About Pearson

Pearson is the world's learning company, with presence across 70 countries worldwide. Our unique insights and world-class expertise comes from a long history of working closely with renowned teachers, authors and thought leaders, as a result of which, we have emerged as the preferred choice for millions of teachers and learners across the world.

We believe learning opens up opportunities, creates fulfilling careers and hence better lives. We hence collaborate with the best of minds to deliver you class-leading products, spread across the Higher Education and Test Preparation spectrum.

Superior learning experience and improved outcomes are at the heart of everything we do. This product is the result of one such effort.

Your feedback plays a critical role in the evolution of our products and you can contact us - reachus@pearson.com. *We look forward to it.*

CLASS

10

Trishna's

PEARSON IIT FOUNDATION

Mathematics

Thirteenth Edition

2025

Pearson

Photo Credits

Chapter 1 Opener: zizou7 / Shutterstock
Chapter 2 Opener: benjaminec / 123RF
Chapter 3 Opener: HL Studios / Pearson Education Ltd
Chapter 4 Opener: IconBunny / Shutterstock
Chapter 5 Opener: benjaminec / Shutterstock
Chapter 6 Opener: GraphicsRF / Shutterstock
Chapter 7 Opener: Evgeniy Goncharenko / 123RF
Chapter 8 Opener: olegdudko / 123RF
Chapter 9 Opener: HL Studios / Pearson Education Ltd
Chapter 10 Opener: Margarita Vin / Shutterstock
Chapter 11 Opener: Pearson Education Ltd
Chapter 12 Opener: YoGinta / Shutterstock
Chapter 13 Opener: alejandro dans neergaard / Shutterstock
Chapter 14 Opener: Leremy / Shutterstock
Chapter 15 Opener: wisitporn / 123RF
Chapter 16 Opener: Kheng Guan Toh / Shutterstock
Chapter 17 Opener: USBFCO / Shutterstock
Chapter 18 Opener: Bradford Calkins / 123RF
Chapter 19 Opener: Elena Khramova / 123RF
Chapter 20 Opener: benjaminec / 123RF

ISBN 978-93-6159-861-6

First Impression

Published by Pearson India Education Services Pvt. Ltd, CIN: U72200TN2005PTC057128.
Head Office: 1st Floor, Berger Tower, Plot No. C-001A/2, Sector 16B, Noida - 201 301, Uttar Pradesh, India.
Registered Office: Featherlite, 'The Address' 5th Floor, Survey No 203/10B, 200 Ft MMRD Road, Zamin Pallavaram, Chennai – 600 044.
Website: in.pearson.com, Email: companysecretary.india@pearson.com

Compositor: Saksham Printographics, Delhi
Printer in India at: Rahul Print O Pack

Brief Contents

UNIT VII: BRIDGE TO GRADE XI

Contents

Preface

"If you have a great ambition, take as big a step as possible in the direction of fulfilling it. The step may only be a tiny one, but trust that it may be the largest one possible for now.".

Mildred McAfee

The *Pearson IIT Foundation* Series has been created keeping in mind the learner's ambition to excel in a competitive examination like IIT-JEE. The series can be used in addition to the books being studied in school to attain that extra edge required to strengthen the concepts and prepare well for future endeavours.

Why Start Early with Pearson Foundation Series

Classes VI to X are the base years of a learner's academic life. In these years learner explore their interests and determine the goals they wish to attain. *Pearson IIT Foundation* series is filled with interactive learning that not only nurtures a learner's interest in science and mathematics but also strengthens their concepts.

The series uses real-life examples and application-based problems to teach theoretical concepts. The objective of this series is to help learners cultivate an analytical mind.

Most of the lessons to be learnt are introduced to the learners in the books for class VI. As they get promoted to higher classes, new topics are added to these lessons. This additive method helps the learners' span their learning over four standards, from VI-X. Thus, learners are not overwhelmed by the introduction of completely new lessons every time they are promoted to a new class.

While their learning is being spanned across five years, so is their ability to resolve doubts for further conceptual clarity. For instance, they can use concepts learnt in class VI to solve questions in class VII. If, in case, they get stuck while answering a question, the learners can infer for themselves that they might be lacking in conceptual clarity. They can then approach their teachers, requesting them to explain the concept once again. This helps the learner to clarify their concepts while revising the lessons previously learnt.

Since classes VI-X are deemed to be a student's formative years, we, at Pearson, aim to provide a foundation level course which serves more than just a standard curriculum.

Here is how it makes a difference to a learner's overall learning...

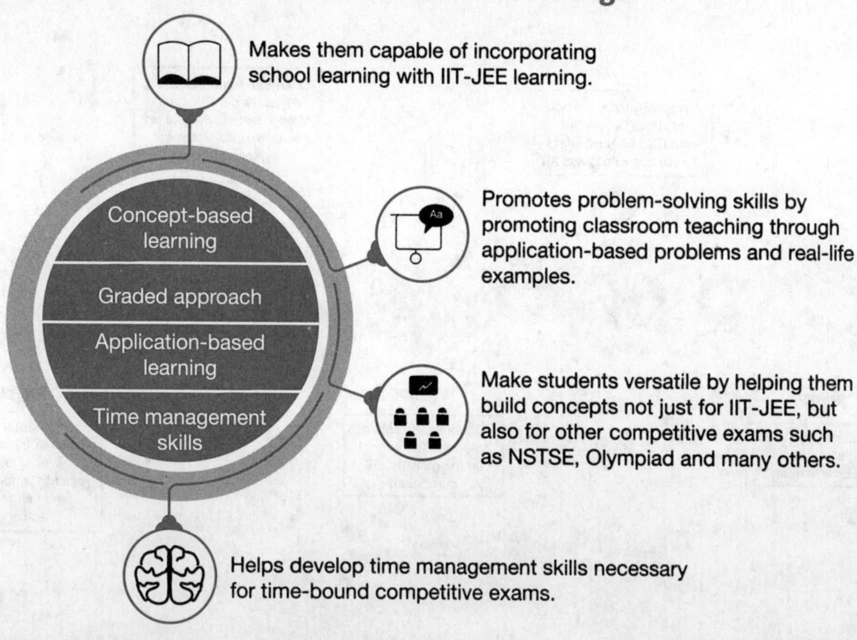

Other Uses of the Series

Instead of limiting themselves to IIT-JEE, a learner can also use this series to prepare for several other competitive examinations such as NSTSE, National and International Olympiads, NEET, BITSAT, etc. This series offers a level of concept learning that empowers learners to handle the challenging nature of questions posed in these examinations. Moreover, this will also allow the learners to have an early insight into their key strengths as well as improvement areas and help them work on themselves.

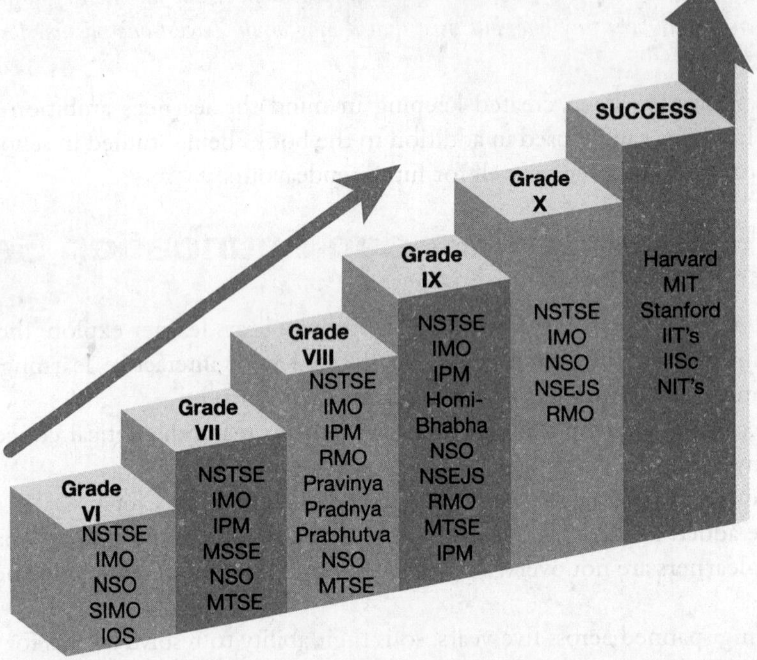

[IMO: International Mathematics Olympiad; NSO: National Science Olympiad, IOS: International Olympiad of Science, NSTSE: National Level Science Talent Search Examination, MTSE: Maharashtra Talent Search Examination, RMO: Regional Mathematical Olympiad, PPP: Pravinya Pradnya Prabhutva, NSEJS: National Standard Examination in Junior Science, IIT: Indian Institute of Technology, IISc: Indian Institute of Science, NIT: National Institute of Technology.]

Highlights of the Series

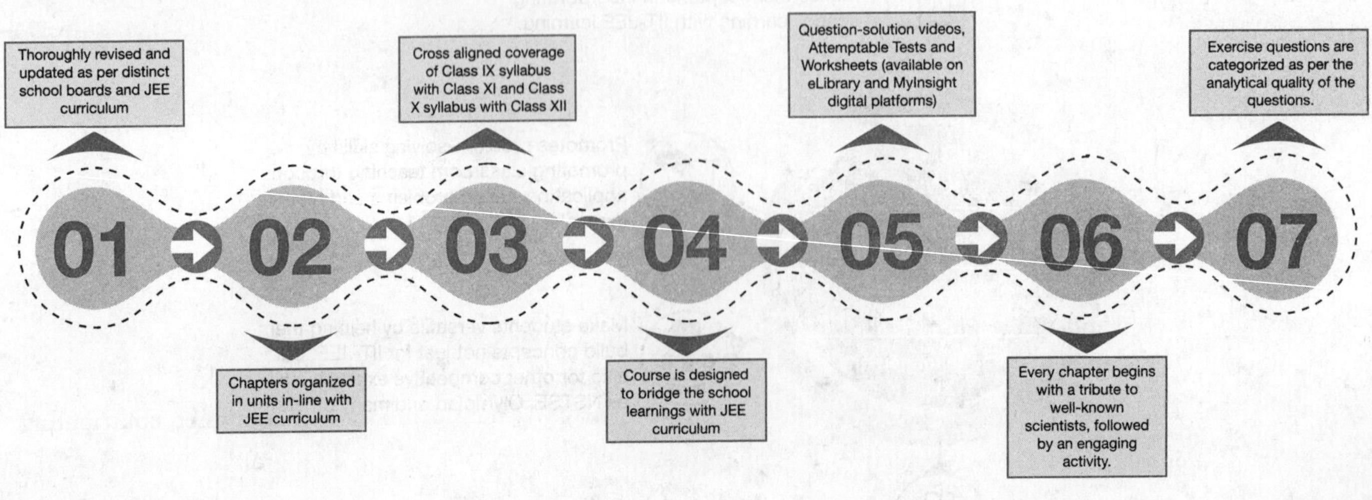

Pearson IIT Foundation series provides a perfect blend of learning through theory and practice questions with a fusion of school and JEE curriculum. It is imperative to note that this series would be as profound as you want it to be. Therefore, to get maximum benefit from this book, were commend following the given study plan.

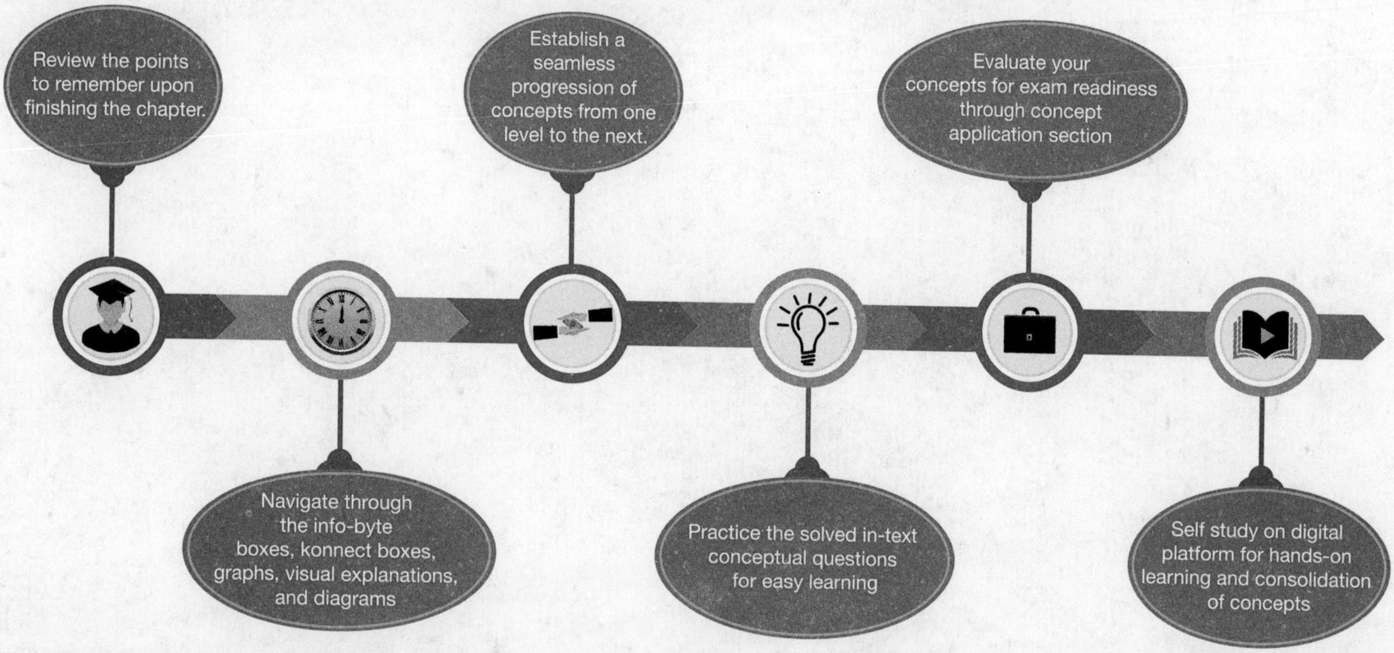

To provide a graded learning approach,the exercise part of each chapter is categorized by using four icons for question tagging. The question categorization helps the learners assess their own problem-solving and analytical skills and motivates them to improve to reach their objectives.

The following icons are used to categorize the questions with specific meanings:

Real-life Situations Questions: 

Analytical Questions: 

Conceptual Questions: 

Value-based Questions: 

With this refined and well-tuned course from Pearson, students will become more confident when they enter the competitive world for actual IIT-JEE preparation. The effort put in today will transform into a valuable asset, contributing to success in future competitive examinations.

Chapter Insights

Remember

Before beginning this chapter, you should be able to:

- Review the types of numbers and understand representation of numbers on a number line
- Study properties of numbers

Remember section will help them to memorize and review the previous learning on a particular topic

Key points will help the students to identify the essential points in a chapter

Key Ideas

After completing this chapter, you should be able to:

- Study Euclid's division lemma
- Learn fundamental arithmetic theorem

Scientific Crypt

A Tribute to Euclid (300 BC)

Euclid, who is called the 'Father of Geometry', was a Greek mathematician. *Elements*, one of his works, was used as the main textbook for teaching mathematics from the time of its publication until the late 19th century. This is one of the greatest contributions to the field of Mathematics. Euclid also wrote works on perspective, conic sections, spherical geometry, number theory, etc.

FUN TIME

CROSSWORD

Scientific Crypt provides information about well-known scientists related to the chapter. The engaging activity is also given in the form of a crossword to keep the learners interested.

Introduction section helps to lay the foundation of the following chapter and leads the way for further learning

INTRODUCTION

In this chapter, we will learn about HCF and LCM of polynomials and the method of finding them. A polynomial is any finite sum of terms. As subtraction can be written in terms of addition, finite differences are also included in this definition. Further we will learn about rational expressions and also the method of expressing them in their lowest terms.

Irrational Numbers

A number which cannot be written in the form $\frac{p}{q}$, where p and q are integers and $q \neq 0$, is an irrational number.

Example: $\sqrt{2}, \sqrt{3}, \sqrt{6}, \sqrt{7}, \sqrt{8}, \sqrt{10}$, 0.123421635, …, etc.

Theorem 1

If p divides x^3, then p divides x, where x is a positive integer and p is a prime number.

Proof: Let $x = p_1 p_2 \cdots p_n$, where $p_1, p_2, p_3, \ldots, p_n$ are primes, not necessarily distinct.

$\Rightarrow$ $$x^3 = p_1^3 p_2^3 \cdots p_n^3$$

Given that p divides x^3.

By fundamental theorem, p is one of the primes of x^3.

Concepts are explained in a well-structured and lucid manner

Konnect boxes are some add-on information of related topic

Konnect

Euclid's division algorithm is stated for only positive integers, it can be also extended for all negative integers.

Info Bytes!

In general $a = p_1 p_2 p_3 \ldots p_n$, where $p_1, p_2, p_3, \ldots, p_n$ are primes in ascending order.

Info bytes are interesting trivia and facts that engage young minds and keep the grey cells ticking!

EXAMPLE 1.13 Prove that $\sqrt{5}$ is irrational.

SOLUTION

Let us assume that $\sqrt{5}$ is not irrational.

$\therefore$ $\sqrt{5}$ is rational.

$\Rightarrow \sqrt{5} = \frac{p}{q}$ (p, q be co-primes.)

Taking squares on both the sides,

$\Rightarrow 5 = \frac{p^2}{q^2}$

$\Rightarrow p^2 = 5q^2$ (1)

$\Rightarrow$ 5 divides p^2

$\Rightarrow$ 5 divides p

$\therefore$ For some integer r,

$p = 5r$ (2)

From Eqs. (1) and (2),

$25r^2 = 5q^2$

$\Rightarrow q^2 = 5r^2$

$\Rightarrow$ 5 divides q^2

$\Rightarrow$ 5 divides q

$\therefore$ p and q have at least 5 as a common factor.

But it contradicts the fact that p and q are co-primes.

$\therefore$ $\sqrt{5}$ is irrational.

Examples are given in the form of in-text exercises to reinforce the concepts learnt in a particular chapter

Illustrative examples solved in a logical and step-wise manner

POINTS TO REMEMBER

- ✔ Euclid's division algorithm is used for finding the greatest common divisor of two numbers.
- ✔ Every composite number can be expressed as the product of prime factors uniquely.
- ✔ A number which cannot be written in the form $\frac{p}{q}$, where p and q are integers and $q \neq 0$, is an irrational number.
- ✔ $\sqrt{2}$ is irrational.
- ✔ If p divides x^3, then p divides x, where x is a positive integer and p is a prime number.

Points to remember summarises the concepts and topics presented in each chapter

PRACTICE QUESTIONS CLASSROOM WING

Very Short Answer Type Questions

Directions of questions from 1 to 8:
Fill in the blanks.

1. $1011_{(2)} + 1101_{(2)} + 1110_{(2)} =$ ________.
2. $11011_{(2)} - 10101_{(2)} =$ ________.
3. If $360 = 2^x \times 3^y \times 5^z$, then $x + y + z =$ ________.
4. If $a = 2 + \sqrt{3}$ and $b = \sqrt{2} - \sqrt{3}$, then $a + b$ is

7. Product of LCM and HCF of 25 and 625 is ________.
8. For ________ values of x, $2^x \times 5^x$ ends in 5.

Directions of questions from 9 to 11:
State whether the following statements are true or false.

9. $\frac{7^3}{5^4}$ is a non-terminating repeating decimal. (True/ ...se)

...19 divides a^3 (where a is a positive integer), then 19

Short Answer Type Questions

Directions of questions from 12 to 13:
Select the correct alternative from the given choices.

12. The binary number equivalent to 250 is ____.
(a) $10111011_{(2)}$ (b) $11111010_{(2)}$
(c) $11001010_{(2)}$ (d) $11111110_{(2)}$

Essay Type Questions

Directions of questions from 21 to 26:
Answer the following questions.

21. (A) The LCM and the HCF of two numbers are 468 and 3, respectively. Find the minimum possible sum of the numbers.

23. Aloukya and M... and they take 18... to complete one... 9 am from the sa... them to meet a... point?

Different typologies of questions have been included in the *Classroom Wing* which help students to develop the problem-solving skill

Competition Wing at the end of the chapter incorporated for competitive examination inline with JEE syllabus

PRACTICE QUESTIONS COMPETITION WING

Level 1: Apply your Concepts

Directions of questions from 1 to 5: **Fill in the blanks.**

1. 1 is equivalent to ____ (in binary system).
2. $(10)_2$ is equivalent to ____ (in decimal system).
3. In binary system, $1 + 1 + 1 + 1 =$ ____.
4. In binary system, $1 + 1 + 0 =$ ____.
5. ...

(a) 1 (b) 3
(c) 5 (d) 7

14. The LCM of two numbers is 1200. Which of the following cannot be their HCF?
(a) 600 (b) 500
(c) 200 (d) 400

...ainder when the square of any number is

Level 2: Review Your Concepts

23. Find the decimal equivalent of the binary number $(1111)_2$.
(a) 15 (b) 10
(c) 12 (d) 14

24. Find the binary equivalent of the decimal number $(111)_{10}$.
(a) $(1011111)_2$ (b) $(1110001)_2$
(c) $(1101111)_2$ (d) $(1011001)_2$

25. Find the decimal number equivalent of $(1100)_2$.
(a) 8 (b) 10

(b) Any surd of the form... by a surd... are surds.
(c) Both (a)...
(d) Neither...

28. The sum of... If their LCM... product of t...
(a) 203400
(c) 198400

Level 3: Assess Your Concepts

30. Find the decimal number equivalent of $(110011)_2$.
(a) 51 (b) 54
(c) 56 (d) 60

31. Find the binary number equivalent of 144.
(a) $(10001001)_2$ (b) $(10010000)_2$
(c) $(1001001)_2$ (d) $(1001101)_2$

32. Find the remainder when the square of any prime number greater than 3 is divided by 6.

Graded as per complexity: Level 1; Level 2; and Level 3

Directions of questions from 6 to 22: **Select the correct alternative from the given choices.**

6. Add $11101_{(2)}$ and $11001_{(2)}$.
(a) $(10100)_2$ (b) $(11110)_2$
(c) $(101010)_2$ (d) $(110110)_2$

7. Subtract $10011_{(2)}$ from $11110_{(2)}$.
(a) $(1011)_2$ (b) $(1101)_2$
(c) $(1001)_2$ (d) $(1001)_2$

8. Find the decimal equivalent of the binary numb... $(111110110)_2$.
(a) 402 (b) 502
(c) 602 (d) 702

9. If n is a natural number, then $9^{2n} - 4^{2n}$ is always divi... ible by ________.

...divided by 4.
(a) 0 (b) 1
(c) Either (a) or (b) (d) Neither (...

16. Ashok has two vessels which contain 720 m... of milk, respectively. Milk in each vessel is... glasses of equal capacity to their brim. Fi...

(a) 1 (b) 3
(c) 5 (d) 7

14. The LCM of two numbers is 1200. Which of the following cannot be their HCF?
(a) 600 (b) 500
(c) 200 (d) 400

15. Find the remainder when the square of any number is divided by 4.
(a) 0 (b) 1
(c) Either (a) or (b) (d) Neither (a) nor (b)

The icons are used for categorisation of the questions in Classroom Wing and Competition Wing

PRACTICE QUESTIONS JEE SPECIAL WING

Multiple-Answer Type Questions

Directions for questions 1 to 5: Each question has FOUR options (a), (b), (c), and (d). ONE OR MORE THAN ONE of these four option(s) is/are the correct answer(s).

1. The LCM and the HCF of two numbers are 660 and 22. Which of the following can be the sum of the two numbers?
   (a) 242 (b) 286
   (c) 330 (d) 374
2. The prime factors of a number are 2 and 3 only. If the number of factors of the number is 12, then which of the following can be the sum of the digits of the number?
   (a) 9 (b) 12
   (c) 15 (d) 18
3. The LCM of two numbers is their product. What do you know about the numbers?
   (a) Consecutive odd numbers
   (b) Consecutive prime numbers
   (c) Consecutive even numbers
   (d) Consecutive composite numbers
4. Which of the following is a RF of $\sqrt[3]{3} - \sqrt[3]{2}$?
   (a) $\sqrt[3]{72} + \sqrt[3]{64} + \sqrt[3]{48}$ (b) $\sqrt[3]{162} + \sqrt[3]{216} + \sqrt[3]{243}$
   (c) $\sqrt[3]{81} + \sqrt[3]{72} + \sqrt[3]{54}$ (d) $\sqrt[3]{6} + \sqrt[3]{8} + \sqrt[3]{10}$
5. Kourav has 252 pigeons and 294 parrots. He wants to arrange them in separate nets. He wants to arrange equal number and same kind of birds. If the number of birds in each net is an odd number, find the total number of nets required.

JEE Special Wing is curated specifically for targeted preparation of JEE examinations.

Hints and Explanations

Classroom Wing

Very Short Answer Type Questions

1. $1011_{(2)} + 1101_{(2)} + 1110_{(2)} + 11 + 13 + 14 = 38 = 2^5 + 2^2 + 2^1 = 100110_{(2)}$
2. $11011_{(2)} - 10101_{(2)} = 27 - 21 = 6 = 2^2 + 2^1 = 110_{(2)}$
3. $360 = 5 \times 3 \times 3 \times 2 \times 2 \times 2$

11. Explanation with example.
    Let 1st irrational no. be $\sqrt{2}$
    Let 2nd irrational no. be $\sqrt{2}$
    $\sqrt{2} \times \sqrt{2} = 2$
    So, it is not always true.

Hints and Explanations for key questions of classroom wing, competition wing and JEE special wing along with highlights on the common mistakes that students usually make in the examinations

Competition Wing

Level 1: Apply Your Concepts

1. $(1)_{10} = (1)_2$
2. $(10)_2 = (2)^1{}_1 + (2)^0{}_0 = (2)_{10}$
3. In binary system, $1 + 1 + 1 + 1 = 4 = (100)_2$
4. In binary system, $1 + 1 + 0 = (10)_2$
5. $0.\bar{5} - 0.\bar{49} = 0.\bar{06}$
6.
$$\begin{array}{r} 1\quad\ \ 1\quad\quad\quad \\ 1\ 1\ 1\ 0\ 1_{(2)} \\ \oplus\ 1\ 1\ 0\ 0\ 1_{(2)} \\ \hline 1\ 1\ 0\ 1\ 1\ 0_{(2)} \end{array}$$
7.
$$\begin{array}{r} 0\ 2\ 2\ \to \text{Borrow} \\ 1\ 1\ 1\ 1\ 0_{(2)} \\ \oplus\ 1\ 0\ 0\ 1\ 1_{(2)} \\ \hline 1\ 0\ 1\ 1_{(2)} \end{array}$$
8. $(111110110)_2 = 2^8 + 2^7 + 2^6$ - ... $2^1 + 0(2^0) = 502$

17. (i) $3^{2n} + 2^{2n} = 9^n + 4^n$.
    (ii) $a^n + b^n$ is divisible by $(a + b)$ when n is odd.
18. For no value of x, $2^x \times 5^x$ ends in 5.
19. Only $\frac{1}{2}$ is terminating decimal.

JEE Special Wing

Multiple-Answer Type Questions

1. Given that LCM = 660 and HCF = 22.
   As the HCF of the numbers is 22, the numbers are multiples of 22.
   Let the numbers be $22x$ and $22y$, where x and y are coprime.
   We have the product of two numbers is equal to the product of their LCM and their HCF.
   $\Rightarrow 22x \times 22y = 660 \times 22$
   $\Rightarrow x \times y = 30$, where x and y are coprime.
   $\Rightarrow (x, y)$ can be $(1, 30), (2, 15), (3, 10)$ or $(5, 6)$
   $\Rightarrow (22x, 22y)$ can be $(22, 660), (44, 330), (66, 220)$ or $(110, 132)$
   $\Rightarrow$ The sum of the numbers can be 682, 374, 286 and 242.
   Hence, the correct options are (a, b, d).
2. Given that the prime factors of a number are 2 and 3.
   Let the number be $2^x \times 3^y$.
   The number of factors $= (x+1)(y+1)$, where each of
4. We have $(a-b)(a^2 + ab + b^2) = a^3 - b^3$.
   So, an RF of $\sqrt[3]{3} - \sqrt[3]{2}$ is $\sqrt[3]{3^2} + \sqrt[3]{3 \times 2} + \sqrt[3]{2^3}$
   $= \sqrt[3]{9} + \sqrt[3]{6} + \sqrt[3]{8}$.
   Also, any multiple of $\sqrt[3]{9} + \sqrt[3]{6} + \sqrt[3]{8}$ is also an RF of $\sqrt[3]{3} - \sqrt[3]{2}$.
   Choice (1): $\sqrt[3]{72} + \sqrt[3]{64} + \sqrt[3]{48}$
   $= \sqrt[3]{8 \times 9} + \sqrt[3]{8 \times 8} + \sqrt[3]{8 \times 6} = 2(\sqrt[3]{9} + \sqrt[3]{8} + \sqrt[3]{6})$
   which is an RF of $\sqrt[3]{3} - \sqrt[3]{2}$.
   Choice (2): $\sqrt[3]{162} + \sqrt[3]{216} + \sqrt[3]{243}$
   $= \sqrt[3]{27 \times 6} + \sqrt[3]{27 \times 8} + \sqrt[3]{27 \times 9} = 3(\sqrt[3]{6} + \sqrt[3]{8} + \sqrt[3]{9})$
   which is an RF of $\sqrt[3]{3} - \sqrt[3]{2}$.
   Choice (3): $\sqrt[3]{81} + \sqrt[3]{72} + \sqrt[3]{54}$
   $= \sqrt[3]{9 \times 9} + \sqrt[3]{9 \times 8} + \sqrt[3]{9 \times 6}$ which is not an RF of $\sqrt[3]{3} - \sqrt[3]{2}$, since 9 is not a perfect cube.
   Clearly Choice (4): $\sqrt[3]{6} + \sqrt[3]{8} + \sqrt[3]{10}$ is not an RF of $\sqrt[3]{3} - \sqrt[3]{2}$.
   Hence, the correct options are (a and b).

DW

WORKSHEET
CHAPTER 2: DYNAMICS

Directions for questions from 1 to 5:
Select the correct alternative from the following options.

1. A bullet of mass 100 g moving with a velocity of 100 m s^{-1} is stopped by a plank. If the bullet travels a distance of 10 cm in the plank before it comes to rest, find the average force exerted by the plank.
   (a) 100 N (b) 1000 N
   (c) 2500 N (d) 5000 N
2. Find the power developed by an engine in filling water of 2000 L from a well of depth 20 m in 20 s.
   (a) 6 kW (b) 20 kW

a rough surface, the total work done by the frictional force is zero.

8. The orbital velocity of a satellite is inversely proportional to the radius of the orbit.
9. When a stone is tied to a string and rotated in a circular path, the work done by the tension of the string is zero.
10. A satellite revolving in an orbit closer to the surface of the earth has more speed than one which is moving in an orbit of higher radius.

Directions for questions from 11 to 15:
Answer the following questions.

DW: Downloadable worksheets supplementing textual exercises for hand-on learning

AT

AI Assessments

What is the value of *x* in the following $(8^x)^3 = (3^x)^2$?

- 4
- 3
- 2
- 0

Questions 1 of 4

Next

AT: Attemptable Tests for assessing understanding of concepts and getting a clear picture of your exam readiness

(B) Find the sum: $\frac{1}{2+\sqrt{5}} + \frac{1}{\sqrt{5}+\sqrt{6}} + \ldots$ up to 96 terms.
(a) 8 (b) 7
(c) 6 (d) 5

Video icon: Audio and visual learning to difficult questions for effective learning and retention

Unit I

Number System

In this Unit

- **Chapter 1** Real Numbers

CHAPTER 1

Real Numbers

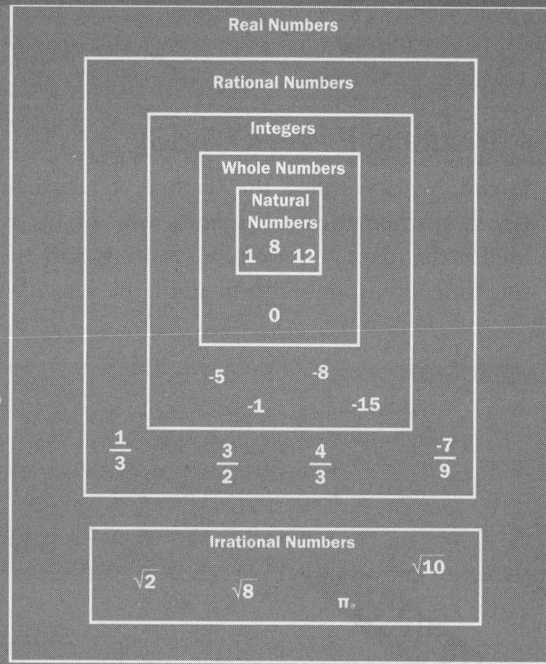

Remember

Before beginning this chapter, you should be able to:

- Review the types of numbers and understand representation of numbers on a number line
- Study properties of numbers

Key Ideas

After completing this chapter, you should be able to:

- Study Euclid's division lemma
- Learn fundamental arithmetic theorem
- Prove theorems related to irrational numbers and rational numbers
- Study proof of irrationality

Scientific Crypt

A Tribute to Euclid (300 BC)

Euclid, who is called the 'Father of Geometry', was a Greek mathematician. *Elements*, one of his works, was used as the main textbook for teaching mathematics from the time of its publication until the late 19th century. This is one of the greatest contributions to the field of Mathematics. Euclid also wrote works on perspective, conic sections, spherical geometry, number theory, etc.

FUN TIME

CROSSWORD

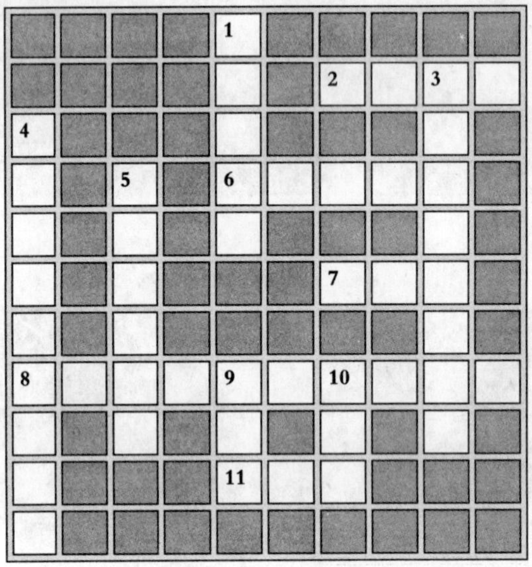

Across

2. In digital electronics, the digit which represents the state OFF.
6. The number of different digits that can be used in the Octal system.
7. The HCF of two consecutive even numbers.
8. The numbers which cannot be written in the form of p/q, where p and q are coprime.
11. The HCF of two consecutive odd numbers.

Down

1. The number of different digits that can be used in the Septenary system.
3. The numbers which can be written in the form of p/q, where p and q are coprime.
4. The process of solving particular problems.
5. The number system used by computers
9. The base of the binary system
10. In digital electronics, the digit which represents the state ON

INTRODUCTION

Earlier we have learnt about number line, irrational numbers, how to represent irrational numbers on the number line, real numbers and their decimal representation, representing real numbers on the number line, and operations on the number line. We shall now present a detailed study of Euclid's division algorithm and fundamental theorem of arithmetic. Further, we continue the revision of irrational numbers and the decimal expansion of rational numbers. We are very familiar with the division rule.

That is, dividend = (divisor × quotient) + remainder.

Euclid's division lemma is based on this rule. We use this result to obtain the HCF of two numbers and also we know that, every composite number can be expressed as the product of primes in a unique way. This is the fundamental theorem of arithmetic. This result is used to prove the irrationality of a number.

In the previous class, we have studied about rational numbers. In this chapter, we shall explore when exactly the decimal expansion of a rational number say p/q ($q \neq 0$) is terminating and when it is non-terminating and repeating.

Euclid's Division Lemma

For any two positive integers, say x and y, there exist unique integers say q and r satisfying $x = yq + r$, where $0 \leq r < y$.

Example: Consider the integers 9 and 19. It implies $19 = 9 \times 2 + 1$

Example: Consider the integers 6 and 24. It implies $24 = 6 \times 4 + 0$

Konnect

1. Euclid's division algorithm is used for finding the greatest common divisor of two numbers.
2. An algorithm is a process of solving particular problems.

EXAMPLE 1.1

Find the HCF of 250 and 30.

SOLUTION

By using Euclid's division lemma, we get,

$250 = 30 \times 8 + 10$

Now consider, the divisor and remainder.

Again by using Euclid's division lemma, we get,

$30 = 10 \times 3 + 0$

Here, we notice that the remainder is zero and we cannot proceed further.

The divisor at this stage is 10.

The HCF of 250 and 30 is 10.

It can be verified by listing out all the factors of 250 and 30.

Info Bytes!

This lemma has been in use since ancient times and is attributed to the ancient Greek mathematician Euclid, who is often referred to as the 'father of geometry' for his work in the field.

Euclid's division algorithm has several applications. The following examples give the idea of the applications.

EXAMPLE 1.2

Show that every positive even integer is of the form 2n and every positive odd integer is of the form 2n + 1.

SOLUTION

For any integer x and $y = 2$, $x = 2n + r$, where $n \geq 0$.

But $0 \leq r < 2$ $\Rightarrow r = 0$ or 1

When $r = 0$, $x = 2n$ $\Rightarrow x$ is a positive even integer

When $r = 1$, $x = 2n + 1$ $\Rightarrow x$ is a positive odd integer.

It can be verified by listing out all the factors of 250 and 30.

Konnect

Euclid's division algorithm is stated for only positive integers, it can be also extended for all negative integers.

EXAMPLE 1.3

A trader has 612 Dettol soaps and 342 Pears soaps. He packs them in boxes and each box contains exactly one type of soap. If every box contains the same number of soaps, then find the number of soaps in each box such that the number of boxes are the least.

SOLUTION

The required number is HCF of 612 and 342.

This number gives the maximum number of soaps in each box and the number of boxes with them be the least.

By using Euclid's division algorithm, we have,

$$612 = 342 \times 1 + 270$$
$$342 = 270 \times 1 + 72$$
$$270 = 72 \times 3 + 54$$
$$72 = 54 \times 1 + 18$$
$$54 = 18 \times 3 + 0$$

Here we notice that the remainder is zero, and the divisor at this stage is 18.

$\therefore$ HCF of 612 and 342 is 18.

So, the trader can pack 18 soaps per box.

Fundamental Theorem Of Arithmetic

Every composite number can be expressed as the product of prime factors uniquely.

Let us see the applications of fundamental theorem.

EXAMPLE 1.4

Write 1800 as product of prime factors.

SOLUTION

2 | 1800
2 | 900
2 | 450
3 | 225
3 | 75
5 | 25
5

$\therefore 1800 = 2^3 \times 3^2 \times 5^2$.

Info Bytes!

In general $a = p_1\, p_2\, p_3 \ldots p_n$, where $p_1, p_2, p_3, \ldots, p_n$ are primes in ascending order.

EXAMPLE 1.5 Check whether there is any value of x for which 6^x ends with 5.

SOLUTION

If 6^x ends with 5, then 6^x would contain the prime number 5.

But, $6^x = (2 \times 3)^x = 2^x \times 3^x$

$\Rightarrow$ The prime numbers in the factorization of 6^x are 2 and 3

By uniqueness of fundamental theorem, there are no prime numbers other than 2 and 3 in 6^x.

$\therefore$ 6^x never ends with 5.

EXAMPLE 1.6 Show that $5 \times 3 \times 2 + 3$ is a composite number.

SOLUTION

$5 \times 3 \times 2 + 3 = 3(5 \times 2 + 1) = 3(11) = 3 \times 11$

$\therefore$ The given number is a composite number.

EXAMPLE 1.7 Find the HCF and LCM of 48 and 56 by prime factorization method.

SOLUTION

$48 = 2^4 \times 3^1$

$56 = 2^3 \times 7^1$

HCF = 2^3 (The product of common prime factors with the least index).

LCM = $2^4 \times 3^1 \times 7^1$ (The product of common prime factors with greater index).

EXAMPLE 1.8 Find the HCF and LCM of 36, 48, and 60 by prime factorization method.

SOLUTION

$36 = 2^2 \times 3^2$

$48 = 2^4 \times 3^1$

$60 = 2^2 \times 3^1 \times 5^1$

HCF = $2^2 \times 3^1 = 12$

LCM = $2^4 \times 3^2 \times 5^1 = 720$.

EXAMPLE 1.9 Two bells toll at intervals of 24 minutes and 36 minutes, respectively. If they toll together at 9 am, after how many minutes do they toll together again, at the earliest?

SOLUTION

The required time is LCM of 24 and 36.

$24 = 2^3 \times 3^1$

$36 = 2^2 \times 3^2$

$\therefore$ LCM of 24 and 36 is $2^3 \times 3^2 = 72$.

So, they will toll together after 72 minutes at the earliest.

EXAMPLE 1.10 A company delivers three different variety of soaps only in cartons. Each carton contains either 720 Life, or 560 Nivel or 900 Pinky soaps. If a dealer wants to purchase equal number of soaps of each variety but possibly the minimum number of soaps in total, then find the least number of cartons that the company should deliver to the dealer.

SOLUTION

The LCM of 720, 560 and 900 = 25200

The number of cartons required $= \dfrac{25200}{720} + \dfrac{25200}{560} + \dfrac{25200}{900} = 35 + 45 + 28 = 108$

EXAMPLE 1.11 The HCF of the two numbers is 24 and the product of those numbers is 4032. How many pairs of such numbers exist?

SOLUTION

Let the two numbers be a and b.

And $a = 24x$, $b = 24y$ where x and y are co-primes.

$\Rightarrow a \times b = 24x \times 24y = 4032$

$\Rightarrow xy = 7 = 1 \times 7$

$\Rightarrow$ The possible values of x and y: (1,7).

There exists only one pair.

EXAMPLE 1.12 What is the greatest possible length of a scale (in cm) which can be used to measure exactly 1 m 35 cm, 4 m 50 cm and 2 m 40 cm?

SOLUTION

The greatest possible length of a scale = HCF of 1 m 25 cm, 4 m 50 cm and 2 m 40 cm.

1 m 35 cm = 135 cm

4 m 50 cm = 450 cm

2 m 40 cm = 240 cm

$135 = 33 \times 5$

$450 = 2 \times 32 \times 52$

$240 = 24 \times 3 \times 5$

The HCF of 135, 450 and 240 = $3 \times 5 = 15$

$\therefore$ Required length of the scale = 15 cm.

Irrational Numbers

A number which cannot be written in the form $\dfrac{p}{q}$, where p and q are integers and $q \neq 0$, is an irrational number.

Example: $\sqrt{2}, \sqrt{3}, \sqrt{6}, \sqrt{7}, \sqrt{8}, \sqrt{10}$, 0.123421635, …, etc.

Theorem 1

If p divides x^3, then p divides x, where x is a positive integer and p is a prime number.

Proof: Let $x = p_1 p_2 \ldots p_n$, where $p_1, p_2, p_3, \ldots, p_n$ are primes, not necessarily distinct.

$\Rightarrow$ $$x^3 = p_1^3 p_2^3 \cdots p_n^3$$

Given that p divides x^3.

By fundamental theorem, p is one of the primes of x^3.

By the uniqueness of fundamental theorem, the distinct primes of x^3 are same as the distinct primes of x.

$\Rightarrow p$ divides x

Hence proved.

Similarly, if p divides x^2, then p divides x, where p is a prime number and x is a positive integer.

Theorem 2

Prove that $\sqrt{2}$ is irrational.

Proof: Let us assume that, $\sqrt{2}$ is not irrational.

So, $\sqrt{2}$ is rational.

$\Rightarrow \sqrt{2} = \frac{x}{y}$, where x, y are integers and $y \neq 0$

Let x and y be co-primes.

Taking squares on both sides,

$2 = \frac{x^2}{y^2}$

$\Rightarrow 2y^2 = x^2$

$\Rightarrow 2$ divides x^2

$\Rightarrow 2$ divides x (1)

$\therefore$ For some integer z,

$x = 2z$ (2)

From Eqs. (1) and (2),

$2y^2 = 4z^2$

$\Rightarrow y^2 = 2z^2$

$\Rightarrow 2$ divides y^2

$\Rightarrow 2$ divides y

$\therefore$ x and y have at least 2 as a common factor.

But it contradicts the fact that x and y are co-primes.

$\therefore$ $\sqrt{2}$ is irrational.

EXAMPLE 1.13

Prove that $\sqrt{5}$ is irrational.

SOLUTION

Let us assume that $\sqrt{5}$ is not irrational.

$\therefore$ $\sqrt{5}$ is rational.

$\Rightarrow \sqrt{5} = \frac{p}{q}$ (p, q be co-primes.)

Taking squares on both the sides,

$\Rightarrow 5 = \frac{p^2}{q^2}$

$\Rightarrow p^2 = 5q^2$ (1)

$\Rightarrow 5$ divides p^2

$\Rightarrow 5$ divides p

$\therefore$ For some integer r,

$p = 5r$ (2)

From Eqs. (1) and (2),

$25r^2 = 5q^2$

$\Rightarrow q^2 = 5r^2$

$\Rightarrow 5$ divides q^2

$\Rightarrow 5$ divides q

$\therefore$ p and q have at least 5 as a common factor.

But it contradicts the fact that p and q are co-primes.

$\therefore$ $\sqrt{5}$ is irrational.

EXAMPLE 1.14

Show that $3+\sqrt{2}$ is irrational.

SOLUTION

Let us assume that $3+\sqrt{2}$ is rational.

$\therefore 3+\sqrt{2}=\frac{p}{q}$, where p and q are integers.

$\Rightarrow \sqrt{2}=\frac{p}{q}-3 \Rightarrow \sqrt{2}=\frac{p-3q}{q}$

Since p and q are integers, $\frac{p-3q}{q}$ is rational.

But $\sqrt{2}$ is irrational.

It contradicts our assumption that $3+\sqrt{2}$ is rational.

$\therefore$ Our assumption is wrong.

Hence, $3+\sqrt{2}$ is irrational.

EXAMPLE 1.15

If $a=\sqrt{11}+\sqrt{3}$, $b=\sqrt{12}+\sqrt{2}$ and $c=\sqrt{6}+\sqrt{4}$, then which of the following holds true?

(a) $c>a>b$ (b) $a>b>c$ (c) $a>c>b$ (d) $b>a>c$

SOLUTION

$a=\sqrt{11}+\sqrt{3}$

$a^2=(\sqrt{11}+\sqrt{3})^2=14+2\sqrt{33}$

$b=\sqrt{12}+\sqrt{2}$

$b^2=(\sqrt{12}+\sqrt{2})^2=14+2\sqrt{24}$

As $\sqrt{33}>\sqrt{24}$, $a^2>b^2$, hence $a>b$.

$c=\sqrt{6}+\sqrt{4}$

$c^2=(\sqrt{6}+\sqrt{4})^2=10+2\sqrt{24}$

As $14>10$, $b^2>c^2$, hence $b>c$.

Hence, $a>b>c$.

EXAMPLE 1.16

The value of $\frac{1}{\sqrt{11}+\sqrt{9}}+\frac{1}{\sqrt{13}+\sqrt{11}}+\ldots\ldots+\frac{1}{\sqrt{2025}+\sqrt{2023}}$ is _____.

SOLUTION

$$\frac{1}{\sqrt{11}+\sqrt{9}}=\frac{\sqrt{11}-\sqrt{9}}{\sqrt{11}+(\sqrt{9})^2}=\frac{\sqrt{11}-\sqrt{9}}{2}$$

$$\frac{1}{\sqrt{13}+\sqrt{11}}=\frac{\sqrt{13}-\sqrt{11}}{(\sqrt{13})^2-(\sqrt{11})^2}=\frac{\sqrt{13}-\sqrt{11}}{2}$$

$$\vdots \quad \vdots \quad \vdots$$

$$\frac{1}{\sqrt{2025}+\sqrt{2025}}=\frac{\sqrt{2025}-\sqrt{2023}}{(\sqrt{2025})^2-(\sqrt{2023})^2}$$

$$=\frac{\sqrt{2025}-\sqrt{2023}}{2}$$

The required sum $=\left(\frac{-\sqrt{9}}{2}+\frac{\sqrt{2025}}{2}\right)=\left(\frac{-3+45}{2}\right)=21$

Rational Numbers

Numbers which can be written in the form of $\frac{p}{q}$ $(q \neq 0)$, where p, q are integers, are called rational numbers.

> **Info Bytes!**
> Every terminating decimal and non-terminating repeating decimal can be expressed in the form $\frac{p}{q}$ $(q \neq 0)$.

Examples:

1. $0.27 = \frac{27}{100} = \frac{27}{2^2 \times 5^2}$
2. $2.356 = \frac{2356}{1000} = \frac{2^2 \times 589}{2^3 \times 5^3} = \frac{589}{2 \times 5^3}$
3. $2.0325 = \frac{20325}{10000} = \frac{3 \times 5^2 \times 271}{2^4 \times 5^4} = \frac{3 \times 271}{2^4 \times 5^2}$

From the above examples, we notice that every terminating decimal can be written in the form of $\frac{p}{q}$ $(q \neq 0)$, where p and q are co-primes and q is of the form $2^m \cdot 5^n$ (m and n are non-negative integers).

Let us write this result formally.

Theorem 3

Let a be a terminating decimal. Then a can be expressed as $\frac{p}{q}$ $(q \neq 0)$, where p and q are co-primes, and the prime factorization of q is of the form $2^m \cdot 5^n$.

Let us observe the following examples:

1. $\frac{1}{4} = \frac{1}{2^2} = \frac{1 \times 5^2}{2^2 \times 5^2} = \frac{2}{25} = 0.25$
2. $\frac{7}{25} = \frac{7}{5^2} = \frac{7 \times 2^2}{5^2 \times 2^2} = \frac{28}{100} = 0.28$
3. $\frac{23}{125} = \frac{23}{5^3} = \frac{23 \times 2^3}{5^3 \times 2^3} = \frac{184}{1000} = 0.184$
4. $\frac{147}{50} = \frac{147}{2 \times 5^2} = \frac{147 \times 2}{2^2 \times 5^2} = \frac{294}{100} = 2.94$

From the above examples, we notice that every rational number of the form $\frac{p}{q}$ $(q \neq 0)$, where q is of the form $2^m \cdot 5^n$ can be written as $\frac{x}{y}$, where y is of the form 10^k, k being a natural number.

Let us write this result formally.

Theorem 4

If $\frac{p}{q}$ is a rational number where q is of the form $2^m \cdot 5^m$ $(m \in W)$, then $\frac{p}{q}$ has a terminating decimal expansion.

Let us observe the following examples.

Examples:

1. $\frac{5}{3} = 1.66666... = 1.\overline{6}$
2. $\frac{8}{7} = 1.\overline{142857}$
3. $\frac{1}{11} = 0.\overline{09}$

Theorem 5

If $\frac{p}{q}$ is a rational number and q is not of the form $2^m \cdot 5^n$ (m and $n \in W$), then $\frac{p}{q}$ has a non-terminating repeating decimal expansion.

EXAMPLE 1.17 Which of the following rational numbers can be expressed as a non-terminating repeating decimal?

(a) $\frac{13 \times 18 \times 5}{9 \times 16 \times 25}$ (b) $\frac{28 \times 19 \times 10}{38 \times 16 \times 25}$ (c) $\frac{12 \times 14 \times 15}{7 \times 16 \times 45}$ (d) $\frac{12 \times 24 \times 15}{81 \times 16 \times 25}$

SOLUTION

The simplest form of choice (d) is $\frac{2}{15}$, where $15 \neq 2^m \times 5^n$

∴ Choice (d) can be expressed as non-terminating repeating decimal.

Decimal and Binary Systems

The numbers that are commonly used are the decimal numbers which involve ten symbols, namely 0, 1, 2, 3, 4, 5, 6, 7, 8, and 9. If we consider the number 526 in the decimal system, it means $5 \times 10^2 + 2 \times 10^1 + 6 \times 10^0$. Likewise, 85.67 means $8 \times 10^1 + 5 \times 10^0 + 6 \times 10^{-1} + 7 \times 10^{-2}$.

The role played by "10" in the decimal system is termed as the "base" of the system. In this chapter, we see the numbers expressed to the base 10 and to the base 2.

Konnect

1. The base of a number system can be any integer greater than 1.
2. Base is also termed as radix or scale of notation.

Base: It is a number which decides the place value of a symbol or a digit in a number. Alternatively, it is the number of distinct symbols that are used in that number system.

The following table lists some number systems along with their respective base and symbols.

Number System	Base	Symbols
Binary	2	0,1
Septenuary	7	0,1,2,3,4,5,6
Octal	8	0,1,2,3,4,5,6,7
Decimal	10	0,1,2,3,4,5,6,7,8,9

Representation: Let N be any integer, r be the base of the system and let $a_0, a_1, a_2, \ldots\ldots, a_n$ be the required digits by which N is expressed. Then,

$$N = a_n r^n + a_{n-1} r^{n-1} + a_{n-2} r^{n-2} + \ldots + a_1 r + a_0, \text{ where } 0 \le a_i < r.$$

We now look into some representations and their meaning in decimal system.

Examples:

1. $(10011)_2 = 1 \times 2^4 + 0 \times 2^3 + 0 \times 2^2 + 1 \times 2^1 + 1 \times 2^0$
2. $(5437)_{10} = 5 \times 10^3 + 4 \times 10^2 + 3 \times 10^1 + 7 \times 10^0$

Conversions

1. **Decimal to binary:**

EXAMPLE 1.18 Convert $(252)_{10}$ to its binary equivalent.

SOLUTION

Step 1: Divide 252 by 2, write the quotient and the remainder

Step 2: Now divide the quotient obtained in step 2 (i.e. 126) and divide 126 by 2, write the quotient and the remainder.

Step 3: Continue this process until we get zero as the quotient.

Step 4: Write the remainders from the bottom to top

$\therefore (252)_{10} = (11111100)_2$

2	252
2	126 - 0
2	63 - 0
2	31 - 1
2	15 - 1
2	7 - 1
2	3 - 1
2	1 - 1
	0 - 1

2. Binary to decimal:

EXAMPLE 1.19 Convert $(101011001)_2$ to its decimal equivalent.

SOLUTION

$$(101011001)_2 = 1 \times 2^8 + 0 \times 2^7 + 1 \times 2^6 + 0 \times 2^5 + 1 \times 2^4 + 1 \times 2^3 + 0 \times 2^2 + 0 \times 2^1 + 1 \times 2^0$$
$$= 256 + 0 + 64 + 0 + 16 + 8 + 0 + 0 + 1 = (345)_{10}$$

EXAMPLE 1.20 Find the minimum number of bits required to represent the decimal number 295 in binary system.

SOLUTION

We have, $295 = 2^8 + 2^5 + 2^2 + 2^1 + 2^0$. So, the minimum number of bits required is 9.

Binary Arithmetic

Addition: Elementary Rules

- $0 + 0 = 0$
- $0 + 1 = 1$
- $1 + 0 = 1$
- $1 + 1 = 10$ (1 will be regarded as carry as we do in decimal system)

EXAMPLE 1.21 Add $(100101)_2$ and $(110)_2$.

SOLUTION

```
1          →      carry
1 0 0 1 0 1
0 0 0 1 1 0  (Introduce leading zeros)
-----------
1 0 1 0 1 1
```

Subtraction: Elementary Rules

- $0 - 0 = 0$
- $1 - 0 = 1$
- $1 - 1 = 0$
- $0 - 1 = 1$

(with a borrow 1 from the next higher column which turns to 2 in this column)

EXAMPLE 1.22 Subtract $(1101)_2$ from $(11010)_2$.

SOLUTION

Say N = 11010. As 1 cannot be subtracted from 0, we borrow 2 from the next place. This gives 2 – 1 = 1, as the right most digit of the result. The penultimate digit of N would become 0. A similar calculation gives the 3rd digit of the result from the right as 1 and the 4th digit of N from the right becomes 0.We now borrow a 2 from the 5th digit of N, this makes the 4th digit of N as 2, thereby resulting in 2 – 1 = 1 as the 4th digit of the result.

```
         2
      0 0 2 0 2 → carry
      1 1 0 1 0
    –   1 1 0 1
result →  1 1 0 1
```

EXAMPLE Let x = 0.00010101.................. where the digit in the nth place is 1 and n is a composite number, then the decimal is a/an ______ decimal.

(a) terminating
(b) non-terminating and non-recurring
(c) non-terminating and recurring
(d) None of these

SOLUTION

x = 0.1001010111............is a non-terminating non-repeating decimal.

POINTS TO REMEMBER

- ✔ Euclid's division algorithm is used for finding the greatest common divisor of two numbers.
- ✔ Every composite number can be expressed as the product of prime factors uniquely.
- ✔ A number which cannot be written in the form $\frac{p}{q}$, where p and q are integers and $q \neq 0$, is an irrational number.
- ✔ $\sqrt{2}$ is irrational.
- ✔ If p divides x^3, then p divides x, where x is a positive integer and p is a prime number.

PRACTICE QUESTIONS CLASSROOM WING

Very Short Answer Type Questions

Directions of questions from 1 to 8:
Fill in the blanks.

1. $1011_{(2)} + 1101_{(2)} + 1110_{(2)} =$ ________.
2. $11011_{(2)} - 10101_{(2)} =$ ________.
3. If $360 = 2^x \times 3^y \times 5^z$, then $x + y + z =$ ________.
4. If $a = 2 + \sqrt{3}$ and $b = \sqrt{2} - \sqrt{3}$, then $a + b$ is ________. (rational/irrational)
5. If $0.\overline{7} = \frac{p}{q}$, then $p + q =$ ________.
6. $101101_{(2)} - 110011_{(2)} =$ ________.
7. Product of LCM and HCF of 25 and 625 is ________.
8. For ________ values of x, $2^x \times 5^x$ ends in 5.

Directions of questions from 9 to 11:
State whether the following statements are true or false.

9. $\frac{7^3}{5^4}$ is a non-terminating repeating decimal. (True/False)
10. If 19 divides a^3 (where a is a positive integer), then 19 divides a. (True/False)
11. Product of two irrational numbers is an irrational number. (True/False)

Short Answer Type Questions

Directions of questions from 12 to 13:
Select the correct alternative from the given choices.

12. The binary number equivalent to 250 is ____.
    (a) $10111011_{(2)}$ (b) $11111010_{(2)}$
    (c) $11001010_{(2)}$ (d) $11111110_{(2)}$
13. If n is a natural number, then $4^n - 3^n$ ends with a digit x. The number of possible values of x is ____.
    (a) 3 (b) 8
    (c) 5 (d) 6

Directions for question 14:
Match the column A with column B.

14.

Column A	Column B
(i) The HCF of 2 consecutive prime numbers	(A) 1
(ii) The HCF of 2 consecutive even composite numbers	(B) 2
(iii) The HCF of the smallest composite number and the smallest two-digit perfect number	(C) 3
(iv) The smallest odd prime number	(D) 4

Directions of questions from 15 to 20:
Answer the following questions.

15. Show that 1000001 is a composite number in any system.
16. Find the HCF of 72 and 264 by using Euclid's division algorithm.
17. (A) Show that $7 \times 5 \times 3 \times 2 + 7$ is a composite number.

    (B) If p is the LCM of 6, 4, 8, 12, and q is the HCF of p, 8, 24, 16, and r is the LCM of q, 2, 16, 6. Find $\frac{(p^3 + q^3 + r^3 - 3pqr)}{(p^2 + q^2 + r^2 - pq - qr - pr)}$.
18. Find the HCF and LCM of 108 and 360 by prime factorization method.
19. (A) Prove that $\sqrt{6}$ is irrational.

    (B) If $z = (16)^{7x} + (15)^{11x}$. $x \in N$, find the unit's digit of z for all $x \in N$.
20. Without performing the actual division, check whether the following rational numbers are terminating or non-terminating.

    (i) $\frac{23}{175}$ (ii) $\frac{125}{325}$

    (iii) $\frac{73}{40}$ (iv) $\frac{157}{125}$

Essay Type Questions

Directions of questions from 21 to 26:
Answer the following questions.

21. (A) A fruit vendor has 732 apples and 942 oranges. He distributes these fruits among the students of an orphanage, such that each of them gets either only apples or only oranges in equal number. Find the least possible number of students.

    (B) Five persons *P*, *Q*, *R*, *S*, *T* start running around a circular track, simultaneously. If they complete one round in 64, 120, 36, 16, 24 seconds respectively, after how much time they will next meet at starting point for the 2nd time? Also find the number of complete rounds made by each person, before they meet.

22. There are 60 boys and 36 girls in a class. These students are arranged in rows for prayer in such a way that each row has either boys or girls, and every row has an equal number of students. Find the minimum number of rows in which all the students can be arranged.

23. Aloukya and Manoghna run around a circular track and they take 180 seconds and 150 seconds respectively to complete one revolution. If they start together at 9 am from the same point, how long it would take for them to meet again for the first time at the starting point?

24. Prove that $5-\sqrt{5}$ is irrational.

25. Express $23.3\overline{24}$ in $\dfrac{p}{q}$ form, where *p* and *q* are integers.

26. Find the value of $12.\overline{35} + 123.\overline{5} + 1.2\overline{35}$.

PRACTICE QUESTIONS COMPETITION WING

Level 1: Apply your Concepts

Directions of questions from 1 to 5: **Fill in the blanks.**

1. 1 is equivalent to ____ (in binary system).
2. $(10)_2$ is equivalent to ____ (in decimal system).
3. In binary system, $1 + 1 + 1 + 1 =$ ____.
4. In binary system, $1 + 1 + 0 =$ ____.
5. $0.\overline{5} - 0.\overline{49} =$ ________.

Directions of questions from 6 to 22: **Select the correct alternative from the given choices.**

6. Add $11101_{(2)}$ and $11001_{(2)}$.
   (a) $(10100)_2$ (b) $(11110)_2$
   (c) $(101010)_2$ (d) $(110110)_2$
7. Subtract $10011_{(2)}$ from $11110_{(2)}$.
   (a) $(1011)_2$ (b) $(1101)_2$
   (c) $(1001)_2$ (d) $(1001)_2$
8. Find the decimal equivalent of the binary number $(111110110)_2$.
   (a) 402 (b) 502
   (c) 602 (d) 702
9. If n is a natural number, then $9^{2n} - 4^{2n}$ is always divisible by ________.
   (a) 5 (b) 13
   (c) Both (a) and (b) (d) Neither (a) nor (b)
10. N is a natural number such that when N^3 is divided by 9, it leaves remainder a. It can be concluded that-
   (a) a is a perfect square. (b) a is a perfect cube.
   (c) Both (a) and (b) (d) Neither (a) nor (b)
11. The remainder of any perfect square divided by 3 is ________.
   (a) 0 (b) 1
   (c) Either (a) or (b) (d) Neither (a) nor (b)
12. Find the HCF of 432 and 504 using prime factorization method.
   (a) 36 (b) 72
   (c) 96 (d) 108
13. If n is any natural number, then $6^n - 5^n$ always ends with________.
   (a) 1 (b) 3
   (c) 5 (d) 7
14. The LCM of two numbers is 1200. Which of the following cannot be their HCF?
   (a) 600 (b) 500
   (c) 200 (d) 400
15. Find the remainder when the square of any number is divided by 4.
   (a) 0 (b) 1
   (c) Either (a) or (b) (d) Neither (a) nor (b)
16. Ashok has two vessels which contain 720 ml and 405 ml of milk, respectively. Milk in each vessel is poured into glasses of equal capacity to their brim. Find the minimum number of glasses which can be filled with milk.
   (a) 45 (b) 35
   (c) 25 (d) 30
17. If n is an odd natural number, $3^{2n} + 2^{2n}$ is always divisible by:
   (a) 13 (b) 5
   (c) 17 (d) 19
18. For what values of x, $2^x \times 5^x$ ends in 5?
   (a) 0 (b) 1
   (c) 2 (d) No value of x
19. Which of the following is a terminating decimal?
   (a) $\frac{4}{7}$ (b) $\frac{3}{7}$
   (c) $\frac{2}{3}$ (d) $\frac{1}{2}$
20. LCM of two co-primes (say x and y) is ________.
   (a) $x + y$ (b) $x - y$
   (c) xy (d) $\frac{x}{y}$
21. HCF of two co-primes (say x and y) is ________.
   (a) x (b) y
   (c) xy (d) 1
22. If we apply Euclid's division lemma for two numbers 15 and 4, then we get,
   (a) $15 = 4 \times 3 + 3$. (b) $15 = 4 \times 2 + 7$.
   (c) $15 = 4 \times 1 + 11$. (d) $15 = 4 \times 4 + (-1)$.

Level 2: Review Your Concepts

23. Find the decimal equivalent of the binary number $(1111)_2$.
(a) 15 (b) 10
(c) 12 (d) 14

24. Find the binary equivalent of the decimal number $(111)_{10}$.
(a) $(1011111)_2$ (b) $(1110001)_2$
(c) $(1101111)_2$ (d) $(1011001)_2$

25. Find the decimal number equivalent of$(1100)_2$.
(a) 8 (b) 10
(c) 12 (d) 14

26. Given that the units digits of A^3 and A are the same, where A is a single digit natural number. How many possibilities can A assume?
(a) 6 (b) 5
(c) 4 (d) 3

27. Which of the following is/are always true?
(a) Every irrational number is a surd.
(b) Any surd of the form $\sqrt[n]{a}+\sqrt[n]{b}$ can be rationalized by a surd of the form $\sqrt[n]{a}-\sqrt[n]{b}$, where $\sqrt[n]{a}$ and $\sqrt[n]{b}$ are surds.
(c) Both (a) and (b)
(d) Neither (a) nor (b)

28. The sum of LCM and HCF of two numbers is 1260. If their LCM is 900 more than their HCF, find the product of two numbers.
(a) 203400 (b) 194400
(c) 198400 (d) 205400

29. The following are the steps involved in finding the LCM of 72 and 48 by prime factorization method. Arrange them in sequential order.
(A) $72 = 2^3 \times 3^2$ and $48 = 2^4 \times 3^1$
(B) LCM $= 2^4 \times 3^2$
(C) All the distinct factors with highest exponents are 24 and 32
(a) ABC (b) ACB
(c) CAB (d) BCA

Level 3: Assess Your Concepts

30. Find the decimal number equivalent of $(110011)_2$.
(a) 51 (b) 54
(c) 56 (d) 60

31. Find the binary number equivalent of 144.
(a) $(10001001)_2$ (b) $(10010000)_2$
(c) $(1001001)_2$ (d) $(1001101)_2$

32. Find the remainder when the square of any prime number greater than 3 is divided by 6.
(a) 1 (b) 3
(c) 2 (d) 4

33. If HCF $(72, q) = 12$ then how many values can q take? (Assume q be a product of a power of 2 and a power of 3 only)
(a) 1 (b) 2
(c) 3 (d) 4

34. Find the HCF of 120 and 156 using Euclid's division algorithm.
(a) 18 (b) 12
(c) 6 (d) 24

35. (A) $\sqrt{3+\sqrt{5}} =$ ______.
(a) $\sqrt{2}+1$ (b) $\sqrt{\frac{5}{2}}+\sqrt{\frac{1}{2}}$
(c) $\sqrt{\frac{7}{2}}-\sqrt{\frac{1}{2}}$ (d) $\sqrt{\frac{9}{2}}-\sqrt{\frac{3}{2}}$

(B) Find the sum: $\frac{1}{2+\sqrt{5}}+\frac{1}{\sqrt{5}+\sqrt{6}}+\ldots$ up to 96 terms.
(a) 8 (b) 7
(c) 6 (d) 5

36. The value of $(37)^{3^x}-(33)^{3^x}$ ends in ______ $(x \in N)$.
(a) 4 (b) 6
(c) 0 (d) Either (a) or (b)

37. $P = 2(4)(6)\ldots(20)$ and $Q = 1(3)(5)\ldots(19)$. What is the HCF of P and Q?
(a) $3^3 \cdot 5 \cdot 7$ (b) $3^4 \cdot 5$
(c) $3^4 \cdot 5^2 \cdot 7$ (d) $3^3 \cdot 5^2$

38. The LCM and the HCF of two numbers are 1001 and 7, respectively. How many such pairs are possible?
(a) 0 (b) 1
(c) 2 (d) 7

39. There are 96 apples and 112 oranges. These fruits are packed in boxes in such a way that each box contains

fruits of the same variety, and every box contains an equal number of fruits. Find the minimum number of boxes in which all the fruits can be packed.

(a) 12 (b) 13
(c) 14 (d) 15

40. Two runners A and B are running on a circular track. A takes 40 seconds to complete every round and B takes 30 seconds to complete every round. If they start simultaneously at 9:00 am, then which of the following is the time at which they can meet at the starting point?

(a) 9:05 am (b) 9:10 am
(c) 9:15 am (d) 9:13 am

41. In how many ways can 1500 be resolved into two factors?

(a) 18 (b) 12
(c) 24 (d) 36

42. Four bells toll at intervals of 10 seconds, 15 seconds, 20 seconds, and 30 seconds, respectively. If they toll together at 10:00 am, at what time will they toll together for the first time after 10 am?

(a) 10:01 am (b) 10:02 am
(d) 10:00:30 am (d) 10:00:45 am

43. If $a = \sqrt[8]{6} - \sqrt[8]{5}$, $b = \sqrt[8]{6} + \sqrt[8]{5}$, $c = \sqrt[6]{6} + \sqrt[6]{5}$, $d = \sqrt[4]{6} + \sqrt[4]{5}$, and $e = \sqrt{6} + \sqrt{5}$, then which of the following is a rational number?

(a) *abcde* (b) *abde*
(c) *ab* (d) *cd*

44. Find the units digit of $(12)^{3^x} + (18)^{3^x}$ $(x \in N)$.

(a) 2 (b) 8
(c) 0 (d) 1

45. If $X = 28 + (1 \times 2 \times 3 \times 4 \times \ldots \times 16 \times 28)$ and $Y = 17 + (1 \times 2 \times 3 \times \ldots \times 17)$, then which of the following is/are true?

(A) X is a composite number
(B) Y is a prime number
(C) $X - Y$ is a prime number
(D) $X + Y$ is a composite number

(a) Both (A) and (D) (b) Both (B) and (C)
(c) Both (B) and (D) (d) Both (A) and (B)

46. P is the LCM of 2, 4, 6, 8, 10, Q is the LCM of 1, 3, 5, 7, 9, and L is the LCM of P and Q. Then, which of the following is true?

(a) $L = 21P$ (b) $L = 4Q$
(c) $L = 63P$ (d) $L = 16Q$

47. The LCM and the HCF of two numbers are 144 and 12, respectively. How many such pairs of numbers are possible?

(a) 0 (b) 1
(c) 2 (d) 10

48. Two bells toll in every 45 seconds and 60 seconds. If they toll together at 8:00 am, then which of the following is the probable time at which they can toll together?

(a) 8:55 am (b) 8:50 am
(c) 8:45 am (d) 8:40 am

PRACTICE QUESTIONS JEE SPECIAL WING

Multiple-Answer Type Questions

Directions for questions 1 to 5: **Each question has FOUR options (a), (b), (c), and (d). ONE OR MORE THAN ONE of these four option(s) is/are the correct answer(s).**

1. The LCM and the HCF of two numbers are 660 and 22. Which of the following can be the sum of the two numbers?
   (a) 242 (b) 286
   (c) 330 (d) 374

2. The prime factors of a number are 2 and 3 only. If the number of factors of the number is 12, then which of the following can be the sum of the digits of the number?
   (a) 9 (b) 12
   (c) 15 (d) 18

3. The LCM of two numbers is their product. What do you know about the numbers?
   (a) Consecutive odd numbers
   (b) Consecutive prime numbers
   (c) Consecutive even numbers
   (d) Consecutive composite numbers

4. Which of the following is a RF of $\sqrt[3]{3} - \sqrt[3]{2}$?
   (a) $\sqrt[3]{72} + \sqrt[3]{64} + \sqrt[3]{48}$ (b) $\sqrt[3]{162} + \sqrt[3]{216} + \sqrt[3]{243}$
   (c) $\sqrt[3]{81} + \sqrt[3]{72} + \sqrt[3]{54}$ (d) $\sqrt[3]{6} + \sqrt[3]{8} + \sqrt[3]{10}$

5. Kourav has 252 pigeons and 294 parrots. He wants to arrange them in separate nets. He wants to arrange equal number and same kind of birds. If the number of birds in each net is an odd number, find the total number of nets required.
   (a) 39 (b) 78
   (c) 91 (d) 182

Match The Column

Directions for questions 6 to 10:
Read the paragraph given below and answer the questions.

$A = 123.\overline{63}$
$B = 431.\overline{6}$
$C = 232.1\overline{4}$
$D = 322.\overline{8}$

Column A	Column B
6. A + B	(a) $108.\overline{7}$
7. C + D	(b) $108.5\overline{08}$
8. C − A	(c) $108.\overline{08}$
9. B − D	(d) $522.4\overline{1}$
10. B + D − C	(e) $555.0\overline{3}$
	(f) $555.\overline{30}$

Comprehension-Based Questions

Directions for questions 11 to 15:
Read the paragraph given below and answer the questions.

Mr Sprinter, Mr Hurdler, and Mr Breezer are good friends. They are health conscious since childhood. They participate in every marathon which is conducted by the rotary club in their city. They want to participate in a marathon on April 7th on the occasion of World Health Day. The marathon route is a circular shape with a length of 12 km. Sprinter, Hurdler, and Breezer can each complete one round in 4 hours, 3 hours, and 2 hours respectively. The three friends start from a point B at 9 am.

11. At what time will they next meet at the point B for the first time after 9 am?
    (a) 12 noon (b) 2 pm
    (c) 6 pm (d) 9 pm

12. Find the sum of the number of rounds they make before they meet at the point B for the first time after 9 am.

(a) 13 (b) 12
(c) 11 (d) 10

13. Find the distance travelled by Hurdler before they meet at the point B for the first time after 9 am.

(a) 36 km (b) 48 km
(c) 72 km (d) 96 km

14. If Breezer takes 250 ml of water for every 9 km he runs, what is the total quantity (in litres) of water that he takes before they meet at the point B for the first time after 9 am?

(a) 4 (b) 3
(c) 2 (d) 1

15. Find the difference between the distances travelled by Breezer and Hurdler before they meet at the point B for the first time after 9 am.

(a) 12 km (b) 24 km
(c) 30 km (d) 36 km

Assertion and Reason Type Questions

Directions for questions 16 to 20:

Read the options given below and answer the questions.

In the light of the given statements, choose the most appropriate answer from the options given below.

(a) Both assertion (A) and reason (R) are true, and reason (R) is the correct explanation of assertion.
(b) Both assertion (A) and reason (R) are true, and reason (R) is not the correct explanation of assertion.
(c) Assertion (A) is true, but reason (R) is false.
(d) Assertion (A) is false, and reason (R) is true.

16. **Assertion:** The HCF and the LCM 1024 and 1025 are 1 and 1049600 respectively.

Reason: Any two consecutive positive integers are co-primes.

17. **Assertion:** The unit's digit of $\left[(2024)^{2028} - (2019)^{2027}\right]$ is 3.

Reason: 4^x ends in 4 or 6.

18. **Assertion:** $\frac{9949}{2^{24} \times 5^{12}}$ has a terminating decimal expansion.

Reason: If $\frac{x}{y}$ is a rational number and $y = 2^m \times 5^n$, where m and n are whole numbers, then $\frac{x}{y}$ has a terminating decimal expansion.

19. **Assertion:** If the HCF and LCM of two numbers are 7 and 49 respectively, there exists only one pair of numbers.

Reason: The HCF two consecutive even natural numbers is 1.

20. **Assertion:** $\left(\sqrt{1375} + \sqrt{1125}\right)\left(\sqrt{1125} - \sqrt{1375}\right)$ is a rational number.

Reason: If $n = 2$, x and y are rational numbers, then $\left(\sqrt[n]{x} + \sqrt[n]{y}\right)\left(\sqrt[n]{x} - \sqrt[n]{y}\right)$ is a rational number since $\left(\sqrt[n]{x} + \sqrt[n]{y}\right)\left(\sqrt[n]{x} - \sqrt[n]{y}\right) = x - y$ for $n = 2$.

ANSWER KEYS

Crossword

Across

2. Zero 6. Eight 7. Two 8. Irrational 11. One

Down

1. Seven 3. Rational 4. Algorithm 5. Binary 9. Two
10. One

Classroom Wing

Very Short Answer Type Questions

1. $100110_{(2)}$ 2. $110_{(2)}$ 3. 6 4. irrational 5. 16
6. $1100000_{(2)}$ 7. 15625 8. No value of x 9. False 10. True
11. False

Short Answer Type Questions

12. (b) 13. (c) 14. (i) → (A); (ii) → (B); (iii) → (D); (iv) → (C)
16. 24 17. (B) 80 18. 36, 1080 19. (B) 11
20. (i), (ii) are non-terminating and (iii), (iv) are terminating.

Essay Type Questions

21. (A) 279 (B) 5760; 90,48,160,360,240 22. 8 23. 9:15 am 25. $\frac{23091}{990}$
26. $\frac{12343}{90}$

Competition Wing

Level 1: Apply Your Concepts

1. $(1)_2$ 2. $(2)_{10}$ 3. $(100)_2$ 4. $(10)_2$ 5. $0.\overline{06}$
6. (d) 7. (a) 8. (b) 9. (c) 10. (b)
11. (c) 12. (b) 13. (a) 14. (b) 15. (c)
16. (c) 17. (a) 18. (d) 19. (d) 20. (c)
21. (d) 22. (a)

Level 2: Review Your Concepts

23. (a) 24. (c) 25. (c) 26. (b) 27. (d)
28. (b) 29. (b)

Level 3: Assess Your Concepts

30. (a) 31. (b) 32. (a) 33. (a) 34. (b)
35. (A) (b) (B) (a) 36. (d) 37. (c) 38. (c)
39. (b) 40. (b) 41. (b) 42. (a) 43. (b)
44. (c) 45. (a) 46. (a) 47. (c) 48. (c)

JEE Special Wing

Multiple-Answer Type Questions

1. (a, b, d)	2. (a, c, d)	3. (a, b)	4. (a, b)	5. (b, d)

Match The Column

6. (f)	7. (e)	8. (b)	9. (a)	10. (d)

Comprehension-Based Questions

11. (d)	12. (a)	13. (b)	14. (c)	15. (b)

Assertion and Reason Type Questions

16. (b)	17. (d)	18. (a)	19. (c)	20. (a)

Hints and Explanations

Classroom Wing

Very Short Answer Type Questions

1. $1011_{(2)} + 1101_{(2)} + 1110_{(2)} + 11 + 13 + 14 = 38 = 2^5 + 2^2 + 2^1 = 100110_{(2)}$

2. $11011_{(2)} - 10101_{(2)} = 27 - 21 = 6 = 2^2 + 2^1 = 110_{(2)}$

3. $360 = 5\times3\times3\times2\times2\times2$

$= 5\times3^2\times2^3$

On comparing,

$x = 3, y = 2, z = 1$

$x + y + z = 6$

4. $a = 2+\sqrt{3}$

$b = \sqrt{2}-\sqrt{3}$

$a + b = 2+\sqrt{3}+\sqrt{2}-\sqrt{3}$

$= 2+\sqrt{2}$

i.e., it is irrational.

5. $0.\overline{7} = \frac{p}{q}$

$\frac{p}{q} = \frac{7}{9}$

$p + q = 16$

6. $101101_{(2)} = 1\times2^5 + 0\times2^4 + 1\times2^3 + 1\times2^2\times0\times2^1 + 1\times2^0 = 45$

$110011_{(2)} = 1\times2^5 + 1\times2^4 + 0\times2^3 + 0\times2^2\times1\times2^1 + 1\times2^0 = 51$

$\therefore 45 + 51 = 96 = 2^6 + 2^5 = 1100000_{(2)}$

7. LCM of 25 and 625 = 625

HCF of 25 and 625 = 25

Product of HCF and LCM = 625×25

= 15,625.

8. $2^x\times5^x$

By law, multiplication of 2 and 5 will always end with a zero. Therefore, for no value of x it will end in 5.

9. $\frac{7^3}{5^4} = \frac{343}{625}$

$= 0.5488$

10. 19 divides a^3 means $\frac{a\times a\times a}{19}$ is correct

So, $\frac{a}{9}$, i.e., also true.

11. Explanation with example.

Let 1st irrational no. be $\sqrt{2}$

Let 2nd irrational no. be $\sqrt{2}$

$\sqrt{2}\times\sqrt{2} = 2$

So, it is not always true.

Short Answer Type Questions

12. $250 = 2^7 + 2^6 + 2^5 + 2^4 + 2^3 + 2^1 = 11111010_{(2)}$

Hence, the correct option is (b).

13. 4^n ends in either 4 or 6.

3^n ends in 3, 9, 7, or 1.

$\therefore 4^n - 3^n$ ends in 1, 5, 7, 3, or 9.

There are 5 possible units digits.

Hence, the correct option is (c).

14. (i) → (A); (ii) → (B); (iii) → (D); (iv) → (C)

15. Let 1000001 be in p system.

$\therefore 1000001_{(p)} = p^6 + 1 = (p^2)^3 + 1^3$

$= (p^2 + 1)(p^4 - p^2 + 1)$

As p is a positive integer and

$1000001_{(p)} = (p^2 + 1)(p^4 - p^2 + 1)$,

Given number is composite number.

16. HCF of 72 and 26

Using Euclid's division algorithm,

Since, $264 > 72$

We divide 264 by 72

$$\begin{array}{r|l} 72 & 264 \; (3 \\ & -216 \\ \hline & 48 \end{array}$$

Since remainders are not zero, we divide 72 by 48

$$\begin{array}{r|l} 48 & 72 \; (1 \\ & -48 \\ \hline & 24 \end{array}$$

Since remainders are not zero, we divide 48 by 24

$$\begin{array}{r|l} 24 & 48 \; (2 \\ & -48 \\ \hline & 0 \end{array}$$

Hence, the HCF is 24.

17. (A) Using BODMAS rule

$7 \times 5 \times 3 \times 2 \times 7 = 217$

Factors of $217 = 7 \times 31 \times 1$

Hence, it is composite number

(B)

2	6, 4, 8, 12
2	3, 2, 4, 6
3	3, 1, 2, 3
	1, 1, 2, 1

$p = 2 \times 2 \times 3 \times 2 = 24$

8	24, 8, 24, 16
3	3, 1, 3, 2
	1, 1, 1, 2

$q = 8$

2	8, 2, 16, 6
2	4, 1, 8, 3
2	2, 1, 4, 3
	1, 1, 2, 3

$r = 2 \times 2 \times 2 \times 2 \times 3 = 48$

we have $(p^3 + q^3 + r^3 - 3pqr)$

$= (p + q + r)\,(p^2 + q^2 + r^2 - pq - qr - rp)$

$$\Rightarrow \frac{p^3 + q^3 + r^3 - 3pqr}{p^2 + q^2 + r^2 - pq - qr - rp} = p + q + r$$

$= 24 + 8 + 48 = 80.$

18. LCM using prime factorization

2	108
2	54
3	27
3	9
3	3
	1

2	360
2	180
2	90
3	45
3	15
5	5
	1

$108 = 2^2 \times 3^3$

$360 = 2^3 \times 3^2 \times 5$

LCM = product of all factors with highest powers

$2^3 \times 3^3 \times 5 = 1080$

HCF = Common factor of 108 and 360

$= 2^2 \times 3^2$

$= 4 \times 9 = 36$

19. (A) Let's assume that the square root of 6 is rational. By definition, that means there are two integers *a* and *b* with no common divisors where

$$\frac{a}{b} = \sqrt{6}$$

So, let's multiply both sides by themselves:

$$\frac{a}{b} \times \frac{a}{b} = \sqrt{6} \times \sqrt{6}$$

$a^2 = 6b^2$

But this statement means the RHS is even, because it is a product of integers and one of those integers (at least) is even. So a^2 must be even. But any odd number times itself is odd, so if a^2 is even, then *a* is even. Since *a* is even, there is some integer *c* that is half of *a*,

$2c = a$

Now, lets replace *a* with $2c$

$a^2 = 6b^2$

$(2c)^2 = (2)(3)(b)^2$

$2c^2 = 3b^2$

But now, we can argue the same thing for *b*, This is a contradiction to all assumption. Hence, $\sqrt{6}$ is irrational.

(B) If we take any power of 6, the unit's digit would be 6. Also, if we take any power of 5, the unit's digit would be 5.

So $(16)^{7x}$ has unit's digit 6 and $(15)^{11x}$ has unit's digits 5 for all $x \in N$

$Z = (16)^{7x} + (15)^{11x}$ has unit's digit is 1 as $5 + 6 = 11$.

20. (i) $\frac{23}{175}$

Denominator = 175

5	175
5	35
7	7
	1

Denominator $= 5^2 \times 7$

Not in form of $2^n 5^m$

Hence, it is non-terminating

(ii) $\frac{125}{325}$

Denominator = 325

5	325
5	65
13	13
	1

Not in form of $2^n 5^m$

Hence, it is non-terminating

(iii) $\frac{73}{40}$

2	40
2	20
2	10
5	5
	1

Denominator $= 2^3 \times 5^1$

in the form of $2^n 5^m$

Hence, it is terminating

(iv) $\frac{157}{125}$

5	125
5	25
5	5
	1

$= 2^0 \times 5^3$

In the form of $2^n 5^m$

Hence, it is terminating

Essay Type Questions

21. (A) Find HCF of 732 and 942.

2	732
2	366
2	183
61	61
	1

2	942
3	471
157	157
	1

$\text{HCF} = 2 \times 3 = 6$

Divide both numbers by 6.

$6\sqrt{732} = 122$, only those who got apples

$6\sqrt{942} = 157$, only those who got oranges

Least possible number of students = 122 + 157

= 279.

(B) Take the LCM of 64, 120, 36, 16, 24

2	64, 120, 36, 16, 24
2	32, 60, 18, 8, 12
2	16, 30, 9, 4, 6
2	8, 15, 9, 2, 3
3	4, 15, 9, 1, 3
	4, 5, 3, 1, 1

$\text{LCM} = 2 \times 2 \times 2 \times 2 \times 3 \times 4 \times 5 \times 3 = 2880.$

They will meet at the starting point for the second time after 2 × LCM i.e. 5760 seconds.

Number of complete rounds

for $P = \frac{5760}{64} = 90$

for $Q = \frac{5760}{120} = 48$

for $R = \frac{5760}{36} = 160$

for $S = \frac{5760}{16} = 360$

for $T = \frac{5760}{24} = 240.$

22. $60 = 36 \times 1 + 24,\ 36 = 24 \times 1 + 12,\ 24 = 12 \times 2 + 0$

HCF of 60, 36 is 12.

∴ The maximum number of students for each row is 12.

Total number of rows $= \frac{60}{12} + \frac{36}{12}$

$= 5 + 3 = 8$

23. They will meet again in $\frac{60}{4}$ minute, i.e., 15 minutes 9:15 A.M.

24. $\frac{p}{q} = 5 - \sqrt{5}$

$\frac{p^2}{q^2} = (5 - \sqrt{5})(5 - \sqrt{5})$

$p^2 = (5 - \sqrt{5})^2 q^2$

Let $p = 5c$

$25c^2 = (5 - \sqrt{5})^2 q^2$

$c^2 = \frac{(5 - \sqrt{5})^2}{25} q^2$

Therefore, $(5 - \sqrt{5})$ should be a factor contradiction, hence, it is irrational.

25. Let $n = 23.3\overline{24}$

$10^n = 233.\overline{24}$

As there are two numbers under bar, multiply by 100,

$1000^n = 23324.\overline{24}$

Subtract 10^n from both sides:

$$1000n = 23324.\overline{24}$$

$$10n = 233.\overline{24}$$

$$(-) \quad (-)$$

$$990n = 23091 \text{ (bar cancel)}$$

$$n = \frac{23091}{990}$$

26. $12.\overline{35} + 123.\overline{5} + 1.\overline{235}$

$$= \frac{1235-12}{99} + \frac{1235-123}{9} + \frac{1235-12}{990}$$

$$= \frac{1223}{99} + \frac{1112}{9} + \frac{1223}{990}$$

$$= \frac{12230+122320+1223}{990}$$

$$= \frac{135773}{990} = \frac{12343}{90}.$$

Competition Wing

Level 1: Apply Your Concepts

1. $(1)_{10} = (1)_2$
2. $(10)_2 = (2)^1{}_1 + (2)^0{}_0 = (2)_{10}$
3. In binary system, $1 + 1 + 1 + 1 = 4 = (100)_2$
4. In binary system, $1 + 1 + 0 = (10)_2$
5. $0.\bar{5} - 0.\overline{49} = 0.\overline{06}$
6.
$$\begin{array}{r} 1 \quad\; 1 \qquad \\ 1\ 1\ 1\ 0\ 1_{(2)} \\ \oplus\ 1\ 1\ 0\ 0\ 1_{(2)} \\ \hline 1\ 1\ 0\ 1\ 1\ 0_{(2)} \\ \hline \end{array}$$
7.
$$\begin{array}{r} 0\ 2\ 2 \rightarrow \text{Borrow} \\ 1\ 1\ 1\ \ 1\ 0_{(2)} \\ \oplus\ 1\ 0\ 0\ \ 1\ 1_{(2)} \\ \hline 1\ \ 0\ \ 1\ 1_{(2)} \\ \hline \end{array}$$
8. $(111110110)_2 = 2^8 + 2^7 + 2^6 + 2^5 + 2^4 + 0(2^3) + 2^2 + 2^1 + 0(2^0) = 502$
9. (i) Given expression is in the form of $a^2 - b^2$.

   (ii) $a^{2n} - b^{2n}$ is divisible by both $(a - b)$ and $(a + b)$.
10. Apply trial and error method.
11. Apply trial and error method.
12. (i) Express 432 and 504 as the product of prime factors and proceed.
    (ii) Write 432 and 504 as the product of prime factors.
    (iii) HCF is the product of common prime factors with least exponents.
13. For any natural number n, 6^n and 5^n end with 6 and 5, respectively.
14. (i) Apply the method of prime factorization for finding the HCF of the given numbers.

    (ii) Then find the possibilities for q.
15. (i) Multiply and divide $3+\sqrt{5}$ by 2.

    (ii) Convert the expression $\sqrt{x+2\sqrt{y}}$ in the form of $\sqrt{(\sqrt{m})^2 + (n)^2 + 2(mn)}$.
16. (i) First of all find the HCF of 720 and 405.

    (ii) The required number is $\dfrac{720}{\text{HCF}} + \dfrac{405}{\text{HCF}}$.
17. (i) $3^{2n} + 2^{2n} = 9^n + 4^n$.

    (ii) $a^n + b^n$ is divisible by $(a + b)$ when n is odd.
18. For no value of x, $2^x \times 5^x$ ends in 5.
19. Only $\dfrac{1}{2}$ is terminating decimal.
20. LCM of two co-primes is their product.
21. HCF of two co-primes is 1.
22. $15 = 4 \times 3 + 3$.

Level 2: Review Your Concepts

23. $(1111)_2 = (2^3)1 + (2^2)1 + (2^1)1 + (2^0)1 = 15$
24. $(111)_{10} = (2^6)1 + (2^5)1 + (2^4)0 + (2^3)1 + (2^2)1 + (2^1)1 + (2^0)1 = (1101111)_2$
25. $(1100)_2 = 2^3 + 2^2 = 12$
26. (i) Write cubes of 1 to 9.

    (ii) Then check their unit digits.
27. (i) Recall the concepts of surds and irrational numbers.

    (ii) Recall the concepts of RF.
28. Form the equations in LCM and HCF and solve for LCM and HCF.
29. ACB is the required sequential order.

Level 3: Assess Your Concepts

30. $(110011)_2 = (2^5)1 + (2^4)1 + (2^3)0 + (2^2)0 + (2^1)1 + (2^0)1 = 32 + 16 + 0 + 0 + 2 + 1 = 51$.
31. $144 = 2^7 + 2^4 = (10010000)_2$
32. Any prime number greater than 3 is in the form $6k \pm 1$, where k is a natural number.
33. HCF is the factor of LCM.
34. (i) Write $156 = 1 \times 120 + 36$ and proceed further.

    (ii) $156 = 120 \times 1 + 36$

    $120 = 36 \times 3 + 12$.

    (iii) Use division algorithm until we get zero as remainder.
35. (A) $\sqrt{3+\sqrt{5}}$

    $= \sqrt{\dfrac{6}{2} + \dfrac{2}{2}\sqrt{5}}$

$$= \sqrt{\frac{5}{2} + \frac{1}{2} + 2\sqrt{\frac{5}{1} \times \frac{1}{2}}}$$

$$= \sqrt{\left(\sqrt{\frac{5}{2}} + \sqrt{\frac{1}{2}}\right)^2}$$

$$= \sqrt{\frac{5}{2}} + \sqrt{\frac{1}{2}}$$

(B) $\frac{1}{2+\sqrt{5}} + \frac{1}{\sqrt{5}+\sqrt{6}} + \ldots +$ 96th term.

$= \frac{1}{\sqrt{4}+\sqrt{5}} + \frac{1}{\sqrt{5}+\sqrt{6}} + \ldots +$ 96th term.

$= \frac{\sqrt{4}-\sqrt{5}}{-1} + \frac{\sqrt{5}-\sqrt{6}}{-1} + \ldots +$ 96th term

$= \sqrt{5} - \sqrt{4} + \sqrt{6} - \sqrt{5} + \ldots + 10 - \sqrt{99}$

$=10 - \sqrt{4} = 10 - 2 = 8.$

36. For all $x \in N$,

$(37)^{3x}$ ends in 3 or 7 and $(33)^{3x}$ ends in 7 or 3.

If $(37)^{3x}$ ends in 3, then $(33)^{3x}$ ends 7.

In this case $(37)^{3x} - (33)^{3x}$ ends in 6 (1)

If $(37)^{3x}$ ends in 7, then $(33)^{3x}$ ends in 3.

In this case, $(37)^{3x} - (33)^{3x}$ ends in 4 (2)

From Eqs. (1) and (2), option (d) follows.

37. In *P*, the prime numbers that occur are 2, 3, 5, 7.

In Q, there are no 2's. So the HCF of *P*, *Q* has only 3's, 5's, 7's.

The 3's in *P* come from 6, 12, 18, i.e., 3^4 is the greatest power of 3 that is a factor of *P*, while for *Q* the 3's come from 3, 9, 15, i.e., 3^4 is also a factor of Q.

Similarly, 5^2 is the greatest power of 5 that for both *P* and Q and 7^1 is the greatest power of 7 for both *P* and Q.

∴ The HCF of *P*, *Q* is $3^4(5^2)(7)$.

38. Given LCM = 1001 and HCF = 7.

Let the two numbers be x and y.

∴ $x = 7a$ and $y = 7b$, where a and b are co-primes.

We have, $x \times y = \text{LCM} \times \text{HCF}$

$7a \times 7b = 1001 \times 7$

$ab = 143 \Rightarrow (a, b) = (1, 143)$ or $(11, 13)$

⇒ There are two pairs of numbers.

39. For number of boxes to be the least, the number of fruits in each box should be maximum.

As per the given data, the number of fruits in each box is equal to the HCF of 96 and 112, i.e., 16

∴ Minimum number of boxes $= \frac{96}{16} + \frac{112}{16} = 13.$

40. LCM of 40 seconds and 30 seconds is 120 seconds, i.e., 2 minutes.

∴ A and B meet in every 2 minutes.

∴ Option (b) follows.

41. Number of ways in which 1500 can be resolved into two factors worked out using the concept given by

$$\frac{\text{Number of factors of 1500}}{2}$$

$1500 = 3 \times 5^3 \times 2^2.$

Number of factors of $1500 = (1 + 1)(3 + 1)(2 + 1) = 24.$

Number of ways in which 1500 can be resolved into two factors $= \frac{24}{2} = 12.$

42. The time interval between simultaneous tolling of the bells = LCM (10, 15, 20, 30) seconds = 60 seconds = 1 minute.

Hence the bells will toll together again for the first time after 10:00 am at 10:01 am.

43. Given that, $a = \sqrt[8]{6} - \sqrt[8]{5},\ b = \sqrt[8]{6} + \sqrt[8]{5}$

$$c = \sqrt[6]{6} + \sqrt[6]{5}$$

$$d = \sqrt[4]{6} + \sqrt[4]{5},\ e = \sqrt{6} + \sqrt{5}$$

By inspection, we can reject *ab*, *cd*.

$ab = \sqrt[4]{6} + \sqrt[4]{5}$

∴ $abd = \sqrt{6} - \sqrt{5}$ and $abde = 6 - 5 = 1.$

∴ *abde* is a rational number.

44. For all $x \in N$,

$(12)^{3x}$ ends in either 8 or 2 and $(18)^{3x}$ ends in either 2 or 8

If $(12)^{3x}$ ends in 8, then $(18)^{3x}$ ends in 2.

If $(12)^{3x}$ ends in 2, then $(18)^{3x}$ ends in 8.

∴ $(12)^{3x} + (18)^{3x}$ ends in 0 only.

45. $X = 28 + (1 \times 2 \times 3 \times \cdots \times 16 \times 28)$

$\Rightarrow X = 28\ [1 + (1 \times 2 \times 3 \times \cdots \times 16)]$

∴ X is a composite number.

$Y = 17 + (1 \times 2 \times 3 \times 4 \times \cdots \times 17) = 17$

$[1 + (1 \times 2 \times \cdots \times 16)]$

$\therefore$ Y is a composite number.

Now, $X - Y = [1 + (1 \times 2 \times 3 \times \cdots \times 16)]$

$(28 - 17) = [1 + (1 \times 2 \times 3 \times \cdots \times 16)]\ (11)$

$\therefore$ $X - Y$ is a composite number.

$X + Y = [1 + (1 \times 2 \times 3 \times \cdots)]$

$\therefore$ $X + Y$ is a composite number.

$\therefore$ Option (a) follows.

46. P is the LCM of 2, 4, 6, 8, 10.

$\therefore$ $P = 3(8)(5)$

Q is the LCM of 1, 3, 5, 7, 9.

$\therefore$ $Q = 5(7)(9)$

L is the LCM of P, Q

$\therefore$ $L = 3(8)(5)21$ or $5(7)(9)8$, i.e., $21P$ or $8Q$.

47. Given LCM = 144 and HCF = 12

Let the two numbers be x and y.

$\therefore$ $x = 12a$ and $y = 12b$

Where a and b are co-primes.

We have, $x \times y$ = LCM × HCF

$12a \times 12b = 144 \times 12$

$ab = 12 \Rightarrow (a, b) = (1, 12)$ or $(3, 4)$

There are two pairs of numbers.

48. LCM of 45 seconds and 60 seconds is 180 seconds, i.e., 3 minutes.

$\therefore$ They toll together in every 3 minutes

$\therefore$ Option (c) follows.

JEE Special Wing

Multiple-Answer Type Questions

1. Given that LCM = 660 and HCF = 22.

   As the HCF of the numbers is 22, the numbers are multiples of 22.

   Let the numbers be $22x$ and $22y$, where x and y are coprime.

   We have the product of two numbers is equal to the product of their LCM and their HCF.

   $\Rightarrow 22x \times 22y = 660 \times 22$

   $\Rightarrow x \times y = 30$, where x and y are coprime.

   $\Rightarrow (x, y)$ can be $(1, 30), (2, 15), (3, 10)$ or $(5, 6)$

   $\Rightarrow (22x, 22y)$ can be $(22, 660), (44, 330), (66, 220)$ or $(110, 132)$

   $\Rightarrow$ The sum of the numbers can be 682, 374, 286 and 242.

   Hence, the correct options are (a, b, d).

2. Given that the prime factors of a number are 2 and 3.

   Let the number be $2^x \times 3^y$.

   The number of factors $= (x+1)(y+1)$, where each of x and y is an integer more than 1.

   Also given that $(x+1)(y+1) = 12$.

   $(x+1)(y+1) = 2 \times 6$ or 3×4

   $= (1+1) \times (5+1)$ or $(2+1) \times (4+1)$.

x	y	$2^x \times 3^y$	Sum of the Digits
1	5	$2^1 \times 3^5 = 486$	18
5	1	$2^5 \times 3^1 = 96$	15
2	4	$2^2 \times 3^4 = 162$	9
4	2	$2^4 \times 3^2 = 144$	9

   The sum of the digits can be 9, 15, or 18.

   Hence, the correct options are (a, c, d).

3. Given that the LCM of two numbers is their product.

   Hence, the numbers must be coprime.

   We know that consecutive odd numbers are coprime.

   Consecutive prime numbers are coprime.

   Consecutive even numbers are not coprime.

   Consecutive composite numbers need not necessarily be coprime.

   Hence, the correct options are (a and b).

4. We have $(a-b)(a^2+ab+b^2) = a^3 - b^3$.

   So, an RF of $\sqrt[3]{3} - \sqrt[3]{2}$ is $\sqrt[3]{3^2} + \sqrt[3]{3 \times 2} + \sqrt[3]{2^3}$

   $= \sqrt[3]{9} + \sqrt[3]{6} + \sqrt[3]{8}$.

   Also, any multiple of $\sqrt[3]{9} + \sqrt[3]{6} + \sqrt[3]{8}$ is also an RF of $\sqrt[3]{3} - \sqrt[3]{2}$.

   Choice (1): $\sqrt[3]{72} + \sqrt[3]{64} + \sqrt[3]{48}$

   $= \sqrt[3]{8 \times 9} + \sqrt[3]{8 \times 8} + \sqrt[3]{8 \times 6} = 2(\sqrt[3]{9} + \sqrt[3]{8} + \sqrt[3]{6})$

   which is an RF of $\sqrt[3]{3} - \sqrt[3]{2}$.

   Choice (2): $\sqrt[3]{162} + \sqrt[3]{216} + \sqrt[3]{243}$

   $= \sqrt[3]{27 \times 6} + \sqrt[3]{27 \times 8} + \sqrt[3]{27 \times 9} = 3(\sqrt[3]{6} + \sqrt[3]{8} + \sqrt[3]{9})$

   which is an RF of $\sqrt[3]{3} - \sqrt[3]{2}$.

   Choice (3): $\sqrt[3]{81} + \sqrt[3]{72} + \sqrt[3]{54}$

   $= \sqrt[3]{9 \times 9} + \sqrt[3]{9 \times 8} + \sqrt[3]{9 \times 6}$ which is not an RF of $\sqrt[3]{3} - \sqrt[3]{2}$, since 9 is not a perfect cube.

   Clearly Choice (4): $\sqrt[3]{6} + \sqrt[3]{8} + \sqrt[3]{10}$ is not an RF of $\sqrt[3]{3} - \sqrt[3]{2}$.

   Hence, the correct options are (a and b).

5. Kourav has 252 pigeons and 294 parrots.

   He wants to arrange them in separate nets.

   He wants to arrange equal number and same kind of birds.

   The number of birds that can be arranged in each net = The HCF of 252 and 294 = 42.

   The factors of 42 are 1, 2, 3, 6, 7, 14, 21, and 42.

   As he wants to arrange odd number of birds in each net, the possible number of nets required is as follows:

Number of Birds in Each Net	Number of Nets
1	$\dfrac{252+294}{1} = 546$
3	$\dfrac{252+294}{3} = 182$
7	$\dfrac{252+294}{7} = 78$
21	$\dfrac{252+294}{2} = 26$

   Hence, the correct options are (b and d).

Match The Column

Common Solutions for questions 6 to 10:

6. $123.\overline{63} = 123.6363636363\ldots$

$431.\overline{6} = 431.6666666666\ldots$

On adding, $= 555.30303030\ldots$

$A + B = 555.\overline{30}$

Hence, the correct option is (f).

7. $232.1\overline{4} = 232.1444444444\ldots$

$322.\overline{8} = 322.8888888888\ldots$

On adding, $= 555.0333333333\ldots$

$C + D = 555.0\overline{3}$

Hence, the correct option is (e).

8. $232.1\overline{4} = 232.1444444444\ldots$

$123.\overline{63} = 123.6363636363\ldots$

On subtracting,

$= 108.508080808\ldots$

$C - A = 108.5\overline{08}$

Hence, the correct option is (b).

9. $431.\overline{6} = 431.6666666666\ldots$

$322.\overline{8} = 322.8888888888\ldots$

On subtracting,

$= 108.777777777\ldots$

$B - D = 108.\overline{7}$

Hence, the correct option is (a).

10. $431.\overline{6} = 431.6666666666\ldots$

$322.\overline{8} = 322.8888888888\ldots$

On adding,

$B + D = 754.5555555554\ldots$

$B + D = 754.5555555554\ldots$

$C = 232.1444444444\ldots$

On subtracting,

$B + D - C = 522.41111111\ldots$

$B - D = 522.4\overline{1}$

Hence, the correct option is (d).

COMPREHENSION-BASED QUESTIONS

Common Solutions for questions 11 to 15:

The length of the route = 12 km.

Sprinter, Hurdler, and Breezer can complete one round in 4 hours, 3 hours, and 2 hours respectively.

11. The time taken to meet for the first time after 9 am = LCM (4 hours, 3 hours, and 2 hours) = 12 hours.

Hence, the required time = 9 am + 12 hours = 9 pm.

Hence, the correct option is (d).

12. The number of rounds made by Sprinter before they meet for the first time after 9 am $= \dfrac{12 \text{ hours}}{4 \text{ hours}} = 3.$

The number of rounds made by Hurdler before they meet for the first time after 9 am $= \dfrac{12 \text{ hours}}{3 \text{ hours}} = 4.$

The number of rounds made by Breezer before they meet for the first time after 9 am $= \dfrac{12 \text{ hours}}{2 \text{ hours}} = 6.$

Hence, the sum of the number of rounds made by them before they meet at the point B for the first time after 9 am = 3 + 4 + 6 = 13.

Hence, the correct option is (a).

13. The number of rounds made by Hurdler before they meet for the first time after 9 am = 4.

Hence, the distance travelled by Hurdler = 4 × 12 = 48 km.

Hence, the correct option is (b).

14. The number of rounds made by Breezer before they meet for the first time after 9 am = 6.

Hence, the distance travelled by Breezer = 6 × 12 = 72 km.

The quantity of water for every 9 km he runs = 250 ml.

Hence, the total quantity of water $= \dfrac{72}{9} \times 250$ ml = 2000 ml = 2 litres.

Hence, the correct option is (c).

15. The distance travelled by Breezer = 72 km.

The number of rounds made by Hurdler before they meet for the first time after 9 am = 4.

Hence, the distance travelled by Hurdler = 4 × 12 = 48 km.

Hence, the required difference = 72 km – 48 km = 24 km.

Hence, the correct option is (b).

ASSERTION AND REASON TYPE QUESTIONS

16. Given that

Assertion: The HCF and the LCM 1024 and 1025 are 1 and 1049600 respectively.

Since 1024 and 1025 are consecutive positive integers, they are coprime to each other.

Hence, the HCF (1024 and 1025) is 1.

The LCM (1024 and 1025) is $1024 \times 1025 = 1049600$.
Hence, the **Assertion** is true.

Reason: Any two consecutive positive integers are co-primes.

The statement of **Reason** is true, but it is not the correct explanation of **Assertion.**

Hence, the correct option is (b).

17. **Assertion:** The unit's digit of $(2024)^{2028}$ is 6.

The unit's digit of $(2019)^{2027}$ is 9.

The unit's digit of $\left[(2024)^{2028} - (2019)^{2027}\right] = 7.$

So, the **Assertion** is false.

Reason: 4^x ends in 4 and 6 when x is odd and even positive integers respectively.

So, the **Reason** is true.

Hence, the correct option is (d).

18. **Assertion:** $\frac{9949}{2^{24} \times 5^{12}}$ has a terminating decimal expansion, since the denominator is in the form of $2^m \times 5^n$, where m and n are whole numbers. So, Assertion is true.

Reason: If $\frac{x}{y}$ is a rational number and $y = 2^m \times 5^n$, where m and n are whole numbers, then $\frac{x}{y}$ has a terminating decimal expansion. It is a true statement and is the correct explanation of **Assertion.**

Hence, the correct option is (a).

19. **Assertion:** Given that the HCF and LCM of two numbers are 7 and 49.

Let the numbers be $7x$ and $7y$, where x and y are co-prime to each other.

We have the product of two numbers = Product of their HCF and LCM.

$\Rightarrow 7x \times 7y = 7 \times 49$

$\Rightarrow x \times y = 7 = 1 \times 7$, where 1 and 7 are co-prime to each other.

The numbers are 7×1 and 7×7 i.e., 7 and 49.

So, there exists only one pair of numbers.

Hence, **Assertion** is true.

Reason: The HCF two consecutive even natural numbers is 2.

Hence, **Reason** is false.

Hence, the correct option is (c).

20. **Assertion:**

$\left(\sqrt{1375} + \sqrt{1125}\right)\left(\sqrt{1125} - \sqrt{1375}\right)$

$= \left(\sqrt{1125} + \sqrt{1375}\right)\left(\sqrt{1125} - \sqrt{1375}\right)$

$= \left(\sqrt{1125}\right)^2 - \left(\sqrt{1375}\right)^2$

$= 1125 - 1375 = -250$ which is a rational number.

Hence, Assertion is true.

Reason: For $n = 2$, $\left(\sqrt[n]{x} + \sqrt[n]{y}\right)\left(\sqrt[n]{x} - \sqrt[n]{y}\right)$

$= \left(\sqrt{x} + \sqrt{y}\right)\left(\sqrt{x} - \sqrt{y}\right)$

$= \left(\sqrt{x}\right)^2 - \left(\sqrt{y}\right)^2$

$= x - y$ which is a rational number since x and y are rational numbers. Hence, **Reason** is true and is the correct explanation of **Assertion**.

Hence, the correct option is (a).

Unit II

Algebra

In this Unit

- ✶ **Chapter 2** Polynomials
- ✶ **Chapter 3** Remainder and Factor Theorem
- ✶ **Chapter 4** Pair of Linear Equations in Two Variables
- ✶ **Chapter 5** Quadratic Equations
- ✶ **Chapter 6** Progressions

CHAPTER 2

Polynomials

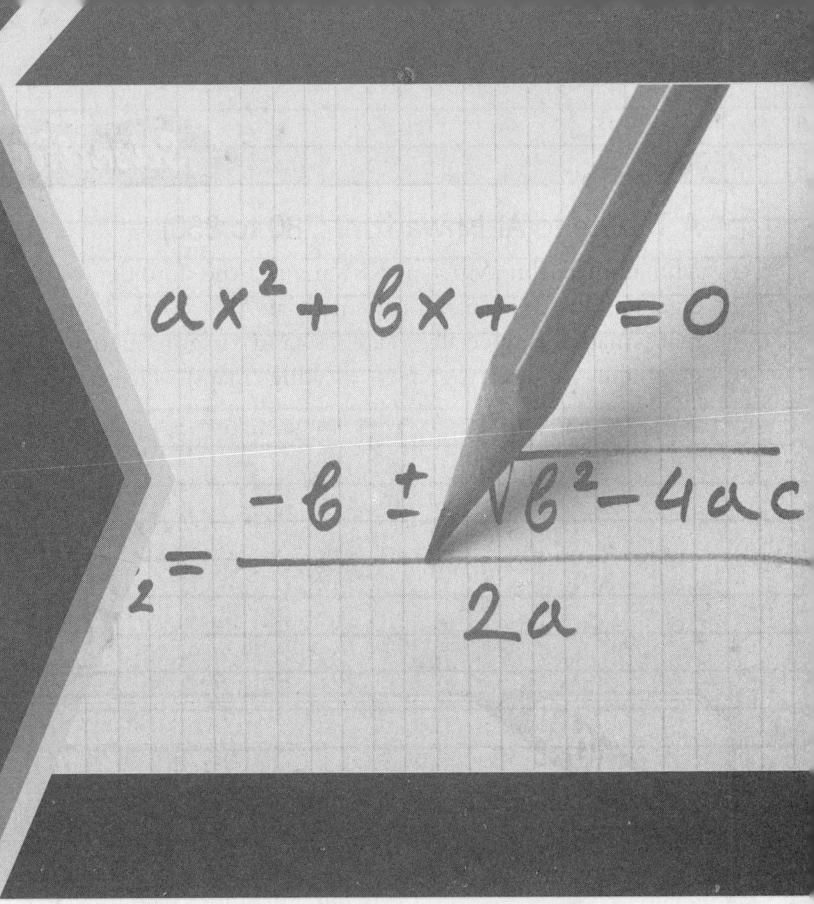

Remember

Before beginning this chapter, you should be able to:

- Explain about polynomials, their types and basic operations on polynomials
- Work on factorization of polynomials

Key Ideas

After completing this chapter, you should be able to:

- Define terms such as HCF and LCM
- Understand the methods to find LCM and HCF of polynomials
- Study relation among the LCM, the HCF and the product of polynomials
- Learn fundamental operations on rational expressions

Scientific Crypt

A Tribute to Al-Khwarizmi (780 to 850)

Muhammad ibn Musa al-Khwarizmi, the founder of algebra, was a Persian mathematician. He worked on mathematics (especially algebra and trigonometry), geography and cartography (making maps). He gave systematic methods for solving linear and quadratic equations. He gave tables for sines and cosines. His work on arithmetic was responsible for introducing the Hindu-Arabic numerals to the Western world.

FUN TIME

CROSSWORD

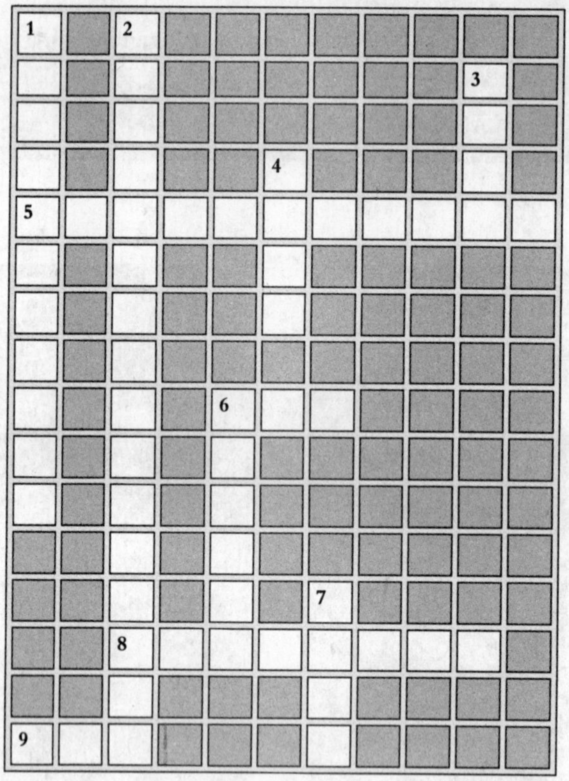

Across

5. The degree of the sum of two bi-quadratic polynomials (two words).
6. The quotient of the product of two polynomials and their HCF.
8. *f* and *g* are two non-zero polynomials. Then *f*/*g* is ____ expression.
9. *f* and *g* are two polynomials in *x*. *f* and *g* have no common factor in *x*. The HCF of *f* and *g*.

Down

1. *f*/*g* is a rational expression. Then *f* and *g* are
2. The sum of two polynomials *f* and *g* is a zero polynomial. How f is related to *g*? (two words)
3. The degree of the product of a cubic and a quadratic polynomial.
4. The degree of a constant polynomial.
6. $(x + y) / (x - y)$ is said to be in its ____ terms.
7. The HCF of $8xyz$ and $12pqr$.

INTRODUCTION

In this chapter, we will learn about HCF and LCM of polynomials and the method of finding them. A polynomial is any finite sum of terms. As subtraction can be written in terms of addition, finite differences are also included in this definition. Further we will learn about rational expressions and also the method of expressing them in their lowest terms.

Polynomial of Nth Degree

The expression of the form $a_0x^n + a_1x^{n-1} + \ldots + a_{n-1}x + a_n$ is a polynomial of nth degree ($a_0 \neq 0$) in one variable. Here a_0, a_1, …, a_n are real numbers.

The degree of a polynomial with one variable is the highest power to which the variable is raised in any one term.

Degree of polynomial is further divided as:

1. Polynomial of degree 0 is called constant polynomial.

   Example has degree 0

2. Polynomial of degree 1 is called linear polynomial.

   Example $5x - 3$ has degree 1

3. Polynomial of degree 2 is called quadratic polynomial.
4. Polynomial of degree 3 is called cubic polynomial.

   For example $6x^3 - 5x^2 + 2x - 1$ has degree 3.

5. Polynomial of degree 4 is called biquadratic polynomial.

> **Konnect**
>
> A polynomial of nth degree has at most terms.

When polynomials are written in decreasing powers of the variable then the coefficient of the first term is called the leading coefficient, e.g. the leading coefficient of $7x^5 - 3x^4 + 2x^2 - 1$ is 7.

HCF of Given Polynomial

For the given two polynomials, $f(x)$, $g(x)$ and $r(x)$ can be taken as the highest common factor, if

1. $r(x)$ is a common factor of $f(x)$ and $g(x)$ and
2. every common factor of $f(x)$ and $g(x)$ is also a factor of $r(x)$.

Highest common factor is generally referred to as HCF.

Method for Finding HCF of the Given Polynomials

Step 1: Express each polynomial as a product of powers of irreducible factors which also requires the numerical factors to be expressed as the product of the powers of primes.

Step 2: If there is no common factor then HCF is 1 and if there are common irreducible factors, we find the least exponent of these irreducible factors in the factorized form of the given polynomials.

Step 3: Raise the common irreducible factors to the smallest or the least exponents found in step 2 and take their product to get the HCF.

EXAMPLE 2.1 The H.C.F of the polynomials $p(x)$ and $q(x)$ is $4x - 12$, then $p(x)$ and $q(x)$ can be ______.

SOLUTION

H.C.F. $= 4x - 12 = 4(x - 3)$

Going by options,

$4(x - 3)^2 = 4(x - 3)\ (x - 3)$

$8(x - 3) = 2 \times 4\ (x - 3)$

H.C.F $= 4(x - 3)$.

EXAMPLE 2.2 Find the HCF of $96(x - 1)(x + 1)^2(x + 3)^3$ and $64(x^2 - 1)(x + 3)(x + 2)^2$.

SOLUTION

Let $f(x) = 96(x - 1)(x + 1)^2(x + 3)^3$ and $g(x) = 64(x^2 - 1)(x + 3)(x + 2)^2$.

Writing $f(x)$ and $g(x)$ as the product of the powers of irreducible factors,

$f(x) = 2 \times 2 \times 2 \times 2 \times 2 \times 3 \times (x - 1) \times (x + 1)^2 \times (x + 3)^3$

$g(x) = 2 \times 2 \times 2 \times 2 \times 2 \times 2 \times (x - 1)(x + 1)(x + 3)(x + 2)^2$

The common factors with the least exponents are 2^5, $(x - 1)$, $(x + 1)$, $(x + 3)$.

$\therefore$ The HCF of the given polynomials $= 32 \times (x - 1)(x + 1)(x + 3)$

$= 32(x^2 - 1)(x + 3)$.

LCM of the Given Polynomials

Least Common Multiple or the Lowest Common Multiple is the product of all the factors (taken once) of the polynomials given with their highest exponents, respectively.

Method for Finding LCM of the Given Polynomials

Step 1: First express each polynomial as a product of powers of irreducible factors.

Step 2: Consider all the irreducible factors (only once) occurring in the given polynomials. For each of these factors, consider the greatest exponent in the factorized form of the given polynomials.

Step 3: Now raise each irreducible factor to the greatest exponent and multiply them to get the LCM.

EXAMPLE 2.3 The LCM of $12p^3q^2$ and $18p^aq^3$ is $36p^3q^3$. Find the number of possible value(s) of a.

SOLUTION

$12p^3q^2 = 2^2 \times 3 \times p^3 \times q^2$

$18p^aq^3 = 2 \times 3^2 \times p^a \times q^3$

L.C.M $= 36p^3.q^3$

The value of 'a' can be 0, 1, 2 or 3

The number of integer values of a is 4.

EXAMPLE 2.4 If the LCM of $(x - 5)^6 (x + 3)^m$ and $(x - 5)^m (x + 3)^n$ is $(x - 5)^7 . (x + 3)^m$, then the maximum value of $(m + n)$ is _______.

SOLUTION

The LCM of $(x - 5)^6(x + 3)^m$ and $(x - 5)^m(x + 3)^n$ is $(x - 5)^7 (x + 3)^m$

Here, m should be 7 and the maximum value of n is 7.

$m + n = 7 + 7 = 14.$

Relation among the HCF, the LCM and the Product of the Polynomials

If $f(x)$ and $g(x)$ are two polynomials then we have the following relation,

$$(\text{HCF of } f(x) \text{ and } g(x)) \times (\text{LCM of } f(x) \text{ and } g(x)) = \pm (f(x) \times g(x)).$$

EXAMPLE 2.5 Let $f(x) = (x + 3)^2(x - 1)(x + 2)^3$ and $g(x) = (x + 3)(x - 1)^2(x + 2)^2$ be two polynomials.

SOLUTION

The common factors with the least exponents are $(x + 3)$, $(x - 1)$, $(x + 2)^2$.

$\Rightarrow$ HCF $= (x - 1)(x + 3)(x + 2)^2$

All the factors (taken only once) with the highest exponents are $(x + 3)^2$, $(x - 1)^2$, $(x + 2)^3$.

$\Rightarrow$ LCM $= (x - 1)^2(x + 2)^3(x + 3)^2$

Now, $f(x) \times g(x) = \{(x + 3)^2(x - 1)(x + 2)^3\} \times \{(x + 3)(x - 1)^2(x + 2)^2\} = (x - 1)^3(x + 2)^5 (x + 3)^3$

LCM $\times$ HCF $= \{(x - 1)(x + 3)(x + 2)^2\} \times \{(x - 1)^2(x + 2)^3(x + 3)^2\} = (x - 1)^3(x + 3)^3 (x + 2)^5$

Thus, we say, LCM $\times$ HCF = Product of two polynomials.

EXAMPLE 2.6 If $f(x) = (x - 2)(x^2 - x - a)$, $g(x) = (x + 2)(x^2 + x - b)$ and their HCF is $x^2 - 4$, then find the value of $(a - b)$ (a and b are constants) from the following options.

(a) 2 (b) 3 (c) −4 (d) 0

SOLUTION

$f(x) = (x - 2)(x^2 - x - a)$

$g(x) = (x + 2)(x^2 + x - b)$

HCF $= x^2 - 4 = (x + 2)(x - 2)$

$\therefore x + 2$ is a factor of $(x^2 - x - a)$

$\therefore (-2)^2 - (-2) - a = 0 \Rightarrow a = 6$

$x - 2$ is a factor of $x^2 + x - b$

$\therefore 2^2 + 2 - b = 0$

$b = 6 \therefore a - b = 0.$

EXAMPLE 2.7 If the LCM of the polynomials $f(x) = (x + 1)^5 (x + 2)^a$ and $g(x) = (x + 1)^b (x + 2)^5$ is $(x + 1)^a (x + 2)^b$, then find the minimum value of $a + b$ from the following options.

(a) is 10 (b) is 14 (c) is 15 (d) Cannot say

SOLUTION

$f(x) = (x + 1)^5 (x + 2)^a$

$g(x) = (x + 1)^b (x + 2)^5$

LCM = $(x + 1)^a (x + 2)^b$

As $(x + 1)^a$ is a multiple of both $(x + 1)^5$ and $(x + 1)^b$, $a \geq 5$ and $a \geq b$ (1)

As $(x + 2)^b$ is a multiple of both $(x + 2)^a$ and $(x + 2)^5$, $b \geq 5$ and $b \geq a$ (2)

From (1) and (2),

$a = b$, $a \geq 5$ and $b \geq 5$

$\therefore$ Minimum value of $a + b$ is 5 + 5, i.e., 10.

Rational Expressions

We know that any number of the form $\frac{p}{q}$, where p, $q \in Z$ and $q \neq 0$, is called a rational number. As integers and polynomials behave in the same manner, we observe most of the properties satisfied by rational numbers are also satisfied by the algebraic expressions of the form $\frac{f(x)}{g(x)}$ which are called rational expressions. Rational expression is an algebraic expression which is of the form $\frac{f(x)}{g(x)}$, where $f(x)$ and $g(x)$ are polynomials and $g(x)$ is not a zero polynomial.

For any rational number of the form $\frac{p}{q}$, where $p, q \in Z$ and $q \neq 0$, p and q are called numerator and denominator respectively. Even though p and q are integers $\frac{p}{q}$, need not be an integer. Similarly, for any rational expression $\frac{f(x)}{g(x)}$, $f(x)$ is called numerator and $g(x)$ is called denominator.

Even though $f(x)$ and $g(x)$ are polynomials, $\frac{f(x)}{g(x)}$ need not be a polynomial.

Konnect

1. Every polynomial is a rational expression as $f(x)$ can be written as $\frac{f(x)}{1}$.
2. $\frac{f(x)}{g(x)}$ is not a rational expression if either numerator $f(x)$ or denominator $g(x)$ or both $f(x)$ and $g(x)$ are not polynomials.

For Examples:

1. $\frac{2x-1}{x^2-3x+1}$ is a rational expression.
2. $\frac{x^3+5x^2-\sqrt{3}x+\sqrt{5}}{2x^2-\sqrt{5}x+8}$ is a rational expression.
3. $\frac{x^2-5\sqrt{x}-1}{3x-5}$ is not a rational expression as the numerator is not a polynomial.

EXAMPLE 2.8 Which of the following algebraic expressions is/are not polynomials?

(A) $x^3+2x^3+\sqrt{7}x+4$ (B) $5x^2+4\sqrt{x}-11$

(C) $\frac{x^3+3x^2-8x+11}{4x\sqrt{x}-3x+3}$ (D) $\frac{x^3+3x^2-6x+13}{x^2+1}$

(a) A, B and C (b) A and C (c) B and C (d) A and D

SOLUTION

Recall definition of polynomials.

Rational Expressions in Lowest Terms

Let $f(x)$ and $g(x)$ have integer coefficients and HCF of $f(x)$ and $g(x)$ is 1, then the rational expression $\frac{f(x)}{g(x)}$ is said to be in its lowest terms.

If HCF of $f(x)$ and $g(x)$ is not equal to 1, then by cancelling HCF of $f(x)$ and $g(x)$ from both numerator and denominator, we can reduce the given rational expression in its lowest terms.

EXAMPLE 2.9 Verify whether the rational expression $\frac{x^2-1}{(2x+1)(x+2)}$ is in its lowest terms or not.

SOLUTION

The given rational expression can be written as $\frac{(x+1)(x-1)}{(2x+1)(x+2)}$ and clearly HCF of numerator and denominator of the given expression is 1.

∴ It is in its lowest terms.

EXAMPLE 2.10 The rational expression $\frac{(x-3)\left(x^2-x-2\right)}{(x-2)\left(x^2-x-6\right)}$ in its lowest terms is ______.

SOLUTION

$$\frac{(x-3)\left(x^2-x-2\right)}{(x-2)\left(x^2-x-6\right)}$$

$$=\frac{(x-3)(x-2)(x+1)}{(x-2)(x-3)(x+2)}$$

$$=\frac{x+1}{x+2}.$$

Addition/Subtraction of Rational Expressions

The sum of any two rational expressions $\frac{f(x)}{g(x)}$ and $\frac{h(x)}{p(x)}$ is written as,

$$\frac{f(x)}{g(x)}+\frac{h(x)}{p(x)}=\frac{f(x)\,p(x)+h(x)\,g(x)}{g(x)\,p(x)}$$

If the denominators $g(x)$ and $p(x)$ are equal then,

$$\frac{f(x)}{g(x)}+\frac{h(x)}{p(x)}=\frac{f(x)+h(x)}{g(x)}.$$

The difference of the above rational expressions can be written as,

$$\frac{f(x)}{g(x)}-\frac{h(x)}{p(x)}=\frac{f(x)\,p(x)-h(x)\,g(x)}{g(x)\,p(x)}.$$

Info Bytes!

1. Sum or difference of two rational expressions is also a rational expression.
2. For any rational expression $\frac{-f(x)}{g(x)}$ is called the additive inverse of $\frac{f(x)}{g(x)}$.

   That is, $\frac{f(x)}{g(x)}+\left(\frac{-f(x)}{g(x)}\right)=0$.

EXAMPLE 2.11 Simplify $\frac{x+1}{2x-1}+\frac{3x-2}{x-1}$.

SOLUTION

$$\frac{x+1}{2x-1}+\frac{3x-2}{x-1}=\frac{(x+1)(x-1)+(3x-2)(2x-1)}{(2x-1)(x-1)}=\frac{x^2-1+6x^2-7x+2}{2x^2-3x+1}=\frac{7x^2-7x+1}{2x^2-3x+1}.$$

EXAMPLE 2.12 Find the sum of the rational expressions $\frac{2x-3}{x^2+x-2}$ and $\frac{3x-1}{2x^2+5x+2}$.

SOLUTION

$$\frac{2x-3}{x^2+x-2}+\frac{3x-1}{2x^2+5x+2}=\frac{2x-3}{(x+2)(x-1)}+\frac{3x-1}{(2x+1)(x+2)}$$

$$=\frac{(2x-3)(2x+1)+(3x-1)(x-1)}{(x-1)(x+2)(2x+1)}$$

$$=\frac{4x^2-4x-3+3x^2-4x+1}{(x-1)(x+2)(2x+1)}=\frac{7x^2-8x-2}{2x^3+3x^2-3x-2}.$$

EXAMPLE 2.13 If $A=\frac{x+1}{2x-1}$, $B=\frac{2x-1}{3x+2}$ and $C=\frac{4x-5}{2x^2+5x-3}$, then find $4A-3B+C$.

SOLUTION

$$4A-3B+C=\frac{4(x+1)}{2x-1}-\frac{3(2x-1)}{3x+2}+\frac{4x-5}{(2x-1)(x+3)} \quad (\because 2x^2+5x-3=(2x-1)(x+3))$$

$$=\frac{4(x+1)(3x+2)(x+3)-3(2x-1)^2(x+3)+(4x-5)(3x+2)}{(2x-1)(3x+2)(x+3)}$$

$$=\frac{4(3x^3+14x^2+17x+6)-3(4x^3+8x^2-11x+3)+12x^2-7x-10}{(2x-1)(3x+2)(x+3)}$$

$$=\frac{44x^2+94x+5}{6x^3+19x^2+x-6}.$$

EXAMPLE 2.14 What should be added to $\left(\frac{5}{x-3}+\frac{5}{x+3}\right)$ to get $\frac{14x}{x^2-9}$?

SOLUTION

Let k should be added to $\left(\frac{5}{x-3}+\frac{5}{x+3}\right)$ to $\frac{14x}{x^2-9}$

$$\left(\frac{5}{x-3}+\frac{5}{x+3}\right)+k=\frac{14x}{x^2-9}$$

$$k=\frac{14x}{x^2-9}-\left(\frac{5}{x-3}+\frac{5}{x+3}\right)=\frac{14x}{x^2-9}-\frac{10x}{x^2-9}=\frac{4x}{x^2-9}$$

Multiplication of Rational Expressions

The product of two rational expressions $\frac{f(x)}{g(x)}$ and $\frac{h(x)}{p(x)}$ is given by

$$\frac{f(x)}{g(x)}\times\frac{h(x)}{p(x)}=\frac{f(x)\cdot h(x)}{g(x)\cdot p(x)}.$$

Konnect

1. The process of finding the
   (i) product of two rational expressions is similar to the process of finding the product of two rational numbers.
   (ii) product of two rational expressions is also a rational expression.
2. After finding the product of two rational expressions the resultant rational expression must be put in its lowest terms.

EXAMPLE 2.15 Find the product of the rational expressions $\frac{3x^2+8x-3}{2x^2-x-6}$ and $\frac{x^2-4}{x+3}$.

SOLUTION

Product of the given expressions is

$$\frac{3x^2+8x-3}{2x^2-x-6}\times\frac{x^2-4}{x+3}$$

$$=\frac{(x+3)(3x-1)}{(2x+3)(x-2)}\times\frac{(x-2)(x+2)}{(x+3)}$$

$$=\frac{(3x-1)(x+2)}{2x+3}=\frac{3x^2+5x-2}{2x+3}.$$

EXAMPLE 2.16 Simplify $\left[\frac{2x-1}{x+3}-\frac{x^2-4}{2x+1}\right]\times\frac{2x^2+7x+3}{x+2}$.

SOLUTION

$$\left[\frac{2x-1}{x+3}-\frac{x^2-4}{2x+1}\right]\times\frac{2x^2+7x+3}{x+2}$$

$$=\frac{(2x-1)(2x+1)-(x^2-4)(x+3)}{(x+3)(2x+1)}\times\frac{(x+3)(2x+1)}{x+2}$$

$$=\frac{4x^2-1-x^3-3x^2+4x+12}{x+2}=\frac{-(x^3-x^2-4x-11)}{x+2}.$$

Konnect

For every rational expression of the form $\frac{f(x)}{g(x)}$, $(g(x)\neq 0)$ there exists a rational expression of the form $\frac{g(x)}{f(x)}$ such that $\frac{f(x)}{g(x)}\times\frac{g(x)}{f(x)}=1$, then $\frac{g(x)}{f(x)}$ is called the multiplicative inverse of $\frac{f(x)}{g(x)}$ and vice versa.

Division of Rational Expressions

Let $\frac{f(x)}{g(x)}$ and $\frac{h(x)}{p(x)}$ be two non-zero rational expressions, then $\frac{f(x)}{g(x)}\div\frac{h(x)}{p(x)}=\frac{f(x)}{g(x)}\times\frac{p(x)}{h(x)}$. That is, $\frac{f(x)p(x)}{g(x)h(x)}$ which is also a rational expression.

EXAMPLE 2.17 Express $\frac{2x^2+6x}{3x^2+7x+2}\div\frac{x^2+x-6}{3x^2+7x+2}$ as a rational expression in its lowest terms.

SOLUTION

Given, $\frac{2x^2+6x}{3x^2+7x+2}\div\frac{x^2+x-6}{3x^2+7x+2}$

$$=\frac{2x(x+3)}{3x^2+7x+2}\times\frac{3x^2+7x+2}{(x+3)(x-2)}$$

$$=\frac{2x}{x-2}.$$

Info Bytes!

The process of dividing two rational expressions is similar to the process of dividing two rational numbers.

EXAMPLE 2.18 If $A = 2x3 + 5x^2 + 4x + 1$ and $B = 2x^2 + 3x + 1$, then find the quotient from the following four options, when A is divided by B.

(a) $x - 1$ (b) $x + 1$ (c) $2x + 1$ (d) $2x - 1$

SOLUTION

$$\frac{A}{B} = \frac{2x^3 + 5x^2 + 4x + 1}{2x^2 + 3x + 1}$$

$$= \frac{2x^3 + (3x^2 + 2x^2) + (x + 3x) + 1}{2x^2 + 3x + 1}$$

$$= \frac{(2x^3 + 3x^2 + x) + (2x^2 + 3x + 1)}{2x^2 + 3x + 1}$$

$$= \frac{(2x^2 + 3x + 1)(x + 1)}{2x^2 + 3x + 1} = x + 1.$$

POINTS TO REMEMBER

- ✔ Polynomial of degree 4 is called biquadratic polynomial.
- ✔ If $f(x)$ and $g(x)$ are two polynomials then we have the following relation,
- ✔ (HCF of $f(x)$ and $g(x)$ × (LCM of $f(x)$ and $g(x)$ $= \pm(f(x) \times g(x))$
- ✔ Every polynomial is a rational expression as $f(x)$ can be written as $f(x)/1$.
- ✔ For any rational expression $\frac{-f(x)}{g(x)}$ is called the additive inverse of $\frac{f(x)}{g(x)}$.

  That is, $\frac{f(x)}{g(x)} + \left(\frac{-f(x)}{g(x)}\right) = 0$.
- ✔ The product of two rational expressions $\frac{f(x)}{g(x)}$ and $\frac{h(x)}{p(x)}$ is given by $\frac{f(x)}{g(x)} \times \frac{h(x)}{p(x)} = \frac{f(x) \cdot h(x)}{g(x) \cdot p(x)}$.
- ✔ For every rational expression of the form $\frac{f(x)}{g(x)}$, $(g(x) \neq 0)$ there exists a rational expression of the form $\frac{g(x)}{f(x)}$ such that $\frac{f(x)}{g(x)} \times \frac{g(x)}{f(x)} = 1$, then $\frac{g(x)}{f(x)}$ is called the multiplicative inverse of $\frac{f(x)}{g(x)}$ and vice versa.

PRACTICE QUESTIONS CLASSROOM WING

Very Short Answer Type Questions

Directions of questions from 1 to 16:
Fill in the blanks.

1. If the degree of polynomial $f(x).g(x)$ is 15, where $f(x)$, $g(x)$, and $\frac{f(x)}{g(x)}$ are polynomials in x, then the degree of $f(x)$ can be ________.
2. The HCF of the polynomials $(x + 5)^2 (x - 2) (x + 1)^2$ and $(x + 1)^3(x + 5)$ is ________.
3. The HCF of $(x + 2)(x^2 - 7x + k)$ and $(x - 3)(x^2 + 3x + l)$ is $(x + 2)(x - 3)$. Then the values of k and l are _____ respectively.
4. The LCM of $x^2 + 2x - 8$ and $x^2 + 3x - 4$ is _____.
5. The additive inverse of $\frac{x^2+1}{x^2-1}$ is _____.
6. $\frac{x^2}{x^2-1} \div \frac{x^3}{x^2+1} =$ _____.
7. The HCF of the polynomials $8a^3b^2c$, $16a^2bc^3$ and $20ab^3c^2$ is _____.
8. The LCM of the polynomials $8(x^3 + 8)$ and $12(x^2 - 4)$ is _____.
9. The HCF of the polynomials $12xy^2z^3$, $18x^2y^2z$ and $28x^3yz^2$ is _____.
10. The LCM of the polynomials $15a^2b(a^2 - b^2)$ and $40ab^2(a - b)$ is _____.
11. The HCF of the polynomials $15(a + 1)^2 (a - 2)$, $65(a - 1)^2 (a + 1)$ and $90 (a - 2)^2 (a - 1)$ is _____.
12. The HCF of the polynomials $(x + 3)^2 (x - 2)(x + 1)^2$ and $(x + 1)^3 (x + 3)(x + 4)$ is _____.
13. The LCM of the polynomials $x^2 - 1$, $x^2 + 1$ and $x^4 - 1$ is _____.
14. The multiplicative inverse of $x - \frac{x-1}{1-x}$ is _____.
15. __________ is the algebraic expressions from the following polynomials?
$x^3 - \sqrt{7}x + 13$; $3x^4 + 2x^3 - \sqrt{5}x + 8$;
$11 - x^2 + x\sqrt{x} + 7x$; $-\sqrt{3}x^3 + 8x^2 - 9$
16. The additive inverse of $\frac{x+1}{x^2-1}$ is _____.

Directions of questions from 17 to 22:
State whether the following statements are true or false

17. The rational expression $\frac{x^2+1}{x^2+4x+3}$ is not in its lowest terms. (True/False)
18. The product of two rational expressions is not always a rational expression. (True/False)
19. The reciprocal of $x - \frac{1}{x}$ is $\frac{1}{x} - x$. (True/False)
20. Every polynomial is a rational expression. (True/False)
21. $\frac{x^3 + \sqrt{6}x^2 - 7}{2x^3 + \sqrt{x} + 1}$ is a rational expression. (True/False)
22. If $A = \frac{p(x)}{q(x)}$ and $B = \frac{f(x)}{g(x)}$ are two rational expressions where $q(x)$, $g(x) \neq 0$, then $A + B$ and $A - B$ are also rational expressions. (True/False)

Short Answer Type Questions

23. (A) Find the HCF and the LCM of the following monomials.
(i) x^3y^6 and x^2y^8
(ii) $3a^2b^3c^4$ and $9a^4b^3c^2$
(iii) $p^4q^2r^3$ and $q^3p^6r^5$

(B) Find the product of additive inverse and multiplicative inverse of $\frac{x^2-4x+3}{x^2-2x-3}$.

24. Find the LCM and HCF of the polynomials $(x^2-4)(x^2-x-2)$ and $(x^2+4x+4)(x^2-3x+2)$. Verify that the product of the LCM and HCF is equal to the product of the polynomials.

25. If HCF of the two polynomials $(x-1)(x-6)(x-2)$ and $(x-6)^3(x-4)(x-2)^2$ is $(x-6)(x-2)$, then find their LCM.

26. (A) If LCM of the two polynomials $(x^2+3x)(x^2+3x+2)$ and $(x^2+6x+8)(x^2+kx+6)$ is $x(x+1)(x+2)^2(x+3)(x+4)$, then find k.

(B) If the LCM of $(x-3)^4(x+4)^a$ and $(x-3)^a(x+4)^b$ is $(x-3)^5(x+4)^a$, then find the minimum value and maximum value of $a+b$.

27. If $(x+2)(x+5)$ is the HCF of the polynomials $(x+2)(x^2+6x+a)$ and $(x+5)(x^2+8x+b)$, then find the values of a and b.

28. If the LCM and HCF of the two polynomials are $(x-1)^2(x-2)^2(x-3)^3$ and $(x-1)(x-2)(x-3)$, respectively, and one of the polynomials is $(x-1)(x-2)^2(x-3)$, then find the other polynomial.

29. The HCF and LCM of the two polynomials are $(x-3)(x+1)$ and $(x^2-9)(x^2-1)$, respectively. If one of the polynomial is $(x-3)(x^2-1)$, then find the second polynomial.

30. Find the sum of the following rational expressions. $\dfrac{x+1}{(x-1)^2}$ and $\dfrac{x-2}{x^2-1}$.

31. If $P=\dfrac{3x+1}{3x-1}$ and $Q=\dfrac{3x-1}{3x+1}$, then find $P-Q$ and $P+Q$.

32. If $X=\dfrac{1+a}{1-a}$ and $Y=\dfrac{1-a}{1+a}$, then find X^2+Y^2+XY.

33. What should be added to $\dfrac{a}{a-b}+\dfrac{b}{a+b}$ to get 1?

34. Simplify: $\dfrac{x+1}{x-1}-\dfrac{x-1}{x+1}+\dfrac{8x}{1+x^2}-\dfrac{12x^3}{x^4-1}$.

Essay Type Questions

35. The sum of $\dfrac{2x-5}{x^2+x-2}$ and $\dfrac{3x-2}{2x^2+5x+2}$ is ________.

36. Express $\dfrac{x^2+x-6}{3x^2+7x+2}\div\dfrac{3x^2-9x}{3x^2+7x+2}$ as rational expression in its lowest terms.

37. $\dfrac{x-1}{x+1}-\dfrac{x+1}{x-1}-\dfrac{8x}{1+x^2}+\dfrac{12x^3}{x^4-1}=?$

38. If $f(x)=(x-3)(x^2-x-a)$, $g(x)=(x+3)(x^2+x-b)$, and their HCF is x^2-9, then find $a+b$, where 'a' and 'b' are constants.

39. If $A=\dfrac{x+1}{2x+1}$, $B=\dfrac{2x-1}{x+2}$, and $C=\dfrac{4x-7}{2x^2+5x+2}$, find $4A-B-C$.

40. If the LCM of $(x^2+6x+8)(x^2-kx-5)$ and $(x^2-3x-10)(x^2-2x-3)$ is $(x-5)(x^2+5x+4)(x^2-x-6)$, then find the value of k.

41. Simplify: $\dfrac{2x}{x^4-3x^2+1}+\dfrac{1}{x^2+x-1}-\dfrac{1}{x^2-x-1}$

PRACTICE QUESTIONS COMPETITION WING

Level 1: Apply Your Concepts

Directions of questions from 1 to 5:
Fill in the blanks.

1. The LCM of $18x^2y^3$ and $8x^3y^2$ is _____.
2. If the LCM of two polynomials $8a^2\ b^3$ and $12a^3\ b^k$ is $24a^3b^3$, then the number of integer values satisfying k is _____.
   (a) 3 (b) 4
   (c) 2 (d) 5
3. The HCF of $9a^2 - 16b^2$ and $12a^2 - 16ab$ is _____.
4. The LCM of $2(x - 3)^2$ and $3(x - 2)^2$ is _____.
5. The HCF of $24x^5$ and $36x^6y^k$ is $12x^5$, then the value of k is _____.

Directions of questions from 6 to 28:
Select the correct alternative from the given choices.

6. The multiplicative inverse of the product of the additive inverse of $x + 1$ and the multiplicative inverse of $x^2 - 1$ is _____.
   (a) $x - 1$ (b) $1 - x$
   (c) $1 - x^2$ (d) $x^2 - 1$
7. The LCM of the polynomials $f(x) = 9(x^3 + x^2 + x)$ and $g(x) = 3(x^3 + 1)$ is _____.
   (a) $27x(x + 1)(x^2 + x + 1)$
   (b) $9x(x + 1)(x^2 + x + 1)(x^2 - x + 1)$
   (c) $9(x + 1)(x^2 - x + 1)(x^2 + x + 1)$
   (d) $9x(x + 1)(x^2 + x + 1)$
8. If HCF and LCM of two polynomials $P(x)$ and $Q(x)$ are $x(x + p)$ and $12x^2\ (x - p)(x^2 - p^2)$ respectively. If $P(x) = 4x^2\ (x + p)$, then $Q(x) =$ _____.
   (a) $3x(x - p)^2\ (x + p)$ (b) $3x(x - p)(x + p)$
   (c) $3x(x + p)(x^2 - p^2)$ (d) $3x(x + p)(x^2 + p^2)$
9. The product of HCF and LCM of two polynomials is $(x^2 - 1)(x^4 - 1)$, then the product of the polynomials is _____.
   (a) $(x^2 - 1)(x^2 + 1)$ (b) $(x^2 - 1)(x^2 + 1)^2$
   (c) $(x^2 - 1)^2\ (x^2 + 1)$ (d) None of these
10. Find the LCM of $x^3 - x^2 + x - 1$ and $x^3 - 2x^2 + x - 2$.
    (a) $(x + 1)(x - 1)$
    (b) $x - 1$
    (c) $(x^2 + 1)(x - 1)(x - 2)$
    (d) $(x^2 + 1)(x + 1)(x - 2)$
11. The HCF of the polynomials $p(x)$ and $q(x)$ is $6x - 9$, then $p(x)$ and $q(x)$ could be _____.
    (a) $3, 2x - 3$ (b) $12x - 18, 2$
    (c) $3(2x - 3)^2, 6(2x - 3)$ (d) $3(2x - 3), 6(2x + 3)$
12. If the HCF of the polynomials $f(x)$ and $g(x)$ is $4x - 6$, then $f(x)$ and $g(x)$ could be _____.
    (a) $2, 2x - 3$ (b) $8x - 12, 2$
    (c) $2(2x - 3)^2, 4(2x - 3)$ (d) $2(2x + 3), 4\ (2x + 3)$
13. If the HCF of the polynomials $f(x) = (x + 3)(3x^2 - 7x - a)$ and $g(x) = (x - 3)(2x^2 + 3x + b)$ is $(x + 3)(x - 3)$, then $a + b =$ _____.
    (a) 3 (b) −15
    (c) −3 (d) 15
14. Find the HCF of the polynomials $f(x) = x^3 + x^2 + x + 1$ and $g(x) = x^3 - x^2 + x - 1$.
    (a) $x(x + 1)$ (b) $x - 1$
    (c) $x^2 + 1$ (d) $x + 1$
15. If the HCF of $x^3 + 2x^2 - ax$ and $2x^3 + 5x^2 - 3x$ is $x(x + 3)$, then $a =$ _____.
    (a) 3 (b) −3
    (c) 6 (d) −4
16. The HCF of the polynomials $70(x^3 - 1)$ and $105(x^2 - 1)$ is _____.
    (a) $15(x - 1)$ (b) $35(x - 1)$
    (c) $35(x^2 - 1)(x^2 + x + 1)$ (d) $15(x^2 - 1)$
17. What should be subtracted from $\frac{7x}{(x^2 - x - 12)}$ to get $\frac{3}{x + 3}$?
    (a) $\frac{5}{x + 4}$ (b) $\frac{4}{x - 4}$
    (c) $\frac{2}{x - 4}$ (d) $\frac{1}{x - 4}$

18. The product of additive inverses of $\frac{x^2-9}{2+x}$ and $\frac{x^2-4}{3-x}$ is ______.
(a) x^2+5x+6 (b) x^2+x-6
(c) x^2-x-6 (d) x^2-5x+6

19. What should be added to $\frac{1}{x^2-7x+12}$ to get $\frac{2}{x^2-6x+8}$?
(a) $\frac{2}{(x+3)(x-2)}$ (b) $\frac{4}{(x+3)(x+2)}$
(c) $\frac{1}{x^2-5x+6}$ (d) $\frac{-1}{x^2+5x-6}$

20. The rational expression $\frac{x^3-3x^2+2x}{x^2y-2xy}$ in lowest terms is ______.
(a) $\frac{x-2}{y}$ (b) $\frac{x+1}{xy}$
(c) $\frac{x-1}{y}$ (d) $\frac{x+1}{y}$

21. If $(x-4)$ is the HCF of $p(x)=x^2-nx-12$ and $q(x)=x^2-mx-8$, then the simplest form of $\frac{p(x)}{q(x)}$ is ______.
(a) $\frac{x-3}{x+2}$ (b) $\frac{x+3}{x-2}$
(c) $\frac{x+2}{x+3}$ (d) $\frac{x+3}{x+2}$

22. The LCM of the polynomials $8(x^2-2x)(x-6)^2$ and $2x(x^2-4)(x-6)^2$ is ______.
(a) $8(x^2-4)(x^2-6x)^2$ (b) $(x^3-4x)(x-6)^2$
(c) $8(x^3-4x)(x-6)^2$ (d) $8x(x^2+4)(x-6)^2$

23. The HCF of polynomials $(x^2-2x+1)(x+4)$ and $(x^2+3x-4)(x+1)$ is ______.
(a) $(x+4)(x-1)$ (b) $(x+1)(x+4)$
(c) $(x+1)(x-4)$ (d) $(x^2-1)(x+4)$

24. If the zeroes of the rational expression $(3x+2a)(2x+1)$ are $\frac{-1}{2}$ and $\frac{b}{3}$, then the value of a is ______.
(a) $-2b$ (b) $\frac{-b}{2}$
(c) $\frac{-b}{3}$ (d) None of these

25. The LCM of the polynomials $(x^2-8x+16)(x^2-25)$ and $(x^2-10x+25)(x^2-2x-24)$ is ______.
(a) $(x^4-41x+400)(x-6)$
(b) $(x^4+41x+400)(x^2-9x+20)$
(c) $(x^4-41x+400)(x^2-9x+20)(x-6)$
(d) $(x^4-41x+400)(x^2-9x+20)(x+6)$

26. If the HCF of the polynomials $(x^2+8x+16)(x^2-9)$ and $(x^2+7x+12)$ is $x^2+7x+12$, then their LCM is ______.
(a) $(x+4)(x^2-9)$ (b) $(x+4)^2(x^2-9)$
(c) $(x^2-4)(x^2+9)$ (d) $(x+4)^2(x+3)$

27. If $h(y)=y^3$ and $g(z)=z^4$, then HCF of $h(b)-h(a)$ and $g(b)-g(a)$ is ______.
(a) $b-a$ (b) b^2-a^2
(c) b^3-a^3 (d) b^2+ab+a^2

28. If the HCF of the polynomials $(x+4)(2x^2+5x+a)$ and $(x+3)(x^2+7x+b)$ is $(x^2+7x+12)$ then $6a+b$ is ______.
(a) -6 (b) 5
(c) 6 (d) -5

Level 2: Review Your Concepts

29. If the zeroes of the rational expression $(ax+b)(3x+2)$ are $\frac{-2}{3}$ and $\frac{1}{2}$, then $a+b=$ ______.
(a) -1 (b) 0
(c) $-b$ (d) $-a$

30. Simplify:
$$\frac{x^2-(y-2z)^2}{x-y+2z}+\frac{y^2-(2x-z)^2}{y+2x-z}+\frac{z^2-(x-2y)^2}{z-x+2y}.$$
(a) 0 (b) 1
(c) $x+y+z$ (d) None of these

31. If the HCF of the polynomials x^2+px+q and x^2+ax+b is $x+l$, then their LCM is ______.
(a) $(x+a-l)(x+l-p)$
(b) $(x-(l+a))(x+l-p)(x+l)$
(c) $(x+a-l)(x+p-l)(x+l)$
(d) $(x-l+a)(x-p+l)(x+l)$

32. The expression $\frac{1}{1-x}-\frac{1}{1+x}-\frac{x^3}{1-x}+\frac{x^2}{1+x}$ in lowest terms is ______.
(a) $2x^3+1$ (b) x^2+2
(c) x^2+2x (d) x^2-2x

33. Simplify: $\dfrac{a^2-(b-c)^2}{(a+c)^2-b^2}+\dfrac{b^2-(a-c)^2}{(a+b)^2-c^2}+\dfrac{c^2-(a-b)^2}{(b+c)^2-a^2}$.

(a) 0 (b) 1
(c) $a+b+c$ (d) $\dfrac{1}{a+b+c}$

34. Simplify: $\dfrac{x+1}{x-1}+\dfrac{x-1}{x+1}-\dfrac{2x^2-2}{x^2+1}$.

(a) $\dfrac{4x^4+2}{x^4-1}$ (b) $\dfrac{4x^2}{x^4-1}$
(c) $\dfrac{8x^2}{x^4-1}$ (d) 1

35. If the LCM of the polynomials $x^9+x^6+x^3+1$ and x^6-1 is $x^{12}-1$, then their HCF is ______.

(a) x^3+1 (b) x^6+1
(c) x^3-1 (d) x^6-1

36. If x^2+x-1 is a factor of $x^4+px^3+qx^2-1$, then the values of p and q can be:

(a) 2, 1 (b) 1, –2
(c) –1, –2 (d) –2, –1

37. If the HCF of the polynomials x^3+px+q and x^3+rx^2+lx+m is x^2+ax+b, then their LCM is ______. $(r \neq 0)$

(a) $(x^2+ax+b)(x+a)(x+a-r)$
(b) $(x^2+ax+b)(x-a)(x-a+r)$
(c) $(x^2+ax+b)(x-a)(x-a-r)$
(d) $(x^2-ax+b)(x-a)(x-a+r)$

38. If the HCF of the polynomials $(x-3)(3x^2+10x+b)$ and $(3x-2)(x^2-2x+a)$ is $(x-3)(3x-2)$, then the relation between a and b is ______.

(a) $3a+8b=0$ (b) $8a-3b=0$
(c) $8a+3b=0$ (d) $a-2b=0$

39. The HCF of the polynomials $12(x+2)^3(x^2-7x+10)$ and $18(x^2-4)(x^2-6x+5)$ is ______.

(a) $(x^2+3x+10)(x-2)$ (b) $6(x^2+3x+10)(x+2)$
(c) $(x^2-3x-10)(x-2)$ (d) $6(x^2-3x-10)(x-2)$

40. The HCF of the polynomials $(x^2-4x+4)(x+3)$ and $(x^2+2x-3)(x-2)$ is ______.

(a) $x+3$ (b) $x-2$
(c) $(x+3)(x-2)$ (d) $(x+3)(x-2)^2$

41. The HCF of the polynomials $5(x^2-16)(x+8)$ and $10(x^2-64)(x+4)$ is ______.

(a) $x^2+12x+32$ (b) $5(x^2+12x+32)$
(c) $x^2-12x+32$ (d) $5(x^2-12x+32)$

42. Find the HCF of $6x^4y$ and $12xy$.

(a) $6x^2y$ (b) $6x$
(c) $6y$ (d) $6xy$

43. Find the LCM of $p^4q^2r^3$ and $q^3p^6r^5$.

(a) $p^4q^3r^3$ (b) $p^4q^2r^5$
(c) $p^6q^3r^5$ (d) $p^6q^2r^5$

44. The LCM of the polynomials $12(x^3+27)$ and $18(x^2-9)$ is ______.

(a) $6(x+3)$
(b) $36(x^2-9)(x^2+3x+9)$
(c) $36(x+3)^2(x^2+3x+9)$
(d) $36(x^2-9)(x^2-3x+9)$

45. The rational expression $\dfrac{x^2+2x+3}{x^4+4x^3+4x^2-9}$ in its lowest terms is ______.

(a) $\dfrac{1}{x^2+3x+3}$ (b) $\dfrac{1}{x^2+2x-3}$
(c) $\dfrac{1}{x^2+4x-3}$ (d) $\dfrac{1}{x^2+2x+3}$

46. The LCM of the polynomials $(x+3)^2(x-2)(x+1)^2$ and $(x+1)^3(x+3)(x^2-4)$ is ______.

(a) $(x+1)^3(x+3)(x^2-4)$
(b) $(x+3)^2(x+1)^3(x^2-4)$
(c) $(x+3)^2(x+1)^3(x+2)$
(d) $(x+3)^2(x+1)^2(x-2)$

Level 3: Assess Your Concepts

47. Simplify: $\dfrac{x+2}{x-2}+\dfrac{x-2}{x+2}-\dfrac{3x^2-3}{x^2+4}$.

(a) $\dfrac{-x^4+31x^2+20}{x^4-16}$ (b) $\dfrac{x^4+31x^2+20}{x^4-16}$
(c) $-\dfrac{x^4+31x^2-20}{x^4-16}$ (d) $-\dfrac{x^4-21x^2+20}{x^4-16}$

48. If $P=\dfrac{x+1}{x-1}$ and $Q=\dfrac{x-1}{x+1}$, then $P^2+Q^2-2PQ=$ ______.

(a) $\dfrac{16x^2}{x^4-2x+1}$ (b) $\dfrac{4x^4+8x^2+4}{x^4-2x+1}$
(c) $\dfrac{4x^2}{x^4+2x^2+1}$ (d) $\dfrac{8x^2}{x^4-2x^2+1}$

49. Simplify: $\frac{81x^4 - 16x^2 + 32x - 16}{9x^2 - 4x + 4}$.

(a) $9x^2 + 4x - 4$ (b) $9x^2 - 4x - 4$
(c) $9x^2 - 2x - 8$ (d) $9x^2 + 2x - 8$

50. The rational expression $A = \left(\frac{x+1}{x-1} - \frac{x-1}{x+1} - \frac{4x}{x^2+1}\right)$ is multiplied with the additive inverse of $B = \frac{1-x^4}{4x}$ to get C. Then, $C =$ ______.

(a) $\frac{32x^2}{x^4-1}$ (b) $\frac{2x}{x^4-1}$
(c) 2 (d) 1

51. If the HCF of $x^3 + qx^2 + px$ and $qx^3 + 11x^2 - 4x$ is $x(x + 4)$, then $p =$ ______.

(a) −4 (b) 3
(c) −2 (d) 5

52. If degree of both $f(x)$ and $[f(x) + g(x)]$ is 18, then degree of $g(x)$ can be ______.

(a) 18 (b) 9
(c) 6 (d) Any one of these

53. The product of additive inverse and multiplicative inverse of $\frac{x-2}{x^2-4}$ is ______.

(a) $x^2 + 4x + 4$ (b) $x^2 - 4x + 4$
(c) $x^2 - 6x + 9$ (d) None of these

54. What should be multiplied to $(2x^2 + 3x - 4)$ to get $4x^4 - 9x^2 + 24x - 16$?

(a) $2x^2 - 3x - 4$
(b) $2x^2 + 24x - 16$
(c) $2x^2 + 3x + 4$
(d) $2x^2 - 3x + 4$

55. If $f(x) = (x + 2)^7 (x + 4)^p$, $g(x) = (x + 2)^q (x + 4)^9$ and the LCM of $f(x)$ and $g(x)$ is $(x + 2)^q (x + 4)^9$, then find the maximum value of $p - q$.

(a) 4 (b) 3
(c) 2 (d) 1

56. If $f(x) = x^2 - 7x + 12$ and $g(x) = x^2 - 8x + 15$, then find the HCF of $f(x)$ and $g(x)$.

(a) $x - 4$ (b) $x - 3$
(c) $x - 5$ (d) $x - 6$

57. If $f(x) = (x + 2)(x^2 + 8x + 15)$ and $g(x) = (x + 3)(x^2 + 9x + 20)$, then find the LCM of $f(x)$ and $g(x)$.

(a) $(x + 2)(x + 3)(x + 4)(x + 5)$
(b) $(x + 2)^2 (x + 3)(x + 5)$
(c) $(x + 2)(x + 3)(x + 5)(x + 1)$
(d) $(x + 2)^2 (x + 3)(x + 4)$

58. If $f(x) = x^2 + 6x + a$, $g(x) = x^2 + 4x + b$, $h(x) = x^2 + 14x + c$ and the LCM of $f(x)$, $g(x)$ and $h(x)$ is $(x + 8)(x - 2)(x + 6)$, then find $a + b + c$. (a, b and c are constants).

(a) 20 (b) 16
(c) 32 (d) 10

59. Simplify: $\frac{(x^2+11x+28)}{(x^2+13x+40)} \div \frac{(x^2+6x+8)}{(x^2+11x+24)}$.

(a) $\frac{(x+2)(x+7)}{(x+3)(x+3)}$ (b) $\frac{x+4}{x+8}$
(c) $\frac{x+8}{x+4}$ (d) $\frac{(x+3)(x+7)}{(x+2)(x+5)}$

60. If LCM of $f(x)$ and $g(x)$ is $6x^2 + 13x + 6$, then which of the following cannot be the HCF of $f(x)$ and $g(x)$?

(a) $2x + 3$ (b) $3x + 1$
(c) $(2x + 3)(3x + 2)$ (d) $3x + 2$

61. If the LCM of $f(x)$ and $g(x)$ is $a^6 - b^6$, then their HCF can be ______.

(a) $a - b$ (b) $a^2 + ab + b^2$
(c) $a^2 - ab + b^2$ (d) All of these

AT

PRACTICE QUESTIONS JEE SPECIAL WING

Multiple-Answer Type Questions

Directions for questions 1 to 5:
Each question has FOUR options (a), (b), (c), and (d). ONE OR MORE THAN ONE of these four option(s) is/are the correct answer(s).

1. If $f(x)$ and $g(x)$ are two polynomials of degree 25 each, then which of the following can be the of the degree polynomial $f(x)+g(x)$?
   (a) 25 (b) 20
   (c) 15 (d) 10
2. Which of the following is/are factor(s) of $729x^6 - 64y^6$?
   (a) $9x^2 - 4y^2$
   (b) $81x^4 + 16y^4 + 36x^2y^2$
   (c) $27x^3 + 36x^2y + 24xy^2 + 8y^3$
   (d) $81x^2 - 36xy + 16y^2$
3. Which of the following is/are true about the rational expression $\frac{f(x)}{g(x)}$?
   (a) $f(x)$, $g(x)$ and $\frac{f(x)}{g(x)}$ are polynomials.
   (b) $g(x)$ is not a zero polynomial.
   (c) $\frac{f(x)}{g(x)}$ need not be a polynomial.
   (d) If $\frac{f(x)}{g(x)}$ is a polynomial, the degree of $\frac{f(x)}{g(x)}$ is the difference of that of $f(x)$ and $g(x)$.
4. The LCM of two polynomials is $x^4 + x^2y^2 + y^4$. Which of the following can be the HCF of the polynomials?
   (a) $x^2 + y^2 + 2xy$ (b) $x^4 + y^4 + x^2y^2$
   (c) $x^2 + y^2 + xy$ (d) $x^2 + y^2 - 2xy$
5. If $f(x)$ and $g(x)$ are two polynomials and the degree of polynomial $f(x) - g(x)$ is 2025. Which of the following statements is/are false?
   (a) The degree of polynomial $f(x)$ is 7.
   (b) The degree of polynomial $g(x)$ is 7.
   (c) The degree of at least one of the polynomials $f(x)$ and $g(x)$ is 7.
   (d) The degree of polynomial $f(x)+g(x)$ is 7.

Match The Column

Directions for questions 6 to 10:
Read the paragraph given below and answer the questions.
Given that $f(p, q, r, s) = p^w q^{14} r^x s^{16}$ and $g(p, q, r, s) = p^{19} q^y r^{12} s^z$.
The HCF of $f(p, q, r, s)$ and $g(p, q, r, s)$ is $p^{13} q^{11} r^{12} s^z$

Column A	Column B
6. The maximum value of $y - x$	(a) −4
7. The minimum value of $w + z$	(b) − 2
8. The minimum value of $x - z$	(c) −1
9. The difference of y and w	(d) 2
10. The maximum value of $z - x$	(e) 4
	(f) 13

Comprehension-Based Questions

Directions for questions 11 to 15:
Read the paragraph given below and answer the questions.
Given that $p(x) = (x+1)^p (x+2)^{15} (x+3)^q$ and $q(x) = (x+1)^{25} (x+2)^{20} (x+3)^r$. The LCM of $p(x)$ and $q(x)$ is $(x+1)^{25} (x+2)^q (x+3)^{40}$. Also, the values of p, q, and r are positive integers.

11. The value of $p + q - r$ is ______ .
    (a) 0 (b) 5
    (c) 15 (d) Cannot be determined
12. The minimum value of $r - p$ is ______ .
    (a) 15 (b) 20
    (c) 35 (d) 40

13. The maximum value of $q + p$ is ______ .

(a) 65 (b) 55
(c) 45 (d) 35

14. If the LCM of p and r is 40, then find the number of possible values that p can take.

(a) 1 (b) 6
(c) 7 (d) More than 7

15. If the HCF of p and q is 2, then find the number of possible values that p can take.

(a) 1 (b) 5
(c) 6 (d) More than 7

Assertion and Reason Type Questions

Directions for questions 16 to 20:

Read the options given below and answer the questions.

In the light of the given statements, choose the most appropriate answer from the options given below.

(a) Both assertion (A) and reason (R) are true, and reason (R) is the correct explanation of assertion.
(b) Both assertion (A) and reason (R) are true, and reason (R) is not the correct explanation of assertion.
(c) Assertion (A) is true, but reason (R) is false.
(d) Assertion (A) is false, and reason (R) is true.

16. **Assertion:** If $p(x)=(x-1)(x^2-1)(x^3-1)(x^4-1)\ldots(x^{10}-1)$ and $q(x)=(x^{14}-1)(x^{15}-1)(x^{16}-1)$, the degree of $p(x)\times q(x)$ is 100.

Reason: The degrees of two polynomials $f(x)$ and $g(x)$ are m and n, then the degree of $f(x)\times g(x)$ is $m+n$.

17. **Assertion:** If the LCM of two polynomials is (x^3-1000), then the HCF of the polynomials can be $x^2+10x+100$.

Reason: The degree of the HCF of two polynomials is less than that of the LCM of the polynomials.

18. **Assertion:** $\dfrac{x^{12}-y^{12}}{x^4-y^4}$ is a polynomial.

Reason: If $f(x)$, and $g(x) \neq 0$ are polynomials, then $\dfrac{f(x)}{g(x)}$ need not be a polynomial.

19. **Assertion:** If $p(x)=\dfrac{x^2-7x+12}{x^2-x-30}$ and $q(x)=\dfrac{x^2-8x+15}{x^2-2x-24}$, then the product of the additive inverse and the multiplicative inverse of $\dfrac{p(x)}{q(x)}$ is -1.

Reason: For any two polynomials $p(x)$, and $q(x)\neq 0$, the product of the additive inverse and the multiplicative inverse of $\dfrac{p(x)}{q(x)}$ is -1.

20. **Assertion:** If the HCF of two polynomials is x^2-2x+1, then their LCM can be x^4+x^2+1.

Reason: The LCM of two polynomials is a multiple of their HCF.

ANSWER KEYS

Crossword

Across

5. Not defined 6. LCM 8. Rational 9. One

Down

1. Polynomials 2. Additive inverse 3. Five 4. Zero 6. Lowest
7. Four

Classroom Wing

Very Short Answer Type Questions

1. 8, 9, 10, ..., 15
2. $(x + 5)(x + 1)^2$
3. 12, 2
4. $(x - 1)(x - 2)(x + 4)$
5. $\dfrac{x^2+1}{1-x^2}$
6. $\dfrac{x^2+1}{x(x^2-1)}$
7. $4abc$
8. $24(x + 2)^2 (x - 2)(x^2 - 2x + 4)$
9. $2xyz$
10. $120\ a^2b^2 (a^2 - b^2)$
11. 5
12. $(x + 3)(x + 1)^2$
13. $(x^2 + 1)(x^2 - 1)$
14. $\dfrac{1}{1+x}$
15. $x^3 - \sqrt{7}x + 13; - \sqrt{3}x^3 + 8x^2 - 9$
16. $\dfrac{1}{1-x}$
17. False
18. False
19. False
20. True
21. False
22. True

Short Answer Type Questions

23. (A) (i) HCF = x^2y^6
LCM = x^3y^8
(ii) HCF = $3a^2b^3c^2$, LCM = $9a^4b^3c^4$
(iii) HCF = $p^4q^2r^3$ and LCM = $p^6q^3r^5$
(B) –1
24. HCF = $(x + 2)(x - 2)$
LCM = $(x + 2)^2(x - 2)^2 (x + 1)(x - 1)$
25. LCM = $(x - 1)(x - 2)^2 (x - 4)(x - 6)^3$
26. (A) $k = 5$ (B) 5, 10
27. $a = 5, b = 12$
28. $(x - 1)^2 (x - 2)(x - 3)^3$
29. $(x + 1)(x^2 - 9)$
30. $\dfrac{2x^2 - x + 3}{(x-1)^2(x+1)}$
31. $P - Q = \dfrac{12x}{(3x-1)(3x+1)}$
$P + Q = \dfrac{2(9x^2+1)}{(9x^2-1)}$
32. $\dfrac{(a^2+3)(3a^2+1)}{(1-a^2)^2}$
33. $\dfrac{2ab}{b^2-a^2}$
34. $\dfrac{4x}{1-x^4}$

Essay Type Questions

35. $\dfrac{7x^2-13x-3}{2x^3+3x^2-3x-2}$ 36. $\dfrac{x-2}{3x}$ 37. $\dfrac{4x}{x^4-1}$ 38. 24

39. $\dfrac{8}{2x+1}$ 40. 4 41. 0

Competition Wing

Level 1: Apply Your Concepts

1. $72x^3y^3$ 2. (b) 3. $3a - 4b$ 4. $6(x-2)^2(x-3)^2$
5. any whole number 6. (b) 7. (b) 8. (a) 9. (c)
10. (c) 11. (c) 12. (c) 13. (c) 14. (c)
15. (a) 16. (b) 17. (b) 18. (b) 19. (c)
20. (c) 21. (d) 22. (c) 23. (a) 24. (b)
25. (c) 26. (b) 27. (a) 28. (a)

Level 2: Review Your Concepts

29. (c) 30. (a) 31. (c) 32. (c) 33. (b)
34. (c) 35. (a) 36. (a) 37. (b) 38. (b)
39. (d) 40. (c) 41. (b) 42. (d) 43. (c)
44. (d) 45. (b) 46. (b)

Level 3: Assess Your Concepts

47. (a) 48. (a) 49. (a) 50. (c) 51. (a)
52. (d) 53. (d) 54. (d) 55. (c) 56. (b)
57. (a) 58. (a) 59. (d) 60. (b) 61. (d)

JEE Special Wing

Multiple-Answer Type Questions

1. (a, b, c, d) 2. (a, b, c) 3. (b, c, d) 4. (b, c) 5. (a, b, c, d)

Match The Column

6. (c) 7. (f) 8. (a) 9. (d) 10. (e)

Comprehension-Based Questions

11. (d) 12. (a) 13. (c) 14. (b) 15. (c)

Assertion and Reason Type Questions

16. (a) 17. (c) 18. (b) 19. (a) 20. (d)

Hints and Explanations

Classroom Wing

Very Short Answer Type Questions

1. The degree of $f(x).g(x)$ is 15.
   The degree of $f(x) \leq 15$ (1)
   As $\frac{f(x)}{g(x)}$ is a polynomial, the degree of $f(x) \geq$ the degree of $g(x)$
   $\therefore$ The degree of $f(x) \geq 8$ (2)
   From Eqs (1) and (2), the degree of $f(x)$ can be 8, 9, 10, …, 15.

2. Let $p(x) = (x + 5)^2 (x - 2) (x + 1)^2$ and
   $q(x) = (x + 1)^3 (x + 5)$
   HCF $= (x + 5)(x + 1)^2$

3. For HCF to be $(x+2)(x-3)$, there has to be a factor of $(x-3)$ in first equation and factor of $(x+2)$ in second equation.
   Therefore, $x = 3$ is a solution of $x^2 - 7x + k$
   $(3)^2 - 7(3) + k = 0$
   $k = 12$
   Similarly, $(-2)^2 + 3(-2) + 1 = 0$
   $l = 2$

4. $f(x) = x^2 + 2x - 8$
   $= x^2 + 4x - 2x - 8$
   $= x(x+4) - 2(x+4)$
   $= (x-2)(x+4)$

   $g(x) = x^2 + 3x - 4$
   $= x^2 + 4x - x - 4$
   $= x(x+4) - 1(x+4)$
   $= (x-1)(x+4)$

   LCM $= (x-1)(x+4)(x-2)$

5. $\frac{x^2+1}{x^2-1}$

   Additive inverse $\frac{-(x^2+1)}{x^2-1}$

   $= \frac{(x^2+1)}{(1-x^2)}$

6. $\frac{x^2}{x^2-1} \times \frac{(x^2+1)}{x^3} = \frac{(x^2+1)}{x(x^2-1)}$

7. $8a^3b^2c = 2\times2\times2\times a\times a\times a\times b\times b\times c$
   $16a^2bc^3 = 2\times2\times2\times2\times a\times a\times b\times c\times c\times c$
   $20ab^3c^2 = 2\times2\times5\times a\times b\times b\times b\times c\times c$
   $\text{HCF} = 2\times2\times a\times b\times c$
   $= 4abc$

8. $f(u) = 2\times2\times2(x^3+2^3)$
   $= 2\times2\times2(x+2)(x^2+2^2-2x)$
   $g(u) = 2\times2\times3\times(x-2)(x+2)$
   $\text{LCM} = 4\times3\times2(x+2)^2(x-2)(x^2+4-2x)$
   $= 24(x+2)^2(x-2)(x^2+4-2x)$

9. $12xy^2z^3 = 2\times2\times3\times x\times y\times y\times z\times z\times z$
   $18x^2y^2z = 2\times3\times3\times x\times x\times y\times y\times z$
   $28x^3yz^2 = 2\times2\times7\times x\times x\times x\times y\times z\times z$
   $\text{HCF} = 2\times x\times y\times z$
   $= 2xyz$

10. $15a^2b(a^2-b^2) = 3\times5\times a\times a\times b\times(a+b)\times(a-b)$
    $40ab^2(a-b) = 2\times2\times2\times5\times a\times b\times b\times(a-b)$
    $\text{LCM} = 120\times a\times a\times b\times b\times(a-b)\times(a+b)$
    $= 120a^2b^2(a^2-b^2)$

11. $15(a+1)^2(a-2) = 15(a+1)(a+1)(a-2)$
    $65(a-1)^2(a+1) = 5\times13\times(a-1)(a-1)(a+1)$
    $90(a-2)^2(a-1) = 5\times2\times9\times(a-2)(a-2)(a-1)$
    HCF = 5.

12. $f(x) = (x+3)(x+3)(x-2)(x+1)(x+1)$
    $g(x) = (x+1)(x+1)(x+1)(x+3)(x+4)$
    $\text{HCF} = (x+3)(x+1)(x+1)$
    $= (x+3)(x+1)^2$

13. $x^2 - 1 = (x+1)(x-1)$
    $(x^4-1) = (x^2+1)(x^2-1)$
    $\text{LCM} = (x^2+1)(x^2-1)$

14. Multiplicative inverse

$$f(u) = x - \frac{(x-1)}{(1-x)}$$

$$\text{MI} = \frac{1}{\left(\frac{x(1-x)-(x-1)}{1-x}\right)}$$

$$= \frac{1-x}{x-x^2-x+1}$$

$$= \frac{1-x}{-(x^2-1)}$$

$$= \frac{-(x-1)}{-(x+1)(x-1)}$$

$$= \frac{1}{x+1}$$

15. $x^3 - \sqrt{7}x + 13; -\sqrt{3}x^3 + 8x^2 - 9$

16. Additive inverse

$$f(u) = \frac{(x+1)}{(x^2-1)}$$

$$\Rightarrow \frac{-(x+1)}{(x+1)(x-1)}$$

$$\Rightarrow -\frac{1}{x-1} \Rightarrow \frac{1}{1-x}$$

17. $f(u) = x^2 + 4x + 3$

$= x^2 + 3x + x + 3$

$= x(x+3) + 1(x+3)$

$= (x+1)(x+3)$

$g(u) = x^2 + 1$

Therefore, it is not in its lowest terms.

18. False

19. $x - \frac{1}{x}$

$$\text{Reciprocal} = \frac{1}{x - \frac{1}{x}} = \frac{x}{x^2-1}$$

Therefore, it is false.

20. True **21.** False **22.** True

Short Answer Type Questions

23. (A) (i) x^3y^6 and x^2y^8

$x^3y^6 = x \times x \times x \times y \times y \times y \times y \times y \times y$

$x^2y^8 = x \times x \times y \times y \times y \times y \times y \times y \times y \times y$

$\text{HCF} = x \times x \times y^6$

$= x^2 \times y^6$

$\text{LCM} = x^3y^8$

(ii) $3a^2b^3c^4 = 3 \times a \times a \times b^3 \times c^2 \times c^2$

$9a^4b^3c^2 = 3 \times 3 \times a^2 \times a^2 \times b^3 \times c^2$

$\text{HCF} = 3 \times a^2 \times b^3 \times c^2$

$= 3a^2b^3c^2$

$\text{LCM} = 9a^4b^3c^4$

(iii) $p^4q^2r^3 = p^4 \times q^2 \times r^3$

$q^3p^6r^5 = p^4 \times p^2 \times q^2 \times q \times r^3 \times r^2$

$\text{HCF} = p^4q^2r^3 \quad \text{LCM} = p^6q^3r^5$

(B) Let the given expression be $\frac{f(x)}{g(x)}$

$\therefore$ The additive inverse $= -\frac{f(x)}{g(x)}$

The multiplicative inverse $= \frac{g(x)}{f(x)}$

The required product $= \frac{-f(x)}{g(x)} \times \frac{g(x)}{f(x)} = -1.$

24. $f(u) = (x+2)(x-2)(x-2)(x+1)$

$g(u) = (x+2)(x+2)(x-2)(x-1)$

$\text{HCF} = (x+2)(x-2)$

$\text{LCM} = (x+2)^2(x-2)^2(x+1)(x-1)$

Product of HCF and LCM = product of $f(u)$ and $g(u)$.

25. $f(u) = (x-1)(x-6)(x-2)$

$g(u) = (x-6)(x-6)(x-6)(x-4)(x-2)(x-2)$

$\text{LCM} = (x-1)(x-6)^3(x-2)^2(x-4)$

26. (A) $f(x) = (x^2+3x)(x^2+3x+2)$

$= x(x+3)(x+1)(x+2)$

$g(x) = (x^2+4)(x+2)(x^2+kx+6)$

$\text{LCM} = x(x+1)(x+2)^2(x+3)(x+4)$

LCM always takes highest power factor for $(x+2)^2$ in LCM.

There should be one more $(x+2)$ in $g(x)$, therefore (-2) is a rest.

$(-2)^2 - 2k + 6 = 0$

$-2k = -10 \quad k = 5$

(B) Given, $(x-3)^4 (x+4)^a$ and $(x-3)^a(x+4)^b$
LCM = $(x-3)^5 (x+4)^a$
Clearly, $a = 5$
Max $\{a, b\} = a$
Because $b \le a$
$0 \le b \le 5$
The minimum value of $b = 0$
The maximum value of $b = 5$
The minimum of $a + b = 5 + 0 = 5$
The maximum of $a + b = 5 + 5 = 10$.

27. HCF = $(x+2)(x+5)$

$g(x) = (x+2)(x^2+6x+a)$

$f(x) = (x+5)(x^2+8x+b)$

$g(x)$ should have $x+5$ and $f(x)$ should have $(x+2)$

$\Rightarrow (-5)^2 + 6(-5) + a = 0$

$25 - 30 + a = 0 \Rightarrow a = 5$

$\Rightarrow (-2)^2 + 8(-2) + b = 0$

$4 - 16 + b = 0 \quad b = 12$

28. LCM takes product of all factors with highest power. Therefore, $(x-1)^2$ should be included $(x-2)$ is because HCF takes common factor. $(x-3)^3$ because LCM has this.
Other polynomial $= (x-1)^2(x-2)(x-3)^3$

29. HCF takes common factor so $(x+1)$ should be there in 2nd polynomial LCM takes product of factors with highest factors. Therefore, x^2-9 should be included 2nd polynomial $= (x+1)(x^2-9)$

30. $\dfrac{x+1}{(x-1)^2} + \dfrac{x-2}{x^2-1}$

$\Rightarrow \dfrac{x+1}{(x-1)(x-1)} + \dfrac{x-2}{(x+1)(x-1)}$

$\Rightarrow \dfrac{(x+1)^2 + (x-2)(x-1)}{(x-1)^2(x+1)}$

$\Rightarrow \dfrac{x^2+2x+1+x^2-3x+2}{(x-1)^2(x+1)} = \dfrac{2x^2-x+3}{(x-1)^2(x+1)}$

31. $P+Q \Rightarrow \dfrac{3x+1}{3x-1} + \dfrac{3x-1}{3x+1}$

$= \dfrac{(3x+1)^2 + (3x-1)^2}{(3x-1)(3x+1)}$

$= \dfrac{9x^2+1+6x+9x^2+1-6x}{9x^2-1} = \dfrac{18x^2+2}{9x^2-1}$

$P-Q \Rightarrow \dfrac{3x+1}{3x-1} - \dfrac{3x-1}{3x+1}$

$= \dfrac{(3x+1)^2 - (3x-1)^2}{(3x-1)(3x+1)}$

$= \dfrac{9x^2+1+6x-9x^2-1+6x}{(3x-1)(3x+1)}$

$= \dfrac{12x}{(3x-1)(3x+1)}$

32. $X = \dfrac{1+a}{1-a} \qquad Y = \dfrac{1-a}{1+a}$

$X^2 = \dfrac{(1+a)^2}{(1-a)^2} \qquad Y^2 = \dfrac{(1-a)^2}{(1+a)^2}$

$XY = \dfrac{(1+a)(1-a)}{(1-a)(1+a)} = 1$

$X^2 + Y^2 + XY = \dfrac{(1+a)^2}{(1-a)^2} + \dfrac{(1-a)^2}{(1+a)^2} + 1$

$= \dfrac{2(1+a)^2(1-a)^2 + 1}{(1-a^2)(1+a^2)}$

$= \dfrac{(a^2+3)(3a^2+1)}{(1-a^2)^2}$

33. $\dfrac{a}{a-b} + \dfrac{b}{a+b}$

$\Rightarrow \dfrac{a(a+b) + b(a-b)}{(a-b)(a+b)}$

$\Rightarrow \dfrac{a^2+ab+ab-b^2}{a^2-b^2}$

$= \dfrac{a^2-b^2+2ab}{a^2-b^2}$

$= 1 - \dfrac{a^2-b^2+2ab}{a^2-b^2}$

$= \dfrac{a^2-b^2-a^2+b^2-2ab}{a^2-b^2}$

$= \dfrac{-2ab}{a^2-b^2} = \dfrac{2ab}{b^2-a^2}$

34. $= \dfrac{(x+1)^2 - (x-1)^2}{(x-1)(x+1)}$

$= \dfrac{x^2+1+2x-x^2-1+2x}{x^2-1} = \dfrac{4x}{x^2-1}$

$\Rightarrow \dfrac{4x}{x^2-1} + \dfrac{8x}{(1+x^2)}$

$$\Rightarrow \frac{4x(x^2+1)+8x(x^2-1)}{(x^2-1)(x^2+1)}$$

$$\Rightarrow \frac{4x^3+4x+8x^3-8x}{x^4-1}$$

$$= \frac{12x^3-4x}{x^4-1}$$

$$= \frac{12x^3-4x}{x^4-1}+\frac{12x^3}{x^4-1}$$

$$= \frac{-4x}{x^4-1} = \frac{4x}{1-x^4}$$

Essay Type Questions

35. $\dfrac{2x-5}{x^2+x-2}+\dfrac{3x-2}{2x^2+5x+2}$

$$= \frac{2x-5}{x^2+2x-1x-2}+\frac{3x-2}{2x^2+4x+1x+2}$$

$$= \frac{2x-5}{(x+2)(x-1)}+\frac{3x-2}{(2x+1)(x+2)}$$

$$= \frac{(2x-5)(2x+1)+(3x-2)(x-1)}{(x+2)(x-1)(2x+1)}$$

$$= \frac{4x^2-10x+2x-5+3x^2-2x-3x+2}{(x^2+x-2)(2x+1)}$$

$$= \frac{7x^2-13x-3}{2x^3+3x^2-3x-2}$$

36. $\dfrac{x^2+x-6}{3x^2+7+2} \div \dfrac{3x^2+9x}{3x^2+7x+2}$

$$= \frac{x^2+x-6}{3x^2+7x+2}\times\frac{3x^2+7x+2}{3x^2+9x}$$

$$= \frac{x^2+x-6}{3x^2+9x}$$

$$= \frac{(x+3)(x-2)}{3x(x+3)}$$

$$= \frac{x-2}{3x}$$

37. $\dfrac{x-1}{x+1}-\dfrac{x+1}{x-1}-\dfrac{8x}{1+x^2}+\dfrac{12x^3}{x^4-1}$

$$= \frac{(x-1)^2(x^2+1)-(x+1)^2(x^2+1)-8x(x^2-1)+12x^3}{x^4-1}$$

$$= \frac{(x^2+1)\left[(x-1)^2-(x+1)^2\right]-8x(x^2-1)+12x^3}{x^4-1}$$

$$= \frac{-4x^3-4x+8x+4x^3}{x^4-1}$$

$$= \frac{4x}{x^4-1}$$

38. $f(x) = (x-3)(x^2-x-a)$

$g(x) = (x+3)(x^2+x-b)$

HCF of $f(x)$ and $g(x) = (x^2-9) = (x+3)(x-3)$

$\Rightarrow (x+3)(x-3)$ is a factor of $(x-3)(x^2-x-a)$.

$\therefore (x+3)$ is a factor of (x^2-x-a).

$\therefore (-3)^2-(-3)-a = 0$

$a = 12$

$(x+3)(x-3)$ is a factor of $(x+3)(x^2+x-b)$.

$\Rightarrow (x-3)$ is a factor of (x^2+x-b).

$\Rightarrow 9+3-b = 0$

$b = 12$

$a+b = 12+12 = 24$

39. $4A-B-C$

$$= \frac{4(x+1)}{2x+1}-\frac{2x-1}{x+2}-\frac{4x-7}{2x^2+5x+2}$$

$$= \frac{4(x+1)(x+2)-(2x-1)(2x+1)-(4x-7)}{2x^2+5x+2}$$

$$= \frac{4x(x^2+3x+2)-(4x^2-1)-4x+7}{2x^2+5x+2}$$

$$= \frac{4x^2+12x+8-4x^2+1-4x+7}{2x^2+5x+2}$$

$$= \frac{8x+16}{(2x+1)(x+2)}$$

$$= \frac{8(x+2)}{(2x+1)(x+2)}$$

$$= \frac{8}{2x+1}$$

40. Given $f(x) = (x^2+6x+8)(x^2-kx-5)$,

$g(x) = (x^2-3x-10)(x^2-2x-3)$

$f(x) = (x+2)(x+4)(x^2-kx-5)$

$g(x) = (x+2)(x-5)(x+1)(x-3)$

LCM $= (x-5)(x^2+5x+4)(x-x-6)$

$\Rightarrow (x-5)(x+1)(x+4)(x+2)(x-3)$

Clearly, $(x-5)$ and $(x+1)$ are factors (x^2-kx-5)

Let $f(x) = x^2-kx-5$

$\Rightarrow (x-5)(x+1) = (x^2-kx-5)$

$\Rightarrow x^2-4x-5 = x^2-kx-5$

$k = 4$.

41. Given

$$\frac{2x}{x^4-3x^2+1}+\frac{1}{x^2+x-1}-\frac{1}{x^2-x-1}\ \frac{1}{x^2-x-1}$$

$$=\frac{2x}{x^4-3x^2+1}+\left[\frac{x^2-x-1-x^2-x+1}{\left(x^2+x-1\right)\left(x^2-x-1\right)}\right]$$

$$=\frac{2x}{x^4-3x^2+1}+\left[\frac{-2x}{x^4-3x^2+1}\right]=0.$$

Competition Wing

Level 1: Apply Your Concepts

1. LCM of $18x^2y^3$ and $8x^3y^2$

2	$18x^2y^3$
3	$9x^2y^3$
3	$3x^2y^3$
x^2	x^2y^3
y^3	$1y^3$
	1

2	$8x^3y^2$
2	$4x^3y^2$
2	$2x^3y^2$
x^3	x^3y^2
y^2	$1y^2$
	1

$$18x^2y^3 = 2\times 3\times 3\times x^2\times y^3$$
$$8x^3y^2 = 2\times 2\times 2\times x^3\times y^2$$
$$\text{LCM} = 2^3\times 3^2\times x^3\times y^3$$
$$= 72x^3y^3$$

2. k can take the values 0, 1, 2, or 3.
   ∴ The number of possible integer values of k is 4.
   Hence, the correct option is (b).

3. HCF of $9a^2 - 16b^2$ and $12a^2 - 16ab$

$$f(u) = 9a^2 - 16b^2$$
$$g(u) = 12a^2 - 16ab$$
$$f(u) = (3a)^2 - (4b)^2$$
$$= (3a+4b)(3a-4b)$$
$$g(u) = 4a(3a-4b)$$
$$\text{HCF} = 3a - 4b$$

4. $f(u) = 2(x-3)^2$
$$= 2(x-3)(x-3)$$
$$g(u) = 3(x-2)(x-2)$$
$$\text{LCM} = 3(x-2)^2\cdot 2(x-3)^2$$
$$= 6(x-2)^2(x-3)^2$$

5. Since HCF has only common factors of both, and there is no y in HCF. y can be any whole number, it will not effect the HCF.

6. The product $= -(x+1)\times\dfrac{1}{x^2-1}$
$$= \frac{-1}{x-1}$$
   Its multiplicative inverse is $1 - x$.
   Hence, the correct option is (b).

7. Factorize the given polynomials. The product of all the factors with highest exponents is LCM.

8. We gave, $P(x)\ Q(x) = \text{LCM}\times\text{HCF}$.

9. We have, $P(x)\ Q(x) = \text{LCM}\times\text{HCF}$.

10. Factorize the given polynomials. The product of all the factors with highest exponents is LCM.

13. If $(x - k)$ is a factor of $f(x)$, then $f(k) = 0$.

14. Factorize the given polynomials.

15. If $(x - k)$ is a factor of $f(x)$, then $f(k) = 0$.

17. Factorize the given polynomials. The product of all the factors with highest exponents is LCM.

19. Subtract the first expression from the second expression.

20. Factorize numerator and denominator and eliminate the common factors.

22. (i) Factorize the given polynomials.
    (ii) $x^2 - 2x = x(x - 2)$
    $x^2 - 4 = (x + 2)(x - 2)$.

23. (i) Factorize the given polynomials.
    (ii) $x^2 - 2x + 1 = (x - 1)^2$
    $x^2 + 3x - 4 = (x + 4)(x - 1)$.

24. (i) Equate the given expression to zero and compare with the given values.
    (ii) As zero of $2x + 1$ is $-\dfrac{1}{2}$, zero of the expression $3x + 2a$ is $\dfrac{b}{3}$.

25. (i) Factorize the given polynomials.
    (ii) $(x^2 - 8x + 16)(x^2 - 25)$
    $= (x - 4)^2\ (x + 5)(x - 5)$
    $(x^2 - 10x + 25)(x^2 - 2x - 24)$
    $= (x - 5)^2\ (x - 6)(x + 4)$.

26. (i) $\text{LCM}\times\text{HCF} = \pm f(x)\times g(x)$
    (ii) $x^2 + 8x + 16 = (x + 4)^2$.

27. (i) Divide the given polynomials with $(x + l)$.
    (ii) $h(b) - h(a) = b^3 - a^3$, $g(b) - g(a) = b^4 - a^4$.
    (iii) Now, factorize the above expressions.

28. (i) Find the values of a and b using the concept of HCF then obtain the required relation.
(ii) $x^2 + 7x + 12 = (x + 4)(x + 3)$.
(iii) $x + 3$ is a factor of $2x^2 + 5x + a$ and $x + 4$ is a factor of $x^2 + 7x + b$.

Level 2: Review Your Concepts

29. (i) Equate the given expression to zero to get the values of a and b then find $a + b$.
(ii) As the zero of $3x + 2$ is $\frac{-2}{3}$, zero of $ax + b$ is $\frac{1}{2}$.

30. (i) Factorize and then simplify.
(ii) $x^2 - (y - 2z)^2 = (x + y - 2z)(x - y + 2z)$ and so on.

31. (i) If $(x - k)$ is a of factor $f(x)$, then $f(k) = 0$.
(ii) Find the quotients by dividing each of the expressions by $x + l$.

32. (i) Add the terms which have the same denominators.
(ii) LCM of denominators is $(1 - x)(1 + x)$.
(iii) $a^2 - 1 = (a + 1)(a - 1)$; $a^3 - 1 = (a - 1)(a^2 + a + 1)$.

33. (i) Factorize numerator and denominator then simplify.
(ii) $a^2 - (b - c)^2 = (a + b - c)(a - b + c)$; $(a + c)^2 - b^2 = (a + c + b)(a + c - b)$.

34. (i) Simplify the first two terms.
(ii) LCM of denominators is $(x^2 - 1)(x^2 + 1)$.

35. (i) We have, $P(x)\ Q(x) = \text{LCM} \times \text{HCF}$.
(ii) $P^2 + Q^2 - 2PQ = (P - Q)^2$.
(iii) Find $P - Q$ and then find $(P - Q)^2$.

37. Find the quotients by dividing each of the given expressions by $x^2 + ax + b$.

38. (i) Find the values of a, b using the concept of HCF then obtain the relation between a and b.
(ii) $3x - 2$ is a factor of $3x^2 + 10x + b$.
(iii) $x - 3$ is a factor of $x^2 - 2x + a$.
(iv) Apply remainder theorem to find the values of a and b.

39. (i) Factorize the given polynomials.
(ii) $x^2 - 7x + 10 = (x - 5)(x - 2)$
$(x^2 - 6x + 5) = (x - 5)(x - 1)$.

41. (i) Factorize the given polynomials.
(ii) $x^2 - 16 = (x + 4)(x - 4)$
$x^2 - 64 = (x + 8)(x - 8)$.

42. The factors of $6x^4y$ and $12xy$ are $(6xy)x^3$ and $(6xy)\cdot 2$, respectively.
$\therefore$ HCF is $6xy$.

43. The factors of $p^4q^2r^3$ and $q^3p^6r^5$ are $(p^4q^2r^3)$ and $(p^4q^2r^3)$ p^2qr^2, respectively.
$\therefore$ LCM is $p^6q^3r^5$.

44. Let $f(x) = 12(x^3 + 27)$ and $g(x) = 18(x^2 - 9)$
$f(x) = 12(x^3 + 3^3) = 12(x + 3)(x^2 - 3x + 9)$
$g(x) = 18(x^2 - 3^2) = 18(x + 3)(x - 3)$.
LCM of 12 and 18 is 36.
$\therefore$ LCM of $f(x)$ and $g(x)$ is $36(x + 3)(x - 3)(x^2 - 3x + 9) = 36(x^2 - 9)(x^2 - 3x + 9)$.

45. $\frac{x^2 + 2x + 3}{x^4 + 4x^3 + 4x^2 - 9}$
$= \frac{x^2 + 2x + 3}{(x^2 + 2x)^2 - 3^2}$
$= \frac{x^2 + 2x + 3}{(x^2 + 2x + 3)(x^2 + 2x - 3)} = \frac{1}{x^2 + 2x - 3}$.

46. Let $f(x) = (x + 3)^2\ (x - 2)(x + 1)^2$ and
$g(x) = (x + 1)^3\ (x + 3)(x^2 - 4)$
$g(x) = (x + 1)^3\ (x + 3)(x + 2)(x - 2)$
$\therefore$ LCM of $f(x)$ and $g(x)$ is $(x + 3)^2\ (x + 1)^3\ (x + 2)(x - 2)$
$= (x + 3)^2\ (x + 1)^3\ (x^2 - 4)$.

Level 3: Assess Your Concepts

48. (i) $P^2 + Q^2 - 2PQ = (P - Q)^2$.
(ii) Find $P - Q$ and then find $(P - Q)^2$.

50. (i) Simplify the expression A
(ii) Find additive inverses of the expression B and then multiply with A.

51. Let $f(x) = x^3 + qx^2 + px = x(x^2 + qx + p)$ and $g(x) = qx^3 + 11x^2 - 4x = x(qx^2 + 11x - 4)$.
Given, HCF $= x(x + 4)$
$\Rightarrow x + 4$ is the factor of $g(x)$
$\Rightarrow g(-4) = 0$
$\Rightarrow q(-4)^2 + 11(-4) - 4 = 0$
$\Rightarrow q = 3$
$x + 4$ is also factor of $f(x)$
$\Rightarrow f(-4) = 0$
$\Rightarrow (-4)^2 + 3\ (-4) + p = 0 \Rightarrow p = -4$.

52. Degree of $f(x) = 18$

Degree of $[f(x) + g(x)] = 18$

$\therefore$ The degree of $g(x)$ can be less than or equal to 18.

53. $\dfrac{x-2}{x^2-4} = \dfrac{1}{x+2}$

Additive inverse of $\dfrac{1}{x+2}$ is $\dfrac{-1}{x+2}$

Multiplicative inverse of $\dfrac{1}{x+2}$ is $x + 2$

$\therefore$ The required product is $\left(\dfrac{-1}{x+2}\right)(x+2)$, i.e., -1.

54. Let A be the required expression

$\therefore A(2x^2 + 3x - 4) = 4x^4 - 9x^2 + 24x - 16$

$$\Rightarrow A = \frac{4x^4 - (9x^2 - 24x + 16)}{2x^2 + 3x - 4}$$

$$= \frac{(2x^2)^2 - (3x - 4)}{2x^2 + 3x - 4}$$

$$= \frac{(2x^2 + 3x - 4)(2x^2 - 3x + 4)}{(2x^2 + 3x - 4)}$$

$$= 2x^2 - 3x + 4.$$

55. Given

$f(x) = (x + 2)^7 (x + 4)^p$

$g(x) = (x + 2)^q (x + 4)^9$

$\text{LCM} = (x + 2)^q (x + 4)^9$

$\therefore q \geq 7$ and $p \leq 9$

For maximum value of $p - q$, p is maximum and q is minimum.

$\therefore$ maximum value of $p - q$ is $9 - 7 = 2$.

56. Given

$f(x) = x^2 - 7x + 12 = (x - 3)(x - 4)$

$g(x) = x^2 - 8x + 15 = (x - 3)(x - 5)$

$\therefore \text{HCF} = x - 3.$

57. Given $f(x) = (x + 2)(x^2 + 8x + 15)$

$= (x + 2)(x + 3)(x + 5)$

$g(x) = (x + 3)(x^2 + 9x + 20)$

$= (x + 3)(x + 4)(x + 5)$

$\text{LCM} = (x + 2)(x + 3)(x + 4)(x + 5).$

58. $f(x) = x^2 + 6x + a$

$g(x) = x^2 + 4x + b$

$h(x) = x^2 + 14 + c$

$\text{LCM} = (x + 8)(x - 2)(x + 6)$

As three given polynomials are quadratic and their LCM is cubic, each polynomial is the product of two of the factors of LCM. By inspection method,

$f(x) = x^2 + 6x + a = (x + 8)(x - 2)$

$\Rightarrow a = -16$

$g(x) = x^2 + 4x + b = (x + 2)(x + 6)$

$\Rightarrow b = -12$

$h(x) = x^2 + 14x + c = (x + 8)(x + 6)$

$\Rightarrow c = 48$

$a + b + c = -16 - 12 + 48 = 20.$

59. $\dfrac{(x^2 + 11x + 28)}{(x^2 + 13x + 40)} \div \dfrac{(x^2 + 6x + 8)}{(x^2 + 11x + 24)}$

$$= \frac{(x+4)(x+7)}{(x+5)(x+8)} \div \frac{(x+2)(x+4)}{(x+3)(x+8)}$$

$$= \frac{(x+4)(x+7)(x+3)(x+8)}{(x+5)(x+8)(x+2)(x+4)}$$

$$= \frac{(x+7)(x+3)}{(x+5)(x+2)}.$$

60. LCM of $f(x)$ and $g(x) = 6x^2 + 13x + 6$

$= (2x + 3)(3x + 2).$

We know that, HCF is a factor of LCM.

$\therefore 3x + 1$ cannot be the HCF.

61. LCM of $f(x)$ and $g(x)$ is $a^6 - b^6$

HCF of $f(x)$ and $g(x)$ is a factors $a^6 - b^6$

All $(a - b)$, $(a^2 + ab + b^2)$

and $(a^2 - ab + b^2)$ are factors of $a^6 - b^6$.

JEE Special Wing

Multiple-Answer Type Questions

1. Given that the degree of each of the polynomials $f(x)$ and $g(x)$ is 25.

If $f(x)=x^{25}$ and $g(x)=2x^{25}$, $f(x)+g(x)=3x^{25}$.

If $f(x)=x^{25}-x^{24}$ and $g(x)=-x^{25}-x^{24}$, $f(x)+g(x)=-2x^{24}$.

The degree of the polynomial $f(x)+g(x)$ can be 25, 24, 23, … (or) 0.

If $f(x)+g(x)=0$, the degree of $f(x)+g(x)$ is not defined.

Hence, the choices (a), (b), (c) and (d) follow.

2. $729x^6-64y^6=\left(27x^3\right)^2-\left(8y^3\right)^2$

$=\left(27x^3-8y^3\right)\left(27x^3+8y^3\right)$

$=\left[(3x)^3-(2y)^3\right]\left[(3x)^3+(2y)^3\right]$

$=(3x-2y)\left(9x^2+6xy+4y^2\right)(3x+2y)\left(9x^2-6xy+4y^2\right)$

Now,

(i) $(3x-2y)(3x+2y)=9x^2-4y^2$ is a factor.

(ii) $(3x+2y)\left(9x^2+6xy+4y^2\right)$

$=(3x)\left(9x^2+6xy+4y^2\right)+(2y)\left(9x^2+6xy+4y^2\right)$

$=27x^3+18x^2y+12xy^2+18x^2y+12xy^2+8y^3$

$=27x^3+36x^2y+24xy^2+8y^3$ is also a factor.

(iii) $\left(9x^2+6xy+4y^2\right)\left(9x^2-6xy+4y^2\right)$

$=\left(9x^2+4y^2\right)^2-(6xy)^2$

$=81x^4+16y^4+72x^2y^2-36x^2y^2$

$=81x^4+16y^4+36x^2y^2$ is also a factor.

Hence, the choices (a), (b) and (c) follow

3. Given that $\dfrac{f(x)}{g(x)}$ is a rational expression.

$f(x)$, and $g(x)$ are polynomials.

$g(x)\neq 0$.

$\dfrac{f(x)}{g(x)}$ need not be a polynomial.

If $\dfrac{f(x)}{g(x)}$ is a polynomial, the degree of $\dfrac{f(x)}{g(x)}$ is the difference of that of $f(x)$ and $g(x)$.

Hence, the choices (b), (c) and (d) follow.

4. $x^4+x^2y^2+y^4=\left(x^2+y^2\right)^2-x^2y^2$

$=\left(x^2+y^2\right)^2-(xy)^2$

$=\left(x^2+y^2+xy\right)\left(x^2+y^2-xy\right)$

We know that the HCF of two polynomials is a factor of their LCM.

So, the HCF can be 1, x^2+y^2+xy, x^2+y^2-xy and $x^4+x^2y^2+y^4$.

Hence, the choices (b) and (c) follow.

5. Given that $f(x)$ and $g(x)$ are two polynomials and the degree of polynomial $f(x)-g(x)$ is 2025.

Let $f(x)=x^8+x^6$ and $g(x)=x^8-x^7$, here each of $f(x)$ and $g(x)$ are two polynomials of degree 8.

Now, $f(x)-g(x)=\left(x^8+x^6\right)-\left(x^8-x^7\right)=x^7+x^6$ which is 7th degree polynomial.

Now, $f(x)+g(x)=\left(x^8+x^6\right)+\left(x^8-x^7\right)$

$=2x^8-x^7+x^6$ which is 8th degree polynomial.

So, the given statements need not be true.

Hence, all the four options are false

Hence, the choices (a), (b), (c) and (d) follow.

Match The Column

Common Solutions for questions 6 to 10:

Given that $f(p,q,r,s)=p^wq^{14}r^xs^{16}$ and $g(p,q,r,s)=p^{19}q^yr^{12}s^z$.

The HCF of $f(p,q,r,s)$ and $g(p,q,r,s)$ is $p^{13}q^{11}r^{12}s^z$

$\Rightarrow w=13$

x can be 12, 13, 14, 15, …

$y=11$

z can be 0, 1, 2, 3, 4, … 16.

6. The maximum value of $y-x=$ The value of $y-$ The minimum value of x

$=11-12=-1$.

Hence, the correct option is (c).

7. The minimum value of $w+z=$ The value of $w+$ The minimum value of z

$=13+0=13$.

Hence, the correct option is (f).

8. The minimum value of $x-z=$ The minimum value of $x-$ The maximum value of z

$=12-16=-4$.

Hence, the correct option is (a).

9. The difference of y and $w = 13 - 11 = 2$.

Hence, the correct option is (d).

10. The maximum value of $z - x =$ The maximum value of $z -$ The minimum value of $x = 16 - 12 = 4$.

Hence, the correct option is (e).

Comprehension-Based Questions

Common Solutions for questions 11 to 15:

Given that $p(x) = (x+1)^p (x+2)^{15} (x+3)^q$ and $q(x) = (x+1)^{25} (x+2)^{20} (x+3)^r$. The LCM of $p(x)$ and $q(x)$ is $(x+1)^{25} (x+2)^q (x+3)^{40}$.

Also, the values of p, q, and r are positive integers.

As the LCM of $(x+1)^p$ and $(x+1)^{25}$ is $(x+1)^{25}$, p can be 1, 2, 3 ... (or) 25.

As the LCM of $(x+2)^{15}$ and $(x+2)^{20}$ is $(x+2)^q$, $q = 20$.

As the LCM of $(x+3)^q$ and $(x+3)^r$ is $(x+3)^{40}$ and $q = 20$, $r = 40$.

11. The value of $p + q - r$ cannot be determined as there is no fixed value for p.

Hence, the correct option is (d).

12. The minimum value of $r - p =$ The value of $r -$ The maximum value of p

$= 40 - 25 = 15$.

Hence, the correct option is (a).

13. The maximum value of $q + p =$ The value of $q +$ The maximum value of p

$= 20 + 25 = 45$.

Hence, the correct option is (c).

14. We know that p can be 1, 2, 3 ... (or) 25 and $r = 40$.

Given that the LCM of p and r is 40.

That is the LCM of p and 40 is 40.

So, the value of p is a factor of 40.

Therefore, p can be 1, 2, 4, 5, 8, 10, 20.

Hence, p can take 7 values.

Hence, the correct option is (b).

15. We know that p can be 1, 2, 3 ... (or) 25 and $q = 20$.

Given that the HCF of p and q is 2.

That is the HCF of p and 20 is 2.

Therefore, p can be 2, 6, 10, 14, 18, 22.

Hence, p can take 6 values.

Hence, the correct option is (c).

Assertion and Reason Type Questions

16. Given that $p(x) = (x-1)(x^2-1)(x^3-1)(x^4-1)\ldots(x^{10}-1)$ The term which has the highest degree of $p(x)$ is $x \times x^2 \times x^3 \times x^4 \times \ldots \times x^{10} = x^{1+2+3+4+\ldots+10} = x^{55}$.

Also, $q(x) = (x^{14}-1)(x^{15}-1)(x^{16}-1)$.

The term which has the highest degree of $q(x)$ is $x^{14} \times x^{15} \times x^{116}$

$= x^{14+15+16} = x^{45}$.

The term which has the highest degree of $p(x) \times q(x)$ is $x^{55} \times x^{45} = x^{55+45} = x^{100}$.

The degree of $p(x) \times q(x)$ is 100, which is the sum of the degrees of $p(x)$ and $q(x)$.

So, **Assertion** is true.

Reason: If the degrees of two polynomials $f(x)$ and $g(x)$ are m and n, then the degree of $f(x) \times g(x)$ is $m+n$. It is a true statement and is the correct explanation of the **Assertion**.

Hence, the correct option is (a).

17. **Assertion:** Given that the LCM of two polynomials is $x^3 - 1000$.

$x^3 - 1000 = x^3 - (10)^2$

$= (x-10)(x^2 + 10x + 100)$

We know that the HCF of two polynomials is a factor of their LCM.

So, the HCF of the polynomials can be 1, $x - 10$, $x^2 + 10x + 100$ or $x^3 - 1000$.

Hence, the **Assertion** is true.

Reason: The degree of the HCF of two polynomials can be lesser than or equal to that of the LCM of the polynomials.

Hence, **Assertion** is true, and **Reason** is false.

Hence, the correct option is (c).

18. **Assertion:** $\dfrac{x^{12} - y^{12}}{x^4 - y^4} = \dfrac{(x^4)^3 - (y^4)^3}{x^4 - y^4}$

$$= \frac{(x^4 - y^4)\left[(x^4)^2 + (y^4)^2 - x^4 \times y^4\right]}{x^4 - y^4}$$

$= (x^4)^2 + (y^4)^2 - x^4 \times y^4$ which is a polynomial.

Hence, the **Assertion** is true.

Reason: If $f(x)$, and $g(x) \neq 0$are polynomials, then $\dfrac{f(x)}{g(x)}$ need not be a polynomial. It is a true statement, but not the correct explanation of the **Assertion**.

Hence, the correct option is (b).

19. Assertion: Given that $p(x)=\dfrac{x^2-7x+12}{x^2-x-30}$ and $q(x)=\dfrac{x^2-8x+15}{x^2-2x-24}$.

$$p(x)=\frac{x^2-7x+12}{x^2-x-30}=\frac{(x-3)(x-4)}{(x-6)(x+5)}$$

$$q(x)=\frac{x^2-8x+15}{x^2-2x-24}=\frac{(x-3)(x-5)}{(x-6)(x+4)}$$

Now $\dfrac{p(x)}{q(x)}=\dfrac{(x-3)(x-4)}{(x-6)(x+5)}\div\dfrac{(x-3)(x-5)}{(x-6)(x+4)}$

$$\frac{p(x)}{q(x)}=\frac{(x-3)(x-4)}{(x-6)(x+5)}\times\frac{(x-6)(x+4)}{(x-3)(x-5)}$$

$$=\frac{(x-4)(x+4)}{(x+5)(x-5)}=\frac{x^2-16}{x^2-25}$$

The additive inverse of $\dfrac{x^2-16}{x^2-25}$ is $-\dfrac{x^2-16}{x^2-25}$.

The multiplicative inverse of $\dfrac{x^2-16}{x^2-25}$ is $\dfrac{x^2-25}{x^2-16}$.

The required product $=-\dfrac{x^2-16}{x^2-25}\times\dfrac{x^2-25}{x^2-16}=-1.$

Reason: The additive inverse of $\dfrac{p(x)}{q(x)}$ is $-\dfrac{p(x)}{q(x)}$.

The multiplicative inverse of $\dfrac{p(x)}{q(x)}$ is $\dfrac{q(x)}{p(x)}$.

The required product $=-\dfrac{p(x)}{q(x)}\times\dfrac{q(x)}{p(x)}=-1.$

For any two polynomials $p(x)$, and $q(x)\neq 0$, the product of the additive inverse and the multiplicative inverse of $\dfrac{p(x)}{q(x)}$ is -1.

Hence, **Reason** is a true statement and is the correct explanation of the **Assertion**.

Hence, the correct option is (a).

20. Assertion: Given that the HCF of two polynomials is x^2-2x+1.

$$x^4+x^2+1=x^4+2x^2+1-x^2$$

$$=\left(x^2+1\right)^2-x^2$$

$$=\left(x^2+1+x\right)\left(x^2+1-x\right)$$

We know that the HCF of two polynomials is a factor of their LCM.

But x^2-2x+1 is not a factor of $\left(x^2+1+x\right)\left(x^2+1-x\right)$ i.e., x^4+x^2+1.

So, Assertion is false.

Reason: Given that the LCM of two polynomials is a multiple of their HCF.

Reason is true.

Hence, the correct option is (d).

CHAPTER 3

Remainder and Factor Theorem

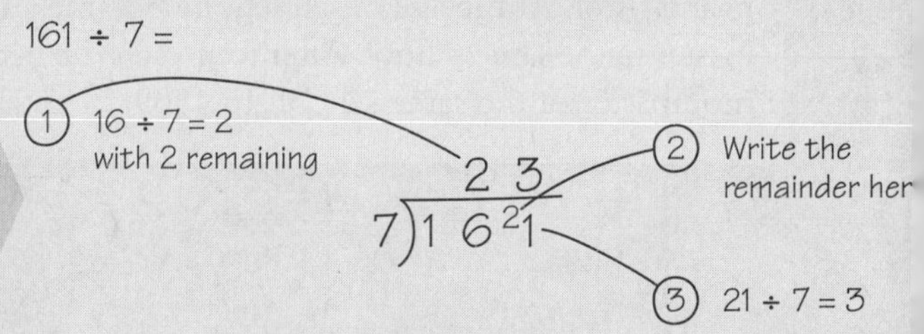

Remember

Before beginning this chapter, you should be able to:

- Define polynomials and its functions

Key Ideas

After completing this chapter, you should be able to:

- Obtain zero of a polynomial
- Prove remainder theorem
- State and prove factor theorem
- Do factorization of polynomials using factor theorem
- Apply Horner's process for synthetic division of polynomials

Scientific Crypt

A Tribute to William George Horner (1786 to 1837)

William George Horner was a British mathematician and schoolmaster. He was educated at Kingswood School, near Bristol. At the age of sixteen, he became an assistant master in the same school. After four years, he became the headmaster of the same school. In 1809, he established a school at Grosvenor Place, Bath. He published a book on solving numerical equations of any degree, now known as Horner's method. We use the Horner's method to divide one polynomial by another.

FUN TIME

CROSSWORD

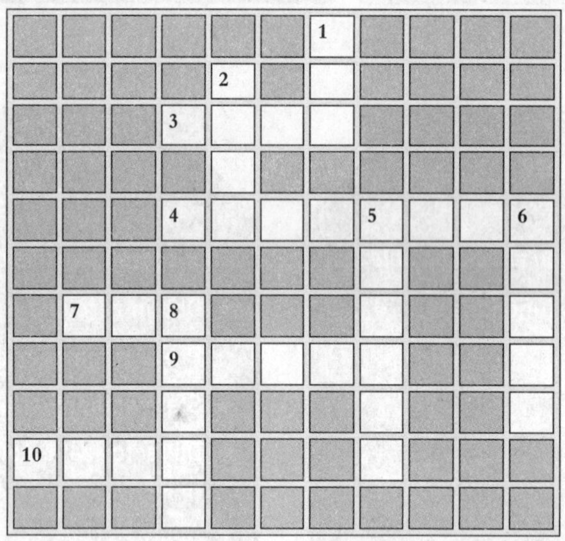

Across

3. It is the value of a variable polynomial at which the polynomial is zero.
4. This polynomial's degree is zero.
7. Is $(x - 3)$ a factor of $x^2 + 4x - 21$?
9. The relation among x, y and z, when $(x - y)^2 + (y - z)^2 + (z - x)^2 = 0$
10. It is a zero of $x^2 - 11x + 18$

Down

1. It is the remainder obtained when $x^2 - 4x + 6$ is divided by $x - 2$.
2. The remainder is obtained when a polynomial (sum of whose coefficients is zero) is divided by $x - 1$.
5. It is the product of the zeroes of $x^2 - 7x + 12$.
6. This can be the maximum number of zeroes of a cubic polynomial.
8. It is the sum of the zeroes of $x^2 - 7x + 12$.

INTRODUCTION

A real valued function $f(x)$ of the form $a_0x^n + a_1x^{n-1} + \cdots + a_n$, $(a_0 \neq 0)$ is called as a polynomial of degree n, where n is a non-negative integer. Here $a_0, a_1, \ldots, a_n$ are the coefficients of various powers of x.

For Examples:

1. $4x^6 + 5x^5 + x^4 + x^2 - 1$ is a polynomial in x of degree 6.
2. $2x^3 + x^2 + 1$ is a polynomial in x of degree 3.

In earlier classes, we have learnt the different operations on polynomials like addition, subtraction, multiplication, and division. Here, we shall learn two important theorems on polynomials.

Remainder Theorem

If $p(x)$ is any polynomial and 'a' is any real number, then the remainder when $p(x)$ is divided by $(x - a)$ is given by $p(a)$.

Proof: Let $q(x)$ and $r(x)$ be the quotient and the remainder respectively when $p(x)$ is divided by $(x - a)$.

$\therefore$ By division algorithm

Dividend = Quotient × Divisor + Remainder,

i.e., $p(x) = q(x)(x - a) + r(x)$

If $x = a$, then

$$p(a) = q(a)(a - a) + r(a) \Rightarrow r(a) = p(a),$$

i.e., $p(x) = (x - a)\, q(x) + p(a)$

Thus, the remainder is $p(a)$.

Konnect

1. If $p(a) = 0$, we say that 'a' is a zero of the polynomial $p(x)$.
2. If $p(x)$ is a polynomial and 'a' is a zero of $p(x)$, then $p(x) = (x - a)\, q(x)$.
3. If $p(x)$ is divided by $ax + b$, then the remainder is given by $p\left(\frac{-b}{a}\right)$.
4. If $p(x)$ is divided by $ax - b$, then the remainder is given by $p\left(\frac{b}{a}\right)$.

EXAMPLE 3.1 What is the remainder when $p(x) = (x + 2)(x - 3)(x + 1) + kx$ is divided by x?

SOLUTION

If $p(x)$ is divided by x, then the remainder is $p(0)$

$p(0) = (0 + 2)(0 - 3)(0 + 1) + k(0)$

$= (2)(-3)(1) = -6$

Factor Theorem

If $p(x)$ is a polynomial of degree n (≥ 1) and a be any real number such that $p(a) = 0$, then $(x - a)$ is a factor of $p(x)$.

Proof: Let $q(x)$ be the quotient and $(x - a)(a \in R)$ be a divisor of $p(x)$.

Given $p(a) = 0$

∴ By division algorithm,

$$\text{Dividend} = \text{Quotient} \times \text{Divisor} + \text{Remainder}$$

$$p(x) = q(x)(x - a) + p(a)$$

$$\Rightarrow \quad p(x) = q(x)(x - a) \qquad (\because p(a) = 0)$$

Therefore, $(x - a)$ is a factor of $f(x)$, which is possible only if $p(a) = 0$.

Hence, $(x - a)$ is a factor of $p(x)$

EXAMPLE 3.2 Determine whether $(x - 3)$ is a factor of $f(x) = x^2 - 5x + 6$.

SOLUTION

Given, $f(x) = x^2 - 5x + 6$

Now, $f(3) = (3)^2 - 5(3) + 6$

$= 9 - 15 + 6$

$= 0 \Rightarrow f(3) = 0$.

Hence, by factor theorem, we can say that $(x - 3)$ is a factor of $f(x)$.

EXAMPLE 3.3 Determine whether $(x - 1)$ is a factor of $x^3 - 6x^2 + 11x - 6$.

SOLUTION

Let $f(x) = x^3 - 6x^2 + 11x - 6$

Now $f(1) = (1)^3 - 6(1)^2 + 11(1) - 6$

$= 1 - 6 + 11 - 6 = 0 \Rightarrow f(1) = 0$.

Hence, by factor theorem, we can say that $(x - 1)$ is a factor of $f(x)$.

Konnect

1. If $p(-a) = 0$, then $(x + a)$ is a factor of $p(x)$.
2. If $p\left(\frac{-b}{a}\right) = 0$, then $(ax + b)$ is a factor of $p(x)$.
3. If $p\left(\frac{b}{a}\right) = 0$, then $(ax - b)$ is a factor of $p(x)$.
4. If sum of all the coefficients of a polynomial is zero, then $(x - 1)$ is one of its factors.
5. If sum of the coefficients of odd powers of x is equal to the sum of the coefficients of even powers of x, then one of the factors of the polynomial is $(x + 1)$.

Factorization of Polynomials Using Factor Theorem

1. Factorize $x^2(y - z) + y^2(z - x) + z^2(x - y)$.

   Let us assume the given expression as a polynomial in x, say $f(x)$

   $f(x) = x^2(y - z) + y^2(z - x) + z^2(x - y)$

   Now, put $x = y$ in the given expression;

   $\Rightarrow f(y) = y^2(y - z) + y^2(z - y) + z^2(y - y)$

   $= y^3 - zy^2 + y^2z - y^3 + 0 = 0 \Rightarrow f(y) = 0$

   $\Rightarrow (x - y)$ is a factor of the given expression.

   Similarly, if we consider the given expression as a polynomial in y, we get $(y - z)$ is a factor of the given expression and we also get $(z - x)$ is a factor of the expression when we consider it as an expression in z.

   Let $x^2(y - z) + yz\ (z - x) + z^2(x - y) = k(x - y)(y - z)(z - x)$

   For $x = 0$, $y = 1$ and $z = 2$, we get

   $0^2(1 - 2) + 1^2(2 - 0) + 2^2(0 - 1) = k(0 - 1)(1 - 2)(2 - 0)$

$\Rightarrow -2 = 2k \Rightarrow k = -1$

$\therefore$ The factors of the given expression are $x - y$, $y - z$ and $z - x$.

2. Use factor theorem to factorize $x^3 + y^3 + z^3 - 3xyz$.

Given expression is $x^3 + y^3 + z^3 - 3xyz$.

Consider the expression as a polynomial in variable x say $f(x)$.

That is, $f(x) = x^3 + y^3 + z^3 - 3xyz$

$$\text{Now, } f[-(y+z)] = [-(y+z)]^3 + y^3 + z^3 - 3[-(y+z)]yz$$
$$= -(y+z)^3 + y^3 + z^3 + 3yz(y+z)$$
$$= -(y+z)^3 + (y+z)^3 = 0 \Rightarrow f[-(y+z)] = 0$$

$\Rightarrow$ According to factor theorem $x - [-(y + z)]$, i.e., $x + y + z$ is a factor of $x^3 + y^3 + z^3 - 3xyz$.

Now, using the long division method we get the other factor as,

$x^2 + y^2 + z^2 - xy - yz - zx$

$\therefore x^3 + y^3 + z^3 - 3xyz = (x + y + z)(x^2 + y^2 + z^2 - xy - yz - zx)$.

Info Bytes!

A constant is considered to be a polynomial of zero degree.

Horner's Process for Synthetic Division of Polynomials

When a polynomial $f(x) = p_0x^n + p_1x^{n-1} + \cdots + p_{n-1}x + p_n$ is divided by a binomial $x - \alpha$, let the quotient be $Q(x)$ and remainder be r.

We can find quotient $Q(x)$ and remainder r by using Horner's synthetic division process as explained below.

α	p_0	p_1	p_2	…	p_{n-1}	p_n	…1st row
left (corner)		$q_0\alpha$	$q_1\alpha$	…	$q_{n-2}\alpha$	$q_{n-1}\alpha$	…2nd row
	q_0	q_1	q_2	…	q_{n-1}	r	…3rd row

Step 1: Write all the coefficients $p_0, p_1, p_2, \ldots, p_n$ of the given polynomial $f(x)$ in the order of descending powers of x as in the first row. When any term in $f(x)$ (as seen with descending powers of x) is missing, we write zero for its coefficient.

Step 2: Divide the polynomial $f(x)$ by $(x - \alpha)$ by writing α in the left corner as shown above $(x - \alpha = 0 \Rightarrow x = \alpha)$.

Step 3: Write the first term of the third row as $q_0 = p_0$, then multiply q_0 by α to get $q_0\alpha$ and write it under p_1, as the first element of the second row.

Step 4: Add $q_0\alpha$ to p_1 to get q_1, the second element of the third row.

Step 5: Again multiply q_1 with α to get $q_1\alpha$ and write $q_1\alpha$ under p_2 and add $q_1\alpha$ to p_2 to get q_2 which is the third element of the third row.

Step 6: Continue this process till we obtain q_{n-1} in the third row. Multiply q_{n-1} with α and write $q_{n-1}\alpha$ under p_n and add $q_{n-1}\alpha$ to p_n to get r in the third row as shown in previous page.

Info Bytes!

If the remainder $r = 0$ then α is one of the roots of $f(x) = 0$ or $x - \alpha$ is a factor of $f(x)$.

In the above process, the elements of the third row, i.e., $q_0, q_1, q_2, \ldots, q_{n-1}$ are the coefficients of the quotient $Q(x)$ in the same order of descending powers starting with x^{n-1}.

$\therefore Q(x) = q_0x^{n-1} + q_1x^{n-2} + \cdots + q_{n-2}x + q_{n-1}$ and the remainder is r, i.e., the last element of the third row.

EXAMPLE 3.4

Factorize $x^4 - 10x^2 + 9$.

SOLUTION

Let $p(x) = x^4 - 10x^2 + 9$

Here, sum of coefficients = 0, and also sum of coefficients of even powers of x = sum of coefficients of odd powers of x.

$\therefore$ $(x - 1)$ and $(x + 1)$ are the factors of $p(x)$.

Multiplier of $x - 1$ is 1 and $x + 1$ is -1

$\therefore$ The quotient is $x^2 - 9$

Hence, $p(x) = (x - 1)(x + 1)(x^2 - 9)$

$\Rightarrow p(x) = (x - 1)(x + 1)(x - 3)(x + 3)$.

1	1	0	−10	0	9
	0	1	1	−9	−9
−1	1	1	−9	−9	0
	0	−1	0	9	
	1	0	−9	0	

EXAMPLE 3.5

Find the value of a if $ax^3 - (a + 1)x^2 + 3x - 5a$ is divisible by $(x - 2)$.

SOLUTION

Let $p(x) = ax^3 - (a + 1)x^2 + 3x - 5a$

If $p(x)$ is divisible by $(x - 2)$, then its remainder is zero, i.e., $p(2) = 0$

$\Rightarrow a(2)^3 - (a + 1)(2)^2 + 3(2) - 5a = 0$

$\Rightarrow 8a - 4a - 4 + 6 - 5a = 0$

$\Rightarrow -a + 2 = 0$

$\Rightarrow a = 2$.

$\therefore$ The required value of a is 2.

EXAMPLE 3.6

If the polynomial $x^3 + ax^2 - bx - 30$ is exactly divisible by $x^2 - 2x - 15$. Find a and b and also the third factor.

SOLUTION

Let $p(x) = x^3 + ax^2 - bx - 30$

Given $p(x)$ is exactly divisible by $x^2 - 2x - 15$, i.e., $(x - 5)(x + 3)$

$\Rightarrow p(x)$ is divisible by $(x + 3)$ and $(x - 5)$

$\therefore p(-3) = 0$ and $p(5) = 0$

Consider $p(-3) = 0$

$\Rightarrow (-3)^3 + a(-3)^2 - b(-3) - 30 = 0$

$\Rightarrow -27 + 9a + 3b - 30 = 0$

$\Rightarrow 9a + 3b - 57 = 0$

$\Rightarrow 3a + b - 19 = 0$ (1)

Now, consider $p(5) = 0$

$\Rightarrow (5)^3 + a(5)^2 - b(5) - 30 = 0$

$\Rightarrow 125 + 25a - 5b - 30 = 0$

$\Rightarrow 25a - 5b + 95 = 0$

$\Rightarrow 5a - b + 19 = 0$ (2)

Adding Eqs. (1) and (2), we get

$8a = 0$

$\Rightarrow a = 0$

Substituting a in Eq. (1), we get $b = 19$.

$\therefore$ The required values of a and b are 0 and 19, respectively.

$\Rightarrow p(x) = x^3 + 0(x^2) - 19x - 30.$

That is, $p(x) = x^3 - 19x - 30.$

−3	1	0	−19	−30
	0	−3	9	30
5	1	−3	−10	0
	0	5	10	
	1	2	0	

Thus, the third factor is $x + 2$.

EXAMPLE 3.7 Find the linear polynomial in x which when divided by $(x - 3)$ leaves 6 as remainder and is exactly divisible by $(x + 3)$.

SOLUTION

Let the linear polynomial be $p(x) = ax + b$

Given, $p(3) = 6$ and $p(-3) = 0$.

$\Rightarrow a(3) + b = 6$ and $a(-3) + b = 0$

$\Rightarrow 3a + b = 6$ (1)

and $-3a + b = 0$ (2)

Adding Eqs. (1) and (2),

$2b = 6 \Rightarrow b = 3$

Substituting the value of b in Eq. (1), we get $a = 1$

$\therefore$ The required linear polynomial is $x + 3$.

EXAMPLE 3.8 A quadratic polynomial in x leaves remainders as 4 and 7, respectively, when divided by $(x + 1)$ and $(x - 2)$. Also it is exactly divisible by $(x - 1)$. Find the quadratic polynomial.

SOLUTION

Let the quadratic polynomial be $p(x) = ax^2 + bx + c$.

Given, $p(-1) = 4$, $p(2) = 7$ and $p(1) = 0$

$p(-1) = a(-1)^2 + b(-1) + c = 4$

$\Rightarrow a - b + c = 4$ (1)

Now, $p(1) = 0$ and $p(2) = 7$

$\therefore a(1)^2 + b(1) + c = 0$ and

$a(2)^2 + b(2) + c = 7$

$\Rightarrow a + b + c = 0$ (2)

$4a + 2b + c = 7$ (3)

Subtracting Eq. (1) from Eq. (2), we have,

$2b = -4 \Rightarrow b = -2.$

Subtracting Eq. (2) from Eq. (3), we have,

$3a + b = 7$

$\Rightarrow 3a - 2 = 7 \quad (\because b = -2)$

$\Rightarrow 3a = 9 \Rightarrow a = 3$

Substituting the values of a and b in Eq. (1), we get $c = -1$

Hence, the required quadratic polynomial is $3x^2 - 2x - 1$.

EXAMPLE 3.9 Find a common factor of the quadratic polynomials $3x^2 - x - 10$ and $2x^2 - x - 6$.

SOLUTION

Consider, $p(x) = 3x^2 - x - 10$ and $q(x) = 2x^2 - x - 6$

Let $(x - k)$ be a common factor of $p(x)$ and $q(x)$.

$\therefore p(k) = q(k) = 0$

$\Rightarrow 3k^2 - k - 10 = 2k^2 - k - 6$

$\Rightarrow k^2 - 4 = 0$

$\Rightarrow k^2 = 4$

$\Rightarrow k = \pm 2$

$\therefore$ The required common factor is $(x - 2)$ or $(x + 2)$.

EXAMPLE 3.10 Find the remainder when x^{999} is divided by $x^2 - 4x + 3$.

SOLUTION

Let $q(x)$ and $mx + n$ be the quotient and the remainder, respectively, when x^{999} is divided by $x^2 - 4x + 3$.

$\therefore x^{999} = (x^2 - 4x + 3)\, q(x) + mx + n.$

$x^2 - 4x + 3 = (x - 1)\,(x - 3)$

If $x = 1$,

$1^{999} = (1 - 4 + 3)\, q(1) + m(1) + n$

$\Rightarrow 1 = 0 \times q(1) + m + n$

$\Rightarrow m + n = 1 \quad (1)$

If $x = 3$,

$3^{999} = (3^2 - 4(3) + 3)\, q(3) + 3m + n$

$\Rightarrow 3^{999} = 0 \times q(3) + 3m + n$

$\Rightarrow 3m + n = 3^{999} \quad (2)$

Subtracting Eq. (1) from Eq. (2), we get,

$2m = 3^{999} - 1$

$m = \frac{1}{2}(3^{999} - 1)$

Substituting m in Eq. (1), we have,

$$n = 1 - \frac{1}{2}(3^{999} - 1) = 1 - \frac{1}{2}3^{999} + \frac{1}{2} = \frac{3}{2} - \frac{1}{2}3^{999}$$

$$n = \frac{3}{2}(1 - 3^{998})$$

$\therefore$ The required remainder is $\frac{1}{2}(3^{999} - 1)x + \frac{3}{2}(1 - 3^{998})$.

EXAMPLE 3.11

Find the remainder when x^5 is divided by $x^3 - 4x$.

SOLUTION

Let $q(x)$ be the quotient and $lx^2 + mx + n$ be the remainder, when x^5 is divided by $x^3 - 4x$.

That is, $x(x - 2)(x + 2)$

$\therefore x^5 = (x^3 - 4x)\, q(x) + lx^2 + mx + n$

Put, $x = 0$

$\Rightarrow 0 = 0 \times q(0) + l(0) + m(0) + n$

$\Rightarrow n = 0$

Put, $x = 2$

$\Rightarrow 2^5 = (8 - 8)\, q(2) + l(2)^2 + m(2) + n$

$\Rightarrow 32 = 4l + 2m + n$

$\Rightarrow 4l + 2m = 32$ $(\because n = 0)$

$\Rightarrow 2l + m = 16$ (1)

Put, $x = -2$

$(-2)^5 = (-8 + 8)\, q(-2) + l(-2)^2 + m(-2) + n$

$\Rightarrow -32 = 4l - 2m + n$

$\Rightarrow 4l - 2m = -32$ $(\because n = 0)$

$\Rightarrow 2l - m = -16$ (2)

Adding Eqs. (1) and (2), we get,

$4l = 0$

$\Rightarrow l = 0$

Substituting l in Eq. (1), we get,

$2(0) + m = 16$

$\Rightarrow m = 16.$

$\therefore$ The required remainder is $0(x^2) + 16x + 0$, i.e., $16x$.

EXAMPLE 3.12

What is the remainder when $(x + a)(x + b)(x + c)\ldots\ldots(x + z)$ is divided by $(x + k)$?

(a) 0 (b) $-k$ (c) k (d) None of these

SOLUTION

Let $p(x)$, $\underset{x=a}{\overset{z}{4}}\,(x + a) = (x + a)(x + b)\ \ldots\ldots(x + k)\ldots.\ (x + z)$

If $p(x)$ is divided by $x + k$, then the remainder is $p(-k)$

$p(-k) = (-k + a)(-k + b)\ldots..\ (-k + k)\ldots\ldots\ (-k + z) = 0$

EXAMPLE 3.13

If $(x - 2)$ and $(x - 3)$ are two factors of $f(x) = x^3 + ax + b$, then find the remainder when $f(x)$ is divided by $x - 5$.

SOLUTION

Given $f(x) = x^3 + ax + b$

$f(2) = 0$ and $f(3) = 0$

$(2)^3 + 2a + b = 0 \Rightarrow 2a + b = -8$ (1)

$(3)^3 + 3a + b = 0 \Rightarrow 3a + b = -27$ (2)

On solving Eqs. (1) and (2), we get

$a = -19$ and $b = 30$

$f(x) = x^3 - 19x + 30$

Now, $f(5) = 5^3 - 19(5) + 30 = 125 - 95 + 30 = 60$.

EXAMPLE 3.14 Find the common factor of the quadratic polynomials $x^2 - x - 6$ and $x^2 + 5x + 6$.

SOLUTION

Let $p(x) = x^2 - x - 6$, $q(x) = x^2 + 5x + 6$

Let $(x - k)$ be a common factor of $f(x)$ and $g(x)$

$\therefore p(k) = q(k) = 0$

$\Rightarrow k^2 - k - 6 = k^2 + 5k + 6$

$\Rightarrow 6k = -12$

$\Rightarrow k = -2$

The required common factor is $(x + 2)$.

EXAMPLE 3.15 When a fourth–degree polynomial $f(x)$ is divided by $(x + 6)$, the quotient is $Q(x)$ and the remainder is -6. And when $f(x)$ is divided by $[Q(x) + 1]$, the quotient is $(x + 6)$ and the remainder is $R(x)$. Find $R(x)$.

SOLUTION

Given,

$f(x) = Q(x)(x + 6) - 6$

$\Rightarrow Q(x)(x + 6) = f(x) + 6$ (1)

And also given,

$f(x) = (x + 6)[Q(x) + 1] + R(x)$

$\Rightarrow f(x) = (x + 6)\ Q(x) + x + 6 + R(x)$

$\Rightarrow f(x) = f(x) + 6 + x + 6 + R(x)$ (from Eq. (1))

$\Rightarrow R(x) = -(x + 12)$.

EXAMPLE 3.16 What is the linear polynomial in x, which when divided by $x - 3$ leaves 9 as the remainder and when it is divided by $x + 3$ leaves 3 as the remainder?

SOLUTION

Let the linear polynomial be $p(x) = ax + b$.

If $p(3) = 9$ and $p(-3) = 3$

$$3a + b = 9$$
$$\underline{-3a + b = 3}$$
$$\underline{2b = 12}$$
$$b = 6$$

$\therefore 3a + 6 = 9$

$3a = 3$

$a = 1$

Required polynomial is $x + 6$

POINTS TO REMEMBER

- ✔ If $p(x)$ is any polynomial and 'a' is any real number, then the remainder when $p(x)$ is divided by $(x - a)$ is given by $p(a)$.
- ✔ If $p(x)$ is a polynomial of degree n (≥ 1) and a be any real number such that $p(a) = 0$, then $(x - a)$ is a factor of $p(x)$.
- ✔ If sum of the coefficients of odd powers of x is equal to the sum of the coefficients of even powers of x, then one of the factors of the polynomial is $(x + 1)$.

DW

PRACTICE QUESTIONS CLASSROOM WING

Very Short Answer Type Questions

Directions of questions from 1 to 10:
Fill in the blanks.

1. If $x + 7$ is a factor of $x^2 - 3x + k$, then find the value of k.
2. If $2x + 3$ is a factor of $6x^2 - 5x + k$, then find the value of k.
3. The remainder when $(x - a)^2 + (x - b)^2$ is divided by x is ______.
4. Find the remainder, when $f(x) = x^2 + 6x + 8$ is divided by $2x - 1$.
5. Find the remainder, when $f(x) = x^3 + 6x^2 - 8x + 1$ is divided by $(x - 2)$.
6. If $(x - 2)^2$ is the factor of an expression of the form $x^3 + bx + c$, then the other factor is ______.
7. The remainder obtained when $x^2 + 3x + 1$ is divided by $(x - 5)$ is ______.
8. If the polynomial $3x^4 - 11x^2 + 6x + k$ is divided by $x - 3$, it leaves a remainder 7. Then the value of k is ______.
9. If $(2x - 1)$ is a factor of $2x^2 + px - 2$, then the other factor is ______.
10. The expression $x^{m^n} - 1$ is divisible by $x + 1$, only if m is ______. (even/odd)

Directions of questions from 11 to 13:
State whether the following statements are true or false.

11. For two odd numbers x and y, if $x^3 + y^3$ is divisible by 2^k, $k \in N$, then $x + y$ is divisible by 2^k. [True/False]
12. The remainder when $f(x)$ is divided by $g(x)$ is $f\left(-\frac{3}{2}\right)$, then $g(x)$ is necessarily $2x + 3$. [True/False]
13. $(7x - 1)$ is a factor of $7x^3 + 6x^2 - 15x + 2$. (True/False)

Directions of questions from 14 to 21:
Answer the following questions.

14. What should be added to $3x^3 + 5x^2 - 6x + 3$ to make it exactly divisible by $x - 1$?
15. Find the remainder when the polynomial $x^2 + 13x + 11$ is divided by $x - 1$.
16. Find the value of the polynomial $a^2 - \frac{1}{6}a + \frac{3}{2}$ when $a = \frac{1}{2}$.
17. The polynomial $7x^2 - 11x + a$ when divided by $x + 1$ leaves a remainder of 8. Then find the value of 'a'.
18. If $x + 2$ is a factor of $f(x)$ and $f(x) = x^3 + 4x^2 + kx - 6$, then find the value of k.
19. Find the value of a if $x - a$ is a factor of the polynomial $x^5 - ax^4 + x^3 - ax^2 + 2x + 3a - 2$.
20. Find the remainder when $x^3 + 3px + q$ is divided by $(x^2 - a^2)$ without actual division.
21. If $x^2 + 5x + 6$ is a factor of $x^3 + 9x^2 + 26x + 24$, then find the remaining factor.

Short Answer Type Questions

Directions of questions from 22 to 36:
Answer the following questions.

22. If $f(x + 4) = x^2 - 7x + 9$, then find the remainder when $f(x)$ is divided by $x + 7$.
23. What should be added to $3x^3 + 5x^2 - 7x + 5$ to make the sum exactly divisible by $(x - 2)$?
24. Prove that $x^m + 1$ is a factor of $x^{mn} - 1$ if n is even.
25. The remainders of a polynomial $f(x)$ in x are 10 and 15, respectively, when $f(x)$ is divided by$(x - 3)$ and $(x - 4)$. Find the remainder when $f(x)$ is divided by $(x - 3)(x - 4)$.
26. If x^{555} is divided by $x^2 - 4x + 3$, then find its remainder.
27. If $(x^2 - 1)$ is a factor of $ax^3 - bx^2 - cx + d$, then find the relation between a and c.
28. When $x^4 - 3x^3 + 4x^2 + p$ is divided by $(x - 2)$, the remainder is zero. Find the value of p.

29. Find the common factors of the expressions $a_1x^2 + b_1x + c_1$ and $a_2x^2 + b_2x + c_1$ where $c_1 \neq 0$.

30. If $(x - 3)$ is a factor of $x^2 + q$ (where $q \in Q$), then find the remainder when $(x^2 + q)$ is divided by$(x - 2)$.

31. If $p + q$ is a factor of the polynomial $p^n - q^n$, then n is ______ (even/odd).

32. The expression $x^{4005} + y^{4005}$ is divisible by ______ $((x + y)$ or $(x - y))$.

33. The value of a for which $x - 7$ is a factor of $x^2 + 11x - 2a$, is ______.

34. If a polynomial $f(x)$ is divided by $(x - 3)$ and $(x - 4)$ it leaves remainders as 7 and 12 respectively, then find the remainder when $f(x)$ is divided by $(x - 3)(x - 4)$.

35. Find the remainder when $5x^4 - 11x^2 + 6$ is divided by $5x^2 - 6$.

36. (A) If $f(x - 2) = 2x^2 - 3x + 4$, then find the remainder when $f(x)$ is divided by $(x - 1)$.

(B) Find the remainder when x^{2017} is divided by $x^2 - 1$.

Essay Type Questions

37. Factorize $x^4 - 2x^3 - 9x^2 + 2x + 8$ using remainder theorem.

38. Find the remainder when x^{2014} is divided by $x^2 - 5x + 6$.

39. If $x^2 - 2x - 1$ is a factor of $px^3 + qx^2 + 1$, (where p, q are integers) then find the value of $p + q$.

40. If $x^2 - x + 1$ is a factor of $x^4 + ax^2 + b$, then the values of a and b are ______ respectively.

41. If $lx^2 + mx + n$ is exactly divisible by $(x - 1)$ and $(x + 1)$ and leaves a remainder 1 when divided by $x + 2$, then find m and n.

42. Given that $f(x)$ is a cubic polynomial. If $f(x)$ is divided by $x - 3$ and $x - 4$, then the remainders are 6 and 7 respectively. Find the remainder when $f(x)$ is divided by $(x - 3)(x - 4)$.

PRACTICE QUESTIONS COMPETITION WING

Level 1: Apply Your Concepts

Directions of questions from 1 to 5:
Fill in the blanks.

1. Let $f(x) = a_0x^n + a_1x^{n-1} + \cdots + a_n$ $(a_0 \neq 0)$ be a polynomial of degree n. If $x + 1$ is one of its factors, then ______.

2. If a polynomial $f(x)$ is divided by $(x + a)$, then the remainder obtained is ______.

3. If $a - b$ is a factor of $a^n - b^n$, then n is ______.

4. If $f(x) = x^3 + 2$ is divided by $x + 2$, then the remainder obtained is ______.

5. The condition for which $ax^2 + bx + a$ is exactly divisible by $x - a$ is ______.

Directions of questions from 6 to 30:
Select the correct alternative from the given choices.

6. If $ax^3 + bx^2 + cx + d$ is exactly divisible by $x + 1$ and $x + 2$, then which of the following is true?
(a) $3a - 4b + d = 0$
(b) $8a - b + 2d = 0$
(c) $5a - 2b + 3d = 0$
(d) $6a - 2b + d = 0$

7. If $px^3 + qx^2 + rx + s$ is exactly divisible by $x + 1$ and $x - 3$, respectively, then which of the following is true?
(a) $6p + 3q + s = 0$ (b) $p + 2q + 3s = 0$
(c) $4p + 2q + s = 0$ (d) $3p + 4q + s = 0$

8. The remainder when $12x^6 - 4x^3 - 9$ is divided by $(x^3 - 5)$ is ______.
(a) 27 (b) 271
(c) 183 (d) 281

9. If both the expressions $x^{1248} - 1$ and $x^{672} - 1$, are divisible by $x^n - 1$, then the greatest integer value of n is ______.
(a) 48 (b) 96
(c) 54 (d) 112

10. When $x^2 - 7x + 2$ is divided by $x - 8$, then the remainder is ______.
(a) 122 (b) 4
(c) 45 (d) 10

11. The expression $2x^3 + 3x^2 - 5x + p$ when divided by $x + 2$ leaves a remainder of $3p + 2$. Find p.
(a) -2 (b) 1
(c) 0 (d) 2

12. $3x - 4$ is a factor of ______.
(a) $18x^4 - 3x^3 - 28x^2 - 3x + 4$
(b) $3x^4 - 10x^3 - 7x^2 + 38x - 24$
(c) $9x^4 - 6x^3 + 5x^2 - 15$
(d) $9x^4 + 36x^3 + 17x^2 - 38x - 24$

13. Which of the following is a factor of $5x^{20} + 7x^{15} + x^9$?
(a) x^{20} (b) x^{15}
(c) x^9 (d) x^{24}

14. If $(x + 3)^2$ is a factor of $f(x) = ex^3 + kx + 6$, then find the remainder obtained when $f(x)$ is divided by $x - 6$.
(a) 1 (b) 0
(c) 5 (d) 4

15. The expression $x^{mn} + 1$ is divisible by $x + 1$, only if
(a) n is odd. (b) m is odd.
(c) both m and n are even. (d) Cannot say

16. If both the expressions $x^{1215} - 1$ and $x^{945} - 1$, are divisible by $x^n - 1$, then the greatest integer value of n is ______.
(a) 135 (b) 270
(c) 945 (d) None of these

17. When $x^3 + 3x^2 + 4x + a$ is divided by $(x + 2)$, the remainder is zero. Find the value of a.
(a) 4 (b) 6
(c) -8 (d) -12

18. If $(x + 1)$ and $(x - 1)$ are the factors of $ax^3 + bx^2 + cx + d$, then which of the following is true?
(a) $a + b = 0$ (b) $b + c = 0$
(c) $b + d = 0$ (d) $a + c = 0$

19. Find the remainder when x^5 is divided by $x^2 - 9$.
(a) $81x$ (b) $81x + 10$
(c) $3^5x + 34$ (d) 81

20. For what values of a and b, the expression $x^4 + 4x^3 + ax^2 - bx + 3$ is a multiple of $x^2 - 1$?

(a) $a = 1, b = 7$ (b) $a = 4, b = -4$
(c) $a = 3, b = -5$ (d) $a = -4, b = 4$

21. When the polynomial $p(x) = ax^2 + bx + c$ is divided by $(x - 1)$ and $(x + 1)$, the remainders obtained are 6 and 10 respectively. If the value of $p(x)$ is 5 at $x = 0$, then the value of $5a - 2b + 5c$ is ______.

(a) 40 (b) 44
(c) 21 (d) 42

22. If $p - q$ is a factor of the polynomial $p^n - q^n$, then n is ______.

(a) a prime number (b) an odd number
(c) an even number (d) All of these

23. When the polynomial $f(x) = ax^2 + bx + c$ is divided by x, $x - 2$ and $x + 3$, remainders obtained are 7, 9 and 49, respectively. Find the value of $3a + 5b + 2c$.

(a) −2 (b) 2
(c) 5 (d) −5

24. If $f(x + 1) = 2x^2 + 7x + 5$, then one of the factors of $f(x)$ is ______.

(a) $2x + 3$ (b) $2x^2 + 3$
(c) $3x + 2$ (d) $2x + 1$

25. If $(x - p)$ and $(x - q)$ are the factors of $x^2 + px + q$, then the values of p and q are ______, respectively.

(a) 1, −2 (b) 2, −3
(c) $\frac{-1}{3}, \frac{-2}{3}$ (d) −2, 1

26. Let $f\left(x - \frac{1}{x}\right) = x^2 + \frac{1}{x^2}$, find the remainder when $f(x)$ is divided by $x - 3$.

(a) $\frac{82}{9}$ (b) $\frac{8}{3}$
(c) 10 (d) 11

27. If $(x - 2)^2$ is a factor of $f(x) = x^3 + px + q$, then find the remainder when $f(x)$ is divided by $x - 1$.

(a) 4 (b) −4
(c) −5 (d) 5

28. A quadratic polynomial in x leaves remainders 4, 4 and 0, respectively when divided by $(x - 1)$, $(x - 2)$ and $(x - 3)$. Find the quadratic polynomial.

(a) $-2x^2 + 6x + 3$ (b) $-2x^2 + 6x$
(c) $-2x^2 + 6x + 5$ (d) $-2x^2 + 6x - 5$

29. If $f(x + 3) = x^2 + x - 6$, then one of the factors of $f(x)$ is ______.

(a) $x - 3$ (b) $x - 4$
(c) $x - 5$ (d) $x - 6$

30. If $(x - 1)^2$ is a factor of $f(x) = x^3 + bx + c$, then find the remainder when $f(x)$ is divided by $(x - 2)$.

(a) 2 (b) −3
(c) 4 (d) −4

Level 2: Review Your Concepts

31. The ratio of the remainders when the expression $x^2 + bx + c$ is divided by $(x - 3)$ and $(x - 2)$, respectively is 4 : 5. Find b and c, if $(x - 1)$ is a factor of the given expression.

(a) $b = \frac{-11}{3}, c = \frac{14}{3}$ (b) $b = \frac{-14}{3}, c = \frac{11}{3}$
(c) $b = \frac{14}{3}, c = \frac{-11}{3}$ (d) None of these

32. If the polynomials $f(x) = x^2 + 9x + k$ and $g(x) = x^2 + 10x + l$ have a common factor, then $(k - l)^2$ is equal to ______.

(a) $9l - 10k$ (b) $10l - 9k$
(c) Both (a) and (b) (d) None of these

33. When $f(x)$ is divided by $(x - 2)$, the quotient is $Q(x)$ and the remainder is zero. And when $f(x)$ is divided by $[Q(x) - 1]$, the quotient is $(x - 2)$ and the remainder is $R(x)$. Find the remainder $R(x)$.

(a) $x + 2$ (b) $-x + 2$
(c) $x - 2$ (d) Cannot be determined

34. Find the values of m and n, if $(x - m)$ and $(x - n)$ are the factors of the expression $x^2 + mx - n$.

(a) $m = -1, n = -2$ (b) $m = 0, n = 1$
(c) $m = \frac{-1}{2}, n = \frac{1}{2}$ (d) $m = -1, n = 2$

35. Let $f\left(x + \frac{1}{x}\right) = x^2 + \frac{1}{x^2}$, find the remainder when $f(x)$ is divided by $2x + 1$.

(a) $\frac{-7}{4}$ (b) $\frac{9}{4}$
(c) $\frac{-9}{4}$ (d) $\frac{11}{4}$

36. A polynomial $f(x)$ leaves remainders 10 and 14, respectively when divided by $(x - 3)$ and $(x - 5)$. Find the remainder when $f(x)$ is divided by $(x - 3)(x - 5)$.

(a) $2x + 6$ (b) $2x - 4$

(c) $2x + 4$ (d) $2x - 6$

37. If $f(x + 3) = x^2 - 7x + 2$, then find the remainder when $f(x)$ is divided by $(x + 1)$.

(a) 8 (b) −4

(c) 20 (d) 46

38. A polynomial $f(x)$ when divided by $(x - 5)$ and $(x - 7)$ leaves remainders 6 and 16, respectively. Find the remainder when $f(x)$ is divided by $(x - 5)(x - 7)$.

(a) $5x + 7$ (b) $5x - 7$

(c) $5x + 19$ (d) $5x - 19$

39. A polynomial $p(x)$ leaves remainders 75 and 15, respectively, when divided by $(x - 1)$ and $(x + 2)$. Then the remainder when $f(x)$ is divided by $(x - 1)(x + 2)$ is ______.

(a) $5(4x + 11)$ (b) $5(4x - 11)$

(c) $5(3x + 11)$ (d) $5(3x - 11)$

40. The leading coefficient of a polynomial $f(x)$ of degree 3 is 2006. Suppose that $f(1) = 5$, $f(2) = 7$ and $f(c) = 9$. Then find $f(x)$.

(a) $2006(x - 1)(x - 2)(x - 3) + 2x + 3$

(b) $2006(x - 1)(x - 2)(x - 3) + 2x + 1$

(c) $2006(x - 1)(x - 2)(x - 3) + 2x - 1$

(d) $2006(x - 2)(x - 3)(x - 1) - (2x - 3)$

41. The ratio of the remainders when the expression $x^2 + ax + b$ is divided by $(x - 2)$ and $(x - 1)$, respectively is 4 : 3. Find a and b if $(x + 1)$ is a factor of the expression.

(a) 9, −10 (b) −9, 10

(c) 9, 10 (d) −9, −10

42. If $x^3 - ax^2 + bx - 6$ is exactly divisible by $x^2 - 5x + 6$, then $\frac{a}{b}$ is ______.

(a) $\frac{6}{11}$ (b) $\frac{-6}{11}$

(c) $\frac{1}{3}$ (d) $-\frac{1}{3}$

43. If $f(x) = x^2 + 5x + a$ and $g(x) = x^2 + 6x + b$ have a common factor, then which of the following is true?

(a) $(a - b)^2 + 5(a - b) + b = 0$

(b) $(a + b)^2 + 5(a + b) + a = 0$

(c) $(a + b)^2 + 6(a + b) + b = 0$

(d) $(a - b)^2 + 6(a - b) + b = 0$

44. If $ax^4 + bx^3 + cx^2 + dx$ is exactly divisible by $x^2 - 4$, then $\frac{a}{c}$ is ______.

(a) $\frac{1}{4}$ (b) $\frac{-1}{4}$

(c) $\frac{-1}{8}$ (d) $\frac{1}{8}$

45. If $x^2 + x + 1$ is a factor of $x^4 + ax^2 + b$, then the values of a and b, respectively, are ______.

(a) 2, 4 (b) 2, 1

(c) 1, 1 (d) 1, 2

46. The following are the steps involved in finding the value of a when $x - 2$ is a factor of $3x^2 - 7x + a$.

Arrange them in sequential order.

(A) $12 - 14 + a = 0 \Rightarrow a = 2$

(B) By factor theorem, $f(2) = 0 \Rightarrow 3(2)^2 - 7(2) + a = 0$

(C) Let $f(x) = 3x^2 - 7x + a$

(a) CBA (b) BCA

(c) CAB (d) BAC

47. Which of the following is a factor of $x^3 + 3px^2 - 3pqx - q^3$? (where p and q are constants)

(a) $x + p$ (b) $x + q$

(c) $x - p$ (d) $x - q$

48. If $(x - k)$ is a common factor of $x^2 + 3x + a$ and $x^2 + 4x + b$, then find the value of k in terms of a and b.

(a) $a + b$ (b) $a - b$

(c) $2a + 3b$ (d) $2a - 3b$

Level 3: Assess Your Concepts

49. Find the remainder when x^{33} is divided by $x^2 - 3x - 4$.

(a) $\left(\frac{4^{33} - 1}{5}\right)x + \left(\frac{4^{33} - 4}{5}\right)$

(b) $\left(\frac{4^{33} + 1}{5}\right)x + \left(\frac{4^{33} - 4}{5}\right)$

(c) $\left(\frac{4^{33} - 4}{5}\right)x + \left(\frac{4^{33} + 1}{5}\right)$

(c) $\left(\frac{4^{33} + 4}{5}\right)x + \left(\frac{4^{33} - 1}{5}\right)$

50. If $6x^2 - 3x - 1$ is a factor of $ax^3 + bx - 1$ (where a, b are integers), then find the value of b.
(a) 1 (b) 3
(c) −5 (d) −7

51. If the polynomials $f(x) = x^2 + 6x + p$ and $g(x) = x^2 + 7x + q$ have a common factor, then which of the following is true?
(a) $p^2 + q^2 + 2pq + 6p - 7q = 0$
(b) $p^2 + q^2 - 2pq + 7p - 6q = 0$
(c) $p^2 + q^2 - 2pq + 6p - 7q = 0$
(d) $p^2 + q^2 + 2pq + 7p - 6q = 0$

52. A polynomial of degree 2 in x, when divided by $(x + 1)$, $(x + 2)$ and $(x + 3)$, leaves remainders 1, 4 and 3, respectively. Find the polynomial.
(a) $\frac{1}{2}(x^2 + 9x + 6)$ (b) $\frac{1}{2}(x^2 - 9x + 6)$
(c) $\frac{-1}{2}(x^2 - 9x + 6)$ (d) $\frac{-1}{2}(x^2 + 9x + 6)$

53. If the expression $x^2 + 3x - 3$, is divided by $(x - p)$, then it leaves remainder 1. Find the value of p.
(a) 1 (b) −3
(c) −4 (d) Either (a) or (c)

54. If $ax^3 - 5x^2 + x + p$ is divisible by $x^2 - 3x + 2$, then find the values of a and p.
(a) $a = 2$, $p = 2$ (b) $a = 2$, $p = 3$
(c) $a = 1$, $p = 3$ (d) $a = 1$, $p = 2$

55. Which of the following should be added to $9x^3 + 6x^2 + x + 2$, so that the sum is divisible by $(3x + 1)$?
(a) −4 (b) −3
(c) −2 (d) −1

56. If the expression $6x^2 + 13x + k$ is divisible by $2x + 3$, then which of the following is the factor of the expression?
(a) $3x + 1$ (b) $3x + 4$
(c) $3x + 2$ (d) $3x + 5$

57. Given $ax^2 + bx + c$ is a quadratic polynomial in x and leaves remainders 6, 11 and 18, respectively, when divided by $(x + 1)$, $(x + 2)$ and $(x + 3)$. Find the value of $a + b + c$.
(a) 1 (b) 2
(c) 3 (d) 4

58. A polynomial $x^4 + 3x^3 - 3px^2 + 5x + 7$ leaves remainder r when it is divided by $x - 1$. Another polynomial $x^4 + px^3 + 6x + 8$ leaves remainder R when it is divided by $x + 2$. Find the value of p if $R + r = 6$.
(a) 2 (b) 3
(c) 4 (d) 5

AT

PRACTICE QUESTIONS JEE SPECIAL WING

Multiple-Answer Type Questions

Directions for questions 1 to 5:
Each question has FOUR options (a), (b), (c), and (d). ONE OR MORE THAN ONE of these four option(s) is/are the correct answer(s).

1. If $f(x) = x^2 - 3x - 3$, the which of the following should be added to $f(x)$ so that the sum is divisible by $x - 3$.
   (a) 3 (b) x
   (c) 6 (d) $x - 3$

2. If $p(x) = a^2 + 1.5ax - x^2$ is divisible by $x + 24$, find the value of a.
   (a) −24 (b) −12
   (c) 36 (d) 48

3. If $x^{105} - y^{105}$ is divisible by $x^n - y^n$, then the value of n can be ____ .
   (a) 35 (b) 21
   (c) 15 (d) 1

4. If $r^{pq} - 1$ is divisible by $r + 1$, then which of the following is/are true?
   (a) Both p and q are even. (b) Both p and q are odd.
   (c) p is even and q is odd. (d) q is even and p is odd.

5. Which of the following is/are divisible by $x + 1$?
   (a) $124x^7 - 73x^6 - 71x^5 + 58x^4 + 18x^3 + 13x^2 - 23x + 50$
   (b) $-15x^5 - 16x^4 + 17x^3 + 18x^2 - 22x - 22$
   (c) $x^8 - 4x^7 + 9x^6 + 16x^5 - 25x^4 - 36x^3 + 13x^2$
   (d) $x^8 - 14x^7 + 19x^6 - 13x^4 + 22x^3 - 12x^2 - 23x + 8$

Match The Column

Directions for questions 6 to 9:
Read the paragraph given below and answer the questions.

Given that $p(x) = x^{660} + y^{660}$

$q(x) = x^{440} - y^{440}$

$r(x) = x^{540} + y^{540}$

$s(x) = x^{480} - y^{480}$

$t(x) = x^{264} - y^{264}$

Column A [Polynomial]	Column B [Factor]
6. $q(x) - r(x)$	(a) $x^6 + y^6$
7. $p(x) + q(x)$	(b) $x^{60} + y^{60}$
8. $r(x) + s(x)$	(c) $x^{20} + y^{20}$
9. $p(x) - t(x)$	(d) $x^{220} + y^{220}$
	(e) $x^{132} + y^{132}$

Comprehension-Based Questions

Directions for questions 10 to 13:
Read the paragraph given below and answer the questions.

Ram, Robert, and Rahim are classmates and good friends. Their teacher asked them to assume three linear factors such that the product of the linear factors is equal to $x(y^2 - z^2) + y(z^2 - x^2) + z(x^2 - y^2)$. They were able to assume the factors correctly in five minutes. Answer the following questions related to the linear factors.

10. Which of the following can be one of the linear factors?
    (a) $x + y$ (b) $y + z$
    (c) Both (a) and (b) (d) None of these

11. What is the sum of the linear factors?
    (a) $3x + 3y + 3z$ (b) $2x + 2y + 2z$
    (c) $x + y + z$ (d) 0

12. Which of the following is a factor of the sum of the squares of the linear factors?
(a) 2 (b) 3
(c) 4 (d) Both (a) and (c)

13. Which of the following is a factor of the sum of the cubes of the linear factors?
(a) 2 (b) 3
(c) 8 (d) 27

Assertion and Reason Type Questions

Directions for questions 14 to 17:
Read the options given below and answer the questions.

(a) Both assertion (A) and reason (R) are true, and reason (R) is the correct explanation of assertion.
(b) Both assertion (A) and reason (R) are true, and reason (R) is not the correct explanation of assertion.
(c) Assertion (A) is true, but reason (R) is false.
(d) Assertion (A) is false, and reason (R) is true.

14. **Assertion:** $6x^6 - 7x^5 + 3x^4 + 12x^3 - 15x^2 - 10x + 11$ is divisible by $x - 1$.
Reason: If the sum of the coefficients of a polynomial in x is zero, then $x - 1$ is a factor of the polynomial.

15. **Assertion:** If $f(x-1) = x^3 - 5x^2 + 13$, then $f(x)$ is divisible by $x - 1$.
Reason: If a polynomial $f(x)$ is divisible by $x - a$, then $f(a) = 0$.

16. **Assertion:** If $f(x) = x^{2025}$ and $f(x)$ is divided by $x^2 - 1$, then the remainder is x.
Reason: If a polynomial $f(x)$ is divided by $x + a$, then the remainder is $f(a)$.

17. **Assertion:** $(29)^{2026} - (15)^{2026}$ is divisible by 14.
Reason: A polynomial $x^n - y^n$ is divisible by $x - y$.

ANSWER KEYS

Crossword

Across

3. Zero 4. Constant 7. Yes 9. Equal 10. Nine

Down

1. Two 2. Zero 5. Twelve 6. Three 8. Seven

Classroom Wing

Very Short Answer Type Questions

1. –70 2. –21 3. $a^2 + b^2$ 4. $\frac{45}{4}$ 5. 17
6. $x + 4$ 7. 41 8. –155 9. $x + 2$ 10. even number
11. True 12. True 13. True 14. –5 15. 25
16. $\frac{5}{3}$ 17. –10 18. 1 19. $\frac{2}{5}$ 20. $(a^2 + 3p)x + q$
21. $(x + 4)$

Short Answer Type Questions

22. 207 23. 35 25. $5(x - 1)$ 26. $\frac{1}{2}(3^{555} - 1)x + \frac{3}{2}(1 - 3^{554})$
27. $a = c$ 28. –8 29. $\left(x + \frac{b_1 - b_2}{a_1 - a_2}\right)$ 30. –5 31. even
32. $x + y$ 33. 63 34. $5x - 8$ 35. 0
36. (A) 13 (B) x

Essay Type Questions

37. $(x - 1)(x + 1)(x + 2)(x - 4)$. 38. $(2^{2014} - 3^{2014})x - (3.2^{2014} + 2.3^{2014})$
39. –3 40. 1, 1 41. $m = 0, n = \frac{-1}{3}$ 42. $x + 3$

Competition Wing

Level 1: Apply Your Concepts

1. $a_1 + a_3 + a_5 + \cdots = a_0 + a_2 + a_4 + \cdots$ 2. $f(-a)$ 3. $n \in N$ 4. –6
5. $a = 0$ or $a^2 + b + 1 = 0$ 6. (d) 7. (a) 8. (b)
9. (b) 10. (d) 11. (d) 12. (a) 13. (c)
14. (b) 15. (b) 16. (a) 17. (a) 18. (c)
19. (a) 20. (d) 21. (b) 22. (c) 23. (a)
24. (a) 25. (a) 26. (d) 27. (d) 28. (b)
29. (c) 30. (c)

Level 2: Review Your Concepts

31. (b) 32. (a) 33. (c) 34. (d) 35. (a)
36. (c) 37. (d) 38. (a) 39. (a) 40. (a)
41. (d) 42. (a) 43. (d) 44. (b) 45. (c)
46. (a) 47. (d) 48. (b)

Level 3: Assess Your Concepts

49. (b) 50. (c) 51. (b) 52. (d) 53. (d)
54. (a) 55. (c) 56. (c) 57. (b) 58. (a)

JEE Special Wing

Multiple-Answer Type Questions

1. (a, b) 2. (b, d) 3. (a, b, c, d) 4. (a, c, d) 5. (a, b)

Match The Column

6. (c) 7. (d) 8. (b) 9. (e)

Comprehension-Based Questions

10. (d) 11. (d) 12. (a) 13. (b)

Assertion and Reason Type Questions

14. (a) 15. (d) 16. (c) 17. (a)

Hints and Explanations

Classroom Wing

Very Short Answer Type Questions

1. Let $f(x) = x^2 - 3x + k$.

$x + 7$ is a factor of $f(x)$.

$\Rightarrow f(-7) = 0 \Rightarrow (-7)^2 - 3(-7) + k = 0$

$\Rightarrow k = -70$

2. Let $f(x) = 6x^2 - 5x + k$.

$2x + 3$ is a factor of $f(x)$.

$$\Rightarrow f\left(\frac{-3}{2}\right) = 0 \Rightarrow 6\left(\frac{-3}{2}\right)^2 - 5\left(\frac{-3}{2}\right) + k = 0$$

$$\Rightarrow \frac{27}{2} + \frac{15}{2} + k = 0$$

$\Rightarrow k = -21$

3. $(x - 0)$ is factor of $(x - a)^2 + (x - b)^2$

$\therefore$ substitute $x = 0$

$(0 - a)^2 + (0 - b)^2 = a^2 + b^2$

= remainder

4. $f(x) = x^2 + 6x + 8$

$$f\left(\frac{1}{2}\right) = \left(\frac{1}{2}\right)^2 + 6\left(\frac{1}{2}\right) + 8$$

$$= \frac{1}{4} + 3 + 8$$

$$= \frac{45}{4}$$

5.

$x = 1$	1	6	−8	1
	0	1	7	−1
	1	7	−1	0

$f(x) = (x^2 + 7x - 1)(x - 1)$

$f(x) = x^3 + 6x^2 - 8x + 1$

Remainder $= f(2)$

$= 2^3 + 6(2)^2 - 8(2)^1$

$= 8 + 24 - 16 + 1$

Quotient $= x^2 + 7x - 1$

$= 17$

6. $x^3 + bx + c$

Factors

$$\frac{x^3 + bx + c}{(x-2)^2}$$

$$= \frac{x^3 + bx + c}{x^2 + 4 - 4x}$$

$x(x^2 + 4 - 4x) + 4(x^2 + 4 - 4x) = 0$

$\therefore (x + 4)$

7. $x = 5$

$f(x) = x^2 + 3x + 1$ when $x = 5$

$(5)^2 + 3(5) + 1 = 25 + 15 + 1$

$= 41$

8. $f(3) = 3x^4 - 11x^2 + 6x + k = 7$

$= 3(3)^4 - 11(3)^2 + 6(3) + k = 7$

$= 243 - 99 + 18 + k = 7$

$= 162 + k = 7$

$k = 7 - 162$

$k = -155$

9. $2x^2 + px - 2 = f(x)$

$x(2x - 1) + 2(2x - 1) = 0$

Hence, the other factor is $(x + 2)$

10. $(x + 1)$ is possible only for relation.

$\therefore mn$ should be even

$\therefore m$ should be even always.

11. $(x^3 + y^3) = \lambda 2^k$

$\Rightarrow (x + y)(x^2 + y^2 - xy) = \lambda 2^k$

$\therefore x + y$ is divisible by 2^k

True

12. $f\left(-\frac{3}{2}\right)$ is remainder

$$\therefore x = \frac{-3}{2}$$

$2x = -3$

$2x + 3$

$\therefore$ True

13. $f(x) = 7x^3 + 6x^2 - 15x + 2$

$x = \frac{1}{7}$

If $f(x) = 0$ then $(7x - 1)$ is factor

$f\left(\frac{1}{7}\right) = 7\left(\frac{1}{7}\right)^3 + 6\left(\frac{1}{7}\right)^2 - 15\left(\frac{1}{7}\right) + 2$

$= \frac{1}{49} + \frac{6}{49} - \frac{15}{7} + 2$

$= \frac{1}{7} - \frac{15}{7} + 2$

$= -2 + 2 = 0$

Hence, it is true.

14. Negative value of remainder should be added

$x = 1$

$3(1) + 5(1) - 6(1) + 3 = 0$

$= 5$

$\therefore -5$ should be added

15. Remainder

$x = 1$

$\therefore (-1)^2 + 13(1) + 11 = 25$

16. $\left(\frac{1}{2}\right)^2 - \frac{1}{6}\left(\frac{1}{2}\right) + \left(\frac{3}{2}\right)$

$\frac{1}{4} - \frac{1}{12} + \frac{3}{2}$

2	4	12	2
2	2	6	1
3	1	3	1

$= \frac{3 - 1 + 18}{12}$

$= \frac{20}{12} = \frac{5}{3}$

17. $x = -1$

$7x^2 - 11x + a = 8$ When $x = -1$

$\therefore 7(-1)^2 - 11(-1) + a = 8$

$7 + 11 + a = 8 \Rightarrow a = -18 + 8 = -10$

18. $x = -2$ should satisfy the polynomial

$\therefore f(x) = x^3 + 4x^2 + kx - 6$

$0 = (-2)^3 + 4(-2)^2 + k(-2) - 6$

$0 = -8 + 16 - 2k - 6$

$2k = 2$

$k = 1$

19. $a^5 - a(a^4) + a^3 - a(a^2) + 2a + 3a - 2 = 0$

$\cancel{a^5} - \cancel{a^5} + \cancel{a^3} - \cancel{a^3} + 2a + 3a - 2 = 0$

$5a = 2$

$a = \frac{2}{5}$

20. $x^2 = a^2$

$x = \pm a$

$f(x) = x^3 + 3px + q$

$= (x^2 + 3p)x + q$

$= (a^2 + 3p)x + q$

21. $x^3 + 9x^2 + 26x + 24$

$x(x^2 + 5x + 6) + 4(x^2 + 5x + 6) = 0$

Hence, the remaining factor $= (x + 4)$

Short Answer Type Questions

22. Given $f(x + 4) = x^2 - 7x + 9$ (1)

When $f(x)$ is divided by $x + 7$, the remainder is $f(-7)$.

$\therefore$ Put $x = -11$ in Eq. (1).

$f(-11 + 4) = (-11)^2 - 7(-11) + 9$

$\Rightarrow f(-7) = 207$

23. Let $f(x) = 3x^3 + 5x^2 - 7x + 5$.

$f(2) = 3(2)^3 + 5(2)^2 - 7(2) + 5$

$= 24 + 20 - 14 + 5$

$= 35$

$\therefore -35$ should be added to $f(x)$, so that the sum is divisible by $x - 2$.

24. $(x^{mn} - 1)$ if n is even

$= ((x^m)^n - 1)$

since $1 = 1^2 = 1^3$ and so on

$\therefore ((x^m)^{2k} - 1^{2k})$

Comparing it with $(a^2 - b^2) = (a + b)(a - b)$

$\therefore (x^m - 1)(x^m + 1)$

$\therefore (x^m + 1)$ is a factor

25. For $x = 3$, $f(x) = 10$

$x = 4$, $f(x) = 15$

Let remainder be $ax + b$

$f(x) = (x - 3)(x - 4)Q(x) + (ax + b)$

$f(3) = 3a + b = 10$

$f(4) = 4a + b = 15$

$\underline{\quad (-)\ (-)\ (-)}$

$-a = -5$

Substitute

$3a + b = 10$

$b = 10 - 15$

$\therefore 5x - 5 = 5(x - 1)$

26. $\dfrac{x^{555}}{x^2 - 4x + 3}$

$f(x) = x^2 - 4x + 3 = (x-1)(x-3)$

Dividend = Divisor × Quotient + Remainder

$\therefore x^{555} = (x^2 - 4x + 3) \times Q(x) + R$

For $x = 1$

$1^{555} = (1 - 4 + 3) \times Q(x) + R$

$R = 1$

If $x = 3$

$(3)^{555} = (3^2 - 4(3) + 3) \times Q(x) + R$

$R = (3)^{555} = ax + b$

$a + b = 1$

$3a + 3 = 3^{555}$

$\underline{(-)\ (-)\ (-)}$

$-2a = 1 - 3^{555}$

$a = \dfrac{1 - 3^{555}}{-2}$

$a = \dfrac{3^{555} - 1}{2}$

$b = 1 - \left(\dfrac{3^{555} - 1}{2}\right) = \dfrac{2 - 3^{555} + 1}{2}$

$= \dfrac{3 - 3^{555}}{2}$

$\dfrac{1}{2}\left(3^{555} - 1\right)x + \dfrac{3}{2}\left(1 - 3^{554}\right)$

27. $f(x) = ax^3 - bx^2 - cx + d$

$x^2 = 1$

$x = \pm 1$

For $x = +1$

$a - b - c + d = 0 \quad (1)$

For $x = -1$

$-a - b + c + d = 0 \quad (2)$

Solving eq. (1) and (2),

$a - b - c + d = 0$

$\underline{-a - b + c + d = 0}$

$-2b + 2d = 0$

$2d = 2b$

$b = d$

Subtract eq. (1) and (2),

$a - b - c + d = 0$

$-a - b + c + d = 0$

$\underline{(+)\ (+)\ (-)\ (-)}$

$2a = 2c$

$a = c$

28. $x^4 - 3x^3 + 4x^2 + p = f(x)$

$x = 2$

$f(2) = (2)^4 - 3(2)^3 + 4(2)^2 + p = 0$

$16 - 24 + 16 + p = 0$

$p = -8$

29. $a_1x^2 + b_1x + c_1$

$a_2x^2 + b_2x + c_1$

$\gcd(a_1x^2 + b_1x + c_1, a_1x^2 + b_1x + c_1)$

$\gcd(a_1x^2 + b_1x + c_1, (a_1 - a_2)x^2 + (b_1 - b_2)x)$

30. $f(x) = x^2 + q$

$f(3) = 9 + q = 0$

$q = -9$

Remainder from $x^2 + q$

$f_1(x) = x^2 - 9$

$x = 2$

$\therefore f_1(2) = 4 - 9 = -5$

31. $f(n) = p^n - q^n$

If $(p + q)$ is factor

$f(p + q) = 0$

$= p^{p+q} - q^{p+q} = 0$

$p^p p^q - q^p q^q = 0$

$p^{p+q} = q^{p+q}$

32. $f(x) = x^{4005} + y^{4005}$

$= x^{4004}x + y^{4004}y$

33. $x^2 + 11x - 2a = f(x)$

$x = 7$

$(7)^2 + 11(7) - 2a = 0$ (since $(x - 7)$ is factor)

$49 + 27 = 2a$

$2a = 126$

$a = 63$

34. For $x = 3$ $f(3) = 7$

$x = 4$ $f(4) = 12$

Let remainder be $ax + b$

$f(x) = (x-3)(x-4)Q(x) + (ax+b)$

$f(3) = 3a + b = 7$

$f(4) = 4a + b = 12$

$\quad (-)(-) \quad (-)$

$-a = -5$

$a = 5$

Substitute $15 + b = 7 \Rightarrow b = -8$

$\therefore 5x - 8$

35. $f(x) = 5x^4 - 11x^2 + 6$

$5x^2 - 6 = 0$

$x^2 = \frac{6}{5}$

$\therefore f(x) = 5\left(\frac{6}{5}\right)^2 - 11\left(\frac{6}{5}\right) + 6$

$= \frac{36}{5} - \frac{66}{5} + 6$

$= 0$

$\therefore$ Remainder $= 0$

36. (A) $f(x-2) = 2x^2 - 3x + 4$

Let $y = x - 2$

$f(y) = 2(y+2)^2 - 3(y+2) + 4$

$= 2(y^2 + 4 + 4y) - (3y + 6) + 4$

$= 2y^2 + 8 + 8y - 3y - 6 + 4$

$f(y) = 2y^2 + 5y + 6$

If $y = 1$

$f(1) = 2(1)^2 + 5(1) + 6$

$= 2 + 5 + 6 = 13$

(B) $x^{2017} = (x^2 - 1)\ Q(x) + ax + b$

Where $Q(x)$ and $ax + b$ are the quotient and the remainder respectively.

Case (i): put $x = 1$

$(1)^{2017} = a + b$

$\Rightarrow a + b = 1 \quad (1)$

Case (ii): put $x = -1$

$(-1)^{2017} = -a + b$

$\Rightarrow -a + b = -1 \quad (2)$

(1) + (2) gives $2b = 0$

$\Rightarrow b = 0$

$\Rightarrow a = 1$

$\therefore$ Remainder $= x$

Essay Type Questions

37. $x^4 - 2x^3 - 9x^2 + 2x + 8$

$(x-1)$ is the factor as $(1)^4 - 2(1)^3 - 9(1)^2 + 2(1) + 8$

$= x^3(x-1) - x^2(x-1) - 10x(x-1) - 8(x-1)$

$= x^3(x-1) - x^2(x-1) - 10x(x-1) - 8(x-1)$

$= (x-1)(x^3 - x^2 - 10x - 8)$

For $x = 4$,

$(x^3 - x^2 - 10x - 8) \Rightarrow (4)^3 - (4)^2 - 10(4) - 8$

$= 64 - 16 - 40 - 8$

$= 0$

$\therefore (x-4)$ is factor

$x^2(x-4) + 3x(x-4) + 2(x-4)$

$= (x^2 + 3x + 2)(x-4)$

For $x = -2$

$(-2)^2 + 3(-2) + 2 = 4 - 6 + 2 = 0$

$\therefore (x+2)$ is factor

$x(x+2) + 1(x+2) = (x+1)(x+2)$

$\therefore (x+1)(x+2)(x-1)(x-4)$

38. Let the quotient be $q(x)$ and the remainder be $ax + b$, when

x^{2014} is divided by $x^2 + 5x + 6$.

$\therefore x^{2014} = (x^2 + 5x + 6)\ q(x) + (ax + b)$

$\Rightarrow x^{2014} = (x + 2)\ (x + 3)\ q(x) + ax + b$

If $x = -2$, then $2^{2014} = -2a + b \quad (1)$

If $x = -3$, then $3^{2014} = -3a + b \quad (2)$

Solving Eqs (1) and (2), we get

$a = 2^{2014} - 3^{2014}$ and $b = 3.2^{2014} + 2.3^{2014}$

$\therefore$ Remainder $= (2^{2014} - 3^{2014})x - (3.2^{2014} + 2.3^{2014})$

40. $x^4 + ax^2 + b$ (1)

$x^2(x^2 - x + 1) + x(x^2 - x + 1) + a(x^2 - x + 1)$

$\therefore (x^2 + x + a)(x^2 - x + 1)$

Since, we have no variable of x

$\therefore + x - ax = 0$

$x = ax$

$a = 1$

For $x = 0$ term

$a = b$

(comparing eq. (1) and the question)

$\therefore b = 1$

41. $lx^2 + mx + n$

For $x = 1,\ l + m + n = 0$ (1)

For $x = -1,\ l - m + n = 0$ (2)

For $x = -2,\ l(4) - 2m + n = 1$

$4l - 2m + n = 1$ (3)

Add eq. (1) and (2),

$2l + 2n = 0$ (4)

For (1),

$2l + 2m + 2n = 0$ (5)

Add (5) and (3),

$$\begin{array}{r} 2l + 2m + 2n = 0 \\ 4l - 2m + n = 1 \\ \hline 6l + 3n = 1 \end{array}$$ (6)

For (4) and (6),

$2l + 2n = 0 \times 3$

$6l + 3n = 1 \times 2$

$$\begin{array}{r} 6l + 6n = 0 \\ 12l + 6n = 2 \\ (-)\ (-)\ \ (-) \\ \hline -6l = -2 \end{array}$$

$l = \frac{1}{3}$

Substitute the value of l in (1) and (2),

$$\begin{array}{r} m + n = -\frac{1}{3} \\ -m + n = -\frac{1}{3} \\ \hline 2n = -\frac{2}{3} \end{array}$$

$n = -\frac{1}{3}$

Substitute in eq. (1),

$l + m + n = 0$

$\frac{1}{3} + m - \frac{1}{3} = 0$

$m = 0$

$\therefore m = 0, n = -\frac{1}{3}$

42. Let the required remainder be ax + b.

Let $f(x) = (x - 3)\ (x - 4)\ Q(x) + ax + b$

(i) Divisor = $x - 3$ and $f(3) = 6$

$\Rightarrow f(3) = 3a + b$

$\Rightarrow 3a + b = 6$ (1)

(ii) Divisor $(x - 4)$ and $f(4) = 7$

$\Rightarrow f(4) = 4a + b \Rightarrow 4a + b = 7$ (2)

On solving (1) and (2), we get

$a = 1$ and $b = 3$

$\therefore$ Remainder = $x + 3$

Competition Wing

Level 1: Apply Your Concepts

1. $f(x) = a_0x^n + a_1x^{n-1} + \cdots a_n$ (1)

Since $(x+1)$ is factor

$x = -1$

Substituting in eq. (1)

$a_0(-1)^n + a_1(-1)^{n-1} + \cdots + a_n$

- If n is even:

  $f(x) = a_0 - a_1 + \cdots + a_n$

  $(a_0 + a_2 + a_4 \cdots) = (a_1 + a_3 + a_5 \cdots)$

- If n is odd:

  $f(x) = a_0(-1)^n + a_1(-1)^{n-1} + \cdots + a_n$

  $= -a_0 + a_1 - a_2 + \cdots + a_n$

  $\therefore (a_1 + a_3 + \cdots) = (a_0 + a_2 + \cdots)$

2. $f(x)$ is divided by $(x+a)$

$x = -a$ by remainder theorem

Remainder $= f(-a)$

3. $x \in N$

Case 1:

n is odd

Eg. $n = 3$

$\therefore a^n - b^n = a^3 - b^3$

$\therefore (a-b)$ is factor

Case 2:

n is even

Eg. $n = 4$

$\therefore a^4 - b^4 = (a^2 - b^2)(a^2 + b^2)$

$= (a+b)(a-b)(a^2+b^2)$

$\therefore a - b$ is factor

$\therefore n \in N$

4. $f(x) = x^3 + 2$

Remainder for $f(x)$

$x = -2$

$f(-2) = -8 + 2 = -6$

5. $(x-a)$ need to be factor of $ax^2 + bx + a$

Substitute $(x = a)$

$a(a^2) + b(a) + a = 0$

$a^3 + ab + a = 0$

$a(a^2 + b + 1) = 0$

$\therefore a = 0$ or $a^2 + b + 1 = 0$

6. Let $f(x) = ax^3 + bx^2 + cx + d$.

$x + 1$ is a factor of $f(x)$.

$\Rightarrow f(-1) = 0 \Rightarrow a(-1)^3 + b(-1)^2 + c(-1) + d = 0$

$\Rightarrow -a + b - c + d = 0 \Rightarrow a + c = b + d$ (1)

$x + 2$ is a factor of $f(x)$.

$\Rightarrow f(-2) = 0 \Rightarrow a(-2)^3 + b(-2)^2 + c(-2) + d = 0$

$\Rightarrow -8a + 4b - 2c + d = 0$

$\Rightarrow 8a + 2c = 4b + d$

$\Rightarrow 8a + 2(b + d - a) = 4b + d$ [from Eq. (1)]

$\Rightarrow 6a - 2b + d = 0$

Hence, the correct option is (d).

7. Let $f(x) = px^3 + qx^2 + rx + s$.

$x + 1$ is a factor of $f(x)$.

$\Rightarrow f(-1) = 0 \Rightarrow p(-1)^3 + q(-1)^2 + r(-1) + s = 0$

$\Rightarrow p + r = q + s$ (1)

$x - 3$ is a factor of $f(x)$.

$\Rightarrow f(3) = 0 \Rightarrow p(3)^3 + q(3)^2 + r(3) + s = 0$

$\Rightarrow 27p + 9q \Rightarrow 3r + s = 0$

$\Rightarrow 27p + 9q + 3(q + s - p) + s = 0$ [from Eq. (1)]

$\Rightarrow 24p + 12q + 4s = 0$

$\Rightarrow 6p + 3q + s = 0$

Hence, the correct option is (a).

8. Let $f(x) = 12x^6 - 4x^3 - 9$.

$f(x^3) = 12(x^3)^2 - 4(x^3) - 9$

$f(y) = 12y^2 - 4y - 9$

$x^3 = y \Rightarrow x^3 - 5 = y - 5$

If $f(y)$ is divided by $(y - 5)$, then the remainder $= f(5)$.

$\Rightarrow f(5) = 12(5)^2 - 4(5) - 9$

$= 300 - 20 - 9 = 271$

Hence, the correct option is (b).

9. The greatest possible value of n is the HCF of 1278 and 672.

10. Use remainder theorem.

11. Use remainder theorem.

12. Use factor theorem.

13. $5x^{20} + 7x^{15} + x^9 = x^9(5x^{11} + 7x^6 + 1)$.

14. Since the coefficient of x^2 is zero, the sum of the roots is zero.

15. Use factor theorem.

16. Largest possible value of n is the HCF of 1215 and 945.

19. Use division algorithm.

20. $(x+1)$ and $(x-1)$ are the factors of the given expression.

21. $P(1) = 6$, $P(-1) = 10$ and $P(0) = 5$.

22. Use division algorithm.

23. $f(0) = 7, f(2) = 9$ and $f(-3) = 49$.

24. Put $x = x - 1$ in $f(x + 1)$ to get $f(x)$.
   (i) Write $2x^2 + 7x + 5$ in terms of $x + 1$.
   (ii) Replace $x + 1$ by x.
   (iii) Apply remainder theorem.

25. (i) $x^2 + px + q = (x - p)(x - q)$.
   (ii) Compare the terms in LHS and RHS.

26. (i) $f\left(x-\frac{1}{x}\right)=\left(x-\frac{1}{x}\right)^2+2.$
   (ii) Replace $\left(x-\frac{1}{x}\right)$ with x.
   (iii) Use remainder theorem to obtain remainder.

27. (i) Since the coefficient of x^2 is 0, the sum of the roots is '0'.
   $\Rightarrow$ Third root is -4.
   (ii) Apply remainder theorem for $f(x) = (x - 2)^2(x + 4)$.

28. (i) Let $f(x) = ax^2 + bx + c$. $f(1) = 4$; $f(2) = 4$; $f(3) = 0$
   (ii) Solve for a, b, and c.

29. (i) Put $x = x - 3$ in $f(x + 3)$ to get $f(x)$.
   (ii) Apply factor theorem.

30. (i) Coefficient of x^2 is 0, therefore sum of roots is 0.
   $\therefore$ Third root $= -2$.
   (ii) Apply factor theorem.
   (iii) To obtain the remainder, use the remainder theorem.

Level 2: Review Your Concepts

31. $\frac{f(3)}{f(2)}=\frac{4}{5}$ and $f(1) = 0$.

32. (i) Let the common factor be $x - a$ and find $f(a)$, and $g(a)$.
   (ii) Obtain the value of a in terms of k and l.

33. Dividend = Divisor × Quotient + Remainder.

34. (i) $x^2 + mx - n = (x - m)(x - n)$.
   (ii) Equate the corresponding terms.

35. (i) $f\left(x+\frac{1}{x}\right)=\left(x+\frac{1}{x}\right)^2-2.$
   (ii) Replace $x+\frac{1}{x}$ by x.
   (iii) Put $x=\frac{1}{2}$.

36. (i) $f(3) = 10$, $f(5) = 14$.
   (ii) Dividend = Divisor × Quotient + Remainder.

39. (i) $f(1) = 75$, $f(-2) = 15$.
   (ii) Dividend = Divisor × Quotient + Remainder.

40. Verify from the options whether $f(1) = 5$, $f(2) = 7$ and $f(3) = 9$ by using remainder theorem.

41. $\frac{f(2)}{f(1)}=\frac{4}{0}$ and $f(-1) = 0$.

42. (i) $x^2 - 5x + 6 = (x - 2)(x - 3)$.
   (ii) $f(2) = 0, f(3) = 0$.

43. (i) Let the common factor be $(x - a)$, then $f(a) = g(a)$, obtain value of 'a'.
   (ii) Substitute value of 'a' in $f(x)$.

44. $f(2) = 0$ and $f(-2)= 0$.

45. $x^4 + x^2 + 1 = (x^2 - x + 1)(x^2 + x + 1)$.

46. CBA is the required sequential order.

47. Let $f(x) = x^3 + 3px^2 - 3pqx - q^3$
   From the options,
   $f(q) = q^3 + 3pq^2 - 3pq^2 - q^3 = 0$
   $x - q$ is a factor of $f(x)$.

48. Given, $x - k$ is a common factor of $x^2 + 3x + a$ and $x^2 + 4x + b$.
   $\therefore (k)^2 + 3k + a = 0$ and $(k)^2 + 4k + b = 0$
   $\Rightarrow k^2 + 4k + b = k^2 + 3k + a$
   $\Rightarrow k = a - b$.

Level 3: Assess Your Concepts

51. (i) Let the common factor be $(x - a)$, then make $f(a) = g(a)$, and get the value of 'a'.
   (ii) Substitute value of 'a' in $f(x)$.

52. Let $f(x) = ax^2 + bx + c$, given $f(-1) = 1$, $f(-2) = 4$ and $f(-3) = 3$.

53. Let $f(x) = x^2 + 3x - 3$

Given, $f(p) = 1$

$\Rightarrow p^2 + 3p - 3 = 1$

$\Rightarrow p^2 + 3p - 4 = 0$

$\Rightarrow (p + 4)(p - 1) = 0$

$\Rightarrow p = -4$ or 1.

54. Let $f(x) = ax^3 - 5x^2 + x + p$

Given, $f(x)$ is divisible $x^2 - 3x + 2$, i.e.,

$\Rightarrow f(x)$ is divisible by $(x - 1)$ and $(x - 2)$

$f(1) = 0$ and $f(2) = 0 \Rightarrow a + p - 4 = 0$

$\Rightarrow a + p = 4$ (1)

$8a + p = 18 = 0 \Rightarrow 8a + p = 18$ (2)

On solving Eqs. (1) and (2), we get $a = p = 2$.

55. Let k should be added to the given expression so that the sum is divisible by $(3x + 1)$.

Let $f(x) = 9x^3 + 6x^2 + x + 2 + k$

Given, $f\left(-\frac{1}{3}\right) = 0$

$\Rightarrow 9\left(-\frac{1}{3}\right)^3 + 6\left(-\frac{1}{3}\right)^2 - \frac{1}{3} + 2 + k = 0$

$\Rightarrow -\frac{1}{3} + \frac{2}{3} - \frac{1}{3} + 2 + k = 0 \Rightarrow 2 + k = 0$

$\Rightarrow k = -2.$

56. Let $f(x) = 6x^2 + 13x + k$

Given $2x + 3$ is a factor of $f(x)$

By factor theorem,

$f\left(-\frac{3}{2}\right) = 0$

$\Rightarrow 6\left(-\frac{3}{2}\right)^2 + 13\left(-\frac{3}{2}\right) + k = 0$

$\Rightarrow \frac{27}{2} - \frac{39}{2} + k = 0 \Rightarrow k = 6$

$\therefore f(x) = 6x^2 + 13x + 6$

$= (2x + 3)(3x + 2)$

$\therefore$ The other factor is $3x + 2$.

57. Let $f(x) = ax^2 + bx + c$.

Given, $f(-1) = 6$, $f(-2) = 11$ and $f(-3) = 18$

$\Rightarrow a - b + c = 6$ (1)

$\Rightarrow 4a - 2b + c = 11$ (2)

$\Rightarrow 9a - 3b + c = 18$ (3)

Eq. (2) – Eq. (1) $\Rightarrow 3a - b = 5$ (4)

Eq. (3) – Eq. (2) $\Rightarrow 5a - b = 7$ (5)

On solving Eqs. (4) and (5), we get

$a = 1$, $b = -2$

Substituting $a = 1$ and $b = -2$ in Eq. (1), we get

$\Rightarrow c = 3$

Now, $a + b + c = 2$.

58. Let $f(x) = x^4 + 3x^3 - 3px^2 + 5x + 7$

Given $f(1) = r$

$\Rightarrow 1 + 3 - 3p + 5 + 7 = r$

$\Rightarrow 3p + r = 16$ (1)

Let $g(x) = x^4 + px^3 + 6x + 8$

Given $g(-2) = R$

$(-2)^4 + p(-2)^3 + 6(-2) + 8 = R$

$\Rightarrow 16 - 8p - 12 + 8 = R$

$\Rightarrow 8p + R = 12$ (2)

On adding (1) and (2), we get

$\Rightarrow 11p + r + R = 28$

$\Rightarrow 11p + 6 = 28$

$\Rightarrow 11p = 22 \Rightarrow p = 2.$

JEE Special Wing

Multiple-Answer Type Questions

1. $f(x) = x^2 - 3x - 3 = x(x-3) - 3$
Divisor is $x - 3$.
Clearly $f(x) + 3 = x(x-3) - 3 + 3 = x(x-3)$ is divisible by $x - 3$.
Also, $f(x) + x = x(x-3) - 3 + x = x(x-3) + x - 3$
$= (x+1)(x-3)$ is divisible by $(x-3)$.
The values in other options will not be possible.
Hence, the choices (a and b) are correct.

2. Given that $p(x) = a^2 + 1.5ax - x^2$ is divisible by $x + 24$.
$\Rightarrow p(-24) = 0.$
$\Rightarrow a^2 + 1.5a(-24) - (-24)^2 = 0$
$\Rightarrow a^2 - 36a - 576 = 0$
$\Rightarrow a^2 - 48a + 12a - 576 = 0$
$\Rightarrow a(a-48) + 12(a-48) = 0$
$\Rightarrow (a-48)(a+12) = 0$
$\Rightarrow a = -12$ or $a = 48$.
Hence, the choices (b and d) are correct.

3. **I Method:**
We know that $x^p - y^p$ is divisible by $x^n - y^n$ where n is a factor of p.
Given that $x^{105} - y^{105}$ is divisible by $x^n - y^n$.
So, n is a factor of 105.
Therefore n can be 1, 3, 5, 7, 15, 21, 35 and 105.
For example:
(i) Let $f(x) = x^{105} - y^{105}$ and the divisor be $x - y$.
By the remainder theorem, $f(y) = y^{105} - y^{105} = 0$.
$\Rightarrow x^{105} - y^{105}$ is divisible by $x - y$.
(ii) $x^{105} - y^{105} = (x^3)^{35} - (y^3)^{35}$
Let $p(x^3) = (x^3)^{35} - (y^3)^{35}$ and the divisor be $x^3 - y^3$.
By the remainder theorem, $p(y^3) = (y^3)^{35} - (y^3)^{35} = 0$.
$\Rightarrow x^{105} - y^{105}$ is divisible by $x^3 - y^3$.
Similarly, we can prove for the remaining value of n.
II Method:
Given that $x^{105} - y^{105}$ is divisible by $x^n - y^n$.
$$x^{105} - y^{105} = (x^n)^{\frac{105}{n}} - (y^n)^{\frac{105}{n}}$$
Let $g(x^n) = (x^n)^{\frac{105}{n}} - (y^n)^{\frac{105}{n}}$
By factor theorem, $g(y^n) = (y^n)^{\frac{105}{n}} - (y^n)^{\frac{105}{n}} = 0$.
Therefore n can be 1, 3, 5, 7, 15, 21, 35 and 105.
Hence, the choices (a, b, c, d) are correct.

4. Given that $r^{pq} - 1$ is divisible by $r + 1$.
Let $p(r) = r^{pq} - 1$.
By factor theorem, $p(-1) = (-1)^{pq} - 1 = 0$.
$\Rightarrow (-1)^{pq} = 1$.
$\Rightarrow pq$ must be even number.
$\Rightarrow$ At least one of p or q is an even number.
Hence, the choices (a, c, d) are correct.

5. The divisor is $x + 1$.
Going by options:
Choice (a): Let $p(x) = 124x^7 - 73x^6 - 71x^5 + 58x^4 + 18x^3 + 13x^2 - 23x + 50$
The sum of the coefficients of even powers of x
$= -73 + 58 + 13 + 50 = 48$.
The sum of the coefficients of odd powers of x
$= 124 - 71 + 18 - 23 = 48$.
As the sum of the coefficients of even powers of x is equal to the sum of the coefficients of odd powers of x, $p(x)$ is divisible by $x + 1$.
Choice (b): Let
$q(x) = -15x^5 - 16x^4 + 17x^3 + 18x^2 - 22x - 22$.
The sum of the coefficients of even powers of x
$= -16 + 18 - 22 = -20$.
The sum of the coefficients of odd powers of x
$= -15 + 17 - 22 = -20$.
As the sum of the coefficients of even powers of x is equal to the sum of the coefficients of odd powers of x, $q(x)$ is divisible by $x + 1$.
Choice (c): Let
$r(x) = x^8 - 4x^7 + 9x^6 + 16x^5 - 25x^4 - 36x^3 + 13x^2$.
The sum of the coefficients of even powers of x
$= 1 + 9 - 25 + 13 = -2$.
The sum of the coefficients of odd powers of x
$= -4 + 16 - 36 = -24$.
As the sum of the coefficients of even powers of x is not equal to the sum of the coefficients of odd powers of x, $r(x)$ is not divisible by $x + 1$.
Choice (d): Let $s(x) = x^8 - 14x^7 + 19x^6 - 13x^4 + 22x^3 - 12x^2 - 23x + 8$.

The sum of the coefficients of even powers of x $= 1 + 19 - 13 - 12 + 8 = 3$

The sum of the coefficients of odd powers of x $= -14 + 22 - 23 = -15$.

As the sum of the coefficients of even powers of x is not equal to the sum of the coefficients of odd powers of x, $s(x)$ is not divisible by $x+1$.

Hence, the choices (a and b) are correct.

Match The Column

Common Solutions for questions 6 to 9:

Given that $p(x) = x^{660} + y^{660}$

$q(x) = x^{440} - y^{440}$

$r(x) = x^{540} + y^{540}$

$s(x) = x^{480} - y^{480}$

$t(x) = x^{264} - y^{264}$

6. $q(x) - r(x) = (x^{440} - y^{440}) - (x^{540} + y^{540})$

$q(x) - r(x)$ is divisible by $x^n + y^n$, where n is a common factor of 540 and 440.

From the options given in Column B, n can be 20.

If $n = 20$, divisor $= x^{20} + y^{20}$.

$q(x) - r(x) = (x^{440} - y^{440}) - (x^{540} + y^{540})$

$= \left[(x^{20})^{22} - (y^{20})^{22}\right] - \left[(x^{20})^{27} + (y^{20})^{27}\right]$

By the remainder theorem, the remainder

$= \left[(-y^{20})^{22} - (y^{20})^{22}\right] - \left[(-y^{20})^{27} + (y^{20})^{27}\right]$

$= \left[(y^{20})^{22} - (y^{20})^{22}\right] - \left[-(y^{20})^{27} + (y^{20})^{27}\right] = 0.$

$\Rightarrow q(x) - r(x)$ is divisible by $x^{20} + y^{20}$.

Hence, the correct option is (c).

7. $p(x) + q(x) = (x^{660} + y^{660}) + (x^{440} - y^{440})$

$p(x) + q(x)$ is divisible by $x^n + y^n$, where n is a common factor of 660 and 440.

From the options given in Column B, n can be 20 or 220.

(i) If $n = 20$, divisor $= x^{20} + y^{20}$.

$p(x) + q(x) = (x^{660} + y^{660}) + (x^{440} - y^{440})$

$= \left[(x^{20})^{33} + (y^{20})^{33}\right] + \left[(x^{20})^{22} - (y^{20})^{22}\right]$

By the remainder theorem, the remainder

$= \left[(-y^{20})^{33} + (y^{20})^{33}\right] + \left[(-y^{20})^{22} - (y^{20})^{22}\right]$

$= \left[-(y^{20})^{33} + (y^{20})^{33}\right] + \left[(y^{20})^{22} - (y^{20})^{22}\right] = 0.$

$\Rightarrow p(x) + q(x)$ is divisible by $x^{20} + y^{20}$.

(ii) If $n = 220$, divisor $= x^{220} + y^{220}$.

$p(x) + q(x) = (x^{660} + y^{660}) + (x^{440} - y^{440})$

$= \left[(x^{220})^3 + (y^{220})^3\right] + \left[(x^{220})^2 - (y^{220})^2\right]$

By the remainder theorem, the remainder

$= \left[(-y^{220})^3 + (y^{220})^3\right] + \left[(-y^{220})^2 - (y^{220})^2\right]$

$= \left[-(y^{220})^3 + (y^{220})^3\right] + \left[(y^{220})^2 - (y^{220})^2\right] = 0.$

$\Rightarrow p(x) + q(x)$ is divisible by $x^{220} + y^{220}$.

Hence, Q. No. 7 can be mapped with options (c) and (d).

As Q. No. 6 is mapped only with option (c), Q. No. 7 must be mapped with option (d).

Hence, the correct option is (d).

8. $r(x) + s(x) = (x^{540} + y^{540}) + (x^{480} - y^{480})$

$r(x) + s(x)$ is divisible by $x^n + y^n$, where n is a common factor of 540 and 480.

From the options given in Column B, n can be 6, 20 or 60.

As Q. No. 6 is mapped only with option (c), let us check for $n = 6$ or 60.

(i) If $n = 6$, divisor $= x^6 + y^6$.

$r(x) + s(x) = (x^{540} + y^{540}) + (x^{480} - y^{480})$

$= \left[(x^6)^{90} + (y^6)^{90}\right] + \left[(x^6)^{80} - (y^6)^{80}\right]$

By the remainder theorem, the remainder

$= \left[(-y^6)^{90} + (y^6)^{90}\right] + \left[(-y^6)^{80} - (y^6)^{80}\right]$

$= \left[(y^6)^{90} + (y^6)^{90}\right] + \left[(y^6)^{80} - (y^6)^{80}\right] = 2(y^6)^{90}.$

$\Rightarrow r(x) + s(x)$ is not divisible by $x^6 + y^6$.

(ii) If $n = 60$, divisor $= x^{60} + y^{60}$.

$r(x) + s(x) = (x^{540} + y^{540}) + (x^{480} - y^{480})$

$= \left[(x^{60})^9 + (y^{60})^9\right] + \left[(x^{60})^8 - (y^{60})^8\right]$

By the remainder theorem, the remainder

$= \left[(-y^{60})^9 + (y^{60})^9\right] + \left[(-y^{60})^8 - (y^{60})^8\right]$

$= \left[-(y^{60})^9 + (y^{60})^9\right] + \left[(y^{60})^8 - (y^{60})^8\right] = 0.$

$\Rightarrow r(x) + s(x)$ is divisible by $x^{60} + y^{60}$.

Hence, the correct option is (b).

9. $p(x)-t(x)=\left(x^{660}+y^{660}\right)-\left(x^{264}-y^{264}\right)$

$p(x)-t(x)$ is divisible by $x^n + y^n$, where n is is a common factor of 660 and 264.

From the options given in Column B, n can be 6 or 132.

(i) If $n = 6$, divisor $= x^6 + y^6$.

$$p(x)-t(x)=\left(x^{660}+y^{660}\right)-\left(x^{264}-y^{264}\right)$$

$$=\left[\left(x^6\right)^{110}+\left(y^6\right)^{110}\right]-\left[\left(x^6\right)^{44}-\left(y^6\right)^{44}\right]$$

By the remainder theorem, the remainder

$$=\left[\left(-y^6\right)^{110}+\left(y^6\right)^{110}\right]-\left[\left(-y^6\right)^{44}-\left(y^6\right)^{44}\right]$$

$$=\left[\left(y^6\right)^{110}+\left(y^6\right)^{110}\right]-\left[\left(y^6\right)^{44}-\left(y^6\right)^{44}\right]=2\left(y^6\right)^{110}$$

$\Rightarrow p(x)-t(x)$ is not divisible by $x^6 + y^6$.

(ii) If $n = 60$, divisor $= x^{132} + y^{132}$.

$$p(x)-t(x)=\left(x^{660}+y^{660}\right)-\left(x^{264}-y^{264}\right)$$

$$=\left[\left(x^{132}\right)^5+\left(y^{132}\right)^5\right]-\left[\left(x^{132}\right)^2-\left(y^{132}\right)^2\right]$$

By the remainder theorem, the remainder

$$=\left[\left(-y^{132}\right)^5+\left(y^{132}\right)^5\right]-\left[\left(-y^{132}\right)^2-\left(y^{132}\right)^2\right]$$

$$=\left[-\left(y^{132}\right)^5+\left(y^{132}\right)^5\right]-\left[\left(y^{132}\right)^2-\left(y^{132}\right)^2\right]=0.$$

$\Rightarrow p(x)-t(x)$ is divisible by $x^{132}+y^{132}$.

Hence, the correct option is (e).

Comprehension-Based Questions

Common Solutions for questions 10 to 13:

(i) Let us consider $f(x)=x\left(y^2-z^2\right)+y\left(z^2-x^2\right)$ $+z\left(x^2-y^2\right)$

Let the divisor be $x - y$.

By the remainder theorem, the remainder $= f(y)$.

$$= y\left(y^2-z^2\right)+y\left(z^2-y^2\right)+z\left(y^2-y^2\right)$$

$$= y^3 - yz^2 + yz^2 - y^3 = 0.$$

$\Rightarrow x - y$ is a factor of $x\left(y^2-z^2\right)+y\left(z^2-x^2\right)$ $+z\left(x^2-y^2\right)$

(ii) Let us consider $f(y)=x\left(y^2-z^2\right)+y\left(z^2-x^2\right)$. $+z\left(x^2-y^2\right)$

Let the divisor be $y - z$.

By the remainder theorem, the remainder $= f(z)$.

$$= x\left(z^2-z^2\right)+z\left(z^2-x^2\right)+z\left(x^2-z^2\right)$$

$$= z^3 - x^2z + x^2z - z^3 = 0.$$

$\Rightarrow y - z$ is a factor of $x\left(y^2-z^2\right)+y\left(z^2-x^2\right)$ $+z\left(x^2-y^2\right)$

(iii) Let us consider

$$f(z)=x\left(y^2-z^2\right)+y\left(z^2-x^2\right)+z\left(x^2-y^2\right).$$

Let the divisor be $z - x$.

By the remainder theorem, the remainder $= f(x)$.

$$= x\left(y^2-x^2\right)+y\left(x^2-x^2\right)+x\left(x^2-y^2\right)$$

$$= xy^2 - x^3 + x^3 - xy^2 = 0.$$

$\Rightarrow z - x$ is a factor of $x\left(y^2-z^2\right)+y\left(z^2-x^2\right)$ $+z\left(x^2-y^2\right)$.

As $x\left(y^2-z^2\right)+y\left(z^2-x^2\right)+z\left(x^2-y^2\right)$ is a polynomial of degree three, it has a maximum of three linear factors.

So, $x\left(y^2-z^2\right)+y\left(z^2-x^2\right)+z\left(x^2-y^2\right)$

$= k(x-y)(y-z)(z-x)$, where k is a constant.

Let us put $x = 1, y = 2$, and $z = 3$.

$$\Rightarrow 1\left(2^2-3^2\right)+2\left(3^2-1^2\right)+3\left(1^2-2^2\right)$$

$$= k(1-2)(2-3)(3-1)$$

$$\Rightarrow -5+16-9 = 2k$$

$$\Rightarrow k = 1.$$

Let us put $x = 0, y = 1$, and $z = 2$.

$$\Rightarrow 0\left(1^2-2^2\right)+1\left(2^2-0^2\right)+2\left(0^2-1^2\right)$$

$$= k(0-1)(1-2)(2-0)$$

$$\Rightarrow 4-2 = 2k \Rightarrow k = 1.$$

For any values of x, y, and z, $k = 1$.

So, $x\left(y^2-z^2\right)+y\left(z^2-x^2\right)+z\left(x^2-y^2\right)$

$= k(x-y)(y-z)(z-x)$.

10. Both $x + y$ and $y + z$ are not linear factors.

Hence, the correct option is (d).

11. The three linear factors are $(x-y), (y-z)$ and $(z-x)$.

The sum of the linear factors

$$=(x-y)+(y-z)+(z-x)=0.$$

Hence, the correct option is (d).

12. The sum of the squares of the linear factors

$$=(x-y)^2+(y-z)^2+(z-x)^2$$

$$= x^2+y^2-2xy+y^2+z^2-2yz+z^2+x^2-2zy$$

$= 2x^2 + 2y^2 + 2z^2 - 2xy - 2yz - 2zy$
$= 2(x^2 + y^2 + z^2 - xy - yz - zy).$

Hence, the correct option is (a).

13. The sum of the cubes of the linear factors

$= (x-y)^3 + (y-z)^3 + (z-x)^3$

$= 3(x-y)(y-z)(z-x)$

$[\because (x-y)+(y-z)+(z-x)=0]$

Hence, the correct option is (b).

Assertion and Reason Type Questions

14. Assertion: Let

$f(x) = 6x^6 - 7x^5 + 3x^4 + 12x^3 - 15x^2 - 10x + 11.$

Divisor $= x - 1$.

By remainder theorem,

$f(1) = 6(1)^6 - 7(1)^5 + 3(1)^4 + 12(1)^3 - 15(1)^2 - 10(1) + 11$

$= 6 - 7 + 3 + 12 - 15 - 10 + 11 = 0.$

So, $6x^6 - 7x^5 + 3x^4 + 12x^3 - 15x^2 - 10x + 11$ is divisible by $x - 1$, is a true statement.

Also, the sum of the coefficients is zero.

Hence, **Assertion** is true.

Reason: If the sum of the coefficients of a polynomial in x is zero, then $x - 1$ is a factor of the polynomial, is a true statement. Also, **Reason** is the correct explanation of **Assertion**.

Hence, the correct option is (a).

15. Assertion: Given that $f(x-1) = x^3 - 5x^2 + 13$.

If $f(x)$ is divisible by $x - 1$, then $f(1) = 0$.

Put $x = 2$ in $f(x-1) = x^3 - 5x^2 + 13$.

$\Rightarrow f(2-1) = 2^3 - 5(2)^2 + 13$

$\Rightarrow f(1) = 1$

So, if $f(x-1) = x^3 - 5x^2 + 13$, then $f(x)$ is divisible by $x - 1$, is a false statement.

Reason: If a polynomial $f(x)$ is divisible by $x - a$, then $f(a) = 0$, is a true statement.

Hence, **Assertion** is false, and **Reason** is true.

Hence, the correct option is (d).

16. Assertion: Given that $f(x) = x^{2025}$.

The divisor is $x^2 - 1 = (x+1)(x-1)$.

Let the Quotient be $q(x)$.

Let the remainder be $ax + b$, since the divisor is a quadratic polynomial.

We have, dividend = divisor × quotient + remainder.

$x^{2025} = q(x)(x+1)(x-1) + (ax+b)$

Substituting $x = 1$, we get $1 = a + b$ (1)

Substituting $x = -1$, we get $-1 = -a + b$ (2)

Eq (1) + Eq (2): $b = 0$.

Substituting $b = 0$, in equation (1) we get $a = 1$.

Hence the remainder is $ax + b = 1(x) + 0 = x$.

Hence, **Assertion** is true.

Reason: If a polynomial $f(x)$ is divided by $x + a$, then the remainder is $f(-a)$.

Hence, **Reason** is false.

17. Assertion: Let $f(29) = (29)^{2026} - (15)^{2026}$.

Divisor = 14 = 29 – 15.

By the remainder theorem, the remainder is $f(15)$.

$= (15)^{2026} - (15)^{2026} = 0.$

Hence, **Assertion** is true.

Reason: For any positive integer value of n, a polynomial $x^n - y^n$ is divisible by $x - y$.

Hence, **Reason** is true and the correct explanation of the **Assertion**.

Hence, the correct option is (a).

CHAPTER

4

Pair of Linear Equations in Two Variables

Remember

Before beginning this chapter, you should be able to:

- Solve simple equations with one or two variable
- Use graphs of linear equations and inequations
- Solve basic word problems on linear equations and inequations

Key Ideas

After completing this chapter, you should be able to:

- Solve linear equations by different methods
- Learn nature of solutions of simultaneous linear equations
- Study solving of word problems on linear equations with two variables
- Find solution of linear equations by graphical methods

Scientific Crypt

A Tribute to Brahmagupta (598 AD to 668 AD)

Brahmagupta was a mathematician and an astronomer who lived in Bhinmal, located in present-day Rajasthan. He was the head of the astronomical observatory at Ujjain. He wrote four texts on Mathematics and Astronomy; the Cadamekela, the Brahmasputa Siddhanta, the Khandakhadyaka and the Durkeamynarda. His most famous work is Brahmasputa Siddhanta, which is the first book that mentions zero as a number. Brahmagupta is considered as a mathematician who found zero. He also gave rules for using zero with other numbers. He discussed the arithmetic operations on positive, negative numbers and zero.

The following are some of his contributions to mathematics:

(i) He gave the solution of general linear equations.

(ii) He developed methods to solve the indeterminate equation of the form $ax + c = b$.

(iii) He gave the solution to the quadratic equation of the form $ax^2 + bx + c = 0$.

(iv) He developed methods to solve quadratic indeterminate equations of the type $ax^2 + c = y^2$, $ax^2 - c = y^2$.

(v) He was the first to give the formula for the area of a cyclic quadrilateral.

FUN TIME

CROSSWORD

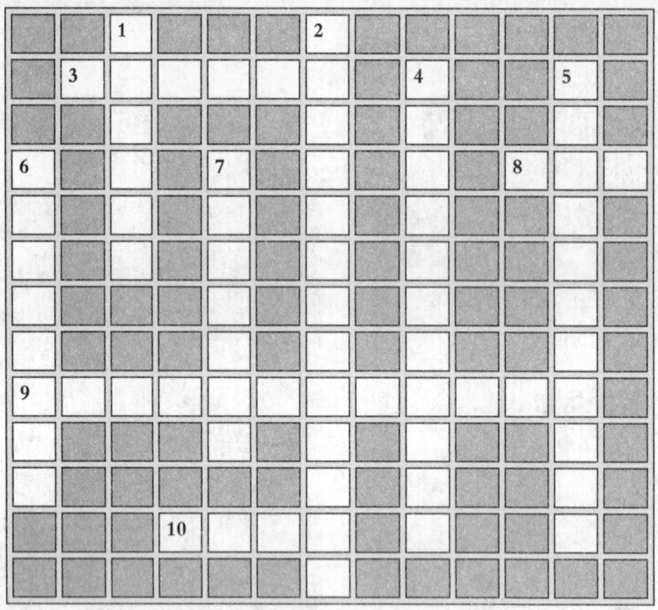

Across

3. An equation, in which the highest index of the unknowns present is one, is a _____equation.
8. The number of solutions for a pair of intersecting lines.
9. If a system of equations has no solution, then the equations are said to be
10. The number of solutions for a pair of parallel lines.

Down

1. A linear equation which has only one unknown is a _____ equation.
2. Moving a term from LHS of an equation to RHS is called
4. If x is greater than or equal to zero, then x is said to be
5. If x is lesser than or equal to zero, then x is said to be
6. A sentence in which there is an equality sign between two algebraic expressions is called
7. The process of finding the value of an unknown in an equation is called _____ the equation.

INTRODUCTION

While solving the problems, in most cases, first we need to frame an equation. In this chapter, we will learn how to frame and solve equations. Framing an equation is more difficult than solving an equation. Now, let us review the basic concepts related to this chapter.

Algebraic Expressions

Expressions of the form $2x$, $(3x + 5)$, $(4x - 2y)$, $2x^2 + 3\sqrt{y}$, $\frac{3x^2}{2}\sqrt{y}$ are algebraic expressions. $3x$ and 5 are the terms of $(3x + 5)$ and $4x$ and $2y$ are the terms of $4x - 2y$. Algebraic expressions are made of numbers, symbols and the basic arithmetical operations. In the term $2x$, 2 is the numerical coefficient of x and x is the variable coefficient of 2.

Equation

An equation is a sentence in which there is an equality sign between two algebraic expressions.

For example, $2x + 5 = x + 3$, $3y - 4 = 20$ and $5x + 6 = x + 1$ are some examples of equations. Here x and y are unknown quantities and 5, 3, 20, etc., are known quantities.

Linear Equation

An equation, in which the highest index of the unknown present is one, is a linear equation.

$2(x + 5) = 18$, $3x - 2 = 5$, $x + y = 20$ and $3x - 2y = 5$ are some linear equations.

Info Bytes!

Many natural phenomena, such as the orbits of planets and the properties of atoms, can be described using algebraic equations

Simple Equation

A linear equation which has only one unknown is a simple equation. $3x + 4 = 16$ and $2x - 5 = x + 3$ are examples of simple linear equations.

The part of an equation which is to the left side of the equality sign is known as the left-hand side, abbreviated as LHS. The part of an equation which is to the right side of the equality sign is known as the right-hand side, abbreviated as RHS. The process of finding the value of an unknown in an equation is called solving the equation. The value/values of the unknown found after solving an equation is/are called the solutions or the roots of the equation.

Before we learn how to solve an equation, let us review the basic properties of equality.

1. When a term is added to both sides of the equality, the equality does not change.

   Example: If $a + b = c + d$, then $a + b + x = c + d + x$.

   This property holds good for subtraction also.

2. When the expressions on the LHS and RHS of the equation are multiplied by a non-zero term, the equation does not change.

   Example: If $a + b = c + d$, then $x(a + b) = x(c + d)$.

   This property holds good for division also.

Solving an Equation in One Variable

The following steps are involved in solving an equation.

Step 1: Always ensure that the unknown quantities are on the LHS and the known quantities or constants on the RHS.
Step 2: Add all the terms containing the unknowns on the LHS and all the knowns on the RHS, so that each side of the equation contains only one term.
Step 3: Divide both sides of the equation by the coefficient of the unknown.

EXAMPLE 4.1 If $4x + 15 = 35$, then find the value of x.

SOLUTION

Step 1: Group the known quantities as the RHS of the equation, i.e., $4x = 35 - 15$.

Step 2: Simplify the numbers on the RHS $\Rightarrow 4x = 20$.

Step 3: Since 4 is the coefficient of x, divide both the sides of the equation by 4.

$$\frac{4x}{4} = \frac{20}{4} \Rightarrow x = 5.$$

EXAMPLE 4.2 Solve: $3x + 11 = 6x - 13$.

SOLUTION

Step 1: $6x - 3x = 11 + 13$

Step 2: $3x = 24$

Step 3: $\frac{3x}{3} = \frac{24}{3} \Rightarrow x = 8.$

EXAMPLE 4.3 A swarm of 62 bees flies in a garden. If 3 bees land on each flower, 8 bees are left with no flowers. Find the number of flowers in the garden.

SOLUTION

Let the number of flowers be x.

Number of bees on the flowers = $3x$

Total number of bees = 62

$\therefore 3x + 8 = 62$

$\Rightarrow 3x = 62 - 8 = 54 \Rightarrow x = 18$

$\therefore$ There are 18 flowers in the garden.

Transposition

In the above problem, $3x + 8 = 62$ can be written as $3x = 62 - 8$. When a term is moved (transposed) from one side of the equation to the other side, the sign is changed. The positive sign is changed to the negative sign and multiplication is changed to division. Moving a term from one side of the equation to the other side is called transposition. Thus solving a linear equation, in general, comprises two kinds of transposition.

Simultaneous Linear Equations

We have learnt to solve an equation with one unknown. Very often we come across equations involving more than one unknown. In such cases we require more than one condition or equation. Generally, when there are two unknowns, we require two equations to solve the problem. When there are three unknowns, we require three equations and so on.

We need to find the values of the unknowns that satisfy all the given equations. Since the values satisfy all the given equations we call them simultaneous equations. In this chapter, we deal with simultaneous (linear) equations in two unknowns.

Let us consider the equation, $2x + 5y = 19$, which contains two unknown quantities x and y.

Here, $5y = 19 - 2x$

$$\Rightarrow \quad y = \frac{19 - 2x}{5} \qquad (1)$$

In the above equation for every value of x, there exists a corresponding value for y.

When $x = 1$, $y = \frac{17}{5}$

When $x = 2$, $y = 3$, and so on.

If there is another equation, of the same kind, say, $5x - 2y = 4$.

From this, we get,

$$y = \frac{5x - 4}{2} \qquad (2)$$

If we need the values of x and y such that both the equations are satisfied, then $\frac{19 - 2x}{5} = \frac{5x - 4}{2}$

$$\Rightarrow \quad 38 - 4x = 25x - 20$$

$$\Rightarrow \quad 29x = 58$$

$$\Rightarrow \quad x = 2$$

On substituting the value of $x = 2$ in Eq. (1), we get,

$$\Rightarrow \quad y = \frac{19 - 2(2)}{5} = \frac{15}{5} = 3$$

$$\Rightarrow \quad y = 3$$

Both the equations are satisfied by the same values of x and y. Thus, we can say that when two or more equations are satisfied by the same values of unknown quantities, then those equations are called simultaneous equations.

When two equations, each in two variables, are given, they can be solved in five ways.

1. Elimination by cancellation
2. Elimination by substitution
3. Adding the two equations and subtracting one equation from the other
4. Cross-multiplication method
5. Graphical method

Elimination by Cancellation

EXAMPLE 4.4 If $2x + 3y = 19$ and $5x + 4y = 37$, then find the values of x and y.

SOLUTION

In this method, the two equations are reduced to a single variable equation by eliminating one of the variables.

Step 1: Here, let us eliminate the y term, and in order to eliminate the y term, we have to multiply the first equation with the coefficient of y in the second equation and the second equation with the coefficient of y in the first equation so that the coefficients of y terms in both the equations become equal.

$(2x + 3y = 19)4 \Rightarrow 8x + 12y = 76$ (1)

$(5x + 4y = 37)3 \Rightarrow 15x + 12y = 111$ (2)

Step 2: Subtract Eq. (2) from Eq. (1),

$(15x + 12y) - (8x + 12y) = 111 - 76$

$\Rightarrow 7x = 35$

$\Rightarrow x = 5.$

Step 3: Substitute the value of x in Eq. (1) or Eq. (2) to find the value of y. Substituting the value of x in the first equation, we get,

$2(5) + 3y = 19$

$\Rightarrow 3y = 19 - 10 \Rightarrow 3y = 9$

$\Rightarrow y = 3.$

$\therefore$ The solution of the given pair of equation is $x = 5$; $y = 3$.

Elimination by Substitution

EXAMPLE 4.5 If $4x - 3y = 32$ and $x + y = 1$, then find the values of x and y.

SOLUTION

In this method, the two equations are reduced to a single variable equation by substituting the value of one variable, obtained from one equation, in the other equation.

Step 1: Using the second equation, find x in terms of y, i.e.,

$x + y = 1$

$\Rightarrow y = 1 - x$ (1)

Step 2: Substitute the value of y in the first equation to find the value of x.

$\therefore 4x - 3(1 - x) = 32$

Step 3: Simplify the equation in terms of x and find the value of x.

$4x - 3 + 3x = 32$

$\Rightarrow 7x = 32 + 3 = 35$

$\Rightarrow x = 5$

Step 4: Substituting the value of x in Eq. (1), we have,

$y = 1 - x = 1 - 5$

$\Rightarrow y = -4.$

$\therefore$ The solution for the given pair of equations is $x = 5$; $y = -4$.

Adding Two Equations and Subtracting One Equation from the Other

EXAMPLE 4.6 Solve $3x + 7y = 32$ and $7x + 3y = 48$.

SOLUTION

Given,

$$3x + 7y = 32 \quad (1)$$
$$7x + 3y = 48 \quad (2)$$

Step 1: Adding both the equations, we get,

$10x + 10y = 80$

$\Rightarrow 10(x + y) = 10 \times 8$

$\Rightarrow x + y = 8$ (3)

Step 2: Subtracting Eq. (1) from Eq. (2), we have,

$(7x + 3y) - (3x + 7y) = 48 - 32$

$\Rightarrow 4x - 4y = 16$

$\Rightarrow 4(x - y) = 4 \times 4$

$\Rightarrow x - y = 4$ (4)

Step 3: Adding the Eqs. (3) and (4), we have,

$x + y + x - y = 12$

$\Rightarrow 2x = 12$

$\Rightarrow x = 6$

Substituting $x = 6$ in any of the Eqs. (1), (2), (3) or (4), we get, $y = 2$.

$\therefore$ The solution of the pair of equations is $x = 6$; $y = 2$.

Cross-multiplication Method

EXAMPLE 4.7 Solve $a_1x + b_1y + c_1 = 0$ and $a_2x + b_2y + c_2 = 0$, where $\frac{a_1}{a_2} \neq \frac{b_1}{b_2}$.

SOLUTION

Given,

$$a_1x + b_1y + c_1 = 0 \quad (1)$$

$$a_2x + b_2y + c_2 = 0 \quad (2)$$

Solving the above equations using elimination by cancellation method, we get,

$$x = \frac{b_1c_2 - b_2c_1}{a_1b_2 - a_2b_1} \text{ and } y = \frac{c_1a_2 - c_2a_1}{a_1b_2 - a_2b_1}.$$

Applying alternendo on the above ratios, we have,

$$\frac{x}{b_1c_2 - b_2c_1} = \frac{1}{a_1b_2 - a_2b_1} \text{ and } \frac{y}{c_1a_2 - c_2a_1} = \frac{1}{a_1b_2 - a_2b_1}$$

$$\Rightarrow \quad \frac{x}{b_1c_2 - b_2c_1} = \frac{y}{c_1a_2 - c_2a_1} = \frac{1}{a_1b_2 - a_2b_1}.$$

The above result can be better remembered using the Fig. 4.1.

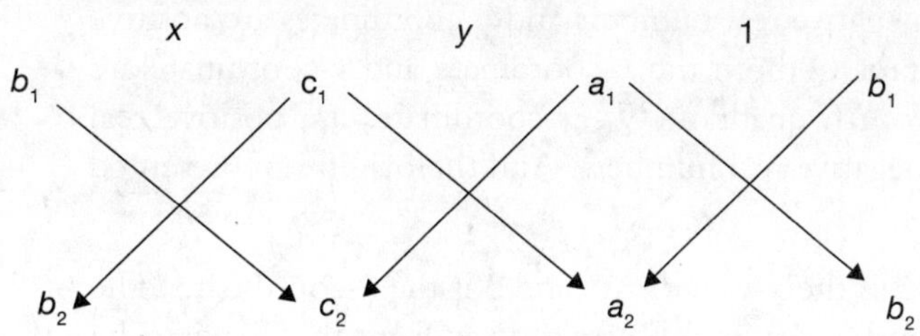

Figure 4.1

The arrows between the two numbers indicate that they are to be multiplied and second product is to be subtracted from the first.

While using this method, the following steps are to be followed.

Step 1: Write the given equations in the form $a_1x + b_1y + c_1 = 0$ and $a_2x + b_2y + c_2 = 0$.

Step 2: Write the coefficients of the equations as mentioned above.

Step 3: Find the values of x and y.

EXAMPLE 4.8 Solve $4x + 5y = 71$ and $5x + 3y = 66$.

SOLUTION

Step 1: Rewriting the equations, we get,

$$4x + 5y - 71 = 0 \quad (1)$$

$$5x + 3y - 66 = 0 \quad (2)$$

Step 2: Write the coefficients of x and y in the specified manner.

x	y	1	
5	−71	4	5
3	−66	5	3

Step 3: Find the values of x and y.

$$\frac{x}{-330+213} = \frac{y}{-355+264} = \frac{1}{12-25}$$

$$\Rightarrow \frac{x}{-117} = \frac{y}{-91} = \frac{1}{-13}$$

$$\Rightarrow x = \frac{-117}{-13}; y = \frac{-91}{-13}$$

$$\Rightarrow x = 9 \text{ and } y = 7.$$

Graphical Method

Plotting the Points

If we consider any point in a plane, then we can determine the location of the given point, i.e., we can determine the distance of the given point from X-axis and Y-axis. Therefore, each point in the plane represents the distance from both the axes. So, each point is represented by an ordered pair and it consists of x-coordinate and y-coordinate. The first element of an ordered pair is called x-coordinate and the second element of an ordered pair is called y-coordinate. In the first quadrant Q_1, both the x-coordinate and y-coordinate are positive real numbers. In the second quadrant Q_2, x-coordinates are negative real numbers and y-coordinates are positive real numbers. In the third quadrant Q_3 both the x-coordinate and y-coordinate are negative real numbers. In the fourth quadrant Q_4, x-coordinates are positive real numbers and y-coordinates are negative real numbers. And the origin is represented by (0, 0).

Consider the point (2, 3). Here 2 is the x-coordinate and 3 is the y-coordinate. The point (2, 3) is 2 units away from the Y-axis and 3 units away from the X-axis. The point (2, 3) belongs to the first quadrant. If we consider the point (–3, –5), –3 is x-coordinate and –5 is y-coordinate. The point (–3, –5) belongs to Q_3 and is 3 units away from the Y-axis and 5 units away from the X-axis.

To plot a point say $P(-3, 4)$, we start from the origin and proceed 3 units towards the left-hand side along the X-axis (i.e., negative direction as x-coordinate is negative), and from there we move 4 units upwards along the Y-axis (i.e., positive direction as y-coordinate is positive). The method of plotting a point in a coordinate plane was explained by Rene Descartes, a French mathematician.

Konnect

Choosing a particular method to solve a pair of equations makes the simplification easier. One can learn as to which method is the easiest to solve a pair of equations by becoming familiar with the different methods of solving the equation.

EXAMPLE 4.9

Plot the following points on the coordinate plane.
$P(2, 3)$, $Q(-4, -5)$, $R(2, -3)$, $S(-4, 4)$, $T(3, 0)$, $U(0, 5)$.

SOLUTION

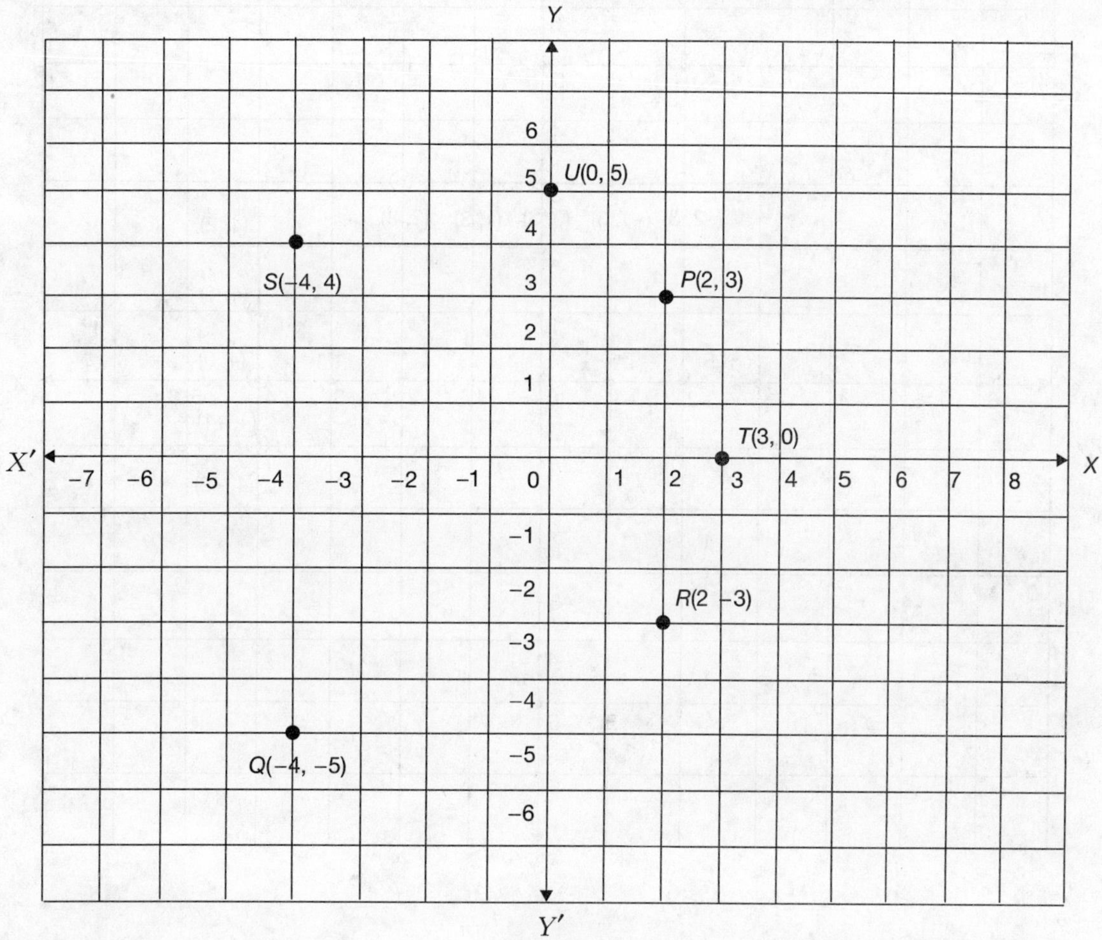

Figure 4.2

EXAMPLE 4.10

Plot the following points on the coordinate plane. What do you observe? (see Fig. 4.3)
(a) (–2, 3), (–1, 3), (0,3), (1, 3), (2, 3)
(b) (4, 2), (4, 1), (4, 0), (4, –1), (4, –2)

SOLUTION

(a) (–2, 3), (–1, 3), (0, 3), (1, 3), (2, 3)

(i) The above points lie on the same straight line which is perpendicular to the Y-axis.
(ii) The y-coordinates of all the given points are the same, i.e., $y = 3$.
(iii) Hence, the straight line passing through the given points is represented by $y = 3$.
(iv) Therefore, the line $y = 3$ is parallel to X-axis which intersects Y-axis at (0, 3).

(b) (4, 2), (4, 1), (4, 0), (4, –1), (4, –2)

(i) The above points lie on the same straight line which is perpendicular to the X-axis.
(ii) The x-coordinates of all the given points is the same, i.e., $x = 4$.
(iii) Hence, the straight line passing through the given points is represented by $x = 4$.
(iv) Therefore, the line $x = 4$ is parallel to the Y-axis which intersects the X-axis at (4, 0).

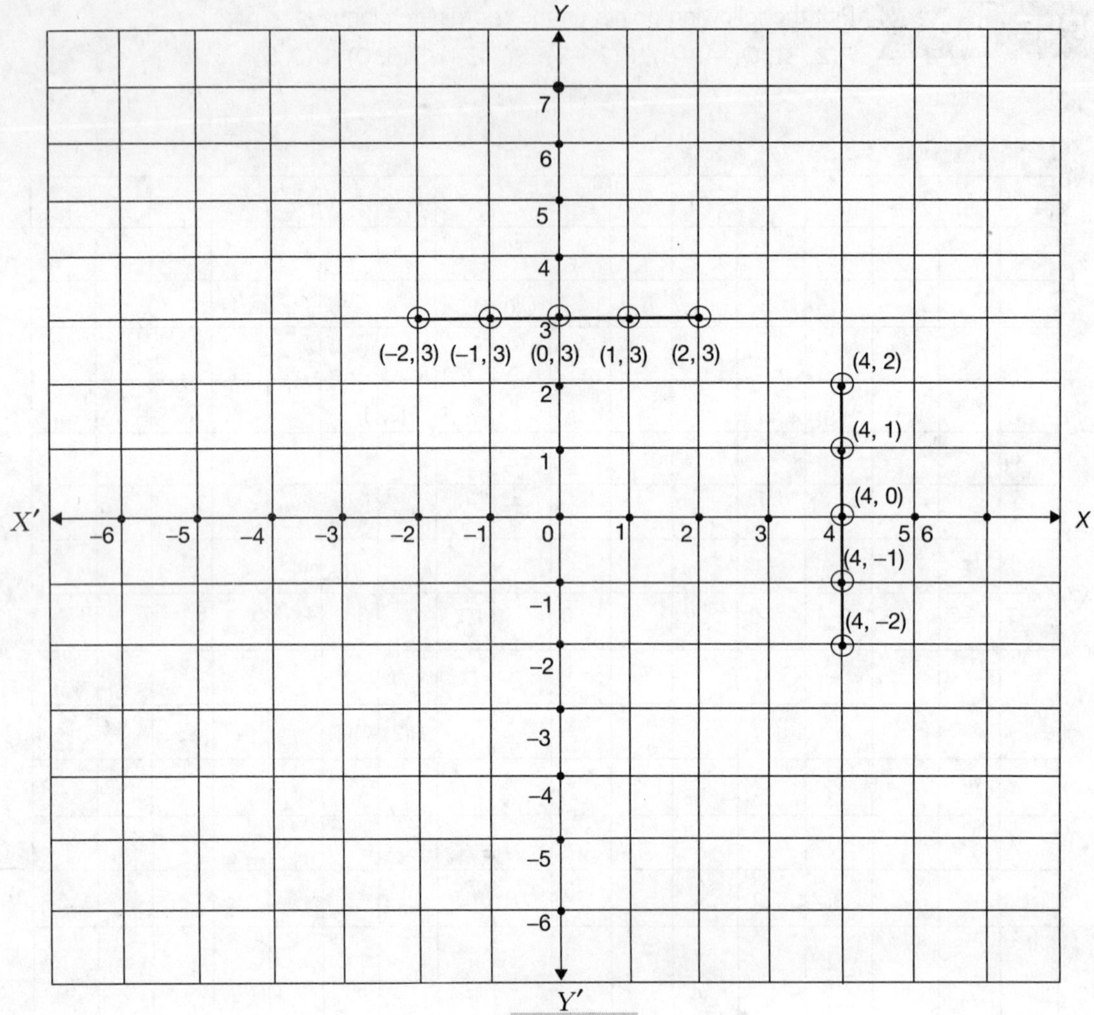

Figure 4.3

Konnect

Every linear equation can be graphed as a straight line, hence the name 'linear'. The **slope** of this line is the coefficient of the variable, and the y-intercept is the constant term.

EXAMPLE 4.11 Plot the following points on the coordinate plane and what do you observe?
(–3, 3), (–2, 2), (–1, 1), (0, 0), (1, –1), (2, –2), (3, –3)

SOLUTION

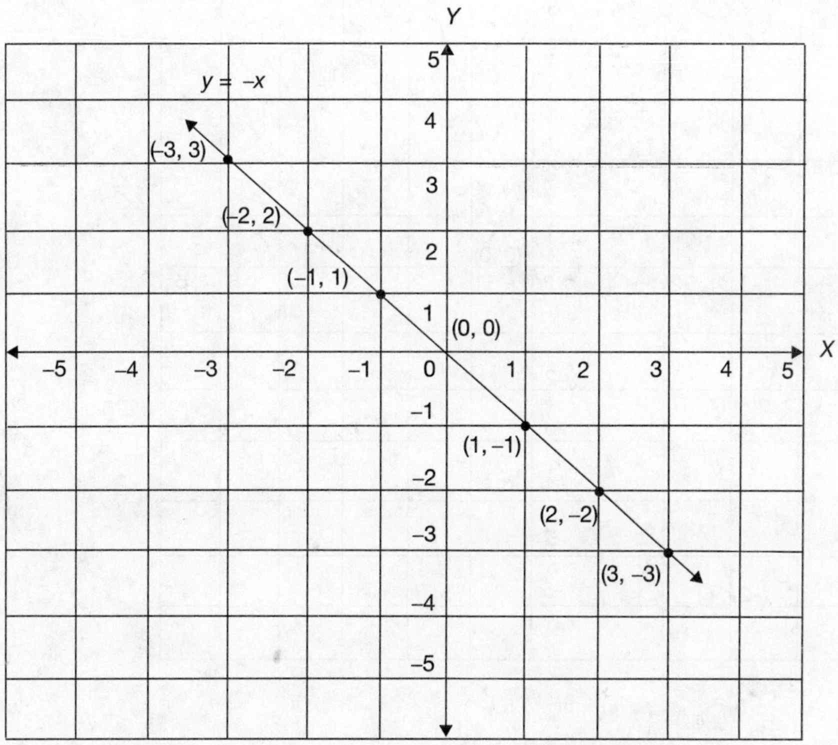

Figure 4.4

Info Bytes!

1. The y-coordinate of every point on the x-axis is zero, i.e., $y = 0$. Therefore the x-axis is denoted by $y = 0$.
2. The x-coordinate of every point on the y-axis is zero, i.e., $x = 0$. Therefore, the y-axis is denoted by $x = 0$.

(a) All the given points lie on the same straight line.
(b) Every point on the straight line represents $y = -x$.
(c) The above line with the given ordered pairs is represented by the equation $y = -x$.

EXAMPLE 4.12 Draw the graph of the equation $y = 3x$ where R is the replacement set for both x and y.

SOLUTION

x	–2	–1	0	1	2
$y = 3x$	–6	–3	0	3	6

Some of the ordered pairs which satisfy the equation $y = 3x$ are (–1, –3), (–2, –6), (0, 0), (1, 3), (2, 6).

By plotting the above points on the graph sheet, we get the following:

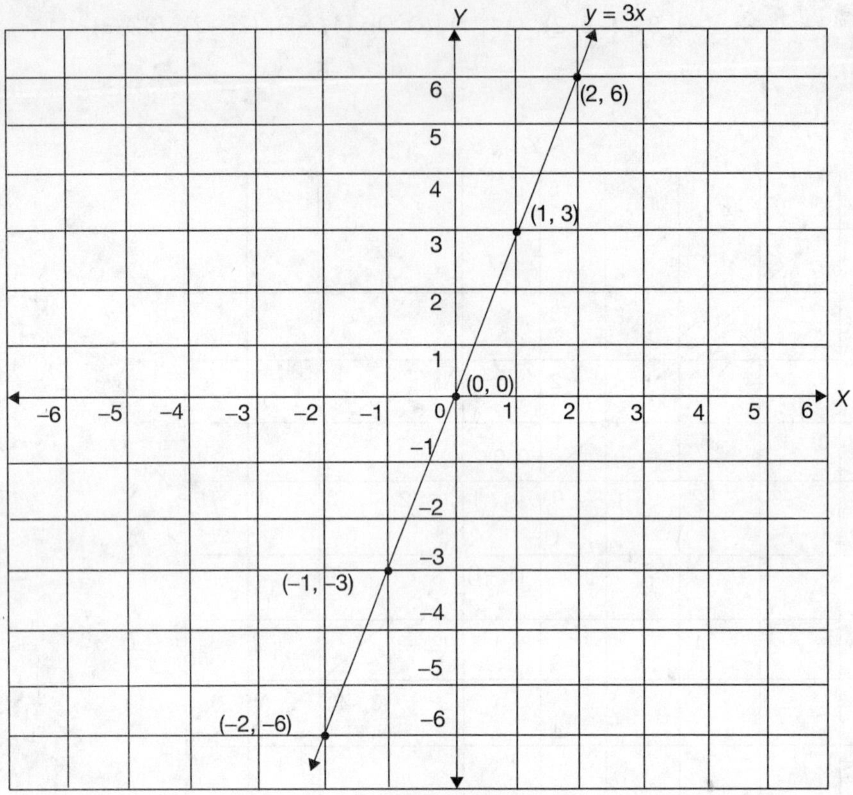

Figure 4.5

EXAMPLE 4.13

Draw the graph of the equations $x + y = -1$ and $x - y = 5$.

SOLUTION

(a) $x + y = -1$

x	–3	–2	–1	0	1	2	3
$y = -1 - x$	2	1	0	–1	–2	–3	–4

Some of the ordered pairs which satisfy the equation $x + y = -1$ are (–3, 2), (–2, 1), (–1, 0), (0, –1), (1, –2), (2, –3), (3, –4).

(b) $x - y = 5$

x	–2	–1	0	1	2	3	4
$y = x - 5$	–7	–6	–5	–4	–3	–2	–1

∴ Some of the ordered pairs which satisfy the equation $x - y = 5$ are (–2, –7), (–1, –6), (0, –5), (1, –4), (2, –3), (3, –2), (4, –1).

The ordered pairs which satisfy the equations $x + y = -1$ and $x - y = 5$ are plotted on a graph paper. We find that each equation represents a line.

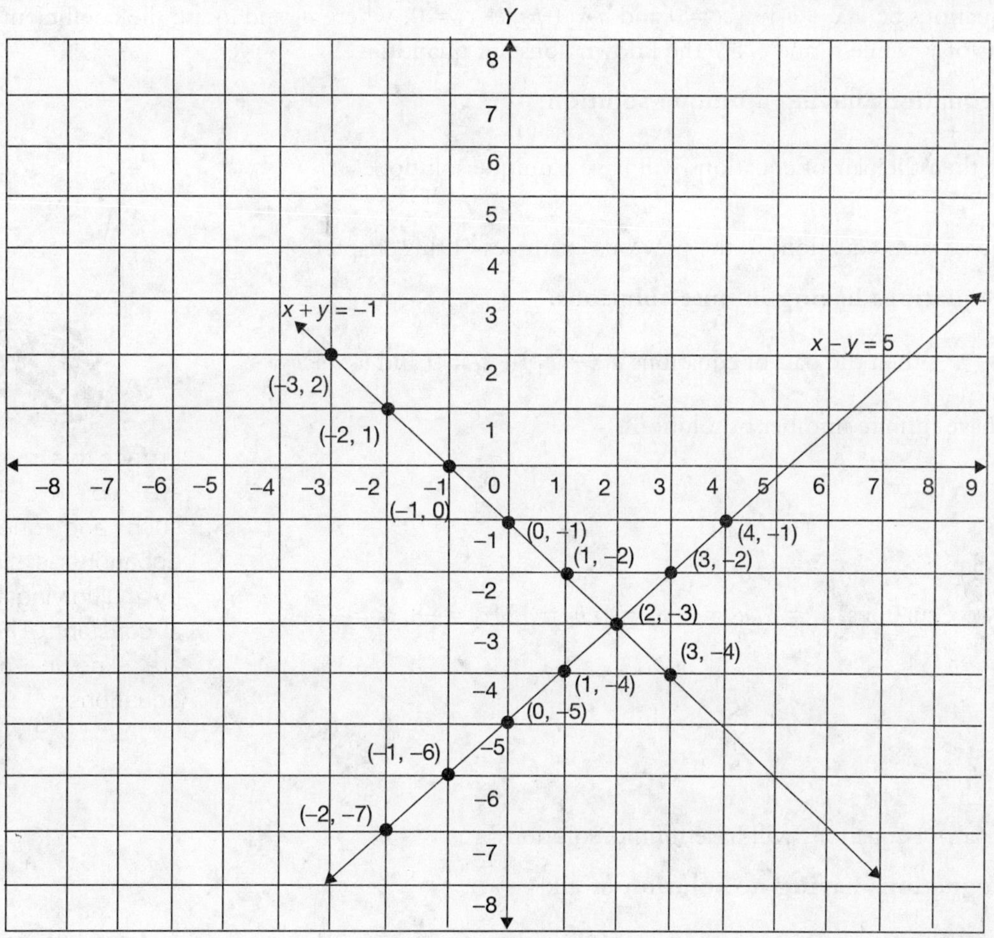

Figure 4.6

From the graph, we notice that the two given lines intersect at the point (2, –3).
That is, lines $x + y = -1$ and $x - y = 5$ have a common point (2, –3). Therefore, (2, –3) is the solution of the equations $x + y = -1$ and $x - y = 5$.

Verification:

$$x + y = -1 \quad (1)$$

$$x - y = 5 \quad (2)$$

Solving Eqs. (1) and (2), we get,

$$x = 2 \text{ and } y = -3.$$

∴ (2, –3) is the solution of $x + y = -1$ and $x - y = 5$.

Info Bytes!

From the above example, we notice that we can find the solution for simultaneous equations by representing them in graphs, i.e., by using the graphical method.

Nature of Solutions

When we try to solve a pair of equations, we could arrive at three possible results. They are:

1. having a unique solution.
2. having an infinite number of solutions.
3. having no solution.

Let the pair of equations be $a_1x + b_1y + c_1 = 0$ and $a_2x + b_2y + c_2 = 0$, where a_1 and a_2 are the coefficients of x; b_1 and b_2 are the coefficients of y; while c_1 and c_2 are the known constant quantities.

1. A pair of equations having a unique solution:

If $\frac{a_1}{a_2} \neq \frac{b_1}{b_2}$, then the pair of equations will have a unique solution.

We have solved such equations in the previous examples of this chapter.

2. A pair of equations having infinite solutions:

If $\frac{a_1}{a_2} = \frac{b_1}{b_2} = \frac{c_1}{c_2}$, then the pair of equations $a_1x + b_1y + c_1 = 0$ and $a_2x + b_2y + c_2 = 0$ will have infinite number of solutions.

Example:

$3x + 4y = 8$

$9x + 12y = 24$

For these two equations, $a_1 = 3$, $a_2 = 9$, $b_1 = 4$, $b_2 = 12$, $c_1 = -8$, $c_2 = -24$

$\therefore \frac{a_1}{a_2} = \frac{b_1}{b_2} = \frac{c_1}{c_2}$

Since, $\frac{3}{9} = \frac{4}{12} = \frac{-8}{-24}$

The above pair of equations will have infinite solutions.

Konnect

In fact this means that there are no two equations as such and one of the two equations is simply obtained by multiplying the other with a constant. These equations are known as dependent equations.

3. A pair of equations having no solution at all:

If $\frac{a_1}{a_2} = \frac{b_1}{b_2} \neq \frac{c_1}{c_2}$, then the pair of equations $a_1x + b_1y + c_1 = 0$ and $a_2x + b_2y + c_2 = 0$ will have no solution.

Example:

$5x + 6y = 30$

$10x + 12y = 40$

For these two equations, $a_1 = 5$, $a_2 = 10$, $b_1 = 6$, $b_2 = 12$, $c_1 = -30$, $c_2 = -40$.

Here,

$\frac{a_1}{a_2} = \frac{b_1}{b_2} \neq \frac{c_1}{c_2}$

$\frac{5}{10} = \frac{6}{12} \neq \frac{-30}{-40}$.

Hence, the pair of equations have no solution at all.

Info Bytes!

1. In other words, the two equations will contradict each other or be inconsistent with each other.
2. A pair of equations issaidtobeconsistent if it has a solution (finite or infinite).

Word Problems and Applications of Simultaneous Equations

In this chapter, we have discussed earlier that it is essential to have as many equations as there are unknown quantities to be determined. In word problems also, it is necessary to have as many independent conditions, as there are unknown quantities to be determined.

Let us understand with the help of the following examples as to how word problems can be solved using simultaneous equations.

EXAMPLE 4.14 The sum of the successors of two numbers is 42 and the difference of their predecessors is 12. Find the numbers.

SOLUTION

Let the two numbers be x, y and $x > y$.

Given that,

$$(x + 1) + (y + 1) = 42$$

$$\Rightarrow \quad x + y = 40 \quad (1)$$

Also,

$$(x - 1) - (y - 1) = 12$$

$$\Rightarrow \quad x - y = 12 \quad (2)$$

Adding Eqs. (1) and (2), we get,

$$\Rightarrow \quad 2x = 52$$

$$\Rightarrow \quad x = 26$$

Substituting $x = 26$ in any one of Eqs. (1) and (2), we get $y = 14$.

∴ The two numbers are 26 and 14.

EXAMPLE 4.15 In a fraction, if numerator is increased by 2 and denominator is decreased by 3, then the fraction becomes 1. Instead, if numerator is decreased by 2 and denominator is increased by 3, then the fraction becomes $\frac{3}{8}$. Find the fraction.

SOLUTION

Let the fraction be $\frac{a}{b}$.

Applying the first condition, we get $\frac{a+2}{b-3} = 1$

$$\Rightarrow \quad a + 2 = b - 3$$

$$\Rightarrow \quad a - b = -5 \quad (1)$$

Applying the second condition, we get $\frac{a-2}{b+3} = \frac{3}{8}$

$$\Rightarrow \quad 8a - 16 = 3b + 9$$

$$\Rightarrow \quad 8a - 3b = 25 \quad (2)$$

Solving Eqs. (1) and (2), using any of the methods discussed earlier, we get $a = 8$ and $b = 13$.

∴ The fraction is $\frac{8}{13}$.

EXAMPLE 4.16 In a box, the total number of ₹2 coins and ₹5 coins is 20. If the total coins amount to ₹76, find the number of coins of each denomination.

SOLUTION

Let the number of ₹2 coins and ₹5 coins be x and y, respectively.

Given,

$$x + y = 20 \quad (1)$$

$$2x + 5y = 76 \quad (2)$$

Solving Eqs. (1) and (2), we get,

$$x = 8 \text{ and } y = 12.$$

That is, The number of ₹2 coins = 8 and number of ₹5 coins = 12.

EXAMPLE 4.17 Four years ago, the age of a person was thrice that of his son. Eight years later, the age of the person will be twice that of his son. Find the present ages of the person and his son.

SOLUTION

Let the present ages of the person and his son be x years and y years, respectively.

Given,

$$x - 4 = 3(y - 4)$$

$$\Rightarrow \quad x - 4 = 3y - 12$$

$$\Rightarrow \quad x - 3y = -8 \qquad (1)$$

Also,

$$x + 8 = 2(y + 8)$$

$$\Rightarrow \quad x + 8 = 2y + 16$$

$$\Rightarrow \quad x - 2y = 8 \qquad (2)$$

Solving Eqs. (1) and (2), we get

$$x = 40 \text{ and } y = 16.$$

EXAMPLE 4.18 For what value of k do the set of equations $4x - (3k + 2)y = 20$ and $(11k - 3)x - 10y = 40$ have infinite solutions?

SOLUTION

Given equations are,

$$4x - (3k + 2)y = 20 \qquad (1)$$

$$(11k - 3)x - 10y = 40 \qquad (2)$$

System of Eqs. (1) and (2) have infinite solutions, if $\frac{4}{11k-3} = \frac{-(3k+2)}{-10} = \frac{-20}{-40}$

$\Rightarrow \frac{4}{11k-3} = \frac{1}{2}$

$\Rightarrow 8 = 11k - 3$

$\Rightarrow 11k = 11$

$\Rightarrow k = 1.$

Linear Inequations

If a is any real number, then a is either positive or negative or zero. When a is positive, we write $a > 0$, which is read as 'a is greater than zero'. When a is negative, we write $a < 0$, which is read as 'a is less than zero'. If a is zero, we write $a = 0$ and in this case, a is neither positive nor negative.

The two signs > and < are called the 'signs of inequalities'.

Notation:

1. '>' denotes 'greater than'.
2. '<' denotes 'less than'.
3. '≥' denotes 'greater than or equal to'.
4. '≤' denotes 'less than or equal to'.

Definition:

For any two non-zero real numbers a and b,

- a is said to be greater than b when $a - b$ is positive, i.e., $a > b$ when $a - b > 0$ and
- a is said to be less than b when $a - b$ is negative. i.e., $a < b$ when $a - b < 0$.

Listed below are some properties/results which are needed to solve problems on inequalities.

The letters a, b, c, d, etc. represent real numbers.

- For any two real numbers a and b, either $a > b$ or $a < b$ or $a = b$. This property is called Law of Trichotomy.
- If $a > b$, then $b < a$.
- If $a > b$ and $b > c$, then $a > c$. This property is called transitive property.
- If $a > b$ then $a + c > b + c$.
- If $a > b$ and $c > 0$, then $ac > bc$.
- If $a > b$ and $c < 0$, then $ac < bc$.
- If $a > b$ and $c > d$, then $a + c > b + d$.
- The square of any real number is always greater than or equal to 0.
- If $a > 0$, then $-a < 0$ and if $a > b$, then $-a < -b$.
- If a and b are positive numbers and $a > b$, then $1/a < 1/b$.
- If a and b are negative numbers and $a > b$, then $1/a < 1/b$.
- If $a > 0$ and $b < 0$, then $1/a > 1/b$.

Inequation: An open sentence which consists of one of the symbols viz., >, <, ≥, ≤ is called an inequation.

Examples:

(i) $3x - 8 > 8$

(ii) $2x^2 - 3x \leq 6$

Continued inequation: Two inequations of the same type (i.e., both consisting of > or ≥ or both consisting of < or ≤) can be combined into a continued inequation as explained below.

Example: If $a < b$ and $b < c$, we can write $a < b < c$. If $a \geq b$ and $b > c$, we can write $a \geq b > c$.

Linear inequation: An inequation in which the highest degree of the variables present is one is called a linear inequation.

Example:

(i) $3x + 4 \leq 8 - 3x$ and $8x - 64 \geq 8 + 5y$ are some of the examples for linear inequations.

(ii) $5x^2 + 6 > 7$ and $6x^3 + 6y^3 \leq 8$ are some of the examples for non-linear inequations.

Solving Linear Inequation in one variable: We are familiar with solving linear equations. Now let us look at solving some linear inequations in one variable.

Example: Solve the following inequations.

(a) $5x - 3 \leq 12,\ x \in N \Rightarrow 5x \leq 15 \Rightarrow x \leq 3 \Rightarrow x \in \{1, 2, 3\}$

(b) $2x - 4 < 4,\ x \in R \Rightarrow 2x < 8 \Rightarrow x < 4$

The set of all the numbers which are less than 4 is the solution set of the given inequation.

(c) $3x - 1 \geq 5,\ x \in Z \Rightarrow 3x \geq 6 \Rightarrow x \geq 2$

The set of all the integers which are greater than 2 is the solution set of the given equation.

Example: Represent the following inequations on the number line.

(a) $x \geq -2$

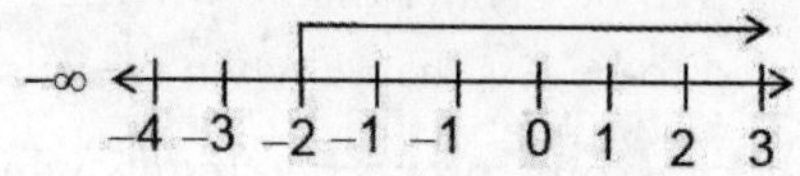

In the above figure, the ray drawn above the number line represents the solution set of the inequation. The end point of the ray is a part of the solution set. This is indicated by placing a solid dot at the end point.

(b) $x \leq 3$

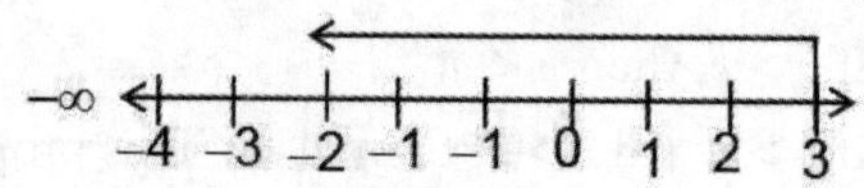

In the given figure, the ray drawn above the number line represents the solution set of the in equation. The end point of the ray is the part of the solution set. This is indicated by placing a solid dot at the end point.

Absolute value: If a is any real number, then,

(i) $|x| \leq a \Rightarrow -a \leq x \leq a$;

(ii) $|x| \geq a \Rightarrow x \geq a$ or $x \leq -a$

Properties of modulus:

(1) $x = 0 \Leftrightarrow |x| = 0$;

(2) For all values of x, $|x| \geq 0$ and $-|x| \leq 0$

(3) For all values of x, $|x + y| \leq |x| + |y|$

(4) $||x| - |y|| \leq |x - y|$

(5) $-|x| \leq x \leq |x|$

(6) $|xy| = |x||y|$

(7) $\left|\frac{x}{y}\right| = \frac{|x|}{|y|}, y \neq 0$

(8) $|x|^2 = x^2$

Interval Notation: We have seen above that the solution set or the range of values that satisfy inequalities are not discrete. Instead, we have, a continuous range of values. Such ranges can be represented using the interval notation.

The set of all real numbers between a and b (where $a < b$) excluding a and b is represented as (a, b) read as "the open interval a, b".$[a, b]$ read as "the closed interval a, b" means all real numbers between a and b including a and b $(a < b)$. $[a, b)$ means all numbers between a and b, with a being included and b excluded $(a < b)$.

EXAMPLE 4.19 Solve $|2x - 3| < 5$.

SOLUTION

$|2x - 3| < 5$

$\Rightarrow -5 < 2x - 3 < 5 \Rightarrow -2 < 2x < 8 \Rightarrow -1 < x < 4$.

$\therefore$ Solution set is $\{x \mid -1 < x < 4\}$ or $x \in (-1, 4)$

EXAMPLE 4.20 Solve $|3x + 2| \geq 7$.

SOLUTION

$|3x + 2| \geq 7$

$3x + 2 \geq 7$ or $3x + 2 \leq -7 \Rightarrow 3x \geq 5$ or $3x \leq -9$

$x \geq 5/3$ or $x \leq -3$.

$\therefore$ Solution set is $\left\{x \mid x \geq \frac{5}{3} \text{ or } x \leq -3\right\}$ or $(-\infty, -3] \cup \left[\frac{5}{3}, \infty\right)$

EXAMPLE 4.21 Solve $|5x - 7| < -18$.

SOLUTION

The modulus of any number has to be 0 or positive. Thus, there are no values of x which satisfy the given inequality. The solution set is φ.

EXAMPLE 4.22 If $|x + 5| < 7$, then find the solution set for the inequality.

SOLUTION

Given $|x + 5| < 7$, $-7 < x + 5 < 7 \Rightarrow -12 < x < 2$.

$\therefore$ Solution is $(-12, 2)$.

EXAMPLE 4.23 If $|x + 3| > -5$, then find the solution set for the inequality.

SOLUTION

Given $|x + 3| > -5$

Clearly $|x + 3|$ is a positive value for all $x \in R$ which is always greater than any negative value, i.e., -5.

$\therefore$ Solution set is R

EXAMPLE 4.24 Solve $|2x + 3| < 2$.

SOLUTION

For $x > -3/2$; $2x + 3 < 2 \Rightarrow x < -1/2$ .... (1)

and for $x < -3/2$; $-(2x + 3) < 2 \Rightarrow -2x < 5 \Rightarrow x > -5/2$ .... (2)

From (1), the solution set is $\left(\frac{-3}{2}, \frac{-1}{2}\right)$ and from (2) the solution set is $\left(\frac{-5}{2}, \frac{-3}{2}\right)$. At $x = -3/2$ also the inequalities holds good.

$\therefore$ Solution for the inequality is $\left(\frac{-5}{2}, \frac{-1}{2}\right)$.

Alternate method:

Given, $|2x + 3| < 2 \Rightarrow -2 < 2x + 3 < 2 \Rightarrow -5 < 2x < -1 \Rightarrow \frac{-5}{2} < x < -1/2 \Rightarrow x \in \left(\frac{-5}{2}, \frac{-1}{2}\right)$

Mathematical Modelling

Mathematical modelling is an attempt to study some part (or form) of the real-life problem in mathematical terms. Mathematical modelling is nothing but a technique and the pedagogy taken from fine arts and not from the basic sciences.

Info Bytes!

Mathematical models are crucial in predicting the spread of diseases and have been invaluable in the fight against pandemics like COVID-19.

POINTS TO REMEMBER

- ✔ An equation is a sentence in which there is an equality sign between two algebraic expressions.
- ✔ An equation, in which the highest index of the unknown present is one, is a linear equation.
- ✔ A linear equation which has only one unknown is a simple equation.
- ✔ The letters a, b, c, d, etc., represent real munbers.
- ✔ For any two real numbers a and b, either $a > b$ or $a < b$ or $a = b$. This property is called Law of Trichotomy.
- ✔ If $a > b$, then $b < a$.
- ✔ If $a > b$ and $b > c$, then $a > c$. This property is called transitive property.
- ✔ If $a > b$, then $a + c > b + c$.
- ✔ If $a > b$ and $c > 0$, then $ac > bc$.
- ✔ If $a > b$ and $c < 0$, then $ac < bc$.
- ✔ If $a > b$ and $c > d$, then $a + c > b + d$.
- ✔ The square of any real number is always greater than or equal to 0.
- ✔ If $a > 0$, then $-a < 0$ and if $a > b$, then $-a < -b$.
- ✔ If a and b are positive numbers and $a > b$, then $1/a < 1/b$.
- ✔ If a and b are negative numbers and $a > b$, then $1/a < 1/b$.
- ✔ If $a > 0$ and $b < 0$, then $1/a > 1/b$.

DW

PRACTICE QUESTIONS CLASSROOM WING

Very Short Answer Type Questions

Directions of questions from 1 to 14:
Fill in the blanks.

1. The solution set of $x + 2 \geq 3$, $x \in W$ is ____.
2. If x:y = 2:7 and $x + y = 81$, then y = ____.
3. The solution set of $|x| < 0$ is ____.
4. If $99x + 101y = 400$ and $101x + 99y = 600$, then $x + y$ is ________.
5. The number of common solutions for the system of linear equations $5x + 4y + 6 = 0$ and $10x + 8y = 12$ is ________.
6. If $a : b = 7 : 3$ and $a + b = 20$, then b = ________.
7. If $\frac{1}{x} + \frac{1}{y} = k$ and $\frac{1}{x} - \frac{1}{y} = k$, then the value of y ________. (is 0/does not exist).
8. If $p + q = k$, $p - q = n$ and $k > n$, then q is ________ (positive/negative).
9. If $a + b = x$, $a - b = y$ and $x < y$, then b is ________ (positive/negative).
10. If $3a + 2b + 4c = 26$ and $6b + 4a + 2c = 48$, then $a + b + c$ = ________.
11. Sum of the ages of X and Y, 12 years ago, was 48 years and sum of the ages of X and Y, 12 years hence will be 96 years. Present age of X is ________.
12. Number of non-negative integral solutions for the equation $2x + 3y = 12$ is ________.
13. If $2x + 3y = 5$ and $3x + 2y = 10$, then $x - y$ = ________.
14. If $a + b = p$ and $ab = p$, then the value of p is ____. (where a and b are positive integers).

Directions of questions from 15 to 16:
State whether the following statements are true or false.

15. If the total cost of 3 chairs and 2 tables is ₹1200 and the total cost of 12 chairs and 8 tables is ₹4800, then the cost of each chair must be ₹200 and each table must be ₹300. (True/False)
16. If the total cost of 2 apples and 3 mangoes is ₹22, then the cost of each apple and each mango must be ₹5 and ₹4, respectively, (where cost of each apple and mango is an integer). (True/False)

Directions of questions from 17 to 20:
Select the correct alternative from the given choices.

17. For what value of k do the system of equations $2x + 3ky = 4$ and $6x + 27y = 12$ has infinite solutions?
    (a) 1 (b) 2
    (c) 3 (d) 4
18. If $|x + 4| < 2$, then find the number of integer values of x.
    (a) 1 (b) 2
    (c) 3 (d) 4
19. For what value of k do the system of equations $5x - 2ky = 10$ and $6x + 8y = 21$ has no solution?
    (a) $\frac{-5}{3}$ (b) $\frac{10}{9}$
    (c) $\frac{5}{9}$ (d) $\frac{-10}{3}$
20. If $|x - 1| \leq 5$, then find the number of integer values of x.
    (a) 10 (b) 11
    (c) 9 (d) 12

Short Answer Type Questions

Directions for question 21:
Match the values of Column A with those of Column B.

21. Match the values of column A with those of column B.

Column A ($a_1x + b_1y + c_1 = 0$) and $a_1x + b_2y + c_2 = 0$	Column B (Number of Solutions)
(i) $\frac{a_1}{a_2} = \frac{b_1}{b_2}$	(A) Infinite
(ii) $\frac{a_1}{a_2} \neq \frac{b_1}{b_2}$	(B) Unique
(iii) $\frac{a_1}{a_2} = \frac{b_1}{b_2} = \frac{c_1}{c_2}$	(C) Zero
(iv) $\frac{a_1}{b_2} = \frac{b_1}{b_2} \neq \frac{c_1}{c_2}$	(D) Cannot be determined

Directions of questions from 22 to 31:
Answer the following questions.

22. For what value of k, will the following system of equations be consistent?
$4x - 5y = 6$ and $16x - 20y = k$

23. Six gallery seats and three balcony seats for a play were sold for ₹162. Four gallery seats and five balcony seats were sold for ₹180. Find the price of a gallery seat and the price of a balcony seat.

24. If the numerator of a fraction is increased by 2 and the denominator is decreased by 4, then it becomes 2. If the numerator is decreased by 1 and the denominator is increased by 2, then it becomes $\frac{1}{3}$. Find the fraction.

25. Solve: $\frac{1}{x} + \frac{1}{y} = 6$, $\frac{1}{y} + \frac{1}{z} = 7$ and $\frac{1}{z} + \frac{1}{x} = 5$.

26. The number of common solutions of $2x + 3y + 4 = 0$ and $4x + 6y + 8 = 0$ is ________.

27. Jaydeep starts his job with a certain monthly salary and earns a fixed increment in his monthly salary at the middle of every year, starting from the first year. If his monthly salary was ₹78000 at the end of 6 years of service and ₹84000 at the end of 12 years of service, find his initial salary and annual increment.

28. Alok was asked to find, $\frac{6}{7}$ of a number but instead he multiplied it by $\frac{7}{6}$. As a result he got an answer,which was more than the correct answer by 299. What was the number?

29. Shriya has certain number of 25 paise and 50 paise coins in her purse. If the total number of coins is 35 and their total value is ₹15.50, find the number of coins of each denomination.

30. (A) For what value of k, will the following pair of linear equations have no solution?
$2x + 3y = 1$ and $(3k - 1)x + (1 - 2k)\,y = 2k + 3$.
(B) If $3x + y - 3z = 11$ and $2x - 2z + 5y = 29$, then what is the value of $x + y - z$?

31. Solve: $\frac{x}{a} + \frac{y}{b} = a^2 + b^2$ and $\frac{x}{a^2} + \frac{y}{b^2} = a + b$.

Essay Type Questions

32. The present age of a father is three times that of his son. Seven years ago, the father's age was five times the son's age. What will be the sum of their present ages (in years)?

33. A two-digit number is 9 more than the sum of its digits. The difference between the digits is k. Find the number of possible values of k.

34. Six years hence, the age of a father will be thrice the age of his son. Three years ago, the father's age was p times his son's age. The value of p cannot be equal to?

35. Tito purchased two varieties of icecream cups, vanilla and strawberry—spending a total amount of ₹330. If each vanilla cup costs ₹25 and each strawberry cup costs ₹40, then in how many different combinations could he have purchased the icecream cups?

36. Amar, Bhavan, Chetan and Dinesh each had some money. Dinesh doubled the amounts with the others. Chetan then doubled the amounts with the others. Bhavan then doubled the amounts with the others. Amar then doubled the amounts with the

others. At this stage, each of them has ₹ 80. Find the initial amount with Chetan (in ₹).

37. Is the age of a person equal to the sum of the ages of his son and wife?

I. The person is two years older than his wife.

II. The age of his son is twelve years, who was born when his wife was 30 years old.

Choice (a) If the question can be answered using one of the statements alone but cannot be answered using the other statement alone.

Choice (b) If the question can be answered using either statement alone.

Choice (c) If the question can be answered using I and II together but not using I or II alone

Choice (d) If the question cannot be answered even using I and II together.

PRACTICE QUESTIONS COMPETITION WING

Level 1: Apply Your Concepts

Directions of questions from 1 to 5:
Fill in the blanks.

1. If $a + b = x$, $a - b = y$ and $x < y$, then b is ____.
2. The solution set of $x + 1 < 2$, $x \in N$ is ____.
3. The solutions set of $|x| < 2$ is ____.
4. The solutions set of $|x| > -5$ is ____.
5. The solution set of $|x| < 1$ is ____.

Directions of questions from 6 to 20:
Select the correct alternative from the given choices.

6. The number of common solution(s) for the system of linear equations $2x + 3y + 5 = 0$ and $4x + 6y - 10 = 0$ is ________.
(a) 0 (b) 1
(c) 2 (d) infinite

7. For what value of k, will the following pair of linear equations have no solution?
$3x + 4y = 5$ and $(3k + 1)x + 8y = k + 2$
(a) $\frac{5}{3}$ (b) $\frac{5}{13}$
(c) $\frac{2}{3}$ (d) $\frac{4}{3}$

8. For what value of k do the equations $3(k - 1)x + 4y = 24$ and $15x + 20y = 8(k + 13)$ have infinite solutions?
(a) 1 (b) 4
(c) 3 (d) 2

9. If the system of equations $4x + py = 21$ and $px - 2y = 15$ has unique solution, then which of the following could be the value of p?
(A) 103 (B) 105
(C) 192 (D) 197
(a) Both (A) and (B)
(b) Both (C) and (D)
(c) (A), (B) and (D)
(d) All of (A), (B), (C) and (D)

10. If the system of equations $2x - 3y = 3$ and $-4x + qy = \frac{p}{2}$ is inconsistent, which of the following cannot be the value of p?
(a) −24 (b) −18
(c) −12 (d) −36

11. The semi-perimeter of a triangle exceeds each of its side by 5, 3, and 2, respectively. What is the perimeter of the triangle?
(a) 12 (b) 10
(c) 15 (d) 20

12. If (p, p) is the solution of system of equations $ax + by + (t - s) = 0$ and $bx + ay + (s - r) = 0$, $(a \neq b)$, then which of the following must be true?
(a) $2r = s + t$ (b) $2t = r + s$
(c) $2s = r + t$ (d) $r + s + t = 0$

13. If $173x + 197y = 149$ and $197x + 173y = 221$, then find (x, y).
(a) (3, −2) (b) (2, 1)
(c) (1, −2) (d) (2, −1)

14. Mallesh has some cows and some hens in his shed. The total number of legs is 92 and the total number of heads is 29. Find the number of cows in his shed.
(a) 12 (b) 14
(c) 17 (d) 19

15. Total cost of 14 pens and 21 books is ₹130 and the total cost of 6 pens and p books is ₹90. Which of the following cannot be the value of p?
(a) 8 (b) 9
(c) 10 (d) 11

16. If an ordered pair satisfying the equations $2x - 3y = 18$ and $4x - y = 16$ also satisfies the equation $5x - py - 23 = 0$, then find the value of p.
(a) 1 (b) 2
(c) −1 (d) −2

17. If we increase the length by 2 units and the breadth by 2 units, then the area of rectangle is increased by 54 square units. Find the perimeter of the rectangle (in units).
(a) 44 (b) 50
(c) 56 (d) 52

18. A mother said to her son, 'the sum of our present ages is twice my age 12 years ago and nine years hence, the

sum of our ages will be thrice my age 14 years ago'. What is her son's present age? (in years)

(a) 8 (b) 12
(c) 15 (d) 10

19. A told B, 'when I was as old as you are now, then your age was four years less than half of my present age'. If the sum of the present ages of A and B is 61 years, what is B's present age? (in years)

(a) 9 (b) 25
(c) 43 (d) 36

20. If the system of equations $4x - 5y = 6$ and $-12x + ay = b$ is inconsistent, which of the following cannot be the value of b?

(a) -16 (b) -18
(c) -20 (d) -22

Level 2: Review Your Concepts

21. What are the real values of x that satisfy the simultaneous inequations $6x + 9 < 3x + 5$ and $4x + 7 > 2x - 5$?

(a) $x \in \left(-6, -\frac{4}{3}\right)$ (b) $x \in \left(-5, -\frac{4}{3}\right)$
(c) $x \in \left(-6, -\frac{3}{3}\right)$ (d) $x \in \left(-7, -\frac{4}{3}\right)$

22. Find the range of the real values of x, if $|9 - x| < 2 - 3x$.

(a) $x \in \left(-, -\frac{3}{2}\right)$ (b) $x \in \left(-, -\frac{9}{2}\right)$
(c) $x \in \left(-, -\frac{5}{2}\right)$ (d) $x \in \left(-, -\frac{7}{2}\right)$

23. If $|x + 2| < 2$, then _____.

(a) $-4 < x < 0$ (b) $x < -6$ or $x > 0$
(c) $x < 0$ or $x > 3$ (d) $x < -3$ or $x > 3$

24. Dheeraj has twice as many sisters as he has brothers. If Deepa, Dheeraj's sister has the same number of brothers as she has sisters, then Deepa has how many brothers?

(a) 2 (b) 3
(c) 4 (d) 6

25. The total cost of six books, five pencils and seven sharpeners is ₹115 and that of eight books, ten pencils, and fourteen sharpeners is ₹190, then which of the following article's cost can be found uniquely?

(a) Book (b) Pencil
(c) Sharpener (d) None of these

26. The sum of the speeds of a boat in still water and the speed the current is 10 kmph. If the boat takes 40% of the time to travel downstream when compared to that upstream, then find the difference of the speeds of the boat when travelling upstream and down stream.

(a) 3 kmph (b) 6 kmph
(c) 4 kmph (d) 5 kmph

27. In a fraction, if the numerator is decreased by 1 and the denominator is increased by 1, then the fraction becomes $\frac{1}{2}$. Instead, if the numerator is increased by 1 and the denominator is decreased by 1, then the fraction becomes $\frac{4}{5}$. Find the numerator of the fraction.

(a) 5 (b) 6
(c) 7 (d) 8

28. Ram has 18 coins in the denominations of ₹1, ₹2 and ₹5. If their total value is ₹54 and the number of ₹2 coins are greater than that of ₹5 coins, then find the number of ₹1 coins with him.

(a) 2 (b) 3
(c) 4 (d) 1

29. If the ordered pair ($\sin\theta$, $\cos\theta$) satisfies the system of equations $mx + ny + a + b = a - b$ and $nx + my + 2b = 0$, then find the value of θ where $0 \le \theta \le 90°$. ($m \ne n$)

(a) 30° (b) 45°
(c) 50° (d) 60°

30. Swaroop can row 16 km downstream and 8 km upstream in 6 hours. He can row 6 km upstream and 24 km downstream in 6 hours. Find the speed of Swaroop in still water.

(a) 6 kmph (b) 8 kmph
(c) 3 kmph (d) 5 kmph

31. A two-digit number is formed by either subtracting 17 from nine times the sum of the digits or by adding 21 to 13 times the difference of the digits. Find the number.

(a) 37 (b) 73
(c) 71 (d) 72

32. Swathi starts her job with certain monthly salary and earns a fixed increment every year. If her salary was ₹22500 per month after 6 years of service and ₹30000

per month after 11 years of service. Find her salary after 8 years of service (in ₹).

(a) 24000 (b) 25500
(c) 26000 (d) 24500

33. A three digit number *abc* is 459 more than the sum of its digits. What is the sum of the 2-digit number *ab* and the 1-digit number *a*?

(a) 71 (b) 61
(c) 51 (d) 41

34. The following sentences are the steps involved in solving the inequation $|5x + 4| > 5x - 4$. Arrange in sequential order from first to last.

(A) $10x < 0$

(B) $5x + 4 < -5x + 4$ or $5x + 4 > 5x - 4$

(C) $x < 0$

(D) $5x + 4 < -5x + 4$

(a) BDAC (b) DBAC
(c) ABDC (d) BADC

Level 3: Assess Your Concepts

35. Find the solution set of the inequation $|x - 2| \leq 3$.

(a) $x \in [-5, 1]$ (b) $x \in [-1, 5]$
(c) $x \in (-5, 1)$ (d) $x \in (-1, 5)$

36. Find the number of integer values of x satisfying the inequation $|x + 3| \leq 5$.

(a) 9 (b) 10
(c) 11 (d) 12

37. Find the solution set of the inequation $|x + 2| < -3$.

(a) 0 (b) 1
(c) 2 (d) No solution

38. Find the solution set of the inequation $|x - 1| > -2$.

(a) $x \in (-, -3)$ (b) $x \in (-, -1)$
(c) $x \in (-,)$ (d) No solution

39. An examination consists of 100 questions. Two marks are awarded for every correct option. If one mark is deducted for every wrong option and half mark is deducted for every question left, then a person scores 135. Instead, if half mark is deducted for every wrong option and one mark is deducted for every question left, then the person scores 133. Find the number of questions left unattempted by the person.

(a) 14 (b) 16
(c) 10 (d) 12

40. Ramu had 13 notes in the denominations of ₹10, ₹50 and ₹100. The total value of the notes with him was ₹830. He had more of ₹100 notes than that of ₹50 notes with him. Find the number of ₹10 notes with him.

(a) 4 (b) 3
(c) 2 (d) 5

41. A, B, C, and D share a certain amount amongst themselves. B sees that the other three get 3 times what he himself gets. C sees that the other three get 4 times what he gets, while D sees that the other three get 5 times what he gets. If the sum of the largest and smallest shares is 99, what is the sum of the other two shares?

(a) 99 (b) 81
(c) 64 (d) 54

42. If $3|x| + 5|y| = 8$ and $7|x| - 3|y| = 48$, then find the value of $x + y$.

(a) 5 (b) –4
(c) 4 (d) The value does not exist

43. A father's present age is 6 times his son's present age. Thirty years hence the father's age will be ten years less than twice the son's age. After how many years will the son's age be half of the father's present age?

(a) 20 (b) 30
(c) 10 (d) 15

44. Ramesh had a total of 30 coins in his purse of denominations ₹5 and ₹2. If the total amount with him is ₹120, then find the number of ₹5 coins.

(a) 20 (b) 10
(c) 4 (d) 12

45. Mukesh has some goats and hens in his shed. Upon counting, Mukesh found that the total number of legs is 112 and the total number of heads is 40. Find the number of hens in his shed.

(a) 18 (b) 20
(c) 22 (d) 24

46. If the length and breadth of a room are increased by 1 m each, its area would increase by 31 m^2. If the length is increased by 1 m and breadth is decreased by 1 m, the area would decrease by 9 m^2. Find the area of the floor of the room, in m^2.

(a) 200 (b) 209
(c) 250 (d) 199

47. A hybrid mango tree, whose life span is 10 years, starts giving fruits from the first year onwards. In the nth year it produces $11n$ raw mangoes. But during the first half of the tree's life, every year, a certain number, which is constant, fail to ripen into fruits. During the second half of the tree's life, every year,the number of raw fruits that fail to ripen is half the corresponding number in the first half of the tree's life. In the fourth year of the tree's life, it produces 36 ripe mangoes. How many mangoes ripen during the 9th year of the tree's life?

(a) 100 (b) 96
(c) 95 (d) 86

48. Sridevi purchased cakes of two varieties of soap, Lux and Dove—spending a total ₹360. If each Lux costs ₹30 and each Dove costs ₹40, then in how many different combinations could she have purchased the cakes?

(a) 3 (b) 4
(c) 5 (d) 2

49. Venu has as many sisters as he has brothers. If Karuna, Venu's sister has thrice as many brothers as she has sisters, then Venu has how many sisters?

(a) 1 (b) 2
(c) 3 (d) 4

50. The cost of two pencils, five erasers and eight sharpeners is ₹47. The cost of three pencils, three erasers and seven sharpeners is ₹42. Find the cost of twelve pencils, three erasers and eighteen sharpeners. (in ₹)

(a) 37 (b) 92
(c) 138 (d) 111

51. Total cost of 15 erasers and 25 pencils is ₹185 and the total cost of 9 erasers and x pencils is ₹106. Which of the following cannot be the value of x?

(a) 12 (b) 10
(c) 13 (d) 15

52. In a fraction, if the numerator is decreased by 1 and the denominator is increased by 1, then the resulting fraction is $\frac{1}{4}$. Instead, if the numerator is increased by 1 and the denominator is decreased by 1, then the resulting fraction is $\frac{2}{3}$. Find the difference of the numerator and the denominator of the fraction.

(a) 2 (b) 3
(c) 4 (d) 5

53. A two-digit number is such that, it exceeds the sum of the number formed by reversing the digits and sum of the digits by 4. Also, the original number exceeds the reversed number by 18. Find the product of the digits.

(a) 48 (b) 36
(c) 42 (d) 56

54. Bhanu has a total of 40 coins of denominations 30 paise and 10 paise. The total amount with him is ₹9. Find the number of 10 paise coins with him.

(a) 25 (b) 35
(c) 15 (d) 20

55. A father's present age is seven years less than 30 times of what his son's age was 20 years ago. Also, the father's present age is 31 years more than his son's present age. Find the sum of their present ages, in years.

(a) 75 (b) 74
(c) 73 (d) 72

56. A and B, have some coins. If A gives 100 coins to B, then B will have twice the number of coins left with A. Instead, if B gives 40 coins to A, then A will have thrice the number of coins left with B. How many more coins does A have than B?

(a) 64 (b) 88
(c) 75 (d) 96

57. Snehal can row 28 km downstream and 12 km upstream in 5 hours. He can row 21 km downstream and 10 km upstream in 4 hours. Find the speed of Snehal in still water.

(a) 9 kmph (b) 8 kmph
(c) 6 kmph (d) 5 kmph

58. The ratio of monthly incomes of Mr X and Mr Y is 3 : 4 and the ratio of their monthly expenditures is 5 : 7. If the ratio of their monthly savings is 3 : 2 and Mr X saves ₹500 more than Mr Y per month, then find the monthly income of Mr Y.

(a) ₹35000 (b) ₹32000
(c) ₹26000 (d) ₹22000

59. A two-digit number is seven times the sum of its digits. The number formed by reversing the digits is 6 more than half of the original number. Find the difference of the digits of the given number.

(a) 2 (b) 3
(c) 4 (d) 5

60. Sanjana travels 660 km, partly by train and partly by car. If she covers 300 km by train and the rest by car, it takes 13.5 hours. But, if she travels 360 km by train

and the rest by car, she takes 30 minutes longer. Find the time taken by Sanjana if she travels 660 km by car. (in hours)

(a) 13 (b) 14
(c) 12 (d) 11

61. In a test of 50 questions, each correct answer fetches two marks and each wrong answer fetches $-\frac{1}{2}$ marks. A candidate attempted all the questions and scored 40 mark. How many questions did he attempt correctly?

(a) 24 (b) 26
(c) 22 (d) 20

62. The average weight of the students of a class is 60 kg. If eight new students of average weight 64 kg join the class, the average weight of the entire class becomes 62 kg. How many students were there in the class initially?

(a) 12 (b) 10
(c) 8 (d) 14

63. A shopkeeper sold a certain number of toys. The number of toys as well as the price of each toy (in ₹) was a two-digit number. By mistake, he reversed the digits of both the number of toys he sold and the price of each toy. As a result, he found that his stock account at the end of the day showed 81 items more than it was. Find the actual number of toys sold.

(a) 68 (b) 95
(c) 81 (d) 90

AT

PRACTICE QUESTIONS JEE SPECIAL WING

Multiple-Answer Type Questions

Directions for questions 1 to 5:
Each question has FOUR options (a), (b), (c), and (d). ONE OR MORE THAN ONE of these four option(s) is/are the correct answer(s).

1. Which of the following satisfies $x^2 - 3x - 180 \geq 0$?
   (a) $(-\infty, -13]$ (b) $(-\infty, 15]$
   (c) $(-12, \infty]$ (d) $[16, \infty)$

2. Which of the following satisfies $|3x - 8| \leq 10$?
   (a) $[-1, 6]$ (b) $[0, 5]$
   (c) $[1, 4]$ (d) $[3, 6]$

3. Which of the following satisfies $\frac{x^2 + x - 8}{x - 3} < x + 3$?
   (a) $(-\infty, -1]$ (b) $(-15, -2]$
   (c) $(-12, 0]$ (d) $[1111, 9999)$

4. For which of the following values of p will $2x - py = 8$ and $(p - 5)x + 3y = 7$ have a unique solution?
   (a) 2 (b) 3
   (c) 5 (d) 7

5. Which of the following satisfies $591x + 788y = 1379$ and $603x + 804y = 1407$?
   (a) (1, 1) (b) (5, –2)
   (c) (–11, 10) (d) (101, –74)

Match The Column

Directions for questions 6 to 9:
Read the paragraph given below and answer the questions.

$P: 2x + 3y = 1$
$Q: 6x + 9y = 12$
$R: 14x + 21y = 28$
$S: 34x + 48y = 72$

Column A [Equation(s)]	Column B [Solution(s)]
6. Q and R	a. $\left(4, \frac{-4}{3}\right)$
7. P and Q	b. Infinite solutions
8. P	c. No common solution
9. R and S	d. $\left(\frac{-1}{2}, \frac{1}{3}\right)$
	e. $\left(\frac{1}{4}, \frac{1}{6}\right)$

Comprehension-Based Questions

Directions for questions 10 to 13:
Read the paragraph given below and answer the questions.

Swaroop is a fruit seller in Mumbai. He sells all kinds of fruits. He is very famous for making all the seasonal fruits available in his shop. The cost of 20 jujube fruits is ₹1, the cost of 1 jackfruit is ₹1, and the cost of 1 pear is ₹5. Kevin went to his shop and bought all the three varieties of fruits by spending ₹100. He counted the fruits after reaching home, surprisingly the total number of fruits was 100.

10. What is the total number of pears he received?
    (a) 19 (b) 17
    (c) 13 (d) 11

11. What is the difference between the number of jujube fruits and jackfruits he received?
    (a) 37 (b) 59
    (c) 73 (d) None of these

12. What is the amount spent on purchasing jackfruits?
(a) 19 (b) 5
(c) 1 (d) None of these

13. What is the difference between the amounts spent on purchasing jujube fruits and pears?
(a) ₹58 (b) ₹62
(c) ₹91 (d) None of these

Assertion and Reason Type Questions

Directions for questions 14 to 17:
Read the options given below and answer the questions.

In the light of the given statements, choose the most appropriate answer from the options given below.

(a) Both assertion (A) and reason (R) are true, and reason (R) is the correct explanation of assertion.
(b) Both assertion (A) and reason (R) are true, and reason (R) is not the correct explanation of assertion.
(c) Assertion (A) is true, but reason (R) is false.
(d) Assertion (A) is false, and reason (R) is true.

14. **Assertion:** $49x - 42y = 91$ and $63x - 54y = 117$ have infinite solutions.

Reason: For a pair of linear equations $a_1x + b_1y = c_1$ and $a_2x + b_2y = c_2$, if $\frac{a_1}{a_2} = \frac{b_1}{b_2} = \frac{c_1}{c_2}$, then the equations have infinite solutions.

15. **Assertion:** If $\frac{1}{x+2} > 0$, then $x > -2$.

Reason: If $|x - 2| \geq 0$, then x is any real number.

16. **Assertion:** The sum of a two-digit number and the number formed by reversing the digits of it can be 165.

Reason: The difference of a two-digit number and the number formed by reversing the digits of it can be 66.

17. **Assertion:** The sum of five times the age A and three times the age of is 117 years. Also, the sum of three times the age A and five times the age of is 115 years. The difference of their ages is 2 years.

Reason: The difference of the ages of two persons when they are alive, is always constant.

ANSWER KEYS

Crossword

Across

3. Linear 8. One 9. Inconsistent 10. Zero

Down

1. Simple 2. Transposition 4. Non-negative 5. Non-positive 6. Equation
7. Solving

Classroom Wing

Very Short Answer Type Questions

1. Set of natural numbers 2. 63 3. Null set 4. 5
5. zero 6. 6 7. Does not exist 8. Positive
9. Negative 10. 10 11. Cannot be determined 12. 3
13. 5 14. 4 15. False 16. True 17. (c)
18. (c) 19. (d) 20. (b)

Short Answer Type Questions

21. (i)-D; (ii)-B; (iii)-A; (iv)-B 22. 24 23. ₹15, ₹24 24. $\frac{4}{7}$
25. $x = \frac{1}{2}, y = \frac{1}{4}$ 26. Infinite solution 27. ₹72000, ₹1000 28. 966
29. Number of 25 paise coins is 8 and number of 50 paise coins is 27.
30. (A) $\frac{5}{13}$ (B) 7 31. $x = a^3$, $y = b^3$

Essay Type Questions

32. 56 years 33. 9 34. 3 35. 2 36. 80
37. (c)

Competition Wing

Level 1: Apply Your Concepts

1. Negative 2. Null set 3. (–2, 2) 4. Set of real numbers
5. (–1, 1) 6. (a) 7. (a) 8. (d) 9. (d)
10. (c) 11. (d) 12. (c) 13. (d) 14. (c)
15. (b) 16. (b) 17. (b) 18. (b) 19. (b)
20. (b)

Level 2: Review Your Concepts

21. (a) 22. (d) 23. (a) 24. (b) 25. (a)
26. (b) 27. (c) 28. (b) 29. (b) 30. (d)
31. (b) 32. (b) 33. (c) 34. (a)

Level 3: Assess Your Concepts

35. (b)	36. (c)	37. (d)	38. (c)	39. (a)
40. (b)	41. (b)	42. (d)	43. (c)	44. (a)
45. (d)	46. (b)	47. (c)	48. (d)	49. (b)
50. (d)	51. (d)	52. (c)	53. (a)	54. (c)
55. (a)	56. (b)	57. (a)	58. (d)	59. (c)
60. (d)	61. (b)	62. (c)	63. (d)	

JEE Special Wing

Multiple-Answer Type Questions

1. (a, d)	2. (b, c, d)	3. (a, b, d)	4. (c, d)	5. (a, b, c, d)

Match The Column

6. (b)	7. (c)	8. (e)	9. (a)

Comprehension-Based Questions

10. (a)	11. (d)	12. (c)	13. (c)

Assertion and Reason Type Questions

14. (a)	15. (b)	16. (c)	17. (d)

Hints and Explanations

Classroom Wing

Very Short Answer Type Questions

1. $x + 2 \geq 3,\ x \in W$
$\Rightarrow x \geq 1,\ x \in W$
$\therefore$ the solutions set is the set of natural numbers

2. Given $x:y = 2:7$
$x = 2k,\ y = 7k$
$x + y = 81$ (Given)
$2k + 7k = 81$
$9k = 81$
$k = 9$
$y = 7k = 7 \times 9 = 63$

3. Given that,
$|x| < 0$
but $|x| \geq 0$
$\therefore$ The solution set is null set.

4. $99x + 101y = 400$
$101x + 99y = 600$
Adding both equations
$200x + 200y = 1000$
$200(x + y) = 1000$
$x + y = 5$

5. $5x + 4y + 6 = 0$
$10x + 8y = 12$
$a_1 = 5,\ a_2 = 10,\ c_1 = -6$
$b_1 = 4,\ b_2 = 8,\ c_2 = 12$
$$\frac{a_1}{a_2} = \frac{b_1}{b_2} \neq \frac{c_1}{c_2}$$
No solution

6. $\dfrac{a}{b} = \dfrac{7}{3}\quad 3a = 7b,\ a = \dfrac{7b}{3}$
$a + b = 20$
$$\frac{7b}{3} + b = 20$$
$$\frac{10b}{3} = 20$$
$b = 3 \times 2$
$b = 6$

7. $$\frac{1}{x} + \frac{1}{y} = k$$
$$\frac{1}{x} - \frac{1}{y} = k$$
$$\frac{2}{x} = 2k$$
$$x = \frac{1}{k}$$
$$k + \frac{1}{y} = k$$
$y = \dfrac{1}{0}$; does not exist.

8. $p + q = k$
$p - q = n$
$(-)\ (+)\ (-)$
$2q = k - n$
$$q = \frac{k-n}{2}$$
Since, $k > n$, it is positive.

9. $a + b = x$
$a - b = y$
$(-)\ (+)\ (-)$
$2b = x - y$
$$b = \frac{x-y}{2}$$
Since $x < y$, b is negative.

10. $3a + 2b + 4c = 26$ (i)
$6b + 4a + 2c = 48$ (ii)
Divide (ii) by 2
$3b + 2a + c = 24$
Add it with (i)
$5a + 5b + 5c = 50$
$5(a + b + c) = 50$
$a + b + c = 10$

11. Let the present age of X be a year the present age of Y be b years

$(a-12)+(b-12)=48$

$a+b=48+24$

$a+b=72$ (1)

$(a+12)+(b+12)=96$

$a+b=96-24$

$a+b=72$ (2)

Since, both the equation are same, it cannot be determined.

12. $2x+3y=12$

$$y=\frac{12-2x}{3}$$

To y be an integer, $12-2x$ should be a multiple of 3.

A little observation tells that n must be 0, 3, 4, beyond this it gives negative result which is not accepted in question.

13. $2x+3y=5$ (×2)

$3x+2y=10$ (×3)

$4x+6y=10$

$9x+6y=30$

(–) (–) (–)

$-5x=-20$

$x=4$

$2(4)+3y=5$

$3y=5-8$

$3y=-3$

$y=-1$

$x-y=4-(-1)$

$=5$

14. $a+b=p$

$ab=p$

$a+b=ab$

This is possible when

$a=2$

$b=2$

$a\times b=4=p$

15. Let cost of 1 chair be x.
Let cost of 1 table by y.
According to question,

$3x+2y=1200$ (1)

$12x+8y=4800$ (2)

Dividing eq. (2) by 4

$3x+2y=1200$

Cannot be determined exact values.

16. Let cost of 1 apple be x.
Let cost of 1 mango by y.

$2x+3y=22$

Putting value given in question

$2(5)+3(4)=22$

i.e., true.

17. $2x+3ky=4$ (1)

$6x+27y=12$ (2)

Given Eqs (1) and (2) have infinite common solutions.

$$\frac{2}{6}=\frac{3k}{27}=\frac{4}{12}\Rightarrow\frac{k}{9}=\frac{1}{3}\Rightarrow k=3$$

Hence, the correct option is (c)

18. $|x+4|<2\Rightarrow -2<x+4<2$

$\Rightarrow -2-4<x<2-4\Rightarrow -6<x<-2$

x can take the values –3, –4, and –5.

∴ The number of integer values of x is 3.

Hence, the correct option is (c).

19. $5x-2ky=10$ (1)

$6x+8y=21$ (2)

Given Eqs (1) and (2) have no common solution.

$$\frac{5}{6}=-\frac{2k}{8}\Rightarrow k=-\frac{20}{6}\Rightarrow k=-\frac{10}{3}$$

Hence, the correct option is (d).

20. $|x-1|\le 5\Rightarrow -5\le x-1\le 5$

$\Rightarrow -4\le x\le 6$

∴ x can take 11 integer values.

Hence, the correct option is (b).

Short Answer Type Questions

21. (i) $\frac{a_1}{a_2}=\frac{b_1}{b_2}\Leftrightarrow$ Can't say anything about the number of solutions.

(ii) $\frac{a_1}{a_2}\neq\frac{b_1}{b_2}\Leftrightarrow$ Unique solution

(iii) $\frac{a_1}{a_2}=\frac{b_1}{b_2}=\frac{c_1}{c_2}\Leftrightarrow$ Infinite solutions

(iv) $\frac{a_1}{a_2} = \frac{b_1}{b_2} \neq \frac{c_1}{c_2} \Leftrightarrow$ Unique solution.

22. Given $4x - 5y = 6$ and $16x - 20y = k$

$\frac{4}{16} = \frac{5}{-20} = \frac{6}{k}$

$\frac{1}{4} = \frac{1}{4} = \frac{6}{k}$

$\frac{6}{k} = \frac{1}{4}$

$k = 24$

23. Let cost of gallery seat $= x$.
Let cost of 1 balcony seat $= y$.

$6x + 3y = 162$ (1)

$4x + 5y = 180$ (2)

Dividing eq. (1) by 3.

$2x + y = 54 \times 5$

$10x + 5y = 270$

$4x + 5y = 180$

(–) (–) (–)

$6x = 90$

$x = 15$

$2x + y = 54$

$30 + y = 54$

$y = 24$

24. Let numerator be x
Let denominator be y

$\frac{x+2}{y-4} = 2$

$x + 2 = 2y - 8$

$\Rightarrow x - 2y = -10$ (1)

$\frac{x-1}{y+2} = \frac{1}{3}$

$\Rightarrow 3x - 3 = y + 2$

$\Rightarrow 3x - y = 5$ (×2)

$6x - 2y = 10$

$x - 2y = -10$

(–) (+) (+)

$5x = 20$

$x = 4$

$3x - y = 5$

$3(4) - y = 5$

$12 - y = 5$

$y = 7$

ratio $= \frac{x}{y} = \frac{4}{7}$

25. Let $\frac{1}{x} = v$

$\frac{1}{y} = w$

$\frac{1}{z} = r$

$v + w = 6$

$w + r = 7; w = 7 - r$

$r + v = 5$

$v + 7 - r = 6$

$v - r = -1$

$v + r = 5$

$2v = 4$

$v = 2$

$\because w = 6 - v$

$\because w = 4$

$\because w = 7 - r$

$4 = 7 - r$

$\Rightarrow r = 3$

$\Rightarrow x = \frac{1}{2}$

$y = \frac{1}{4}$

$z = \frac{1}{3}$

26. Given $2x + 3y + 4 = 0$ and $4x + 6y + 8 = 0$

$\frac{2}{4} = \frac{3}{6} = \frac{4}{8}$

$\frac{1}{2} = \frac{1}{2} = \frac{1}{2}$

$\therefore$ The pair of equations has infinite solutions.

27. Let initial monthly salary be Rs x and increment be y.
Salary of first month $= 6x$
Salary of next 1 year $= 12\ (x + y)$
Salary of next 1 year $= 12(x + 2y)$

Salary of next 1 year [upto $5\frac{1}{2}$] = $12(x+5y)$

Salary of next 6 months = $6(x+6y)$

Monthly salary of last month = $x+6y$

$x+6y = 78000$

Similarly salary at end of 12 years = $x+12y$

$x+12y = 84000$

$x+6y = 78000$

$y = 1000$

Which gives $x = 72000$

28. Let the number be x

$\frac{6}{7}x = \frac{7}{6}x - 299$

$\frac{7}{6}x - \frac{6}{7}x = 299$

$\frac{49x - 36x}{42} = 299$

$\frac{13x}{42} = 299$

$x = \frac{42 \times 299}{13}$

$x = 966$

29. Let 25 p coins be x and 50 p coins be y.

$x + y = 35$

$\frac{25x}{100} + \frac{50y}{100} = 15.50$

$\frac{x}{4} + \frac{y}{2} = 15.50$

$\frac{x+2y}{4} = 15.50$

$x + 2y = 62$

$x + y = 35$

(−) (−) (−)

$y = 27$

$x = 8$

30. (A) for no solution

$\frac{a_1}{a_2} = \frac{b_1}{b_2} \neq \frac{c_1}{c_2}$

$\frac{2}{3k-1} = \frac{3}{1-2k}$

$2 - 4k = 9k - 3$

$2 + 3 = 9k + 4k$

$k = \frac{5}{13}$

(B) $3x + y - 3z = 11$

$\Rightarrow 3(x - z) + y = 11$ (1)

$2(x - z) + 5y = 29$ (2)

Let $x - z = a$

$\Rightarrow 3a + y = 11$ (3)

$2a + 5y = 29$ (4)

(3) × 5 − (4)

$\Rightarrow 13a = 26$

$\Rightarrow a = 2$

$y = 5$

$a = x - z$

$\Rightarrow y + x - z = 5 + 2 = 7$

31. $\frac{x}{a} + \frac{y}{b} = a^2 + b^2$

$\frac{ax}{a^2} + \frac{by}{b^2} = a^2 + b^2$ (1)

$\frac{x}{a^2} + \frac{y}{b^2} = a + b$ (× b)

$\frac{bx}{a^2} + \frac{by}{b^2} = ab + b^2$ (2)

Subtracting (1) and (2),

$\frac{ax}{a^2} + \frac{by}{b^2} = a^2 + b^2$

$\frac{bx}{a^2} + \frac{by}{b^2} = ab + b^2$

(−) (−) (−)

$\frac{ax}{a^2} - \frac{bx}{a^2} = a^2 - ab$

$ax - bx = a^4 - a^3b$

$x(a - b) = a^3(a - b)$

$x = a^3$

and

$y = b^3$

Essay Type Questions

32. Let the present age of the son be x years.

∴ Father's present age = $3x$ years.

Given $3x - 7 = 5(x - 7)$

$\Rightarrow 3x - 7 = 5x - 35 \Rightarrow 2x = 28 \Rightarrow x = 14$

$\therefore$ The sum of their present ages = $4x$.

= 4 (14) = 56 years

33. Let the two-digit number be $10a + b$.

Given $10a + b = a + b + 9$

$\Rightarrow 9a = 9 \Rightarrow a = 1$

$\therefore$ The required numbers are 10, 11, 12, 13, …, 19.

Difference between digits are 1, 0, 1, 2, 3, 4, 5, 6, 7, 8.

$\therefore$ The number of different values of k is 9.

34. Let F be the father's age and S be the son's age

Given $F + 6 = 3(S + 6)$ (1)

$F - 3 = p(S - 3)$ (2)

(1) $\Rightarrow F = 3S + 12$ (3)

(2) $\Rightarrow F = pS - 3p + 3$ (4)

(3) = (4) $\Rightarrow 3S + 12 = 4S - 9$

$$\frac{1}{1} \neq \frac{3}{p}$$

$\Rightarrow p \neq 3$

35. Let cost of vanilla be x.

Cost of strawberry be y.

$25x + 40y = 330$

$5x + 8y = 66$

Now, putting $y = 0, 1, 2, 3...$

We can see that at $y = 2, x = 10$

$y = 7, x = 2$

These are two combinations only.

36. Before doubling, the amounts with Bhavan, Chetan and Dinesh, each of them must have had $\frac{80}{2}$ = ₹ 40.

$\therefore$ Amar must have then had ₹80 + ₹120 i.e. ₹200. Similarly, we can work out the amounts with each of them before the other doubled the amounts. The results are summarized below.

	Amar	Bhavan	Chetan	Dinesh
Finally	80	80	80	80
Before Amar doubles	200	40	40	40
Before Bhavan doubles	100	180	20	20
Before Chetan doubles	50	90	170	10
Before Dinesh doubles	25	45	85	165

37. From statement I, we have man's age = wife's age + 2 years

But to know whether man's age = wife's age + son's age, we should know the ages of at least two of them.

$\therefore$ Statement I alone is not sufficient.

From statement II, we have

son's present age = 12 years

wife's present age = 42 years

But to know whether man's age = wife's age + son's age or not, we should know the relationship between the ages of the man and wife or man and the son.

$\therefore$ Statement II alone is not sufficient.

Using both the statements we have

man's age = 42 + 2 = 44 years

$\therefore$ Clearly, man's age < wife's age + son's age.

Choice (c)

Competition Wing

Level 1: Apply Your Concepts

1. From given equations we have $2b = x - y$

$\Rightarrow b = \dfrac{x-y}{2} < 0.$

Since $x < y$, b is negative.

2. $x + 1 < 2, x \in N$

$\Rightarrow x < 1, x \in N$

$\therefore$ The solution set is null set.

3. $|x| < 2$ and by the definition of modulus, $-2 < x < 2$

4. $|x| > -5$ and by the definition of modulus, the solution set is the set of real numbers.

5. $|x| < 1$ and by the definition of modulus, $-1 < x < 1$

6. Given $2x + 3y + 5 = 0$ and $4x + 6y - 10 = 0$

$\dfrac{2}{3} = \dfrac{3}{6} \neq \dfrac{5}{-10}$

$\Rightarrow \dfrac{1}{2} = \dfrac{1}{2} \neq \dfrac{-1}{2}$

$\therefore$ The pair of equations has no solution.

Hence, the correct option is (a).

7. Using the condition of no solution, the correct option is (a).

8. Condition for infinite solutions is, $\dfrac{a_1}{a_2} = \dfrac{b_1}{b_2} = \dfrac{c_1}{c_2}$.

9. For unique solution, $\dfrac{a_1}{a_2} \neq \dfrac{b_1}{b_2}$.

10. If two equations $a_1x + b_1y + c_1 = 0$ and $a_2x + b_2y + c_2 = 0$ are inconsistent, then $\dfrac{a_1}{a_2} = \dfrac{b_1}{b_2} \neq \dfrac{c_1}{c_2}$.

11. (i) Semi perimeter $(s) = \dfrac{a+b+c}{2}$.

(ii) $a + 5 = s$; $b + 3 = s$; $c + 2 = s$.

12. If $x = y$, then $a_1 = a_2$, $b_1 = b_2$ and $c_1 = c_2$.

13. Add two equations.

14. Each cow has 4 legs and each hen has 2 legs.

15. Frame the linear equation and write $\dfrac{a_1}{a_2} \neq \dfrac{b_1}{b_2}$.

16. Solve the first two equations and substitute (x, y) in the third equation.

17. Frame linear equation by taking length and breadth as l and b respectively.

18. Frame linear equations and solve.

19. (i) Let the present ages of A and B be x years, and y years respectively.

(ii) $y - (x - y) = \dfrac{x}{2} - 4$.

(iii) $x + y = 61$.

20. If the system of equations $a_1x + b_1y + c_1$, $a_2x + b_2y + c_2 = 0$ is inconsistent, $\dfrac{a_1}{a_2} = \dfrac{b_1}{b_2} + \dfrac{c_1}{c_2}$.

Level 2: Review Your Concepts

21. Given,

$6x + 9 < 3x + 5$	:	$4x + 7 > 2x - 5$
$6x - 3x < 5 - 9$	:	$4x - 2x > -5 - 7$
$3x < -4$	:	$2x > -12$
$\Rightarrow x < -4/3$ ... (1)	:	$x > -6$ ... (2)

$\therefore$ From (1) and (2), we have $x \in \left(-6, -\dfrac{4}{3}\right)$

22. Given, $|9 - x| < 2 - 3x$

Let $x < 9$

Then, $9 - x < 2 - 3x \Rightarrow 2x < -7$

$\Rightarrow x < -7/2$ which agrees with $x < 9$

Let $x > 9$

Then, $-(9 - x) < 2 - 3x$

$-9 + x < 2 - 3x$

$4x < 11$

$x < 11/4$ which does not agree with $x > 9$.

$\therefore$ The required solution set $\left(-\infty, -\dfrac{7}{2}\right)$

23. $|x + 2| < 2$

$\Rightarrow -2 < x + 2 < 2$

$\Rightarrow -4 < x < 0$

24. (i) Let the number of sons and daughters that Dheeraj's parents have be b and d, respectively.

(ii) Form the equations and solve them.

25. Let the cost of each book and each pencil and each sharpener be b, p, and s, respectively. Then frame the equations.

27. Let the fraction be $\dfrac{n}{a}$ and frame the linear equations.

28. (i) Let the number of ₹1, ₹2 and ₹5 coins be x, y and z, respectively.

(ii) From the information given, obtain an equation in y and z and proceed.

29. If (p, q) is a solution of $ax + by + c = 0$ and $bx + ay + c = 0$, then $p = q$.

31. (i) $10x + y = 9(x + y) - 17$.
(ii) $10x + y = 13(x - y) + 21$.
(iii) Solve the above equations.

32. Frame linear equations and solve.

33. (i) Let the three digit number be $100x + 10y + z$.
(ii) Frame the equations and solve them.

34. BDAC are in sequential order from first to last.

Level 3: Assess Your Concepts

35. Given, $|x - 2| \leq 3$
$\Rightarrow -3 \leq x - 2 \leq 3$ (by the definition of modulus)
$\Rightarrow -3 + 2 \leq x \leq 3 + 2$
$\Rightarrow -1 \leq x \leq 5$
$\therefore$ The required solution set is $[-1, 5]$.

36. Given, $|x + 3| \leq 5$
$\Rightarrow -5 \leq x + 3 \leq 5$
$\Rightarrow -5 - 3 \leq x \leq 5 - 3$
$\Rightarrow -8 \leq x \leq 2$
$\therefore$ The integers which satisfy the given inequation are $-8, -7, -6, -5, -4, -3, -2, -1, 0, 1$ and 2.
Hence, the required number of integers is 11.

37. For every real value of x, $|x + 2| \geq 0$
So, no real value of x satisfies the inequation $|x+2| < -3$
$\therefore$ There is no solution for the given inequation.

38. For every real value of x, $|x - 1| > -2$
By the definition of modulus, $|x - 1|$ is always non-negative.
$\therefore$ The required solution set is $(-\infty, \infty)$.

39. (i) $x + y + z = 100$, $2x - y - \frac{1}{2}z = 135$;

$2x - \frac{y}{2} - z = 133$

where x, y, and z are the number of correct answers, wrong answers and unattempted questions, respectively.
(ii) Solve the above equations.

41. Let the total amount be $4B$ or $5C$ or $6D$ and $B + D = 99$.

42. (i) Let $|x| = a$ and $|y| = b$ and solve linear equations which are in a and b.
(ii) Let $|x| = k_1$ and $|y| = k_2$ and solve them.
(iii) $|x| = \pm x$, $|y| = \pm y$.

43. Let the present ages of father and son be f and s, respectively.
Then, $f = 6s$ (1)
The second condition gives,
$f + 30 = 2(s + 30) - 10 \Rightarrow f = 2s + 20$
$\therefore 6s - 2s = 20$ ($\because$ from Eq. (1))
$\Rightarrow s = 5$ and $f = 30$
Half the father's present age is 15. After 10 years, the son's age will be 15.

44. Let the number of 5-rupee coins be x.
Let the number of 2-rupee coins be y.
$\therefore x + y = 30$ (1)
Also $5x + 2y = 120$ (2)
Multiplying Eq. (1) by 2, we have,
$2x + 2y = 60$ (3)
subtracting Eq. (3) from Eq. (2),
$3x = 60$
$x = 20$

45. Let the number of goats and hens, be x and y, respectively.
Given, $4x + 2y = 112$ (1)
$x + y = 40$ (2)
Solving Eqs. (1) and (2), we get,
$x = 16$ and $y = 24$
$\therefore$ Number of hens = 24

46. Let the length of the room = 1 m
Breadth of the room = b m
Area of the room = lb m^2.
The length and breadth are increased by 1 m each and the area increases by 31 m^2
$(l + 1)(b + 1) = lb + 31$
$\Rightarrow lb + l + b + 1 = lb + 31$
$\Rightarrow l + b = 30$ (1)
If length increased by 1 m and breadth decreased by 1 m, then the area decreases by 9 m^2, i.e.,
$(l + 1)(b - 1) = lb - 9$
$\Rightarrow lb - l + b - 1 = lb - 9$
$\Rightarrow l - b = 8$ (2)
On solving Eq. (1) and Eq. (2), we get,
$l = 19$, $b = 11$
$\Rightarrow$ Area of the floor = lb = 19 (11)
= 209 m^2

47. Every year in the first half of the tree's life, the number of mangoes that cannot become ripen fruit is y (say).
The number of fruits produced in the xth year $= 11x - y$
Number of fruits produced in 4th year = 36
$\Rightarrow 11(4) - y = 36 \Rightarrow y = 8$
Number of fruits produced in xth year of the second half-life $= 11x - \frac{y}{2}$
Number of fruits produced in the 9th year
$= 11(9) - \frac{8}{2} = 99 - 4 = 95.$

48. Let the number of Lux cakes be x and Dove cakes be y.
Given $30x + 40y = 360$
$\Rightarrow 3x + 4y = 36$
$\Rightarrow x = \frac{36 - 4y}{3}$
$\Rightarrow x = 12 - \frac{4y}{3}$
As x and y are positive integers, $y = 3$ or 6
$\Rightarrow x = 8, 1$
There are two combinations.

49.

No. of Girls	No. of Boys
x	$(x + 1)$ (including Venu)
$(x - 1)$ (without Karuna)	$3(x - 1)$ (including Venu)

$\Rightarrow 3(x - 1) = x + 1$
$\Rightarrow 2x = 4 \Rightarrow x = 2.$

50. Let the cost of each pencils be p.
Let the cost of each sharpner be s.
Let the cost of each eraser be e.
Then, $2p + 5e + 8s = 47$ (1)
$3p + 3e + 7s = 42$ (2)
Multiply Eq. (2) by 2 and subtracting Eq. (1) from Eq. (2), we have,
$4p + e + 6s = 37$ (3)
Multiply Eq. (3) by 3, we get,
$12p + 3e + 18s = 111.$

51. Let the cost of each eraser and each pencil be ₹e and ₹p, respectively.
$\Rightarrow 15e + 25p = 185$ and $9e + xp = 106$
As the cost of these articles is unique,
$\frac{15}{9} \neq \frac{25}{x}$
$\Rightarrow x \neq 15.$

52. Let the fraction be $\frac{x}{y}$.
Case 1:
$\frac{x-1}{x+1} = \frac{1}{4} \Rightarrow 4x - 4 = y + 1$
$\Rightarrow 4x - y = 5$ (1)
Case 2:
$\frac{x+1}{y-1} = \frac{2}{3}$
$\Rightarrow 3x + 3 = 2y - 2$
$\Rightarrow 3x - 2y + 5 = 0$ (2)
Solving Eqs. (1) and (2), we get $x = 3$ and $y = 7$.
$\therefore$ The required difference is 4.

53. Let x, y be the tens and units digits respectively.
Sum of the digits $= x + y$
Value of the number $= 10x + y$
$10x + y = x + y + 4 + 10y + x$
$8x - 10y = 4$ or $4x - 5y = 2$ (1)
Also given that,
$10x + y = 10y + x + 18$
$x - y = 2$ (2)
Multiply Eq. (2) by 4, we have,
$4x - 4y = 8$ (3)
Subtract Eq. (1) from Eq. (3), we get,
$y = 6$
Substitute $y = 6$ in Eq. (2), we have $x = 8$.
The product of the digits = 48.

54. Let the total number of 30 paise coins with him $= x$.
Let the total number of 10 paise coins with him $= y$.
Then $x + y = 40$
Also, $30x + 10y = 900$
Solving for x and y we have $y = 15$.

55. Let the present age of father be f years.
Let son's present age be s years.
Then $f = 30(s - 20) - 7$ (1)
$f = s + 31$ (2)
$s + 31 = 30s - 600 - 7$
$638 = 29s$
$22 = s$
$\Rightarrow f = 53$
Sum of their ages = 75 years.

56. Let A and B have x and y coins, respectively.
Case 1:
If A gives 100 coins to B.
$y + 100 = 2(x - 100)$

$2x - y = 300$ (1)

Case 2:

If B gives 40 coins to A

$x + 40 = 3(y - 40)$

$\Rightarrow x - 3y + 160 = 0$ (2)

Solving Eqs. (1) and (2), we get,

$x = 212$ and $y = 124$

$\therefore$ The required difference $= 212 - 124 = 88$.

57. Let Snehal's speed and the speed of the stream be x kmph and y kmph, respectively.

Given, $\frac{28}{x+y} + \frac{12}{x-y} = 5$ (1)

and, $\frac{21}{x+y} + \frac{10}{x-y} = 4$ (2)

Let $\frac{1}{x+y} = a$ and $\frac{1}{x-y} = b$, then

Eq. (1) $\Rightarrow 28a + 12b = 5$ (3)

and Eq. (2) $\Rightarrow 21a + 10b = 4$ (4)

Solving Eqs. (3) and (4), we get,

$a = \frac{1}{14}$ and $b = \frac{1}{4}$

$\Rightarrow x + y = 14$ and $x - y = 4$

$\Rightarrow x = 9$ and $y = 5$

$\therefore$ Snehal's speed in still water = 9 kmph

58. Let the monthly income of X and Y be $3x$, $4x$ and monthly expenditures be $5y$, $7y$

Savings of $X = 3x - 5y$

Savings of $Y = 4x - 7y$

Given, $\frac{3x - 5y}{4x - 7y} = \frac{3}{2}$ and

$(3x - 5y) - (4x - 7y) = 500$

$\Rightarrow 6x - 10y = 12x - 21y$

$\Rightarrow 6x - 11y = 0$ (1)

and $-x + 2y = 500$ (2)

Solving Eqs. (1) and (2), we get $y = 3000$ and $x = 5500$

$\therefore$ Monthly income of Mr Y = ₹$4x$ = ₹22000.

59. Let the two-digit number be $10x + y$

Given, $10x + y = 7(x + y)$

$\Rightarrow 3x = 6y \Rightarrow x = 2y$ (1)

Also, $10y + x = \frac{1}{2}(10x + y) + 6$

$\Rightarrow -8x + 19y = 12$

$\Rightarrow -16y + 19y = 12$ ($\because$ from Eq. (1))

$\Rightarrow y = 4$ and $x = 8$

$\therefore x - y = 4$.

60. Let the speed of the train and car be t kmph and c kmph, respectively.

$\therefore \frac{300}{t} + \frac{360}{c} = 13.5$ (1)

$\frac{360}{t} + \frac{300}{c} = 14$ (2)

On solving Eqs. (1) and (2), we get

$t = 40$ km/h and $c = 60$ kmph

The time taken by car to travel 660 km

$= \frac{660}{60} = 11$ hours.

61. Let the number of questions which are correct be c and the questions which are wrong be w.

$c + w = 50$ (1)

$2c - \frac{w}{2} = 40$

$4c - w = 80$ (2)

From Eqs. (1) and (2), we have $\Rightarrow 5c = 130 \Rightarrow c = 26$

62. Let there be n students in the class. The total weight of the students after the eight new students join the class.

$60n + 64(8) = 62(n + 8)$

$\Rightarrow 60n + 64(8) = 62n + 62(8)$

$\Rightarrow 62n - 60n = 64(8) - 62(8)$

$\Rightarrow 2n = 8(2) \Rightarrow n = 8$

$\therefore$ Initially, there were 8 students in the class.

63. Let the number of toys sold by the shopkeeper be 'ab'.

Let his initial stock be s.

Actual stock left = s – 'ab'.

Stock as shown on record = s – 'ba'

$s - ba = s - ab + 81$

Given that,

$10a + b - (10b + a) = 81$

$a - b = 9$

$\therefore a = 9$ and $b = 0$

$ab = 90$.

JEE Special Wing

Multiple-Answer Type Questions

1. $x^2 - 3x - 180 \geq 0.$

$\Rightarrow x^2 - 15x + 12x - 180 \geq 0$

$\Rightarrow x(x-15) + 12(x-15) \geq 0$

$\Rightarrow (x+12)(x-15) \geq 0$

$\Rightarrow x \leq -12$ (or) $x \geq 15$

$\Rightarrow x \in (-\infty, -12] \cup [15, \infty)$

Hence, choice (a and c) satisfy the given inequation.

2. $|3x - 8| \leq 10$

$\Rightarrow -10 \leq 3x - 8 \leq 10$

$\Rightarrow -10 + 8 \leq 3x - 8 + 8 \leq 10 + 8$

$\Rightarrow -2 \leq 3x \leq 18$

$\Rightarrow -\frac{2}{3} \leq \frac{3x}{3} \leq \frac{18}{3}$

$\Rightarrow -\frac{2}{3} \leq x \leq 6$

$\Rightarrow x \in \left[-\frac{2}{3}, 6\right]$

Hence, choice (b, c, d) satisfy the given inequation.

3. $\frac{x^2 + x - 8}{x - 3} > x + 3$

$\Rightarrow \frac{x^2 + x - 8}{x - 3} - (x+3) > 0$

$\Rightarrow \frac{x^2 + x - 8 - (x^2 - 3^2)}{x - 3} > 0$

$\Rightarrow \frac{x^2 + x - 8 - x^2 + 9}{x - 3} > 0$

$\Rightarrow \frac{x+1}{x-3} > 0$

$\Rightarrow x < -1 (\text{or}) x > 3$

$\Rightarrow x \in (-\infty, -1] \cup [3, \infty)$

That is $\Rightarrow x \notin (-1, 3)$

Hence, choice (a, b, d) satisfy the given inequation.

4. Given that $2x - py = 8$ and $(p-5)x + 3y = 7$ have a unique solution.

$\Rightarrow \frac{a_1}{a_2} = \frac{b_1}{b_2}$

$\Rightarrow \frac{2}{p-5} \neq \frac{-p}{3}$

$\Rightarrow -p(p-5) \neq 6$

$\Rightarrow -p^2 + 5p - 6 \neq 0$

$\Rightarrow p^2 - 5p + 6 \neq 0$

$\Rightarrow p^2 - 2p - 3p + 6 \neq 0$

$\Rightarrow p(p-2) - 3(p-2) \neq 0$

$\Rightarrow (p-2)(p-3) \neq 0$

$\Rightarrow p \neq 2$ and $p \neq 3$.

Hence, choice (c and d) are correct.

5. Given that $591x + 788y = 1379$ (1)

Also $603x + 804y = 1407$ (2)

Let us divide the first equation by 197.

$\Rightarrow 3x + 4y = 7$

Let us divide the first equation by 201.

$\Rightarrow 3x + 4y = 7$

So, both the equations represent coincidental lines. Hence, the solution of $3x + 4y = 7$ is also a solution of the given equations.

(1, 1), (5, –2), (–11, 10), and (101, –74) will satisfy the equation $3x + 4y = 7$.

Hence, choice (a, b, c, d) are correct.

Match The Column

Common Solutions for questions 6 to 9:

Given that:

$P: 2x + 3y = 1$

$Q: 6x + 9y = 12$

$R: 14x + 21y = 28$

$S: 34x + 48y = 72$

6. $Q: 6x + 9y = 12$

$R: 14x + 21y = 28$

$\frac{a_1}{a_2} = \frac{6}{14} = \frac{3}{7}$

$\frac{b_1}{b_2} = \frac{9}{21} = \frac{3}{7}$

$\frac{c_1}{c_2} = \frac{12}{28} = \frac{3}{7}$

$\Rightarrow \frac{a_1}{a_2} = \frac{b_1}{b_2} = \frac{c_1}{c_2}$

Hence, the equations Q and R have infinite solutions.

Hence, the correct option is (b).

7. $P: 2x + 3y = 1$

$Q: 6x + 9y = 12$

$\frac{a_1}{a_2} = \frac{2}{6} = \frac{1}{3}$

$\frac{b_1}{b_2} = \frac{3}{9} = \frac{1}{3}$

$\frac{c_1}{c_2} = \frac{1}{12}$

$\Rightarrow \frac{a_1}{a_2} = \frac{b_1}{b_2} \neq \frac{c_1}{c_2}$

Hence, the equations P and Q have no common solution.

Hence, the correct option is (c).

8. $P: 2x + 3y = 1.$

An equation in two variables have infinite solutions.

Also $\left(\frac{1}{4}, \frac{1}{6}\right)$ satisfies the equation P.

So, it can be mapped with either **(b)** or **(e)**.

As already Qno. 6 is mapped with only **(b),** Qno. 8 can be mapped with (e).

Hence, the correct option is (e).

9. $R: 14x + 21y = 28$ (1)

$S: 34x + 48y = 72$ (2)

$\frac{a_1}{a_2} = \frac{14}{34} = \frac{7}{17}$

$\frac{b_1}{b_2} = \frac{21}{48} = \frac{7}{16}$

$\Rightarrow \frac{a_1}{a_2} \neq \frac{b_1}{b_2}$

Hence, the equations P and Q have unique solution.

Dividing each term of the equation (1) by 7, we get

$2x + 3y = 4$ (3)

Eqn (2): $34x + 48y = 72$

Eqn (3) × 17: $34x + 51y = 68$

On subtracting,

$-3y = 4$

$y = \frac{-4}{3}$

Substituting $y = \frac{-4}{3}$ in equation (3) we get

$2x + 3\left(\frac{-4}{3}\right) = 4.$

$2x - 4 = 4$

$2x = 8$

$x = 4.$

Hence, $(x, y) = \left(4, \frac{-4}{3}\right).$

Hence, the correct option is (a).

Comprehension-Based Questions

Common Solutions for questions 10 to 13:

Given that:

The cost of 20 jujube fruits = ₹1.

The cost of 1 jack fruit = ₹1.

The cost of 1 pear = ₹5.

Let the number of jujube, jackfruits and pears purchased be x, y, and z respectively.

Total number of fruits = 100.

$x + y + z = 100$ (1)

Total cost of the fruits = ₹100

$\frac{x}{20} + y + 5z = 100$ (2)

Eqn (1) – Eqn (2): $\frac{19x}{20} - 4z = 0.$

$\frac{19x}{20} = 4z$

$\frac{x}{z} = \frac{80}{19}$

As x is a multiple of 80 and the $x + y + z = 100$, x can not be taken as more than 80.

$\Rightarrow x = 80$, and $z = 19$.

$\Rightarrow y = 100 - 80 - 19 = 1.$

10. The total number of pears (z) = 19.

Hence, the correct option is (a).

11. The difference between the number of jujube fruits and jackfruits = $x - y = 80 - 1 = 79$.

Hence, the correct option is (d).

12. The amount spent on purchasing jackfruits = y × ₹1 = ₹1.

Hence, the correct option is (c).

13. The difference between the amounts spent on purchasing jujube fruits and pears

$= ₹\left(5z - \frac{x}{20}\right)$

$= ₹\left(5 \times 19 - \frac{80}{20}\right)$

= ₹91.

Hence, the correct option is (c).

Assertion and Reason Type Questions

14. Assertion: Given that $49x - 42y = 91$ and $63x - 54y = 117$.

$\frac{a_1}{a_2} = \frac{49}{63} = \frac{7}{9}$

$\frac{b_1}{b_2} = \frac{-42}{-54} = \frac{7}{9}$

$\frac{c_1}{c_2} = \frac{91}{117} = \frac{7}{9}$

As $\frac{a_1}{a_2} = \frac{b_1}{b_2} = \frac{c_1}{c_2}$, $49x - 42y = 91$ and $63x - 54y = 117$ have infinite solutions.

So, **Assertion** is true.

Reason: For a pair of linear equations $a_1x + b_1y = c_1$ and $a_2x + b_2y = c_2$, if $\frac{a_1}{a_2} = \frac{b_1}{b_2} = \frac{c_1}{c_2}$, then the equations have infinite solutions. It is a true statement and is the correct explanation of **Assertion**.

Hence, the correct option is (a).

15. Assertion: $\frac{1}{x+2} > 0$

$\Rightarrow x + 2 > 0$

$\Rightarrow x > -2$.

So, **Assertion** is true.

Reason: $|x - 2| \geq 0$ is true for any real value of x, since the absolute value of any number is always greater than or equal to 0. So, **Reason** is true, but not the correct explanation of **Assertion**.

Hence, the correct option is (b).

16. Assertion: Let the two-digit number be $10a + b$.

The required sum $= (10a + b) + (10b + a) = 11(a + b)$.

Hence, the sum of a two-digit number and the number formed by reversing the digits of it is always divisible by 11.

The maximum possible sum can be $11(9 + 9) = 198$.

As 165 is divisible by 11 and lesser than 198, **Assertion** is true.

Reason:

The required difference

$= |(10a + b) - (10b + a)| = |9(a - b)|$.

Hence, the difference of a two-digit number and the number formed by reversing the digits of it is always divisible by 9.

The minimum possible difference can be $9(1 - 0) = 9$.

As 66 is not divisible by 9, **Reason** is false.

Hence, the correct option is (c).

17. Assertion: Let the present ages of A and B be x years and y years respectively.

From the given data: $5x + 3y = 117$ and $3x + 5y = 115$.

Subtracting one equation from the other, we get $2x - 2y = 2$.

$x - y = 1$.

So, **Assertion** is false.

Reason: The difference of the ages of two persons when they are alive, is always constant. It is a true statement.

Hence, the correct option is (d).

CHAPTER

5

Quadratic Equations

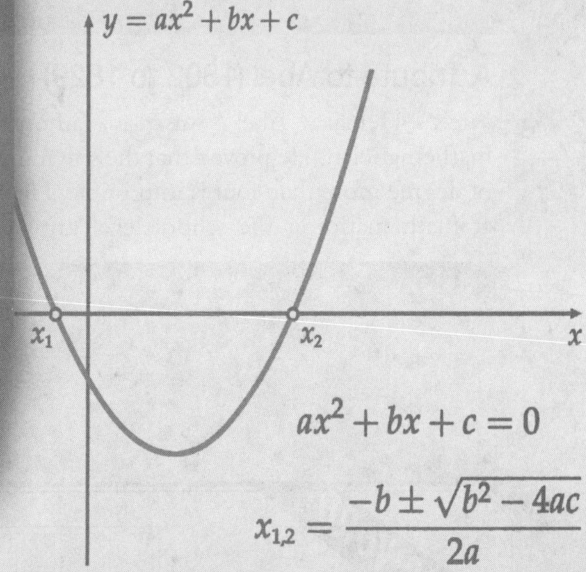

$$ax^2 + bx + c = 0$$

$$x_{1,2} = \frac{-b \pm \sqrt{b^2 - 4ac}}{2a}$$

Remember

Before beginning this chapter, you should be able to:

- Know the terms, such as quadratic expression, zero in a equation
- Understand reciprocal equation and maximum or minimum value of a quadratic equation

Key Ideas

After completing this chapter, you should be able to:

- Find the roots of a quadratic equation by factorization, using a formula, and graphical method
- Study nature and signs of the roots
- Construct a quadratic equation
- Solve word problems on quadratic equations

Scientific Crypt

A Tribute to Abel (1802 to 1829)

Niels Henrik Abel was a famous Norwegian mathematician. He proved that the solving of an equation of degree more than four is impossible. He was very good at mathematics at the school level but he struggled in other subjects. Euler proved that the binomial theorem is valid for only rational numbers. But Abel proved that it is valid for all numbers.

FUN TIME

CROSSWORD

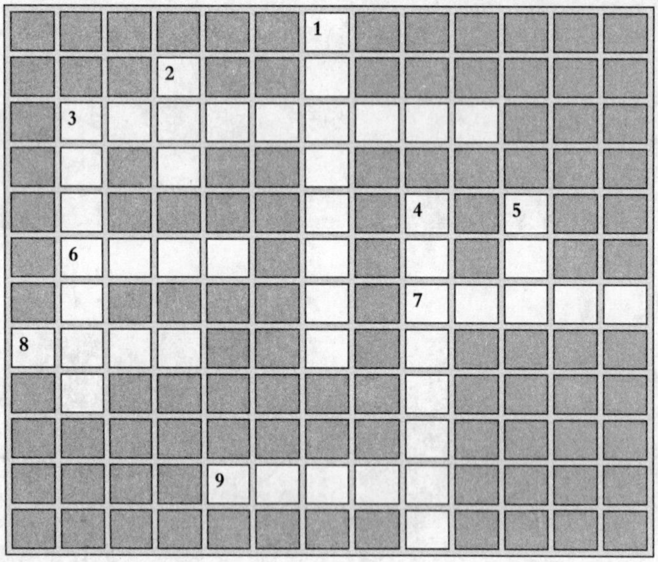

Across

3. If the roots of a quadratic equation are irrational, then they are ________ to each other.
6. In a quadratic equation, if the coefficient of x is zero, then the equation is said to be
7. The values of the variable that satisfy the equation are called ______ of the equation.
8. If the discriminant of a quadratic equation is greater than or equal to zero, then the roots are
9. If the discriminant of a quadratic equation is zero, then the roots are

Down

1. If the product of roots is positive and their sum is negative, then the roots are
2. If the sum of the coefficients of a quadratic equation is zero, then one of its roots.
3. If the discriminant of a quadratic equation is less than zero, then the roots are
4. The shape of the graph of a quadratic equation.
5. The sum of the roots of $x + 1/x = 2$

INTRODUCTION

Very often we come across many equations involving several powers of one variable. If the indices of all these powers are integers then the equation is called a polynomial equation. If the highest index of a polynomial equation in one variable is two, then it is a quadratic equation.

A quadratic equation is a second-degree polynomial in x usually equated to zero. In other words, for an equation to be a quadratic, the coefficient of x^2 should not be zero and the coefficients of any higher power of x should be 0.

The general form of a quadratic equation is $ax^2 + bx + c = 0$, where $a \neq 0$ (and a, b, c are real). The following are some examples of quadratic equations.

1. $x^2 - 5x + 6 = 0$ (1)
2. $x^2 - x - 6 = 0$ (2)
3. $2x^2 + 3x - 2 = 0$ (3)
4. $2x^2 + x - 3 = 0$ (4)

A quadratic polynomial or expression is a polynomial of the from $ax^2 + bx + c$ where a, b, c, are real numbers and $a \neq 0$, and a quadratic equation is obtained by setting it equal to 0, that is, a quadratic equation is an equation of the form $ax^2 + bx + c = 0$, where a, b, c are real numbers and $a \neq 0$.

Roots of the Equation

Just as a first-degree equation in x has one value of x satisfying the equation, a quadratic equation in x has two values of x that satisfy the equation. The values of x that satisfy the equation are called the roots of the equation. These roots may be real or complex.

The roots of the four quadratic equations given above are:

For Eq. (1), $x = 2$ and $x = 3$

For Eq. (2), $x = -2$ and $x = 3$

For Eq. (3), $x = \frac{1}{2}$ and $x = -2$

For Eq. (4), $x = 1$ and $x = \frac{-3}{2}$

Info Bytes!

A quadratic equation may have two real roots, one real root, or no real roots at all.

In general, the roots of a quadratic equation can be found in two ways:

1. By factorizing the expression on the left-hand side.
2. By using the standard formula.

All the expressions may not be easy to factorize, whereas applying the formula is simple and straightforward.

Finding the Roots by Factorization

If the quadratic equation $ax^2 + bx + c = 0$ $(a \neq 0)$ is written in the form, $(x - \alpha)(x - \beta) = 0$, then the roots of the equation are α and β.

To find the roots of a quadratic equation, we should first express it in the form of $(x - \alpha)(x - \beta) = 0$, i.e., the left-hand side, $ax^2 + bx + c$ of the quadratic equation $ax^2 + bx + c = 0$ should be factorized.

For this purpose, we should go through the following steps with the help of above equations.

Consider Equation (1)

Step 1: The equation is, $x^2 - 5x + 6 = 0$. Here $a = 1$, $b = -5$, and $c = 6$.

First write down b (the coefficient of x) as the sum of two quantities whose product is equal to ac. In this case, -5 has to be written as the sum of two quantities whose product is 6. We write -5 as $(-3) + (-2)$, because the product of (-3) and (-2) is equal to 6.

Step 2: Now, rewrite the equation. In this case, the given equation can be written as $x^2 - 3x - 2x + 6 = 0$.

Step 3: Consider the first two terms and rewrite them together after taking out their common factor. Similarly, the third and the fourth terms should be rewritten after taking out their common factor. In this process, we should ensure that what is left from the first and the second terms (after removing the common factor) is the same as that left from the third and fourth terms (after removing their common factor).
In this case, the equation can be rewritten as $x(x - 3) -2(x - 3) = 0$; now $(x - 3)$ is a common factor.

Step 4: If we take out $(x - 3)$ as the common factor, we can rewrite the given equation as $(x - 3)(x - 2) = 0$.
We know that α and β are the roots of the given quadratic equation $(x - \alpha)(x - \beta) = 0$.
Hence, the roots of the given equation are 3 and 2.

Consider Equation (2)

The equation is $x^2 - x - 6 = 0$. Here, the coefficient of x is -1, which can be rewritten as $(-3) + (2)$, because the product of (-3) and 2 is -6, which is equal to 'ac' (1 multiplied by -6). Then, we can rewrite the equation as $(x - 3)(x + 2) = 0$ to get the roots as 3 and -2.

Consider Equation (3)

The equation is $2x^2 + 3x - 2 = 0$. Here, the coefficient of x is 3, which can be rewritten as $(4) + (-1)$ so that their product is -4, which is the value of 'ac' (-2 multiplied by 2). Then, we can rewrite the equation as $(2x - 1)(x + 2) = 0$, obtaining the roots as $\frac{1}{2}$ and -2.

Consider Equation (4)

The equation is $2x^2 + x - 3 = 0$. Here, the coefficient of x is 1, which can be rewritten as $(3) + (-2)$ because their product is -6, which is equal to 'ac' (2 multiplied by -3). Then we can rewrite the given equation as $(x - 1)(2x + 3) = 0$ to get the roots as 1 and $\frac{-3}{2}$.

Discriminant

In the case of quadratic equation $ax^2 + bx + c = 0$, the discriminant can be defined as:

$$\Delta = b^2 - 4ac$$

$b^2 - 4ac$ determines the nature of the roots of the quadratic equation.

For the quadratic equation $ax^2 + bx + c = 0$, we can use the standard formula given below to find out the roots of the equation.

$$x = \frac{-b \pm \sqrt{b^2 - 4ac}}{2a}.$$

Sum and Product of Roots of a Quadratic Equation

For the quadratic equation $ax^2 + bx + c = 0$, let α and β be the roots, then the sum of the roots, $(\alpha + \beta) = \frac{-b}{a}$ the product of the roots, $(\alpha\beta) = \frac{c}{a}$.

These two rules will be very helpful in solving problems on quadratic equation.

Nature of the Roots

We have already learnt that the roots of a quadratic equation with real coefficients can be real or complex. When the roots are real, they can be rational or irrational and, also, they can be equal or unequal.

A quadratic equation has real roots only if $b^2 - 4ac \geq 0$.

If $b^2 - 4ac < 0$, then the roots of the quadratic equation are complex conjugates.

The following table gives us a clear idea about the nature of the roots of a quadratic equation, when *a*, *b*, and *c* are all rational.

Condition	Nature of Roots
when $b^2 - 4ac < 0$	the roots are complex conjugates
when $b^2 - 4ac = 0$	the roots are rational and equal
when $b^2 - 4ac > 0$ and a perfect square	the roots are rational and unequal
when $b^2 - 4ac > 0$ and not a perfect square	the roots are irrational and unequal

Konnect

1. Whenever the roots of the quadratic equation are irrational, (a, b, c being rational), are of the form $a+\sqrt{b}$ and $a-\sqrt{b}$, i.e., whenever $a+\sqrt{b}$ is one root of a quadratic equation, $a-\sqrt{b}$ is the other root of the quadratic equation and vice-versa. In other words, if the roots of a quadratic equation are irrational, then they are conjugate to each other.
2. If the sum of the coefficients of a quadratic equation, say $ax^2 + bx + c = 0$, is zero, then its roots are 1 and $\frac{c}{a}$.

   That is, if $a + b + c = 0$, then the roots of $ax^2 + bx + c = 0$ are 1 and $\frac{c}{a}$.

Signs of the Roots

We can comment on the signs of the roots, i.e., whether the roots are positive or negative, based on the sign of the sum of the roots and the product of the roots of the quadratic equation. The following table indicates the signs of the roots when the signs of the sum and the product of the roots are given.

Sign of Product of the Roots	Sign of Sumof the Roots	Sign of the Roots
+ve	+ve	Both the roots are positive.
+ve	–ve	Both the roots are negative.
–ve	+ve	One root is positive and the other negative. The numerically greater root is positive.
–ve	–ve	One root is positive and the other negative. The numerically greater root is negative.

Constructing a Quadratic Equation

We can build a quadratic equation in the following cases:

1. When the roots of the quadratic equation are given.
2. When the sum of the roots and the product of the roots of the quadratic equation are given.

Case 1: If the roots of the quadratic equation are α and β, then its equation can be written as $(x - \alpha)(x - \beta) = 0$, i.e., $x^2 - x(\alpha + \beta) + \alpha\beta = 0$.

Case 2: If p is the sum of the roots of the quadratic equation and q is their product, then the equation can be written as $x^2 - px + q = 0$.

Constructing a New Quadratic Equation by Changing the Roots of a Given Quadratic Equation

If we are given a quadratic equation, we can build a new quadratic equation by changing the roots of this equation in the manner specified to us.

For example, consider the quadratic equation $ax^2 + bx + c = 0$ and let its roots be α and β, respectively. Then, we can build new quadratic equations as per the following points:

1. A quadratic equation whose roots are $\frac{1}{\alpha}$ and $\frac{1}{\beta}$, i.e., the roots are reciprocal to the roots of the given quadratic equation, can be obtained by substituting $\left(\frac{1}{x}\right)$ for x in the given equation, which gives us $cx^2 + bx + a = 0$, i.e., we get the equation required by interchanging the coefficient of x^2 and the constant term.
2. A quadratic equation whose roots are $(\alpha + k)$ and $(\beta + k)$ can be obtained by substituting $(x - k)$ for x in the given equation.
3. A quadratic equation whose roots are $(\alpha - k)$ and $(\beta - k)$ can be obtained by substituting $(x + k)$ for x in the given equation.
4. A quadratic equation whose roots are $(k\alpha)$ and $(k\beta)$ can be obtained by substituting $\left(\frac{x}{k}\right)$ for x in the given equation.
5. A quadratic equation whose roots are $\left(\frac{\alpha}{k}\right)$ and $\left(\frac{\beta}{k}\right)$ can be obtained by substituting (kx) for x in the given equation.
6. A quadratic equation whose roots are $(-\alpha)$ and $(-\beta)$ can be obtained by replacing x by $(-x)$ in the given equation.

Finding the Roots of a Quadratic Equation by Graphical Method

First Method

First, let us learn how to draw the graph of $y = x^2$.

We assume certain real values for x, i.e., we substitute some values for x in $y = x^2$. We can find the corresponding values of y. We tabulate the values, as shown in next page:

x	5	4	3	2	1	0	–1	–2	–3	–4	–5
$y = x^2$	25	16	9	4	1	0	1	4	9	16	25

Plotting the points corresponding to the ordered pairs (5, 25), (4, 16), (3, 9), (2, 4), (1, 1), (0, 0) (–1, 1), (–2, 4), (–3, 9), (–4, 16), and (–5, 25) on the graph paper and joining them with a smooth curve, we obtain the graph of $y = x^2$, as shown in the Fig. 5.1.

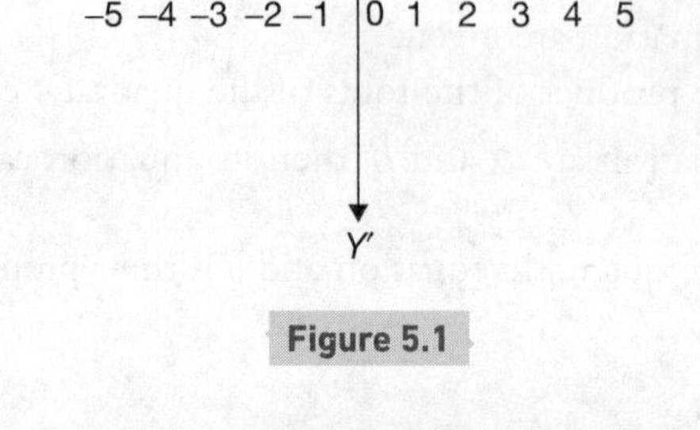

Figure 5.1

We observe the following about the graph of $y = x^2$.

1. It is a U-shaped graph and it is called a parabola. The arms of the 'U' spread outwards.
2. For every value of x ($\neq 0$), we notice that y is always positive. Hence, the graph lies entirely in the first and second quadrants.
3. When $x = 0$, $y = 0 \Rightarrow y = x^2$ passes through origin.
4. The graph is symmetric about the Y-axis.
5. Using the graph of $y = x^2$, we can find the square of any real number as well as the square root of any non-negative real number.
   (i) for any given value of x, the corresponding value of y on the graph is its square and
   (ii) for any given value of y (≥ 0), the corresponding value of x on the graph is its square root.
6. The graph of $y = kx^2$, when $k > 0$ lies entirely in Q_1 and Q_2 and when $k < 0$ the graph lies entirely in Q_3 and Q_4 (see Fig. 5.2).

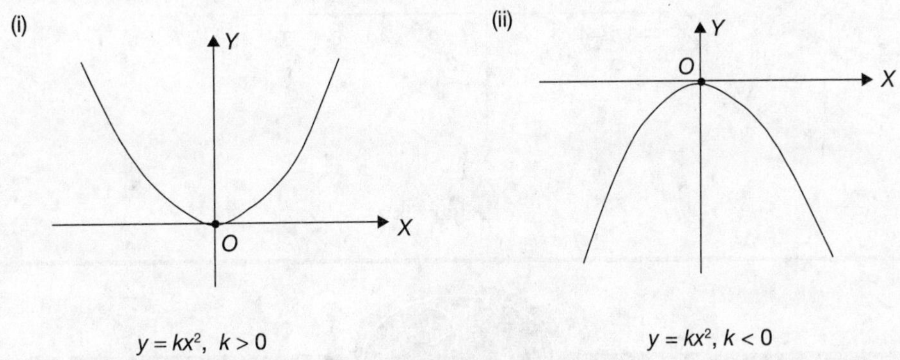

Figure 5.2

The method of solving the quadratic equation of the form $px^2 + qx + r = 0$, whose roots are real is shown in the following example.

EXAMPLE 5.1 Solve $x^2 - 5x + 6 = 0$ using the graphical method.

SOLUTION

Let $y = x^2 - 5x + 6$

Prepare the following table by assuming different values for x.

x	0	1	2	3	−1	−2	4	5
x^2	0	1	4	9	1	4	16	25
$5x$	0	5	10	15	−5	−10	20	25
$y = x^2 - 5x + 6$	6	2	0	0	12	20	2	6

Plot the points (0, 6), (1, 2), (2, 0), (3, 0), (−1, 12), (−2, 20), (4, 2) and (5, 6) on the graph and join the points with a smooth curve, as shown in the Fig. 5.3.

Here, we notice that the given graph (parabola) intersects the X-axis at (2, 0) and (3, 0).

The roots of the given quadratic equation $x^2 - 5x + 6 = 0$ are $x = 2$ and $x = 3$.

∴ The roots of the given equation are the x-coordinates of the points of intersection of the curve with X-axis.

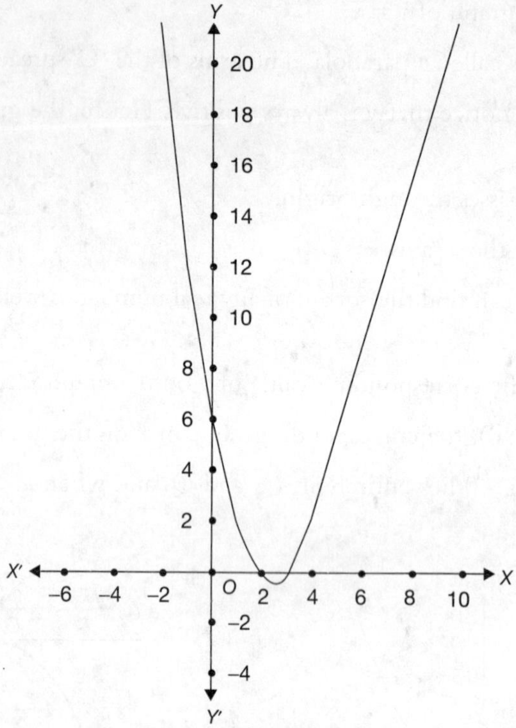

Figure 5.3

Konnect

1. If the graph meets the X-axis at two distinct points, then the roots of the given equation are real and distinct (see Fig. 5.4).

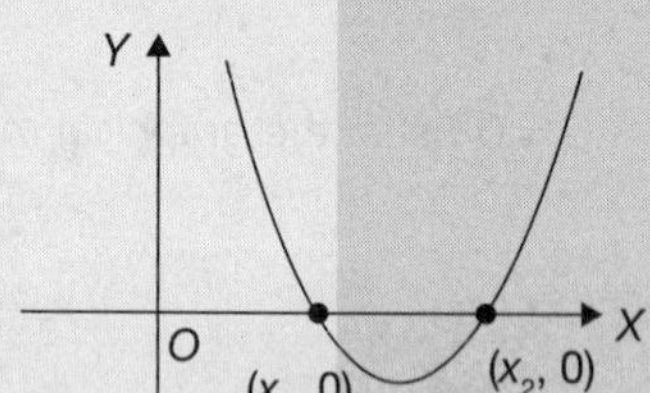

Figure 5.4

2. If the graph touches the X-axis at only one point, then the roots of the quadratic equation are real and equal (see Fig. 5.5).

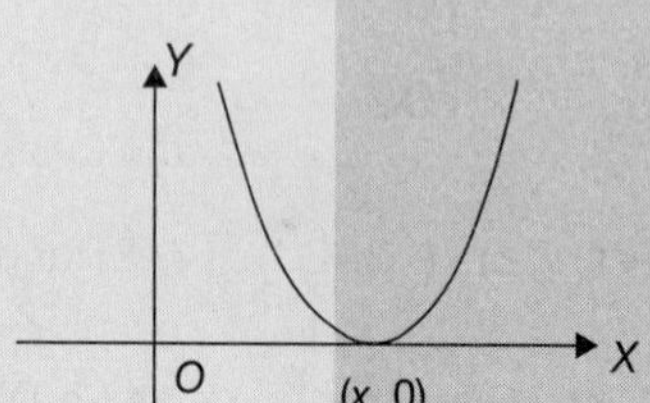

Figure 5.5

3. If the graph does not meet the X-axis, then the roots of the quadratic equation are not real, i.e., they are complex (see Fig. 5.6).

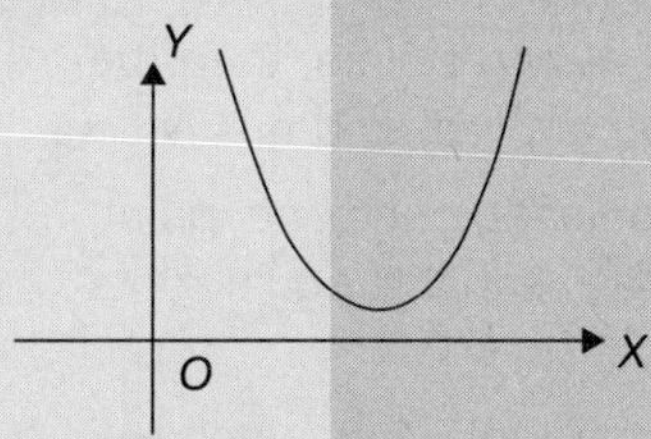

Figure 5.6

Second Method

We can also solve the quadratic equation $px^2 + qx + r = 0$ by considering the following equations:

$$y = px^2 \quad (1)$$

and

$$y = -qx - r \quad (2)$$

Clearly, $y = px^2$ is a parabola and $y = -qx - r$ is a straight line.

Step 1: Draw the graph of $y = px^2$ and $y = -qx - r$ on the same graph paper.

Step 2: Draw perpendiculars from the points of intersection of parabola and the straight line onto the X-axis. Let the points of intersection on the X-axis be $(x_1, 0)$ and $(x_2, 0)$.

Step 3: The x-coordinates of the points in Step (2), i.e., x_1 and x_2 are the two distinct roots of $px^2 + qx + r = 0$.

EXAMPLE 5.2 Solve $2x^2 - x - 3 = 0$.

SOLUTION

Given: $2x^2 - x - 3 = 0, \Rightarrow 2x^2 = x + 3$. Let $y = 2x^2 \Rightarrow y = x + 3$

We know that the roots of $2x^2 - x - 3 = 0$ are the x-coordinates of the points of intersection of the parabola, $y = 2x^2$ and the straight line, $y = x + 3$.

(1) $y = 2x^2$

x	0	1	2	−1	−2
$y = 2x^2$	0	2	8	2	8

(2) $y = x + 3$

x	0	1	2	−1	−2	−3
$y = x + 3$	3	4	5	2	1	0

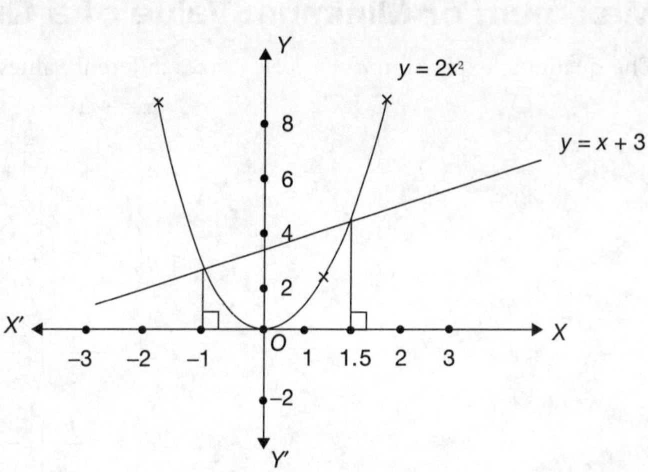

Figure 5.7

Draw the graph of $y = 2x^2$ and $y = x + 3$ (see Fig. 5.7).

Clearly, the perpendiculars drawn from the points of intersection of parabola and the line meet the X-axis at $\left(\frac{3}{2}, 0\right)$ and $(-1, 0)$.

$\therefore$ The roots of the given quadratic equation $2x^2 - x - 3 = 0$ are $\frac{3}{2}$ and -1.

Konnect

1. If the line meets the parabola at two points, then the roots of the quadratic equation are real and distinct.
2. If the line touches the parabola at only one point, then the quadratic equation has real and equal roots (see Fig. 5.8).
3. If the line does not meet the parabola, i.e., when the line and the parabola have no points in common, then the quadratic equation has no real roots. In this case, the roots of the quadratic equation are imaginary (see Fig. 5.9).

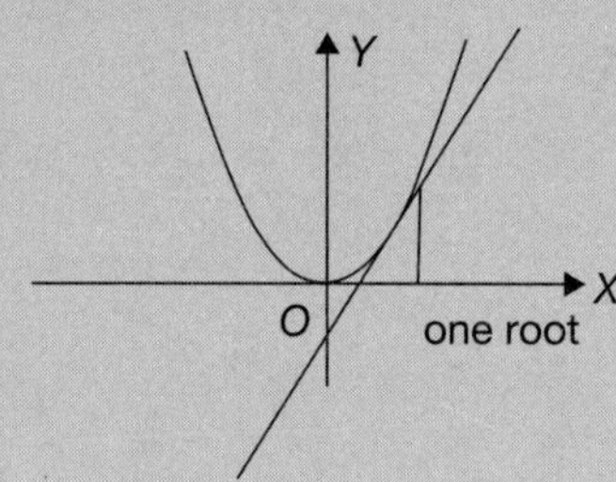

Figure 5.8

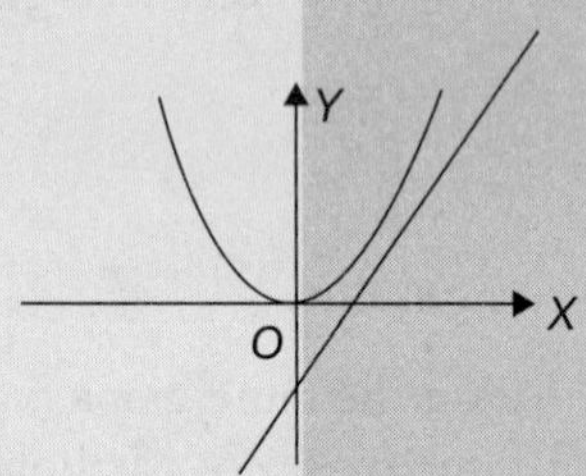

Figure 5.9

Equations of Higher Degree

The index of the highest power of x in the equation is called the degree of the equation. For example, if the highest power of x in the equation is x^3, then the degree of the equation is 3. An equation whose degree is 3 is called a cubic equation. A cubic equation will have three roots.

Info Bytes!

An equation whose degree is n will have n roots.

Maximum or Minimum Value of a Quadratic Expression

The quadratic expression $ax^2 + bx + c$ takes different values, as x takes different values.

$$
\begin{aligned}
& ax^2 + bx + c \\
&= a\left(x^2 + \frac{b}{a}x\right) + c \\
&= a\left(x^2 + 2\left(\frac{b}{2a}\right)x + \frac{b^2}{4a^2} - \frac{b^2}{4a^2}\right) + c \\
&= a\left(x + \frac{b}{2a}\right)^2 + c - \frac{b^2}{4a} \\
&= a\left(x + \frac{b}{2a}\right)^2 + \frac{4ac - b^2}{4a}
\end{aligned}
$$

For all the values of x, as x varies from $-\infty$ to $+\infty$, (i.e., when x is real), the quadratic expression $ax^2 + bx + c$:

1. has a minimum value if $a > 0$ (i.e., a is positive). The minimum value of the quadratic expression is $\frac{(4ac - b^2)}{4a}$ and it occurs at $x = \frac{-b}{2a}$.

2. has a maximum value if $a < 0$ (i.e., a is negative). The maximum value of the quadratic expression is $\dfrac{(4ac - b^2)}{4a}$ and it occurs at $x = \dfrac{-b}{2a}$.

EXAMPLE 5.3

Find the roots of the equation $x^2 + 3x - 4 = 0$.

SOLUTION

$x^2 + 3x - 4 = 0$

$\Rightarrow x^2 - x + 4x - 4 = 0$

$\Rightarrow x(x - 1) + 4(x - 1) = 0$

$\Rightarrow (x + 4)(x - 1) = 0.$

$\therefore x = -4$ or $x = 1$.

EXAMPLE 5.4

Find the roots of the equation $4x^2 - 13x + 10 = 0$.

SOLUTION

$4x^2 - 13x + 10 = 0$

$\Rightarrow 4x^2 - 8x - 5x + 10 = 0$

$\Rightarrow 4x(x - 2) -5(x - 2) = 0$

$\Rightarrow (4x - 5)(x - 2) = 0.$

$\Rightarrow 4x - 5 = 0$ or $x - 2 = 0$.

$\therefore x = \dfrac{5}{4}$ or $x = 2$.

EXAMPLE 5.5

Find the roots of the equation $26x^2 - 43x + 15 = 0$.

SOLUTION

We have to write 43 as the sum of two parts whose product should be equal to (26×15).

$26 \times 15 = 13 \times 30$ and $13 + 30 = 43$

$\therefore 26x^2 - 43x + 15 = 0$

$\Rightarrow 26x^2 - 13x - 30x + 15 = 0$

$\Rightarrow (13x - 15)(2x - 1) = 0$

$\Rightarrow x = \dfrac{15}{13}$ or $x = \dfrac{1}{2}$

We can also find the roots of the equation by using the formula.

$$x = \frac{-b \pm \sqrt{b^2 - 4ac}}{2a} = \frac{43 \pm \sqrt{(43)^2 - (1560)}}{52}$$

$$= \frac{43 \pm \sqrt{(1849) - (1560)}}{52}$$

$$= \frac{43 \pm \sqrt{289}}{52} \Rightarrow x = \frac{43 \pm 17}{52}$$

$$\Rightarrow x = \frac{43 + 17}{52} \text{ or } \frac{43 - 17}{52} = \frac{60}{52} \text{ or } \frac{26}{52}$$

$$\therefore x = \frac{15}{13} \text{ or } \frac{1}{2}.$$

EXAMPLE 5.6 Discuss the nature of the roots of the equation $4x^2 - 2x + 1 = 0$.

SOLUTION

Discriminant $= b^2 - 4ac = (-2)^2 - 4(4)(1) = 4 - 16 = -12 < 0$.

Since the discriminant is negative, the roots are imaginary.

EXAMPLE 5.7 If the sum of the roots of the equation $kx^2 - 3x + 9 = 0$ is $\frac{3}{11}$, then find the product of the roots of that equation.

SOLUTION

Compare the given equation with $ax^2 + bx + c = 0$.

Sum of roots of the equation $= \frac{-b}{a} = \frac{3}{k} = \frac{3}{11}$ (given)

$\therefore k = 11$.

In the given equation, product of the roots $= \frac{9}{k}$.

As $k = 11$, product of the roots $= \frac{9}{11}$.

EXAMPLE 5.8 Form quadratic equation whose roots are 2 and 7.

SOLUTION

Sum of the roots $= 2 + 7 = 9$

Product of the roots $= 2 \times 7 = 14$

We know that if p is the sum of the roots and q is the product of the roots of a quadratic equation, then its equation is $x^2 - px + q = 0$.

Hence, the required equation is $x^2 - 9x + 14 = 0$.

EXAMPLE 5.9 Form a quadratic equation with rational coefficients, one of whose roots is $4 - \sqrt{3}$, is ______.

SOLUTION

One root is $4 - \sqrt{3}$.

$\therefore$ The other root is $4 + \sqrt{3}$.

Required quadratic equation is

$$x^2 - \left(4 - \sqrt{3} + 4 + \sqrt{3}\right)x + \left(4 - \sqrt{3}\right)\left(4 + \sqrt{3}\right) = 0$$

$$x^2 - 8x + 13 = 0.$$

EXAMPLE 5.10 A person can buy 15 books less for ₹900, when the price of each book goes up by ₹3. Find the original price and the number of copies he could buy at the initial price.

SOLUTION

Let the number of books bought initially for ₹900 be 'x'. The original price of the each book was $\frac{900}{x}$. Now the price of the each book is increased by ₹3.

That is, the new price of each book is $\left(\frac{900}{x}\right) + 3$.

And the number of books bought is reduced by 15, i.e., $(x - 15)$.

Since the total amount spent is still ₹900, the product of the price of each book and the number of books are still 900.

$$\left[\left(\frac{900}{x}\right) + 3\right](x - 15) = 900$$

$\Rightarrow (900 + 3x)\ (x - 15) = 900x$

$\Rightarrow 3x^2 + 855x - 13500 = 900x$

$\Rightarrow 3x^2 - 45x - 13500 = 0$

$\Rightarrow x^2 - 15x - 4500 = 0$

$\Rightarrow x^2 - 75x + 60x - 4500 = 0$

$\Rightarrow x(x - 75) + 60(x - 75) = 0$

$\Rightarrow (x - 75)\ (x + 60) = 0$

$\Rightarrow x = 75$ or -60.

Since x cannot be negative, $x = 75$.

Thus, the original price of the book $= \dfrac{900}{75} = 12$.

EXAMPLE 5.11 If α and β are the roots of $2x^2 - 3x + 4 = 0$, then the equation whose roots are $(2 + \alpha)$ and $(2 + \beta)$ is ______.

SOLUTION

Let $f(x) = 2x^2 - 3x + 4$

The quadratic equation whose roots are $\alpha + 2$ and $\beta + 2$ is $f(x - 2) = 0$

$2(x - 2)^2 - 3(x - 2) + 4 = 0$

$2(x^2 - 4x + 4) - 3x + 6 + 4 = 0$

$2x^2 - 8x + 8 - 3x + 6 + 4 = 0$

$2x^2 - 11x + 18 = 0$

EXAMPLE 5.12 Solve for x: $3^{x+1} + 3^{2x+1} = 270$.

SOLUTION

$3^{x+1} + 3^{2x+1} = 270$

$\Rightarrow 3 \cdot 3^x + 3^{2x} \cdot 3 = 270$

$\Rightarrow 3^x + 3^{2x} = 90$.

Substituting $3^x = a$, we get,

$a + a^2 = 90$

$\Rightarrow a^2 + a - 90 = 0$

$\Rightarrow a^2 + 10a - 9a - 90 = 0$

$\Rightarrow (a + 10)(a - 9) = 0$

$\Rightarrow a = 9$ or $a = -10$.

If $3^x = 9$, then $x = 2$.

If $3^x = -10$, which is not possible.

$\therefore x = 2$.

EXAMPLE 5.13 Solve $|x|^2 - 7|x| + 12 = 0$.

SOLUTION

Given equation is $|x|^2 - 7|x| + 12 = 0$

$\Rightarrow (|x| - 3)(|x| - 4) = 0$

$\Rightarrow |x| = 3$ or $|x| = 4$

$\Rightarrow x = \pm 3$ or $x = \pm 4$.

EXAMPLE 5.14 Solve $|x|^2 - 7|x| + 10 = 0$.

SOLUTION

Given equation is $|x|^2 - 7|x| + 10 = 0$

$\Rightarrow (|x| - 2)(|x| - 5) = 0$

$\Rightarrow |x| = -3$ or $|x| = -5$

But, the absolute value of any number can never be negative.

$\therefore$ No roots are possible for the given equation.

EXAMPLE 5.15 For what value of a, $(1 + a^2)x^2 + 2(x - a)(1 + ax) = 1$ has no real roots?

(a) For any real value of a
(b) For no real value of a
(c) $-2 < a < 2$
(d) $a > 2$

SOLUTION

$$(1+a^2)x^2 + 2(x-a)(1+ax) = 1$$

$$(1+a^2)x^2 + 2x + 2ax^2 - 2a - 2a^2x - 1 = 0$$

$$(1+a^2+2a)x^2 + 2(1-a^2)x - (2a+1) = 0$$

$$(1+a)^2x^2 + 2(1-a^2)x - (2a+1) = 0$$

Since above equation has no real roots,

$$[2(1-a^2)]^2 + 4(a+1)^2(2a+1) < 0$$

$$4(1-a^2)^2 + 4(a+1)^2(2a+1) < 0$$

$$4((1+a)(1-a))^2 + 4(1+a)^2(2a+1) < 0$$

$$4(1+a)^2\left[(1-a)^2 + (2a+1)\right] < 0$$

$$4(1+a)^2(1+a^2-2a+2a+1) < 0$$

$$4(1+a)^2(a^2+2) < 0. \text{ But } 4(1+a)^2(a^2+2) \geq 0$$

For no value of 'a',

$$4(1+a)^2(a^2+2) < 0$$

Therefore, Choice (b) is the correct answer.

EXAMPLE 5.16 The cost of a certain number of pens is ₹72. If the cost of each pen is decreased by ₹1.50, then 8 more pens can be purchased for the same amount. How many pens can be purchased for the same amount if the cost of each pen is increased by ₹1.50?

SOLUTION

Let the cost of each pen be ₹x and the number of pens be y.

Given that $xy = 72$ -------------(1)

$(x - 1.5)(y + 8) = 72$ -------------(2)

$(x + 1.5)(?) = 72$

From (2)

$$\left(x - \frac{3}{2}\right)(y+8) = 72$$

$(2x - 3)(y + 8) = 2 \times 72$

$2xy + 16x - 3y - 24 = 144$

From (1), $y = \frac{72}{x}$

$2 \times 72 + 16x - 3\left(\frac{72}{x}\right) - 24 = 144$

$16x - \frac{216}{x} - 24 = 0$

$16x^2 - 216 - 24x = 0$

$16x^2 - 24x - 216 = 0$

$4x^2 - 6x - 54 = 0$

$2x^2 - 3x - 27 = 0$

$2x^2 - 9x + 6x - 27 = 0$

$x(2x - 9) + 3(2x - 9) = 0$

$(2x - 9)\ (x + 3) = 0$

$2x - 9 = 0$ or $x + 3 = 0$

$2x = 9$ or $x = -3$

$x = \frac{9}{2} = 4.5$ or $x = -3$ (not applicable)

∴ cost of each pen is ₹4.50

∴ The number of pens

$y = \frac{72}{4.5} = \frac{72}{\left(\frac{9}{2}\right)} = 72 \times \frac{2}{9} = 16$

If the cost is increased by ₹1.50, then the cost would be ₹(4.50 + 1.50) = ₹6.00

The number of pens that can be purchased at ₹6 per each pen= $\frac{72}{6} = 12$.

EXAMPLE 5.17 If $3 \cdot 2^{2x+1} - 5 \cdot 2^{x+2} + 16 = 0$ and x is an integer, find the value of x.

SOLUTION

$3 \times 2^{2x+1} - 5 \times 2^{x+2} + 16 = 0$

$3 \times 2^{2x} \times 2 - 5 \times 2^x \times 2^2 + 16 = 0$

$6(2^x)^2 - 20\ (2^y) + 16 = 0$

Let $2^x = a$.

$6a^2 - 20a + 16 = 0$

$\Rightarrow 6a^2 - 12a - 8a + 16 = 0$

$\Rightarrow 6a(a - 2) - 8(a - 2) = 0$

$\Rightarrow (a - 2)\,(6a - 8) = 0$

$\Rightarrow a - 2 = 0$ or $6a - 8 = 0$

$a = 2$ or $a = \frac{8}{6}$

$2^x = 2^1$ or $2^x = \frac{2^2}{3}$

$\Rightarrow x = 1,$

Since x is integer, $x = 1$.

EXAMPLE 5.18 If $(x + 1)(x + 2)(x + 3)(x + 4) = 168$, then the number of real values of x is ______.

SOLUTION

$(x + 1)(x + 2)(x + 3)(x + 4) = 168$

$(x + 1)(x + 4)(x + 2)(x + 3) = 168$

$(x^2 + 5x + 4)(x^2 + 5x + 6) = 168$

Let $x^2 + 5x + 4 = a$

$(a)(a + 2) = 168$

$a^2 + 2a - 168 = 0$

$a^2 + 14a - 12a - 168 = 0$

$a(a + 14) - 12(a + 14) = 0$

$(a + 14)(a - 12) = 0$

$\Rightarrow (x^2 + 5x + 4 + 14)(x^2 + 5x + 4 - 12) = 0$

$(x^2 + 5x + 18)(x^2 + 5x - 8) = 0$

Let $x^2 + 5x + 18 = 0$ ---------(1)

$x^2 + 5x - 8 = 0$ --------- (2)

For equation (1), discriminate is negative and for equation (2), the discriminate in positive

Hence, there are two real values of x which satisfy the given equation.

POINTS TO REMEMBER

- ✔ In the case of quadratic equation $ax^2 + bx + c = 0$, the discriminant can be defined as

$$\Delta = b^2 - 4ac$$

- ✔ $b^2 - 4ac$ determineds the nature of the roots of the quadratic equation.
- ✔ Whenever the roots of the quadratic equation are irrational, (a, b, c being rational), are of the form $a+\sqrt{b}$ and $a-\sqrt{b}$, i.e., whenever $a+\sqrt{b}$ is one root of a quadratic equation, $a-\sqrt{b}$ is the other root of the quadratic equation and vice-versa. In other words, if the roots of a quadratic equation are irrational, then they are conjugate to each other.
- ✔ If the line meets the parabola at two points, then the roots of the quadratic equation are real and distinct.
- ✔ If the line does not meet the parabola, i.e., when the line and the parabola have no points in common, then the quadratic equation has no real roots. In this case, the roots of the quadratic equation are imaginary.
- ✔ A quadratic equation whose roots are $\frac{1}{\alpha}$ and $\frac{1}{\beta}$, i.e., the roots are reciprocal to the roots of the given quadratic equation, can be obtained by substituting $\left(\frac{1}{x}\right)$ for x in the given equation, which gives us $cx^2 + bx + a = 0$, i.e., we get the equation required by interchanging the coeffficient of x^2 and the constant term.

PRACTICE QUESTIONS CLASSROOM WING

Very Short Answer Type Questions

Directions of questions from 1 to 10:
Fill in the blanks.

1. If one of the roots of a quadratic equation having rational coefficients is $3+\sqrt{2}$, then the quadratic equation is ______.

2. If one of the roots of a quadratic equation having rational coefficients is $5-\sqrt{3}$, then the quadratic equation is ______.

3. The roots of $(x - 3)(x + 2) = 0$ are ________ and ________.

4. The roots of $\left(x+\sqrt{2}\right)\left(x-\sqrt{3}\right) = 0$ are ________.

5. The diagonal of a rectangle is 5 units. If one side is twice the other side, then the length is _____.

6. The positive number which is less than its square by 12 is _____.

7. If the product of two successive even numbers is 48, then the numbers are _____ and _____.

8. The point (1, –6) satisfies the equation $y = x^2 - x - 6$. Is the statement true?

9. The line $y = 5x - 6$ meets the parabola $y = x^2$ in two points, where x-coordinates are _____ and _____.

10. If the product of Shiva's age 3 years ago and his age three years later is 16, then Shiva's present age is _____.

Directions of question 11:
State whether the following statements are true or false.

11. For a quadratic equation $ax^2 + bx + c = 0$, if $a + b + c = 0$, then $x = 1$. (True/False)

Directions of questions from 12 to 14:
Answer the following questions.

12. Find the positive number which is less than its square by 42.

13. Find the dimensions of a rectangular hall, if its length exceeds its breadth by 7 m and the area of the hall being 228 m^2.

14. If $y=\sqrt{k\sqrt{k\sqrt{k\sqrt{k\ldots\infty}}}}$, where $k > 0$; find the value of y.

Short Answer Type Questions

15. Find the nature of the roots of $5x^2 - 2x - 1 = 0$.

16. Find the nature of the roots of $x^2 - x + 1 = 0$.

17. The following steps are involved in finding a number, if the positive number is less than its square by 30. Arrange them in sequential order.
(a) $x^2 - x - 30 = 0$ (b) $x = 6$
(c) $x^2 - x = 30$ (d) $(x + 5)(x - 6) = 0$

18. A number consists of two digits whose product is 18. If 27 is added to the number, the number formed will have the digits in reverse order, when compared to the original number. Find the number.

19. Find the minimum value of $x^2 + 12x$.

20. If the sides of a right triangle are x, $3x + 3$, and $3x + 4$, then find the value of x.

21. Find the roots of the equation $\frac{1}{x}-\frac{1}{x-a}=\frac{1}{b}-\frac{1}{b-a}$, where $a \neq 0$.

22. In a boys' hostel, there are as many boys in each room as the number of rooms. If the number of rooms is doubled and the number of boys in each room is reduced by 10, then the number of boys in the hostel becomes 1200. Find the number of rooms in the hostel.

23. If the equations $x^2 + 3x + 2 = 0$ and $x^2 + kx + 6 = 0$ have a common root, then find the values of k.

24. If $x^4 - 17x^2 + 16 = 0$, then find the sum of the squares of the roots.

25. If the quadratic equation $x^2 - mx - 4x + 1 = 0$ has real and distinct roots, then find the values of m.

26. $\sqrt{y+1}-\sqrt{y-1}=\sqrt{4y-1}$. Find the value of y.

Essay Type Questions

27. Solve $x^2 - 2x + 1 = 0$ graphically.

28. Find the value of $\sqrt{240+\sqrt{240+\sqrt{240+\ldots\infty}}}$.

29. Ramesh rowed a boat 24 km upstream from point A and returned to A in 10 h. If the speed of his boat in still water is 5 kmph, find the speed of the stream (in kmph).

30. Find the value of $\sqrt{132-\sqrt{132-\sqrt{132-\ldots\infty}}}$.

31. A rational number is less than its square by 20. How many such numbers exist?

32. The sum of the maximum value of $-3x^2 + 3x + k$ and the minimum value of $2x^2 + 2x + k$ is equal to 9/4, then find the value of k.

33. Mr. M travels 180 km at a uniform speed. If he wants to reduce the travel time by half an hour, he will have to increase his speed by 5 m/s. Find the time taken by him to travel 180 km at his usual speed.

34. Tap 'A' can fill a tank 15 min faster than tap 'B'. If both the taps can together fill the tank in $\frac{3}{7}$ hours, then find the time taken by B alone to fill the tank.

PRACTICE QUESTIONS COMPETITION WING

Level 1: Apply Your Concepts

Directions of questions from 1 to 5:
Fill in the blanks.

1. If $a = c$, then the roots of $ax^2 + bx + c = 0$ are ______ to each other.
2. If $b = 0$, then $ax^2 + bx + c = 0$ is called ______ quadratic equation.
3. If the sum of the roots of a quadratic equation is positive and the product of the roots is negative, then the numerically greater root is ______.
4. If we divide 8 into two parts such that their product is 15, then the parts are ______ and ______.
5. One side of a rectangle exceeds its other side by 2 cm. If its area is 24 cm^2, then the length and breadth are ______ and ______ respectively.

Directions of questions from 6 to 25:
Select the correct alternative from the given choices.

6. If α and β are the roots of $x^2 - 5x + 7 = 0$, then find $\alpha^2 + \beta^2$.
   (a) 11 (b) 14
   (c) 18 (d) 20
7. Find the number of solutions of the equation $|x|^2 - 5|x|^2 + 6 = 0$
   (a) 0 (b) 2
   (c) 3 (d) 4
8. If a and b are the roots of $x^2 + 2x - 3 = 0$, then find the value of $\frac{a}{b} + \frac{b}{a}$.
   (a) $-\frac{5}{3}$ (b) $-\frac{10}{3}$
   (c) $\frac{5}{4}$ (d) $-\frac{7}{4}$
9. Find the number of roots of the equation $|x|^2 + 7|x| + 12 = 0$.
   (a) 0 (b) 2
   (c) 3 (d) 4
10. The discriminant of $2x^2 - 8x + p = 0$ is -64. The number of values that exist for p is ______.
    (a) 0 (b) 1
    (c) 2 (d) 3
11. If α and β are the roots of the equation $x^2 - 3x + 2 = 0$, then $\frac{1}{a} + \frac{1}{b} =$ ______.
    (a) $\frac{1}{2}$ (b) $\frac{3}{2}$
    (c) $\frac{5}{2}$ (d) $\frac{2}{3}$
12. If the quadratic equation $px^2 + qx - r = 0$ $(p \neq 0)$ is to be solved by the graphical method, then which of the following graphs have to be drawn?
    (a) $y = x^2$, $y = r - qx$ (b) $y = px^2$, $y = qx - r$
    (c) $y = x^2$, $qx + py - r = 0$ (d) $y = x^2$, $qx - py = r$
13. If the roots of the equation $ax^2 + bx + c = 0$ are α and β, then the quadratic equation whose roots are $-\alpha$ and $-\beta$ is ______.
    (a) $ax^2 - bx - c = 0$ (b) $ax^2 - bx + c = 0$
    (c) $ax^2 + bx - c = 0$ (d) $ax^2 - bx + 2c = 0$
14. Find the sum and the product of the roots of the quadratic equation $-x^2 - \frac{25}{3}x + 25 = 0$.
    (a) $\frac{25}{3}, 25$ (b) $\frac{-25}{3}, 25$
    (c) $\frac{25}{3}, -25$ (d) $\frac{-25}{3}, -25$
15. For what value of k, if one root of the quadratic equation $9x^2 - 18x + k = 0$ is double of the other?
    (a) 36 (b) 9
    (c) 12 (d) 8
16. The sum of a number and its square is greater than 6, then the number belongs to ______.
    (a) $(-\infty, 2) \cup (3, \infty)$ (b) $(-\infty, -3) \cup (2, \infty)$
    (c) $(2, 3)$ (d) $[2, 3]$
17. The condition for the sum and the product of the roots of the quadratic equation $ax^2 - bx + c = 0$ to be equal, is ______.
    (a) $b + c = 0$ (b) $b - c = 0$
    (c) $a + c = 0$ (d) $a + b + c = 0$

18. The quadratic equation having rational coefficients and one of the roots as $4+\sqrt{15}$, is ______.
(a) $x^2 - 8x + 1 = 0$ (b) $x^2 + x - 8 = 0$
(c) $x^2 - x + 8 = 0$ (d) $x^2 + 8x + 8 = 0$

19. Find the nature of the roots of the equation $4x^2 - 2x - 1 = 0$.
(a) Real and equal (b) Rational and unequal
(c) Irrational and unequal (d) Imaginary

20. If the sum of the squares of three consecutive odd natural numbers is 155, then their product will be equal to ______.
(a) 99 (b) 105
(c) 693 (d) 315

21. If A and B are the roots of the quadratic equation $x^2 - 12x + 27 = 0$, then $A^3 + B^3$ is ______.
(a) 27 (b) 729
(c) 756 (d) 64

22. By drawing which of the following graphs can the quadratic equation $4x^2 + 6x - 5 = 0$ be solved by graphical method?
(a) $y = x^2$, $3x - 2y - 5 = 0$
(b) $y = 4x^2$, $6x - 2y - 5 = 0$
(c) $y = x^2$, $6x - y - 5 = 0$
(d) $y = 2x^2$, $6x + 2y - 5 = 0$

23. If the quadratic equation $(a^2 - b^2)x^2 + (b^2 - c^2)x + (c^2 - a^2) = 0$ has equal roots, then which of the following is true?
(a) $b^2 + c^2 = a^2$ (b) $b^2 + c^2 = 2a^2$
(c) $b^2 - c^2 = 2a^2$ (d) $a^2 = b^2 + 2c^2$

24. Which of the following are the roots of the equation $|x|^2 + |x| - 6 = 0$?
(A) 2 (B) −2
(C) 3 (D) −3
(a) Both (A) and (B) (b) Both (C) and (D)
(c) Both (A) and (C) (d) (A), (B), (C) and (D)

25. What are the values of x which satisfy the equation, $\sqrt{5x-6} + \frac{1}{\sqrt{5x-6}} = \frac{10}{3}$?
(a) 3 (b) $4, \frac{11}{9}$
(c) $\frac{11}{9}$ (d) $3, \frac{11}{9}$

Level 2: Review Your Concepts

26. If the roots of the equation $3ax^2 + 2bx + c = 0$ are in the ratio 2 : 3, then ______.
(a) $8ac = 25b$
(b) $8ac = 9b^2$
(c) $8b^2 = 9ac$
(d) $8b^2 = 25ac$

27. Find the roots of the equation $l^2(m^2 - n^2)x^2 + m^2(n^2 - l^2)x + n^2(l^2 - m^2) = 0$.
(a) $1, \frac{n^2(l^2 - m^2)}{l^2(m^2 - n^2)}$ (b) $1, \frac{-m^2(l^2 - n^2)}{l^2(m^2 - n^2)}$
(c) $1, \frac{n^2(l^2 + m^2)}{l^2(m^2 - n^2)}$ (d) $1, \frac{-m^2(l^2 + n^2)}{l^2(m^2 - n^2)}$

28. For all real values of x, $\frac{x^2 - \left(\frac{x}{2}\right) + 1}{x^2 + 1} - \frac{5}{4}$ is ______.
(a) equal to 1 (b) non-negative
(c) greater than $\frac{1}{4}$ (d) non-positive

29. Find the product of the roots of $x^2 + 8x - 16 = 0$.
(a) 8 (b) −8
(c) 16 (d) −16

Level 3: Assess Your Concepts

30. In a forest, a certain number of apes equal to the square of one-eighth of the total number of their group are playing and having great fun. The rest of them are twelve in number and are on an adjoining hill. The echo of their shrieks from the hills frightens them. They come and join the apes in the forest and play with enthusiasm. What is the total number of apes in the forest?
(a) 16 (b) 48
(c) 16 or 48 (d) 64

31. The roots of the equation $x^2 - px + q = 0$ are consecutive integers. Find the discriminant of the equation.
(a) 1 (b) 2
(c) 3 (d) 4

32. Rohan and Sohan were attempting to solve the quadratic equation, $x^2 - ax + b = 0$. Rohan copied the coefficient of x wrongly and obtained the roots as 4 and 12. Sohan copied the constant term wrongly and obtained the roots as −19 and 3. Find the correct roots.
(a) −2 and −24 (b) 2 and 24
(c) 4 and 12 (d) −4 and −12

33. If $(x + 2)(x + 4)(x + 6)(x + 8) = 945$ and x is an integer, then find x.
(a) −1 or −11 (b) 1 or −11
(c) −1 or 11 (d) 1 or 11

34. The difference of the roots of $2y^2 - ky + 16 = 0$ is $\frac{1}{3}$. Find k.
(a) $\pm\frac{32}{3}$ (b) $\pm\frac{34}{3}$
(c) $\pm\frac{38}{3}$ (d) $\pm\frac{40}{3}$

35. Find the condition to be satisfied by the coefficients of the equation $px^2 + qx + r = 0$, so that the roots are in the ratio 3 : 4.
(a) $12q^2 = 49pr$ (b) $12q^2 = -49pr$
(c) $49q^2 = 12\,pr$ (d) $49q^2 = -12pr$

36. If the roots of the equation $3x^2 + 9x + 2 = 0$ are in the ratio $m : n$, then find $\sqrt{\frac{m}{n}} + \sqrt{\frac{n}{m}}$.
(a) $\frac{-3\sqrt{3}}{\sqrt{2}}$ (b) $\frac{3\sqrt{2}}{2}$
(c) $\frac{3\sqrt{3}}{\sqrt{2}}$ (d) $\frac{-3\sqrt{3}}{2}$

37. If $(p^2 - q^2)\,x^2 + (q^2 - r^2)\,x + r^2 - p^2 = 0$ and $(p^2 - q^2)\,y^2 + (r^2 - p^2)\,y + q^2 - r^2 = 0$ have a common root for all real values of p, q and r, then find the common root.
(a) −1 (b) 1
(c) 2 (d) −2

38. Which of the following are the roots of $|y|^2 - |y| - 12 = 0$?
(A) 4 (B) −4
(C) 3 (D) −3
(a) Both (A) and (B) (b) Both (C) and (D)
(c) Both (A) and (C) (d) (A), (B), (C), and (D)

39. Find the value of $\sqrt{30+\sqrt{30+\sqrt{30+\cdots\infty}}}$.
(a) 6 (b) −5
(c) Either (a) or (b) (d) Neither (a) nor (b)

40. If $y^2 + 6y - 3m = 0$ and $y^2 - 3y + m = 0$ have a common root, then find the possible values of m.
(a) $0, -\frac{27}{16}$ (b) $0, -\frac{81}{16}$
(c) $0, \frac{81}{16}$ (d) $0, \frac{27}{16}$

41. The graphs of $y = 2x^2$ and $y = ax + b$ intersect at two points (2, 8) and (6, 72). Find the quadratic equation in x whose roots are $a + 2$ and $\frac{b}{4} - 1$.
(a) $x^2 + 11x - 126 = 0$ (b) $x^2 - 11x + 126 = 0$
(c) $x^2 + 11x + 126 = 0$ (d) $x^2 - 11x - 126 = 0$

42. The equation $9y^2(m + 3) + 6(m - 3)y + (m + 3) = 0$, where m is real, has real roots. Which of the following is true?
(a) $m = 0$ (b) $m < 0$
(c) Either (a) or (b) (d) Neither (a) nor (b)

43. An engineer drew a blueprint for the construction of a tunnel. The cross-section of the tunnel is shown in the figure. The equation of the curve is $y = 25 - x^2$ and that of BC is $y = 0$. $x^2 - 25 = 0$. The shaded portion represents the masonry portion under the tunnel and ΔPBC is the opening under the tunnel, where P is any point on the curve. What is the area of the biggest such ΔPBC? (The parabola has the maximum area at the vertex of the parabola)

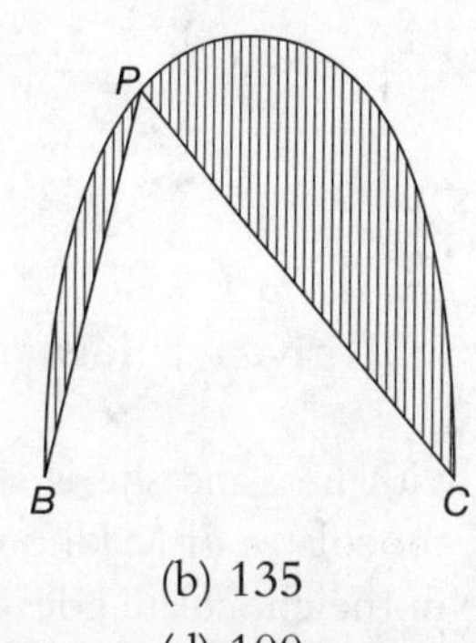

(a) 120 (b) 135
(c) 125 (d) 100

PRACTICE QUESTIONS JEE SPECIAL WING

Multiple-Answer Type Questions

Directions for questions 1 to 5:
Each question has FOUR options (a), (b), (c), and (d). ONE OR MORE THAN ONE of these four option(s) is/are the correct answer(s).

1. The graph of $y = x^2 - 6x + 8$ lies in ____ .
   (a) Q_1 (b) Q_2
   (c) Q_3 (d) Q_4

2. Given that $\alpha < 0$ and $\beta > 0$. α and β are the roots of $ax^2 + bx + c = 0$, where α numerically greater than β. Which of the following is/are true?
   (a) $a > 0, b > 0, c < 0$ (b) $a < 0, b > 0, c > 0$
   (c) $a < 0, b < 0, c > 0$ (d) $a > 0, b < 0, c < 0$

3. If the minimum value of $3x^2 - 3px + p$ is –8, then which of the following is the value of p?
   (a) –4 (b) $\frac{-8}{3}$
   (c) 4 (d) $\frac{4}{3}$

4. Which of the following is true about the vertex of the graph of $-2x^2 + 7x - 6$?
   (a) The x –coordinate is $\frac{3}{8}$
   (b) The y –coordinate is $\frac{-9}{4}$
   (c) The x –coordinate is $\frac{7}{4}$.
   (d) The y –coordinate is $\frac{1}{8}$

5. Which of the following is true about $x^2 - 13|x| + 42 = 0$?
   (a) Sum of the roots is 13.
   (b) The product of the roots is 42.
   (c) Sum of the roots is 0.
   (d) The product of the roots is 1764.

Match The Column

Directions for questions 6 to 10:
Read the paragraph given below and answer the questions.

A : $4x^2 - 16x + 25 = 0$
B : $2x^2 + 7x = 3$
C : $6x^2 - 17x + 12 = 0$
D : $49x^2 + 294x + 441 = 0$
E : $6x^2 + 21x + 6 = 0$

Column A [Equation]	Column B [Roots]
6. *A*	(a) Reciprocal to each other
7. *B*	(b) Negative integers
8. *C*	(c) Rational numbers
9. *D*	(d) Irrational numbers
10. *E*	(e) Imaginary numbers

Comprehension-Based Questions

Directions for questions 11 to 15:
Read the paragraph given below and answer the questions.

Ms Aira has ₹180 with her, and she is able to purchase a certain number of chocolates of Madhur with her pocket money. If the price of the chocolate goes up by ₹3, she can purchase 2 less chocolates. The initial number of chocolates is represented by y and the initial price is represented by x.

11. The equation in terms of x is ____ .
    (a) $x^2 - 3x - 180 = 0$ (b) $x^2 - 2x - 120 = 0$
    (c) $x^2 + 3x - 270 = 0$ (d) $x^2 + 2x - 120 = 0$

12. What is the quadratic equation whose roots are 5 more than that of the equation obtained in the 11th question?
    (a) $x^2 - 13x - 140 = 0$ (b) $x^2 - 12x - 85 = 0$
    (c) $x^2 - 8x - 105 = 0$ (d) $x^2 - 7x - 260 = 0$

13. The equation in terms of y is ____ .
    (a) $y^2 - 3y - 180 = 0$ (b) $y^2 - 2y - 120 = 0$
    (c) $y^2 + 3y - 270 = 0$ (b) $y^2 + 2y - 120 = 0$

14. What is the quadratic equation whose roots are 2 less than that of the equation obtained in the 13th question?

(a) $y^2 + y - 182 = 0$ (b) $y^2 + 7y - 170 = 0$
(c) $y^2 + 2y - 120 = 0$ (b) $y^2 + 6y - 112 = 0$

15. Find the values of x and y.

(a) $x = 15$ and $y = 12$ (b) $x = 12$ and $y = 15$
(c) $x = 18$ and $y = 15$ (d) $x = 15$ and $y = 18$

Assertion and Reason Type Questions

Directions for questions 16 to 19:
Read the options given below and answer the questions.

(a) Both assertion (A) and reason (R) are true, and reason (R) is the correct explanation of assertion.
(b) Both assertion (A) and reason (R) are true, and reason (R) is not the correct explanation of assertion.
(c) Assertion (A) is true, but reason (R) is false.
(d) Assertion (A) is false, and reason (R) is true.

16. Assertion: The maximum value of $-x^2 - 6x + 17$ is 26.

Reason: $ax^2 + bx + c$ has a maximum value, if $a < 0$.

17. Assertion: If one of the roots of $ax^2 + bx + c = 0$, where a, b and c are rational, is $\sqrt{5} - 7$, then the other roots is $-\sqrt{5} - 7$.

Reason: If α and β are the irrational roots of $ax^2 + bx + c = 0$, where a, b and c are rational, then α and β are conjugate to each other.

18. Assertion: The roots of $3x^2 - 5x + 4 = 0$ are imaginary.

Reason: If $b^2 - 4ac < 0$, then $ax^2 + bx + c$ has imaginary roots.

19. Assertion: $\sqrt{240 + \sqrt{240 + \sqrt{240 + \sqrt{240 + \ldots\infty}}}} = 16$

Reason: For any integer value of x, the value of $\sqrt{x + \sqrt{x + \sqrt{x + \sqrt{x + \ldots\infty}}}}$ is an integer.

ANSWER KEYS

Crossword

Across

3. Conjugate 6. Pure 7. Roots 8. Real 9. Equal

Down

1. Negative 2. One 3. Complex 4. Parabola 5. Two

Classroom Wing

Very Short Answer Type Questions

1. $x^2 - 6x + 7 = 0$
2. $x^2 - 10x + 22 = 0$
3. –2, 3
4. $-\sqrt{2}$ and $\sqrt{3}$
5. $2\sqrt{5}$
6. 4
7. 6
8. True
9. 3, 2
10. 5 years
11. True
12. 7
13. Length = 19 m, breadth = 12 m
14. 0, k

Short Answer Type Questions

15. irrational and distinct
16. complex conjugates
17. CADB
18. 36
19. –36
20. $x = 7$
21. b and $(a - b)$
22. 30
23. 5 or 7
24. 34
25. $m \in (-\infty, -6) \cup (-2, \infty)$
26. $\frac{5}{4}$

Essay Type Questions

27. (1, 1)
28. 16
29. 1
30. 11
31. 4 or –5
32. 1
33. $2\frac{1}{2}$ hrs
34. 60

Competition Wing

Level 1: Apply Your Concepts

1. reciprocal
2. pure
3. positive
4. 3, 5
5. 6 cm and 8 cm
6. (a)
7. (d)
8. (b)
9. (a)
10. (b)
11. (b)
12. (c)
13. (b)
14. (d)
15. (d)
16. (b)
17. (b)
18. (a)
19. (c)
20. (d)
21. (c)
22. (d)
23. (b)
24. (a)
25. (d)

Level 2: Review Your Concepts

26. (d)
27. (a)
28. (d)
29. (d)

Level 3: Assess Your Concepts

30. (a)
31. (a)
32. (d)
33. (b)
34. (b)
35. (a)
36. (a)
37. (b)
38. (a)
39. (a)
40. (d)
41. (d)
42. (c)
43. (c)

JEE Special Wing

Multiple-Answer Type Questions

1. (a, b, d) 2. (a, c) 3. (b, c) 4. (c, d) 5. (c, d)

Match The Column

6. (e) 7. (d) 8. (c) 9. (b) 10. (a)

Comprehension-Based Questions

11. (c) 12. (d) 13. (b) 14. (c) 15. (a)

Assertion and Reason Type Questions

16. (b) 17. (a) 18. (a) 19. (c)

Hints and Explanations

Classroom Wing

Very Short Answer Type Questions

1. Given one root is $3+\sqrt{2}$, The other root will be $3-\sqrt{2}$.

$\therefore$ The required quadratic equation is

$x^2-\left[\left(3+\sqrt{2}\right)+\left(3-\sqrt{2}\right)\right]x+\left(3+\sqrt{2}\right)\left(3-\sqrt{2}\right)=0$

$\Rightarrow x^2-6x+7=0$

2. Given one root is $5-\sqrt{3}$, The other root will be $5+\sqrt{3}$.

$\therefore$ The required quadratic equation is

$x^2-\left[\left(5+\sqrt{3}\right)+\left(5-\sqrt{3}\right)\right]x+\left(5+\sqrt{3}\right)\left(5-\sqrt{3}\right)=0$

$x^2-10x+22=0$

3. The roots of $(x-3)(x+2)=0$ are -2, 3.

4. The roots of $\left(x+\sqrt{2}\right)\left(x-\sqrt{3}\right)=0$ are $-\sqrt{2}$ and $\sqrt{3}$.

5. Let one side be a

Second side be b such that, $a=2b$

$\sqrt{a^2+b^2}=5,\ ab=5$

$a^2+b^2=25$

$4a^2+b^2=25$

$5b^2=25$

$b^2=5$

$b=\sqrt{5},\quad a=2\sqrt{5}$

6. Let positive number $= x$

$x^2-x=12$

$x^2-x-12=0$

$x^2-4x+3x-12=0$

$x(x-4)+3(x-4)=0$

$x=-3,\ x=4$

Negative rejected.

7. $x(x+2)=48$

$x^2+2x-48=0$

$x^2+8x-6x-48=0$

$x(x+8)-6(x+8)=0$

$x=6,\ x=-8$

Negative rejected

8. $x=1$

$y=-6$

$y=x^2-x-6$

$-6=(1)-(1)-6$

$-6=-6$

Yes, the statement is true.

9. $y=5x-6,\quad y=x^2$

$x^2=5x-6$

$x^2-5x+6=0$

$x^2-3x-2x+6=0$

$x(x-3)-2(x-3)=0$

$x=2,\ x=3$

10. Let Shiva's present age $= x$

$(x-3)(x+3)=16$

$x^2-3x+3x-9=16$

$x^2=25$

$x=\pm 5$

$x=-5,\ x=5$

Negative rejected.

11. True

12. $x^2-x=42<0$

$x^2-x-42=0$

$x^2-7x+6x-42=0$

$x(x-7)+6(x-7)=0$

$(x+6)(x-7)=0$

$x=7$

$x=-6$

Negative rejected

13. Let the length be xm

breadth $=(x-7)m$

Area $=228$

$x(x-7)=228$

$x^2-7x-228=0$

$x^2-19x+12x-228=0$

$x(x-19)+12(x-19)=0$

$(x+12)(x-19)=0$

$x=-12$ Rejected

$x=19$

Length $=19$ m, Breadth $=12$ m

14. $y=\sqrt{k\sqrt{k\sqrt{k\ldots\infty}}}$

$y=\sqrt{k\sqrt{y}}$

$y^2=ky$

$y^2-ky=0$

$y(y-k)=0$

$y=0, y=k$

Short Answer Type Questions

15. Given $5x^2-2x-1=0$

Discriminant $(\Delta)=b^2-4ac$

$=(-2)^2-4(5)(-1)$

$=4+20$

$=24>0$

The roots are irrational and distinct.

16. Given $x^2-x+1=0$

Discriminant $(\Delta)=b^2-4ac$

$=(-1)^2-4(1)(1)$

$=1-4$

$=-3<0$

The roots are complex conjugates.

17. The required sequential order is CADB.

18. $xy=18$

$10x+y+27=10y+x$

$9x-9y=-27$

$y-x=3$

$\frac{18}{x}-x=3$

$18-x^2=3x$

$x^2+3x-18=0$

$x^2+6x-3x-18=0$

$x(x+6)-3(x+6)=0$

$x=3, x=-6$

Negative rejected

$xy=18$

$(3)y=18\Rightarrow y=6$

Number $=10x+y$

$=10(3)+6=36$

19. x^2+12x

$\frac{d}{du}(x^2+12x)$

$2x+12=0\Rightarrow x=-6$

Minimum value occurs at -6

$=(-6)^2+12(-6)$

$=36-72=-36$

20. Here, $3x+4$ is the largest side

Apply Pythagoras' theorem

$x^2+(3x+3)^2=(3x+4)^2$

$x^2+9x^2+9+18x=9x^2+16+24x$

$x^2+9+18x-16-24x=0$

$x^2-6x-7=0$

$x^2-7x+x-7=0$

$x(x-7)+1(x-7)=0$

$x=7, x=-1$

Negative rejected, $x=7$

21. $\frac{1}{x}-\frac{1}{x-a}=\frac{1}{b}-\frac{1}{b-a}$

$\frac{x-a-x}{x(x-a)}=\frac{b-a-b}{b(b-a)}$

$\frac{-a}{x^2-ax}=\frac{-a}{b^2-ab}$

$x^2-ax=b^2-ab$

$x^2-ax-b^2+ab=0$

Roots $=\frac{a\pm\sqrt{a^2-4(-b^2+ab)}}{2}$

$=\frac{a\pm\sqrt{a^2+4b^2-4ab}}{2}$

$=\frac{a\pm\sqrt{(a-2b)^2}}{2}$

$=\frac{a\pm(a-2b)}{2}$

$\alpha=\frac{a+(a-2b)}{2}$ $\beta=\frac{a-a+2b}{2}$

$\alpha=a-b$ $\beta=b$

22. Let no. of rooms = x
Total rooms = $2x$
And in every room $x - 10$ students
$2x(x-10) = 1200$
$2x^2 - 20x - 1200 = 0$
$x^2 - 30x + 20x - 600 = 0$
$x(x-30) + 20(x-30) = 0$
$(x+20)(x-30) = 0$
$x = 30, x = -20$
Negative rejected

23. $x^2 + 3x + 2 = 0$
$(x+1)(x+2) = 0$
$x = -1$
$x = -2$
$(-1)^2 + k(-1) + 6 = 0$
$+1 - k + 6 = 0$
$k = 7$
Or
$(-2)^2 + k(-2) + 6 = 0$
$4 + (-2k) + 6 = 0$
$k = 5$

24. $x^4 - 17x^2 + 16 = 0$
Let $x^2 = a$
$a^2 - 17a + 16 = 0$
$a^2 - 16a - a + 16 = 0$
$a(a-16) - 1(a-16) = 0$
$(a-1)(a-16) = 0$
$a = 1, a = 16$
$x^2 = 1$
$x = 1, -1$
$x^2 = 16$
$x = +4, -4$
Sum of square of roots,
$1^2 + (-1)^2 + (4)^2 + (-4)^2$
$1 + 1 + 16 + 16$
$= 34$

25. $x^2 - mx - 4x + 1 = 0$
Real and distinct roots
$D > 0$
$b^2 - 4ac > 0$
$(-m-4)^2 - 4(1) > 0$
$m^2 + 16 + 8m - 4 > 0$
$m^2 + 8m + 12 > 0$
$m^2 + 6m + 2m + 12 > 0$
$m(m+6) + 2(m+6) > 0$
$(m+2)(m+6) > 0$
$m > -2, m > -6$
$m \in (-\infty, -6) \cup (-2, \infty)$

26. $\sqrt{y+1} - \sqrt{y-1} = \sqrt{4y-1}$
Squaring both sides
$(y+1) + (y-1) - 2\sqrt{y+1}\sqrt{y-1} = 4y - 1$
$2y - 2\sqrt{y^2-1} = 4y - 1$
$1 - 2y = 2\sqrt{y^2-1}$
Squaring both sides,
$1 + 4y^2 - 4y = 4(y^2 - 1)$
$1 + 4y^2 - 4y = 4y^2 - 4$
$-4y = -5$
$y = \frac{5}{4}$

Essay Type Questions

27. $x^2 - 2x + 1 = 0$
$y = x^2 - 2x + 1$
At $x = 0,\ y = 1$
At $x = 1,\ y = 0$
At $x = 2,\ y = 1$
At $x = 3,\ y = 4$
At $x = -1,\ y = 4$
At $x = -2,\ y = 7$

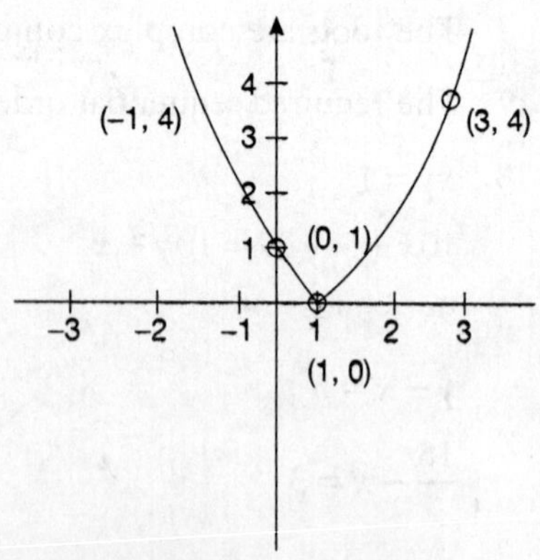

28. Let $x = \sqrt{240 + \sqrt{240 + \sqrt{240 + \ldots\infty}}}$
$\Rightarrow\ x^2 = 240 + \sqrt{240 + \sqrt{240 + \ldots\infty}}$
$\Rightarrow x^2 = 240 + x$
$\Rightarrow x^2 - x - 240 = 0$
$\Rightarrow (x-16)(x+15) = 0$
$\Rightarrow x = 16$ or $x = -15$ (not possible)
$\therefore x = 16$

29. Let the speed of the stream be x kmph.

The speed of boat upstream = $(5 - x)$ kmph

The speed of boat downstream = $(5 - x)$ kmph

$$\Rightarrow \frac{24}{5-x} + \frac{24}{5+x} = 0$$

$$\Rightarrow 24\left(\frac{5+x+5-x}{25-x^2}\right) = 10$$

$$\Rightarrow 25 - x^2 = 24 \Rightarrow x^2 = 1 \Rightarrow x = \pm 1$$

$x = -1$ is not possible.

$\therefore x = 1$

30. Let $y = \sqrt{132 - \sqrt{132 - \sqrt{132 - \ldots\infty}}}$

$y^2 = 132 - \sqrt{132 - \sqrt{132 - \ldots\infty}}$

$y^2 = 132 - y$

$y^2 = y - 132 = 0$

$(y + 12)(y - 11) = 0$

$y = -12$ (not possible) or $y = 11$

$\therefore y = 11$

31. Let the number be x

Given $x^2 - x = 20$

$x^2 - x - 20 = 0$

$x^2 + 5x - 4x - 20 = 0$

$x(x + 5) - 4(x + 5) = 0$

$(x + 5)(x - 4) = 0$

$x = 4$ or -5

Two numbers are follows.

32. Maximum value of $-3x^2 + 3x + k$ is $\frac{4ac - b^2}{4a}$

$$= \frac{4\times(-3)(k) - (3)^2}{4\times(-3)} = \frac{-12k - 9}{-12} = \frac{4k+3}{4}$$

Minimum value of $2x^2 + 2x + k = 0$ is

$$\frac{4ac - b^2}{4a} = \frac{4(2)(k) - (2)^2}{4\times 2}$$

$$= \frac{8k-4}{8} = \frac{2k-1}{2}$$

Given that

$$\frac{4k+3}{4} + \frac{15-8}{9+1} = \frac{9}{4}$$

$$\frac{4k+3+4k-2}{4} = \frac{9}{4}$$

$\Rightarrow 8k + 1 = 9 \Rightarrow k = 1.$

33. Let the time taken at his usual speed be x hrs.

We know that $\frac{\text{distance}}{\text{time}}$ = speed.

$$\frac{180}{x - \frac{1}{2}} - \frac{180}{x} = 5 \text{ m/s}$$

$$\frac{180}{\left(\frac{2x-1}{2}\right)} - \frac{180}{x} = 5 \times \frac{18}{5} \text{ km}$$

$$180\left(\frac{2x - (2x-1)}{x(2x-1)}\right) = 18$$

$$\frac{1}{2x^2 - x} = \frac{1}{10}.$$

$2x^2 - x - 10 = 0$

$2x^2 - 5x + 4x - 10 = 0$

$x(2x - 5) + 2(2x - 5) = 0$

$(2x - 5)(x + 2) = 0$

$2x - 5 = 0$ or $x + 2 = 0$

$x = \frac{5}{2}$ or $x = -2$.

Time taken at his usual speed = $\frac{5}{2}$ hrs = $2\frac{1}{2}$ hrs.

34. Let the time taken by tap 'B' to fill the tank be x min.

$\Rightarrow$ A can fill the tank in $(x - 15)$ minutes

Both the taps together can fill the tank in $\frac{3}{7}$ hrs

Part of the tank filled in one minute = $\frac{7}{180}$

$$\frac{1}{x} + \frac{1}{x-15} = \frac{7}{180}$$

$$\frac{x-15+x}{x(x-15)} = \frac{7}{180}$$

$360x - 2700 = 7x^2 - 105x$

$7x^2 - 465x + 2700 = 0$

$7x^2 - 420x - 45x + 2700 = 0$

$(x - 60)(7x - 45) = 0$

$\Rightarrow x - 60 = 0$ or $7x - 45 = 0$

$x = 60$ or $x = \frac{45}{7}$. As $x - 15 > 0$, $x = 60$.

$\therefore$ Tap B alone can fill the tank in 60 mins.

Competition Wing

Level 1: Apply Your Concepts

1. Direct property reciprocal
2. Pure quadratic equation.
3. $\alpha+\beta>0$

   $\alpha\beta<0$

   Greater root should be positive to make sure positive.
4. $a+b=8$

   $a\times b=15$

   $a=\frac{15}{b}$

   $b+\frac{15}{b}=8$

   $b^2+15=8b$

   $b^2-8b+15=0$

   $b^2-5b-3b+15=0$

   $b(b-5)-3(b-5)=0$

   $(b-3)(b-5)=0$

   $b=3$

   $a=5$

   or $b=5$

   $a=3$
5. Let one side be x and other is $x+2$

   Area $=\frac{1}{2}\times x(x+2)=24$

   $x^2+2x-48=0$

   $x^2+8x-6x-48=0$

   $x(x+8)-6(x+6)=0$

   $x=6,\ x=-8$

   second $=6+2=8$
6. $x^2-5x+7=0$

   $a+b=\frac{-(-5)}{1}=5$

   $ab=\frac{7}{1}=7$

   $a^2+b^2=(a+b)^2-2ab=(5)^2-2\times7=25-14=11$

   $(a+b)^2-2ab=(5)^2-2\times7=25-14=11.$

   Hence, the correct option is (a).
7. $|x|^2-5|x|+6=0\Rightarrow|x|^2-3|x|-2|x|+6=0$

   $\Rightarrow(|x|-3)(|x|-2)=0$

   $\Rightarrow|x|=3$ or $|x|=2$

   $x=\pm3$ or $x=\pm2$

   $\therefore$ Number of solutions is 4.

   Hence, the correct option is (d).
8. Given $x^2+2x-3=0$

   $a+b=\frac{-2}{1}=-2$

   $ab=\frac{-3}{1}=-3$

   $\frac{a}{b}+\frac{b}{a}=\frac{a^2+b^2}{ab}=\frac{(a+b)^2-2ab}{ab}$

   $=\frac{(2)^2-2(-3)}{-3}=\frac{4+6}{-3}=\frac{-10}{3}$

   Hence, the correct option is (b).
9. $|x|^2+7|x|+12=0\Rightarrow(|x|+3)(|x|+4)=0$

   $\Rightarrow|x|=-3$ or $|x|=-4$, which are not possible.

   No solution for given equation.

   Hence, the correct option is (a).
10. Given $2x^2-8x+p=0$

    Discriminant $(\Delta)=b^2-4ac=-64$

    $\Rightarrow(-8)^2=4(2)(p)=-64$

    $\Rightarrow 8p=128$

    $p=16$

    Hence, the correct option is (b).
11. Given α and β are the roots of the equation.

    $x^2-3x+2=0$

    $\Rightarrow\alpha+\beta=\frac{-b}{a}=3$

    $\alpha\beta=\frac{c}{a}=2$

    $\frac{1}{a}+\frac{1}{b}=\frac{a+b}{ab}=\frac{3}{2}$

    Hence, the correct option is (b).
12. Take the first-degree expression and the constant on the other side.
13. Use $x^2-(\alpha+\beta)x+\alpha\beta=0$.
14. Use $\alpha+\beta=-\frac{b}{a}$ and $\alpha\beta=\frac{c}{a}$.
15. Simplify and solve by finding $\alpha+\beta$ and $\alpha\beta$. Where $\beta=2\alpha$.
16. Let the number be x and frame the inequations.

17. Find the sum and the product of the roots then equate them.

18. If one of the roots is $a+\sqrt{b}$, this the other root is $a-\sqrt{b}$.

19. Use the formula of discriminant.

20. Let the three consecutive odd natural numbers be $x-2$, x and $x+2$.

21. Find the roots or write A^3+B^3 in terms of $A+B$ and AB.

22. Take $6x-5$ on other side.

23. Observe the coefficient of each term and guess one root.

24. (i) Put $|x| = y$ and frame the equation.
(ii) Solve for y.

25. Find the LCM and then square on both sides.

Level 2: Review Your Concepts

26. If the roots of $ax^2+bx+c=0$ are in the ratio $m : n$, then $(m+n)^2\, a \cdot c = mnb^2$.

27. In the equation $ax^2+bx+c=0$ when $a+b+c=0$, then the roots are 1 and $\frac{c}{a}$.

28. Simplify the expression and identify whether it is non-positive or non-negative.

29. $x^2+8x-16=0$.

The product of the roots $=\frac{c}{a}=-16$.

Level 3: Assess Your Concepts

30. (i) Let the number of apes be equal to n.
(ii) The number of apes which are on the adjoining hills is $n-\frac{n^2}{64}$, which is equal to 12.

31. Let the roots be α and $\alpha+1$.

$\alpha+(\alpha+1)=p$, i.e., $2\alpha+1=p$.

$(\alpha)(\alpha+1)=\frac{q}{1}=q$.

Discriminant $=p^2-4q=(2\alpha+1)^2-4(\alpha)(\alpha+1)=4\alpha^2+4\alpha+1-4\alpha^2-4\alpha=1$.

32. Rohan copied only the coefficient of x wrongly.

$\therefore$ He must have copied the constant term correctly.

$\therefore$ Correct product of the roots $=\frac{b}{1}=4(12)$

$\Rightarrow b=48$

Sohan copied only the constant term wrongly.

$\therefore$ He must have copied the coefficient of x correctly.

$\therefore$ Correct sum of the roots $=a=-19+3=-16$

Correct equation is $x^2-(-16)x+48=0$

$\Rightarrow x^2+16x+48=0$

$\Rightarrow (x+4)(x+12)=0$

$\Rightarrow x=-4$ or -12.

$\therefore$ Correct roots are -4 and -12.

33. As x is an integer.

$\therefore$ $x+2$, $x+4$, $x+6$ and $x+8$ are four consecutive odd/even integers. Their product = 945, which is odd.

$\therefore$ $x+2$, $x-4$, $x+6$ and $x+8$ must be odd.

Factorizing 945 as a product of 4 consecutive odd integers.

We have, $945=3(5)(7)(9)=(-3)(-5)(-7)(-9)$

$\therefore$ The smallest, i.e., $x+2=3$ or -9.

$\therefore$ $x=1$ or $x=-11$.

34. Let the roots of $2y^2-ky+16=0$ be α and β, where with $\alpha \geq \beta$. $\alpha+\beta=\frac{k}{2}$ and $\alpha\beta=8$.

Difference of its roots > 0. $\alpha \neq \beta$

$\therefore$ $\alpha > \beta$

$\therefore$ Difference of its roots $=\alpha-\beta=\frac{1}{3}$

$(\alpha-\beta)^2=(\alpha+\beta)^2-4\alpha\beta$

$$\left(\frac{1}{3}\right)^2=\left(\frac{k}{2}\right)^2-4(8)$$

$$\left(\frac{k}{2}\right)^2=\frac{289}{9}=\left(\frac{17}{3}\right)^2$$

$$\Rightarrow \frac{k}{2}=\pm\frac{17}{3} \Rightarrow k=\pm\frac{34}{3}.$$

35. Let the common factor for the roots be y.

The roots are $3y$ and $4y$, $3y+4y=\frac{-q}{p}$

$$\Rightarrow y=\frac{-q}{7p}$$

$$(3y)(4y)=\frac{r}{p} \Rightarrow y^2=\frac{r}{12p}$$

$$y^2=\left(\frac{-q}{7p}\right)^2=\frac{r}{12p} 12q^2=49pr.$$

36. Let the common factor for the roots be y.
The roots are my and ny.
$my + ny = -3 \Rightarrow (m + n)\, y = -3$
We can take m, n as positive and y as negative
$(my)(ny) = \frac{2}{3}$.
Now, $\sqrt{\frac{m}{n}} + \sqrt{\frac{n}{m}} = \frac{m+n}{\sqrt{mn}}$
Multiplying the numerator denominator by y, we have:
$\frac{m+n}{\sqrt{mn}} = \frac{y(m+n)}{y\sqrt{mn}} = \frac{y(m+n)}{\sqrt{(my)(ny)}}$
$= \frac{-3}{\sqrt{\frac{2}{3}}} = \frac{-3\sqrt{3}}{\sqrt{2}}$.

37. $(p^2 - q^2)\, x^2 + (q^2 - r^2)\, x + (r^2 - p^2) = 0$ (1)
The sum of the coefficients $(p^2 - q^2) + (q^2 - r^2) + (r^2 - p^2) = 0$
$\therefore x = 1$ is a root of Eq. (1)
$(p^2 - q^2)\, y^2 + (r^2 - p^2)\, y + q^2 - r^2 = 0$ (2)
$p^2 - q^2 + r^2 - p^2 + q^2 - r^2 = 0$
$\therefore y = 1$ is a root of Eq. (2)
$\therefore$ 1 is the common root of Eqs. (1) and (2).

38. $|y|^2 - |y| - 12 = 0$
$(|y| - 4)\,(|y| + 3) = 0$
$|y| = 4$ or -3.
But $|y|$ must be non-negative.
$\therefore |y| = 4$, i.e., $y = \pm 4$.

39. $x = \sqrt{30 + x}$
Squaring on both sides, we get $x^2 = 30 + x$
$x^2 - x - 30 = 0$
$(x - 6)(x + 5) = 0$
$x = 6$ or -5.
But x must be positive.
$\therefore x = 6$.

40. Let the common root be c.
$c^2 + 6c - 3m = 0$ and $c^2 - 3c + m = 0$
That is, $3m = c^2 + 6c$ and $m = 3c - c^2$
$\therefore 3m = c^2 + 6c = 3\,(3c - c^2)$
$c^2 + 6c = 9c - 3c^2$
$4c^2 - 3c = 0$
$c = 0$ or $\frac{3}{4}$
If $c = 0$, $m = 0$
If $c = \frac{3}{4}$, $m = \frac{27}{16}$.

41. At (2, 8) and (6, 72), $y = 2x^2 = ax + b$
$8 = 2a + b$ and $72 = 6a + b$.
Solving for a and b, $a = 16$ and $b = -24$.
The required equation is that whose roots are 18 and -7.
Sum of its roots = 11
Product of its roots = -126
$\therefore$ The Required equation is $x^2 - 11x - 126 = 0$.

43.
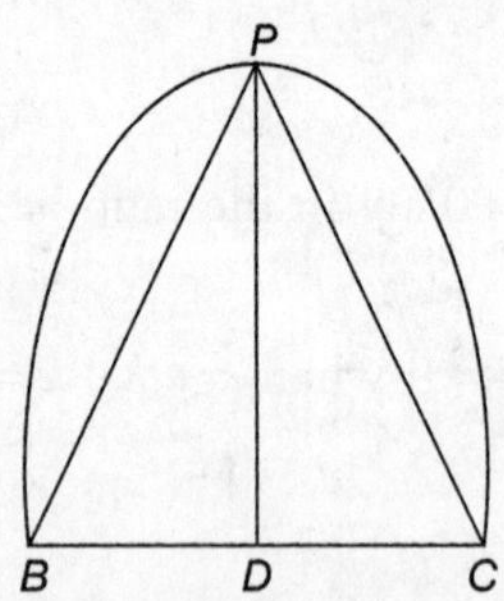

The equation of curve is $y = 25 - x^2$ and that of BC is $y = 0$.
$\Rightarrow x^2 - 25 = 0 \Rightarrow x^2 = 25$ and $x = \pm 5$
$\therefore B(-5, 0)$ and $C(5, 0)$
$BC = 10$ units.
For the biggest ΔPBC, PD is the highest.
For the maximum value of PD(= y), the value of x^2 is minimum.
$\therefore$ The maximum value of x^2 is zero.
$\therefore$ The maximum value of $y = 25 - x^2$
$= 25 - 0 = 25$.
$\therefore PD = 25$ units.
Area of $\Delta ABC = \frac{1}{2}\; BC \times PD$
$= \frac{150}{2} \times 10 \times 25 = 125$ sq.units.

JEE Special Wing

Multiple-Answer Type Questions

1. Given that $y = x^2 - 6x + 8$.
$\Rightarrow y = x^2 - 6x + 9 - 1$
$\Rightarrow y = (x-3)^2 - 1$
We know that $(x-3)^2 \geq 0$ for any real value of x.
When $x = 3$, $y = -1$. So, (x, y) belongs to Q_4.
When x is a positive number other than 3, y is also a positive number.
So, (x, y) belongs to Q_1.
When x is a negative number, y is a positive number.
So, (x, y) belongs to Q_2.
Hence, the graph of $y = x^2 - 6x + 8$ lies in Q_1, Q_2, and Q_4.
Hence, the choices (a, b, d) are correct.

2. Given that α and β are the roots of $ax^2 + bx + c = 0$, where α numerically greater than β, where $\alpha < 0$ and $\beta > 0$.
$\Rightarrow \alpha + \beta < 0$ and $\alpha \times \beta < 0$
$\Rightarrow \frac{-b}{a} < 0$ and $\frac{c}{a} < 0$.
$\Rightarrow \frac{b}{a} > 0$ and $\frac{c}{a} < 0$.
As $\frac{b}{a} > 0$, (i) $b > 0$ and $a > 0$ **(or)** (ii) $b < 0$ and $a < 0$.
When (i) $b > 0$ and $a > 0$, $c < 0$ since $\frac{c}{a} < 0$.
When (ii) $b < 0$ and $a < 0$, $c > 0$ since $\frac{c}{a} < 0$.
Hence, the choices (a and c) are correct.

3. Given that the minimum value of $3x^2 - 3px + p$ is -8.
When compared $3x^2 - 3px + p$ with $ax^2 + bx + c$, $a = 3$, $b = -3p$, and $c = p$.
$\Rightarrow \frac{4ac - b^2}{4a} = -8.$
$\Rightarrow \frac{4 \times 3 \times p - (-3p)^2}{4 \times 3} = -8.$
$\Rightarrow \frac{12p - 9p^2}{4 \times 3} = -8.$
$\Rightarrow \frac{4p - 3p^2}{4} = -8.$
$\Rightarrow 4p - 3p^2 = -32.$
$\Rightarrow 3p^2 - 4p - 32 = 0.$
$\Rightarrow 3p^2 - 12p + 8p - 32 = 0.$
$\Rightarrow 3p(p-4) + 8(p-4) = 0.$
$\Rightarrow (p-4)(3p+8) = 0.$
$\Rightarrow p = 4$ (or) $p = \frac{-8}{3}$.
Hence, the choices (b and c) are correct.

4. If the vertex of the graph of $-2x^2 + 7x - 6$ is (x, y), where $x = \frac{-b}{2a}$ and $y = \frac{4ac - b^2}{4a}$.
That is the $y-$ coordiante of the graph of $-2x^2 + 7x - 6$ is the maximum value of $-2x^2 + 7x - 6$ and the $x-$ coordiante of the graph is the value of x at which $-2x^2 + 7x - 6$ contains the maximum value.
The $x-$ coordiante of the graph $= \frac{-b}{2a} = \frac{-7}{2 \times (-2)} = \frac{7}{4}$.
The $y-$ coordiante of the graph $= \frac{4ac - b^2}{4a}$
$= \frac{4 \times (-2) \times (-6) - 7^2}{4 \times (-2)}$
$= \frac{48 - 49}{-8} = \frac{1}{8}$.
Hence, the choices (c and d) are correct.

5. Given that $x^2 - 13|x| + 42 = 0$.
Let $|x|$ be y.
$\Rightarrow x^2 = y^2$.
$x^2 - 13|x| + 42 = 0 \Leftrightarrow y^2 - 13y + 42 = 0$
$\Rightarrow y^2 - 6y - 7y + 42 = 0$
$\Rightarrow y(y-6) - 7(y-6) = 0$
$\Rightarrow (y-6)(y-7) = 0$
$\Rightarrow y = 6$ (or) $y = 7$
$\Rightarrow |x| = 6$ (or) $|x| = 7$
$\Rightarrow x = \pm 6$ (or) $x = \pm 7$.
The sum of the roots $= -6 + 6 - 7 + 7 = 0$.
The product of the roots $= (-6) \times 6 \times (-7) \times 7 = 1764$.
Hence, the choices **(c and d)** are correct.

Match The Column

Common Solutions for questions 6 to 10:
Given that:
A : $4x^2 - 16x + 25 = 0$
B : $2x^2 + 7x = 3$
C : $6x^2 - 17x = -12$
D : $49x^2 + 294x + 441 = 0$
E : $6x^2 + 21x + 6 = 0$

6. When compared $4x^2 - 16x + 25 = 0$ with $ax^2 + bx + c = 0$, $a = 4$, $b = -16$, and $c = 25$.
Discriminant $= b^2 - 4ac$
$= (-16)^2 - 4 \times 4 \times 25$
$= 256 - 400 = -144 < 0.$
Hence, the roots are imaginary.
Hence, the correct option is (e).

7. When compared $2x^2 + 7x - 3 = 0$ with $ax^2 + bx + c = 0$, $a = 2$, $b = 7$, and $c = -3$.
Discriminant $= b^2 - 4ac$
$= (7)^2 - 4 \times 2 \times -3$
$= 49 + 24 = 73 > 0$, but not a perfect square.
Hence, the roots are irrational.
Hence, the correct option is (d).

8. When compared $6x^2 - 17x + 12 = 0$ with $ax^2 + bx + c = 0$, $a = 6$, $b = -17$, and $c = 12$.
Discriminant $= b^2 - 4ac$
$= (-17)^2 - 4 \times 6 \times 12$
$= 289 - 288 = 1 > 0$, but a perfect square.
Hence, the roots are rational.
$6x^2 - 17x + 12 = 0$
$\Rightarrow 6x^2 - 9x - 8x + 12 = 0$
$\Rightarrow 3x(2x - 3) - 4(2x - 3) = 0$
$\Rightarrow (2x - 3)(3x - 4) = 0$
$\Rightarrow x = \frac{3}{2} \text{ (or) } x = \frac{4}{3}$
Hence, the roots are rational but not integers.
Hence, the correct option is (c).

9. $49x^2 + 294x + 441 = 0 \Leftrightarrow x^2 + 6x + 9 = 0$
When compared $x^2 + 6x + 9 = 0$ with $ax^2 + bx + c = 0$, $a = 1$, $b = 6$, and $c = 9$.
Discriminant $= b^2 - 4ac$
$= (6)^2 - 4 \times 1 \times 9$
$= 36 - 36 = 0.$
Hence, the roots are equal and rational.
$\Rightarrow (x + 3)^2 = 0$
$\Rightarrow x = -3$
So, the roots are negative integers.
Hence, the correct option is (b).

10. When compared $6x^2 + 21x + 6 = 0$ with $ax^2 + bx + c = 0$, $a = 6$, $b = 21$, and $c = 6$.
Discriminant $= b^2 - 4ac$
$= (21)^2 - 4 \times 6 \times 6$
$= 441 - 144 = 297 > 0$, but not a perfect square.
Hence, the roots are irrational. So, $10 \leftrightarrow d$. But 7th question is already mapped with **d**.
The product of the roots is $\frac{c}{a} = \frac{6}{6} = 1.$
Hence, the roots are reciprocal to each other.
Hence, the correct option is (a).

Comprehension-Based Questions

Common Solutions for questions 11 to 15:

11. As the initial cost of each chocolate is ₹x, she will be able to purchase $\frac{180}{x}$ chocolates.
If the cost of each chocolate increases by ₹3, she would be able to purchase $\frac{180}{x+3}$ chocolates.
From the given data, $\frac{180}{x} - \frac{180}{x+3} = 2.$
$\frac{90}{x} - \frac{90}{x+3} = 1.$
$\frac{90(x + 3 - x)}{x(x+3)} = 1$
$\frac{270}{x^2 + 3x} = 1$
$x^2 + 3x = 270$
$x^2 + 3x - 270 = 0.$
Hence, the correct option is (c).

12. For the quadratic equation whose roots are 5 more than that of $x^2 + 3x - 270 = 0$, let us substitute $x = x - 5$ in $x^2 + 3x - 270 = 0$.
$(x - 5)^2 + 3(x - 5) - 270 = 0$
$x^2 - 10x + 25 + 3x - 15 - 270 = 0$
$x^2 - 7x - 260 = 0.$
Hence, the correct option is (d).

13. As the initial number of chocolates is y, the cost of each chocolate is $\frac{₹180}{y}$.
If the number of chocolates decreases by 2, the cost of each chocolate would be $\frac{₹180}{y-2}$.
From the given data, $\frac{₹180}{y-2} - \frac{₹180}{y} = ₹3.$
$\frac{60}{y-2} - \frac{60}{y} = 1.$
$\frac{60(y - y + 2)}{(y-2)y} = 1.$

$$\frac{120}{y^2 - 2y} = 1$$
$y^2 - 2y = 120$
$y^2 - 2y - 120 = 0.$

Hence, the correct option is (b).

14. For the quadratic equation whose roots are 2 less than that of $y^2 - 2y - 120 = 0$, let us substitute $y = y + 2$ in $y^2 - 2y - 120 = 0$.
$(y+2)^2 - 2(y+2) - 120 = 0$
$y^2 + 4y + 4 - 2y - 4 - 120 = 0$
$y^2 + 2y - 120 = 0$
Hence, the correct option is (c).

15. We have $x^2 + 3x - 270 = 0$.
$x^2 + 18x - 15x - 270 = 0.$
$(x+18)(x-15) = 0.$
$x = -18 \,(\text{or})\, x = 15.$
As x cannot be negative, $x = 15$.
Also, $y^2 - 2y - 120 = 0$.
$y^2 - 12y + 10y - 120 = 0$
$y(y-12) + 10(y-12) = 0$
$(y-12)(y+10) = 0.$
$y = 12 \,(\text{or})\, y = -10$
As y| cannot be negative, $y = 12$.
Hence, $x = 15$ and $y = 12$.
Hence, the correct option is (a).

Assertion and Reason Type Questions

16. **Assertion:** If $a < 0$, the maximum value of
$ax^2 + bx + c = \frac{4ac - b^2}{4a}$.
The maximum value of $-x^2 - 6x + 17$
$$= \frac{4 \times (-1) \times (17) - (-6)^2}{4 \times (-1)}$$
$$= \frac{-68 - 36}{-4}$$
$$= \frac{-104}{-4} = 26.$$
So, **Assertion** is true.
Reason: $ax^2 + bx + c$ has a maximum value, if $a < 0$. It is a true statement, but it is not the correct explanation of **Assertion**.
Hence, the correct option is (b).

17. **Assertion:** If one of the roots of $ax^2 + bx + c = 0$, where a, b and c are rational, is $\sqrt{5} - 7$, then the other roots is $-\sqrt{5} - 7$.
It is a true statement, since if the roots are irrational, then they are conjugate to each other.
Reason: If α and β are the irrational roots of $ax^2 + bx + c = 0$, where a, b and c are rational, then α and β are conjugate to each other. It is a true statement and is the correct explanation of the **Assertion**.
Hence, the correct option is (a).

18. **Assertion:** Given that $3x^2 - 5x + 3 = 0$.
Discriminant $= b^2 - 4ac$
$= (-5)^2 - 4(3)(3) = -11 < 0.$
As the discriminant of the quadratic equation is lesser than 0, the roots are imaginary.
So, **Assertion** is true.
Reason: If $b^2 - 4ac < 0$, then $ax^2 + bx + c$ has imaginary roots.
So, **Reason** is true and is the correct explanation of the **Assertion**.
Hence, the correct option is (a).

19. **Assertion:** Let
$$\sqrt{240 + \sqrt{240 + \sqrt{240 + \sqrt{240 + \ldots\infty}}}} = x.$$
$$x^2 = 240 + \sqrt{240 + \sqrt{240 + \sqrt{240 + \ldots\infty}}}$$
$x^2 = 240 + x$
$x^2 - x - 240 = 0$
$x^2 - 16x + 15x - 240 = 0$
$x(x-16) + 15(x-16) = 0$
$(x-16)(x+15) = 0$
$x = 16$ (or) $x = -15$.
As the given number is positive, $x = 16$.
So, **Assertion** is true.
Reason: For any integer value of x, the value of
$\sqrt{x + \sqrt{x + \sqrt{x + \sqrt{x + \ldots\infty}}}}$ is an integer only if x is the product of two consecutive positive integers.
So, **Reason** is false.
Hence, the correct option is (c).

CHAPTER

6

Progressions

Remember

Before beginning this chapter, you should be able to:

- Recall different types of numbers
- Work on factorization of polynomials

Key Ideas

After completing this chapter, you should be able to:

- Understand terms such as sequences, series and progressions
- Study arithmetic progression (AP) and also obtain arithmetic mean (AM)
- Formulate geometric progression (GP)
- Insert harmonic mean (HM) between two numbers
- Study relation between AM, GM, and HM

Scientific Crypt

A Tribute to Carl Friedrich Gauss (1777 AD to 1855 AD)

Carl Friedrich Gauss was a German mathematician and scientist. He worked on many fields like number theory, statistics, analysis, geophysics, astronomy, optics, etc. He is regarded as 'the Prince of Mathematicians'. There is a story of his early genius: one day his teacher asked the class, 'the sum of the first hundred natural numbers.' Gauss arrived at the answer within a few seconds. He found the sum of the first 100 natural numbers as follows:

$S = 1 + 2 + \ldots\ldots\ldots\ldots + 99 + 100$

$S = 100 + 99 + \ldots\ldots\ldots + 2 + 1$

$2S = 101 + 101 + \ldots\ldots\ldots + 101 + 101$

$$\Rightarrow 2S = 101\times100 - S = \frac{101\times100}{2} = 5050$$

Now, most of us are using the above method for finding the sum of the first n numbers of an AP. The following are named in honour of Gauss:

- The crater Gauss on the Moon.
- Asteroid 1001 Gaussia.
- The Gauss Building – University of Idaho (College of Engineering).

At the age of 21, he completed his work on the fundamentals of consolidating number theory which had the title 'Disquistiones Arithmeticae'.

FUN TIME

CROSSWORD

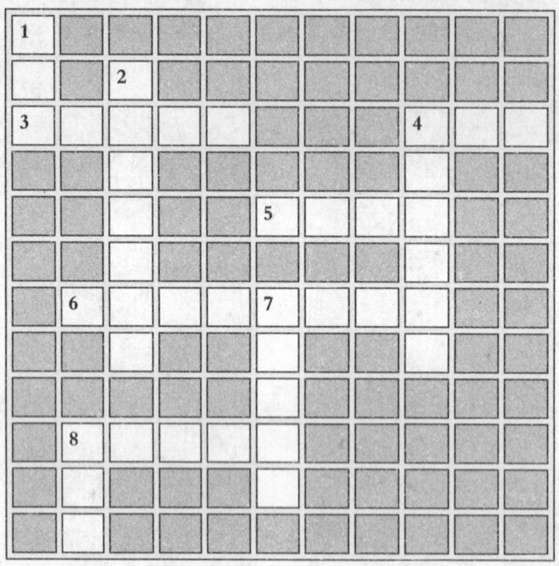

Across

3. AM, GM and HM of two equal numbers
4. This is GM of 4 and 9
5. This is HM of 3 and 6
6. A systematic arrangement of numbers
8. Which term of a sequence is the difference between S_{10} and S_9?

Down

1. It is the sum of $\frac{1}{3}, \frac{2}{9}, \frac{4}{27} \ldots\ldots\infty$
2. $1 + 3 + 5 + \ldots\ldots + 19$
4. The sum of the terms of a sequence
7. The value of $\sum n$, if $\sum n^3 = 64$
8. This is AM of 7 and 13

INTRODUCTION

Let us observe the following pattern of numbers:

- 5, 11, 17, 23, ...
- 6, 12, 24, 48, ...
- 4, 2, 0, –2, –4, ...
- $\frac{2}{3}, \frac{4}{9}, \frac{8}{27}, \frac{16}{81}, \ldots$

In example 1, every number (except 5) is formed by adding 6 to the previous number. Hence, a specific pattern is followed in the arrangement of these numbers. Similarly, in example 2, every number is obtained by multiplying the previous number by 2. Similar cases are followed in examples 3 and 4.

Sequence

A systematic arrangement of numbers according to a given rule is called a sequence.

The numbers in a sequence are called its terms. We refer the first term of a sequence as T_1, second term as T_2, and so on. The nth term of a sequence is denoted by T_n, which may also be referred to as the general term of the sequence.

Finite and Infinite Sequences

1. A sequence which consists of a finite number of terms is called a finite sequence.

Example: 2, 5, 8, 11, 14, 17, 20, 23 is a finite sequence of 8 terms.

2. A sequence which consists of an infinite number of terms is called an infinite sequence.

Example: 3, 10, 17, 24, 31, ... is an infinite sequence.

> **Konnect**
>
> If a sequence is given, then we can find its *n*th term and if the *n*th term of a sequence is given we can find the terms of the sequence.

Examples: Find the first four terms of the sequences whose *n*th terms are given as follows.

(i) $T_n = 3n + 1$

Substituting $n = 1$,

$T_1 = 3(1) + 1 = 4$

Similarly, $T_2 = 3(2) + 1 = 7$

$T_3 = 3(3) + 1 = 10$

$T_4 = 3(4) + 1 = 13$

∴ The first four terms of the sequence are 4, 7, 10, 13.

(ii) $T_n = 2n^2 - 3$

Substituting $n = 1$,

$T_1 = 2(1)^2 - 3 = -1$

Similarly, $T_2 = 2(2)^2 - 3 = 5$

$T_3 = 2(3)^2 - 3 = 15$

$T_4 = 2(4)^2 - 3 = 29$

∴ The first four terms of the sequence are –1, 5, 15, 29.

Series

The sum of the terms of a sequence is called the series of the corresponding sequence.

Example: $1 + 2 + 3 + \cdots + n$ is a finite series of first n natural numbers.

The sum of first n terms of series is denoted by S_n.

Here, $S_n = T_1 + T_2 + \cdots + T_n$.

Here, $S_1 = T_1$

$S_2 = T_1 + T_2$

$S_3 = T_1 + T_2 + T_3$

...

...

$S_n = T_1 + T_2 + T_3 + \cdots + T_n$

We have,

$S_2 - S_1 = T_2$

$S_3 - S_2 = T_3$

Similarly,

$S_n - S_{n-1} = T_n$.

> **Konnect**
>
> **Fibonacci Sequence:** It is a series in which each number is the sum of the two preceding ones, usually starting with 0 and 1. This series appears surprisingly often in nature, e.g., in the arrangement of leaves on a stem or the branching of trees.

EXAMPLE 6.1 In the series, $T_n = 2n + 5$, find S_4.

SOLUTION

$T_n = 2n + 5$

$T_1 = 2(1) + 5 = 7$

$T_2 = 2(2) + 5 = 9$

$T_3 = 2(3) + 5 = 11$

$T_4 = 2(4) + 5 = 13$

$S_4 = T_1 + T_2 + T_3 + T_4 = 7 + 9 + 11 + 13 = 40$.

Progression

Sequences of numbers which follow specific patterns are called progressions. Depending on the pattern, the progressions are classified as follows:

1. Arithmetic Progression
2. Geometric Progression
3. Harmonic Progression.

Arithmetic Progression (AP)

Numbers (or terms) are said to be in arithmetic progression when each one, except the first, is obtained by adding a constant to the previous number (or term).

An arithmetic progression can be represented by $a, a + d, a + 2d, \ldots, [a + (n - 1)d]$. Here, d is added to any term to get the next term of the progression. The term a is the first term of the progression, n is called the number of terms in the progression and d is the common difference.

1. The nth term (general term) of an arithmetic progression is, $T_n = a + (n - 1)d$.
2. Sum to n terms of an AP = $S_n = \frac{n}{2}[2a + (n - 1)d]$.

The sum to n terms of an AP can also be written in a different manner. That is, sum of n terms $= \frac{n}{2}[2a + (n - 1)d]$ $= \frac{n}{2}[a + \{a + (n - 1)d\}]$.

But, when there are n terms in an AP, a is the first term and $\{a + (n - 1)d\}$ is the last term. Hence, $S_n = \left(\frac{n}{2}\right)$[first term + last term].

Let us consider $S_n = a_1 + a_2 + a_3 + ... + a_{n-1} + a_n$ ... (1)

$S_{n-1} = a_1 + a_2 + a_3 + ... + a_{n-1}$ ... (2)

Let us subtract equation (2) from equation (1).

$S_n - S_{n-1} = a_n$

$a_n - S_n - S_{n-1}$

Arithmetic Mean (AM)

The average of all the terms in an AP is called the arithmetic mean (AM) of the AP.

The average of a certain terms $= \frac{\text{Sum of all the terms}}{\text{Number of terms}}$

$\therefore$ AM of n terms in an AP $= \frac{S_n}{n} = \frac{1}{n} \times \frac{n}{2}$ [first term + last term] $= \frac{\text{(first term + last term)}}{2}$,

i.e., the AM of an AP is the average of the first and the last terms of the AP.

The AM of an AP can also be obtained by considering any two terms which are EQUIDISTANT from the two ends of the AP and taking their average, i.e.,

1. the average of the second term from the beginning and the second term from the end is equal to the AM of the AP
2. the average of the third term from the beginning and the third term from the end is also equal to the AM of the AP and so on.

In general, the average of the kth term from the beginning and the kth term from the end is equal to the AM of the AP.

If the AM of an AP is known, the sum to n terms of the series (S_n) can be expressed as $S_n = n$(AM)

In particular, if three numbers are in arithmetic progression, then the middle number is the AM, i.e., if a, b, and c are in AP, then b is the AM of the three terms and $b = \frac{a+c}{2}$.

If a and b are any two numbers, then their AM $= \frac{a+b}{2}$.

Inserting arithmetic mean between two numbers:

When n arithmetic means $a_1, a_2, ..., a_3$ are inserted between a and b, then $a, a_1, a_2, ..., a_n, b$ are in AP.

$\Rightarrow t_1 = a$ and $t_{n+2} = b$ of AP

The common difference of the AP can be obtained as follows:

Given that, n arithmetic means are there between a and b.

$\therefore a = t_1$ and $b = t_{n+2}$

Let d be the common difference.

$\Rightarrow b = t_1 + (n + 1)d$

$\Rightarrow b = a + (n + 1)d$

$\Rightarrow d = \frac{(b-a)}{(n+1)}$.

Konnect

1. If three numbers are in AP, we can take the three terms to be $(a - d)$, a and $(a + d)$.
2. If four numbers are in AP, we can take the four terms to be $(a - 3d)$, $(a - d)$, $(a + d)$ and $(a + 3d)$. The common difference in this case is $2d$ and not d.
3. If five numbers are in AP, we can take the five terms to be $(a - 2d)$, $(a - d)$, a, $(a + d)$ and $(a + 2d)$.

Some Important Results

The sum of first n terms of the following series are quite useful and hence should be remembered by students.

1. Sum of first n natural numbers $= \sum_{i=1}^{n} i = \frac{n(n+1)}{2}$

2. Sum of the squares of first n natural numbers $= \sum_{i=1}^{n} i^2 = \frac{n(n+1)(2n+1)}{6}$

3. Sum of the cubes of first n natural numbers $= \sum_{i=1}^{n} i^3 = \left[\frac{n(n+1)}{2}\right]^2 = \frac{n^2(n+1)^2}{4} = \left[\sum_1^n i\right]^2$

EXAMPLE 6.2 Find the 14th term of an AP whose first term is 3 and the common difference is 2.

SOLUTION

The nth term of an AP is given by $t_n = a + (n - 1)d$, where a is the first term and d is the common difference.

$\therefore t_{14} = 3 + (14 - 1)\,2 = 29.$

EXAMPLE 6.3 Find the first term and the common difference of an AP, if the 3rd term is 6 and the 17th term is 34.

SOLUTION

If a is the first term and d is the common difference, then we have,

$$t_3 = a + 2d = 6 \qquad (1)$$

$$t_{17} = a + 16d = 34 \qquad (2)$$

On subtracting Eq. (1) from Eq. (2), we get,

$$14d = 28 \Rightarrow d = 2$$

Substituting the value of d in Eq. (1), we get $a = 2$.

$\therefore a = 2$ and $d = 2$.

EXAMPLE 6.4 Find the sum of the first 20 terms of the sequence $\frac{1}{30}, \frac{1}{42}, \frac{1}{56}, \ldots\ldots$

SOLUTION

Given Expression $= \frac{1}{5\times6} + \frac{1}{6\times7} + \ldots\ldots + \frac{1}{24\times25}$

$= \left(\frac{1}{5} - \frac{1}{6}\right) + \left(\frac{1}{6} - \frac{1}{7}\right) + \ldots\ldots + \left(\frac{1}{24} - \frac{1}{25}\right)$

$= \left(\frac{1}{5} - \frac{1}{25}\right) = \frac{4}{25} = 0.16.$

EXAMPLE 6.5 Divide 124 into four parts in such a way that they are in AP and the product of the first and the 4th part is 128 less than the product of the 2nd and the 3rd parts.

SOLUTION

Let the four parts be $(a - 3d)$, $(a - d)$, $(a + d)$ and $(a + 3d)$. The sum of these four parts is 124, i.e., $4a = 124 \Rightarrow a = 31$

$(a - 3d)(a + 3d) = (a - d)(a + d) - 128$

$\Rightarrow a^2 - 9d^2 = a^2 - d^2 - 128$

$\Rightarrow 8d^2 = 128 \Rightarrow d = \pm4.$

As $a = 31$, taking $d = 4$, the four parts are 19, 27, 35 and 43.

Info Bytes!

If d is taken as -4, then the same four numbers are obtained, but in decreasing order.

EXAMPLE 6.6 Find the three terms in AP, whose sum is 36 and product is 960.

SOLUTION

Let the three terms of an AP be $(a - d)$, a and $(a + d)$.

Sum of these terms is $3a$.

$3a = 36 \Rightarrow a = 12$

Product of these three terms is:

$(a + d)\ a\ (a - d) = 960$

$\Rightarrow (12 + d)\ (12 - d) = 80$

$\Rightarrow 144 - d^2 = 80 \Rightarrow d = \pm 8.$

Taking $d = 8$, we get the terms as 4, 12, and 20.

> **Info Bytes!**
> If d is taken as -8, then the same numbers are obtained, but in decreasing order.

EXAMPLE 6.7 The sum of five numbers, which are in AP, is 100. The product of the first and the fifth numbers is 300. Find the sum of the 2nd and the 4th numbers.

SOLUTION

Let the 5 parts be $a - 2d, a - d, a, a + d, a + 2d$

Given that its sum is 100

$\therefore\ (a - 2d) + (a - d) + a + (a + d) + (a + 2d) = 100$

$5a = 100$

$a = 20$

Product of first and last parts = 300

$(a - 2d)(a + 2d) = 300$

$a^2 - 4d^2 = 300$

$20^2 - 4d^2 = 300$

$4d^2 = 100$

$d^2 = 25$

$d = \pm 5$

taking $d = 5$

$\therefore$ The four parts are 10, 15, 20, 15, 30.

The sum of 2nd and 4th parts = 15 + 25 = 40.

EXAMPLE 6.8 Find the sum of 100 terms of the series 1(3) + 3(5) + 5(7) + ...

SOLUTION

$1 \cdot 3 + 3 \cdot 5 + 5 \cdot 7 + \ldots$

The series of first factor is 1, 3, 5, 7 ...

$$t_{n_1} = 1 + (n - 1)\ (2)$$

The series of 2nd factor is 3, 5, 7, 9 ...

$t_{n_2} = 3 + (n - 1)\ (2)$

$t_n = t_{n_1} \times t_{n_2}$

$= 1 + (n - 1)2 \times 3 + (n - 1)2$

$= (2n - 1)(2n + 1)$

$t_n = 4n^2 - 1.$

$\Sigma t_n = \Sigma(4n^2 - 1)$

$= 4\Sigma n^2 - \Sigma 1$

$= 4 \times \frac{n(n+1)(2n+1)}{6} - n$

$= \frac{2n(n+1)(2n+1) - 3n}{3}$

$= \frac{n}{3}[2(n+1)(2n+1) - 3].$

$\Sigma t_{100} = \frac{100}{3}[2 \times 101 \times 201 - 3]$

$= \frac{100}{3}[202 \times 201 - 3]$

$= 100[202 \times 67 - 1]$

$= 100[13534 - 1] = 100 \times 13533$

$= 1353300.$

Geometric Progression (GP)

Numbers are said to be in geometric progression when the ratio of any quantity to the number that follows it is the same. In other words, any term of a GP (except the first one) can be obtained by multiplying the previous term by the same constant.

The constant is called the common ratio and is normally represented by r. The first term of a GP is generally denoted by a.

A geometric progression can be represented by a, ar, ar^2, … where a is the first term and r is the common ratio of the GP. The nth term of the GP is ar^{n-1}, i.e., $t_n = ar^{n-1}$.

Sum of first n terms $= S_n = \frac{a(1 - r^n)}{1 - r} = \frac{a(r^n - 1)}{r - 1} = \frac{r(ar^{n-1}) - a}{r - 1}$

∴ The sum of first n terms of a geometric progression can also be written as:

$$S_n = \frac{r(\text{Last term}) - \text{First term}}{r - 1}.$$

Konnect

1. If n terms viz., $a_1, a_2, a_3, \ldots, a_n$ are in GP, then the geometric mean (GM) of these n terms is given by $= \sqrt[n]{a_1 a_2 a_3 \ldots a_n}$.
2. If three terms are in geometric progression, then the middle term is the geometric mean of the GP, i.e., if a, b, and c are in GP, then b is the geometric mean of the three terms.

3. If there are two terms say a and b, then their geometric mean is given by $GM = \sqrt{ab}$.
4. When n geometric means are there between a and b, the common ratio of the GP can be derived as follows. Given that, n geometric means are there between a and b.

   $\therefore \quad a = t_1$ and $b = t_{n+2}$.

   Let 'r' be the common ratio

   $$\Rightarrow b = (t_1)(r^{n+1}) \Rightarrow b = ar^{n+1}$$

   $$\Rightarrow r^{n+1} = \frac{b}{a} \Rightarrow r = \sqrt[(n+1)]{\frac{b}{a}}$$
5. For any two positive numbers a and b, their arithmetic mean is always greater than or equal to their geometric mean, i.e., for any two positive numbers a and b, $\frac{a+b}{2} \geq \sqrt{ab}$.

   The equality holds if and only if $a = b$.
6. When there are three terms in geometric progression, we can take the three terms to be a/r, a, and ar.

Geometric Mean

The Geometric Mean (G.M) of a series containing n observations is the nth root of the product of the values. Consider, if t_1 , t_2 .... t_n are n observation, then the GM is given by $\sqrt[n]{t_1 . t_2 ...... t_n}$ or $(t_1 . t_2 ...... t_n)^{1/n}$

Infinite Geometric Progression

If $-1 < r < 1$ (or $|r| < 1$), then the sum of a geometric progression does not increase infinitely but 'converges' to a particular value, no matter how many terms of the GP we take. The sum of an infinite geometric progression is represented by S_∞ and is given by the formula,

$$S_\infty = \frac{a}{1-r}, \text{ if } |r| < 1.$$

EXAMPLE 6.9 In a GP, if $a_7 \div a_4$ is 343, then find the common ratio.

SOLUTION

Given that $\frac{a_7}{a_4} = 343$

$\frac{ar^6}{ar^3} = 343$

$r^3 = 343$

$r^3 = 7^3$

$r = 7$.

EXAMPLE 6.10 Find the common ratio of the GP whose first and last terms are 25 and $\frac{1}{625}$, respectively, and the sum of the GP is $\frac{19531}{625}$.

SOLUTION

We know that the sum of a GP is $\frac{\text{first term} - r(\text{last term})}{1-r}$

or $\frac{19531}{625}=\frac{25-\left(\frac{r}{625}\right)}{1-r}\Rightarrow\frac{19531}{625}=\frac{15625-r}{(1-r)625}$

$\Rightarrow 19531-15625=-r+19531r$

$\Rightarrow \frac{3906}{19530}=r$

$\therefore r=\frac{1}{5}.$

EXAMPLE 6.11 Find three numbers of a GP whose sum is 26 and product is 216.

SOLUTION

Let the three numbers be a/r, a, and ar.

Given that,

$a/r \cdot a \cdot ar = 216;$

$\Rightarrow a^3 = 216 \Rightarrow a = 6.$

$a/r + a + ar = 26$

or, $6 + 6r + 6r^2 = 26r$

or, $6r^2 - 20r + 6 = 0$

or, $6r^2 - 18r - 2r + 6 = 0$

or, $6r(r-3) - 2(r-3) = 0$

$(r-3)(6r-2) = 0$

or, $r = 1/3$ (or) $r = 3$.

Hence, the three numbers are 2, 6 and 18 (or) 18, 6, and 2.

EXAMPLE 6.12 If $|x| < 1$, then find the sum of the series $2 + 4x + 6x^2 + 8x^3 + \ldots$.

SOLUTION

Let $S = 2 + 4x + 6x^2 + 8x^3 + \cdots$ (1)

$xS = 2x + 4x^2 + 6x^3 + \ldots$ (2)

Eq. (1) – Eq. (2) gives

$S(1-x) = 2 + 2x + 2x^2 + 2x^3 + \cdots$

$= 2(1 + x + x^2 + \ldots)$

$1 + x + x^2 + \cdots$ is an infinite GP with $a = 1$, $r = x$ and $|r| = |x| < 1$

$\therefore$ Sum of the series $=\frac{1}{1-x}$

$\therefore S(1-x)=\frac{2}{(1-x)}$

$\therefore S=\frac{2}{(1-x)^2}.$

EXAMPLE 6.13 Find the sum of the series $1, \frac{2}{5}, \frac{4}{25}, \frac{8}{125}, \ldots \infty$.

SOLUTION

Given that, $a = 1$, $r=\frac{2}{5}$ and $|r|=\left|\frac{2}{5}\right|<1$

$\therefore S_\infty=\frac{a}{1-r}=\frac{1}{1-\frac{2}{5}}=\frac{5}{3}.$

EXAMPLE 6.14 S_{10} is the sum of the first 10 terms of a GP and S_5 is the sum of the first 5 terms of the same GP. If $\frac{S_{10}}{S_5} = 244$, then find the common ratio.

SOLUTION

$$\frac{S_{10}}{S_5} = \frac{\frac{a\cdot(r^{10}-1)}{(r-1)}}{\frac{a(r^5-1)}{r-1}}$$

or, $\frac{S_{10}}{S_5} = \frac{r^{10}-1}{r^5-1} = \frac{(r^5)^2-(1)^2}{r^5-1} = \frac{(r^5+1)(r^5-1)}{(r^5-1)} \Rightarrow r^5+1$

$\Rightarrow 244 = r^5 + 1$

or, $r^5 = 243 \Rightarrow r = 3.$

EXAMPLE 6.15 The difference between two hundred-digit numbers consisting of all 1's and a hundred-digit number consisting of all 2's is equal to:

SOLUTION

Apply the principle $11 = 1 + 10^{2-1}$, $111 = 1 + 10^{3-1}$ and proceed.

Harmonic Progression (HP)

A progression is said to be a harmonic progression if the reciprocal of the terms in the progression form an arithmetic progression.

For example, consider the series $\frac{1}{2}, \frac{1}{5}, \frac{1}{8}, \frac{1}{11}, \ldots$

The progression formed by taking reciprocals of terms of the above series is 2, 5, 8, 11, …. Clearly, these terms form an AP whose common difference is 3.

Hence, the given progression is a harmonic progression.

*n*th term of an HP:

We know that if a, $a + d$, $a + 2d$, … are in AP, then the *n*th term of this AP is $a + (n - 1)d$. Its reciprocal is $\frac{1}{a+(n-1)d}$.

So, *n*th term of an HP whose first two terms are and is $\frac{1}{a}$ and $\frac{1}{a+d}$ is $\frac{1}{a+(n-1)d}$.

Info Bytes! There is no concise general formula for the sum to *n* terms of an HP.

EXAMPLE 6.16 In a HP, 14th and 22nd terms are $\frac{6}{29}$ and $\frac{2}{15}$ respectively. Find the 18th term of the H.P.

SOLUTION

Given, $t_{14} = \frac{1}{a+13d} = \frac{6}{29}$ —— (1)

$t_{22} = \frac{1}{a+21d} = \frac{2}{15}$ —— (2)

$(1) \Rightarrow a + 13d = \frac{29}{6}$

$(2) \Rightarrow a + 21d = \frac{15}{2}$

$$2a + 34d = \frac{37}{3}$$

$$a + 17d = \frac{37}{6}$$

$$\frac{1}{a+17d} = \frac{6}{37}$$

$$t_{18} = \frac{6}{37}$$

Harmonic Mean (HM)

If three terms are in HP, then the middle term is the HM of other two terms.

The harmonic mean of two terms a and b is given by HM $= \frac{2ab}{a+b}$.

Inserting *n* Harmonic Means Between Two Numbers

To insert n harmonic means between two numbers, we first take the corresponding arithmetic series and insert n arithmetic means, and next, we find the corresponding harmonic series.

This is illustrated by the example below:

EXAMPLE 6.17 Insert three harmonic means between $\frac{1}{12}$ and $\frac{1}{20}$.

SOLUTION

After inserting the harmonic means, let the harmonic progression be,

$$\frac{1}{a}, \frac{1}{a+d}, \frac{1}{a+2d}, \frac{1}{a+3d}, \frac{1}{a+4d}$$

Given, $\frac{1}{a} = \frac{1}{12}$ and $\frac{1}{a+4d} = \frac{1}{20} \Rightarrow a = 12$ and $d = 2$

$\therefore$ The required harmonic means are $\frac{1}{14}, \frac{1}{16}$, and $\frac{1}{18}$.

Relation between AM, HM, and GM of Two Numbers

Let x and y be two numbers.

$$\therefore \text{AM} = \frac{x+y}{2}, \text{GM} = \sqrt{xy} \text{ and HM} = \frac{2xy}{x+y}$$

$$\Rightarrow (\text{AM})(\text{HM}) = (\text{GM})^2.$$

EXAMPLE 6.18

The arithmetic mean and the harmonic mean of two positive integers are respectively 6 more and 4 less than the geometric mean. Find the geometric mean.

SOLUTION

$G^2 = A \times H$

$x^2 = (x + 6)(x - 4)$

$x^2 = x^2 + 2x - 24$

$2x = 24$

$x = 12$

$\therefore$ The geometric mean = 12.

POINTS TO REMEMBER

- ✔ A systematic arrangement of numbers according to a given rule is called a sequence.
- ✔ A sequence which consists of a finite number of terms is called a finite sequence.
- ✔ A sequence which consists of an infinite number of terms is called an infinite sequence.
- ✔ Sequences of numbers which follow specific patterns are called progressions.
- ✔ AM of n terms in an AP $= \dfrac{S_n}{n} = \dfrac{1}{n} \times \dfrac{n}{2}$ [first term + last term] $= \dfrac{(\text{first term} + \text{last term})}{2}$,
- ✔ If three numbers are in AP, we can take the three terms to be $(a - d)$, a and $(a + d)$.
- ✔ If four numbers are in AP, we can take the four terms to be $(a - 3d)$, $(a - d)$, $(a + d)$ and $(a + 3d)$. The common difference in this case is $2d$ and not d.
- ✔ If five numbers are in AP, we can take the five terms to be $(a - 2d)$, $(a - d)$, a, $(a + d)$ and $(a + 2d)$.
- ✔ Numbers are said to be in geometric progression when the ratio of any quantity to the number that follows it is the same.
- ✔ The sum of first n terms of a geometric progression can also be written as:
- ✔ $S_n = \dfrac{r(\text{Last term}) - \text{First term}}{r - 1}$.
- ✔ $S_\infty = \dfrac{a}{1 - r}$, if $|r| < 1$.
- ✔ The harmonic mean of two terms a and b is given by HM $= \dfrac{2ab}{a + b}$.
- ✔ Let x and y be two numbers.
- ✔ $\therefore$ AM $= \dfrac{x + y}{2}$, GM $= \sqrt{xy}$ and HM $= \dfrac{2xy}{x + y}$
- ✔ $\Rightarrow$ (AM) (HM) = $(\text{GM})^2$.

PRACTICE QUESTIONS CLASSROOM WING

Very Short Answer Type Questions

Directions of questions from 1 to 13:
Fill in the blanks.

1. If $\frac{a}{2}$ is the first term and d is the common difference of an AP, then the sum of n terms of the AP is ______.
2. In a sequence, if S_n is the sum of n terms and S_{n-1} is the sum of $(n-1)$ terms, then the nth term is ______.
3. If $T_n = 3n + 8$, then $T_{n-1} =$ ______.
4. The sum of the first $(n + 1)$ natural numbers is ______.
5. For a series in geometric progression, the first term is a and the second term is $3a$. The common ratio of the series is ______.
6. In a series, starting from the second term, if each term is twice its previous term, then the series is in ______ progression.
7. If a, b and c are in geometric progression then, a^2, b^2 and c^2 are in ______ progression.
8. Geometric mean of 5, 10 and 20 is ______.
9. The reciprocals of all the terms of a series in geometric progression form a ______ progression.
10. The nth term of the sequence $\frac{1}{100}, \frac{1}{10000}, \frac{1}{1000000}, \ldots$ is ______.
11. If three arithmetic means are inserted between 4 and 5, then the common difference is ______.
12. If the 7th and the 9th terms of a GP are x and y respectively, then the common ratio of the GP is ______.
13. In a series, $T_n = 3 - n$, then $S_5 =$ ______.

Directions of questions from 14 to 18:
State whether the following statements are true or false

14. All the multiples of 3 form a geometric progression. [True/False]
15. If every term of a series in geometric progression is multiplied by a real number, then the resulting series also will be in geometric progression. [True/False]
16. Sum of the infinite terms of the GP, −3, −6, −12, ... is 3. [True/False]
17. The harmonic mean of 1, 2, and 3 is $\frac{3}{2}$. [True/False]
18. If the AM of two numbers is 9 and their HM is 4, then their GM is 6. [True/False]

Directions of questions from 19 to 21:
Answer the following questions.

19. In a series, $T_n = x^{2n-2}$ $(x \neq 0)$, then write the infinite series.
20. Write the first three terms of the sequence whose nth term is $T_n = 8 - 5n$.
21. Write the first three terms of the sequence whose nth term is $T_n = 5^{n+1}$

Short Answer Type Questions

22. Which term of the AP 5, 11, 17, 23, ... is 125?
23. Which term of the AP 7, 3, −1, −5, ... is −153?
24. An nth term of the sequence 7, 16, 25, 34, 43, is 115. Find n.
25. Find the 5th term of a geometric progression whose first term is 8 and the common ratio is 5.
26. Find the geometric mean of 6, 18, 54, and 162.
27. If the ratio of the sum of first three terms of a GP to the sum of first six terms is 448 : 455, then find the common ratio.
28. If in a GP, 5th term and the 12th term are 9 and $\frac{1}{243}$, respectively, find the 9th term of GP.
29. A person opens an account with ₹50 and starts depositing every day double the amount he has deposited on the previous day. Then find the amount he has deposited on the 10th day from the beginning.
30. Find the sum of 5 geometric means between $\frac{1}{3}$ and 243, by taking common ratio positive.

31. Using progressions express the recurring decimal $2 \cdot \overline{123}$ in the form of $\frac{p}{q}$, where p and q are integers.

32. A ball is dropped from a height of 64 m and it rebounces $\frac{3}{4}$ of the distance every time it touches the ground. Find the total distance it travels before it comes to rest.

33. (A) Find the sum to n terms of the series 5 + 55 + 555 + ...

(B) In an infinite GP, each term is double the sum of its succeeding terms. Find the common ratio of the GP.

34. If lth, mth and nth terms of an HP are x, y and z respectively, then find the value of $yz(m - n) + xz(n - l) + xy(l - m)$.

35. (A) The AM of two numbers is 40 more than GM and 64 more than HM. Find the numbers.

(B) Find the ratio of the common differences d_1 and d_2 of two arithmetic progressions if the respective n^{th} terms are in the ratio of $(2n + 3) : (n - 11)$.

Essay Type Questions

36. Find the sum of the first 50 terms of the sequence 7, 77, 777, ...

37. Check whether $\frac{1}{a+b}, \frac{1}{b+c}$, and $\frac{1}{c+a}$ are in AP.

38. Find the sum to infinity of the terms of the sequence 5, $10x$, $15x^2$, $20x^3$, ... where $|x| < 1$.

39. If 3 harmonic means are inserted between $\frac{1}{5}$ and $-\frac{1}{12}$ then find the 2nd harmonic mean inserted.

40. In an AP, if m times the mth term is equal to n times the nth term, then show that $(m + n)^{th}$ term is zero, where $m \neq n$.

41. If S_1, S_2 and S_3 are the sum of first n, $2n$ and $3n$ terms of a geometric progression respectively, then prove that $S_1^2 + S_2^2 = S_1 (S_2 + S_3)$.

42. If $\frac{1}{p^2}, \frac{1}{q^2}, \frac{1}{r^2}$ are in HP, then prove that, $(q + r)$, $(p + r)$ and $(p + q)$ are also in HP.

PRACTICE QUESTIONS COMPETITION WING

Level 1: Apply Your Concepts

Directions of questions from 1 to 5: Fill in the blanks.

1. Third term of the sequence whose nth term is $2n + 5$ is ______.
2. If a is the first term and d is the common difference of an AP, then the $(n + 1)$th term of the AP is ______.
3. If the sum of three consecutive terms of an AP is 9, then the middle term is ______.
4. General term of the sequence 5, 25, 125, 625, … is ______.
5. The arithmetic mean of 7 and 8 is ______.

Directions of questions from 6 to 30: Select the correct alternative from the given choices.

6. If the sum of the first n terms of a sequence is $2n^2 + n$, then find the general term of the sequence.
   (a) 3-n − 1 (b) 5-n − 2
   (c) 3-n − 2 (d) 4-n − 1
7. If the sum of the first n terms of a sequence is $n(3n + 1)$, then find the general term of the sequence.
   (a) $4n - 3$ (b) $6n - 2$
   (c) $10n - 6$ (d) $6n - 3$
8. If there are 5 arithmetic means between 8 and 3, then the 4th arithmetic mean is ______.
   (a) $\frac{7}{6}$ (b) $\frac{10}{3}$
   (c) $\frac{17}{6}$ (d) $\frac{14}{3}$
9. Find the geometric mean of the first 33 powers of 2.
   (a) 2^{17} (b) 2^{18}
   (c) 2^{16} (d) 2^{19}
10. Which of the following is the next term of the series?
   $\frac{5}{16}, \frac{5}{24}, \frac{5}{36}, \frac{5}{54}, \ldots ?$
   (a) $\frac{5}{18}$ (b) $\frac{5}{81}$
   (c) $\frac{7}{18}$ (d) $\frac{11}{18}$
11. If there are 7 A.M's between 5 and 8, find the 7th A.M.
   (a) $\frac{61}{8}$ (b) $\frac{51}{8}$
   (c) $\frac{11}{8}$ (d) $\frac{61}{9}$
12. Find the sum of infinite terms of the series
   $1 + \frac{1}{2} + \frac{1}{2^2} + \frac{1}{2^3} + \frac{1}{2^4} + \ldots$
   (a) $\frac{3}{2}$ (b) 2
   (c) $\frac{5}{2}$ (d) 3
13. The sum of the first 51 terms of the arithmetic progression whose 2nd term is 2 and 4th term is 8, is ______.
   (a) 3774 (b) 3477
   (c) 7548 (d) 7458
14. Find the 15th term of the series 243, 81, 27, ….
   (a) $\frac{1}{3^{14}}$ (b) $\frac{1}{3^8}$
   (c) $\left(\frac{1}{3}\right)^9$ (d) $\left(\frac{1}{3}\right)^{10}$
15. If t_8 and t_3 of a geometric progression are $\frac{4}{9}$ and $\frac{27}{8}$, respectively, then find t_{12} of the geometric progression.
   (a) $\frac{64}{729}$ (b) $\frac{32}{243}$
   (c) $\frac{729}{64}$ (d) $\frac{243}{32}$
16. If $t_n = 3^{n-1}$, then $S_6 - S_5 =$ ______.
   (a) 243 (b) 81
   (c) 77 (d) 27
17. Find the sum of the first 10 terms of geometric progression 18, 9, 4.5, ….

(a) $9\dfrac{(2^{10}-1)}{2^8}$ (b) $9\dfrac{(2^{10}-1)}{2^{10}}$

(c) $36\left(\dfrac{2^{10}-1}{2^8}\right)$ (d) $8\dfrac{(2^{10}-1)}{2^8}$

18. If the 3rd, 7th, and 11th terms of a geometric progression are p, q, and r, respectively, then the relation among p, q, and r is ______.

(a) $p^2 = qr$ (b) $r^2 = qp$

(c) $q^2 = p^2r^2$ (d) $q^2 = pr$

19. Evaluate $\Sigma(3 + 2^r)$, where $r = 1, 2, 3, \ldots, 10$.

(a) 2051 (b) 2049

(c) 2076 (d) 1052

20. Find the sum of the series $\dfrac{27}{8}+\dfrac{9}{4}+\dfrac{3}{2}+\ldots\infty$.

(a) $\dfrac{81}{8}$ (b) $\dfrac{27}{8}$

(c) $\dfrac{81}{16}$ (d) $\dfrac{9}{8}$

21. If $3x - 4$, $x + 4$, and $5x + 8$ are the three positive consecutive terms of a geometric progression, then find the terms.

(a) 2, 8, 32 (b) 2, 10, 50

(c) 2, 6, 18 (d) 12, 6, 3

22. Find the geometric mean of the first twenty-five powers of twenty five.

(a) 5^{13} (b) 5^{19}

(c) 5^{24} (d) 5^{26}

23. Find the sum of 3 geometric means between $\dfrac{1}{3}$ and $\dfrac{1}{48}(r > 0)$.

(a) $\dfrac{1}{4}$ (b) $\dfrac{5}{24}$

(c) $\dfrac{7}{24}$ (d) $\dfrac{1}{3}$

24. The 10th term of harmonic progression $\dfrac{1}{5}, \dfrac{4}{19}, \dfrac{2}{9}, \dfrac{4}{17}, \ldots$ is ______.

(a) $\dfrac{11}{4}$ (b) $\dfrac{13}{4}$

(c) $\dfrac{4}{13}$ (d) $\dfrac{4}{11}$

25. If the ratio of the arithmetic mean and the geometric mean of two positive numbers is 3 : 2, then find the ratio of the geometric mean and the harmonic mean of the numbers.

(a) 2 : 3 (b) 9 : 4

(c) 3 : 2 (d) 4 : 9

26. Find the least value of n for which the sum $1 + 2 + 2^2 + \ldots$ to n terms is greater than 3000.

(a) 8 (b) 10

(c) 12 (d) 15

27. Find the HM of $\dfrac{1}{7}$ and $\dfrac{1}{12}$.

(a) $\dfrac{1}{19}$ (b) $\dfrac{2}{19}$

(c) $\dfrac{3}{19}$ (d) $\dfrac{4}{19}$

28. Number of rectangles in the following figure is ______.

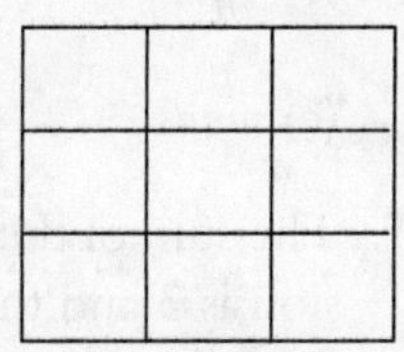

(a) 9 (b) 10

(c) 24 (d) 36

29. In a series, if $t_n = \dfrac{n^2-1}{n+1}$, then $S_6 - S_3 =$ ______.

(a) 3 (b) 12

(c) 22 (d) 25

30. Find the number of terms to be added in the series 27, 9, 3, … so that the sum is $\dfrac{1093}{27}$.

(a) 6 (b) 7

(c) 8 (d) 9

Level 2: Review Your Concepts

31. If $\dfrac{1}{b+c}, \dfrac{1}{c+a}$, and $\dfrac{1}{a+b}$ are in AP, then a^2, b^2 and c^2 are in:

(a) geometric progression

(b) arithmetic progression

(c) harmonic progression

(d) None of these

32. Among the following, which term belongs to the arithmetic progression –5, 2, 9, ...?
(a) 342 (b) 343
(c) 344 (d) 345

33. Five distinct positive integers are in arithmetic progression with a positive common difference. If their sum is 10020, then find the smallest possible value of the last term.
(a) 2002 (b) 2004
(c) 2006 (d) 2008

34. In a right triangle, the lengths of the sides are in arithmetic progression. If the lengths of the sides of the triangle are integers, which of the following could be the length of the shortest side?
(a) 2125 (b) 1700
(c) 1275 (d) 1150

35. If S_1 = 3, 7, 11, 15, ... upto 125 terms and S_2 = 4, 7, 10, 13, 16, ... upto 125 terms, then how many terms are there in S_1 that are there in S_2?
(a) 29 (b) 30 (c) 31 (d) 32

36. The first term and the mth term of a geometric progression are a and n respectively and its nth term is m. Then its $(m + 1 - n)$th term is ______.
(a) $\frac{ma}{n}$ (b) $\frac{na}{m}$
(c) mna (d) $\frac{mn}{a}$

37. The sum of the terms of an infinite geometric progression is 3 and the sum of the squares of the terms is 81. Find the first term of the series.
(a) 5 (b) $\frac{27}{5}$
(c) $\frac{31}{6}$ (d) $\frac{19}{3}$

38. If $\log_{\sqrt{2}} x + \log_{\sqrt{\sqrt{2}}} x + \log_{\sqrt{\sqrt{\sqrt{2}}}} x + \ldots$ upto 7 terms = 1016, the find the value of x.
(a) 4 (b) 16 (c) 64 (d) 2

39. Find the sum of all the multiples of 6 between 200 and 1100.
(a) 96750 (b) 95760
(c) 97560 (d) 97650

40. If the kth term of a HP is λp and the λth term is kp and $k \neq \lambda$, then the pth term is ______.
(a) $k^2\lambda$ (b) k^2p
(c) p^2k (d) λk

41. If six harmonic means are inserted between 3 and $\frac{6}{23}$, then the fourth harmonic mean is:
(a) $\frac{6}{11}$ (b) $\frac{6}{17}$ (c) $\frac{3}{7}$ (d) $\frac{3}{10}$

42. If a, b, and c are positive numbers in arithmetic progression and a^2, b^2, and c^2 are in geometric progression, then a^3, b^3, and c^3 are in:
(A) arithmetic progression
(B) geometric progression
(C) harmonic progression
(a) (A) and (B) only (b) only (C)
(c) (A), (B), and (C) (d) only (B)

43. The infinite sum $\sum_{n=1}^{\infty}\left(\frac{5^n + 3^n}{5^n}\right)$ is equal to:
(a) $\frac{3}{2}$ (b) $\frac{3}{5}$
(c) $\frac{2}{3}$ (d) None of these

44. (i) If $x = 3 + \frac{3}{y} + \frac{3}{y^2} + \frac{3}{y^3} + \cdots + \infty$, then, show that $y = \frac{x}{x-3}$. (Where $|y| < 1$). The following are the steps involved in solving the above problem. Arrange them in sequential order.
(A) $xy - 3y = x$ (B) $x = 3\left(\frac{1}{1-\frac{1}{y}}\right)$
(C) $y(x - 3) = x$ (D) $x = 3\left(\frac{y}{y-1}\right)$
(a) BDCA (b) BDAC
(c) CABD (d) ACBD

Level 3: Assess Your Concepts

45. The numbers $h_1, h_2, h_3, h_4, \ldots, h_{10}$ are in harmonic progression and $a_1, a_2, \ldots, a_{10}$ are in arithmetic progression. If $a_1 = h_1 = 3$ and $a_7 = h_7 = 39$, then the value of $a_4 \times h_4$ is ______.
(a) $\frac{13}{49}$ (b) $\frac{182}{3}$
(c) $\frac{7}{13}$ (d) 117

46. Find the value of

$$\left(1+\frac{1}{2}\right)\left(1+\frac{1}{4}\right)\left(1+\frac{1}{16}\right)\left(1+\frac{1}{256}\right)\ldots\infty.$$

(a) 1 (b) 2

(c) $\frac{1}{3}$ (d) $\frac{1}{4}$

47. The ratio of the sum of n terms of two arithmetic progressions is given by $(2n + 3) : (5n - 7)$. Find the ratio of their nth terms.

(a) $(4n + 5) : (10n + 2)$ (b) $(4n + 1) : (10n - 12)$

(c) $(4n - 1) : (10n + 8)$ (d) $(4n - 5) : (10n - 2)$

48. There are n arithmetic means (were $n \in N$) between 11 and 53 such that each of them is an integer. How many distinct arithmetic progressions are possible from the above data?

(a) 7 (b) 8

(c) 14 (d) 16

49. If $x = \frac{1}{\sqrt{2}} + \frac{1}{2} + \frac{1}{2\sqrt{2}} + \cdots + \infty$, then find the value of $x + \frac{1}{x}$.

(a) $\sqrt{2}$ (b) $2\sqrt{2}$

(c) $3\sqrt{2}$ (d) $4\sqrt{2}$

50. If $x = 3 + \frac{3}{y} + \frac{3}{y^2} + \frac{3}{y^3} + \cdots + \infty$, then $y =$ _____ (where $|y| > 1$).

(a) $\frac{x}{3}$ (b) $\frac{x}{x-3}$

(c) $\frac{1-x}{3}$ (d) $1 - \frac{3}{x}$

51. Find the sum of $\frac{0.3}{0.5} + \frac{0.33}{0.55} + \frac{0.333}{0.555} + \ldots$ to 15 terms.

(a) 10 (b) 9

(c) 3 (d) 5

52. In a GP, if the fourth term is the square of the second term, then the relation between the first term and common ratio is _____.

(a) $a = r$ (b) $a = 2r$

(c) $2a = r$ (d) $r^2 = a$

53. For which of the following values of x is $(0° < x < 90°)$ $16^{1+\cos x+\cos^2 x+\cos^3 x+\ldots\infty} = 256$?

(a) 30° (b) 45°

(c) 60° (d) 15°

54. If t_2 and t_3 of a GP are p and q, respectively, then $t_5 =$ _____.

(a) $p\left(\frac{q}{p}\right)^3$ (b) $p\left(\frac{q}{p}\right)^2$

(c) $\frac{p^2}{q^3}$ (d) p^2q^2

55. If a, b, c, d are in GP, then $(b + c)^2 =$ _____.

(a) $(b + d)(a + d)$ (b) $(a + d)(c + d)$

(c) $(a + b)(c + d)$ (d) $(a + c)(b + d)$

56. a, b, c are in GP. If a is the first term and c is the common ratio, then $b =$ _____.

(a) 1 (b) $\frac{1}{a}$

(c) $\frac{1}{c}$ (d) None of these

57. In a GP of 7 terms, the last term is $\frac{64}{81}$ and the common ratio is $\frac{2}{3}$. Find the 3rd term.

(a) 4 (b) 9

(c) 8 (d) 12

58. An AP starts with a positive fraction and every alternate term is an integer. If the sum of the first 11 terms is 33, then find the fourth term.

(a) 2 (b) 3

(c) 5 (d) 6

59. If the sum of 16 terms of an AP is 1624 and the first term is 500 times the common difference, then find the common difference.

(a) 5 (b) $\frac{1}{2}$

(c) $\frac{1}{5}$ (d) 2

60. Find the sum of the series $1 + (1 + 2) + (1 + 2 + 3) + (1 + 2 + 3 + 4) + \cdots + (1 + 2 + 3 + \cdots + 20)$.

(a) 1470 (b) 1540

(c) 1610 (d) 1370

61. Evaluate $\Sigma 2^i$, where $i = 2, 3, 4, \ldots, 10$.

(a) 2044 (b) 2048

(c) 1024 (d) 1022

PRACTICE QUESTIONS JEE SPECIAL WING

Multiple-Answer Type Questions

Directions for questions 1 to 5:

Each question has FOUR options (a), (b), (c), and (d). ONE OR MORE THAN ONE of these four option(s) is/are the correct answer(s).

1. If the nth term of a sequence is $5n^3 + 6$, then which of the following is/are the term(s) of the sequence?
   (a) 46 (b) 141
   (c) 336 (d) 631

2. If the nth term of a sequence is $n(12 - n)$, then which term of the sequence is 35?
   (a) 5th (b) 6th
   (c) 7th (d) 8th

3. Which of the following numbers belong to the AP: $-153, -146, -139, -132, \ldots$?
   (a) −55 (b) −20
   (c) 155 (d) 330

4. If the sum of the first three terms of an AP is 45 and their product is 3240, the common difference of the AP is ______.
   (a) −3 (b) −2
   (c) 2 (d) 3

5. The sum of the terms of an infinite GP is $r + 1$, where r is the common ratio of the GP. If the first term is $\frac{16}{25}$, then the value of r ______.
   (a) $-\frac{3}{4}$ (b) $-\frac{3}{5}$
   (c) $\frac{3}{5}$ (d) $\frac{3}{4}$

Match The Column

Directions for questions 6 to 9:

Read the paragraph given below and answer the questions.

In an infinite GP, any term is equal to one-fourth of the sum of the terms that follow it. The first term of the GP is $\frac{5}{4}$.

Column A	Column B
6. Common ratio	(a) 1
7. The product of the first three terms	(b) $\frac{4}{5}$
8. The sum of the first four terms	(c) $\frac{25}{4}$
9. The sum of all the terms	(d) $\frac{369}{100}$
	(e) 25

Comprehension-Based Questions

Directions for questions 10 to 14:

Read the paragraph given below and answer the questions.

Welkin and Kevin are very good friends, and they prefer to play games which involve numbers. They have created many such games. One such game is as follows:

The natural numbers from **1 to 2500** are written in order starting from 1, on a sheet of paper. In the first round, Welkin erases all the numbers which are in odd places. The remaining numbers are written in order, and in the second round Kevin erases all the numbers which are in odd places. Again, the remaining numbers are written in order, and in the third round Welkin erases all the numbers which are in odd places. Again, the remaining numbers are written in order, and in the fourth round Kevin erases all the numbers which are in odd places. This process continues till only one number is left.

Welkin wins the game if the sum of the factors of the number left over is a multiple of 6. Kevin wins the game if the sum of the factors of the number left over is a multiple of 9.

10. What is the 29th term of the numbers which are left over after the 3rd round of the game?

(a) 145 (b) 174

(c) 203 (d) 232

11. What is the sum of the numbers which are left over after the 4th round of the game?

(a) 195936 (b) 193440

(c)198448 (d) 190960

12. What is the difference of the smallest and the largest numbers after the 5th round of the game?

(a) 2400 (b) 2432

(c) 2464 (d) 2496

13. What is the nth term of the numbers which are left over after the 6th round of the game? ?

(a) 72 n (b) $64n$

(c) 48 n (d) 32 n

14. Which of the following is a true statement?

(a) The number which is left-over at the end lies between 2000 and 2200 and the winner is Welkin.

(b) The number which is left-over at the end lies between 2200 and 2500 and the winner is Welkin.

(c) The number which is left-over at the end lies between 2000 and 2200 and the winner is Kevin.

(d) The number which is left-over at the end lies between 2200 and 2500 and the winner is Kevin.

Assertion and Reason Type Questions

Directions for questions 15 to 18:

Given below are two statements, one is labeled as Assertion (A) and the other is labeled as Reason (R). In the light of the given statements, choose the most appropriate answer from the options given below.

(a) Both assertion (A) and reason (R) are true, and reason (R) is the correct explanation of assertion.

(b) Both assertion (A) and reason (R) are true, and reason (R) is not the correct explanation of assertion.

(c) Assertion (A) is true, but reason (R) is false.

(d) Assertion (A) is false, and reason (R) is true.

15. Assertion: The nth term of $\frac{1}{a}, \frac{1}{(a+d)}, \frac{1}{(a+2d)}, \frac{1}{(a+3d)} \ldots$ is $\frac{1}{[a+(n-1)d]}$.

Reason: The sum of the first n terms term of $\frac{1}{a}, \frac{1}{(a+d)}, \frac{1}{(a+2d)}, \frac{1}{(a+3d)} \ldots$ is $\frac{1}{\frac{n}{2}[2a+(n-1)d]}$.

16. Assertion: If $a_1, a_2, a_3, a_4, a_5 \ldots a_n$ are in AP, then $2a_1, 2a_2, 2a_3, 2a_4, 2a_5 \ldots 2a_n$ are also in AP.

Reason: If $a_1, a_2, a_3, a_4, a_5 \ldots a_n$ are in GP, then $2a_1, 2a_2, 2a_3, 2a_4, 2a_5 \ldots 2a_n$ are also in GP.

17. Assertion: $9+90+900+9000+\ldots 100$ terms $= 10^{100}-1$.

Reason: If a and r are the first term and the common ratio of a GP, then

$$S_n = \frac{a(r^n-1)}{r-1}.$$

18. Assertion: If x^2, y^2, and z^2 are in AP, then $\frac{1}{(z+y)}, \frac{1}{(x+z)}$, and $\frac{1}{(y+x)}$ are in both AP and GP.

Reason: If the terms of a sequence are in both AP and GP, then the terms the sequence must be non-zero equal numbers.

ANSWER KEYS

Crossword

Across

3. Equal
4. Six
5. Four
6. Sequence
8. Tenth

Down

1. One
2. Hundred
4. Series
7. Eight
8. Ten

Classroom Wing

Very Short Answer Type Questions

1. $\frac{n}{2}[a+(n-1)d]$
2. $S_n - S_{n-1}$
3. $3n+5$
4. $\frac{(n+1)(n+2)}{2}$
5. 3
6. geometric
7. geometric
8. 10
9. geometric
10. $\frac{1}{100^n}$
11. $\frac{1}{4}$
12. $\pm\sqrt{\frac{y}{x}}$
13. 0
14. False
15. True
16. True
17. False
18. True
19. $1+x^2+x^4+x^6+\ldots$
20. 3, –2, –7.
21. 25, 125, 625.

Short Answer Type Questions

22. 21
23. 41
24. 13
25. 5000
26. $18\sqrt{3}$
27. $r=\frac{1}{4}$
28. $\frac{1}{9}$
29. ₹25600
30. 121
31. $\frac{111}{900}$
32. 448 m
33. (A) $\frac{50}{81}(10^n-1)-\frac{5n}{9}$ (B) $\frac{1}{3}$
34. 0
35. (A) 180 and 20 (B) 2 : 1

Essay Type Questions

36. $\frac{70}{81}(10^{50}-1)-\frac{350}{9}$
37. b^2, a^2, and c^2
38. $S=\frac{5}{(1-x)^2}$
39. $\frac{-2}{7}$
40. 0

Competition Wing

Level 1: Apply Your Concepts

1. 11
2. $a+nd$
3. 3
4. 5^n
5. 7.5
6. (c)
7. (b)
8. (d)
9. (a)
10. (a)
11. (a)
12. (b)
13. (a)
14. (c)
15. (a)
16. (a)
17. (a)
18. (d)
19. (c)
20. (a)
21. (c)
22. (d)
23. (c)
24. (d)
25. (c)
26. (c)
27. (b)
28. (d)
29. (b)
30. (b)

Level 2: Review Your Concepts

31. (b)	32. (d)	33. (c)	34. (c)	35. (c)
36. (b)	37. (b)	38. (b)	39. (d)	40. (d)
41. (c)	42. (c)	43. (d)	44. (b)	

Level 3: Assess Your Concepts

45. (d)	46. (b)	47. (b)	48. (c)	49. (b)
50. (b)	51. (b)	52. (a)	53. (c)	54. (a)
55. (c)	56. (a)	57. (a)	58. (a)	59. (c)
60. (b)	61. (a)			

JEE Special Wing

Multiple-Answer Type Questions

1. (a, b, d)	2. (a, c)	3. (a, b, c, d)	4. (a, d)	5. (b, c)

Match The Column

6. (b)	7. (a)	8. (d)	9. (c)

Comprehension-Based Questions

10. (d)	11. (a)	12. (c)	13. (b)	14. (c)

Assertion and Reason Type Questions

15. (c)	16. (b)	17. (a)	18. (d)

Hints and Explanations

Classroom Wing

Very Short Answer Type Questions

1. $S_n = \frac{n}{2}[2a + (n-1)d]$

$S_n = \frac{n}{2}\left[2\times\frac{a}{2} + (n-1)d\right]$

$= \frac{n}{2}[a + (n-1)d]$

2. $S_n = \frac{n}{2}(2a + (n-1)d)$

$S_{n-1} = \frac{n-1}{2}(2a + (n-1-1)d)$

$= \frac{n-1}{2}(2a + (n-2)d)$

nth term $= S_n - S_{n-1}$

3. $T_n = 3n + 8$

$T_{n-1} = 3(n-1) + 8$

$= 3n - 3 + 8$

$= 3n + 5$

4. $S_n = \frac{n}{2}[2a + (n-1)d]$

$S_{n+1} = \frac{n+1}{2}[2\cdot 1 + (n+1-1)\cdot 1]$

$= \frac{n+1}{2}[2+n]$

$= \frac{(n+1)(n+2)}{2}$

5. common ration $= \frac{3a}{a} = 3$

6. Geometric

7. Geometric sequence

8. Geometric year is the central number, i.e., 10.

9. Geometric, because common ratio remains constant again.

10. $a = \frac{1}{100}$

$r = \frac{\frac{1}{10000}}{\frac{1}{100}}$

$= \frac{1}{100}$

$a_n = a(r)^{n-1}$

$= \frac{1}{100}\left(\frac{1}{100}\right)^{n-1}$

$= \frac{1}{(100)^n}$

11. nth term $= a_0 + (n-1)d$

$a_5 = 5$

$a_4 = 4$

$a_5 = a_1 + (5-1)d$

$5 = 4 + 4d$

$d = \frac{1}{4}$

12. $a_n = ar^{n-1}$

$a_7 = a\cdot r^6 = x$

$a_9 = a\cdot r^8 = y$

Dividing $\frac{a_7}{a_9}$

$\frac{r^6}{r^8} = \frac{x}{y}$

$r^2 = \frac{y}{x}$

$r = \pm\sqrt{\frac{y}{x}}$

13. $T_n = 3 - n$

$S_n = \frac{n}{2}[a_0 + a_n]$

$S_5 = \frac{5}{2}[a_0 + a_5]$

$T_1 = 3 - 1$

$= 2$

$T_5 = 3 - 5$

$= -2$

$$S_5 = \frac{5}{2}[2+(-2)]$$
$$= 0$$

14. False

15. True, because common ratio remains the same.

16. True

$$S_\infty = \frac{a}{1-r}$$
$$a = -3$$
$$r = \frac{-6}{-3} = 2$$
$$S_\infty = \frac{-3}{(1-2)} = \frac{-3}{-1} = 3$$

17. False

$$\text{Harmonic mean} = \frac{1^{-1}+2^{-1}+3^{-1}}{3}$$
$$= \frac{3}{1+\frac{1}{2}+\frac{1}{3}}$$
$$= \frac{3\times 6}{6+3+2}$$
$$= \frac{3\times 6}{11}$$
$$= \frac{18}{11}$$

18. $\text{AM} = \frac{a+b}{2} = 9$

$$a+b = 18$$
$$\text{HM} = \frac{a^{-1}+b^{-1}}{2} = 4$$
$$\frac{2}{\frac{1}{a}+\frac{1}{b}} = 4$$
$$\frac{ab}{a+b} = 2$$
$$\frac{ab}{18} = 2$$
$$ab = 36$$

Geometric mean = $\sqrt{36} = 6$

True.

19. $T_1 = x^{2-2}$

$$= x^0 = 1$$
$$T_2 = x^{4-2}$$
$$= x^2$$
$$T_3 = x^{6-2}$$
$$= x^4$$

Infinite series $= 1 + x^2 + x^4 + x^6 + \cdots$

20. $T_n = 8 - 5n$

$$T_1 = 8 - 5$$
$$= 3$$
$$T_2 = 8 - 5(2)$$
$$= -2$$
$$T_3 = 8 - 5(3)$$
$$= 8 - 15$$
$$= -7$$

21. $T_n = 5^{n+1}$

$$T_1 = 5^{1+1}$$
$$= 5^2$$
$$= 25$$
$$T_2 = 5^{2+1}$$
$$= 5^3$$
$$= 125$$
$$T_3 = 5^{3+1}$$
$$= 5^4$$
$$= 625$$

Short Answer Type Questions

22. Here, $a = 5$ and $d = 6$
    $t_n = 125 \Rightarrow a + (n-1)d = 125$
    $\Rightarrow 5 + (n-1)6 = 125$
    $\Rightarrow n - 1 = 20 \Rightarrow n = 21$

23. Here, $a = 7$ and $d = -4$
    $t_n = -153 \Rightarrow a + (n-1)\,d = -153$
    $\Rightarrow 7 + (n-1)(-4) = -153$
    $\Rightarrow n - 1 = 40 \Rightarrow n = 41$

24. Given sequence, 7, 16, 25, 34, 43, … are in AP.
    $a = 7,\ d = 16 - 7 = 9$
    $t_n = a + (n-1)\,d = 115$
    $7 + (n-1)(9) = 115$

$7 + 9n - 9 = 115$

$9n - 2 = 115$

$9n = 177 \Rightarrow n = 13$

25. $a = 8$ and $r = 5$

$t_5 = ar^4$

$= 8(5)^4$

$= 5000$

26. 6, 18, 54, 162, are in GP.

$\text{GM} = \sqrt[4]{6\times18\times54\times162}$

$\sqrt[4]{2^4\times9^4\times3^2}$

$= \sqrt[4]{2^4\times3^{10}}$

$= 2\times9\sqrt{3} = 18\sqrt{3}$

27. $S_n = \dfrac{a(r^n-1)}{r-1}$

$S_3 = \dfrac{a(r^3-1)}{r-1}$

$S_6 = \dfrac{a(r^6-1)}{r-1}$

$\Rightarrow \dfrac{\frac{a(r^3-1)}{r-1}}{\frac{a(r^6-1)}{r-1}} = \dfrac{448}{455}$

$\Rightarrow \dfrac{(r^3-1)}{(r^6-1)} = \dfrac{448}{455}$

$\dfrac{r^3-1}{(r^3+1)(r^3-1)} = \dfrac{448}{455}$

$\dfrac{455}{488} = r^3+1$

$\dfrac{455-448}{448} = r^3$

$r^3 = \dfrac{7}{448}$

$r^3 = \dfrac{1}{64}$

$r = \left(\dfrac{1}{64}\right)^{\frac{1}{3}}$

$r = \dfrac{1}{4}$

28. $a_5 = ar^4 = 9$

$a_{12} = ar^{11} = \dfrac{1}{243}$

Dividing

$\dfrac{ar^4}{ar^{11}} = \dfrac{9}{1/243}$

$r^{-7} = 9\times243$

$r^{-7} = 3^7$

$\left(\dfrac{1}{r}\right)^7 = 3^7$

$r = \dfrac{1}{3}$

$a\left(\dfrac{1}{3}\right)^4 = 9$

$a = 9\times3^4$

$a = 729$

$a_9 = ar^8$

$= 729\left(\dfrac{1}{3}\right)^8$

$= \dfrac{729}{6561}$

$= \dfrac{1}{9}$

29. $50, x, 2x, 4x, 8x, \ldots$

GP

$a = 50$

$r = 2$

$a_{10} = ar^9$

$= 50(2)^9$

$= 25600$

30. $a = \dfrac{1}{3}$

$a_7 = 243$

$ar^6 = 243$

$\dfrac{1}{3}r^6 = 243$

$r^6 = 243\times3$

$r^6 = 3^6$

$r = 3$

$$\text{Sum} = \frac{a(r^n - 1)}{r-1}$$

$$S_7 = \frac{\frac{1}{3}(3^7 - 1)}{2}$$

$$= \frac{1}{6} \times 2186 - \frac{1}{6}$$

$$S_5 = \frac{1}{6} \times 2186 - \frac{1}{6} - 243$$

$$= \frac{2187 - 1 - 1458}{6}$$

$$= \frac{728}{6}$$

$$\approx 121$$

31. $2.1\overline{23}$ in form of p/q

$0.02333... = x$

Periodicity

Add 10 on both side

$$10x = 1.233$$

Subtract both equations

$$10x = 1.233$$

$$x = 0.1233$$

$$9x = 1.1100$$

$$x = \frac{1.11}{9}$$

$$x = \frac{111}{900}$$

32. $a = 64$

$$r = \frac{3}{4}$$

$$64 \times \frac{3}{4} = 48$$

Equation can be written as initial height + twice because of rebound formula for infinite GP $= \frac{a}{1-r}$

$$a = 48$$

$$r = \frac{3}{4}$$

$$\text{Total distance} = 64 + 2\left(\frac{48}{\frac{1}{4}}\right)$$

$$= 64 + 384$$

$$= 448 \text{ m}$$

33. (A) $S_n = 5 + 55 + 555 \cdots$

$$S_n = 5(1 + 11 + 111 + \cdots)$$

Multiplying and dividing by 9,

$$S_n = \frac{5}{9}(9 + 99 + 999 + \cdots)$$

$$S_n = \frac{5}{9}[(10-1) + (10^2 - 1) + (10^3 - 1) + \cdots]$$

$$S_n = \frac{5}{9}[(10 + 10^2 + 10^3 + \cdots) - (1 + 1 + + \cdots)]$$

$10 + 10^2 + 10^3 \cdots$ is GP

$$a = 10$$

$$r = 10$$

$$S_n = \frac{ar^{n-1}}{r-1}$$

$$S_n = \frac{10(10^n - 1)}{9}$$

$$S_n = \frac{10}{9}(10^n - 1)$$

And $1 + 1 + 1 + \cdots = n$

$$S_n = \frac{5}{9}\left[\frac{10}{9}(10^n - 1) - n\right]$$

$$= \frac{50}{81}[10^n - 1] - \frac{5n}{9}.$$

(B) $\frac{\boldsymbol{a}}{\boldsymbol{1-r}} = \boldsymbol{a + ar + ar^2 + \ldots}$

$$\frac{a}{1-r} = a + \frac{a}{2}.$$

$$\frac{\boldsymbol{a}}{\boldsymbol{1-r}} = \frac{\boldsymbol{3a}}{2}.$$

$$\Rightarrow \frac{1}{1-\boldsymbol{r}} = \frac{3}{2}.$$

$$\Rightarrow 1 - \boldsymbol{r} = \frac{2}{3}$$

$$\Rightarrow \boldsymbol{r} = \frac{1}{3}.$$

34. $$\frac{1}{a + (l-1)d} = x \quad (1)$$

$$\frac{1}{a + (m-1)d} = y \quad (2)$$

$$\frac{1}{a + (n-1)d} = z \quad (3)$$

Divide and multiply by xyz,

$$\Rightarrow xyz\left[\frac{m-n}{x}+\frac{n-l}{y}+\frac{l-m}{z}\right]$$

$$\Rightarrow xyz[(m-n)(a+(l-1)d)+(n-l)(a+(n-1)d) + (l-m)(a+(n-1)d)]$$

$$\Rightarrow xyz[\cancel{m}+(l-1)md-\cancel{n}-(l-1)nd+ \cancel{n}+(m-1)nd-\cancel{l}-(m-1)ld+ \cancel{l}+(n-1)ld-\cancel{m}-(n-1)md]$$

$$\Rightarrow xyz[lmd-md-lnd+nd+mnd- nd-mld+ld+nld-ld- mdn+md]$$

$$= xyz\times 0$$

$$= 0$$

35. (A) Let first number be a.

Second number be b.

$\text{GM}=\sqrt{ab}$

$\text{AM}=\dfrac{a+b}{2}$

$\text{HM}=\dfrac{2ab}{a+b}$

$\text{GM}^2=\text{AM}\times\text{HM}$

$\Rightarrow \text{AM}=40+\text{GM}$

$\text{GM}=\text{AM}-40$

$\Rightarrow \text{AM}=64+\text{HM}$

$\text{HM}=\text{AM}-64$

$(\text{AM}-40)^2=(\text{AM})(\text{AM}-64)$

$\text{AM}^2+1600-80AM=\text{AM}^2-64\text{AM}$

$1600=16\text{ AM}$

$\text{AM}=\dfrac{1600}{16}$

$\text{AM}=100$

$\text{GM}=100-40=60$

$\Rightarrow \dfrac{a+b}{2}=100$

$\Rightarrow a+b=200$

$\Rightarrow \sqrt{ab}=60$

$ab=3600$

$a=\dfrac{3600}{b}$

$\Rightarrow \dfrac{3600}{b}+b=200$

$\Rightarrow b^2-200b+3600=0$

$b=180, 20$

$ab=3600$

$a=40$

$b=\dfrac{40}{9}$

(B) $\dfrac{T_n}{t_n}=\dfrac{2n+3}{n-11}$

Let $T_n = k(2n+3)$

$\Rightarrow$ Sequence is $5k, 7k, 9k \ldots \Rightarrow d_1 = 2k$

Let $t_n = k(n-11)$

$\therefore$ The sequence is $-10k, -9k, -8k, \ldots \Rightarrow d_2 = k$

$\therefore \dfrac{d_1}{d_2}=\dfrac{2K}{K}=\dfrac{2}{1}=2:1$

Essay Type Questions

36. $S_n = 7 + 77 + 777 + \ldots\ n$ terms

$= 7[1 + 11 + 111 + \ldots\ n \text{ terms}]$

$=\dfrac{7}{9}[9+99+999+\ldots n\text{ terms}]$

$=\dfrac{7}{9}\left[(10-1)+(100-1)+(1000-1)+\ldots n\text{ terms}\right]$

$=\dfrac{7}{9}\left[\left(10+10^2+10^3+\ldots n\text{ terms}\right)\right.$

$\left.-(1+1+1+\ldots n\text{ terms})\right]$

$S_n=\dfrac{7}{9}\left[\dfrac{10\left(10^n-1\right)}{10-1}-n\right]$

$\therefore S_{50}=\dfrac{7}{9}\left[\dfrac{10\left(10^{50}-1\right)}{9}-50\right]$

$=\dfrac{70}{81}\left(10^{50}-1\right)-\dfrac{350}{9}$

37. Given $\dfrac{1}{a+b}, \dfrac{1}{b+c}$, and $\dfrac{1}{c+a}$ are in AP.

$\Rightarrow \dfrac{1}{b+c}-\dfrac{1}{a+b}=\dfrac{1}{c+a}-\dfrac{1}{b+c}$

$\Rightarrow \dfrac{a+b-b-c}{(b+c)(a+b)}=\dfrac{b+c-c-a}{(c+a)(b+c)}$

$a^2-c^2=b^2-a^2$

$\Rightarrow 2a^2=b^2+c^2$

$\Rightarrow b^2, a^2$, and c^2 are in AP.

38. Let $S = 5 + 10x + 15x^2 + 20x^3 + ...$

$Sx = 5x + 10x^2 + 15x^3 + 20x^4 + ...$

$\Rightarrow S - Sx = 5 + 5x + 5x^2 + 5x^3 + ...$

$\Rightarrow S(1 - x) = 5(1 + x + x^2 + x^3 + ...)$

$$\Rightarrow S(1-x) = 5\left(\frac{1}{1-x}\right)$$

($\because$ $1 + x + x^2 + ...$ is an infinite GP, $|x| < 1$.)

$$\Rightarrow S = \frac{5}{(1-x)^2}$$

Alternate method:

Let $x = 0.0001$. We expect S to be slightly more than 5. In choices 2, 3, and 4, the denominators would be more than 1.

$\therefore$ These choice values are less than 5.

39. After inserting the harmonic means, let the harmonic progression be

$$\frac{1}{a}, \frac{1}{a+d}, \frac{1}{a+2d}, \frac{1}{a+3d}, \text{ and } \frac{1}{a+4d}.$$

Given $\frac{1}{a} = \frac{1}{5}$ and $\frac{1}{a+4d} = \frac{-1}{12}$

$$\Rightarrow a = 5 \text{ and } d = -\frac{17}{4}$$

The 2nd harmonic mean $= \frac{1}{a+2d}$

$$= \frac{1}{5+2\left(\frac{-17}{4}\right)} = -\frac{2}{7}$$

Note: When N harmonic means are inserted between a and b and N is odd, the middle harmonic mean inserted will be the harmonic mean of a and b. $\therefore$ The 2nd harmonic mean in the given problem is the harmonic mean of $\frac{1}{5}$ and $-\frac{1}{12}$, i.e., $\dfrac{2\left(\frac{1}{5}\right)\left(\frac{-1}{12}\right)}{\frac{1}{5}+\left(\frac{-1}{12}\right)} = \frac{-2}{7}$.

40. $m\ t_m = n\ t_n$

$m\ [a + (m - 1)d] = n[a + (n - 1)d]$

$m([a + md - d] = n[a + nd - d]$

$ma + m^2d - md = na + n^2d - nd$

$ma - na + m^2d - n^2d - md + nd = 0$

$(m - n)\ (a) + (m^2 - n^2)d - (m - n)d = 0$

$(m - n)\ [a + (m + n)\ d - d] = 0$

$(m - n) = 0$ or $a + (m + n)d - d = 0$

Since $m \neq n$, $a + (m + n - 1)\ d = 0$.

$\Rightarrow t_{m+n} = 0.$

41. $$S_n = a\left(\frac{r^n - 1}{r-1}\right) = S_1$$

$$S_{2n} = a\left(\frac{r^{2n} - 1}{r-1}\right) = S_2$$

$$S_{3n} = \frac{a\left(r^{3n}-1\right)}{r-1} = S_3$$

$$S_1^2 + S_2^2 = a^2\left(\frac{r^n-1}{r-1}\right)^2 + a^2\left(\frac{r^{2n}-1}{r-1}\right)^2$$

$$= \frac{a^2}{(r-1)^2}\ [(r^n - 1)^2 + (r^{2n} - 1)^2]$$

$$= \frac{a}{r-1} \times \left[\left(r^n-1\right)^2 + \left(\left(r^n\right)^2 - 1\right)^2\right] \frac{a}{r-1}$$

$$= \frac{a}{r-1}\ [(r^n - 1)^2 + (r^n - 1)^2\ (r^n + 1)^2]\ \frac{a}{r-1}$$

$$= \frac{a}{r-1}\ (r^n - 1)\ [(r^n - 1) + (r^n + 1)^2\ (r^n - 1)]\ \frac{a}{r-1}$$

$$S_1^2 + S_1^2 = S_1\left[\frac{a\left(r^n-1\right)}{r-1}\{1+(r^n+1)^2\}\right]$$

$$= S_1\left[\frac{a}{r-1}\left(r^n-1\right)\left\{r^{2n}+2r^n+2\right\}\right]$$

$$= S_1\left[\frac{a}{r-1}\left(r^{3n}+2r^{2n}+2r^n-r^{2n}-2r^n-2\right)\right]$$

$$= S_1\left[\frac{a}{r-1}\left(r^{3n}+r^{2n}-2\right)\right]$$

$$= S_1\left[\frac{a}{r-1}\left(r^{3n}-1+r^{2n}-1\right)\right]$$

$$= S_1\left[\frac{a\left(r^{3n}-1\right)}{r-1}+\frac{a\left(r^{2n}-1\right)}{r-1}\right]$$

$$= S_1\ [S_3 + S_2]$$

$$\therefore S_1^2 + S_2^2 = S_1\ [S_2 + S_3]$$

42. $\frac{1}{p^2}, \frac{1}{q^2}, \frac{1}{r^2}$ are in HP

$\Rightarrow p^2, q^2, r^2$ are in AP

$\Rightarrow q^2 - p^2 = r^2 - q^2$

$\Rightarrow (q + p)\ (q - p) = (r + q)\ (r - q)$

$$\frac{q-p}{q+r} = \frac{r-q}{p+q}$$

$$\frac{2-3}{1+6} = \frac{r+p-p-q}{p+q}$$

$$\frac{(q+r)-(r+p)}{(q+r)} = \frac{A_3}{120b-27b}$$

Dividing by $(r + p)$ on both sides.

$$\frac{(q+r)-(r+p)}{(q+r)(r+p)} = \frac{6-1}{3+2}$$

$$\Rightarrow \frac{1}{r+p} - \frac{1}{q+r} = \frac{1}{p+q} - \frac{1}{r+p}$$

$$\Rightarrow \frac{1}{(q+r)}, \frac{1}{(r+p)}, \frac{1}{p+q} \text{ are in AP}$$

$\therefore$ $(q + r)$, $(r + p)$ and $(p + q)$ are in HP.

Competition Wing

Level 1: Apply Your Concepts

1. $n = 3$

$\Rightarrow 2(3)+5$

$\Rightarrow 6+5$

$\Rightarrow 11$

2. $a_n = a+(n-1)d$

$a_{n+1} = a+(n+1-1)d$

$= a+nd$

3. Let three consecutive terms are x, $x + 1$, $x + 2$

$x+x+1+x+2=9$

$3x+3=9$

$x=\frac{9-3}{3}$

$x=2$

Middle term $= x+1 = 3$

4. The series is in GP

$a_n = ar^{n-1}$

$a=5$

$r=\frac{25}{5}=5$

$a_n = 5\cdot 5^{n-1}$

$= 5^n$

5. $\frac{7+8}{2}=7.5$

6. Given $S_n = 2n^2 + n$

$tn = S_n - S_{n-1} = 2n^2 + n - [2(n-1)^2 + (n+1)]$

$= 2n^2 + n - 2n^2 + 4n - 2 - n + 1$

$= 4n - 1$

Hence, the correct option is (c).

7. Given $S_n = n(3n + 1)$

$tn = S_n - S_{n-1} = n(3n + 1) - (n-1)(3n - 3 + 1)$

$= 3n^2 + n - (3n^2 - 3n - 2n + 2)$

$= 6n - 2$

Alternate method:

$t_1 = S_1 = 4$. When $n = 1$, the only choices whose values equal 4 are 2 and 3.

$t_2 = S_2 - S_1 = 14 - S_1 = 10$, which is $6(2) - 2$ but not $10(2) - 6$.

$\therefore$ Option (b) follows.

Hence, the correct option is (b).

8. 8, x_1, x_2, x_3, x_4, x_5, and 3 are in AP.

$t_1 = 8$, $t_7 = 3$

$t_7 = a + 6d = 3$

$8 + 6d = 3$

$6d = -5$

$d=\frac{-5}{6}$.

$x_4 = t_5 = a+4d$

$=8+4\left(\frac{-5}{6}\right)$.

$=\frac{24-10}{3}=\frac{14}{3}$

Hence, the correct option is (d).

9. Geometric mean of 'n' terms of a GP $= \sqrt[n]{t_1\times t_2\times\ldots\ldots t_n}$

Required GM $= \sqrt[33]{2^1\times 2^2\times 2^2\times\ldots\times 2^{32}\times 2^{33}}$

$= \sqrt[33]{2^{1+2+3+\ldots+32+33}}$

$= \sqrt[33]{2^{\frac{33\times 34}{2}}} = 2^{17}$

Hence, the correct option is (a).

10. $\frac{5}{16},\frac{5}{24},\frac{5}{26},\frac{5}{54},\ldots$

$r=\frac{t_2}{t_1}=\frac{t_3}{t_2}=\frac{2}{3}$

The given is a GP.

$t_5=\frac{5}{16}\times\left(\frac{2}{3}\right)^4$

$\therefore \frac{5}{18}$ be the term of the series.

Hence, the correct option is (a).

11. $\Rightarrow 5, x_1, x_2, x_3, \ldots x_7, 8$ are in AP.

$a = 5 = t_1$, $t_9 = 8$, $d=\frac{8-5}{7+1}=\frac{3}{8}$

7th AM $= t_8 = a + 7d$

$= 5 + 7 \Rightarrow \frac{3}{8}=5+\frac{21}{8}=\frac{61}{8}$

Hence, the correct option is (a).

12. $a = 1, r = \frac{1}{2}$

$$S_\infty = \frac{a}{1-r}$$

$$= \frac{1}{1-\frac{1}{2}} = \frac{1}{1/2} = 2$$

Hence, the correct option is (b).

13. Find a and d using the given data and use the formula to find S_n of AP.

14. Use the formula to find the nth term of a GP.

15. Find a and r using the given data.

16. $S_6 - S_5 = t_6$.

17. Use the formula of S_n of a GP.

18. $p = ar_1^2, q = ar_1^6$ and $r = ar_1^{10}$.

19. $\Sigma\,(3 + 2^r) = 3\Sigma 1 + \sum_{r=1}^{10} 2^r$.

20. Use the formula to find S_∞ of a GP.

21. If a, b and c are in GP, then $b^2 = ac$.

22. Form the series and use the formula to find S_n.

23. The 3 geometric means are t_2, t_3 and t_4 terms.

24. Use the formula of the nth term of a HP.

25. Use the relation between AM, GM and HM.

26. (i) $S_n = \frac{a(r^n - 1)}{(r-1)}$

(ii) $a = 1$ and $r = 2$

(iii) Given that $S_n > 3000$

(iv) Then find least possible value of n.

27. HM of a and b is $\frac{2ab}{a+b}$.

29. $S_6 - S_3 = T_4 + T_5 + T_6$.

30. Use the formula of S_n of a GP.

Level 2: Review Your Concepts

31. $t_2 - t_1 = t_3 - t_2$.

32. Each term is in the form of $7n + 2$, where $n = -1, 0, 1, 2, 3, \ldots$.

33. Let the five integers be $a - 2d$, $a - d$, a, $a + d$ and $a + 2d$.

34. (i) The sides must be in the ratio 3 : 4 : 5.

(ii) Shortest side should be a multiple of 3.

35. (i) Common terms in S_1 and S_2 are 7, 19, 31, ….

(ii) The first term of S_1 is 3. The 125th term is 499.

The first term of S_2 is 4. The 125th term is 376.

(iii) The last common term is 367 (and not 499).

(iv) $7 = 12(1) - 5$, $19 = 12(2) - 5$, …, $367 = 12(31) - 5$.

36. (i) Use the formula to find nth term of a GP.

(ii) $ar^{m-1} = n$, $ar^{n-1} = m$.

(iii) $(m + 1 - n)$th term $= ar^{m-n}$.

37. (i) Given $S_\infty = \frac{a}{1-r} = 3$.

(ii) $a^2 + a^2r^2 + a^2r^4 + \cdots = 81$.

38. (i) Use $\log_{b^n} a = \frac{1}{n}\log_b a$.

(ii) $S_n = \frac{a(r^n - 1)}{(r-1)}$

(iii) If $\log_a x = b$, then $a^b = x$.

39. Form the series and find the value of n and use the formula $S_n = \frac{n}{2}(2a + (n-1)d)$.

40. $t_n = \frac{1}{a + (n-1)d}$ in HP.

41. (i) $\frac{1}{a} = 3, \frac{1}{a+7d} = \frac{6}{23}$.

(ii) Find a and d by using above relation find t_5 using $\frac{1}{a+4d}$.

42. Use $b = \frac{a+c}{2}$ and $(b^2)^2 = a^2c^2$.

43. (i) $\sum_{n=1}^{\infty}\left(1+\left(\frac{3}{5}\right)^n\right) = 1 + \frac{3}{5} + \left(\frac{3}{5}\right)^2 + \ldots\infty$

(ii) $S_\infty = \frac{a}{1-r}$, where a is the first term and r is the common ratio.

44. BDAC is the sequential order of steps.

Level 3: Assess Your Concepts

45. (i) In AP, $t_n = a + (n-1)d$ and in HP, $t_n = \frac{1}{a+(n-1)d}$.

(ii) Find the values of a and d by using the data.

46. (i) Let $p=\left(1+\frac{1}{2}\right)\left(1+\frac{1}{4}\right)\left(1+\frac{1}{4}\right)\left(1+\frac{1}{4}\right)\ldots$

(ii) Multiply with $\left(1-\frac{1}{2}\right)$ on both sides.

(iii) $(a+b)(a-b)=a^2-b^2\ a,\ n-\infty\ \frac{1}{2^n}=0.$

47. (i) Let a_1 and d_1 be the first term and common difference of the first AP and a_2, d_2 be the corresponding values for the second AP.

(ii) $S_n : S'_n$ has to be converted in the form of $t_n : t'_n$.

48. (i) n arithmetic means are in between a and b;

$$d=\frac{b-a}{n+1}.$$

(ii) Evaluate for how many values of $(n+1)$, d is an integer.

49. $x=\frac{1}{\sqrt{2}}+\frac{1}{2}+\frac{1}{2\sqrt{2}}+\ldots\infty$

$$x=\frac{\frac{1}{\sqrt{2}}}{1-\frac{1}{\sqrt{2}}}=\frac{1}{\sqrt{2}-1}$$

$$x=\frac{1}{\sqrt{2}-1}=\sqrt{2}+1\Rightarrow\frac{1}{x}=\sqrt{2}-1$$

$$\therefore x+\frac{1}{x}=\sqrt{2}+1+\sqrt{2}-1=2\sqrt{2}.$$

50. $x=3+\frac{3}{y}+\frac{3}{y^2}+\frac{3}{y^3}+\cdots+\infty$

$$x=3\left[\frac{1}{1-\frac{1}{y}}\right]$$

$$x=3\left[\frac{y}{y-1}\right]\Rightarrow xy-x=3y$$

$$xy-3y=x$$

$$y(x-3)=x\Rightarrow y=\frac{x}{x-3}.$$

51. $\frac{0.3}{0.5}+\frac{0.33}{0.55}+\frac{0.333}{0.555}+\cdots 15 \text{ terms}$

$$S=\frac{3}{5}+\frac{33}{55}+\frac{333}{555}+\cdots 15 \text{ terms}$$

$$S=\frac{3}{5}\left[1+\frac{11}{11}+\frac{111}{111}+\cdots 15 \text{ terms}\right]$$

$$S=\frac{3}{5}\times 15\Rightarrow S=9.$$

52. $t_4=t_2{}^2$

$$\Rightarrow ar^3=(ar)^2\Rightarrow ar^3=a^2r^2\Rightarrow r=a.$$

53. $16^{1+\cos x+\cos^2 x+\cos^3 x+\ldots\infty}=256$

$$16^{\frac{1}{1-\cos x}}=256\Rightarrow 16^{\frac{1}{1-\cos x}}=16^2$$

$$\Rightarrow\frac{1}{1-\cos x}=2\Rightarrow 1-\cos x=\frac{1}{2}$$

$$1-\frac{1}{2}=\cos x.$$

$$\frac{1}{2}=\cos x\Rightarrow x=60°.$$

54. $t_2=ar=p$

$t_3=ar^2=q$

$$\Rightarrow\frac{t_3}{t_2}=\frac{q}{p}=\frac{ar^2}{ar}\Rightarrow r=\frac{q}{p}$$

$$ar=p$$

$$\Rightarrow a\cdot\frac{q}{p}=p\Rightarrow a=\frac{p^2}{q}$$

$$t_5=a\cdot r^4$$

$$=\frac{p^2}{q}\left(\frac{q}{p}\right)^4$$

$$=\frac{p^2}{q}\times\frac{q^4}{p^4}=\frac{q^3}{p^2}=p\left(\frac{q}{p}\right)^3.$$

55. a, b, c, d are in GP

$a=a,\ b=ar,\ c=ar^2,\ d=ar^3$

$b+c=ar+ar^2=ar(1+r)$

$(b+c)^2=a^2r^2(1+r^2+2r)$

$=a^2r^2+a^2r^4+2a^2r^3$

$=a\cdot ar^2+ar\cdot ar^3+a^{2r3}+a^{2r3}$

$=a\cdot c+bd+bc+ad=a(c+d)+b(c+d)$

$=(a+b)(c+d).$

56. a, b, c are in GP

$$r=\frac{b}{a}=\frac{c}{b}$$

but given that $r=c$

$$\Rightarrow\frac{c}{b}=c\Rightarrow b=1.$$

57. Let a be the first term and r the common ratio of the GP.

$$T_y=ar^6=\frac{64}{81}\Rightarrow a=9$$

Therefore the 3rd term, $T_3 = ar^2$

$$T_3 = 9\left(\frac{2}{3}\right)^2 = 4.$$

58. Given, $\frac{11}{2}[2a + 10d] = 33$

$\Rightarrow a + 5d = 3$

$\Rightarrow a + 3d = 2$

Since, alternate terms are integers and the given sum is positive.

59. $S_n = \frac{n}{2}[2a + (n-1)d]$

$$\frac{16}{2}[2 \times 500d + (16-1)d] = 1624$$

$$8[1000d + 15d] = 1624$$

$$1015d = \frac{1624}{8}$$

$$1015d = 203$$

$$d = \frac{203}{1015} \Rightarrow d = \frac{1}{5}.$$

60. $1 + (1 + 2) + (1 + 2 + 3) + (1 + 2 + 3 + 4) + \ldots$ 20 terms

$= 1 + 3 + 6 + 10 + 15 + 21 + 28 + 36 + 45 + 55 + 66 + 78 + 91 + 105 + 120 + 136 + 153 + 171 + 190 + 210$

$= 1540.$

Alternative method:

$1 + (1 + 2) + (1 + 2 + 3) + \ldots$

nth term of the series is

$$1 + 2 + 3 + 4 + \ldots n = \frac{n(n+1)}{2}$$

Sum of n terms of the series

$$= \Sigma t_n$$

$$= \Sigma \frac{n(n+1)}{2} \Rightarrow = \frac{1}{2}\Sigma(n^2 + n)$$

$$= \frac{1}{2}\left(\Sigma n^2 + \Sigma n\right)$$

$$= \frac{1}{2}\left[\frac{n(n+1)(2n+1)}{6} + \frac{n(n+1)}{2}\right]$$

$$= \frac{n(n+1)}{4}\left(\frac{2n+1}{3} + 1\right)$$

$$\Rightarrow \frac{n(n+1)(2n+4)}{12} = \frac{n(n+1)(n+2)}{6}.$$

If $n = 20$

$$\Sigma t_{20} = \frac{20(21)(22)}{6}$$

$$\Rightarrow \frac{10 \times 21 \times 22}{3} = 1540.$$

61. $\Sigma 2^i, i = 2, 3, \ldots 10$

$$= (2^2 + 2^3 + \cdots + 2^{10})$$

$$= 2^2 \times \frac{(2^9 - 1)}{2 - 1}$$

$$= \frac{2^{11} - 2^2}{1}$$

$$= 2044.$$

JEE Special Wing

Multiple-Answer Type Questions

1. Given that $t_n = 5n^3 + 6$.

Going by options:

(a) Let $5n^3 + 6 = 46$.
$\Rightarrow 5n^3 = 40$
$\Rightarrow n^3 = 8$
$\Rightarrow n = 2$
$\Rightarrow$ 46 is a term of the sequence.

(b) Let $5n^3 + 6 = 141$.
$\Rightarrow 5n^3 = 135$
$\Rightarrow n^3 = 27$
$\Rightarrow n = 3$
$\Rightarrow$ 141 is a term of the sequence.

(c) Let $5n^3 + 6 = 336$.
$\Rightarrow 5n^3 = 330$
$\Rightarrow n^3 = 66$ which is not a perfect cube.
$\Rightarrow$ 336 is not a term of the sequence.

(d) Let $5n^3 + 6 = 631$.
$\Rightarrow 5n^3 = 625$
$\Rightarrow n^3 = 125$
$\Rightarrow n = 5$
$\Rightarrow$ 631 is a term of the sequence.

Hence, the choices (a, b, d) are correct.

2. Given that $t_n = n(12 - n)$.
Also, $n(12 - n) = 35$.
$n^2 - 12n + 35 = 0$.
$n^2 - 5n - 7n - 35 = 0$.
$n(n-5) - 7(n-5) = 0$.
$(n-5)(n-7) = 0$.
$n = 5$ (or) $n = 7$.

Hence, the choices (a and c) are correct.

3. Given AP: $-153, -146, -139, -132, \ldots$
$a = -153$ and $d = -146 - (-153) = -146 + 153 = 7$.
Now $t_n = a + (n-1)d = -153 + (n-1)7 = 7n - 160$.

Going by options:

(a) Let $7n - 160 = -55$.
$\Rightarrow 7n = 105$
$\Rightarrow n = 15$
$\Rightarrow -55$ is a term of the AP.

(b) Let $7n - 160 = -20$.
$\Rightarrow 7n = 140$
$\Rightarrow n = 20$
$\Rightarrow -20$ is a term of the AP.

(c) Let $7n - 160 = 155$.
$\Rightarrow 7n = 315$
$\Rightarrow n = 45$
$\Rightarrow$ 155 is a term of the AP.

(d) Let $7n - 160 = 330$.
$\Rightarrow 7n = 490$
$\Rightarrow n = 40$
$\Rightarrow$ 330 is a term of the AP.

Hence, the choices (a, b, c, d) are correct.

4. Given that the sum of the first three terms of an AP is 45 and their product is 3240.
Let the first three terms of the AP be $a - d$, a, and $a + d$.
$\Rightarrow (a-d) + a + (a+d) = 45$
$\Rightarrow 3a = 45 \Rightarrow a = 15$.
Also, $(a-d) \times a \times (a+d) = 3240$.
$\Rightarrow (15-d) \times 15 \times (15+d) = 3240$
$\Rightarrow 15^2 - d^2 = 216$
$\Rightarrow d^2 = 225 - 216 = 9$
$\Rightarrow d = \pm 3$

Hence, the choices (a and d) are correct.

5. Given that the sum of the terms of an infinite GP is $r + 1$ and $a = \frac{16}{25}$.
$\Rightarrow \frac{a}{1-r} = r + 1.$
$\Rightarrow \frac{16}{25} = (1+r)(1-r).$
$\Rightarrow \frac{16}{25} = 1 - r^2$
$\Rightarrow r^2 = 1 - \frac{16}{25}$
$\Rightarrow r^2 = \frac{9}{25}$
$\Rightarrow r = \pm\frac{3}{5}.$

Hence, the choices (b and c) are correct.

Match The Column

Common Solutions for questions 6 to 9:

We have $S_\infty = a + ar + ar^2 + ar^3 + ar^4 + ar^5 + ar^6 \ldots$

Given that the sum of any number of consecutive terms is 4 times their preceding term.

$\Rightarrow ar + ar^2 + ar^3 + ar^4 + ar^5 + ar^6 \ldots = 4a.$

$\Rightarrow S_\infty = a + 4a = 5a$

6. $S_\infty = 5a$

$\Rightarrow \dfrac{a}{1-r} = 5a$ (1)

$\Rightarrow \dfrac{1}{1-r} = 5$

$\Rightarrow 1 - r = \dfrac{1}{5}$

$\Rightarrow r = 1 - \dfrac{1}{5} = \dfrac{4}{5}$.

Hence, the correct option is (b).

7. Given that $a = \dfrac{5}{4}$ and $r = \dfrac{4}{5}$.

The product of the first three terms

$= \dfrac{5}{4} \times \left(\dfrac{5}{4} \times \dfrac{4}{5}\right) \times \left(\dfrac{5}{4} \times \left(\dfrac{4}{5}\right)^2\right)$

$= \dfrac{5}{4} \times (1) \times \left(\dfrac{4}{5}\right) = 1.$

Hence, the correct option is (a).

8. The sum of the first four terms $= a + ar + ar^2 + ar^3$

$= \dfrac{5}{4} + \left(\dfrac{5}{4} \times \dfrac{4}{5}\right) + \left(\dfrac{5}{4} \times \left(\dfrac{4}{5}\right)^2\right) + \left(\dfrac{5}{4} \times \left(\dfrac{4}{5}\right)^3\right)$

$= \dfrac{5}{4} + 1 + \dfrac{4}{5} + \left(\dfrac{4}{5}\right)^2$

$= \dfrac{5}{4} + 1 + \dfrac{4}{5} + \dfrac{16}{25}$

$= \dfrac{125 + 100 + 80 + 64}{100} = \dfrac{369}{100}$.

Hence, the correct option is (d).

9. The sum of all the terms $(S_\infty) = \dfrac{a}{1-r}$.

$= 5a$ [From equation (1)]

$= 5 \times \dfrac{5}{4}$

$= \dfrac{25}{4}$.

Hence, the correct option is (c).

Comprehension-Based Questions

Common Solutions for questions 10 to 14:

Given that the number written on the board initially are 1, 2, 3, 4, 5, 6, 7, 8, 9, 10, 11, 12, … 2500.

In the first round, as Welkin erases all the numbers which are in odd places, the numbers left over after the first round are: 2, 4, 6, 8, 10, 12, 14, 16, 18, 20, 22, 24, 26, 28, 32, 34, 36, 38, 40 … which are multiples of 2.

In the second round, as Kevin erases all the numbers which are in odd places, the numbers left over after the second round are: 4, 8, 12, 16, 20, 24, 28, 32, 36, 40, … which are multiples of 4.

10. The numbers left over after the third round are: 8, 16, 24, 32, 40, … are in AP with $a = 8$ and $d = 16 - 8 = 8$.

We have $t_n = a + (n-1)d$.

$\Rightarrow t_n = 8 + (29 - 1)8$

$= 29 \times 8 = 232.$

Hence, the correct option is (d).

11. The numbers left over after the fourth round are: 16, 32, 48, … are in AP with $a = 16$ and $d = 32 - 16 = 16$.

We have $t_n = a + (n-1)d$.

We know that $t_n \le 2500$

$\Rightarrow a + (n-1)d \le 2500$

$\Rightarrow 16 + (n-1)16 \le 2500$

$\Rightarrow 16n \le 2500$

$\Rightarrow n \le \dfrac{2500}{16}$

$\Rightarrow n \le 156.25$

$\Rightarrow$ The number of terms $(n) = 156$.

We have $S_n = \dfrac{n}{2}[2a + (n-1)d]$.

$= \dfrac{156}{2} \times [2 \times 16 + (156 - 1) \times 16]$

$= 78 \times [32 + 2480]$

$= 78 \times 2512 = 195936.$

Hence, the correct option is (a).

12. The numbers left over after the fifth round are: 32, 64, 96… are in AP with $a = 32$ and $d = 64 - 32 = 32$.

We have $t_n = a + (n-1)d$.

We know that $t_n \le 2500$

$\Rightarrow a + (n-1)d \le 2500$

$\Rightarrow 32 + (n-1)32 \le 2500$

$\Rightarrow 32n \le 2500$

$\Rightarrow n \le \dfrac{2500}{32}$

$\Rightarrow n \le 78.125$

$\Rightarrow$ The largest value of $n = 78$.

The largest number in the AP $= a + (n-1)d$.

$= 32 + (78 - 1)32$

$= 78 \times 32 = 2496.$

The required difference $= 2496 - 32 = 2464$.

Hence, the correct option is (c).

13. The numbers left over after the sixth round are: 64, 128, 192… are in AP with $a = 64$ and $d = 128 - 64 = 64$.
We have $t_n = a + (n-1)d$.
$= 64 + (n-1) \times 64 = 64n$.
Hence, the correct option is (b).

14. We notice that the first number in each of the new sets of numbers is a power of 2.
(i.e., $2 = 2^1, 4 = 2^2, 8 = 2^3, 16 = 2^4, 32 = 2^5, 64 = 2^6 \ldots$).
As the process continues till only one number is left, the number which is left over will be the highest power of 2 which is less than or equal to 2500.
The required number is 2048 i.e., 2^{11}, which lies between 2000 and 2200.
The factors are: $2^0, 2^1, 2^2, 2^3, 2^4, 2^5, 2^6 \ldots 2^{11}$
The factors are in GP with $a = 2^0 = 1, r = 2$, and $n = 22$.
We have $S_n = \dfrac{a(r^n - 1)}{r - 1}$.
$S_{12} = \dfrac{1(2^{12} - 1)}{2 - 1}$
$= 4096 - 1 = 4095$ which is multiple of 9 but not 6.
Hence, the winner is Kevin.
Hence, the correct option is (c).

Assertion and Reason Type Questions

15. **Assertion:** $a, (a+d), (a+2d), (a+3d) \ldots$ are in AP.
$\Rightarrow \dfrac{1}{a}, \dfrac{1}{(a+d)}, \dfrac{1}{(a+2d)}, \dfrac{1}{(a+3d)} \ldots$ are in HP.
The nth term of the AP $= [a + (n-1)d]$.
The nth term of the HP is $\dfrac{1}{[a + (n-1)d]}$.
So, **Assertion** is true.
Reason: The sum of the first n terms term of $\dfrac{1}{a}, \dfrac{1}{(a+d)}, \dfrac{1}{(a+2d)}, \dfrac{1}{(a+3d)} \ldots$ is $\dfrac{1}{\frac{n}{2}[2a + (n-1)d]}$. It is a false statement, since we cannot determine a precise formula for the sum of the first n terms term of a HP.
Hence, the correct option is (c).

16. **Assertion:** Given that $a_1, a_2, a_3, a_4, a_5 \ldots a_n$ are in AP.
$\Rightarrow a_2 - a_1 = a_3 - a_2 = a_4 - a_3 = \ldots = d$.
Now $2a_2 - 2a_1 = 2(a_2 - a_1) = 2d$.
$2a_3 - 2a_2 = 2(a_3 - a_2) = 2d$.
$2a_4 - 2a_3 = 2(a_4 - a_3) = 2d$.
Hence, $2a_1, 2a_2, 2a_3, 2a_4, 2a_5 \ldots 2a_n$ are also in AP.
Reason: Given that $a_1, a_2, a_3, a_4, a_5 \ldots a_n$ are in GP.
$\Rightarrow \dfrac{a_2}{a_1} = \dfrac{a_3}{a_2} = \dfrac{a_4}{a_3} = \ldots = r$.
Now $\dfrac{2a_2}{2a_1} = \dfrac{a_2}{a_1} = r$
$\dfrac{2a_3}{2a_2} = \dfrac{a_3}{a_2} = r$
$\dfrac{2a_4}{2a_3} = \dfrac{a_4}{a_3} = r$
Hence, $2a_1, 2a_2, 2a_3, 2a_4, 2a_5 \ldots 2a_n$ are also in GP.
Both Assertion and Reason are true, but Reason is not the correct explanation of Assertion.
Hence, the correct option is (b).

17. **Assertion:** $9 + 90 + 900 + 9000 + \ldots 100$ terms
$= 9[10^0 + 10^1 + 10^2 + 10^3 + \ldots 100 \text{ terms}]$
The terms of the series are in GP with $a = 1, r = 10$ and $n = 100$.
We have $S_n = \dfrac{a(r^n - 1)}{r - 1}$.
$S_{100} = 9 \times \left[\dfrac{1(10^{100} - 1)}{10 - 1}\right] = 10^{100} - 1$.
Reason: If a and r are the first term and the common ratio of a GP, then $S_n = \dfrac{a(r^n - 1)}{r - 1}$.
Both **Assertion** and **Reason** are true, and **Reason** is the correct explanation of **Assertion**.
Hence, the correct option is (a).

18. **Assertion:** Given that x^2, y^2, and z^2 are in AP.
$y^2 - x^2 = z^2 - y^2$
$(y+x)(y-x) = (z+y)(z-y)$
$\dfrac{(y-x)}{(z+y)} = \dfrac{(z-y)}{(y+x)}$
$\dfrac{(y-x)}{(z+y)(x+z)} = \dfrac{(z-y)}{(y+x)(x+z)}$
$\dfrac{1}{(x+z)} - \dfrac{1}{(z+y)} = \dfrac{1}{(y+x)} - \dfrac{1}{(x+z)}$
$\dfrac{1}{(z+y)}, \dfrac{1}{(x+z)}$, and $\dfrac{1}{(y+x)}$ are in AP and these may not be in GP.
So, **Assertion** is false.
Reason: If the terms of a sequence are in both AP and GP, then the terms the sequence must be non-zero equal numbers.
It is a true statement.
Hence, the correct option is (d).

Unit III

Geometry

In this Unit

- **Chapter 7** Geometry
- **Chapter 8** Mensuration
- **Chapter 9** Coordinate Geometry

CHAPTER

7

Geometry

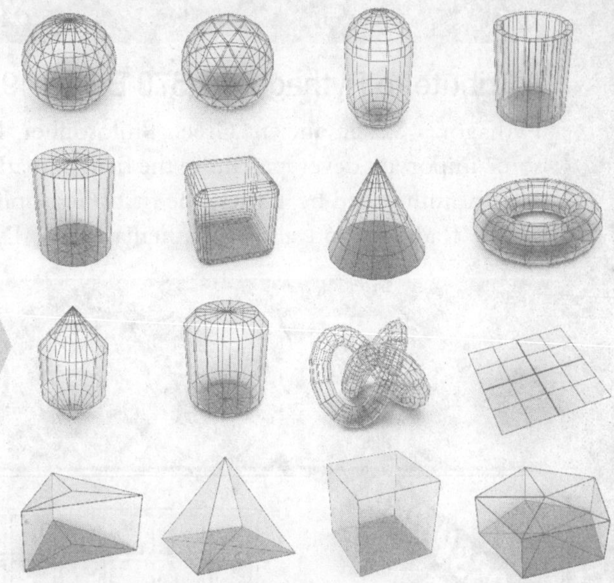

Remember

Before beginning this chapter, you should be able to:

- Know types and properties of quadrilaterals
- Recall Pythagoras theorem and its converse
- Construct polygons, triangles, quadrilaterals, circles

Key Ideas

After completing this chapter, you should be able to:

- Learn about symmetry and similarity of geometrical figures in general
- Explain criteria for similarity of triangles, right angle theorem, results on areas of similar triangle, Pythagorean, Apollonius, Thales, vertical angle bisector theorems
- Understand properties of chords or arcs and prove theorems based on tangents
- Learn construction of geometrical figures
- Study equation of locus

Scientific Crypt

A Tribute to Pythagoras (570 BC to 490 BC)

Pythagoras was an ancient Greek Philosopher. He made some important developments in the field of mathematics. He was influenced by Thales (the first philosopher in the Greek tradition and also a mathematician). Pythagoras theorem is one of his major contributions. This theorem plays a vital role in proving some other theorems (for example, Apollonius theorem) in geometry.

FUN TIME

CROSSWORD

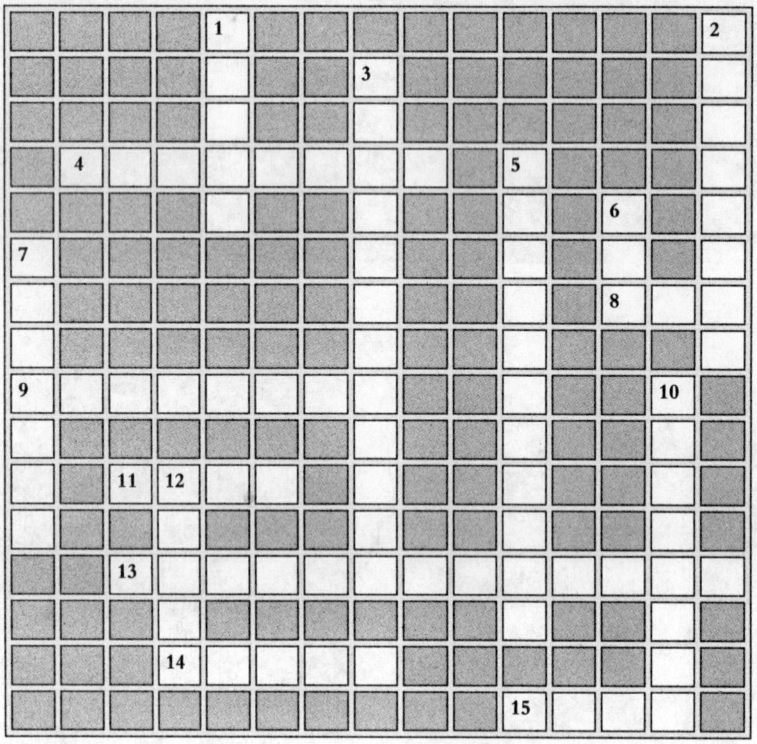

Across

4. The point of concurrence of the bisectors of angles of a triangle
8. The number of points of symmetry of a circle
9. The number of points of symmetry of a straight line.
11. The number of lines of symmetry of a parallelogram.
13. The opposite angles of a cyclic quadrilateral are
14. The collection of all points and only those points that satisfy certain given geometrical conditions is called ______ of a point.
15. The number of lines of symmetry of a square.

Down

1. The number of lines of symmetry of an equilateral triangle.
2. The tangents drawn to a circle at the ends of a diameter are
3. The locus of a point which is equidistant from the vertices of a triangle.
5. Equal chords of the circle are _____ from the centre of the circle.
6. The number of common tangents drawn to two intersecting circles at different points.
7. Any two squares are
10. For all triangles, the centroid lies _____ of the triangles
12. The corresponding angles of two similar triangles are

INTRODUCTION

In this chapter, we shall learn about symmetry, similarity of geometrical figures in general, triangles in particular. We shall understand similarity through size transformation. Further we shall learn about concurrent lines, geometric centres in triangles, basic concepts of circles, and related theorems. We shall also focus on some constructions related to polygons and circles. Finally, we shall discuss the concept of locus.

Symmetry

Let us examine the following figures (Fig. 7.1) drawn on a rectangular piece of paper:

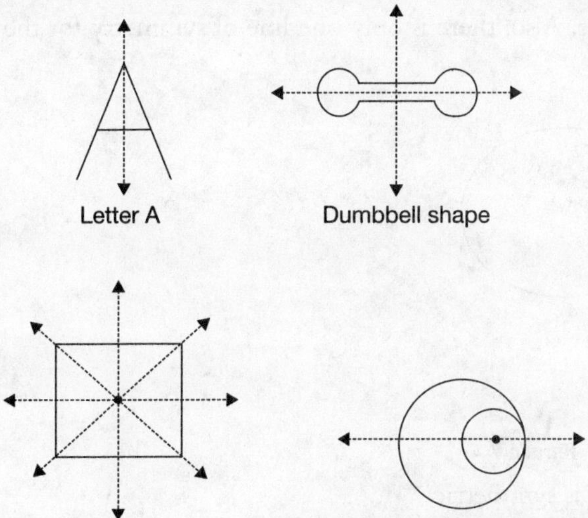

Figure 7.1

> **Info Bytes!**
> In ancient architecture, the Greeks extensively used symmetry and geometric proportions to build temples and structures, aiming to achieve a divine and harmonious aesthetic. The Parthenon is a prime example of the application of geometric symmetry in architecture.

What do you infer? We can observe that when these figures are folded about the dotted lines, the two parts on either side of the dotted lines coincide. This property of geometrical figures is called symmetry.

In this chapter, we shall discuss two basic types of symmetry—**line symmetry and point symmetry**. Then we shall see how to obtain the image of a point, a line segment, and an angle about a line.

Line Symmetry

Trace a geometrical figure on a rectangular piece of paper as shown in adjacent figure.

Now fold the paper along the dotted line. You will find that the two parts of the figure on either sides of the line coincide. Thus the line divides the figure into two identical parts. In this case, we say that the figure is symmetrical about the dotted line or Line Symmetric. Also, the dotted line is called the Line of Symmetry or The Axis of Symmetry.

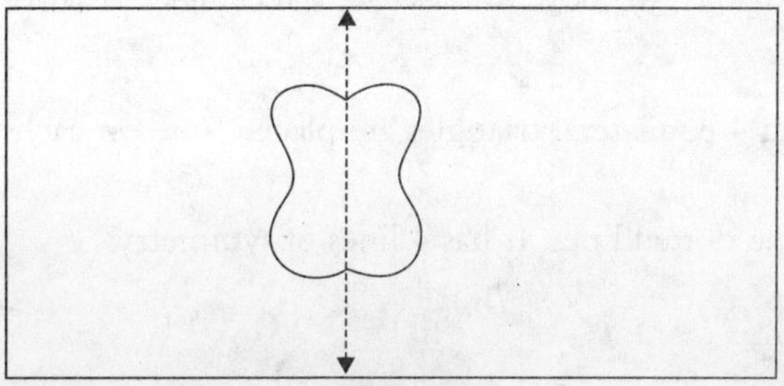

Figure 7.2

So, a geometrical figure is said to be line symmetric or symmetrical about a line if there exists at least one line in the figure such that the parts of the figure on either sides of the line coincide, when it is folded about the line.

Example: Consider the following figure (Fig. 7.3).

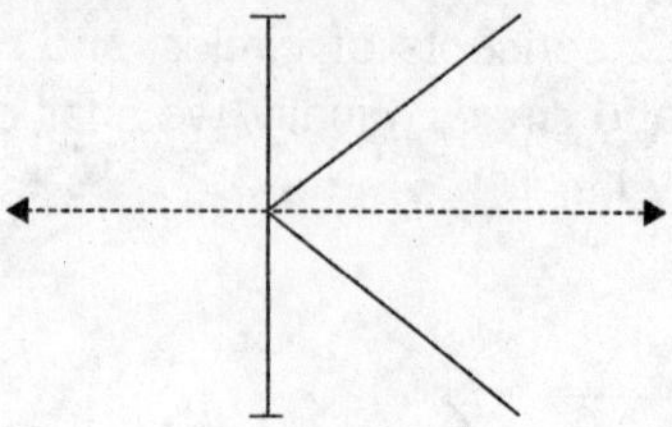

Figure 7.3

The above figure is symmetrical about the dotted line. Also, there is only one line of symmetry for the figure.

Example: Observe the figure given below (Fig. 7.4).

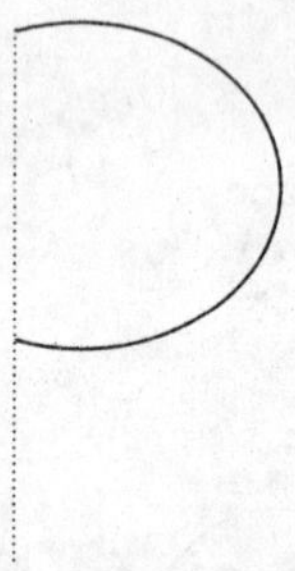

Figure 7.4

There is no line in the figure about which the figure is symmetric.

Example: Consider a rectangle as shown in the Fig. 7.5.

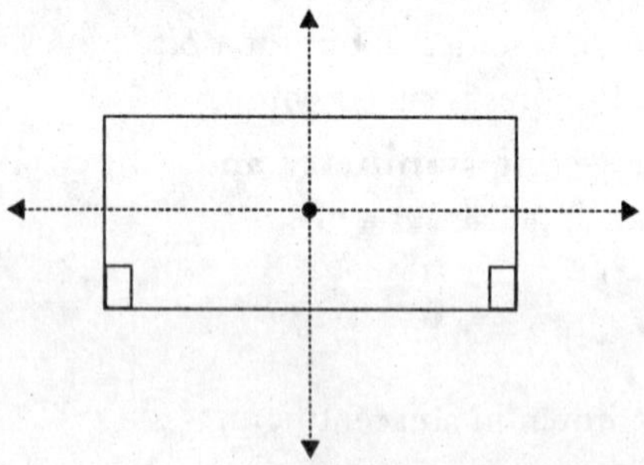

Figure 7.5

The rectangle is symmetrical about the two dotted lines. So, a rectangle has two lines of symmetry.

Example: Consider a figure in which 4 equilateral triangles are placed, one on each side of a square as shown below.

The figure is symmetrical about the dotted lines. It has 4 lines of symmetry.

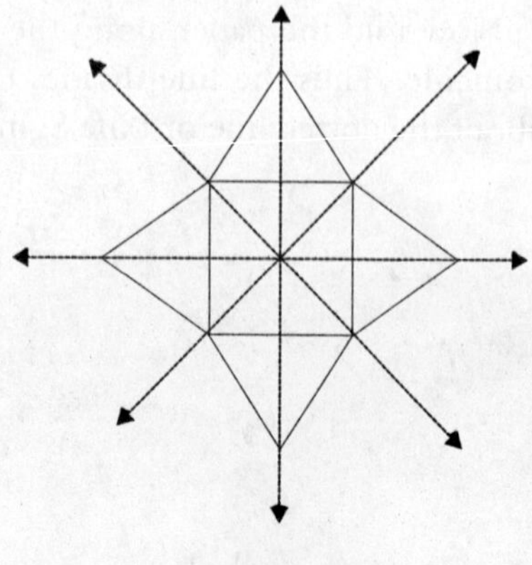

Figure 7.6

Example: A circle has an infinite number of lines of symmetry, some of which are shown in the Fig. 7.7.

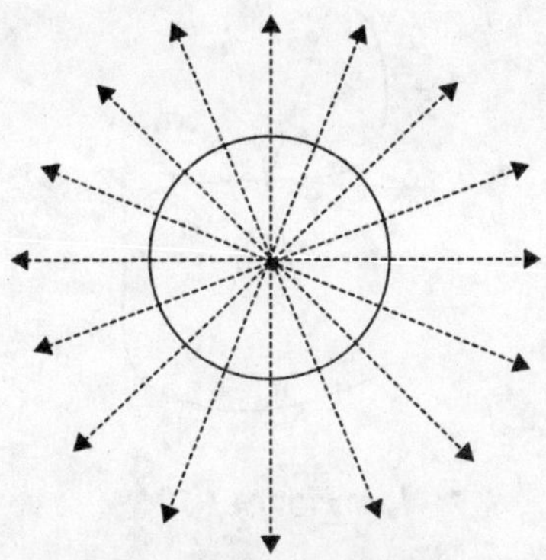

Figure 7.7

From the above illustrations, we observe the following:

1. A geometrical figure may not have a line of symmetry, i.e., a geometric figure may not be line symmetric.
2. A geometrical figure may have more than one line of symmetry, i.e., a geometrical figure may be symmetrical about more than one line.

Point Symmetry

Trace the letter N on a rectangular piece of paper as shown in Fig. 7.8. Let P be the mid-point of the inclined line in the figure. Now draw a line segment through the point P touching the two vertical strokes of N. We find that the point P divides the line segment into two equal parts. Thus, every line segment drawn through the point P and touching the vertical strokes of N is bisected at the point P. Also, when we rotate the letter N about the point P through an angle of 180°, we find that it coincides exactly with the initial position. This property of geometrical figures is called *Point Symmetry*. In this case, we say that the point P is the point of symmetry of the figure.

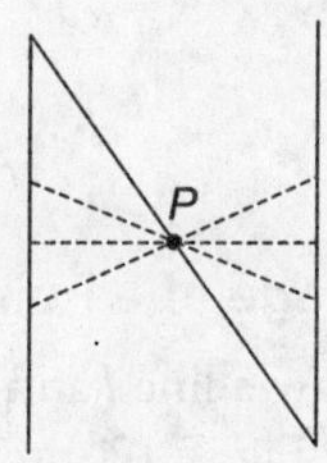

Figure 7.8

So, a geometrical figure is said to have symmetry about a point P if every line segment through the point P touching the boundary of the figure is bisected at the point P.

(Or)

A geometrical figure is said to have point symmetry if the figure does not change when rotated through an angle of 180°, about the point P.

Here, point P is called the centre of symmetry.

Illustrations

Example: Consider a rectangle $ABCD$. Let P be the point of intersection of the diagonals AC and BD. Then, the rectangle $ABCD$ has the point symmetry about the point P.

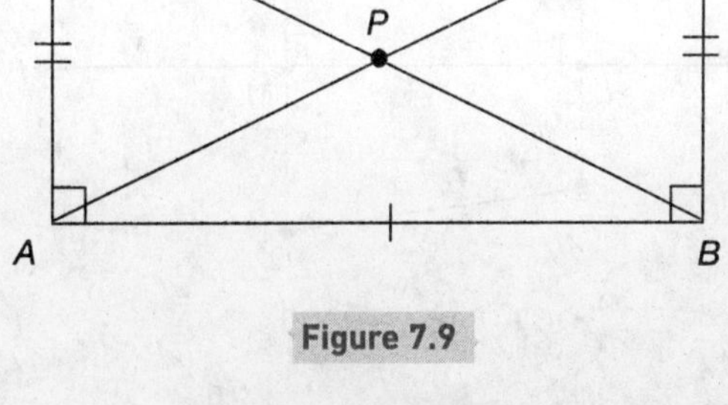

Figure 7.9

Example: The letter '*S*' has a point of symmetry about the turning point in *S*.

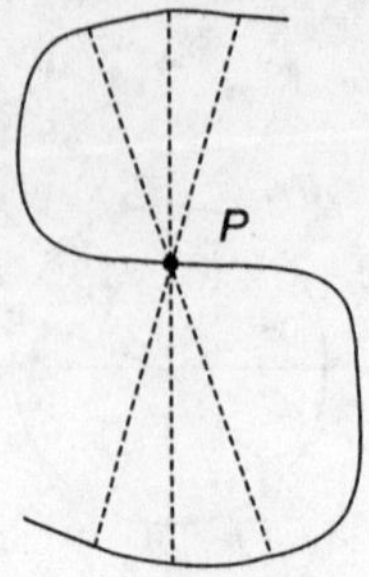

Figure 7.10

Example: A circle has a point of symmetry. This point is the centre of the circle.

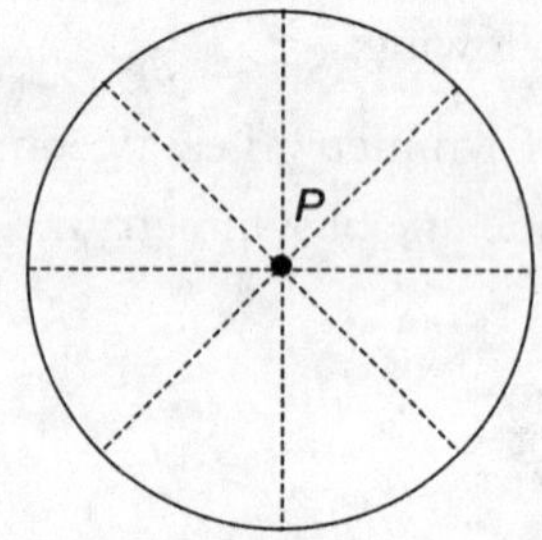

Figure 7.11

Image of a Point About a Line

Draw a line *l* and mark a point *A* on a rectangular piece of paper as shown in the Fig. 7.12.

Draw *AM* perpendicular to *l* and produce it to *B* such that $AM = MB$. Then the point *B* is said to be the image of the point *A* about the line *l*.

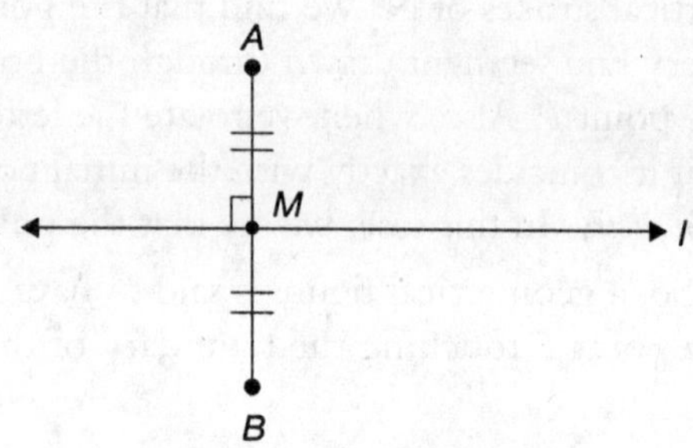

Figure 7.12

Image of a Line Segment About a Line

Draw a line *l* and a line segment *PQ* on a rectangular piece of paper as shown in the Fig. 7.13.

Draw perpendiculars *PL* and *QM* from the points *P* and *Q*, respectively, to the line *l*and produce them to P' and Q', respectively, such that $PL = LP'$ and $QM = MQ'$. Join the points P', Q'. Then the line segment $P'Q'$ is called the image of the line segment *PQ* about the line *l*.

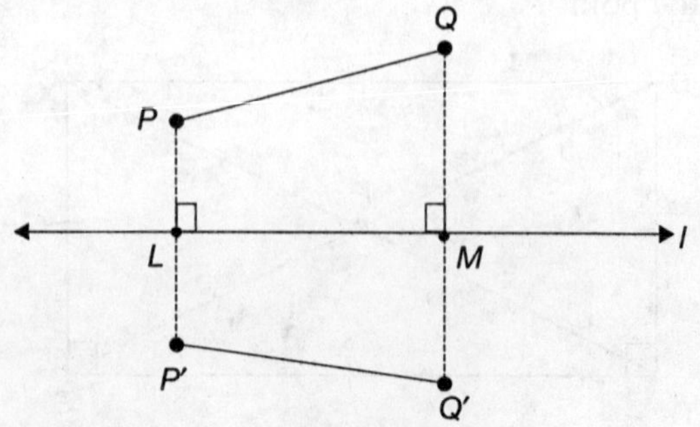

Figure 7.13

Image of an Angle About a Line

Draw a line l and an angle PQR on a piece of paper as shown below:

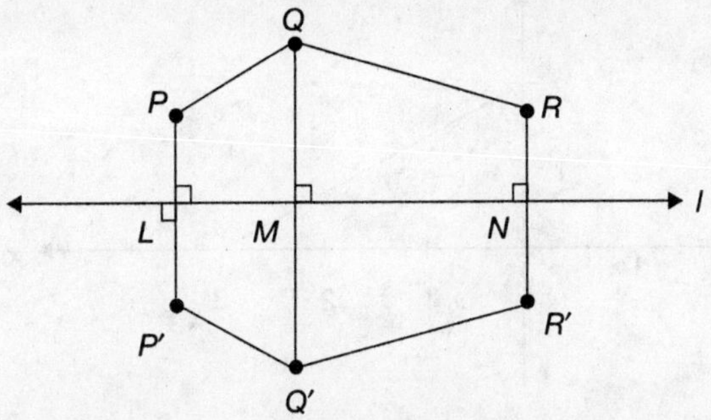

Figure 7.14

Draw perpendiculars PL, QM, and RN from the points P, Q and R respectively to the line l and produce them to P', Q', and R', respectively, such that $PL = LP'$, $QM = MQ'$ and $RN = NR'$. Join the points P', Q' and Q', R'. Then, the angle $P'Q'R'$ is called the image of the angle PQR about the line l.

EXAMPLE 7.1 Determine the line of symmetry of a triangle ABC in which $\angle A = 40°$, $\angle B = 70°$ and $\angle C = 70°$.

SOLUTION

The line which bisects $\angle A$ is the line of symmetry of the given triangle ABC.

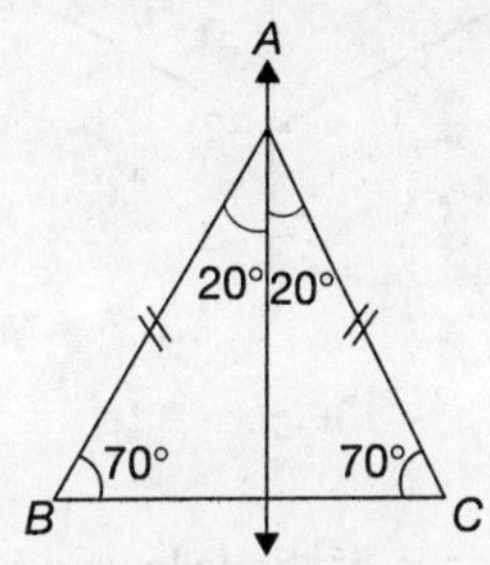

Figure 7.15

EXAMPLE 7.2 Determine the point of symmetry of a regular hexagon.

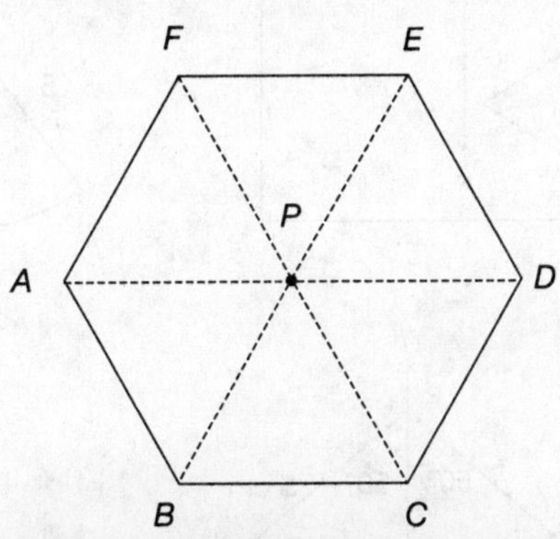

Figure 7.16

SOLUTION

The point of intersection of the diagonals of regular hexagon is the required point of symmetry.

EXAMPLE 7.3

Complete adjacent figure so that X-axis and Y-axis are the lines of symmetry of the completed figure.

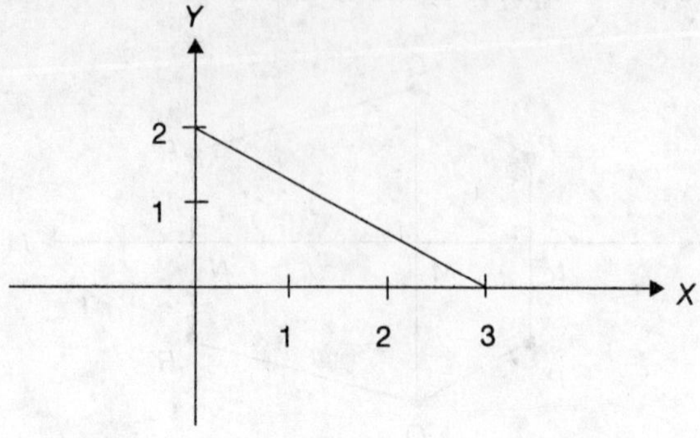

Figure 7.17

SOLUTION

Required figure is a rhombus of side $\sqrt{13}$ units.

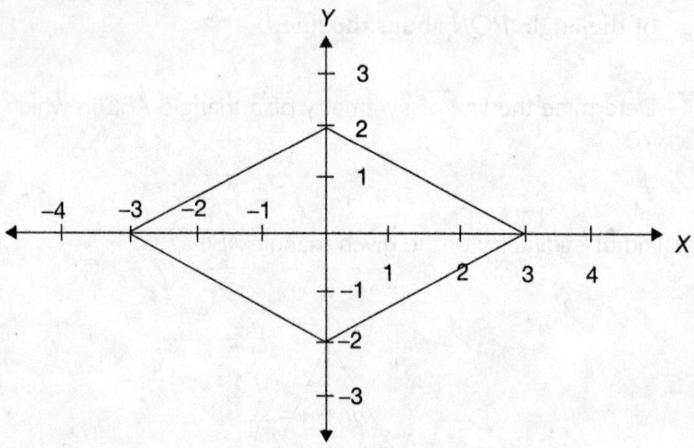

Figure 7.18

EXAMPLE 7.4

Determine the images of the following figure about the given line:

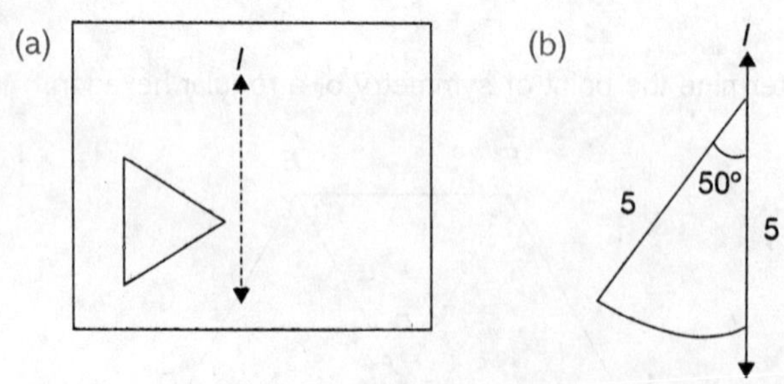

SOLUTION

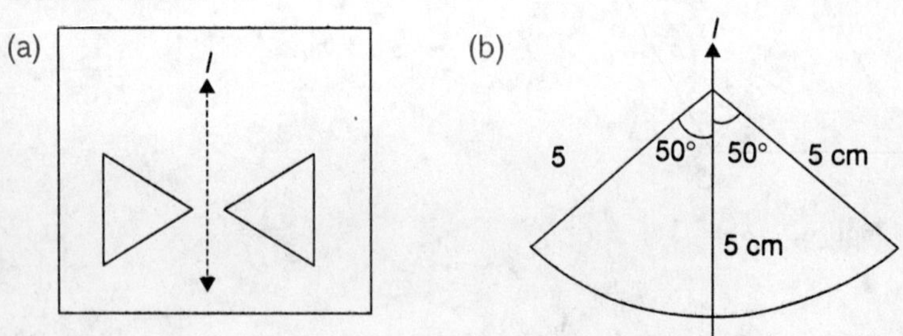

Similarity

Similarity of Geometrical Figures

Two geometrical figures of same shape, but not necessarily of same size are said to be similar.

Examples:

1. Any two circles are similar.
2. Any two squares are similar.
3. Any two equilateral triangles are similar.

Two circles C_1 and C_2 are similar, since their shapes are the same.

C_1 and C_2 may have an equal area.

While considering the circles C_1 and C_3 they may not be of equal area, but their shapes are the same.

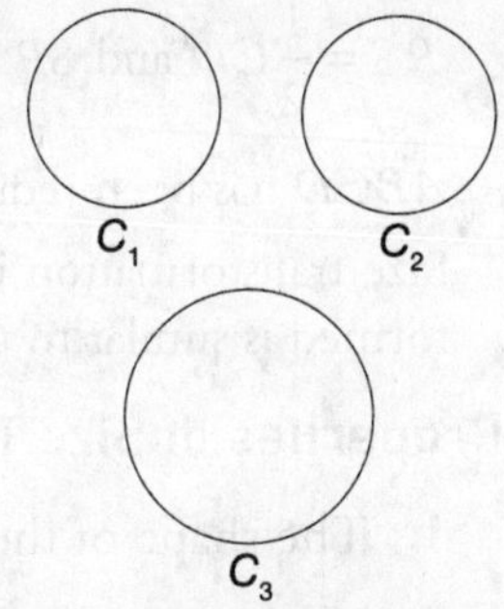

Figure 7.19

C_1 and C_2 are of the same shape and of same size.

C_1 and C_3 are of the same shape but of different sizes.

In both the cases, they are of the same shape.

Hence C_1, C_2, and C_3 are similar circles.

Similarity as a Size Transformation

Enlargement

Consider triangle ABC.

Construct triangle PQR whose sides are twice the corresponding sides of triangle ABC, as shown in the following figure.

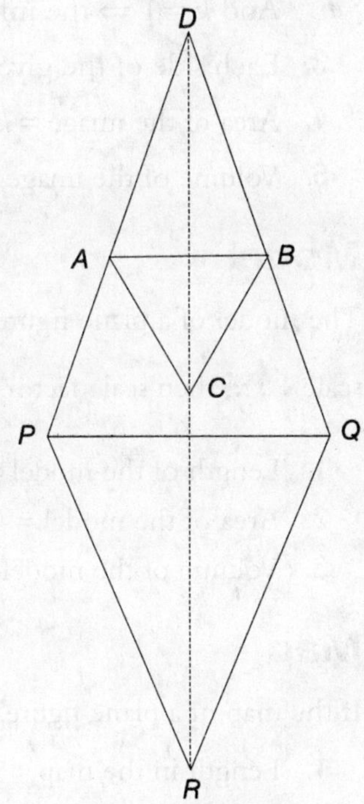

Figure 7.20

Construction: First draw the triangle ABC. Take a point D outside the triangle. Join DA, DB, and DC.

Now, extend DA, DB and DC to the points P, Q, and R respectively, such that $DP = 2DA$, $DQ = 2DB$ and $DR = 2DC$.

PQR is the enlarged image of ABC.

On verification, we find that $PQ = 2AB$

$QR = 2BC$ and $RP = 2AC$.

It can be defined that triangle ABC has been enlarged by a scale factor of 2 about the centre of the enlargement D to give image PQR.

Reduction

Consider square $ABCD$. One can draw a square $PQRS$ whose side is half the length of the side of $ABCD$.

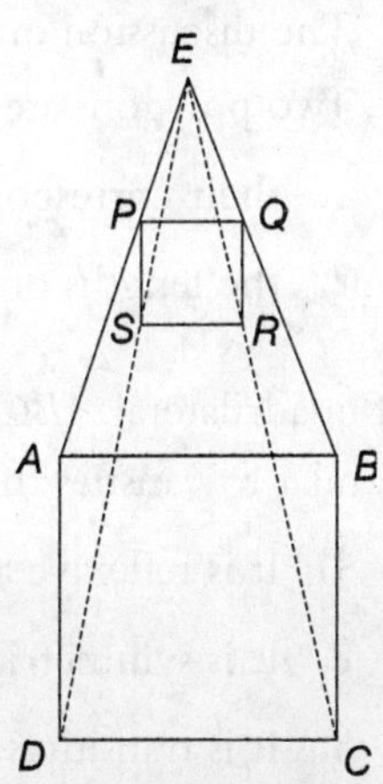

Figure 7.21

Construction: Draw square $ABCD$.

Take a point E outside the square.

Join EA, EB, EC, and ED. Mark the points P, Q, R, and S on $\overline{EA}$, $\overline{EB}$, $\overline{EC}$, and $\overline{ED}$, such that

$$EP = \frac{1}{2}EA,\ EQ = \frac{1}{2}EB,\ ER = \frac{1}{2}EC \text{ and } ES = \frac{1}{2}ED$$

Square $PQRS$ is the reduced image of square $ABCD$.

We find that,

$$PQ = \frac{1}{2}AB,\ QR = \frac{1}{2}BC,$$

$$RS = \frac{1}{2}CD \text{ and } SP = \frac{1}{2}AD$$

$ABCD$ has been reduced by a scale factor $\frac{1}{2}$ about the centre of reduction E to give the image $PQRS$.
Size transformation is the process which a geometrical figure is enlarged or reduced by a scale k, such that the image formed is similar to the given figure.

Properties of Size Transformation

1. The shape of the given figure remains the same.
2. If k is the scale factor of a given size transformation and $k > 1 \Rightarrow$ the image is enlarged and $k < 1$ $\Rightarrow$ the image is reduced.

   And $k = 1 \Rightarrow$ the image is identical to the original figure.
3. Each side of the given geometrical figure = k (The corresponding side of the given figure).
4. Area of the image = k_2 (Area of the given geometrical figure).
5. Volume of the image, if it is a 3-dimensional figure, is equal to k^3 (Volume of the original figure).

Model

The model of a plane figure and the given figure are similar to each other. If the model of a plane figure is drawn to the scale 1 : x, then scale factor, $k = \frac{1}{x}$.

1. Length of the model = k (Length of the original figure)
2. Area of the model = k^2 (Area of the original figure)
3. Volume of the model = k^3 (Volume of the original figure)

Map

If the map of a plane figure, is drawn to the scale 1 : x, then, scale factor, $k = \frac{1}{x}$.

1. Length in the map = k (Original length)
2. Area in the map = k^2 (Original area)

The discussion on similarity can be extended further as follows:
Two polygons are said to be similar to each other if

1. their corresponding angles are equal and
2. the lengths of their corresponding sides are proportional.

Info Bytes!

'~' is the symbol used for 'is similar to'.

If quadrilateral $ABCD$ is similar to quadrilateral $PQRS$, we denote this as ▱ $ABCD$ ~ ▱ $PQRS$. The relation 'is similar to' satisfies the following properties.

1. It is reflexive as every figure is similar to itself.
2. It is symmetric as A is similar to B, then B is also similar to A.
3. It is transitive as, if A is similar to B and B is similar to C, then A is similar to C.

∴ The relation is 'similar to' is an equivalence relation.

Criteria for Similarity of Triangles

Similar Triangles

In two triangles, if either the corresponding angles are equal or the ratio of corresponding sides are equal, then the two triangles are similar to each other.

In ΔABC and ΔDEF, if,

1. $\angle A = \angle D$, $\angle B = \angle E$ and $\angle C = \angle F$ or
2. $\dfrac{AB}{DE} = \dfrac{BC}{EF} = \dfrac{AC}{DF}$,

then $\Delta ABC \sim \Delta DEF$ or ΔABC is similar to ΔDEF.

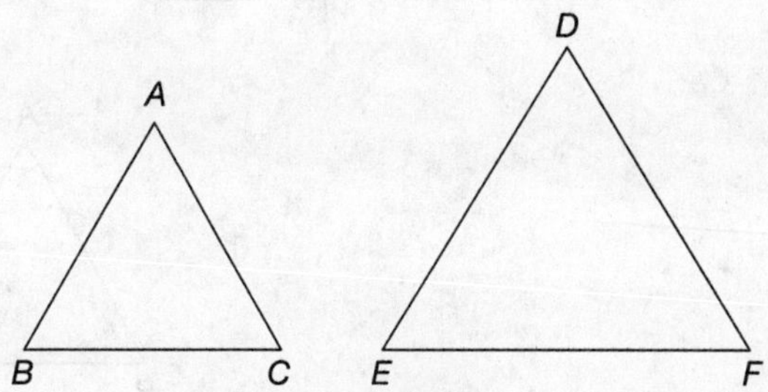

Figure 7.22

Three Similarity Axioms for Triangles

1. **AA–Axiom or AAA–Axiom:** In two triangles, if corresponding angles are equal, then the triangles are similar to each other.

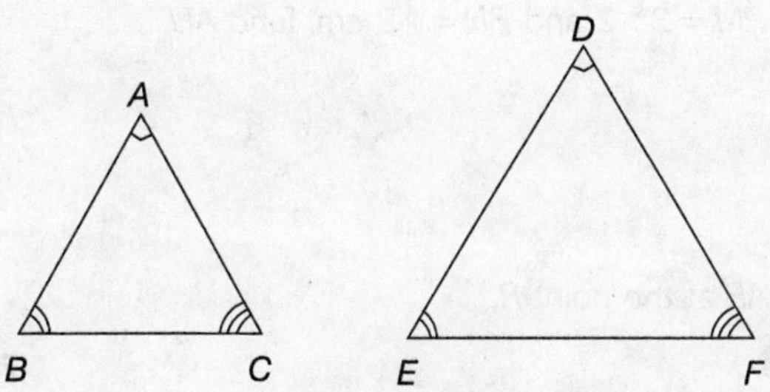

Figure 7.23

In ΔABC and ΔDEF, $\angle A = \angle D$, $\angle B = \angle E$ and $\angle C = \angle F$.

$\therefore \Delta ABC \sim \Delta DEF$.

2. **SSS–Axiom:** In two triangles, if the corresponding sides are proportional, then the two triangles are similar to each other.

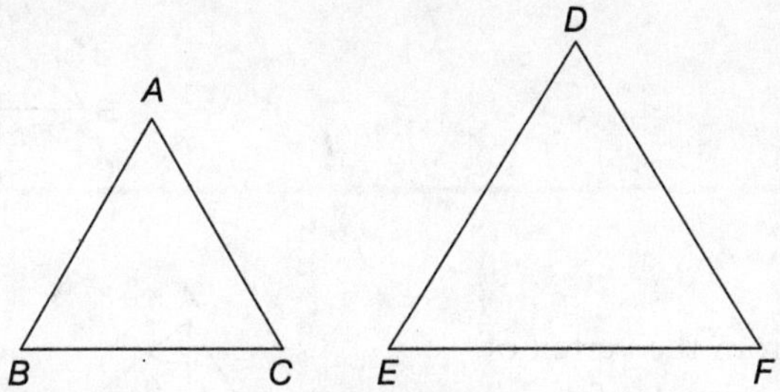

Figure 7.24

Konnect

In two triangles, if two pairs of corresponding angles are equal then the triangles are similar to each other, because the third pair corresponding angles will also be equal.

In ΔABC and ΔDEF, if $\dfrac{AB}{DE} = \dfrac{BC}{EF} = \dfrac{CA}{FD}$

$\Rightarrow \Delta ABC \sim \Delta DEF$.

3. **SAS–Axiom:** In two triangles, if one pair of corresponding sides are proportional and the included angles are equal then the two triangles are similar.

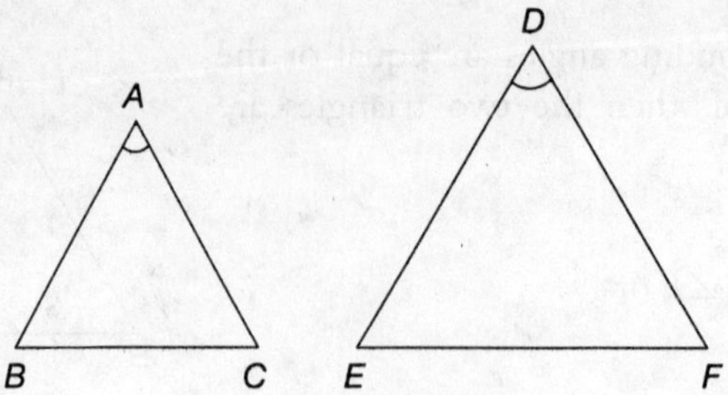

Figure 7.25

In ΔABC and ΔDEF,

If $\frac{AB}{DE} = \frac{AC}{DF}$ and $\angle A = \angle D$, then $\Delta ABC \sim \Delta DEF$.

EXAMPLE 7.5 In the given figure (not to scale), $AM : MC = 3 : 4$, $BP : PM = 3 : 2$ and $BN = 12$ cm. Find AN.

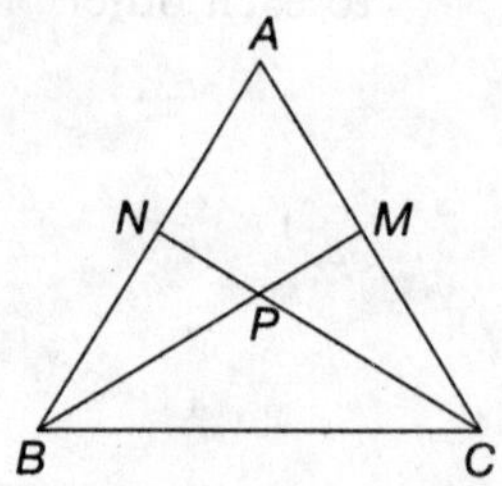

SOLUTION

Given, $AM : MC = 3 : 4$

$BP : PM = 3 : 2$ and $BN = 12$ cm

Draw MR parallel to CN which meets AB at the point R,

Consider ΔBMR,

$PN \parallel MR$ (Construction)

By BPT,

$$\frac{BN}{NR} = \frac{BP}{PM} \Rightarrow \frac{12}{NR} = \frac{3}{2}$$

$NR = 8$ cm

Consider ΔANC, $RM \parallel NC$ (By construction)

By BPT,

$$\frac{AR}{RN} = \frac{AM}{MC} \Rightarrow \frac{AR}{8} = \frac{3}{4} \Rightarrow AR = 6 \text{ cm}$$

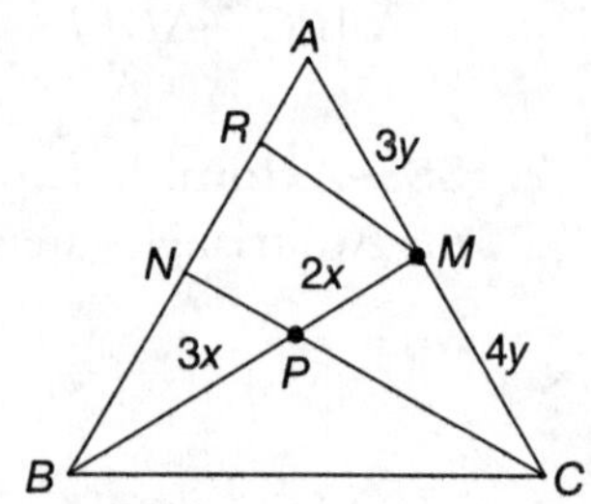

$\therefore AN = AR + RN = 6 + 8 = 14$ cm.

Right Angle Theorem

In a right-angled triangle, if a perpendicular is drawn from the vertex of the right angle to the hypotenuse, then the two right triangles formed on either side of the perpendicular are similar to each other and similar to the given triangle.

In the figure, ΔABC is right angled at A. $\overline{AD}$ is the perpendicular drawn from A to BC.

Let $\angle ABD = \theta$

Then, $\angle BAD = 90° - \theta$

$\angle DAC = \angle BAC - \angle BAD = 90° - (90° - \theta)$

$\Rightarrow \angle DAC = \theta$

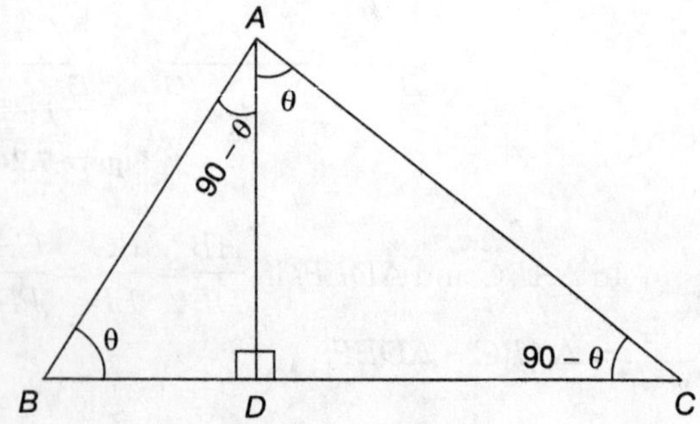

Figure 7.26

$\therefore \angle DCA = 90° - \theta$

In triangles DBA, DAC, and ABC, three corresponding angles are equal. Therefore, the triangle ABC is similar to triangle DAC or triangle DBA.

In triangles DBA and DAC,

$$\because \frac{BD}{AD} = \frac{AD}{DC}$$

$$\Rightarrow AD^2 = BD \times DC$$

AD is the mean proportional of BD and DC.

$$\Rightarrow AD^2 = BD \cdot DC.$$

Info Bytes!

The right angle theorem is pivotal in the creation of astrolabes, ancient devices used for solving problems related to time and the position of the stars, by measuring angles in degrees.

Results on Areas of Similar Triangles The ratio of areas of the two similar triangles is equal to the ratio of the squares of any two corresponding sides of the triangles.

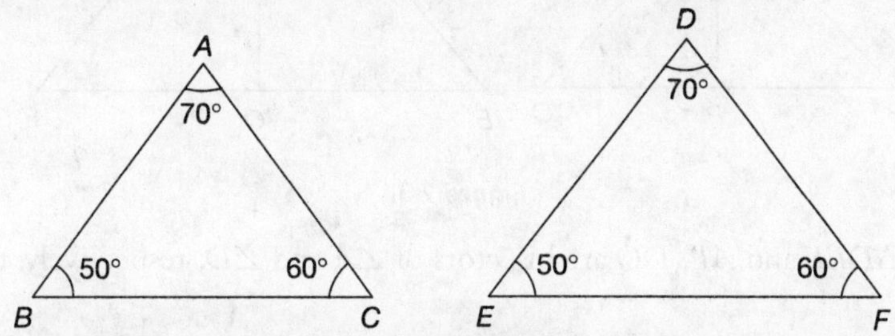

Figure 7.27

$$\Delta ABC \sim \Delta DEF \Rightarrow \frac{\text{Area of } \Delta ABC}{\text{Area of } \Delta DEF} = \frac{AB^2}{DE^2} = \frac{BC^2}{EF^2} = \frac{CA^2}{FD^2}.$$

1. The ratio of areas of two similar triangles is equal to the ratio of the squares of their corresponding altitudes. In the following figures, $\Delta ABC \sim \Delta DEF$ and AX, DY are the altitudes.

Then, $\dfrac{\text{Area of } \Delta ABC}{\text{Area of } \Delta DEF} = \dfrac{AX^2}{DY^2}.$

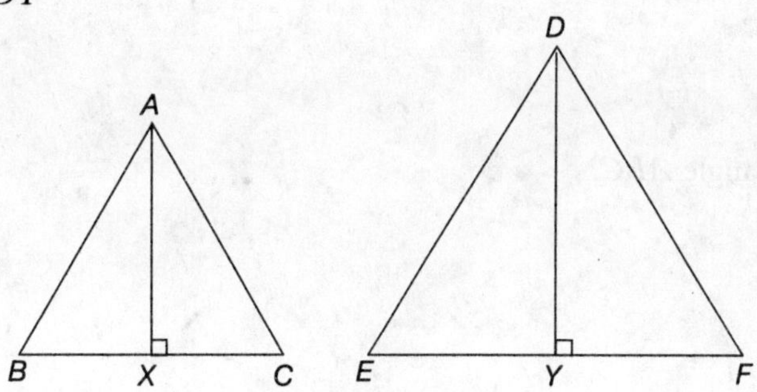

Figure 7.28

2. The ratio of areas of two similar triangles is equal to the ratio of the squares on their corresponding medians (see Fig. 7.29).

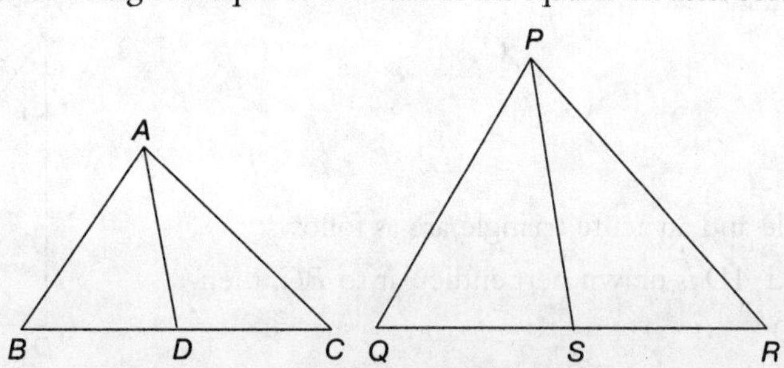

Figure 7.29

In the above figure, $\Delta ABC \sim \Delta PQR$ and AD and PS are medians.

Then, $\dfrac{\text{Area of } \Delta ABC}{\text{Area of } \Delta PQR} = \dfrac{AD^2}{PS^2}$.

3. The ratio of areas of two similar triangles is equal to the ratio of the squares of their corresponding angle bisector segments.

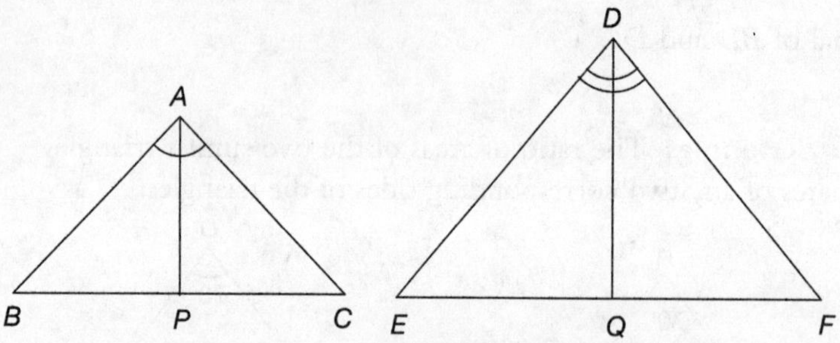

Figure 7.30

In the figure, $\Delta ABC \sim \Delta DEF$ and AP, DQ are bisectors of $\angle A$ and $\angle D$, respectively, then,

$\dfrac{\text{Area of } \Delta ABC}{\text{Area of } \Delta DEF} = \dfrac{AP^2}{DQ^2}$.

Pythagoras Theorem

In a right-angled triangle, the square of the hypotenuse is equal to the sum of the squares of the other two sides.

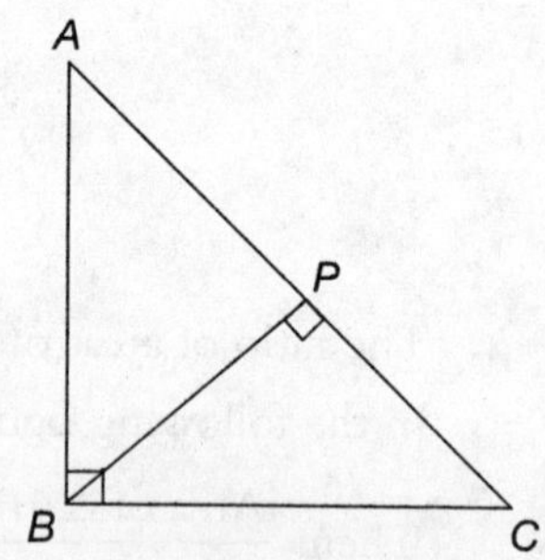

Figure 7.31

To prove: $AC^2 = AB^2 + BC^2$

Construction: Draw BP perpendicular to AC.

Proof: In triangles APB and ABC,

$\angle APB = \angle ABC$ (right angles)

$\angle A = \angle A$ (common)

$\therefore$ Triangle APB is similar to triangle ABC.

$\Rightarrow \dfrac{AP}{AB} = \dfrac{AB}{AC}$

$\Rightarrow AB^2 = (AP)(AC)$

Similarly, $BC^2 = (PC)(AC)$

$\therefore AB^2 + BC^2 = (AP)(AC) + (PC)(AC)$

$AB^2 + BC^2 = (AC)(AP + PC)$

$AB^2 + BC^2 = (AC)(AC)$

$\Rightarrow AC^2 = AB^2 + BC^2$

Hence proved.

Info Bytes!

The square root of 2, discovered through the Pythagorean theorem, was one of the first known irrational numbers

The results in an obtuse triangle and an acute triangle are as follows:

In ΔABC, $\angle ABC$ is obtuse and AD is drawn perpendicular to BC, then,

$AC^2 = AB^2 + BC^2 + 2BC \cdot BD$

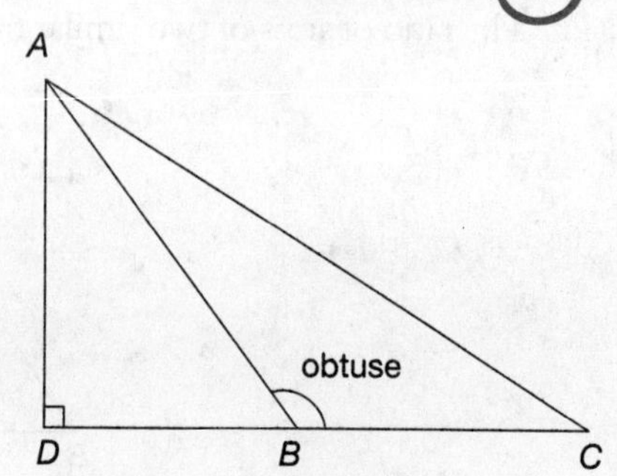

Figure 7.32

ΔABC is an acute-angled triangle, acute angle at B and AD is drawn perpendicular to BC, then $AC^2 = AB^2 + BC^2 - 2BC \cdot BD$.

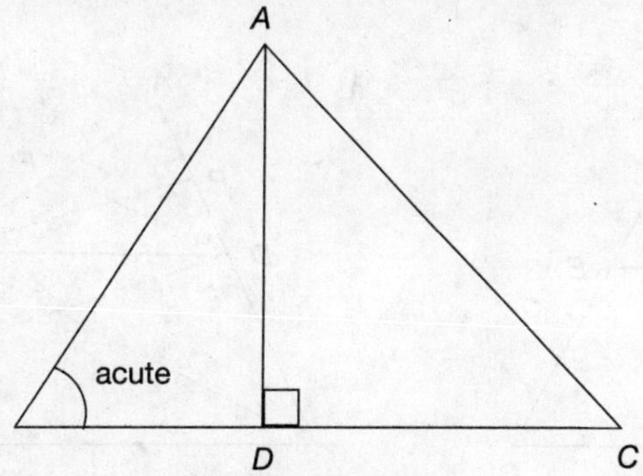

Figure 7.33

Apollonius Theorem

In a triangle, the sum of the squares of two sides of a triangle is equal to twice the sum of the square of the median which bisects the third side and the square of half the third side.

Given: In ΔABC, AD is the median.

RTP: $AB^2 + AC^2 = 2(AD^2 + DC^2)$ or $2(AD^2 + BD^2)$

Construction: Draw AE perpendicular to BC.

Case 1: If $\angle ADB = \angle ADC = 90°$

According to Pythagoras theorem,

In ΔABD, $AB^2 = BD^2 + AD^2$ (1)

In ΔADC, $AC^2 = CD^2 + AD^2$ (2)

Adding Eqs. (1) and (2), we have,

$AB^2 + AC^2 = BD^2 + CD^2 + 2AD^2 = 2BD^2 + 2AD^2$. [$\because CD = BD$]

or $2[CD^2 + AD^2]$

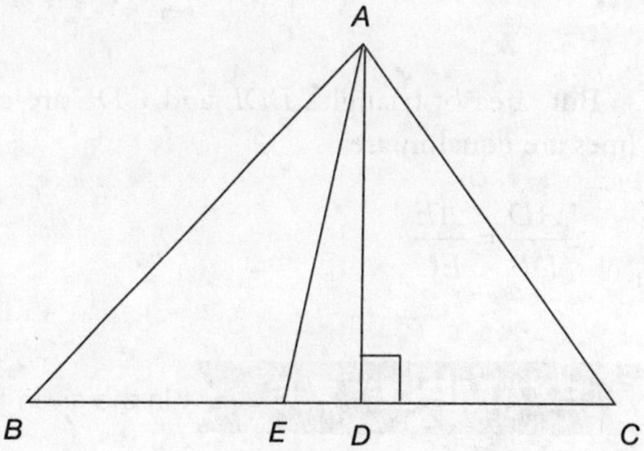

Figure 7.34

Case 2: If $\angle ADC$ is acute and $\angle ADB$ is obtuse.

In triangle ADB,

$AB^2 = AD^2 + BD^2 + 2 \times BD \times DE$

In triangle ADC,

$AC^2 = AD^2 + DC^2 - 2 \times CD \times DE$

But $BD = CD$

$\therefore AB^2 + AC^2 = 2AD^2 + 2BD^2$ or $2(AD^2 + CD^2)$

Hence proved.

Basic Proportionality Theorem In a triangle, if a line is drawn parallel to one side of a triangle, then it divides the other two sides in the same ratio.

Given: In ΔABC, $\overline{DE} \parallel \overline{BC}$

RTP: $\dfrac{AD}{DB} = \dfrac{AE}{EC}$

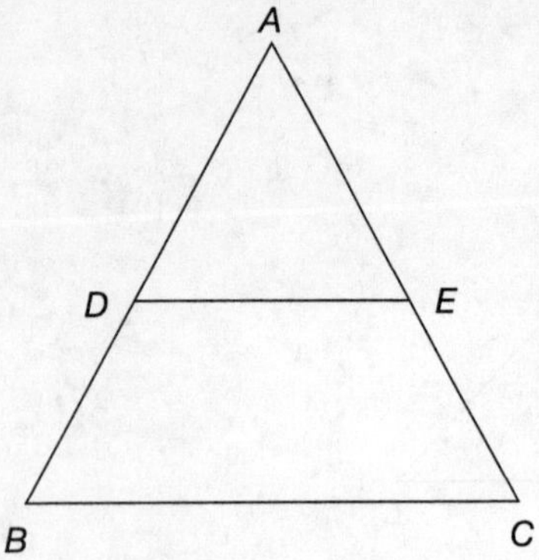

Figure 7.35

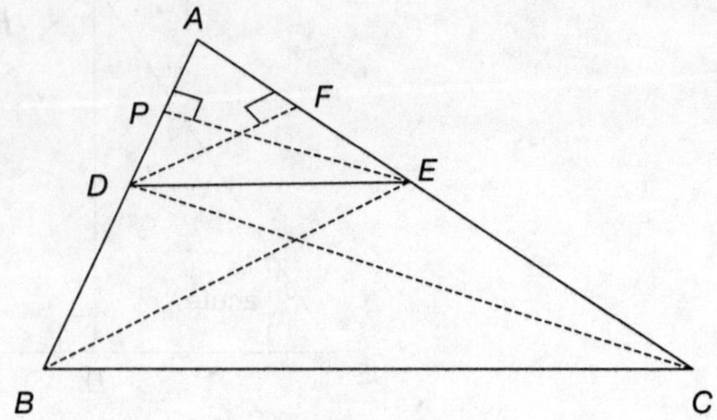

Figure 7.36

Construction: Draw $EP \perp AB$ and $DF \perp AC$. Join $\overline{DC}$ and $\overline{BE}$.

Proof: $$\frac{\text{Area of triangle } ADE}{\text{Area of triangle } BDE} = \frac{\frac{1}{2} \times AD \times PE}{\frac{1}{2} \times BD \times PE} = \frac{AD}{BD}$$

and $$\frac{\text{Area of triangle } ADE}{\text{Area of triangle } CDE} = \frac{\frac{1}{2} \times AE \times DF}{\frac{1}{2} \times EC \times DF} = \frac{AE}{EC}$$

But, area of triangles BDE and CDE are equal. (Two triangles lying on the same base and between the same parallel lines are equal in area).

$$\therefore \frac{AD}{DB} = \frac{AE}{EC}$$

EXAMPLE 7.6

In the given figure, $\overline{DE} \parallel \overline{AC}$. Find the value of x.

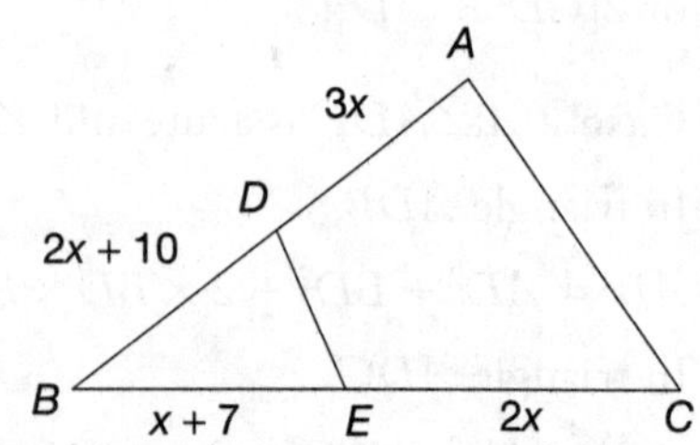

SOLUTION

In ΔABC,

$DE \parallel AC$

$\therefore \frac{BD}{DA} = \frac{BE}{EC}$ (Basic proportionality theorem)

$\Rightarrow \frac{2x+10}{3x} = \frac{x+7}{2x}$

$\Rightarrow 2x(2x+10) = 3x(x+7)$

$\Rightarrow 4x^2 + 20x = 3x^2 + 21x$

$\Rightarrow x^2 - x = 0$

$\Rightarrow x(x-1) = 0$

$\Rightarrow x - 1 = 0$

$\Rightarrow x = 1$

Info Bytes!

From the above result we can prove that $\frac{AB}{AD} = \frac{AC}{AE}$ and $\frac{AB}{BD} = \frac{AC}{CE}$

Converse of Basic Proportionality Theorem

If a line divides two sides of a triangle in the same ratio, then that line is parallel to the third side.

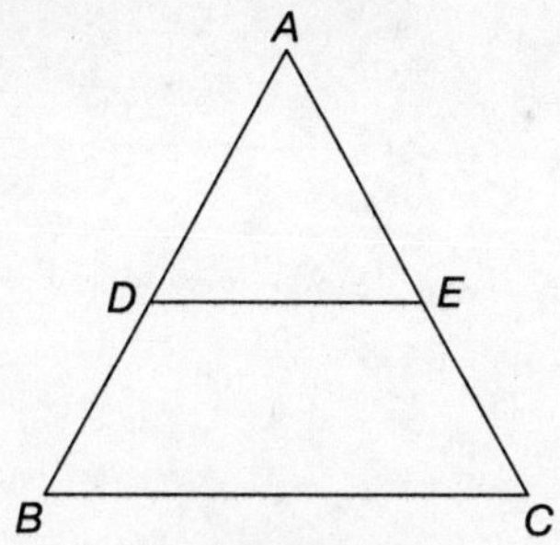

Figure 7.37

In the figure given, $\frac{AD}{DB} = \frac{AE}{EC} \Rightarrow \overline{DE} \parallel \overline{BC}$.

Vertical Angle Bisector Theorem

The bisector of the vertical angle of a triangle divides the base in the ratio of the other two sides.

Given: In ΔABC, AD is the bisector of $\angle A$.

RTP: $\frac{BD}{DC} = \frac{AB}{AC}$

Construction: Draw CP parallel to AD to meet BA produced at P.

Proof: $\angle DAC = \angle ACP$ (alternate angles and $AD \parallel CP$)

$\angle BAD = \angle APC$ (corresponding angles)

But $\angle BAD = \angle DAC$ (given)

$\therefore \angle ACP = \angle APC$

In triangle APC,

$AC = AP$ (sides opposite to equal angles are equal)

In triangle BCP,

$\frac{BD}{DC} = \frac{BA}{AP}$ (by basic proportionality theorem)

$\Rightarrow \frac{BD}{DC} = \frac{BA}{AC}$ ($\because AP = AC$)

Hence proved.

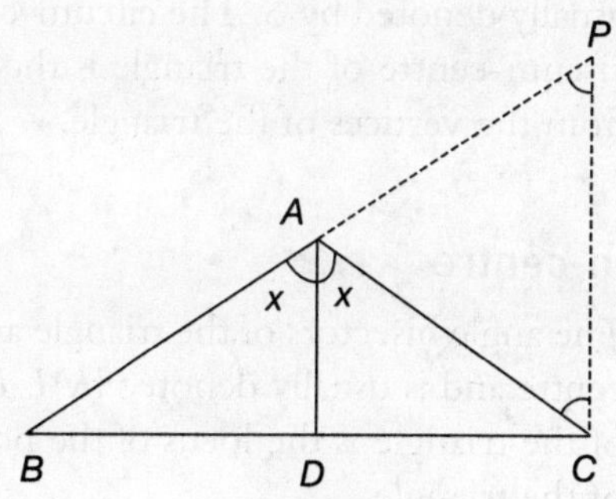

Figure 7.38

Converse of Vertical Angle Bisector Theorem

If a line that passes through a vertex of a triangle, divides the base in the ratio of the other two sides, then it bisects the angle.

In the adjacent figure, AD divides BC in the ratio $\frac{BD}{DC}$ and if $\frac{BD}{DC} = \frac{AB}{AC}$, then AD is the bisector of $\angle A$.

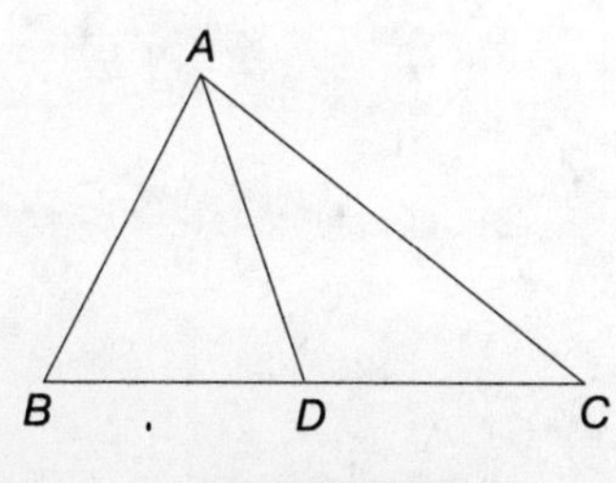

Figure 7.39

EXAMPLE 7.7 In the figure above (not to scale), $\overline{AB} \perp \overline{CD}$ and AD is the bisector of $\angle BAE$. $AB = 3$ cm and $AC = 5$ cm. Find CD.

SOLUTION

Let BD be x cm.

Given $AB = 3$ cm, $AC = 5$ cm and $\angle ABC = 90°$

$\therefore$ BC = 4 cm

And also given, AD is the bisector of $\angle BAE$.

$\therefore$ By vertical angle bisector theorem.

$$\frac{AB}{AC} = \frac{BD}{CD} \Rightarrow \frac{3}{5} = \frac{x}{4+x}$$

$\Rightarrow 12 + 3x = 5x \Rightarrow x = 6$ cm.

$\therefore CD = 4 + 6 = 10$ cm.

Concurrency—Geometric Centres of a Triangle

Let us recall that if three or more lines pass through a fixed point, then those lines are said to be concurrent and that fixed point is called the point of concurrence. In this context, we recall different concurrent lines and their points of concurrence associated with a triangle, also called geometric centres of a triangle.

Circum-centre

The locus of the point equidistant from the end points of the line segment is the perpendicular bisector of the line segment. The three perpendicular bisectors of the three sides of a triangle are concurrent and the point of their concurrence is called the circum-centre of the triangle and is usually denoted by S. The circum-centre is equidistant from all the vertices of the triangle. The circum-centre of the triangle is the locus of the point in the plane of the triangle, equidistant from the vertices of the triangle.

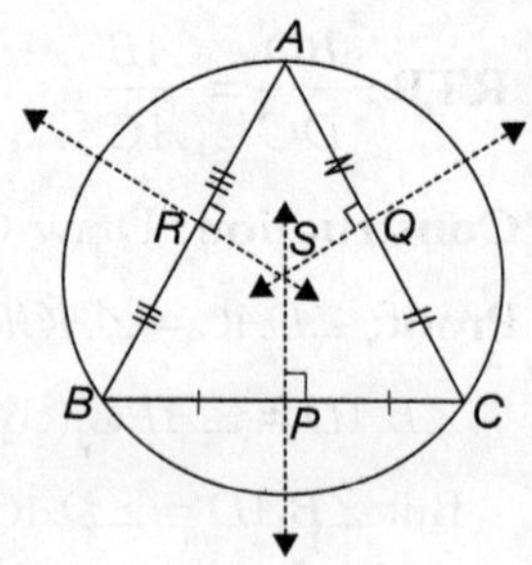

Figure 7.40

In-centre

The angle bisectors of the triangle are concurrent and the point of concurrence is called the in-centre and is usually denoted by I. I is equidistant from the sides of the triangle. The in-centre of the triangle is the locus of the point, in the plane of the triangle, equidistant from the sides of the triangle.

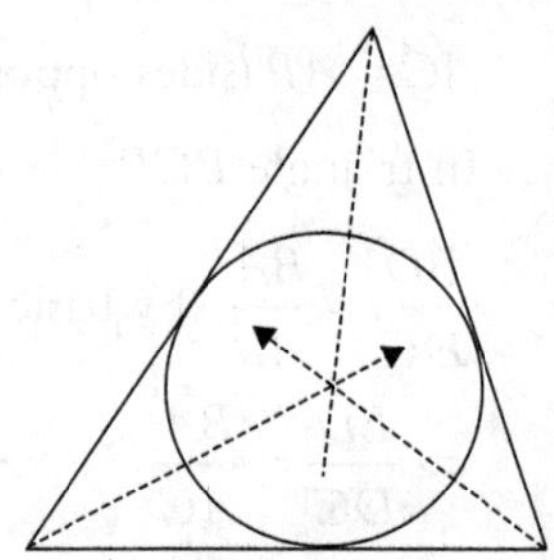

Figure 7.41

Ortho-centre

The altitudes of the triangle are concurrent and the point of concurrence of the altitudes of a triangle is called ortho-centre and is usually denoted by O.

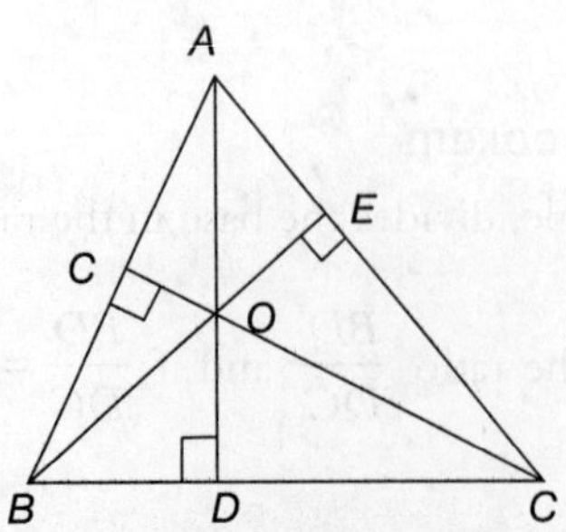

Figure 7.42

Centroid

The medians of a triangle are concurrent and the point of concurrence of the medians of a triangle is called the centroid and it is usually denoted by G. The centroid divides each of the medians in the ratio 2 : 1, starting from vertex, i.e., in the figure given below, $AG : GD = BG : GE = CG : GF = 2 : 1$.

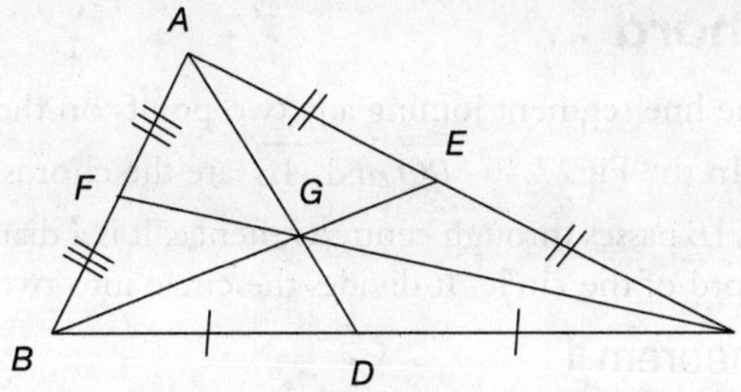

Figure 7.43

Some Important Points

1. In an equilateral triangle, the centroid, the ortho-centre, the circum-centre and the in-centre all coincide.
2. In an isosceles triangle, the centroid, the ortho-centre, the circum-centre and the in-centre all lie on the median to the base.
3. In a rightangled triangle the length of the median drawn to the hypotenuse is equal to half of the hypotenuse. The median is also equal to the circum-radius. The mid-point of the hypotenuse is the circum-centre.
4. In an obtuse-angled triangle, the circum-centre and ortho-centre lie outside the triangle and for an acute angled triangle the circum-centre and the ortho-centre lie inside the triangle.
5. For all triangles, the centroid and the in-centre lie inside the triangle.

Circles

A circle is a set of points in a plane which are at a fixed distance from a fixed point.

The fixed point is the centre of the circle and the fixed distance is the radius of the circle.

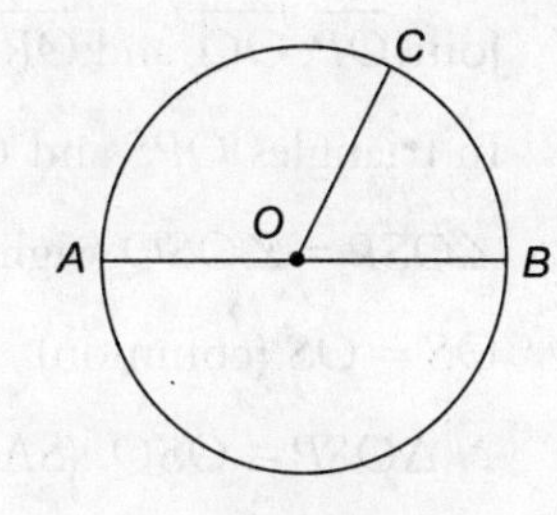

Figure 7.44

In the Fig. 7.44, O is the centre of the circle and OC is a radius of the circle.

AB is a diameter of the circle. OA and OB are also the radii of the circle.

The diameter is twice the radius.

The centre of the circle is generally denoted by O, diameter by d and radius by r.

$d = 2r$.

The perimeter of the circular line is called the circumference of the circle.

The circumference of the circle is π times the diameter.

In the Fig. 7.45 with centre O; A, B, and C are three points in the plane in which the circle lies. The points O and A are in the interior of the circle. The point B is located on the circumference of the circle.

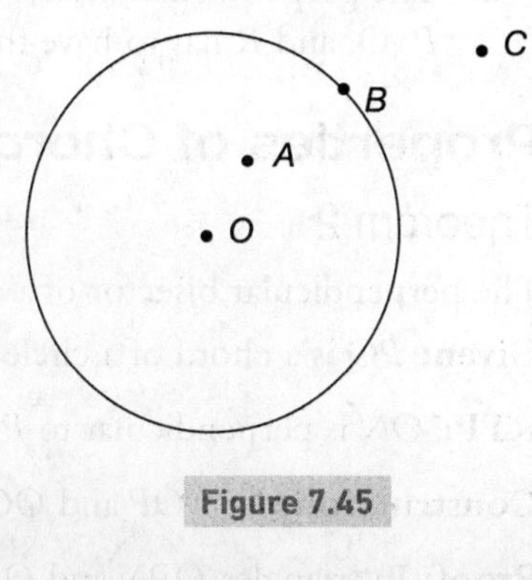

Figure 7.45

Hence, B belongs to the circle.

C is located in the exterior of the circle.

If $OB = r$, B is a point on the circumference of the circle.

As $OA < r$, A is a point in the interior of the circle.

As $OC > r$, C is a point in the exterior of the circle.

Chord

The line segment joining any two points on the circumference of a circle is a chord of the circle.

In the Fig. 7.46, $\overline{PQ}$ and $\overline{AB}$ are the chords.

AB passes through centre *O*, hence, it is a diameter of the circle. A diameter is the longest chord of the circle. It divides the circle into two equal parts.

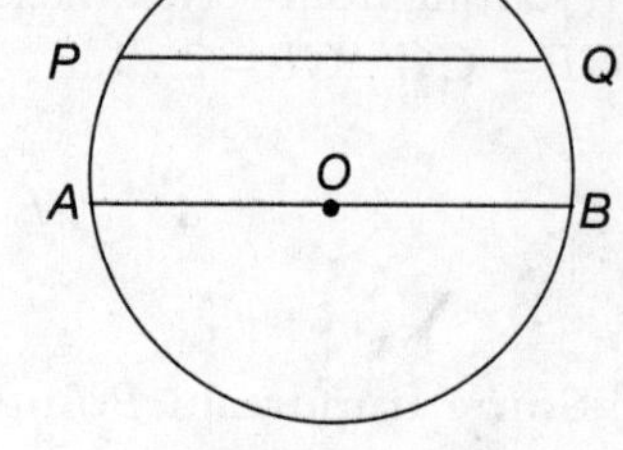

Figure 7.46

Theorem 1

One and only one circle exists through three non-collinear points.

Given: *P*, *Q*, and *R* are three non-collinear points.

RTP: One and only one circle passes through the points *P*, *Q*, and *R*.

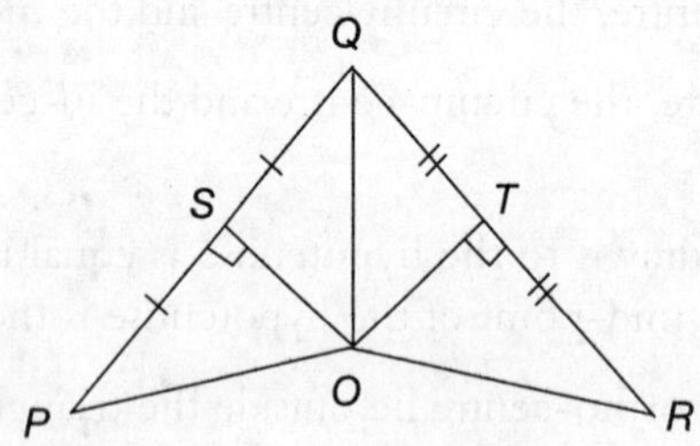

Figure 7.47

Construction:

1. Join *PQ* and *RQ* and draw the perpendicular bisectors of *PQ* and *RQ*.

   Let them meet at the point *O*.

   Join $\overline{OP}$, $\overline{OQ}$, and $\overline{OR}$.

   In triangles *OPS* and *OQS*, $PS = SQ$

   $\angle OSP = \angle OSQ$ (right angles)

   $OS = OS$ (common)

   $\therefore \Delta OSP \cong OSQ$. (SAS Congruence Property)

   $\therefore OQ = OP$

   Similarly, it can be proved that $OQ = OR$.

   $\therefore OP = OQ = OR$. Therefore, the circle with *O* as the centre and passing through *P*, also passes through *Q* and *R*.

2. The perpendicular bisectors of *PQ* and *QR* intersect at only one point and that point is *O*. A circle passing through *P*, *Q*, and *R* has to have this point as the centre. Thus, there can only be one circle passing through *P*, *Q*, and *R*.

Info Bytes!

Art and Design: The principles of circles and chords play a vital role in creating designs and patterns. They are the basis of mandalas, a spiritual and ritual symbol in Hinduism and Buddhism, representing the universe.

Properties of Chords and Related Theorems

Theorem 2

The perpendicular bisector of a chord of a circle passes through the centre of the circle.

Given: *PQ* is a chord of a circle with centre *O*. *N* is the mid-point of chord *PQ*.

RTP: *ON* is perpendicular to *PQ*.

Construction: Join *OP* and *OQ*.

Proof: In triangles *OPN* and *OQN*,

$OP = OQ$ (radius of the circle)

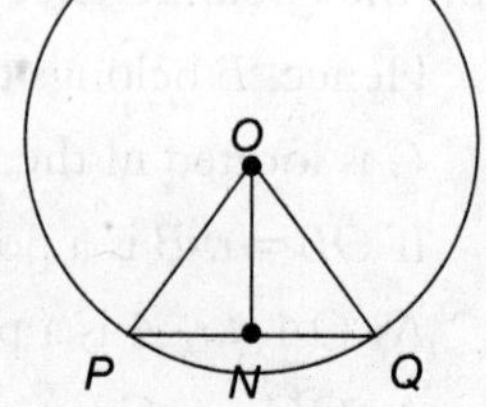

Figure 7.48

$PN = QN$ (given)

ON is common.

By SSS Congruence Property,

$\Delta OPN \cong \Delta OQN$.

$\therefore \angle ONP = \angle ONQ$

But,

$\angle ONP + \angle ONQ = 180°$ (straight line)

$\Rightarrow \angle ONP = \angle ONQ = 90°$

$\therefore$ ON is perpendicular to chord PQ.

Konnect

The converse of the above theorem is also true, i.e., the diameter which is perpendicular to a chord of a circle bisects the chord.

Theorem 3

Two equal chords of a circle are equidistant from the centre of the circle.

Given: In a circle with centre O, chord PQ = chord RS.

$OM \perp PQ$ and $ON \perp RS$.

RTP: $OM = ON$

Construction: Join OP and OR.

Proof: Since PQ is a chord of the circle and OM is perpendicular to PQ, OM bisects PQ (theorem 1).

Similarly, ON bisects RS.

$PQ = RS$ (given)

$\frac{1}{2}PQ = \frac{1}{2}RS$

$\Rightarrow PM = RN$

$\angle OMP = \angle ONR$ (right angles)

$OP = OR$ (radii of the circle)

In triangles OMP and ONR,

$OP = OR$,

$PM = RN$ and $\angle OMP = \angle ONR$

$\therefore \Delta OMP \cong \Delta ONR$ (SAS axiom)

$\therefore OM = ON$

Hence proved.

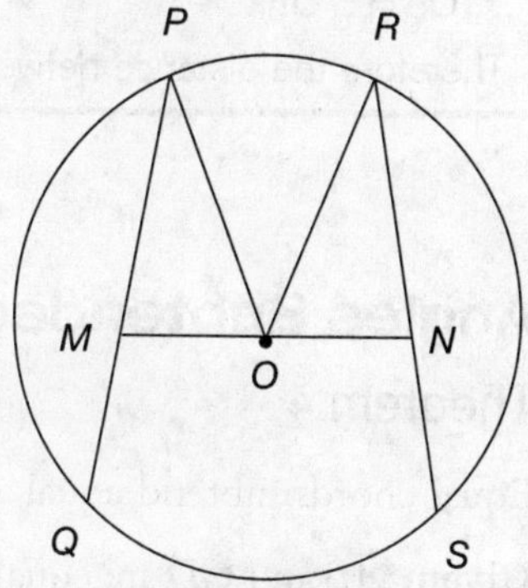

Figure 7.49

The converse of the above theorem, is also true, i.e., two chords which are equidistant from the centre of a circle are equal in length.

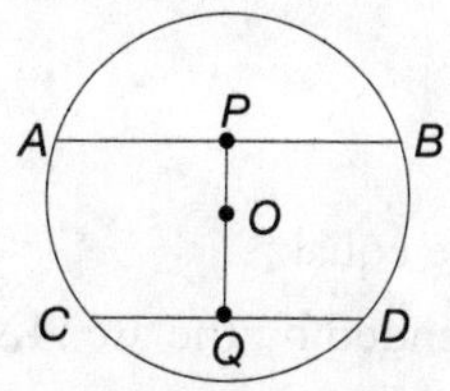

Figure 7.50

Info Bytes!

Longer chords are closer to the centre and shorter chords are farther from the centre.

In the given figure, AB and CD are two chords of the circle with centre at O and $AB > CD$. OP is perpendicular to chord AB and OQ is perpendicular to chord CD. By observation, we can say that $OQ > OP$.

EXAMPLE 7.8 *AB* and *CD* are two equal and parallel chords of lengths 24 cm each, in a circle of radius 13 cm. What is the distance between the chords?

SOLUTION

In the given circle with centre *O*, *AB* and *CD* are the two chords each of length 24 cm and are equidistant from the centre of the circleJoin OB and draw OE ⊥ AB

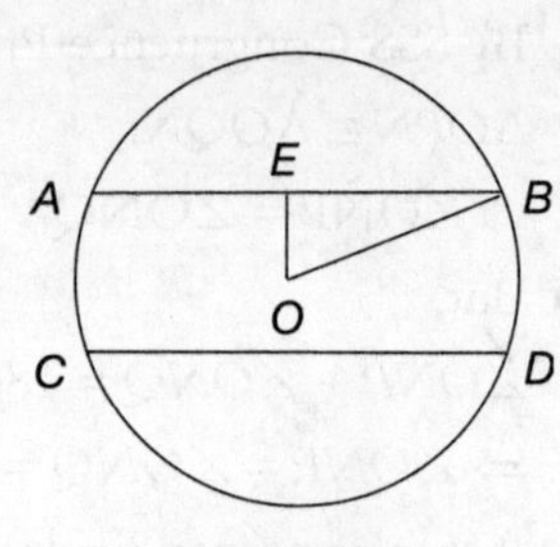

Figure 7.51

In ΔOEB,

$OE^2 = OB^2 - BE^2$

$OE^2 = (13)^2 - \left(\frac{24}{2}\right)^2$

$= 169 - 144$

$= 25$

$\therefore$ OE = 5 cm.

Therefore the distance between *AB* and *CD* = 5 + 5 = 10 cm.

Angles Subtended by Equal Chords at the Centre

Theorem 4

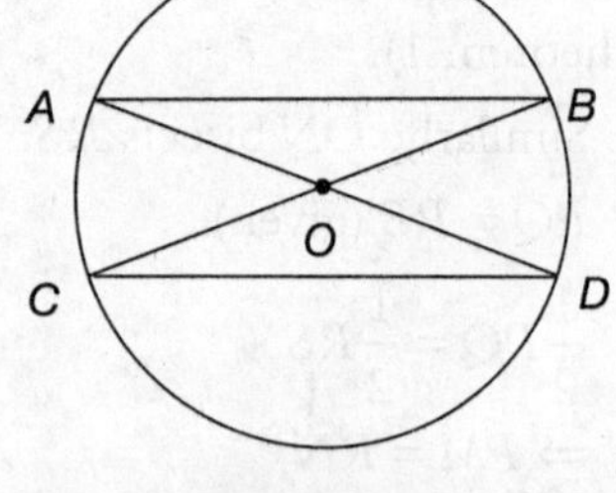

Figure 7.52

Equal chords subtend equal angles at the centre of the circle.

Given: *AB* and *CD* are equal chords of a circle with centre *O*. Join *OA*, *OB*, *OC*, and *OD*.

RTP: $\angle AOB = \angle COD$.

Proof: In triangles *ABO* and *CDO*,

OA = *OC*, (radii of the same circle)

OB = *OD*

AB = *CD* (given)

By SSS (side-side-side congruence property), triangles *ABO* and *CDO* are congruent. Hence, the corresponding angles are equal.

$\angle AOB = \angle COD$

Hence proved.

The converse of the theorem is also true, i.e., chords of a circle subtending equal angles at the centre are equal.

Angles Subtended by an Arc

Property 1

Angles subtended by an arc at any point on the rest of the circle are equal.

In the given circle, *AXB* is an arc of the circle. The angles subtended by the arc *AXB* at *C* and *D* are equal, i.e., $\angle ADB = \angle ACB$.

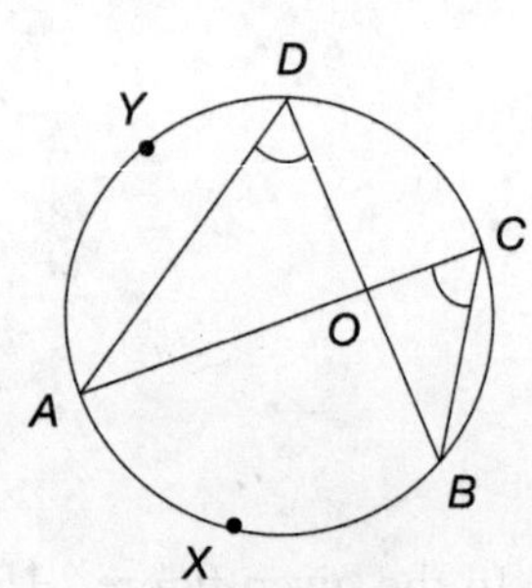

Figure 7.53

Property 2

Angle subtended by an arc at the centre of a circle is double the angle subtended by it at any point on the remaining part of the circle.

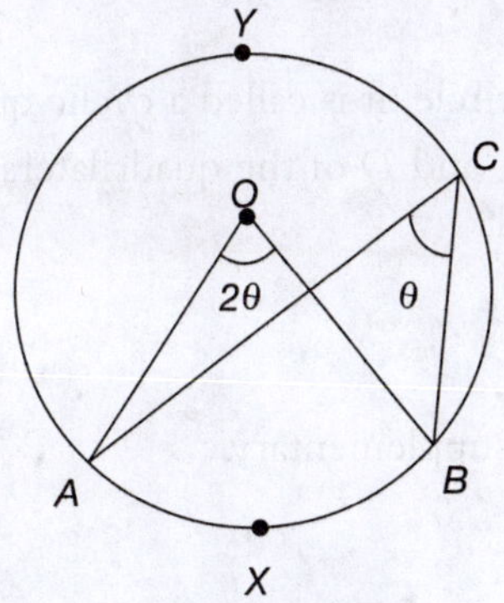

Figure 7.54

In the above figure, AXB is an arc of the circle. $\angle ACB$ is subtended by the arc AXB at the point C (a point on the remaining part of the circle), i.e., arc AYB. If O is the centre of the circle,

$$\angle AOB = 2\ \angle ACB.$$

EXAMPLE 7.9

In the adjacent figure, 'O' is the centre of the circle, PA and PB are tangents to the circle at points A and B. If ∠APB = 60°, then find ∠AOB.

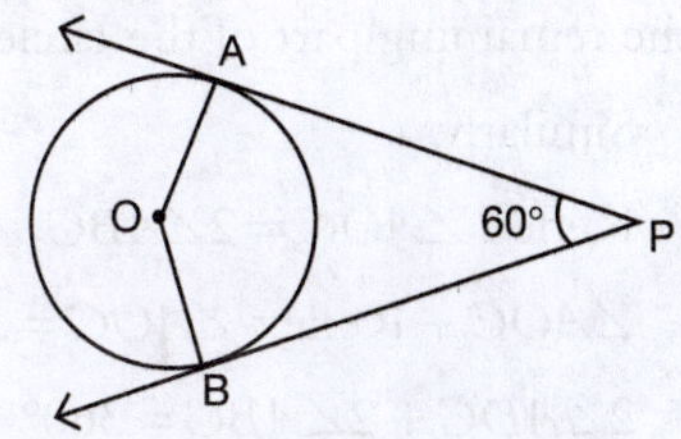

SOLUTION

In the quadrilateral PAOB, ∠PAO = ∠PBO = 90° (angle between tangent and radius)

∴ ∠AOB = 360° – (90° + 90° + 60°) = 120°.

EXAMPLE 7.10

In the figure, 'O' is the centre of the circle, ∠BDC = 110° and ∠ABO = 40°. Find ∠ACO.

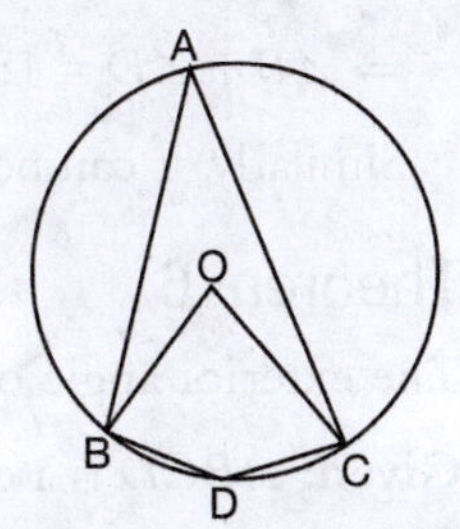

SOLUTION

ABCD is a cyclic quadrilateral.

∴ opposite angles are supplementary.

∴ ∠BDC = 110° ⇒ ∠BAC = 180 – 110° = 70°

∴ ∠BOC = 140° (angle subtended by an arc at the centre)

Reflex ∠BOC = 360° – 140° = 220°

In the quadrilateral ABOC, ∠BAC = 70°, ∠ABO = 40°,

Reflex ∠BOC = 220°

∴ ∠ACO = 360° – (70° + 40° + 220°) = 360° – 330° = 30° (∵ sum of angles of a quadrilateral is 360°)

EXAMPLE 7.11

In the adjacent figure, PT is the tangent segment to the circle with centre 'O'. If ∠QPT = 60° and ∠RQO = 35°, then find ∠RPO.

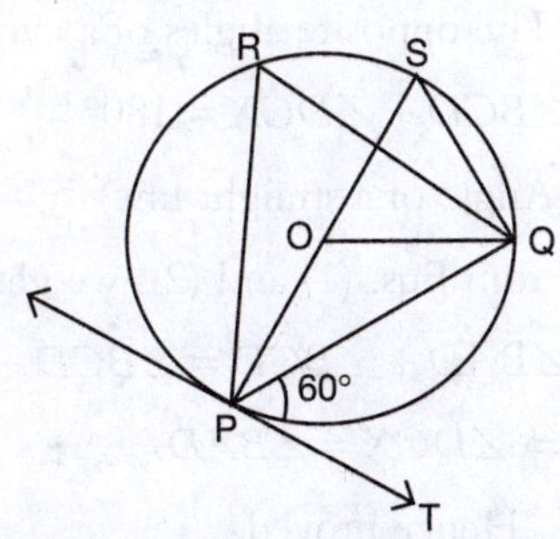

SOLUTION

∠QPT = 60°

∴∠PRQ = 60° (by alternate segment theorem)

⇒ ∠POQ = 120° (angle subtended by an arc at the centre)

Reflex ∠POQ = 360° – 120° = 240°

In the quadrilateral POQR, ∠PRQ = 60°, ∠RQO = 35°

Reflex ∠POQ = 240°

∴∠RPO = 360 – (240 + 60 + 35) = 360 – 335 = 25°

Cyclic Quadrilateral

If all the four vertices of a quadrilateral lie on a circle, it is called a cyclic quadrilateral.

In the given figure, the four vertices, A, B, C, and D of the quadrilateral $ABCD$ lie on the circle. Hence, $ABCD$ is a cyclic quadrilateral.

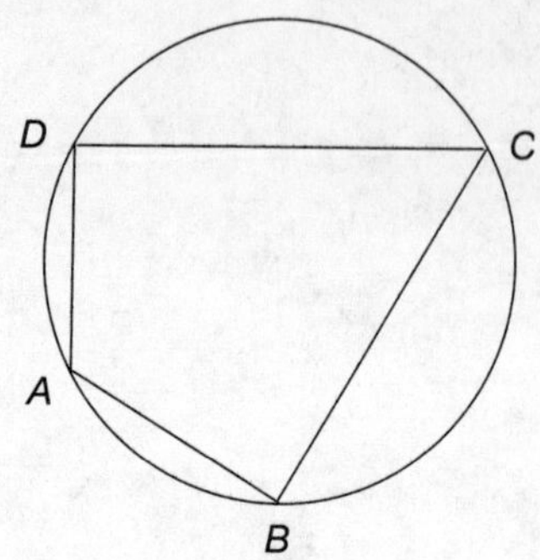

Figure 7.58

Theorem 5

The opposite angles of a cyclic quadrilateral are supplementary.

Given: $ABCD$ is a cyclic quadrilateral.

RTP:

$\angle A + \angle C = 180°$ or $\angle B + \angle D = 180°$

Construction: Join OA and OC, where O is the centre of the circle.

$$\angle AOC = 2\angle ADC$$

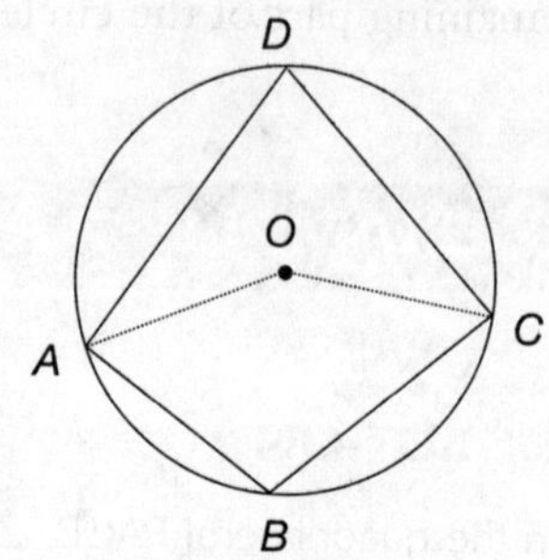

Figure 7.59

Angle subtended by arc ABC is double the angle subtended by arc ABC at any point on the remaining part of the circle and D is such a point.

Similarly,

Reflex $\angle AOC = 2\angle ABC$

$\angle AOC +$ Reflex $\angle AOC = 360°$

$2\angle ADC + 2\angle ABC = 360°$

$\Rightarrow \angle ADC + \angle ABC = 180°$

$\Rightarrow \angle B + \angle D = 180°$

Similarly, it can be proved that $\angle A + \angle C = 180°$.

Theorem 6

The exterior angle of a cyclic quadrilateral is equal to the interior opposite angle.

Given: $ABCD$ is a cyclic quadrilateral.

Construction: Extend BC to X.

RTP: $\angle DCX = \angle BAD$.

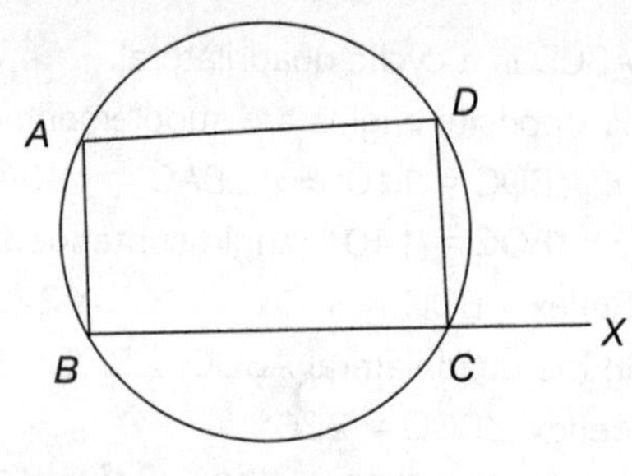

Figure 7.60

Proof:

$\angle BAD + \angle BCD = 180°$ (1)

(The opposite angles of a cyclic quadrilateral are supplementary).

$\angle BCD + \angle DCX = 180°$ (2)

(Angle of a straight line)

From Eqs. (1) and (2), we get,

$\angle BAD + \angle BCD = \angle BCD + \angle DCX$

$\Rightarrow \angle DCX = \angle BAD$.

Hence proved.

We are already familiar with what a circle is and studied some of its properties. Now, we shall study the properties of tangents and chords.

Tangents

When a line and a circle are drawn in the same plane we have the following cases:

1. The line and the circle may not intersect at all, as shown in the Fig. 7.61(a). This means the line and the circle do not meet.
2. The line may intersect the circle at two points as shown in Fig. 7.61(b).
3. The line may touch the circle at only one point as shown in Fig. 7.61(c).

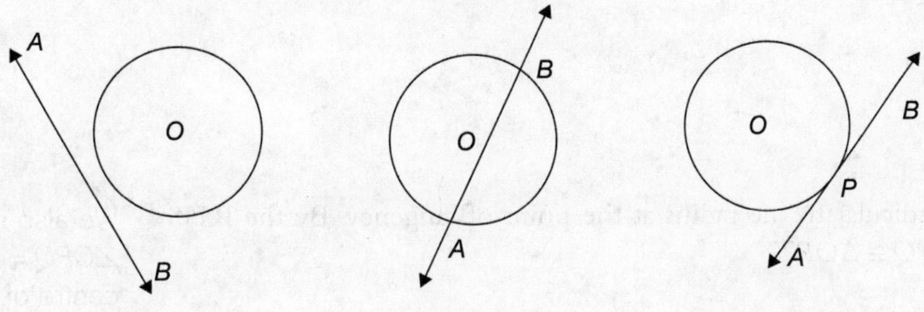

Figure 7.61

(i) If a line meets a circle at two points, then the line is called a secant of the circle.

(ii) When a line touches the circle at only one point or a line meets a circle at only one point, then the line is called a tangent to the circle at that point and that point is called point of contact or the point of tangency.

(iii) At a point on a circle, only one tangent can be drawn.

(iv) From any given external point, two tangents can be drawn to a circle.

(v) From any point inside a circle, no tangent can be drawn to the circle.

Theorem 7

The tangent at any point on a circle is perpendicular to the radius through the point of contact.

Given: PQ is a tangent to a circle with centre O. Point of contact of the tangent and the circle is A.

RTP: OA is perpendicular to PQ.

Construction: Take another point B on PQ and join OB.

Proof: Since B is a point other than A, B may lie inside or outside the circle.

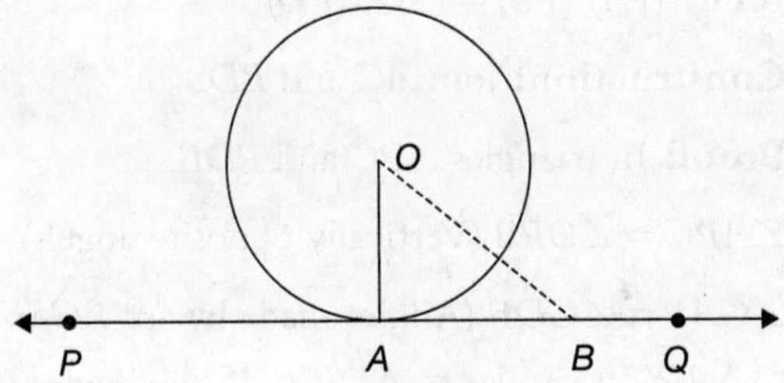

Figure 7.62

Case 1: If point B lies inside the circle but on the line PQ, then PQ cannot be a tangent to the circle. Hence B does not lie inside the circle.

Case 2: If B lies outside the circle, $OB > OA$, i.e., among all the segment joining a point on the line to the point O, OA is the shortest.

But, among all the line segments joining point O to a point on PQ, the shortest is the perpendicular line.

$\therefore$ OA is perpendicular to PQ.

Converse of the Theorem

A line drawn through the end point of a radius of a circle and perpendicular to it is a tangent to the circle.

Theorem 8

Two tangents drawn to a circle from an external print are equal in length.

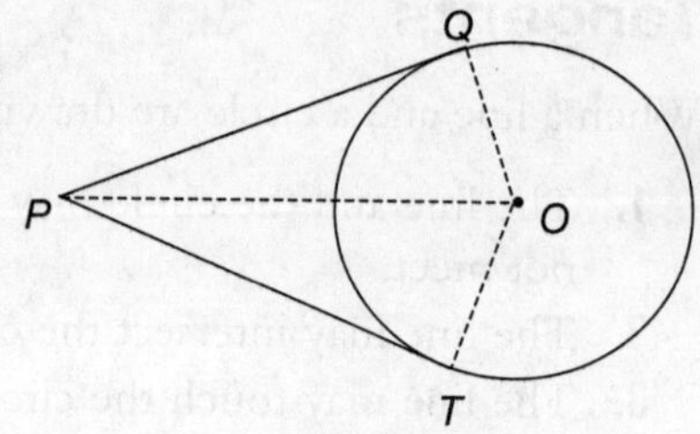

Figure 7.63

Given *PQ* and *PT* are two tangents drawn from point *P* to circle with centre *O*.

RTP: $PQ = PT$

Construction: Join *OP*, *OQ* and *OT*.

Proof: In triangles *OPQ* and *OPT*,

$OP = OP$ (Common)

$\angle OQP = \angle OTP = 90°$

$OQ = OT$ (Radius)

The tangent is perpendicular to the radius at the point of tangency. By the RHS congruence axiom, $\Delta OPQ \cong \Delta OPT$

$\Rightarrow PQ = PT.$

Konnect

We also note that $\angle OPQ = \angle OPT$, i.e., the centre of a circle lies on the bisector of the angle formed by the two tangents.

Chords

A line joining any two points on a circle is a chord of the circle. If *AB* is a chord of a circle and *P* is a point on it, *P* is said to divide *AB* internally into two segments *AP* and *PB*. Similarly, if *Q* is a point on the line *AB*, outside the circle, *Q* is said to divide *AB* externally into two segments *AQ* and *QB*.

Theorem 9

If two chords of a circle intersect each other, then the products of the lengths of their segments are equal.

Case 1: Let the two chords intersect internally.

Given: *AB* and *CD* are two chords intersecting at point *P* in the circle.

RTP: $(PA)\ (PB) = (PC)\ (PD)$

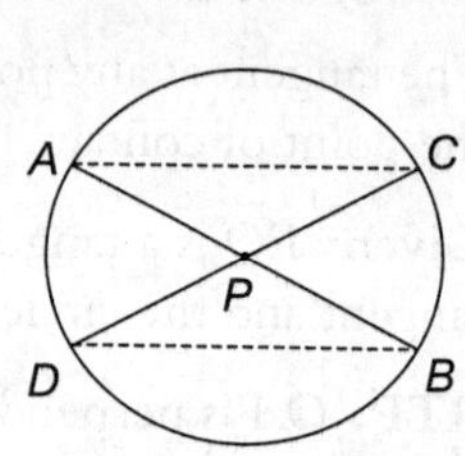

Construction: Join *AC* and *BD*.

Proof: In triangles *APC* and *PDB*,

$\angle APC = \angle DPB$ (Vertically opposite angels)

$\angle CAP = \angle CDB$ (Angles made by arc *BC* in the same segment)

ΔAPC is similar to ΔDPB. (If two angles of one triangle are equal to the corresponding angles of another triangle, the two triangles are similar or the *AA* Similarity Property)

$$\therefore \frac{PA}{PD} = \frac{PC}{PB} \Rightarrow (PA)(PB) = (PC)(PD)$$

Case 2: Let the two chords intersect externally.

Given: Two chords *BA* and *CD* intersect at point *P* which lies outside the circle.

RTP: $(PA)(PB) = (PC)(PD)$

Construction: Join *AC* and *BD*.

Proof: In triangles *PAC* and *PDB*,

$\angle PAC = \angle PDB$ and $\angle PCA = \angle PBD$ (An external angle of a cyclic quadrilateral is equal to the interior angle at the opposite vertex.

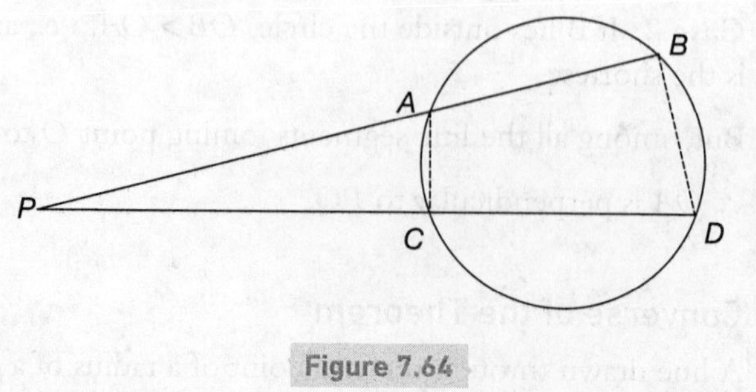

Figure 7.64

$\frac{PA}{PD} = \frac{PC}{PB}$ (The *AA* Similarity Property)

$\Rightarrow (PA)(PB) = (PC)(PD)$.

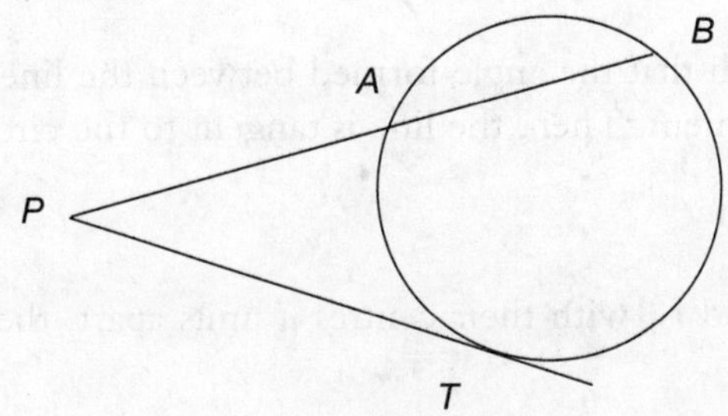

Figure 7.65

Konnect

1. The converse of the above theorem is also true, i.e., if two line segments *AB* and *CD* intersect at *P* and (*PA*) (*PB*) = (*PC*) (*PD*), then the four points are concyclic.
2. If one of the secants (say *PCD*) is rotated around *P* so that it becomes a tangent, i.e., points *C* and *D* say at *T*, coincide. We get the following result:

If *PAB* is a secant to a circle intersecting the circle at *A* and *B* and *PT* is the tangent drawn from *P* to the circle, then $PA \cdot PB = PT^2$

P is any point out side the circle with centre *O* and *PAB* is these cant drawn from *P* and *PT* is the tangent. Then $(PA)(PB) = PT^2$.

Alternate Segment and Its Angles

AB is a chord in a circle with centre *O*. A tangent is drawn to the circle at *A*. Chord *AB* makes two angles with the tangents $\angle BAY$ and $\angle BAX$. Chord *AB* divides the circle into two segments *ACB* and *ADB*. The segments *ACB* and *ADB* are called alternate segments to angles $\angle BAY$ and $\angle BAX$, respectively.

Angles made by the tangent with the chord are $\angle BAY$ and $\angle BAX$. *ACB* and *ADB* are alternate segments to those angles, respectively.

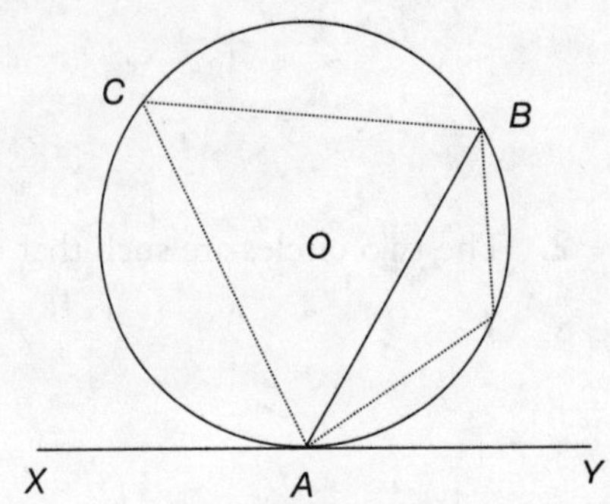

Figure 7.66

Theorem 10—Alternate Segment Theorem

If a line touches the circle at a point and if a chord is drawn from the point of contact then the angles formed between the chord and the tangent are equal to the angles in the alternate segments.

Given: *XY* is a tangent to the given circle with centre *O* at the point *A*, which lies in between *X* and *Y*. *AB* is a chord. *C* and *D* are points on the circle either side of line *AB*.

RTP: $\angle BAY = \angle ACB$ and $\angle BAX = \angle ADB$.

Construction: Draw the diameter *AOP* and join *PB*.

Proof: $\angle ACB = \angle APB$ (Angles in the same segment)

$\angle ABP = 90°$ (Angle in a semi-circle)

In the triangle *ABP*,

$\angle APB + \angle BAP = 90°$ (1)

$\angle PAY = 90°$ (the radius makes a right angle with the tangent at the point of tangency).

$\Rightarrow \angle BAP + \angle BAY = 90°$ (2)

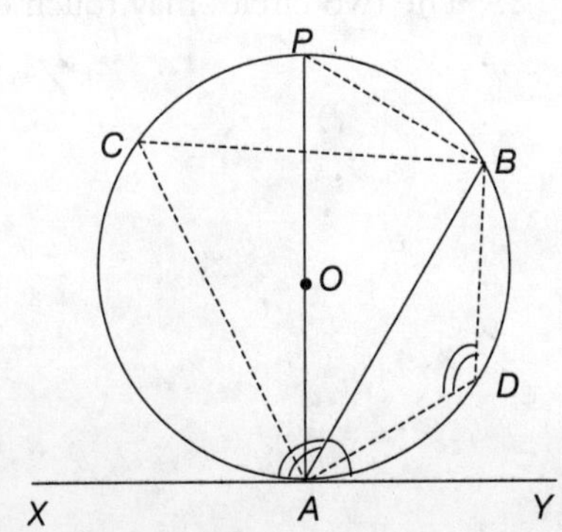

Figure 7.67

From the Eqs. (1) and (2), we get,

$\angle APB = \angle BAY$

$\Rightarrow \angle ACB = \angle BAY.$ ($\because \angle APB = \angle ACB$)

Similarly, it can be proved that

$\angle BAX = \angle ADB.$

Converse of Alternate Segment Theorem

A line is drawn through the end point of a chord of a circle such that the angle formed between the line and the chord is equal to the angle subtended by the chord in the alternate segment. Then, the line is tangent to the circle at the point.

Common Tangents to Circles

When two circles are drawn on the same plane with radii r_1 and r_2, with their centres d units apart, then we have the following possibilities.

1. The two circles are concentric, then $d = 0$. The points C_1 and C_2 coincide.

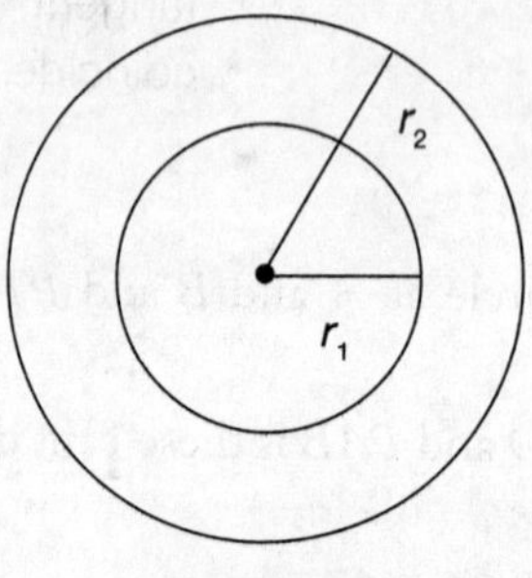

Figure 7.68

2. The two circles are such that one lies in side the other, then $|r_1 - r_2| > d$.

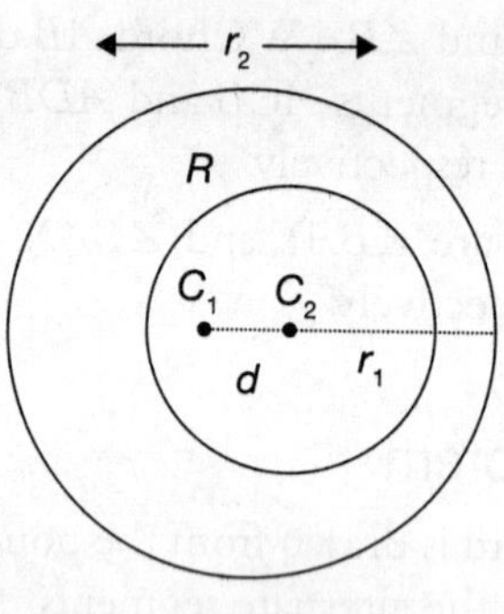

Figure 7.69

3. The two circles may touch each other internally, then $d = |r_1 - r_2|$.

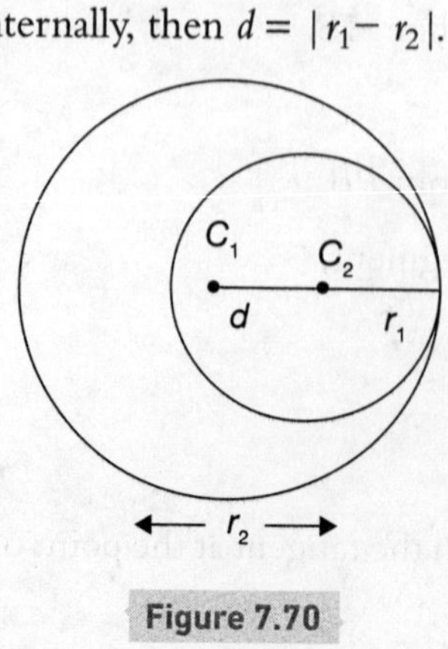

Figure 7.70

4. The two circles intersect at two points, in which case, $|r_1 - r_2| < d < r_1 + r_2$.

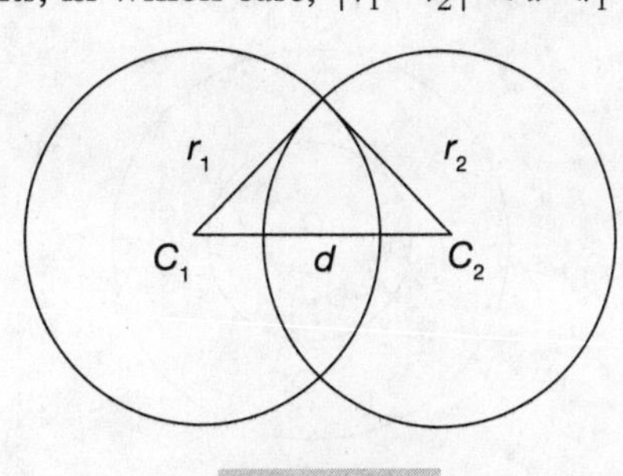

Figure 7.71

5. The two circles may touch each other externally, then $d = r_1 + r_2$.

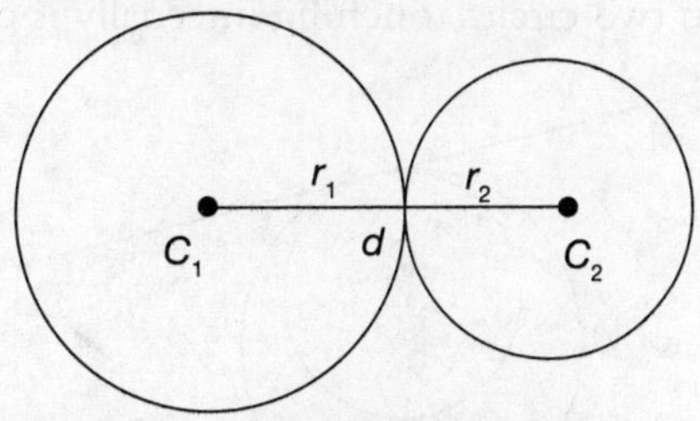

Figure 7.72

6. The two circles do not meet each other, then $d > r_1 + r_2$.

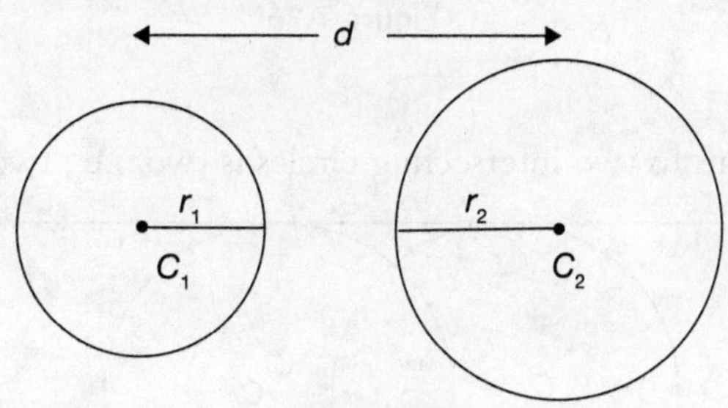

Figure 7.73

Common Tangent

If the same line is tangent to two circles drawn on the same plane, then the line is called a common tangent to the circles. The distance between the point of contacts is called the length of the common tangent.

In the figure, PQ is a common tangent to the circles, C_1 and C_2. The length of PQ is the length of the common tangent.

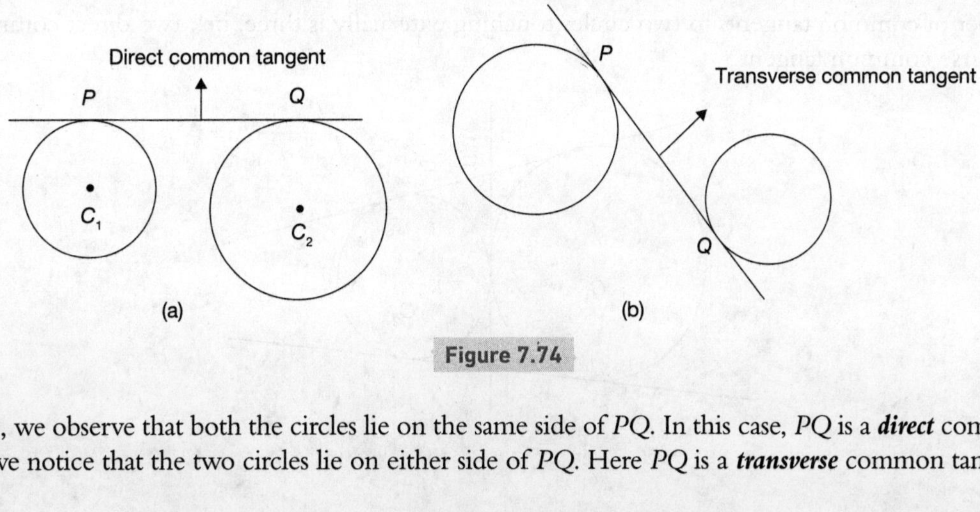

Figure 7.74

In Fig. 7.74(a), we observe that both the circles lie on the same side of PQ. In this case, PQ is a ***direct*** common tangent and in Fig. 7.74(b), we notice that the two circles lie on either side of PQ. Here PQ is a ***transverse*** common tangent.

1. The number of common tangents to the circles, one lying inside the other is zero.

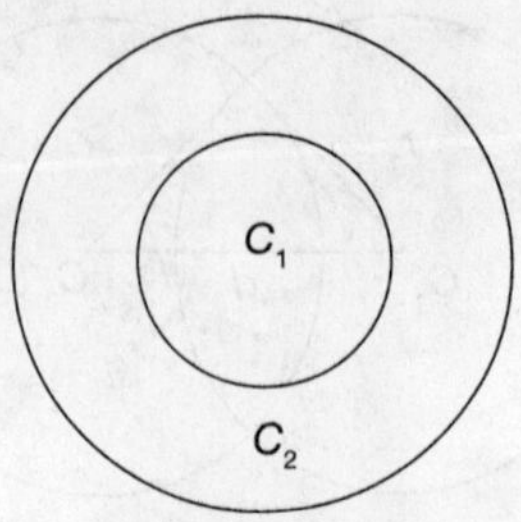

Figure 7.75

2. The number of common tangents to two circles touching internally is one.

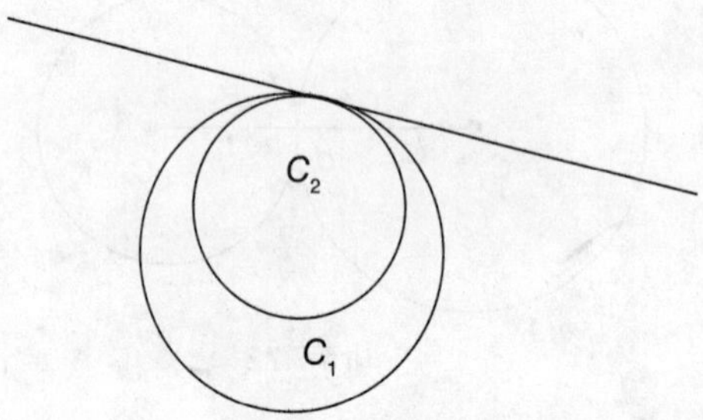

Figure 7.76

3. The number of common tangents to two intersecting circles is two, i.e., two direct common tangents.

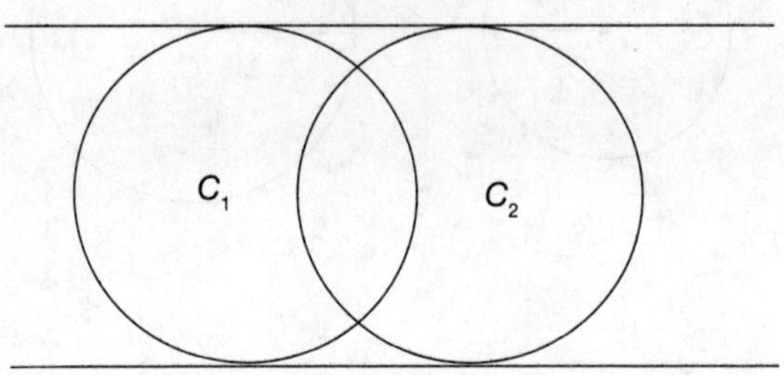

Figure 7.77

4. The number of common tangents to two circles touching externally is three, i.e., two direct common tangents and one transverse common tangent.

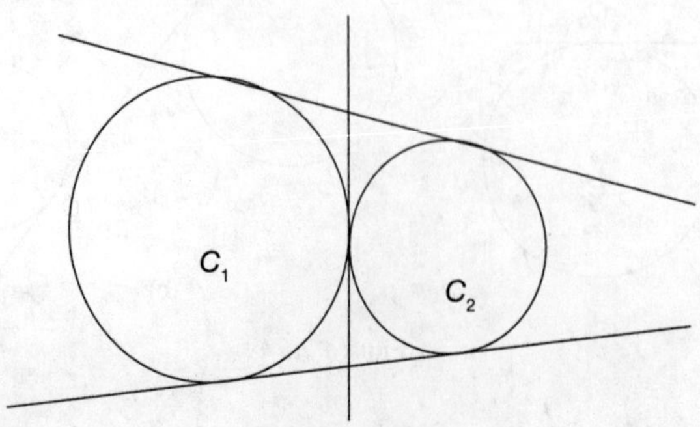

Figure 7.78

5. The number of common tangents to non-intersecting circles is four, i.e., 2 direct common tangents and 2 transverse common tangents.

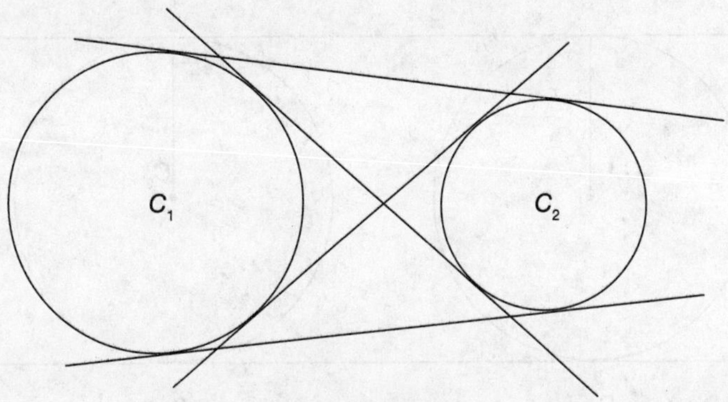

Figure 7.79

Properties of Common Tangents

1. When two circles touch each other internally or externally, then the line joining the centres is perpendicular to the tangent drawn at the point of contact of the two circles.

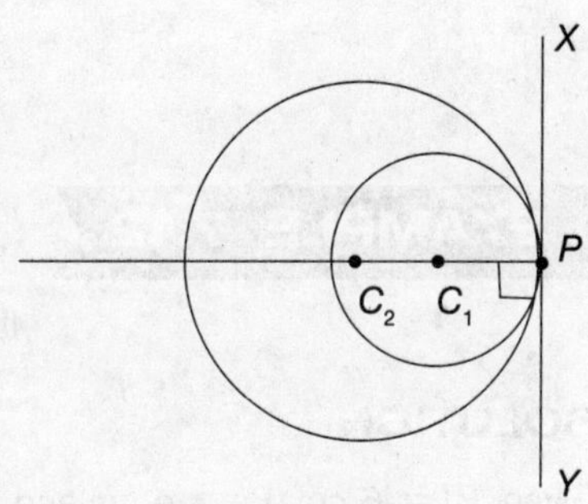

Figure 7.80

Case 1: Two circles with centres C_1 and C_2 touch each other internally at P. C_2C_1P is the line drawn through the centres and XY is the common tangent drawn at P which is common tangent to both the circles.
$\therefore$ C_1C_2 is perpendicular to XY.

Case 2: The given two circles with centres C_1 and C_2 touch each other externally at P.
C_1PC_2 is the line joining the centres of the circles and XY is the common tangent to the two circles drawn at P.

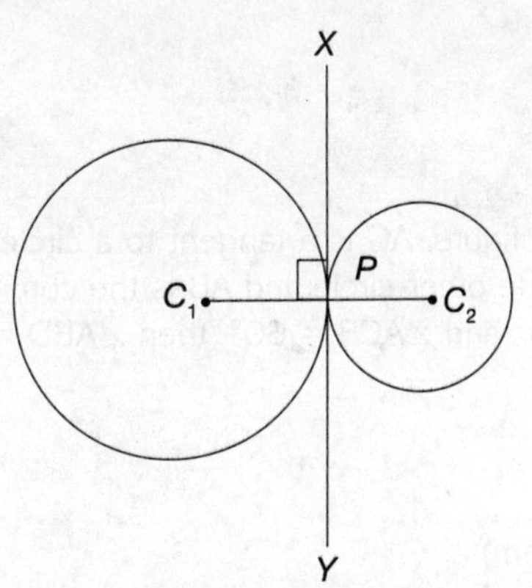

Figure 7.81

$\therefore$ C_1C_2 is perpendicular to XY.

2. The direct common tangents to two circles of equal radii are parallel to each other.

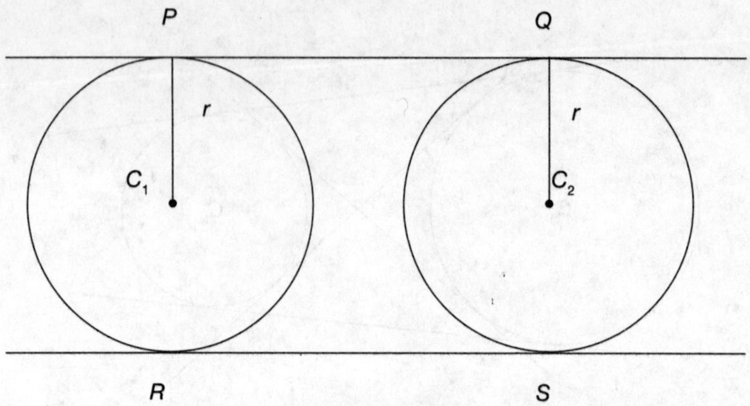

Figure 7.82

Let two circles of equal radii '*r*' have centres C_1 and C_2 and *PQ* and *RS* be the direct common tangents drawn to the circles. Then *PQ* is parallel to *RS*.

EXAMPLE 7.12

In the given figure, PT is a tangent, PB is a secant intersecting the circle at A and B.

If PT = 6 cm, PA = 4 cm and AB = x cm, then x = ____ cm.

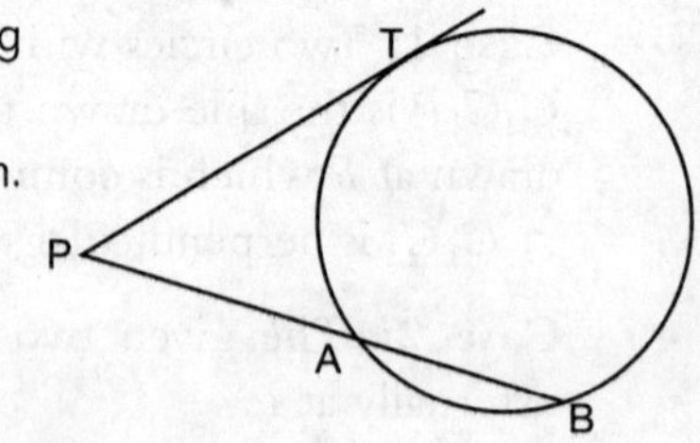

SOLUTION

Given, PT = 6 cm, PA = 4 cm and AB = x cm

Then PB = (4 + x) cm

We know that $PT^2 = PA.\ PB$

$6^2 = 4(4 + x)$

$9 = 4 + x$

$x = 5$

EXAMPLE 7.13

In the given figure, AC is a tangent to a circle and AD is a tangent to the other circle and AB is the common chord. If $\angle CAB = 55°$ and $\angle ACB = 60°$, then $\angle ABD$ = _____.

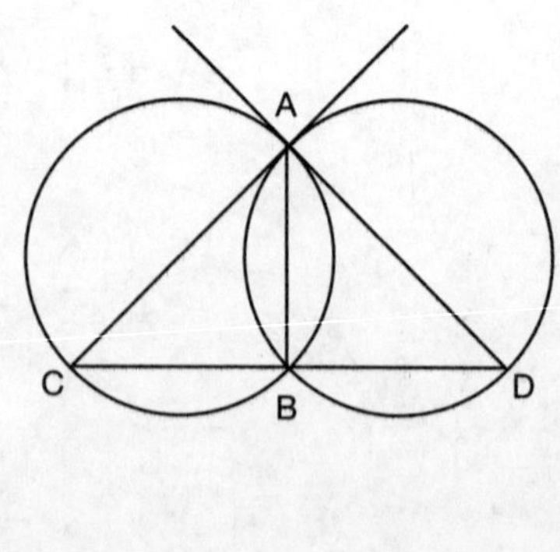

SOLUTION

In Δ ABC and Δ ABD

$\angle BAC = \angle ADB$ (By alternate segment theorem)

$\angle ACB = \angle BAD$ (By alternate segment theorem)

∴ By A.A. similarity axiom

Δ ACB ~ Δ DAB

$\angle ABD = \angle ABC = 180° - (55° + 60°)$

$= 180° - 115°$

$= 65°$

EXAMPLE 7.14 In the given figure (not to scale), PQ is a tangent segment, drawn to the circle with centre O at P and $QR = RO$. If $PQ = 3\sqrt{3}$ cm, and ORQ is a line segment, then find the radius of the circle.

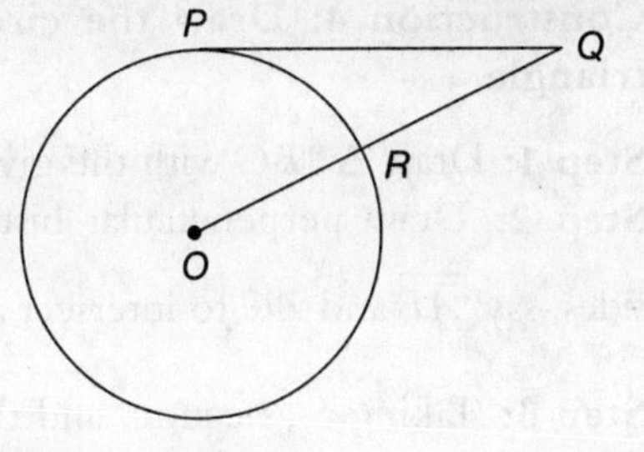

SOLUTION

Let radius of the circle be x.

$\therefore OR = RQ = x$ (given $OR = RQ$)

Join OP

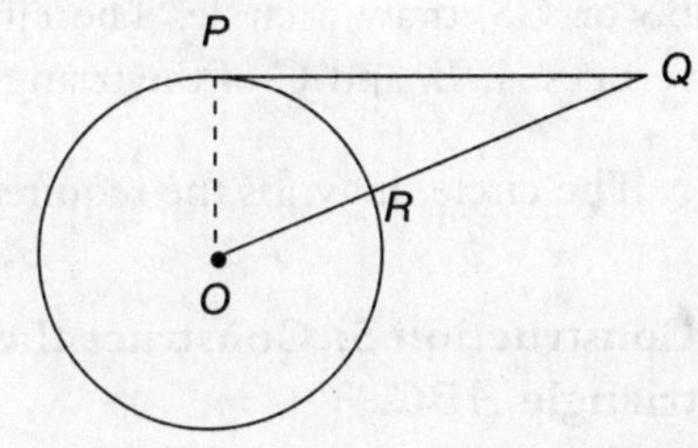

$\therefore \overline{OP} \perp \overline{PQ}$

$OP^2 + PQ^2 = OQ^2$

$\Rightarrow x^2 + (3\sqrt{3})^2 = (2x)^2$

$\Rightarrow 3x^2 = 27 \Rightarrow x^2 = 9 \Rightarrow x = \pm 3$

But x is positive.

$\therefore x = 3$ cm.

Constructions Related to Circles

Construction 1: To construct a segment of a circle, on a given chord and containing a given angle.

Example: Construct a segment of a circle on a chord of length 8.5 cm, containing an angle of 65°(θ)

Step 1: Draw a line segment BC of the given length, 8.5 cm.

Step 2: Draw $\overrightarrow{BX}$ and $\overrightarrow{CY}$ such that $\angle CBX = \angle BCY = \dfrac{180 - 2\theta}{2} = 25°$.

Step 3: Mark the intersection of $\overrightarrow{BX}$ and $\overrightarrow{CY}$ as O.

Step 4: Taking O as centre and OB or OC as radius, draw BAC

Step 5: In ΔBOC, $\angle BOC = 130°$

$\Rightarrow \angle BAC = (1/2)\ \angle BOC = (1/2)(130°) = 65°$

$\angle BAC = 65°$.

The segment bounded by $\overparen{BAC}$ and $\overline{BC}$ is the required segment.

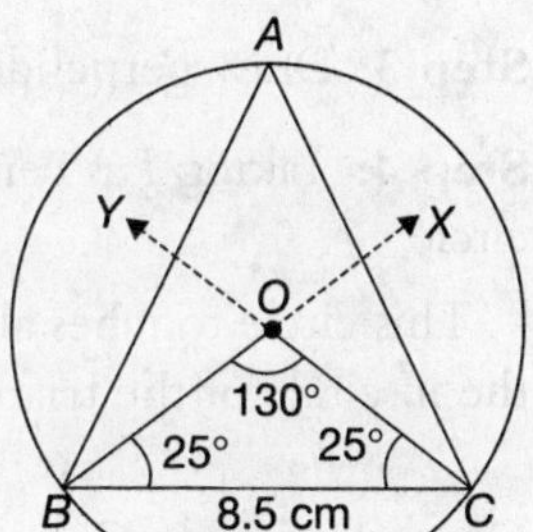

Figure 7.84

Construction 2: Construct an equilateral triangle inscribed in a circle of radius 3.5 cm.

Step 1: Draw a circle of radius 3.5 cm and mark its centre as O.

Step 2: Draw radii $\overline{OA}, \overline{OB}$, and $\overline{OC}$ such that $\angle AOB = \angle BOC = 120°$.

($\therefore \angle COA = 120°$)

Step 3: Join AB, BC and CA which is the required equilateral ΔABC in the given circle.

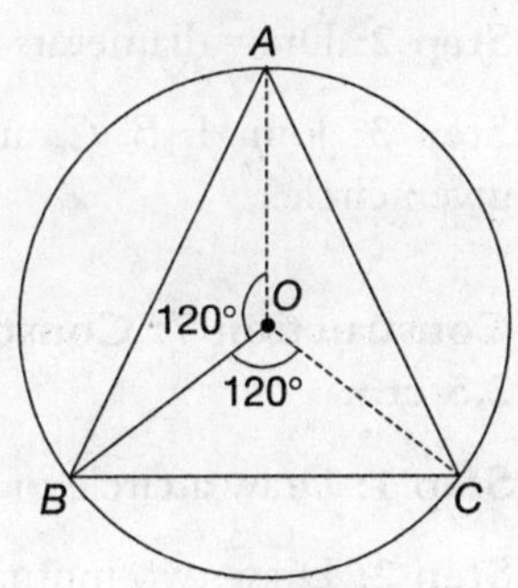

Figure 7.85

Construction 3: Construct an equilateral triangle circumscribed over a circle of radius 3 cm.

Step 1: Draw a circle of radius 3 cm with centre O.

Step 2: Draw radii $\overline{OP}$, $\overline{OQ}$, and $\overline{OR}$ such that $\angle POR = \angle ROQ = 120°$.

($\therefore \angle QOP = 120°$)

Step 3: At P, Q, and R draw perpendiculars to $\overline{OP}$, $\overline{OQ}$, and $\overline{OR}$, respectively, to form ΔABC. ΔABC is the required circumscribing equilateral triangle.

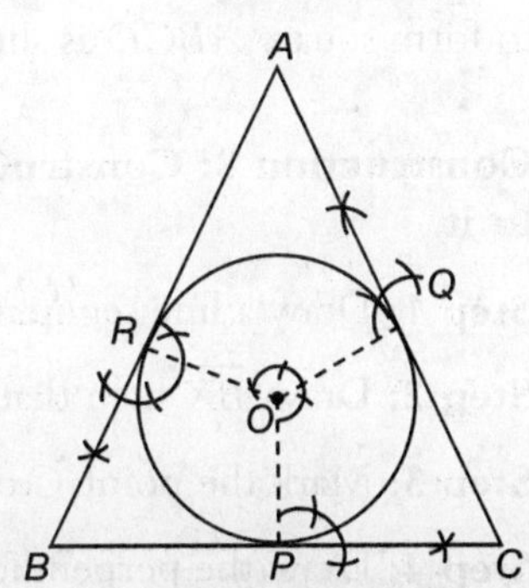

Figure 7.86

Construction 4: Draw the circum-circle of a given triangle.

Step 1: Draw ΔABC with the given measurements.

Step 2: Draw perpendicular bisectors of the two of the sides, say $\overline{AB}$ and AC to intersect at S.

Step 3: Taking S as centre, and the radius equal to AS or BS or CS, draw a circle. The circle passes through all the vertices A, B, and C of the triangle.

∴ The circle drawn is the required circum-circle.

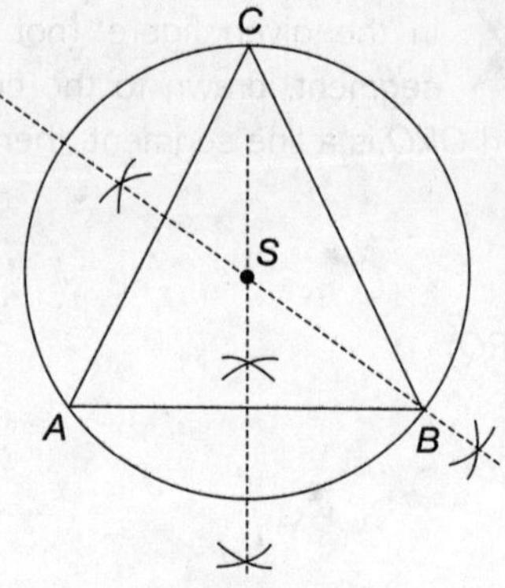

Figure 7.87

Info Bytes!

The circum-centre is equidistant from the vertices of the triangle.

Construction 5: Construct the in circle of a given triangle *ABC*.

Step 1: Draw a ΔABC with the given measurements.

Step 2: Draw bisectors of two of the angles, say $\angle B$ and $\angle C$ to intersect at I.

Step 3: Draw perpendicular $\overline{IM}$ from I onto $\overline{BC}$.

Step 4: Taking I as centre and IM as the radius, draw a circle.

This circle touches all the sides of the triangle. This is the in circle of the triangle.

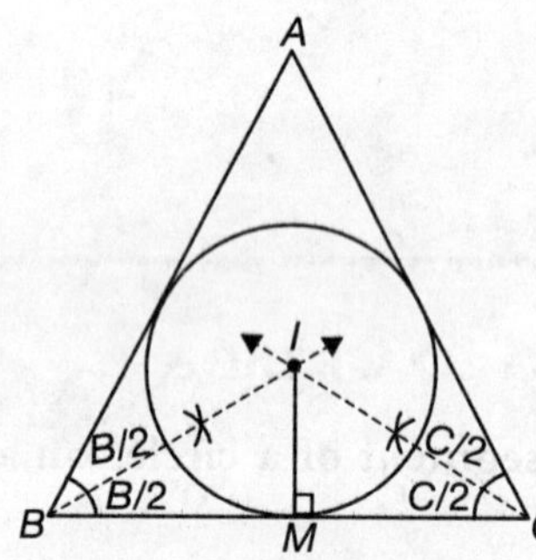

Figure 7.88

Konnect

The in-centre is equidistant from all the sides of the triangle.

Construction 6: Construct a square inscribed in a circle of radius 3 cm.

Step 1: Draw a circle of radius 3 cm and mark centre as 'O'.

Step 2: Draw diameters $\overline{AC}$ and $\overline{BD}$ such that $\overline{AC} \perp \overline{BD}$.

Step 3: Join A, B, C, and D. Quadrilateral $ABCD$ is the required square inscribed in the given circle.

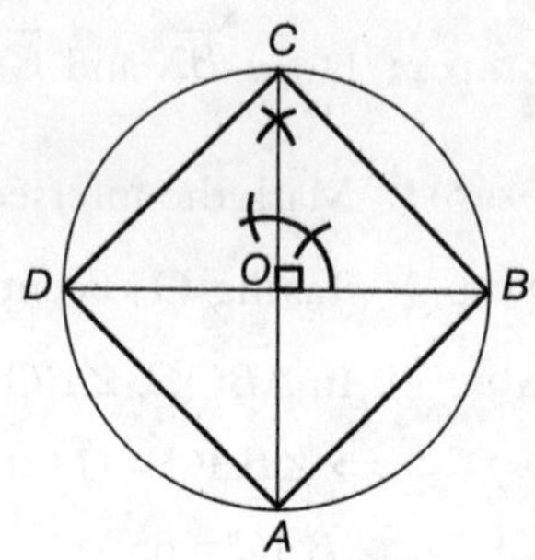

Figure 7.89

Construction 7: Construct a square circumscribed over the given circle of radius 2.5 cm.

Step 1: Draw a circle of radius 2.5 cm.

Step 2: Draw two mutually perpendicular diameters $\overline{PR}$ and $\overline{SQ}$.

Step 3: At P, Q, R, and S, draw lines perpendicular to OP, OQ, OR, and OS respectively to form square $ABCD$ as shown in the figure.

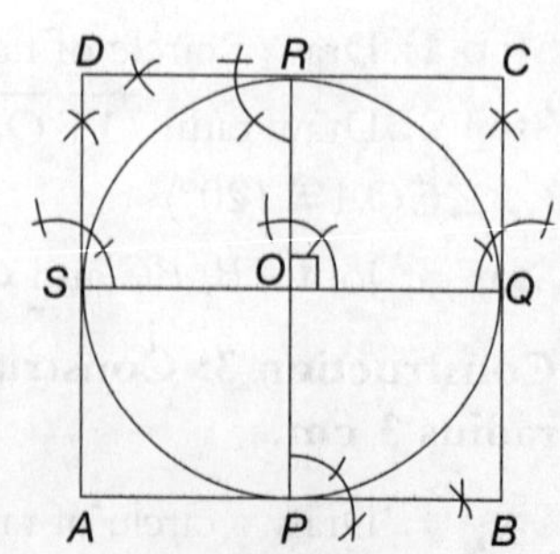

Figure 7.90

Construction 8: Construct a regular pentagon of side 4 cm. Circumscribe a circle to it.

Step 1: Draw a line segment, $AB = 4$ cm.

Step 2: Draw $\overrightarrow{BX}$ such that $\angle ABX = 108°$.

Step 3: Mark the point C on $\overrightarrow{BX}$ such that $BC = 4$ cm.

Step 4: Draw the perpendicular bisectors of $\overline{AB}$ and $\overline{BC}$ and mark their intersecting point as O.

Step 5: With *O* as centre and *OA* as radius draw a circle. And it passes through the points *B* and *C*.

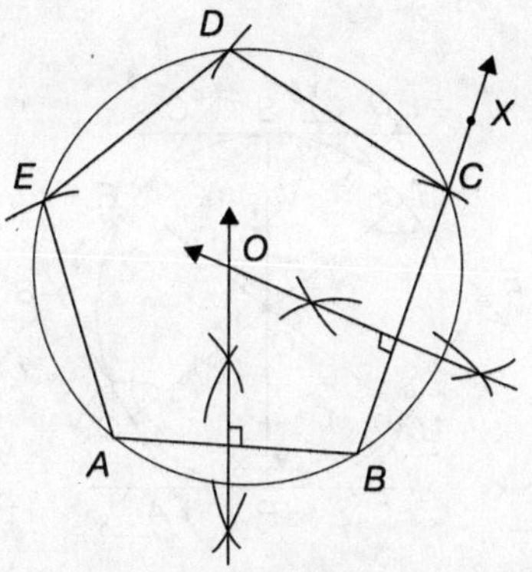

Figure 7.91

Step 6: With *C* as centre and 4 cm as radius draw an arc which cuts the circle at the point *D*.

Step 7: With *D* as centre and 4 cm as radius draw an arc which cuts the circle at the point *E*.

Step 8: Join *CD*, *DE*, and *AE*.

Step 9: *ABCDE* is the required pentagon.

Construction 9: Construct a regular pentagon in a circle of radius 4 cm.

Step 1: Construct a circle with radius 4 cm.

Step 2: Draw two radii $\overline{OA}$ and $\overline{OB}$ such that $\angle AOB = 72°$.

Step 3: Join *AB*.

Step 4: With *A* as centre and *AB* as radius draw an arc which cuts the circle at the point *E*.

Step 5: With *E* as centre and *AB* as radius draw an arc which cuts the circle at the point *D*.

Step 6: With *D* as centre and *AB* as radius draw an arc which cuts the circle at the point *C*.

Step 7: Join *AE*, *ED*, *DC*, and *CB*.

Step 8: *ABCDE* is the required pentagon.

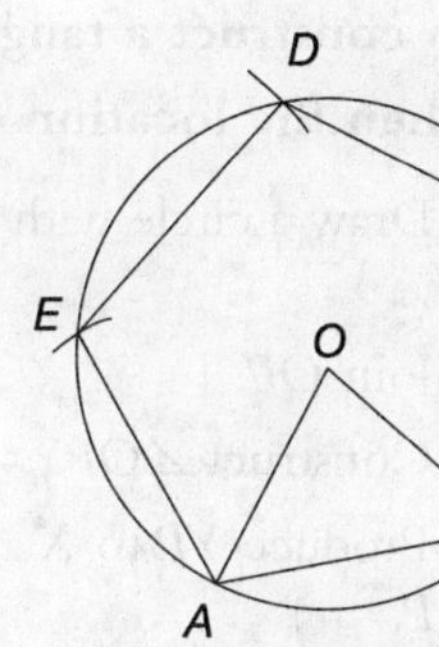

Figure 7.92

Construction 10: Construct a regular pentagon about a circle of radius 3.5 cm.

Step 1: Construct a circle with radius 3.5 cm.

Step 2: Draw radii *OP*, *OQ*, *OR*, *OS*, and *OT* such that the angle between any two consecutive radii is 72°.

Step 3: Draw tangents to the circle at the points *P*, *Q*, *R*, *S*, and *T*.

Step 4: Mark the intersecting points of the tangents as *A*, *B*, *C*, *D*, and *E*.

Step 5: *ABCDE* is the required pentagon.

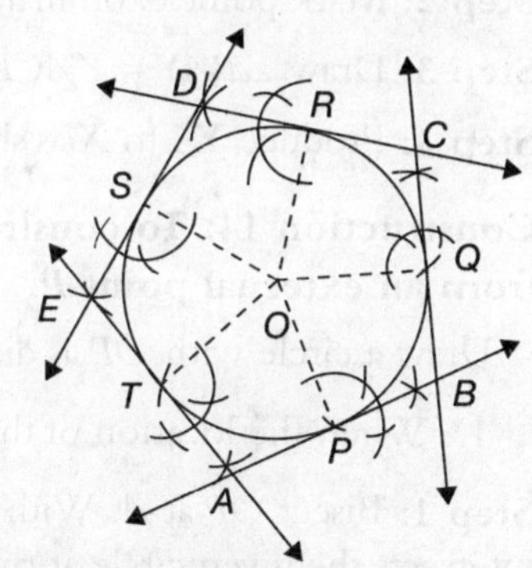

Figure 7.93

Construction 11: Construct a regular hexagon circumscribed over a circle of radius 3.5 cm.

Step 1: Draw a circle of radius 3.5 cm and mark its centre as *O*.

Step 2: Draw radii $\overline{OP}, \overline{OQ}, \overline{OR}, \overline{OS}, \overline{OT}$, and $\overline{OU}$ such that the angle between any two adjacent radii is 60°.

Step 3: Draw lines at *P*, *Q*, *R*, *S*, *T*, and *U* perpendicular to $\overline{OP}, \overline{OQ}, \overline{OR}, \overline{OS}, \overline{OT}$, and $\overline{OU}$, respectively, to form the required circumscribed hexagon *ABCDEF*.

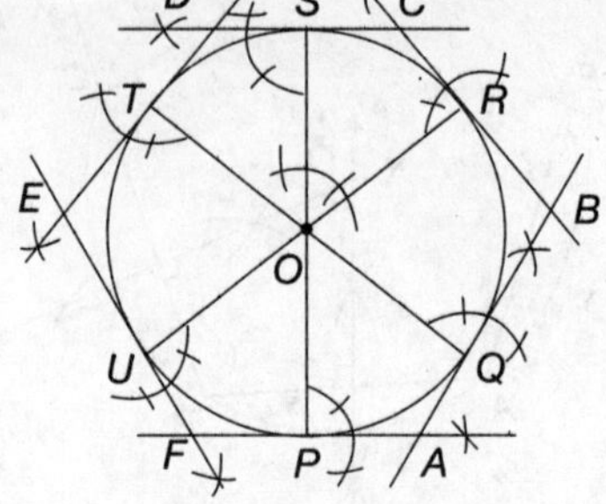

Figure 7.94

Construction 12: Inscribe a regular hexagon in a circle of radius 3 cm.

Step 1: Draw a circle of radius 3 cm taking the centre as *O*.

Step 2: Draw radius $\overline{OA}$. With radius, equal to *OA* and starting with *A* as the centre, mark points *B*, *C*, *D*, *E*, and *F* one after the other.

Step 3: Join *A*, *B*, *C*, *D*, *E*, and *F*. Polygon *ABCDEF* is the required hexagon.

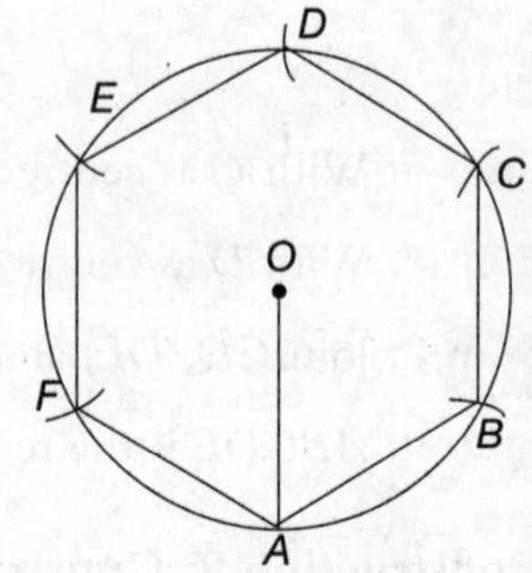

Figure 7.95

Construction 13:

1. **To construct a tangent to a circle at a point on it. When the location of the centre is known.**

Step 1: Draw a circle with centre *O* with any radius. Let *P* be a point on the circle.

Step 2: Join *OP*.

Step 3: Construct $\angle OPY = 90°$.

Step 4: Produce *YP* to *X* and *XPY* is the required tangent to the given circle at point *P*.

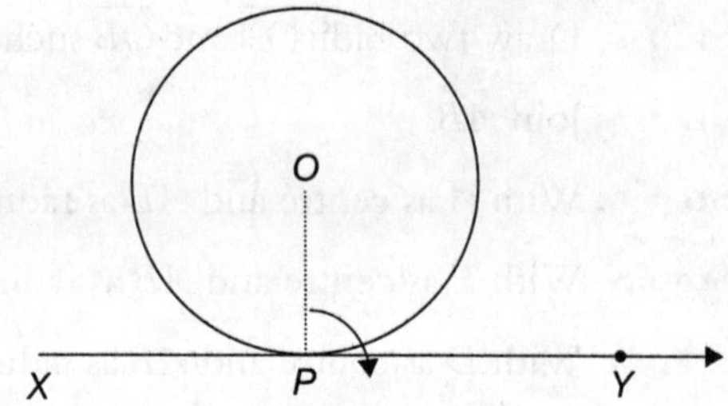

Figure 7.96

2. We have a circle, but we do not know where the centre is located.

Step 1: Draw a chord *AB*.

Step 2: Mark point *C* on major arc *ACB*. Join *BC* and *AC*.

Step 3: Draw $\angle BAY = \angle ACB$.

Step 4: Produce *YA* to *X* as shown in the figure. *XAY* is the required tangent at *A*.

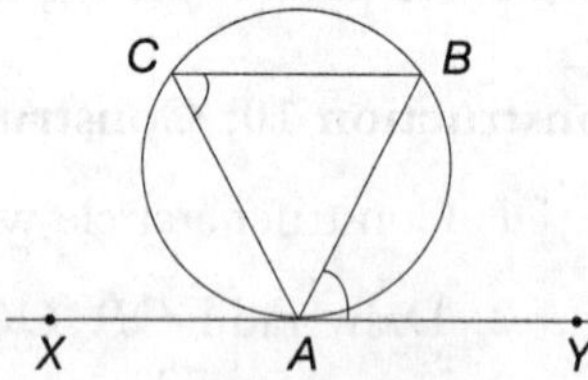

Figure 7.97

Construction 14: To construct the two tangents to a circle with centre at O, from an external point P.

Draw a circle with *OP* as diameter.

1. When the location of the centre is known.

Step 1: Bisect *OP* at *A*. With centre *A* and radius equal to *OA* or *AP*, draw a circle that intersects the given circle at two points *T* and *Q*.

Step 2: Join *PT* and *PQ*, which are the required tangents from *P*.

2. When the location of the centre is not known.

Step 1: Draw a circle of radius 2.5 cm. Mark a point *P* outside the circle.

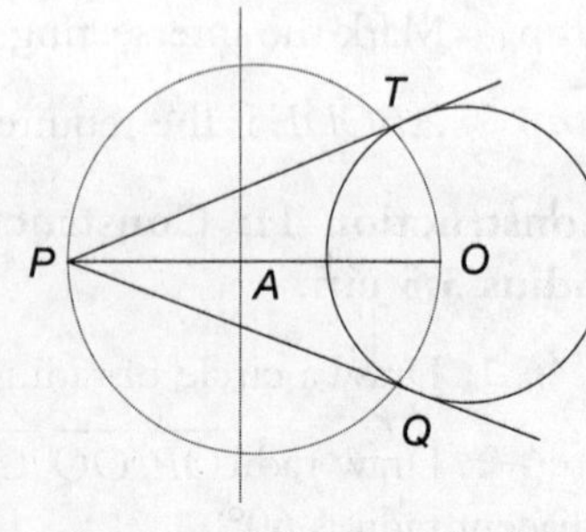

Figure 7.98

Step 2: Draw a secant PQR through 'P' to intersect the circle at Q and R.

Step 3: Produce QP to S, such that $PS = QP$.

Step 4: With SR as diameter, construct a semi-circle.

Step 5: Construct a line perpendicular to SR at P to intersect the semi-circle at U.

Step 6: Draw arcs with PU as radius and P as the centre to intersect the given circle at T and T_1.

Step 7: Join PT and PT_1. These are the required tangents from P to the given circles.

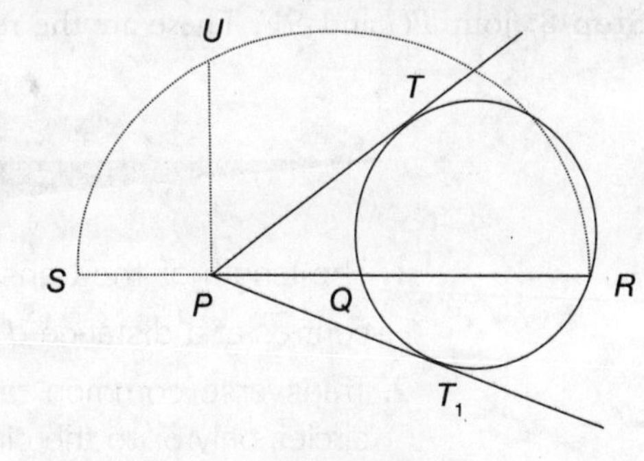

Figure 7.99

Construction 15: To construct the direct common tangents to the circles of radii 3.5 cm and 1.5 cm whose centres are 6.5 cm apart.

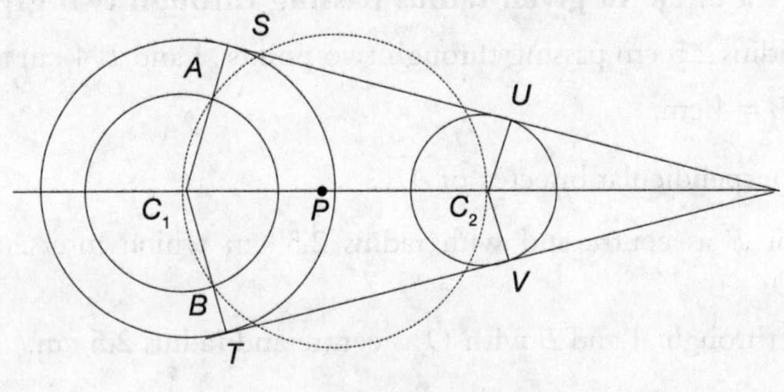

Figure 7.100

Step 1: Draw line segment, $C_1C_2 = 6.5$ cm.

Step 2: Draw circles with radii 3.5 cm and 1.5 cm, respectively, with C_1 and C_2 as centres.

Step 3: Bisect C_1C_2 at P and draw a circle taking P as centre and radius equal to PC_1 or PC_2.

Step 4: Draw another circle with radius equal to $(3.5 - 1.5) = 2$ cm, taking the centre of larger circle C_1 intersecting the circle drawn in step 3 at A and B.

Step 5: Join C_1A and C_1B and produce C_1A and C_1B to meet the outer circle at S and T, respectively.

Step 6: Draw line segments C_2U and C_2V, such that $C_2U \,||\, C_1S$ and $C_2V \,||\, C_1T$, where U, V are points on the circle with centre C_2.

Step 7: Join SU and TV. These are the required direct common tangents.

Konnect

The length of a direct common tangent to two circles with radii r_1 and r_2 and centres d units apart, is given by $\sqrt{d^2 - (r_1 - r_2)^2}$.

Construction 16: To construct the transverse common tangents to two circles with radii 2.5 cm and 1.5 cm, with centres at a distance of 6 cm from each other.

Step 1: Draw a line segment, $C_1C_2 = 6$ cm.

Step 2: Draw circles of radii 2.5 cm and 1.5 cm respectively with C_1 and C_2 as centres.

Step 3: Bisect C_1C_2. Let M be the mid-point of C_1C_2.

Step 4: Draw a circle with M as centre and C_1M or C_2M as radius.

Step 5: With C_2 as centre and radius equal to $(2.5 + 1.5)$ or 4 cm, mark off 2 points A and B on the circle in step 4.

Step 6: Join C_2A and C_2B to meet the other circle with centre C_2 at S and T, respectively.

Step 7: Draw lines, C_1U and C_1V such that $C_1U \,||\, C_2B$ and $C_1V \,||\, C_2A$, where U, V are points on the circle with centre at C_1.

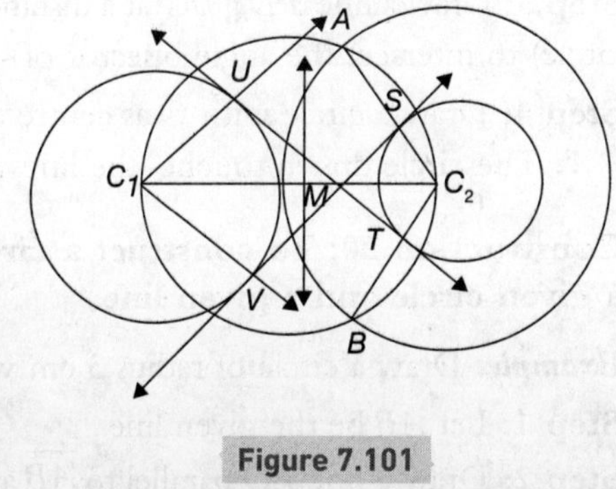

Figure 7.101

Step 8: Join TU and SV. These are the required transverse common tangents.

Konnect

1. The length of the transverse common tangent of two circles with radii r_1 and r_2 and centres at a distance d ($d > r_1 + r_2$) is $\sqrt{d^2 - (r_1 + r_2)^2}$.
2. Transverse common tangents can be drawn to non-intersecting and non-touching circles only or to the circles that satisfy the condition, $d > r_1 + r_2$.

Construction 17: To construct a circle of given radius passing through two given points.

Example: Construct a circle of radius 2.5 cm passing through two points A and B 4 cm apart.

Step 1: Draw a line segment, $AB = 4$ cm.

Step 2: Bisect $\overline{AB}$ by drawing a perpendicular bisector of $\overline{AB}$.

Step 3: Draw an arc with A or B as centre and with radius 2.5 cm which intersect the perpendicular bisector of $\overline{AB}$ at O.

Step 4: Draw a circle that passes through A and B with O as centre and radius 2.5 cm.

$\therefore$ This is the required circle with given radius and passing through the given points A and B.

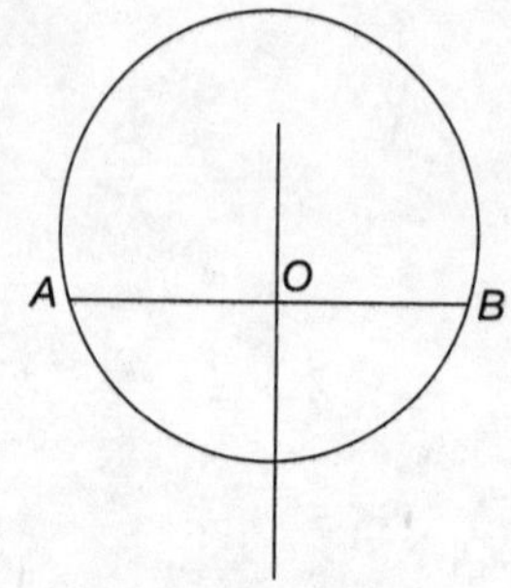

Figure 7.102

Construction 18: To draw a circle touching a given line AB at a given point P and passing through a given point Q.

Step 1: Draw a line AB and mark point P on it.
Step 2: Draw PR at P such that $PR \perp AB$, i.e., $\angle APR = 90°$.
Step 3: Join PQ and draw the perpendicular bisector of PQ to intersect PR at O.
Step 4: Draw a circle, touches line AB at P and passes through the given point Q with O as centre and OP as radius.

$\therefore$ The circle drawn is the required circle.

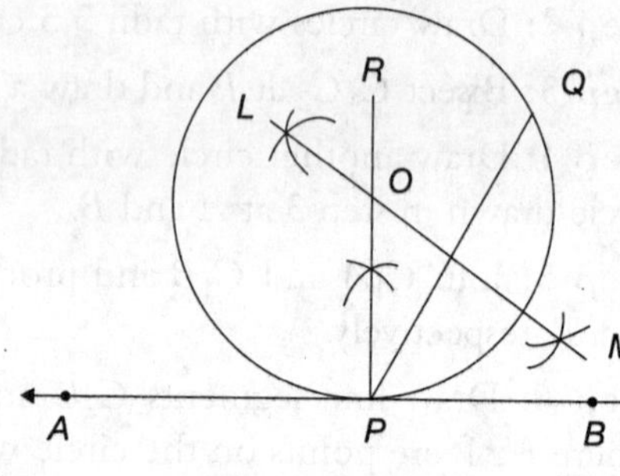

Figure 7.103

Construction 19: To construct a circle with a given radius and touching the two given intersecting lines.

Example: Construct an angle of 70° and draw a circle of radius 2.5 cm touching the arms of the angle.

Step 1: Draw an angle $\angle ABC = 70°$.

Step 2: Draw BD, the bisector of the angle ABC.

Step 3: Draw a line $\overline{PD} \parallel \overline{BC}$ at a distance of 2.5 cm (equal to the radius of the circle) to intersect the angle bisector of step 2 at O.

Step 4: Draw a circle with O as centre and radius 2.5 cm

$\therefore$ The circle drawn touches the lines at X and Y.

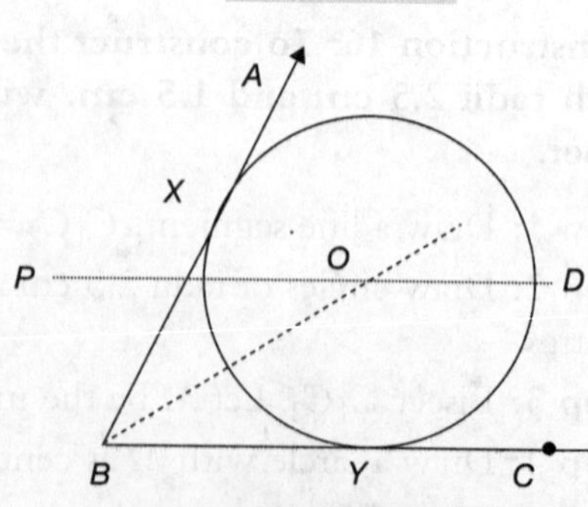

Figure 7.104

Construction 20: To construct a circle of given radius which touches a given circle and a given line.

Example: Draw a circle of radius 3 cm which touches a given line AB and a given circle of radius 2 cm with centre C.

Step 1: Let AB be the given line.

Step 2: Draw a line PQ parallel to $\overline{AB}$ at a distance 3 cm from $\overline{AB}$.

Step 3: Draw an arc with C as centre and with radius equal to $(2 + 3) = 5$ cm to cut PQ at point O.

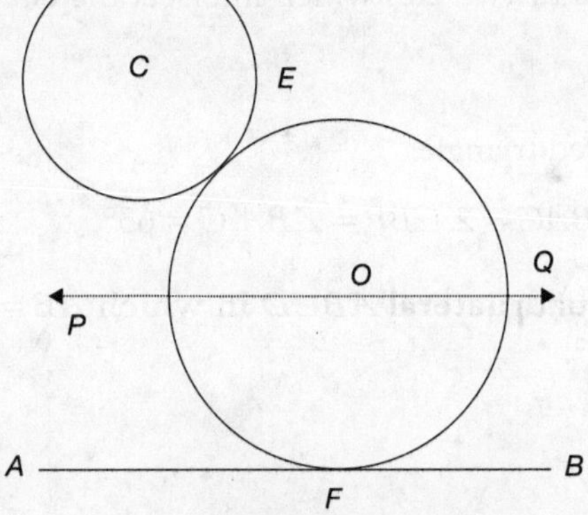

Figure 7.105

Step 4: Draw a circle which touches the given circle at E and the given line AB at F with O as centre and radius 3 cm.

∴ The circle drawn in step 4 is the required circle.

Construction 21: Construct a triangle ABC in which $BC = 6$ cm, $\angle A = 60°$ and altitude through A is 4 cm.

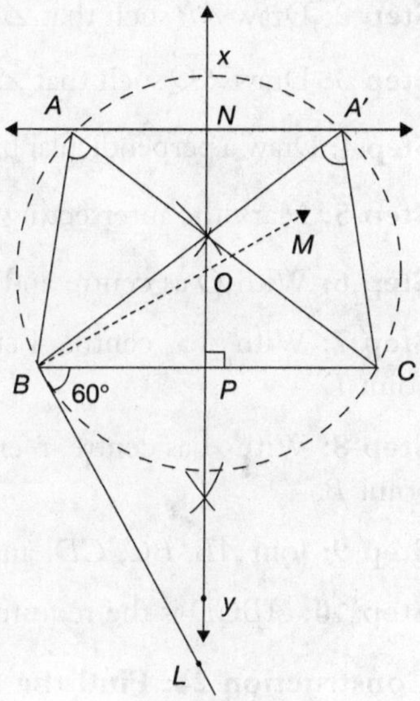

Figure 7.106

Step 1: Draw a line segment, $BC = 6$ cm.

Step 2: Draw $\overrightarrow{BL}$ such that $\angle CBL = 60°$.

Step 3: Draw $\overrightarrow{BM}$ such that $\angle MBL = 90°$.

Step 4: Draw a perpendicular bisector $\left(\overleftrightarrow{XY}\right)$ of $\overline{BC}$ which intersects $\overline{BC}$ at the point P.

Step 5: Mark the intersecting point of $\overleftrightarrow{XY}$ and $\overrightarrow{BM}$ as O.

Step 6: With O as centre and OB as radius draw a circle.

Step 7: Mark the point N on $\overleftrightarrow{XY}$ such that $PN = 4$ cm.

Step 8: Through N, draw a line parallel to $\overrightarrow{BC}$ which intersects the circle at points A and A'.

Step 9: Join AB, AC and $A'B$, $A'C$.

Step 10: Now, ABC or $A'BC$ is required triangle.

Proof: By alternate segment theorem, $\angle BAC = \angle CBL = \angle BA'C = 60°$.

Altitude through A = Altitude through $A' = PN = 4$ cm.

Construction 22: Construct a triangle ABC in which $BC = 7$ cm, $\angle A = 65°$ and median AT is 5 cm.

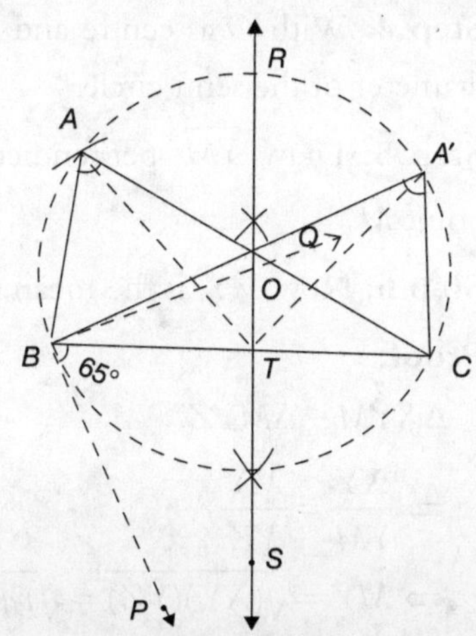

Figure 7.107

Step 1: Draw a line segment, $BC = 7$ cm.

Step 2: Draw $\overrightarrow{BP}$ such that $\angle CBP = 65°$.

Step 3: Draw $\overrightarrow{BQ}$ such that $\angle PBQ = 90°$.

Step 4: Draw a perpendicular bisector $\left(\overleftrightarrow{RS}\right)$ of $\overline{BC}$ which intersects $\overline{BC}$ at the point T.

Step 5: Mark the intersecting point of $\overleftrightarrow{RS}$ and $\overrightarrow{BQ}$ as O.

Step 6: With O as centre and OB as radius draw circle.

Step 7: With T as centre 5 cm as radius draw two arcs which intersect the circle at the points A and A'.

Step 8: Join AB and AC and A' and $A'C$.

Step 9: Now, ABC or $A'BC$ is the required triangle.

Proof: By alternate segment theorem, $\angle BAC = \angle CBP = \angle BA'C = 65°$.

Construction 23: Construct a cyclic quadrilateral $ABCD$ in which $AB = 3$ cm, $AD = 4$ cm, $AC = 6$ cm and $\angle D = 70°$.

Rough figure:

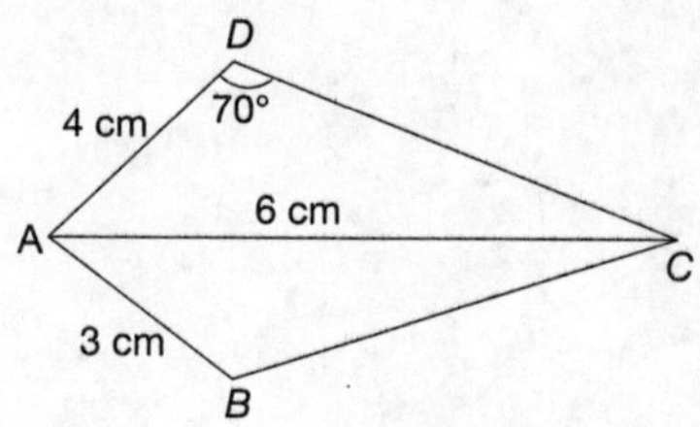

Figure 7.108

Step 1: Draw a line segment, $AC = 6$ cm.

Step 2: Draw $\overrightarrow{AP}$ such that $\angle CAP = 70°$.

Step 3: Draw $\overrightarrow{AQ}$ such that $\angle PAQ = 90°$.

Step 4: Draw a perpendicular bisectors $\left(\overleftrightarrow{RS}\right)$ of $\overline{AC}$ which intersects $\overline{AC}$ at the point T.

Step 5: Mark the intersecting point of $\overleftrightarrow{RS}$ and $\overrightarrow{AQ}$ as O.

Step 6: With O as centre and OA as radius draw a circle.

Step 7: With A as centre, 4 cm as radius draw an arc which intersects the circle atthe point D.

Step 8: With A as centre, 3 cm as radius draw an arc which intersects the circle at the point B.

Step 9: Join AB, BC, CD, and AD.

Step 10: $ABCD$ is the required cyclic quadrilateral.

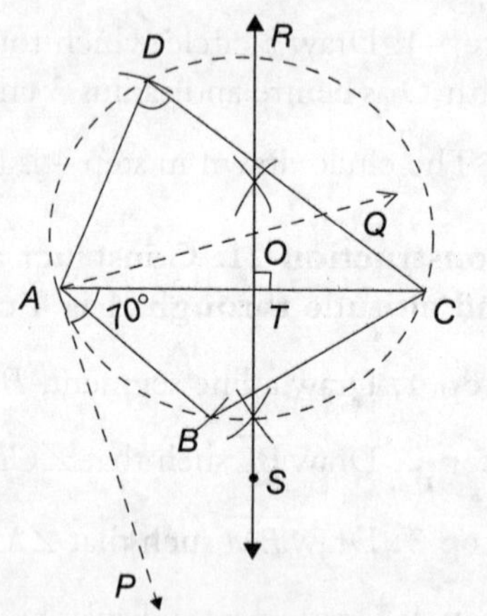

Figure 7.109

Construction 24: Find the mean proportional of the given segments p cm and q cm.

Step 1: Draw $\overline{XZ}$.

Step 2: Mark the point Y on $\overline{XZ}$ such that $XY = p$ cm and $YZ = q$ cm.

Step 3: Draw the perpendicular bisector $\left(\overleftrightarrow{AB}\right)$ of $\overline{XZ}$ which meets $\overline{XZ}$ at the point O.

Step 4: With O as centre and OX as radius draw a semi circle. $\overline{XZ}$ is the diameter of the semi circle.

Step 5: Draw $\overrightarrow{YM}$ perpendicular to $\overline{XZ}$ which meets semicircle at the point M.

Step 6: Now MY, is the mean proportional of XY and YZ, i.e., p and q.

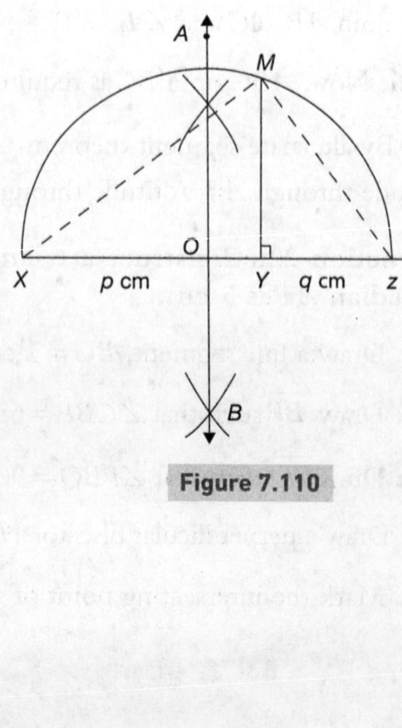

Figure 7.110

Proof:

$$\Delta XYM \sim \Delta MYZ$$

$$\Rightarrow \frac{XY}{YM} = \frac{MY}{YZ}$$

$$\Rightarrow MY = \sqrt{(XY)(YZ)} = \sqrt{pq}.$$

Uses: By using this construction, square root ($\sqrt{12}, \sqrt{15}, \ldots$) can be found.

Construction 25: Construct a square whose area is equal to the area of the rectangle.

Step 1: Produce $\overline{AB}$ of rectangle $ABCD$ to the point E such that $BE = BC$.

Step 2: Construct mean proportional (BF) of AB and BE.

Step 3: Construct a square with side BF.

Step 4: $BFGH$ is the required square.

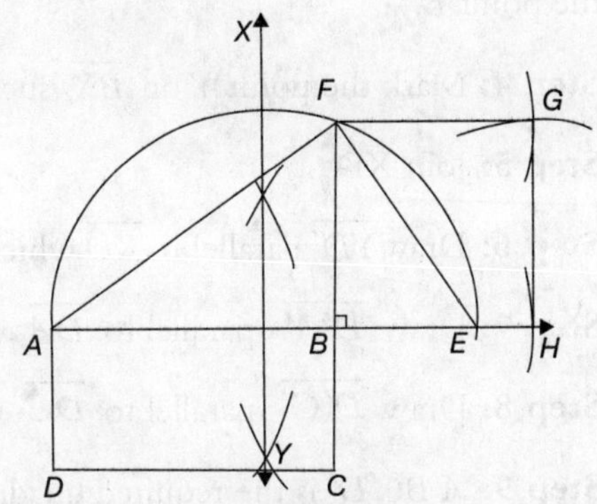

Figure 7.111

Proof: BF is the mean proportional of AB and BE.

$\Rightarrow (BF)^2 = AB \times BE$

$\Rightarrow (BF)^2 = AB \times BC$ ($\because BC = BE$)

$\Rightarrow$ Area of square $BFGH$ = Area of rectangle $ABCD$.

Construction 26: Construct a triangle similar to a given triangle ABC with its sides equal to $\left(\frac{5}{9}\right)$ th of the corresponding sides of ΔABC.

Step 1: ABC is the given triangle.

Step 2: Draw $\overrightarrow{BD}$ which makes non-zero angle with $\overline{BC}$ and D is 9 cm away from the point B.

Step 3: Mark the point E on $\overrightarrow{BD}$ such that $BE = 5$ cm.

Step 4: Join $\overline{CD}$.

Step 5: Draw $\overline{EC'}$ parallel to $\overline{DC}$ which meets $\overline{BC}$ at the point C'.

Step 6: Draw $\overline{C'A'}$ parallel to $\overline{CA}$ which meets $\overline{BA}$ at the point A'.

Step 7: $A'BC'$ is the required triangle.

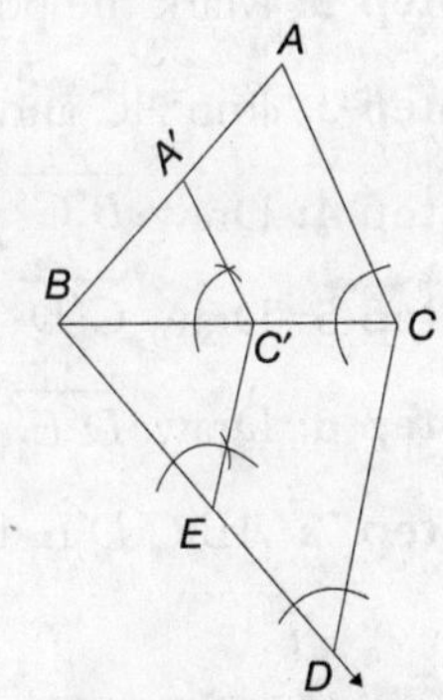

Figure 7.112

Proof: In ΔBCD, $\frac{BE}{BD} = \frac{5}{9}$ and $\overline{DC} \parallel \overline{EC'}$

$\therefore \Delta BEC' \sim \Delta BDC$

$\therefore \frac{BC'}{BC} = \frac{5}{9}$

In ΔBCA, $\frac{BC'}{BC} = \frac{5}{9}$ and $\overline{C'A'} \parallel \overline{CA}$

$\therefore \Delta BCA \sim \Delta BC'A'$

$\therefore \frac{BC'}{BC} = \frac{BA'}{BA} = \frac{A'C'}{AC} = \frac{5}{9}$

Construction 27: Construct a quadrilateral similar to a given quadrilateral $ABCD$ with its sides equal to $\left(\frac{6}{10}\right)$ th of the corresponding sides of $ABCD$.

Step 1: $ABCD$ is the given quadrilateral.

Step 2: Join BD.

Step 3: Draw $\overrightarrow{BX}$ which makes non zero angle with BD and X is 10 cm away from the point B.

Step 4: Mark the point Y on $\overrightarrow{BX}$ such that $BY = 6$ cm.

Step 5: Join XD.

Step 6: Draw $\overline{YD'}$ parallel to $\overline{XD}$ which meets BD at the point D'.

Step 7: Draw $\overline{D'A'}$ parallel to $\overline{DA}$ which meets $\overline{AB}$ at the point A'.

Step 8: Draw $\overline{D'C'}$ parallel to $\overline{DC}$ which meets $\overline{BC}$ at the point C'.

Step 9: $A'BC'D'$ is the required quadrilateral.

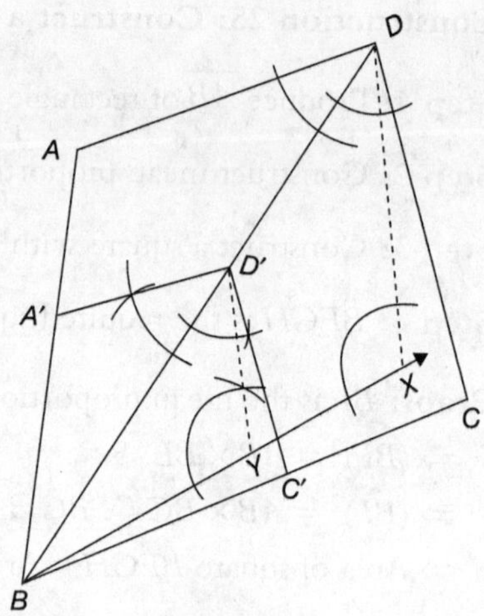

Figure 7.113

Construction 28: Construction of a pentagon similar to the given pentagon on a side of given length.

Step 1: $ABCDE$ is a given pentagon and $\overline{XY}$ is the given line segment.

Step 2: Mark the point B' on $\overline{AB}$ such that $AB' = XY$.

Step 3: Join AC and AD.

Step 4: Draw $\overline{B'C'}$ parallel to $\overline{BC}$ which meets $\overline{AC}$ at the point C'.

Step 5: Draw $\overline{C'D'}$ parallel to $\overline{CD}$ which meets $\overline{AD}$ at the point D'.

Step 6: Draw $\overline{D'E'}$ parallel to $\overline{DE}$ which meets AE at the point E'.

Step 7: $AB'C'D'E'$ is the required pentagon.

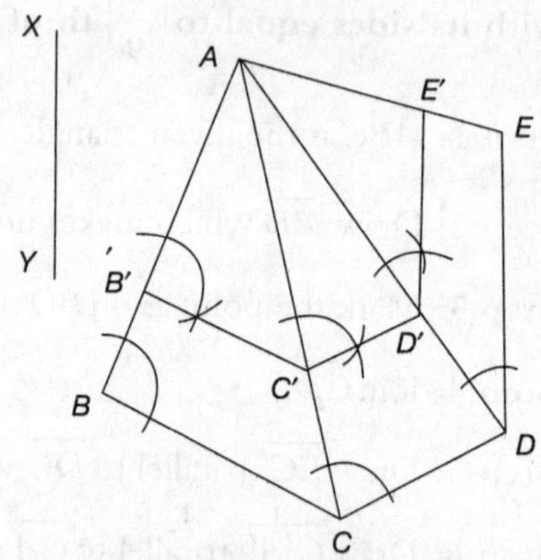

Figure 7.114

Locus

Mark a fixed point O on a sheet of paper. Now, start marking points P_1, P_2, P_3, P_4, … on the sheet of paper such that $OP_1 = OP_2 = OP_3 = \ldots = 4$ cm. What do we observe on joining these points by a smooth curve? We observe a pattern, which is circular in shape such that any point on the circle obtained is at a distance of 4 cm from the point O.

It can be said that whenever a set of points satisfying a certain condition are plotted, a pattern is formed. This pattern formed by all possible points satisfying the given condition is called the locus of points. In the above given example, we have a locus of points which are equidistant (4 cm) from the given point O.

The collection (set) of all points and only those points which satisfy certain given geometrical conditions is called **locus of a point.**

Alternatively, locus can be defined as the path or curve traced by a point in a plane when subjected to some geometrical conditions.

Basic Locus Theorem

Locus Theorem 1: The locus of the point in a plane which is at a constant distance 'r' from a fixed point 'O' is a circle with centre O and radius r units.

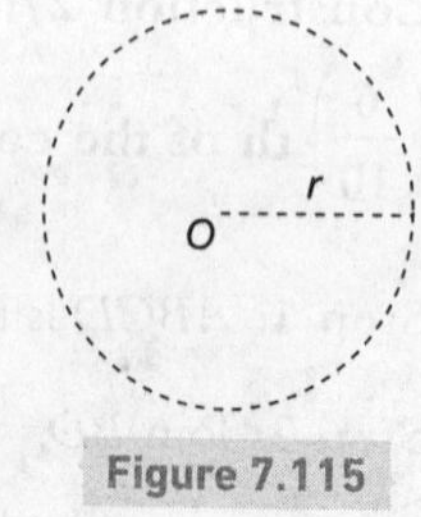

Figure 7.115

Locus Theorem 2: The locus of the point in a plane which is at a constant distance from a fixed straight line is a pair of lines, parallel to the fixed line. Let the fixed line be l. The lines m and n form the set of all points which are at a constant distance from l. The locus of a point in a plane, which is equidistant from a given pair of parallel lines is a straight line, parallel to the two given lines and lying midway between them.

In the given above, *m* and *n* are the given lines and line *l* is the locus.

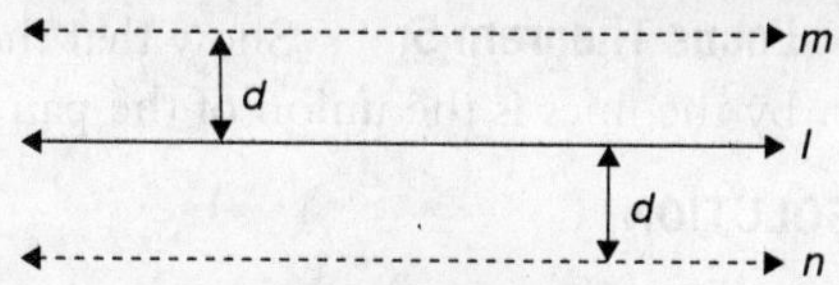

Figure 7.116

Locus Theorem 3: The locus equidistant from two parallel lines, m and n, is a line parallel to both m and n and halfway between them.

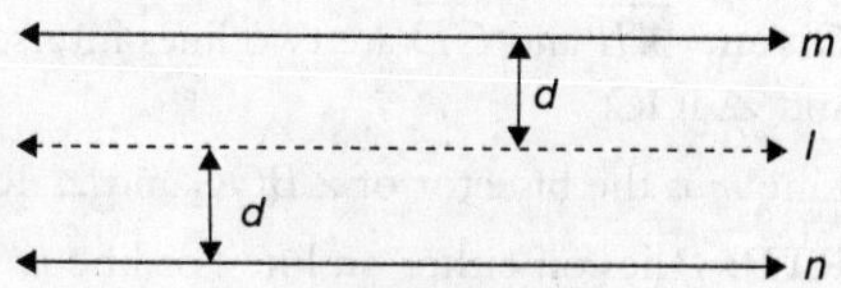

Figure 7.117

Locus Theorem 4: Show that the locus of a point equidistant from the end points of a line segment is the perpendicular bisector of the segment.

SOLUTION

The proof will be taken up in two steps:

Step 1: We, initially prove that any point equidistant from the end points of a line segment lies on the perpendicular bisector of the line segment.

Given: *M* and *N* are two points on a plane. *A* is a point in the same plane such that $AM = AN$.

RTP: A lies on the perpendicular bisector of *MN*.

Proof: Let *M* and *N* be the two fixed points in a plane.

Let *A* be a point such that $AM = AN$ and *L* be the mid-point of $\overline{MN}$.

If *A* coincides with *L*, then *A* lies on the bisector of *MN*.

Suppose *A* is different from *L*.

Then, in ΔMLA and ΔNLA,

$ML = NL$, $AM = AN$ and *AL* is a common side.

$\therefore$ By SSS congruence property, $\Delta MLA \cong \Delta NLA$.

$\Rightarrow \angle MLA = \angle NLA$ ($\because$ Corresponding elements of congruent triangles are equal) (1)

But $\angle MLA + \angle NLA = 180°$ ($\because$ They form a straight angle)

$\Rightarrow 2\angle MLA = 180°$ (using (1))

$\therefore \angle MLA = \angle NLA = 90°$

So, $\overline{AL} \perp \overline{MN}$ and hence $\overline{AL}$ is the perpendicular bisector of $\overline{MN}$.

$\therefore$ *A* lies on the perpendicular bisector of $\overline{MN}$.

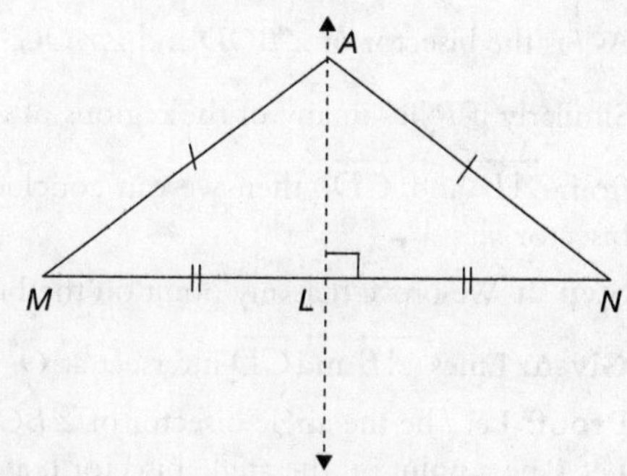

Figure 7.118

Step 2: Now, we prove that any point on the perpendicular bisector of the line segment is equidistant from the end points of the line segment.

Given: *MN* is a line segment and *P* is a point on the perpendicular bisector. *L* is the mid-point of *MN*.

RTP: $MP = NP$.

Proof: If *P* coincides with *L*, then $MP = NP$.

Suppose *P* is different from *L*. Then, in ΔMLP and *NLP*,

$ML = LN$

LP is the common side and

$\angle MLP = \angle NLP = 90°$

$\therefore$ By the SAS congruence property, $\Delta MLP \cong \Delta NLP$.

So, $MP = PN$ ($\because$ The corresponding elements of congruent triangles are equal)

$\therefore$ Any point on the perpendicular bisector of $\overline{MN}$ is equidistant from the points *M* and *N*.

Hence, from the steps 1 and 2 of the proof it can be said that the locus of the point equidistant from two fixed points is the perpendicular bisector of the line segment joining the two points.

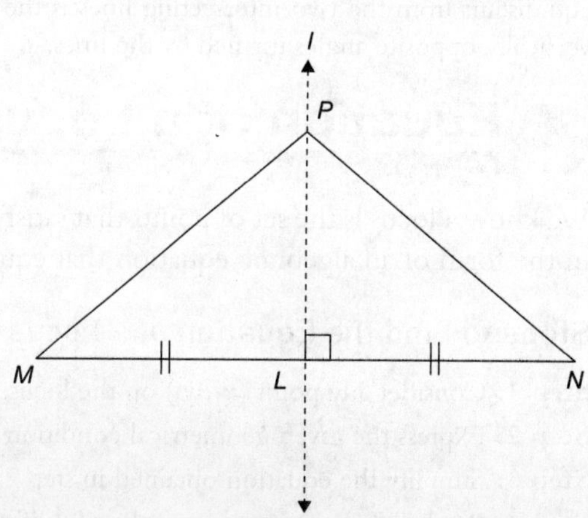

Figure 7.119

Locus Theorem 5: Show that the locus of a point equidistant from two intersecting lines in the plane determined by the lines is the union of the pair of lines bisecting the angles formed by given lines.

SOLUTION

Step 1: We initially prove that any point equidistant from two given intersecting lines lies on one of the lines bisecting the angles formed by given lines.

Given: $\overleftrightarrow{AB}$ and $\overleftrightarrow{CD}$ are two lines intersecting at O. P is the point on the plane such that $PM = PN$. Line l is the bisector of $\angle BOD$ and $\angle AOC$.

Line m is the bisector of $\angle BOC$ and $\angle AOD$.

RTP: P lies on either on line l or line m.

Proof: In ΔPOM and ΔPON, $PM = PN$,

OP is a common side and $\angle PMO = \angle PNO = 90°$

$\therefore$ By RHS congruence property, $\Delta POM \cong \Delta PON$.

So, $\angle POM = \angle PON$, i.e., P lies on the angle bisector of $\angle BOD$.

As l is the bisector of $\angle BOD$ and $\angle AOC$, P lies on the line l.

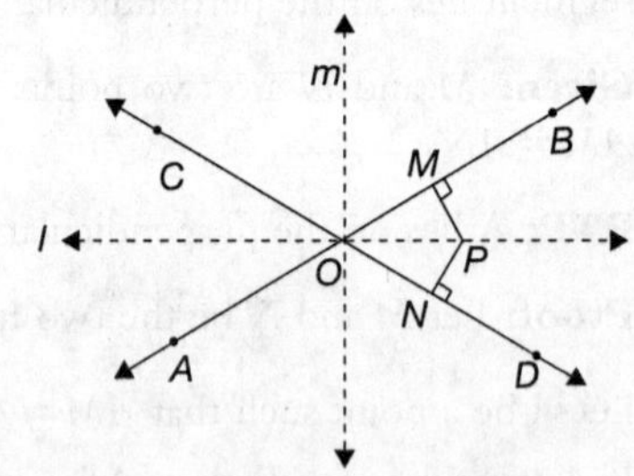

Figure 7.120

Similarly if P lies in any of the regions of $\angle BOC$, $\angle AOC$, or $\angle AOD$, such that it is equidistant from $\overleftrightarrow{AB}$ and $\overleftrightarrow{CD}$, then we can conclude that P lies on the angle bisector l or on the angle bisector m.

Step 2: We prove that any point on the bisector of one of angles formed by two intersecting lines is equidistant from the lines.

Given: Lines $\overleftrightarrow{AB}$ and $\overleftrightarrow{CD}$ intersect at O. Lines l and m are the angle bisectors.

Proof: Let l be the angle bisector of $\angle BOD$ and $\angle AOC$, and m be the angle bisector of $\angle BOC$ and $\angle AOD$.

Let P be a point on the angle bisector l, as shown in the figure.

If P coincides with O, then P is equidistant from the line $\overline{AB}$ and $\overline{CD}$.

Suppose P is different from O.

Draw the perpendiculars $\overline{PM}$ and $\overline{PN}$ from the point P onto the lines $\overline{AB}$ and $\overline{CD}$, respectively.

Then in ΔPOM and ΔPON, $\angle POM = \angle PON$, $\angle PNO = \angle PMO = 90°$ and OP is a common side.

$\therefore$ By the AAS congruence property $\Delta POM \cong \Delta PON$

So, $PN = PM$ ($\because$ Corresponding sides), i.e.,

P is equidistant from the lines $\overleftrightarrow{AB}$ and $\overline{CD}$.

Hence, from the steps 1 and 2 of the proof it can be said that the locus of the point which is equidistant from the two intersecting lines is the pair of the angle bisectors of the two pairs of vertically opposite angles formed by the lines.

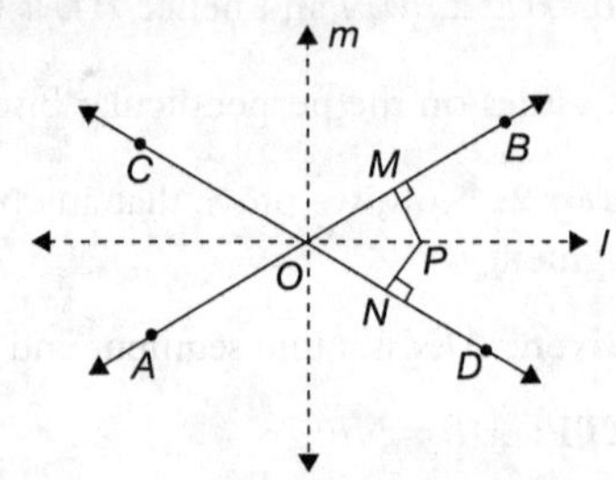

Figure 7.121

Equation of a Locus

We know a locus is the set of points that satisfy a given geometrical condition. When we express the geometrical condition in the form of an algebraic equation that equation is called the equation of the locus.

Steps to Find the Equation of a Locus

Step 1: Consider any point (x_1, y_1) on the locus.

Step 2: Express the given geometrical condition in the form of an equation using x_1 and y_1.

Step 3: Simplify the equation obtained in step 2.

Step 4: Replace (x_1, y_1) by (x, y) in the simplified equation obtained in step 3, which gives the required equation of the locus.

The following formulae will be helpful in finding the equation of a locus.

1. Distance between two points $A(x_1, y_1)$ and $B(x_2, y_2)$ is $AB = \sqrt{(x_2 - x_1)^2 + (y_2 - y_1)^2}$.
2. Area of the triangle formed by joining the points (x_1, y_1), (x_2, y_2) and (x_3, y_3) is $\frac{1}{2}\begin{vmatrix} x_1 - x_2 & x_2 - x_3 \\ y_1 - y_2 & y_2 - y_3 \end{vmatrix}$, where the value of $\begin{vmatrix} a & b \\ c & d \end{vmatrix} = ad - bc$.
3. Equation of the circle with centre (a, b) and radius r is given by $(x - a)^2 + (y - b)^2 = r^2$.
4. The perpendicular distance from a point $P(x_1, y_1)$ to a given line $ax + by + c = 0$ is $\left|\frac{ax_1 + by_1 + c}{\sqrt{a^2 + b^2}}\right|$.

EXAMPLE 7.15 Find the equation of the locus of a point that forms a triangle of area 5 units with the points $A(2, 3)$ and $B(-1, 4)$.

SOLUTION:

Let $P(x_1, y_1)$ be point on the locus, $(x_2, y_2) = (2, 3)$ and $(x_3, y_3) = (-1, 4)$

Given area of ΔPAB = 5 sq. units.

$$\therefore \frac{1}{2}\begin{vmatrix} x_1 - 2 & 2-(-1) \\ y_1 - 3 & 3-4 \end{vmatrix} = 5$$

$$\begin{vmatrix} x_1 - 2 & 3 \\ y_1 - 3 & -1 \end{vmatrix} = 10$$

$-(x_1 - 2) - 3(y_1 - 3) = \pm 10$

$x_1 + 3y_1 + 11 = \pm 10$

Required equation is $x + 3y = 10 - 11$ or $x + 3y = -10 - 11$

$\therefore x + 3y + 1 = 0$ or $x + 3y + 21 = 0$.

Euclid's Geometry

Euclidean geometry can be defined as the study of geometry (especially for the shapes of geometrical figures) which is attributed to the Alexandrian mathematician Euclid who has explained in his book on geometry which is known as Euclid's Elements of Geometry.

POINTS TO REMEMBER

- ✔ In an equilateral triangle, the centroid, the ortho-centre, the circum-centre, and the incentre all coincide.
- ✔ In an isosceles triangle, the centroid, the ortho-centre, the circum-centre, and the incentre all lie on the median to the base.
- ✔ In a right triangle, the length of the median drawn to the hypotenuse is equal to half of the hypotenuse. The median is also equal to the circum-radius. The mid-point of the hypotenuse is the circum-centre.
- ✔ In an obtuse-angled triangle, the circum-centre and ortho-centre lie outside the triangle. for an acute-angled triangle, the circum-centre and the ortho-centre lie inside the triangle.
- ✔ For all triangles, the centroid and the in-centre lie inside the triangle.
- ✔ For all triangles, the ex-centre lies outside the triangle.

PRACTICE QUESTIONS CLASSROOM WING

Very Short Answer Type Questions

Directions of questions from 1 to 22:
Fill in the blanks.

1. The distance between the centres of two circles with radii 4 cm and 5 cm is 10 cm. The length of their direct common tangent is ______ (in cm).
2. The distance between the centres of two circles with radii 3 cm and 5 cm is 8 cm. The length of their transverse common tangent is ________ cm.
3. In the following figure, $PT = 4$ cm, $TQ = 6$ cm and $RT = 3$ cm, then $TS =$ ______.

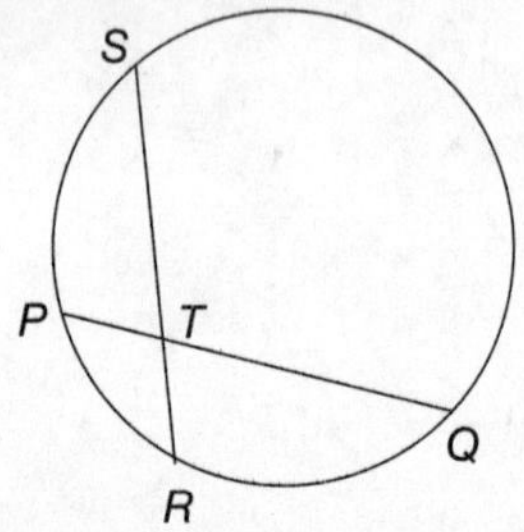

4. If two circles touch each other externally, then the number of transverse common tangents is ______.
5. In the following figure, to find $\angle PQR$, ______ must be given. ($\angle PRQ/\angle QPT/\angle RPT$)

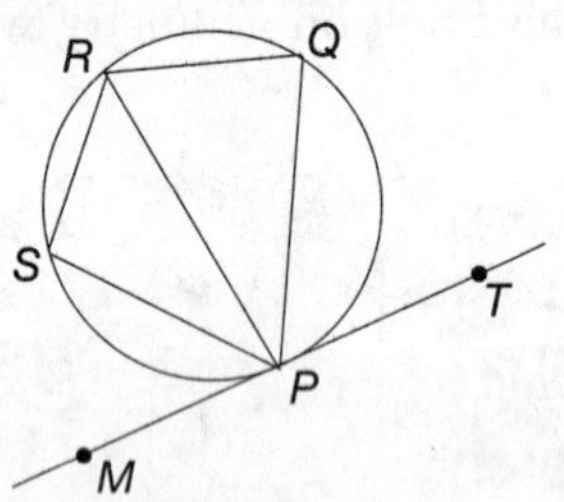

6. From a point P which is at a distance of 13 cm from the centre of the circle of radius 5 cm, a tangent is drawn to the circle. The length of the tangent is ______.
7. Distance between two circles with radii R and r is d units. If $d^2 = R^2 + r^2$ then the two circles ______ (intersect at one point/do not intersect/intersect at two distinct points).
8. Two circles with radii r_1 and r_2 touch externally. The length of their direct common tangent is ______.
9. In a circle, angle made by an arc in the major segment is 60°. Then the angle made by it in the minor segment is ______.
10. If a trapezium is cyclic, then its ______ are equal. (parallel sides/oblique sides)
11. In a circle, two chords PQ and RS bisect each other. Then $PRQS$ is ______.
12. The locus of the tip of a seconds hand of a watch is a ______.
13. If the length of an enlarged rectangle is 12 cm and the scale factor is $\frac{3}{2}$, then the length of the original rectangle is ______.
14. Centroid divides the median from the vertex in the ratio ______.
15. Any point on the perpendicular bisector of a line segment joining two points is ______ from the two points.
16. ______ is the locus of a point in a plane which is at a distance of p units from the circle of radius q units ($p \neq q$).
17. If A and B are two fixed points, then the locus of a point P, such that $\angle APB = 90°$ is ______.
18. The locus of the point equidistant (in a plane) from the three vertices of a triangle is ______.
19. The locus of the point in a plane which is equidistant from two intersecting lines is ______.
20. The line segment joining the vertex of a triangle and the mid-point of its opposite side is called ______.
21. The locus of the centre of the circles (in a plane) passing through two given points is the ______ of the line segment joining the two points.
22. If the altitude of an equilateral triangle is 6 units, then the radius of its incircle is ______.

Directions of questions from 23 to 35:
State whether the following statements are true or false

23. There are no congruent figures which are similar. (True/False)
24. Two triangles with measures 3 cm, 4 cm, 5 cm and 0.60 cm, 0.8 cm, 1 cm are similar. (True/False)

25. A triangle is formed by joining the mid-points of the sides of a given triangle. This process is continued indefinitely. All such triangles formed are similar to one another. (True/False)

26. All the similar figures are congruent if their areas are equal. (True/False)

27. The ratio of corresponding sides of two similar triangles is 2 : 3, then the ratio of the perimeters of two triangles is 4 : 9. (True/False)

28. Which of the following is/are true?

(a) All triangles are similar.

(b) All circles are similar.

(c) All squares are similar.

29. Two equal chords of a circle are always parallel. (True/False)

30. In the following figure, $AD = DB$ and $DE \parallel BC$, then $AE = EC$. (True/False)

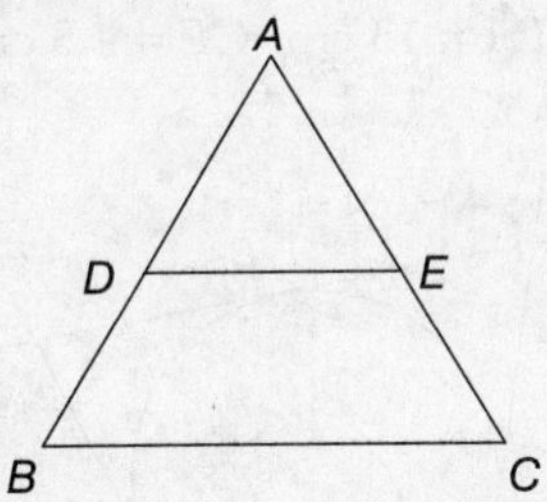

31. In the following figure, $ST \parallel QR$, then $\Delta PST \sim \Delta PQR$. (True/False)

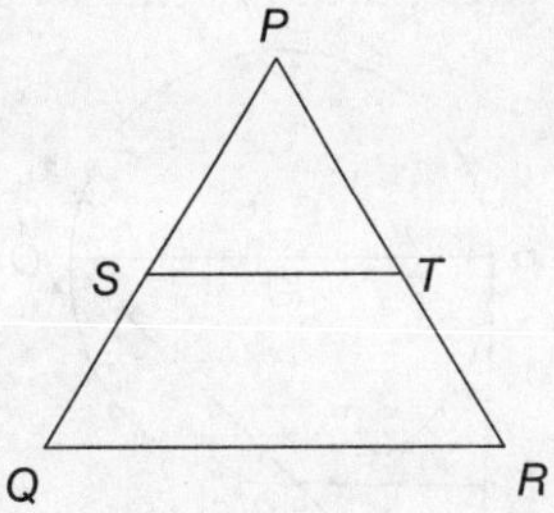

32. A line drawn from the centre of a circle to a chord always bisects it. (True/False)

33. Line joining the centers of two intersecting circles always bisect their common chord. (True/False)

34. A parallelogram has no line of symmetry. (True/False)

35. Is the statement 'In ΔABC, a point equidistant from AB and AC lies on the median', true?

Short Answer Type Questions

Directions of questions from 36 to 57:
Answer the following questions.

36. In the given figure (not to scale), PQ || BC and AQ:QC = 3:2. If PQ = 15 cm, then find the length of BC (in cm).

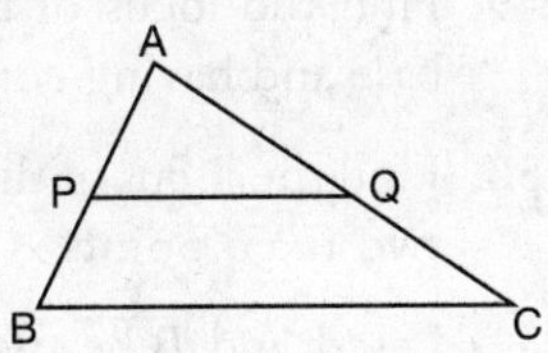

37. In the given figure (not to scale), AD is the bisector of ∠A. If AB:AC = 3:4 and BC = 21 cm, then find the length of BD (in cm).

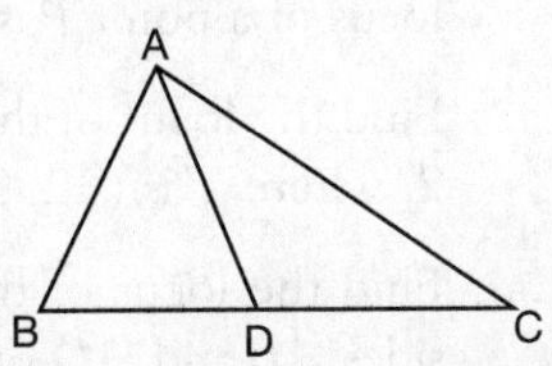

38. In ΔABC, D is a point on AC such that BD ⊥ AC. If ∠ABC = 90°, AB = 15 cm and BC = 36 cm, then find the length of BD (in cm).

39. In ΔPQR, A and B are two points on PQ and PR, respectively, such that AB || QR. If PA = $2x + 3$, AQ = $6x - 16$ and PB:BR = 3:4, then what will be the value of x?

40. The chords RQ and TS of a circle are produced to meet at P. If PQ = 6 cm, QR = 9 cm, and PS = 5 cm, then find the length of ST (in cm).

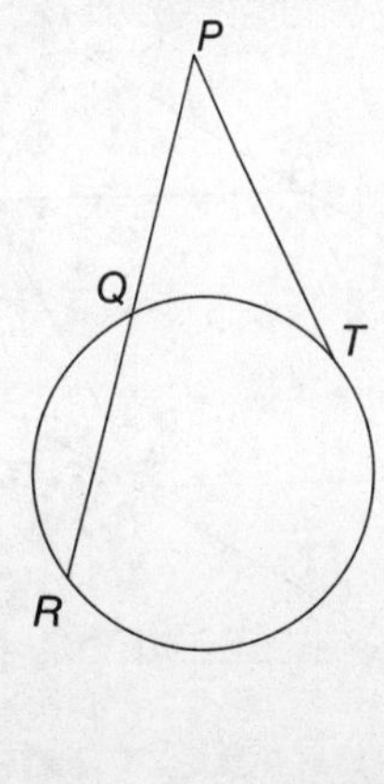

41. In the following figure, PQ is the diameter of the circle with radius 5 cm. If AT is the tangent and equal to the radius of the circle, then find the length of AR.

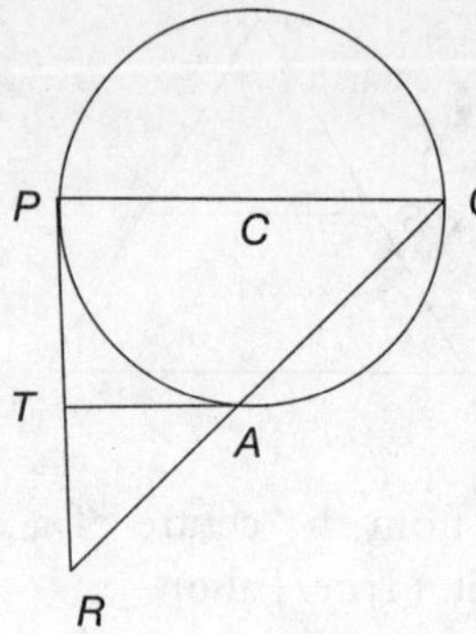

42. The distance between two buildings is 24 m. The height of the buildings are 12 m and 22 m. Find the distance between the tops.

43. Find the distance between the centres of the two circles, if their radii are 11 cm and 7 cm, and the length of the transverse common tangent is $\sqrt{301}$ cm.

44. In the figure given along side, AB is the diameter of the circle, C is the centre of the circle and CQR is an isosceles triangle, such that $CQ = QR$. Prove that $\angle DCA = 3 \cdot \angle QCR$.

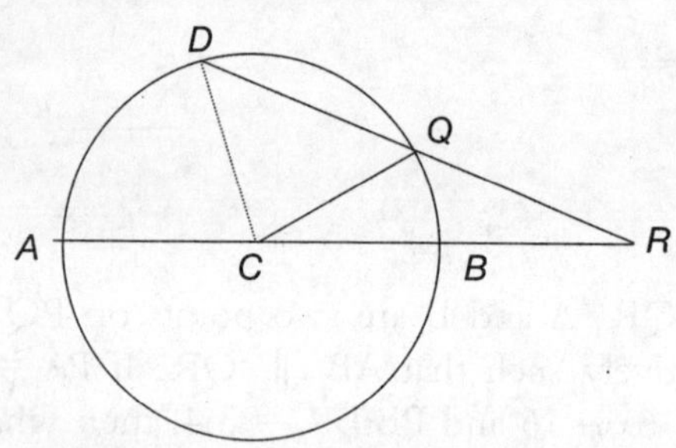

45. In the following figure, $PQRS$ is a rhombus formed by joining the mid-points of a quadrilateral $YMXN$, show that $3PQ^2 = SN^2 + NR^2 + QX^2 + XR^2 + PY^2 + YS^2$.

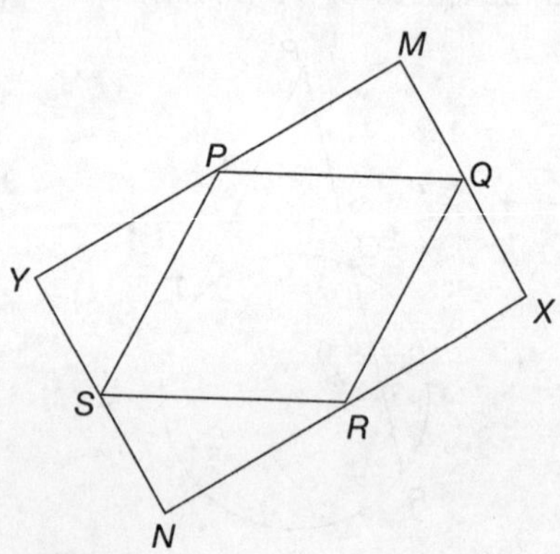

46. Find the locus of a point which is at a distance of 5 units from $(-1, -2)$.

47. In the following figure, PR and SQ are chords, of the circle with centre O, intersecting at T and $TQ = x$; $TP = y$.

Show that $(TS + TR) : (TS - TR) = (x + y) : (y - x)$.

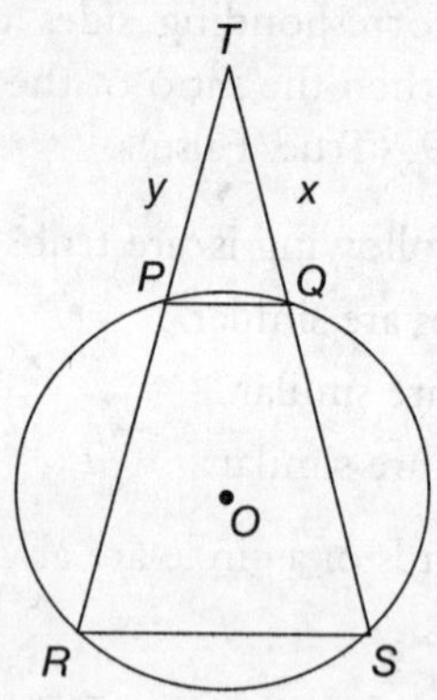

48. In the given figure, PA, PB, EC and ED are tangents to the circle. If $PA = 13$ cm, $CE = 4.5$ cm and $FE = 9$ cm, then find PF.

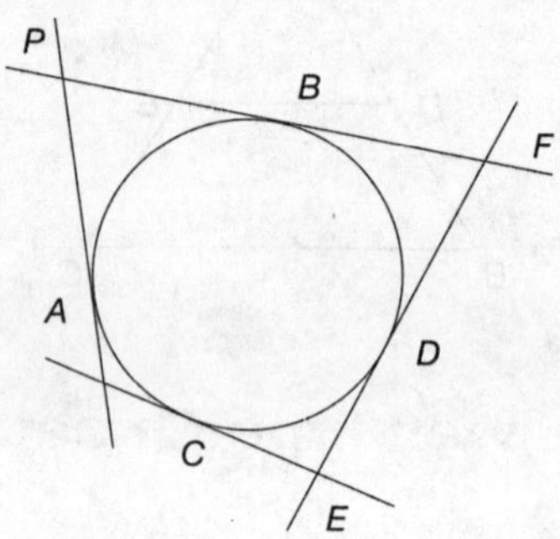

49. Find the locus of the vertex of a triangle with fixed base and having constant area.

50. Find the locus of the centre of a circle passing through two fixed points A and B.

51. Let A and B be two fixed points in a plane. Find the locus of a point P, such that $PA^2 + PB^2 = AB^2$.

52. Find the locus of the point P, such that $TP : MP = 3 : 2$, where T is $(-2, 3)$ and M is $(4, -5)$.

53. Find the locus of the point which is equidistant from sides AB and AD of a rhombus $ABCD$.

54. In the following figure (not to scale), ABC is a right isosceles triangle, right-angled at B and $\overline{BD} \perp \overline{AC}$. If the triangle ABC is rotated about the hypotenuse, then find the locus of the triangle ABC.

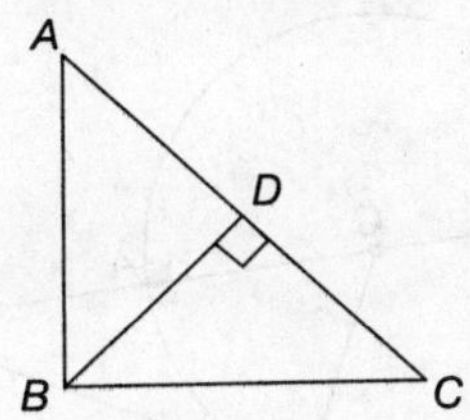

55. Show that the locus of a point, equidistant from three distinct given collinear points in a plane does not exist.

56. Find the locus of the point which is equidistant from the sides AB and AC of triangle ABC.

57. (A) ΔAPQ, ΔBPQ and ΔCPQ are three isosceles triangles with the same base PQ. Show that the points A, B and C are collinear.

(B) In the figure, P, Q and R are the midpoints of BC, CA and AB of ΔABC respectively. If $\angle BPR = \angle APR$ and $PB = 15$ cm, and $CQ = 12$ cm, find the length of AB.

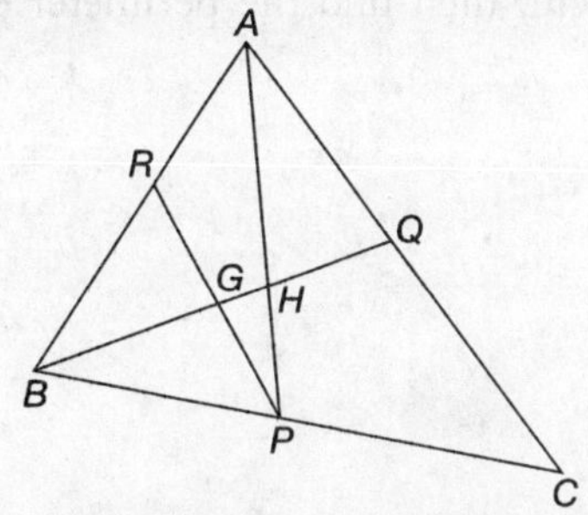

Essay Type Questions

58. In the following figure (not to scale), ABCD is rectangle, if AB = 20 cm, BC = 12 cm, and AF: FE = 3:2, then find the length of FE (in cm).

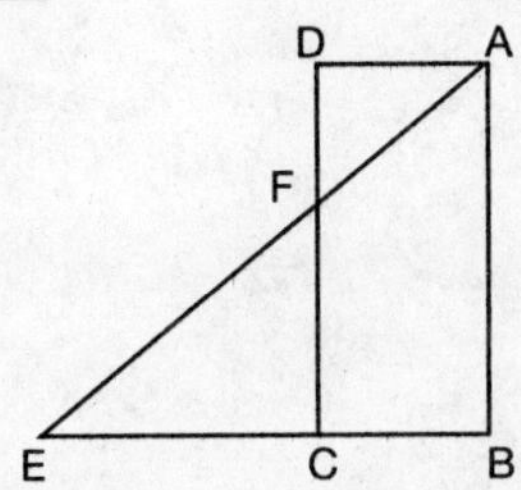

59. In the given figure (not to scale), 'O' is the centre of the circle, and AB and PC are the tangents to the circle at A and P, respectively. If $\angle$PAB = 40°, then find the measure of $\angle$PCA.

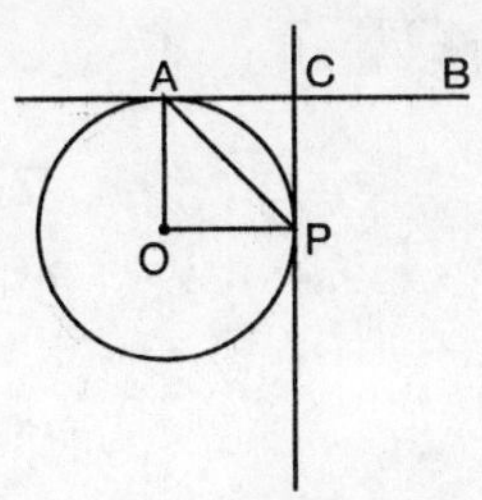

60. In the given figure (not to scale), ABCD is a square of side 10 cm. If CE = 15 cm, then find the length of FE (in cm).

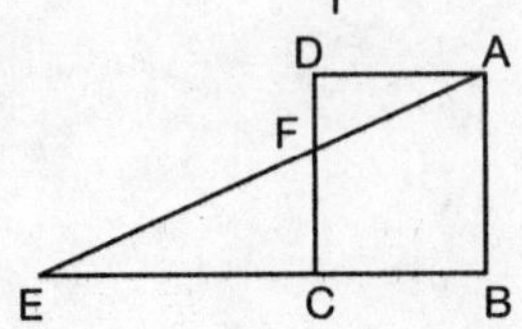

61. In the given figure (not to scale), AB = 3 cm and CD = 4 cm. The perimeter of the quadrilateral ABCD (in cm) is ________.

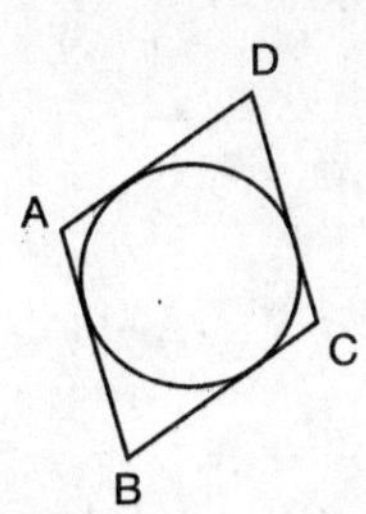

62. In the given figure (not to scale), 'O' is the centre of the circle, and PA and PB are the tangents to the circle at A and B, respectively. If $\angle$OAB = 25°, then find the measure of $\angle$APB.

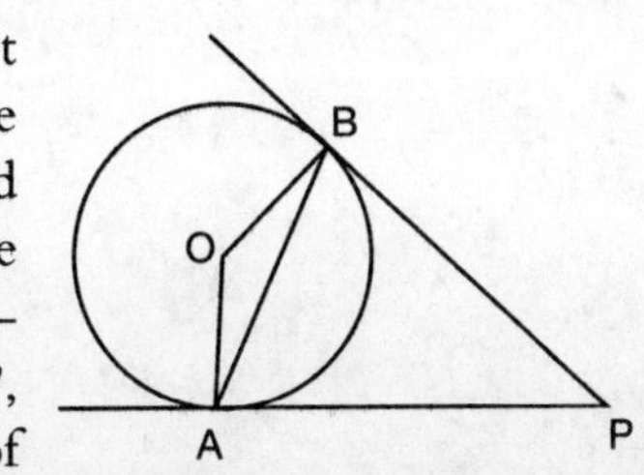

63. If $P(x, y)$ and $Q(1, 4)$ are the points on the circle whose centre is $C(5, 7)$, then find the locus of P.

64. If two lines intersect at P at right angles and pass through $A(1, 1)$ and $B(1, 0)$, respectively then what is the locus of P?

65. If P is a point on the circle with AB as a diameter, where A and B are $(0, 2)$ and $(2, 4)$ respectively, then what is the locus of P ?

66. In the figure, $KP \perp LM$. If $\angle KQM$ is an obtuse angle, then prove that

(i) $KM^2 > KQ^2 + QM^2$.

(ii) $KL^2 < LQ^2 + KQ^2$.

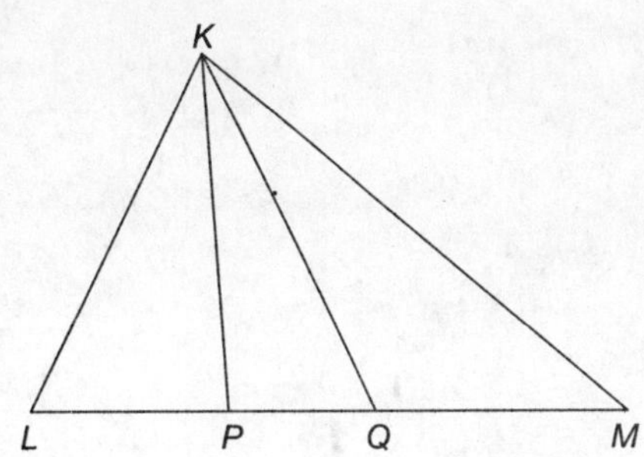

67. The distance between the centres of two circles is 10 cm. The radii of two circles are 9 cm and 3 cm. $\overline{ABP}$ is the common tangent touches the circles at A and B. $\overline{PQCRS}$ is a straight line, where C is the centre of the smaller circle. If $PB = 3$ cm, find the length of

(i) PA.	(ii) PQ.

68. In the given figure, PQ is a tangent at Q, $\overline{CQ} \,||\, \overline{BR}$ and PB is a secant of the circle and is passing through C, the centre of the circle. If $PA = 8$ cm, and $PQ = 12$ cm, then find the perimeter of the triangle PBR.

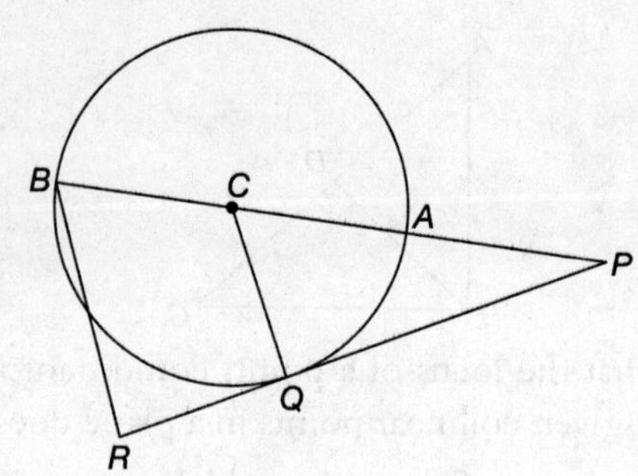

PRACTICE QUESTIONS COMPETITION WING

Level 1: Apply Your Concepts

Directions of questions from 1 to 5: **Fill in the blanks.**

1. Number of circles that pass through three collinear points is ______.

2. In the following figure, $\angle ABC = 90°$, $BC = 10$ cm, $CD = 6$ cm, then $AD =$ ______.

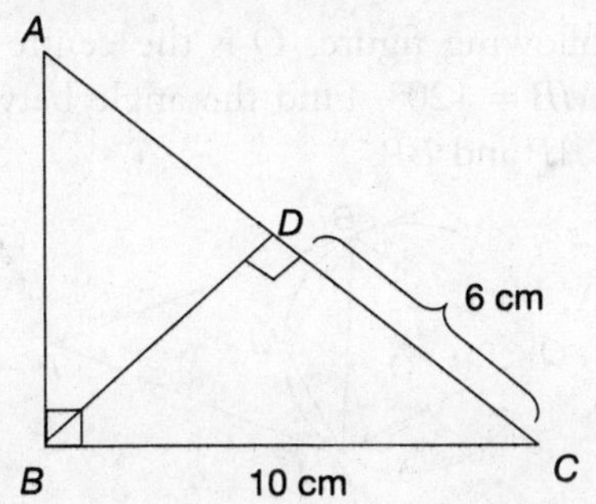

3. In the following figure (not to scale), if $BC = 20$ cm and $\angle BAD = \angle CAD$, then $BD =$ ______.

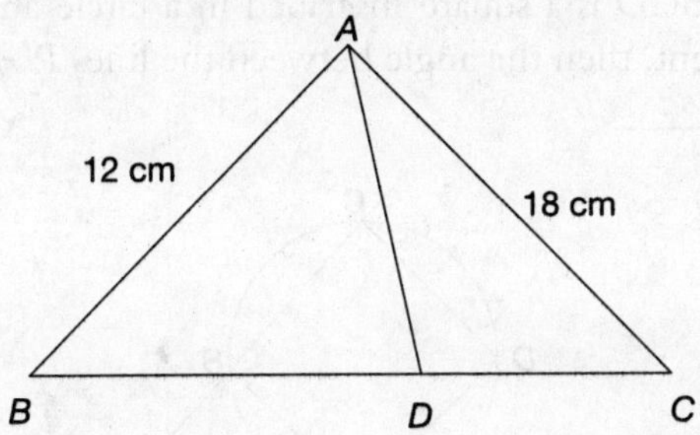

4. The number of tangents drawn from an external point to a circle is ______.

5. If two circles intersect at two distinct points, then the number of common tangents is ______.

Directions of questions from 6 to 49: **Select the correct alternative from the given choices.**

6. In the given figure (not to scale), PA : AQ = 1:3 and $\overline{AB} \parallel \overline{QR}$. If QR = 10 cm, then find the length of AB (in cm).

(a) 2.5
(b) 3
(c) 3.5
(d) 4

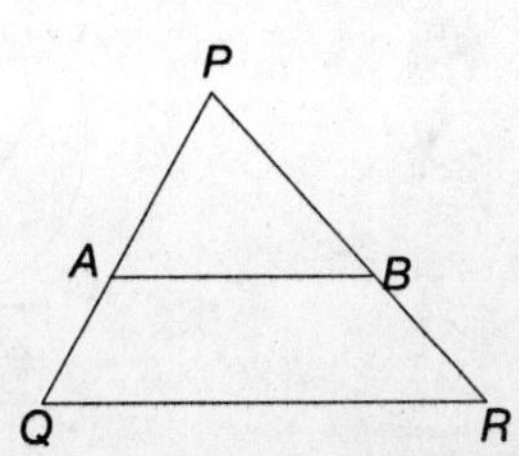

7. In the given figure (not to scale), AD is the bisector of ∠A. If AB = 9 cm, AC = 12 cm, and BC = 14 cm, then find the length of CD (in cm).

(a) 7
(b) 6
(c) 8
(d) 9

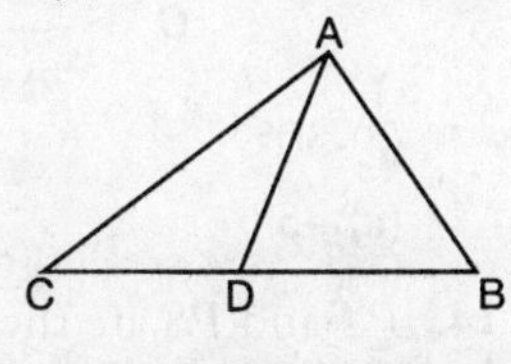

8. In ΔABC, D is a point on AC such that BD ⊥ AC. If ∠ABC = 90°, AB = 15 cm, and BD = 12 cm, then find the length of BC (in cm).

(a) 20 (b) 18
(c) 16 (d) 25

9. In ΔABC, P and Q are on AB and AC, respectively, such that PQ ∥ BC. If AP = $3x - 2$, PB = $2x + 7$ and AQ:QC = 2:3, then the value of x is ______.

(a) 16 (b) 3
(c) 6 (d) 4

10. In the given figure (not to scale), PT is a tangent to the circle at T. PQR is a straight line. If PT = 12 cm and QR = 7 cm, then find the length of PQ (in cm).

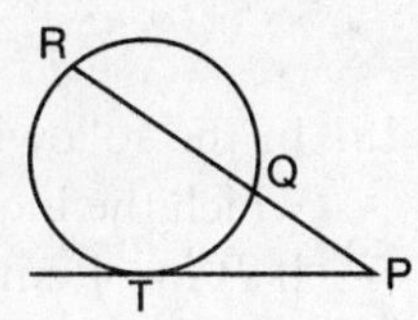

(a) 8 (b) 9
(c) 10 (d) 16

11. A man travels on a bicycle, 10 km east from the starting point *A* to reach point *B*, then he cycles 15 km south to reach point *C*. Find the shortest distance between *A* and *C*.

(a) 25 km (b) 5 km
(c) $25\sqrt{13}$ km (d) $5\sqrt{13}$ km

12. In the following figure, O is the centre of the circle. If $\angle BAC = 60°$, then $\angle OBC =$ ______.

(a) 120° (b) 30°
(c) 40° (d) 60°

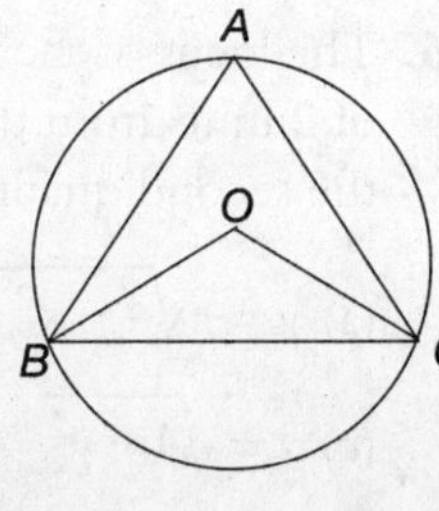

13. In the following figure (not to scale), $AB = CD$ and $\overline{AB}$ and $\overline{CD}$ are produced to meet at the point P. If $\angle BAC = 70°$, then find $\angle P$.

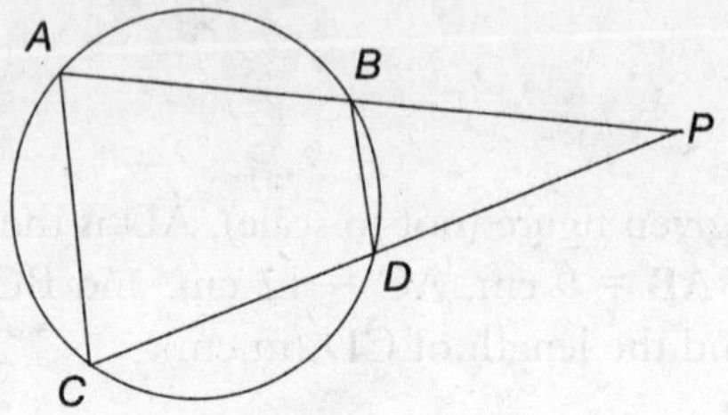

(a) 30° (b) 40°
(c) 45° (d) 50°

14. PT and PS are the tangents to the circle with centre O. If $\angle TPS = 65°$, then $\angle OTS =$ ______.

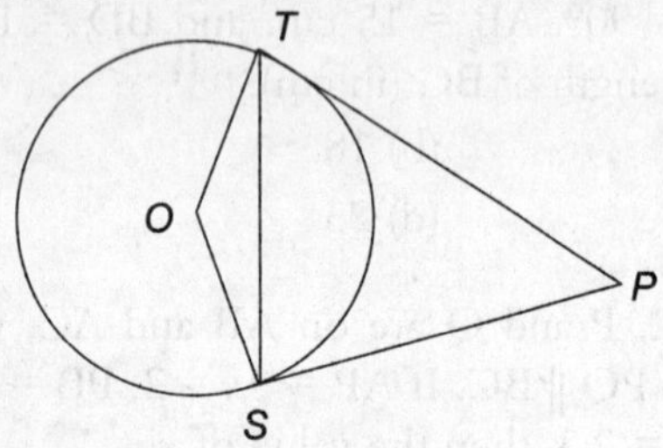

(a) 32° (b) 45°
(c) $57\frac{1}{2}°$ (d) $32\frac{1}{2}°$

15. In the following figure X, Y, and Z are the points at which the incircle touches the sides of the triangle. If $PX = 4$ cm, $QZ = 7$ cm, and $YR = 9$ cm, then the perimeter of triangle PQR is,

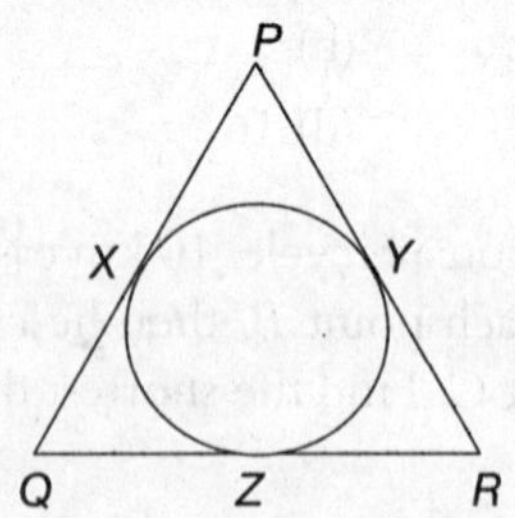

(a) 20 cm (b) 46 cm
(c) 40 cm (d) 80 cm

16. The locus of the point P which is at a constant distance of 2 units from the origin and which lies in the first or the second quadrants is ______.

(a) $y = -\sqrt{4 - x^2}$ (b) $y = \sqrt{4 - x^2}$
(c) $x = \sqrt{4 - y^2}$ (d) $x = -\sqrt{4 - y^2}$

17. If PAB is a triangle in which $\angle B = 90°$ and $A(1, 1)$ and $B(0, 1)$, then the locus of P is ______.

(a) $y = 0$ (b) $xy = 0$
(c) $x = y$ (d) $x = 0$

18. In the following figure, if the angle between two chords AB and AC is 65°, then the angle between two tangents which are drawn at B and C is ______.

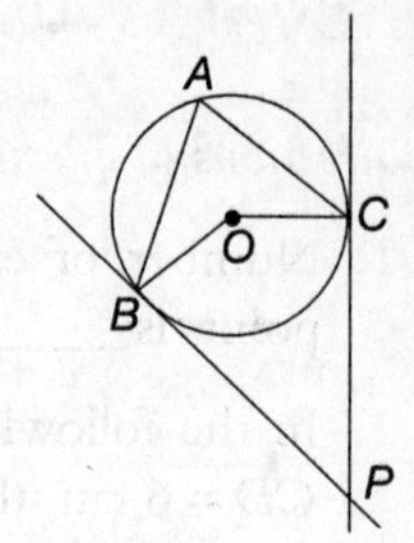

(a) 50° (b) 30°
(c) 60° (d) 40°

19. In the following figure, O is the centre of the circle and $\angle AMB = 120°$, Find the angle between the two tangents AP and BP.

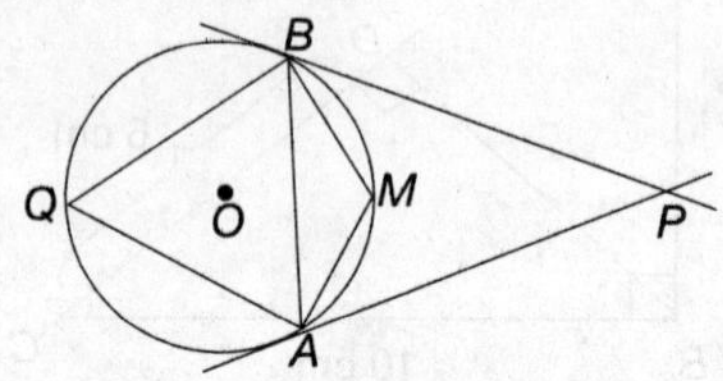

(a) 30° (b) 45°
(c) 70° (d) 60°

20. If $ABCD$ is a square inscribed in a circle and PA is a tangent, then the angle between the lines $P'A$ and $P'B$ is ______.

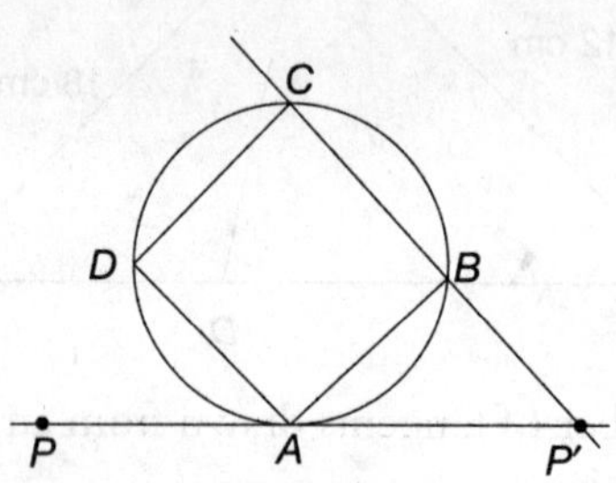

(a) 30° (b) 20°
(c) 40° (d) 45°

21. In the following figure, if l and m are two tangents and AB is a chord making an angle of 60° with the tangent l, then the angle between l and m is ______.

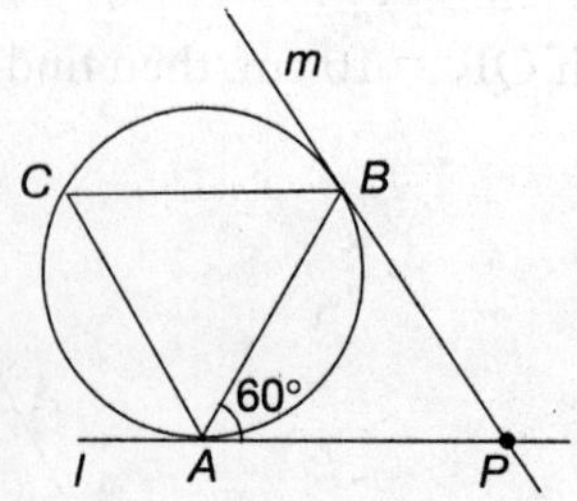

(a) 45° (b) 30°
(c) 60° (d) 90°

22. Find the length of a transverse common tangent of the two circles whose radii are 3.5 cm, 4.5 cm and the distance between their centres is 10 cm.
(a) 36 cm (b) 6 cm
(c) 64 cm (d) 8 cm

23. If *ABCD* is a trapezium, *AC* and *BD* are the diagonals intersecting each other at point *O*. Then *AC* : *BD* = ______.
(a) $AB : CD$ (b) $AB + AD : DC + BC$
(c) $AO^2 : OB^2$ (d) $AO - OC : OB - OD$

24. In the following figure (not to scale), $\overline{PA}$ and $\overline{PB}$ are equal chords and *ABCD* is a cyclic quadrilateral. If $\angle DCE = 80°$, $\angle DAP = 30°$, then find $\angle APB$.

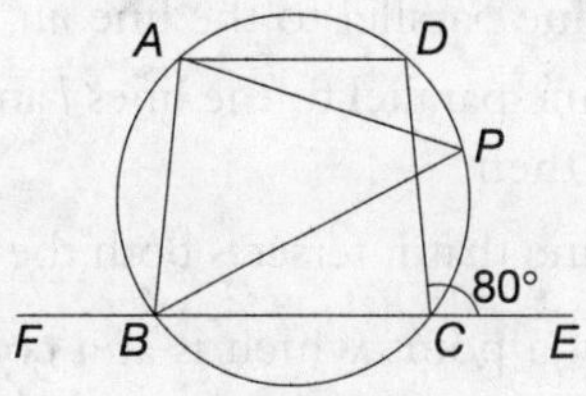

(a) 40° (b) 80°
(c) 90° (d) 160°

25. In trapezium *KLMN*, *KL* and *MN* are parallel sides. A line is drawn, from the point *A* on *KN*, parallel to *MN* meeting *LM* at *B*. *KN* : *LM* is equal to ______.
(a) *KL* : *NM*
(b) (*KL* + *KA*) : (*NM* + *BM*)
(c) (*KA* – *AN*) : (*LB* – *BM*)
(d) $KL^2 : MN^2$

26. In the following figure, *ABCD* is a square and *AED* is an equilateral triangle. Find the value of *a*.

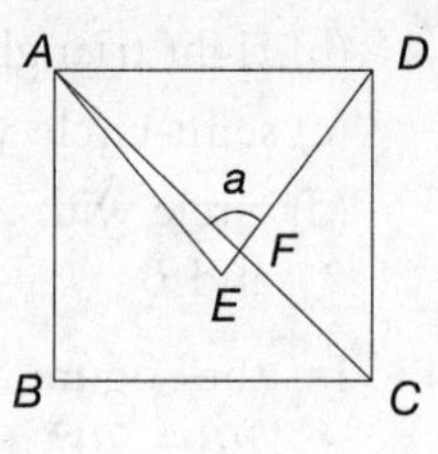

(a) 30° (b) 45°
(c) 60° (d) 75°

27. A circle with centre O is inscribed in a quadrilateral *ABCD* as shown in the figure. Which of the following statements is/are true?

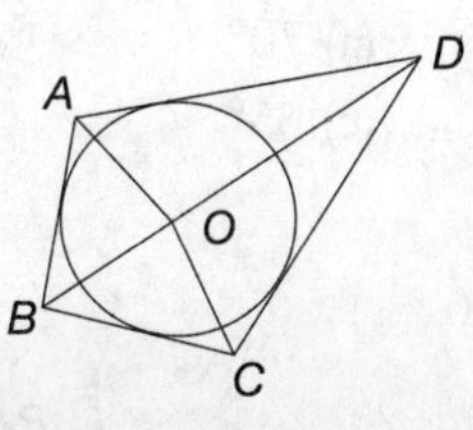

(A) $\angle AOD + \angle BOC = 180°$
(B) $\angle AOB$ and $\angle COD$ are complementary.
(C) *OA*, *OB*, *OC* and *OD* are the angle bisectors of $\angle A$, $\angle B$, $\angle C$, and $\angle D$, respectively.

(a) Both (A) and (B)
(b) Both (B) and (C)
(c) Both (A) and (C)
(d) All the three

28. In the following figure, O is the centre of the circle and if $\angle OAB = 30°$, then the acute angle between *AB* and the tangent *PQ* at *B* is ______.

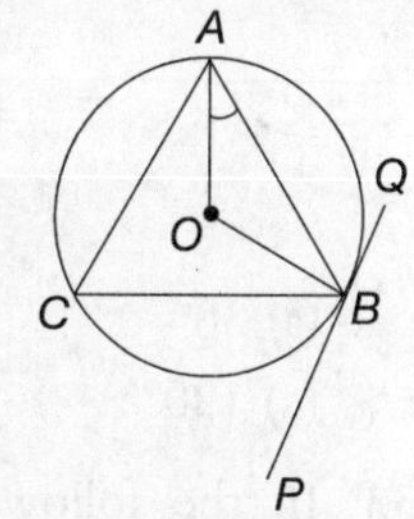

(a) 30° (b) 60°
(c) 45° (d) 90°

29. In the following figure, *AB* = *OB* and *CT* is the tangent to the circle at *O*. If $\angle COA = 125°$, then $\angle OAB$ is ______.

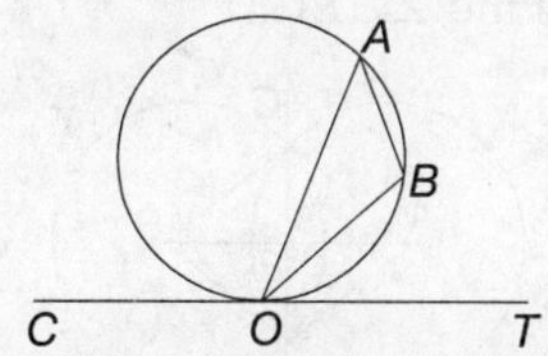

(a) 55° (b) $27\frac{1}{0}°$
(c) $82\frac{1}{2}°$ (d) 45°

30. *AR* and *BS* are the tangents to the circle, with centre *O*, touching at *P* and *Q*, respectively and *PQ* is the chord. If $\angle OQP = 25°$, then $\angle RPQ =$ ______.

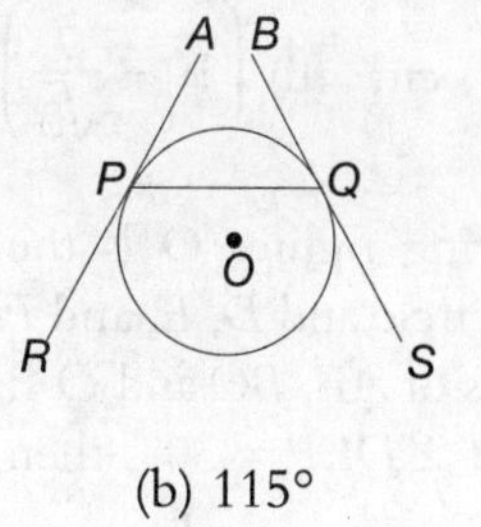

(a) 100° (b) 115°
(c) 150° (d) 90°

31. In the diagram, if $\angle BCP' = \angle ABQ = 60°$, then the triangle *ABC* is ______.

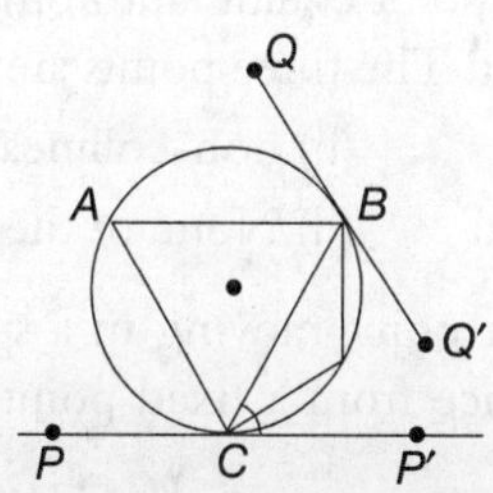

(a) scalene (b) equilateral
(c) right angled (d) acute angled

32. In the following figure, AQ is a tangent to the circle at A. If $\angle ACB = 60°$, then $\angle BAQ =$ ______.

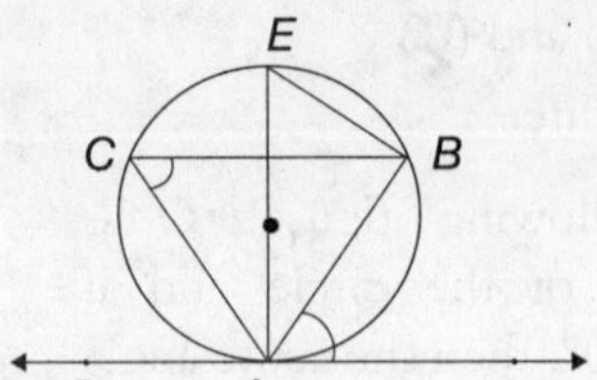

(a) 30° (b) 60°
(c) 120° (d) 45°

33. In the following figure, two circles X and Y with centres A and B respectively intersect at C and D. The radii AC and AD of circle X are tangents to the circle Y. Radii BC and BD of circle Y are tangents to the circle X. Find $\angle AEC$.

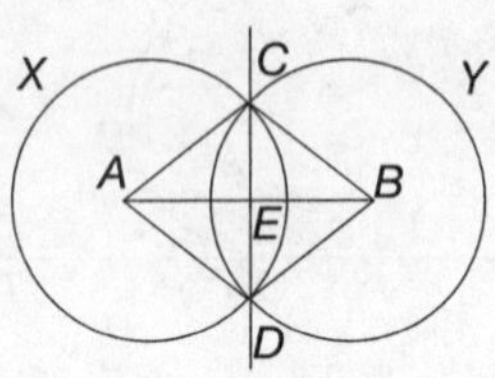

(a) 45° (b) 60°
(c) 90° (d) Cannot be determined

34. The tangent AB touches a circle, with centre O, at the point P. If the radius of the circle is 5 cm, $OB = 10$ cm and $OB = AB$, then find AP.
(a) $5\sqrt{5}$ cm (b) $10\sqrt{5}$ cm
(c) $(10 - 5\sqrt{3})$ cm (d) $\left(10 - \frac{5}{\sqrt{3}}\right)$ cm

35. In the following figure, O is the centre of the circle and D, E, and F are mid-points of AB, BO and OA, respectively. If $\angle DEF = 30°$, then find $\angle ACB$.

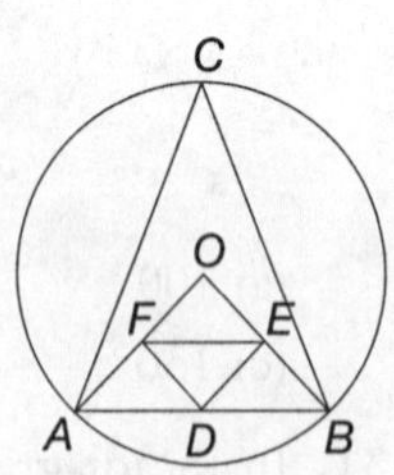

(a) 30° (b) 60°
(c) 90° (d) 120°

36. The locus of a point equidistant from three fixed points is a single point. The three points are ______.
(a) collinear (b) non-collinear
(c) coincidental (d) None of these

37. The locus of a point moving in a space which is at a constant distance from a fixed point in space is called a ______.
(a) square (b) sphere
(c) circle (d) triangle

38. The locus of the centre of the circle that touch a given circle internally is a ______.
(a) straight line (b) hellix
(c) circle (d) None of these

39. In ΔABC, $\angle A = \angle B + \angle C$, then the circum-centre is at ______.
(a) A (b) B
(c) C (d) the mid-point of BC

40. The locus of a point equidistant from three points does not exist. This implies that the three points are ______.
(a) collinear (b) non-collinear
(c) coincidental (d) None of these

41. The locus of a point which is equidistant from two non-intersecting lines l and m is a ______.
(a) straight line parallel to the line l
(b) straight line parallel to the line m
(c) straight line parallel to the lines l and m and midway between them
(d) straight line that intersects both the lines l and m

42. The locus of a point which is at a constant distance k from Y-axis is ______.
(a) $x = \pm k$ (b) $y = \pm k$
(c) $x = 0$ (d) $y = 0$

43. The locus of the centre of a wheel rolling on a straight road is a ______.
(a) concentric circle (b) straight line
(c) curve path (d) parabola

44. If A and B are two fixed points, then the locus of a point P, such that $PA^2 + PB^2 = AB^2$ is a/an ______.
(a) circle with AB as the diameter
(b) right triangle with $\angle P = 90°$
(c) semi-circle with AB as the diameter
(d) circle with AB as the diameter, excluding points A and B

45. In the figure, $\overline{RX} \perp \overline{PA}$, $\overline{RY} \perp \overline{PB}$, $RX = RY$ and $\angle APB = 70°$. Find $\angle APQ$.
(a) 70° (b) 140°
(c) 35° (d) 50°

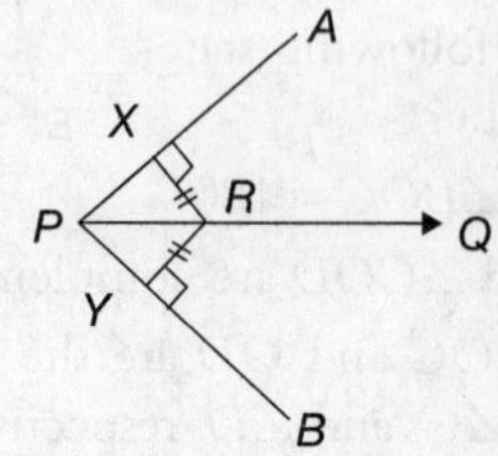

46. Consider a point M inside a quadrilateral $PQRS$. If M be the point of intersection of angle bisectors PE and QF, then ______.

(a) M is nearer to $\overline{PS}$ than to $\overline{QR}$

(b) M is equidistant from opposite sides $\overline{PS}$ and $\overline{QR}$

(c) M is nearer to $\overline{QR}$ than to $\overline{PS}$

(d) M is equidistant from opposite sides $\overline{PQ}$ and $\overline{SR}$

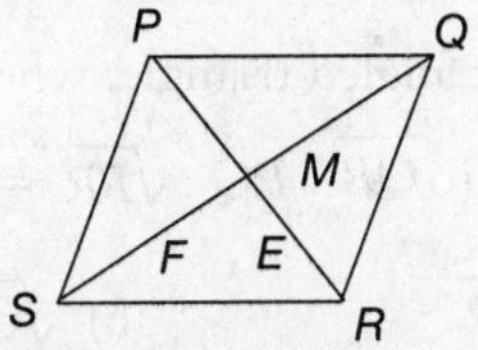

47. The locus of the point which is equidistant from the three lines determined by the sides of a triangle is ______.

(a) the in-centre (b) the ex-centre

(c) the ortho-centre (d) either (a) or (b)

48. Find the locus of any fixed point on the circumference of a coin when the coin is rolling on a straight path.

(a) Circle (b) Straight line

(c) Sphere (d) Helix

49. The locus of a point which is equidistant from the coordinate axes can be a ______.

(a) line making a non-zero intercept on X-axis

(b) line making a non-zero intercept on Y-axis

(c) line passing through the origin making an angle of 45° with X-axis

(d) None of the above

Level 2: Review Your Concepts

50. In the figure given below, ABC is an equilateral triangle and $PQRS$ is a square of side 6 cm. By how many cm² is the area of the triangle more than that of the square?

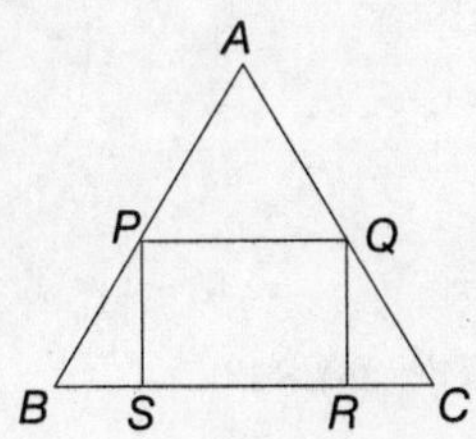

(a) $\frac{21}{\sqrt{3}}$ (b) 21

(c) $21\sqrt{3}$ (d) 63

51. In the following figure (not to scale) $ABCD$ is a rectangle, BC = 24 cm, DP = 10 cm and CD = 15 cm. Then, AQ and CQ, respectively, are ______.

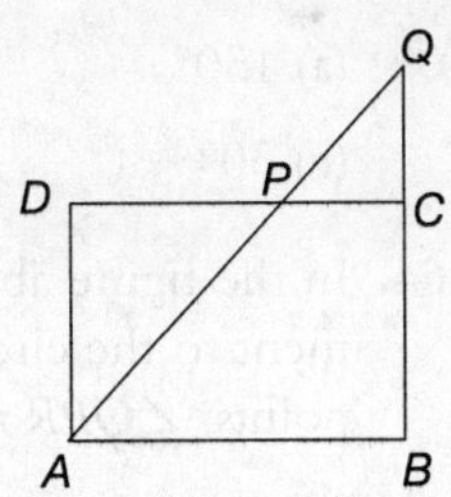

(a) 39 cm, 13 cm

(b) 13 cm, 12 cm

(c) 25 cm, 13 cm

(d) 39 cm, 12 cm

52. At a particular time, the shadow cast by a tower is 6 m long. If the distance from top of the tower to the end of the shadow is 10 m long, determine the height of the tower.

(a) 4 m (b) 8 m

(c) 16 m (d) 12 m

53. In the following figure, $\angle ABC = 90°$, $AD = 15$ and $DC = 20$. If BD is the bisector of $\angle ABC$, what is the perimeter of the triangle ABC?

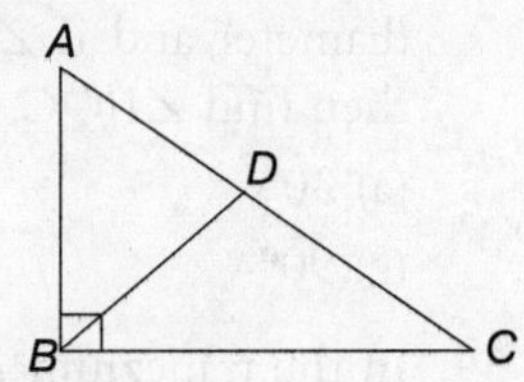

(a) 74 (b) 84

(c) 91 (d) 105

54. In the triangle ABC, $\angle ABC$ or $\angle B = 90°$. $AB : BD : DC = 3 : 1 : 3$. If $AC = 20$ cm, then what is the length of AD (in cm)?

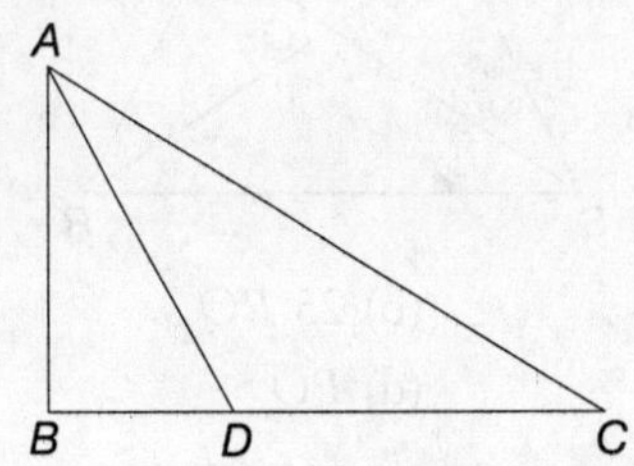

(a) $5\sqrt{2}$ (b) $6\sqrt{3}$

(c) $4\sqrt{5}$ (d) $4\sqrt{10}$

55. In the following figure, find AD.

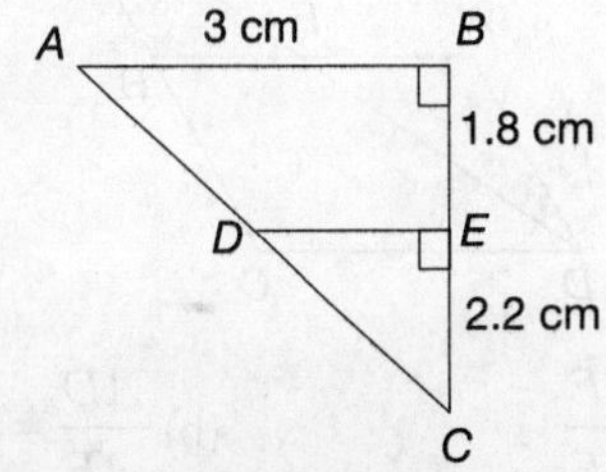

(a) 1.8 cm (b) 2.25 cm

(c) 2.2 cm (d) 1.85 cm

56. In the given figure, AB is a diameter, O is the centre of the circle and $\angle OCB = 50°$, then find $\angle DBC$.

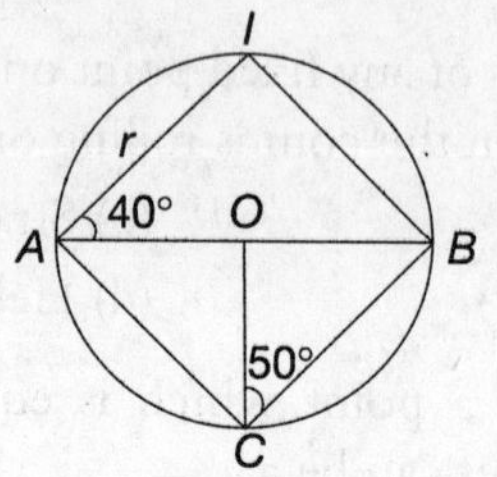

(a) 80° (b) 100°
(c) 120° (d) 140°

57. In the following figure, O is the centre of the circle and AD is the diameter. If $\angle ACB = 135°$, then find $\angle DOB$.

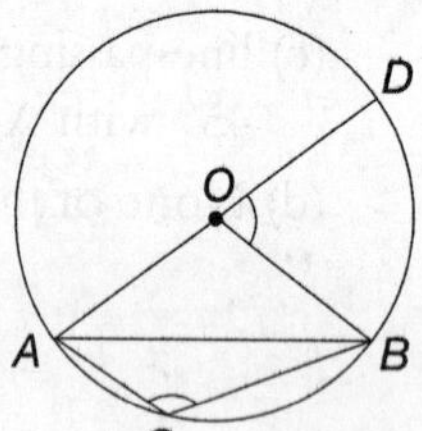

(a) 135° (b) 60°
(c) 90° (d) 45°

58. In the following figure, O is the centre of the circle, AC is the diameter and if $\angle APB = 120°$, then find $\angle BQC$.

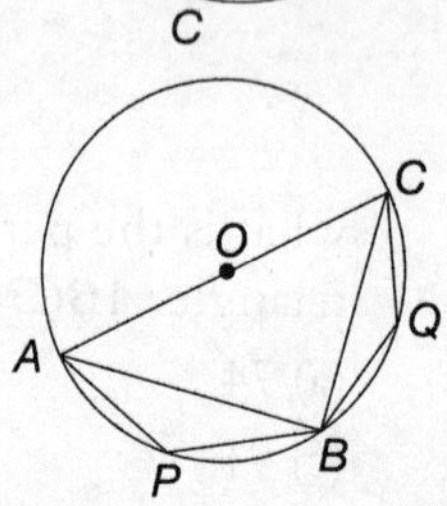

(a) 30° (b) 150°
(c) 90° (d) 120°

59. In the trapezium $PQRS$, PQ is parallel to RS and the ratio of the areas of the triangle POQ to triangle ROS is 225 : 900. Then SR = ______.

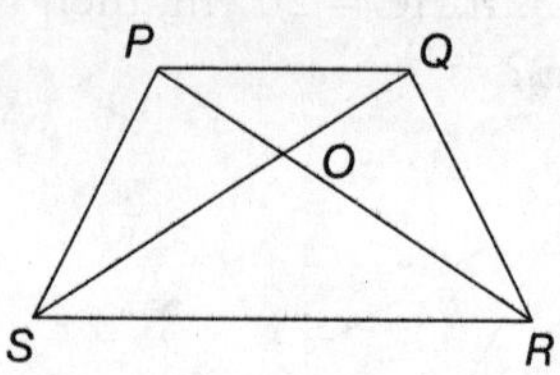

(a) 30 PQ (b) 25 PQ
(c) 2 PQ (d) PQ

60. In the following figure, $ABCD$ is a parallelogram, CB is extended to F and the line joining D and F intersect AB at E. Then ______.

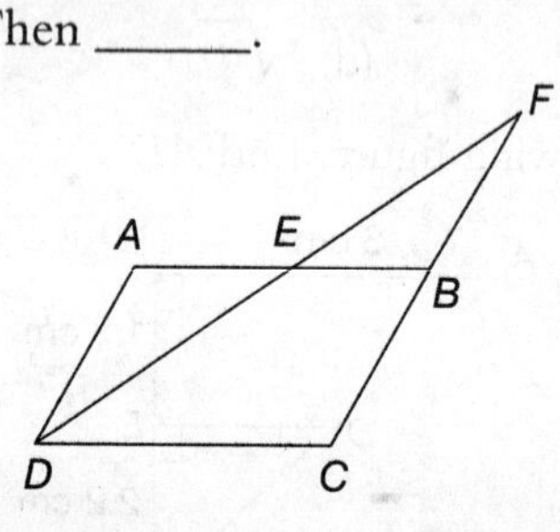

(a) $\frac{AD}{AE} = \frac{BF}{BE}$ (b) $\frac{AD}{AE} = \frac{CF}{CD}$
(c) $\frac{BF}{BE} = \frac{CF}{CD}$ (d) All of these

61.

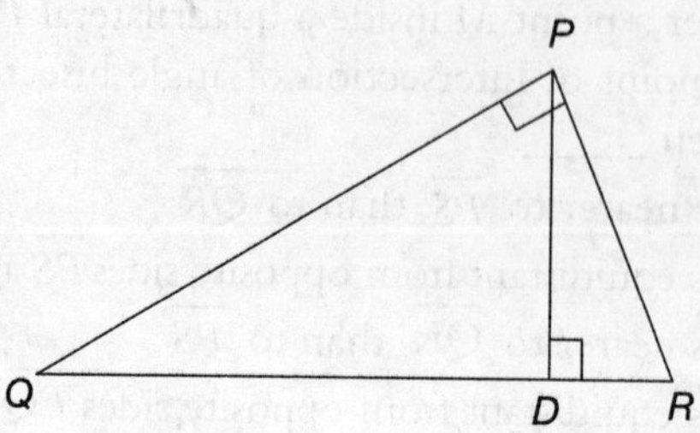

PQR is a right angled triangle, where $\angle P = 90°$. $\overline{PD}$ is perpendicular to $\overline{QR}$. $PQ : \sqrt{PR}$ = ______.

(a) $QD : \sqrt{DR}$ (b) $\sqrt{QD} : \sqrt{DR}$
(c) $QD^2 : \sqrt{RD^2}$ (d) None of these

62. Two circles intersect at two points P and S. QR is a tangent to the two circles at Q and R. If $\angle QSR = 72°$, then $\angle QPR$ = ______.

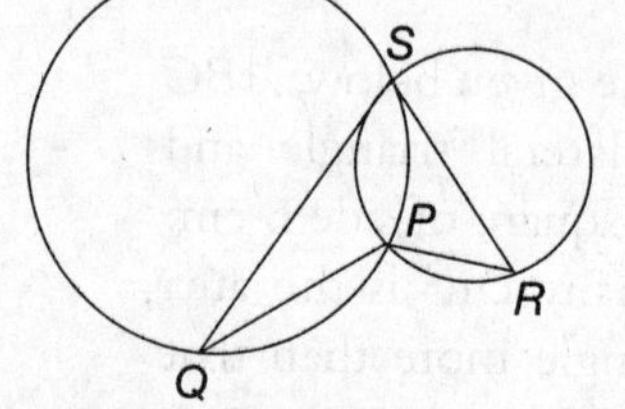

(a) 84° (b) 96°
(c) 102° (d) 108°

63. An equilateral triangle CDE is constructed on a side CD of square $ABCD$. The measure of $\angle AEB$ can be ______.

(a) 150° (b) 45°
(c) 30° (d) 20°

64. In the figure above (not to scale), PQ is a tangent segment to the circle at P. If P, R, S, and T are concyclic points, $\angle QPR = 40°$ and $PR = RQ$, then find $\angle PTS$.

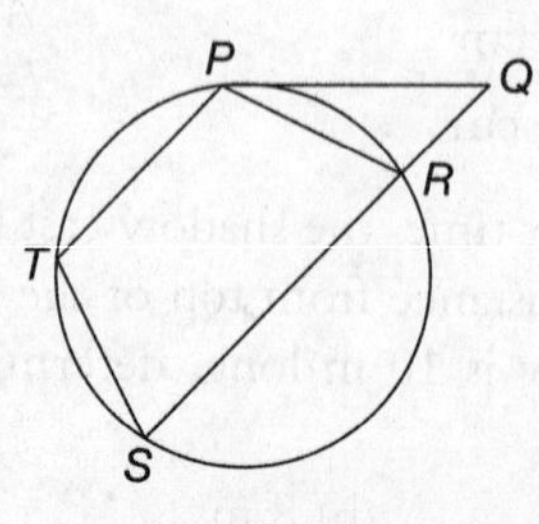

(a) 80° (b) 100°
(c) 60° (d) 120°

65. Construct the incircle of a given triangle ABC. The following sentences are the steps involved in the above construction. Arrange them in sequencial order from first to left.

(A) Draw perpendicular $\overline{IM}$ from I onto $\overline{BC}$.

(B) Taking I as centre and IM as the radius, draw a circle.

(C) Draw a $DABC$ with the given measurements.

(D) Draw bisectors of two of the angles, say $\angle B$ and $\angle C$ to intersect at I.

(a) DCAB (b) CDAB
(c) CADB (d) DACB

66. In the figure following figure, O is the centre of the circle and $\overline{AL} \perp \overline{MN}$. If $\angle AOB = 90°$, then find $\angle AOP$.

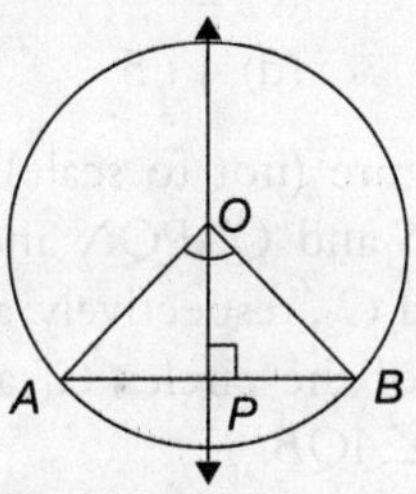

(a) 60° (b) 20°
(c) 30° (d) 45°

67. The solid formed when a right triangle is rotated about one of the sides containing the right angle is a ______.

(a) prism (b) cylinder
(c) cone (d) sphere

68. In the figure (not to scale), $AB = AC$ and $BD = CD$. Find $\angle ADB$.

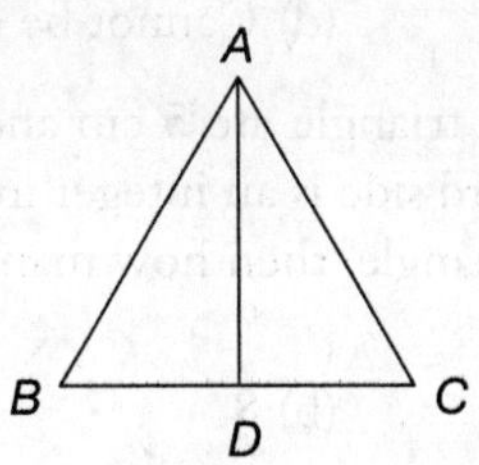

(a) 60° (b) 90°
(c) 120° (d) Cannot be determined

69. If PAB is a triangle of area 4 sq. units and A is (2, 5) and B is (3, 4), then part of the locus of P is ______.

(a) $x - y + 15 = 0$
(b) $x - y - 15 = 0$
(c) $x + y - 15 = 0$
(d) $x + y + 15 = 0$

70. Given, triangle PBC and parallelogram $ABCD$ lie between the same parallel lines. On the same base, BC and the area of parallelogram is 2 sq. units. The points B and C are (2, 4) and (4, 4), respectively. Which of the following lines is a part of the locus of P?

(a) $y = 4$ (b) $y = 7$
(c) $y = 5$ (d) $y = 6$

71. If PAB is a triangle in which $\angle B = 90°$ and $A(1, 1)$ and $B(0, 1)$, then the locus of P is ______.

(a) $y = 0$ (b) $xy = 0$
(c) $x = y$ (d) $x = 0$

72. The locus of P whose distance from the X-axis is thrice the distance from the line $x = 5$ is ______.

(a) $x - y - 5 = 0$
(b) $3x - y - 15 = 0$
(c) $3x + y + 15 = 0$
(d) $x + y + 5 = 0$

73. Two of the vertices of a triangle ABC are $A(1, 1)$, $B(-1, -3)$ and the area of ΔABC is 6 sq. units. If P is the centroid of the ΔABC, then find the locus of P.

(a) $2x - y + 1 = 0$ (b) $2x - y - 3 = 0$
(c) $2x + y + 3 = 0$ (d) Both (a) and (b)

74. In a circle with radius 25 cm, what is the area of the region determined by the locus of the mid-points of chords of length 48 cm?

(a) 154 cm^2 (b) 254 cm^2
(c) 72 cm^2 (d) None of these

75. The locus of a rectangle, when the rectangle is rotated about one of its sides, is a ______.

(a) plane (b) sphere
(c) cone (d) cylinder.

76. If the ortho-centre of a triangle ABC is B, then which of the following is true?

(a) $AC^2 = AB^2 + BC^2$
(b) $AC^2 > AB^2 + BC^2$
(c) $AC^2 < AB^2 + BC^2$
(d) None of these

77. In ΔABC, $\angle A = \angle B + \angle C$. The point which is equidistant from A, B, and C is ______.

(a) mid-point of AB
(b) mid-point of AC
(c) mid-point of BC
(d) None of these

Level 3: Assess Your Concepts

78. Side of a square $PQRS$ is 4 cm long. $\overline{PR}$ is produced to the point M such that $PR = 2RM$. Find SM.

(a) $\sqrt{10}$ cm (b) $\sqrt{5}$ cm

(c) $2\sqrt{5}$ (d) $2\sqrt{10}$ cm

79. ABC is an equilateral triangle of side 6 cm. If a circle of radius 1 cm is moving inside and along the sides of the triangle, then locus of the centre of the circle is an equilateral triangle of side ________.

(a) 5 cm (b) 4 cm

(c) $(6 - 2\sqrt{3})$ cm (d) $(3 + \sqrt{3})$ cm

80. In the following figure (not to scale), STM and MQ are tangents to the circle at T and Q respectively. SRQ is a straight line. $SR = TR$ and $\angle TSR = 25°$. Find $\angle QMT$.

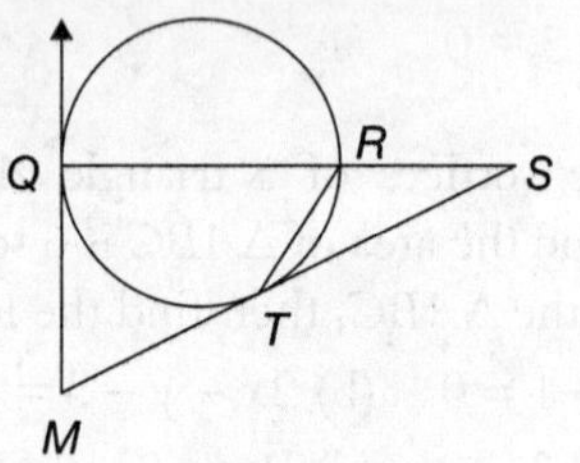

(a) 55° (b) 60°

(c) 75° (d) 80°

81. PQ is the direct common tangent of two circles (S, 9 cm) and (R, 4 cm) which touch each other externally. Find the area of the quadrilateral $PQRS$. (in cm^2)

(a) 72 (b) 65

(c) 78 (d) 69

82. Diagonal AC of a rectangle $ABCD$ is produced to the point E such that $AC : CE = 2 : 1$. $AB = 8$ cm and $BC = 6$ cm. Find the length of DE.

(a) $2\sqrt{19}$ cm (b) 15 cm

(c) $3\sqrt{17}$ cm (d) 13 cm

83. In ΔPQR, $PQ = 6$ cm, $PR = 9$ cm and M is a point on QR such that it divides QR in the ratio 1 : 2. $PM \perp QR$. Find QR.

(a) $\sqrt{18}$ cm (b) $3\sqrt{12}$ cm

(c) $3\sqrt{15}$ cm (d) $\sqrt{20}$ cm

84. In the following figure (not to scale), $ABCD$ is an isosceles trapezium. $\overline{AB} \parallel \overline{CD}$, $AB = 9$ cm and $CD = 12$ cm. $AP : PD = BQ : QC = 1 : 2$. Find PQ.

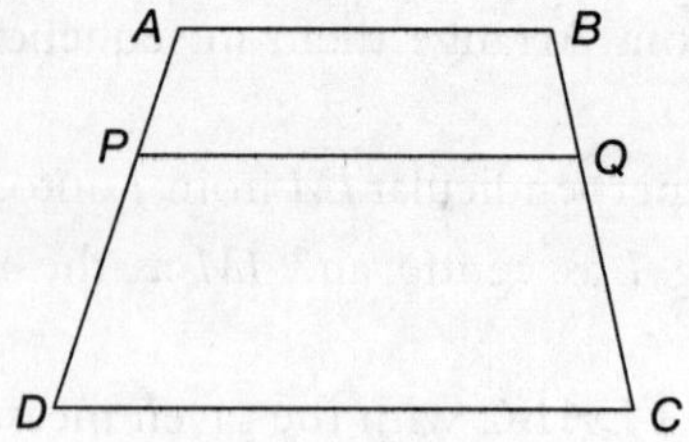

(a) 11 cm (b) 10.5 cm

(c) 10 cm (d) 9.5 cm

85. P, Q, and R are on AB, BC, and AC of the equilateral triangle ABC, respectively. $AP : PB = CQ : QB = 1 : 2$. G is the centroid of the triangle PQB and R is the mid-point of AC. Find $BG : GR$.

(a) 1 : 2 (b) 2 : 3

(c) 3 : 4 (d) 4 : 5

86. In the given figure (not to scale), two circles C_1 and C_2 intersect at S and Q. PQN and RQM are tangents drawn to C_1 and C_2, respectively, at Q. MAB and ABN are the chords of the circles C_1 and C_2. If $\angle NQR = 85°$, then find $\angle AQB$.

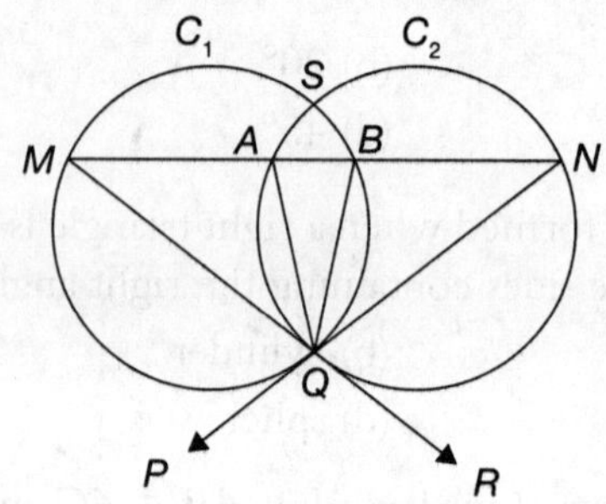

(a) 5° (b) 10°

(c) 15° (d) Cannot be determined

87. Two sides of a triangle are 5 cm and 12 cm long. The measure of third side is an integer in cm. If the triangle is an obtuse triangle, then how many such triangles are possible?

(a) 9 (b) 8

(c) 7 (d) 6

88. In a ΔPQR, M lies on PR and between P and R such that $QR = QM = PM$. If $\angle MQR = 40°$, then find $\angle P$.

(a) 35° (b) 25°

(c) 45° (d) 55°

89. In the following figure, (not to scale), AB is the common tangent to the circles C_1 and C_2. C_1 and C_2 are touching externally at C. AD and DC are two chords of the circle C_1 and BE and CE are two chords of the circle C_2. Find the measure of $\angle ADC + \angle BEC$.

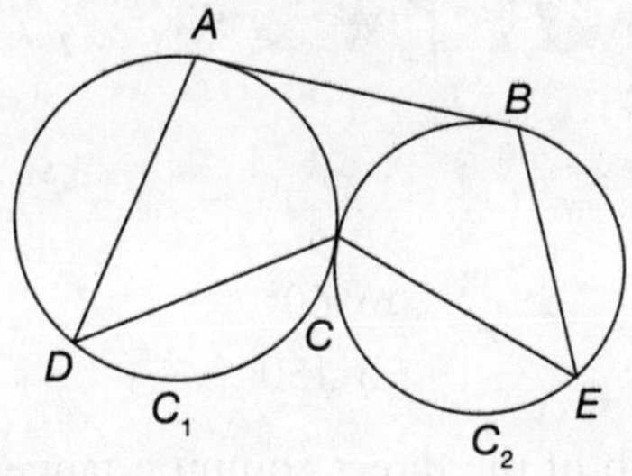

(a) 60° (b) 90°
(c) 120° (d) 100°

90. The area of ΔPQR is 4 sq. units Q and R are (1, 1) and (1, 0), respectively. Which of the following lines is a part of the locus of P?
(a) $x - 6 = 0$ (b) $x - 7 = 0$
(c) $x + 8 = 0$ (d) $x + 7 = 0$

91. What is the locus of the point $P(x, y)$ (where $xy > 0$), which is at a distance of 2 units from the origin?
(a) $x^2 + y^2 = 4$
(b) $x^2 + y^2 = 4, x > 0, y > 0$
(c) $x^2 + y^2 = 4, x < 0, y < 0$
(d) None of these

92. The locus of a point, which is at a distance of 8 units from (0, –7), is ______.
(a) $x^2 + y^2 + 6x + 14y - 15 = 0$
(b) $x^2 + y^2 + 14y - 15 = 0$
(c) $y^2 + 14y - 8 = 0$
(d) $x^2 + y^2 + 14x + 14y - 15 = 0$

93. The area of ΔABC is 2 sq. units. If $A = (2, 4)$ and $B = (4, 4)$, then find the locus of $C(x, y)$.
(a) $y - 6 = 0$
(b) $y - 2 = 0$
(c) Both (a) and (b)
(d) None of these

94. Find the locus of a point which is a constant distance of 4 units away from the point (2, 4).
(a) $x^2 + y^2 - 4x - 8y + 4 = 0$
(b) $x^2 + 4x + 16 = 0$
(c) $y^2 - 8y + 12 = 0$
(d) None of these

95. P is the point of intersection of the diagonals of a square $READ$. P is equidistant from ______.
(a) the vertices R, E, A and D
(b) $\overline{RE}$ and $\overline{EA}$
(c) $\overline{EA}$ and $\overline{AD}$
(d) All of these

96. A coin of radius 1 cm is moving along the circumference and interior of a square of side 5 cm. Find the locus of centre of the coin.
(a) A square of side 6 cm
(b) A square of side 4 cm
(c) A square of side 3 cm
(d) A square of side 2 cm

97. ABC is a triangle in which $AB = 40$ cm, $BC = 41$ cm and $AC = 9$ cm. Then ortho-centre of ΔABC lies ______.
(a) interior of the triangle
(b) exterior of the triangle
(c) on the triangle
(d) at the mid-point of the triangle

98. O is an interior point of a rhombus, $ABCD$, and O is equidistant from BC and CD. Then O lies on ______.
(a) $\overline{AC}$ (b) $\overline{BD}$
(c) Either (a) or (b) (d) Neither (a) nor (b)

99. The locus of a point, equidistant from the coordinate axes is ______.
(a) $x = |y|$ (b) $y = |x|$
(c) Both (a) and (b) (d) None of these

100. P is an interior point of an equilateral triangle ABC. If P is equidistant from AB and BC, BC and AC, then $\angle BPC$ = ______.
(a) 120° (b) 90°
(c) 60° (d) 150°

101. A park is in the shape of a regular pentagon. A path of uniform width is constructed around and outside of it. The sides of the pentagons formed are in the ratio 20: 21.and the area of the path is 820 sq m. Find the area of the park.
(a) 9500 (b) 1400
(c) 1600 (d) 8000

AT

PRACTICE QUESTIONS JEE SPECIAL WING

Multiple-Answer Type Questions

Directions for questions 1 to 5:
Each question has FOUR options (a), (b), (c), and (d). ONE OR MORE THAN ONE of these four option(s) is/are the correct answer(s).

1. If two sides of an obtuse triangle are 21 cm and 29 cm, then which of the following can be the measure of the third side?
   (a) 18 (b) 28
   (c) 38 (d) 48

2. If two sides of an acute triangle are 17 cm and 22 cm, then which of the following can be the measure of the third side?
   (a) 7 (b) 17
   (c) 27 (d) 37

3. T, R, and S are three points lie on a circle. PT is a tangent drawn to the circle at T from an external point P. If $\angle PTR = 30°$, then which of the following can be the measure of $\angle TSR$?
   (a) 30° (b) 60°
   (c) 120° (d) 150°

4. The length of the direct common tangent of two circles of radii 12 cm and 3 cm is 12 cm. Which of the following is true about the given information?
   (a) Two direct common tangents can be drawn to the circles.
   (b) Two transverse common tangents can be drawn to the circles.
   (c) The maximum number of common tangents which can be drawn to the circles is 4.
   (d) The maximum number of common tangents which can be drawn to the circles is 3.

5. P is a point on the side RT of a triangle RST such that $PR = 20$ cm, $PT = 16$ cm, and $\angle TSR = \angle SPT$. Which of the following can be the measure of the perimeter (in cm) of the triangle RST?
   (a) 80 (b) 90
   (c) 100 (d) 110

Match The Column

Directions for questions 6 to 9:
Read the paragraph given below and answer the questions.

In the given diagram, OD is a tangent at D and OVG is a secant drawn to a circle. $GV = 5$ cm, $VO = 4$ cm, and $DG = 6$ cm.

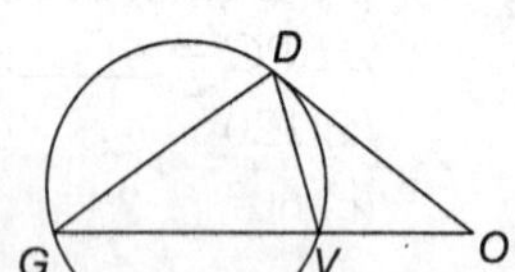

Column A	Column B
6. DO	(a) Acute Triangle
7. DV	(b) Obtuse Triangle
8. ΔDGV	(c) Right Triangle
9. ΔDVO	(d) 9 cm
	(e) 6 cm
	(f) 4 cm

Comprehension-Based Questions

Directions for questions 10 to 14:
Read the paragraph given below and answer the questions.

Aara is enthusiastic student. She made a model with the help of two circular rings and aluminium wire as shown in the given diagram.

V and U are the centres of the circular rings. PQR is a tangent drawn to the circles with centres V and U at Q and R respectively. PST is another tangent drawn to the circles with centres V and U at S and T respectively. The radii of the circles with centres V and U are 20 cm and 45 cm respectively.

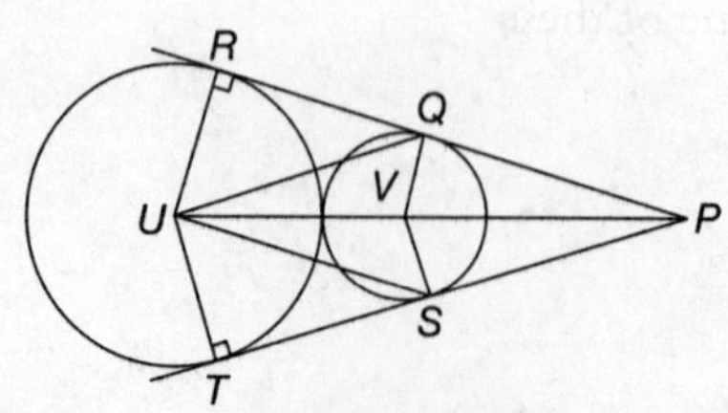

10. What is the length of the wire used to make quadrilateral $RQVU$?

(a) 190 cm (b) 180 cm
(c) 175 cm (d) 170 cm

11. What is the length of the wire QU?

(a) 60 cm (b) 75 cm
(c) 80 cm (d) 90 cm

12. What is the difference between the lengths of the wires PQ and PV?

(a) 6 cm (b) 5 cm
(c) 4 cm (d) 3 cm

13. If the measure of $\angle SPV = x$, what is the measure of reflex $\angle RUT$?

(a) $180° - 2x$ (b) $180° - x$
(c) $180° + x$ (d) $180° + 2x$

14. How many pairs of congruent triangles do visible in the diagram?

(a) 3 (b) 4
(c) 5 (d) More than 5

Assertion and Reason Type Questions

Directions for questions 15 to 18:

Read the options given below and answer the questions.

In the light of the given statements, choose the most appropriate answer from the options given below.

(a) Both assertion (A) and reason (R) are true, and reason (R) is the correct explanation of assertion.
(b) Both assertion (A) and reason (R) are true, and reason (R) is not the correct explanation of assertion.
(c) Assertion (A) is true, but reason (R) is false.
(d) Assertion (A) is false, and reason (R) is true.

15. **Assertion:** If $\Delta ABC \sim \Delta PQR$ and the ratio of their areas of the triangles is 9 : 15, then the ratio of their perimeters is $\sqrt{3} : \sqrt{5}$.

Reason: The ratio of the areas of two similar triangles is the square of the ratio of their perimeters.

16. **Assertion:** If PA and PB are the tangents drawn to a circle at A and B respectively from an eternal point P, then $PA = PB$.

Reason: The tangent at any point on a circle is perpendicular to the radius through the point of contact.

17. **Assertion:** If $ABCD$ is a cyclic quadrilateral and $\angle ABC = 60°$, then $\angle ADC = 120°$.

Reason: In a cyclic quadrilateral, a pair of opposite angles such that one is twice the other.

18. **Assertion:** PT is a tangent at T and PAB is a secant drawn to a circle. If $PT = 24$ cm and $AB = 20$ cm, then $PA = 18$ cm.

Reason: If PT is a tangent at T and PAB is a secant drawn to a circle, then $(PT)^2 = PA \times PB$.

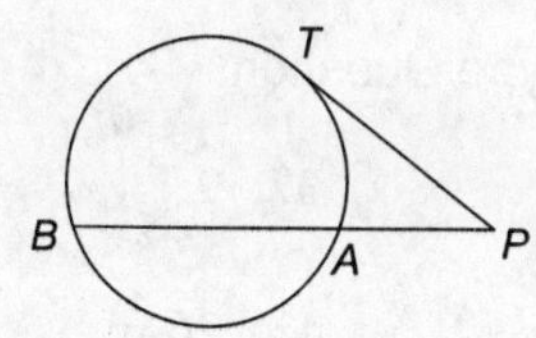

ANSWER KEYS

Crossword

Across

4. Incentre
8. One
9. Infinite
11. Zero
13. Supplementary
14. Locus
15. Four

Down

1. Three
2. Parallel
3. Circumcentre
5. Equidistant
6. Two
7. Similar
10. Interior
12. Equal

Classroom Wing

Very Short Answer Type Questions

1. $\sqrt[3]{11}$ cm
2. 0
3. $\frac{9}{2}$ cm
4. 1
5. $\angle RPT$
6. 12 cm
7. Intersect at two distinct points
8. $2\sqrt{r_1 r_2}$
9. 120°
10. Oblique sides
11. Rectangle
12. Circle
13. 8 cm
14. 2 : 1
15. Equidistant
16. Another circle of radius $(p + q)$ or $(q - p)$ concentric to it.
17. Circle with diameter AB excluding the points A and B.
18. Circum-centre
19. Angle bisectors of the two pairs of vertically opposite angles of intersecting lines.
20. Median
21. Perpendicular bisector
22. 2 units
23. False
24. True
25. True
26. True
27. False
28. b and c.
29. False
30. True
31. True
32. False
33. True
34. True
35. False

Short Answer Type Questions

36. 25 cm
37. 9
38. $\frac{180}{13}$ cm
39. 6
40. 13 cm
41. $5\sqrt{2}$ cm
42. 26 m
43. 25 cm
46. $x^2 + y^2 + 2x + 4y = 0$.
48. 17.5 cm
49. The required locus is a line parallel to the given base.
50. The required locus is the perpendicular bisector of $\overline{AB}$, except the mid-point of $\overline{AB}$.
51. The required locus is the circle with diameter AB, excluding points A and B.
52. $5x^2 + 5y^2 - 88x + 114y + 317 = 0$ is the required locus of point P.
53. The required locus is diagonal AC.
54. According to given conditions, two equal cones of base radius BD and slant height AB or BC are formed in such a way that their bases touch one another.
56. The required locus is the bisector of $\angle BAC$.
57. (B) 18 cm

Essay Type Questions

58. $8\sqrt{2}$ cm
59. 100°
60. $\sqrt[3]{29}$
61. 14 cm
62. 50°
63. $x^2 + y^2 - 10x - 14y + 49 = 0$
64. $x^2 + y^2 - 2x - y + 1 = 0$
65. $x^2 + y^2 - 2x - 6y + 8 = 0$
67. (i) 11 cm (ii) $3(\sqrt{2} - 1)$ cm
68. $BR + RP + PB$

Competition Wing

Level 1: Apply Your Concepts

1. Zero	2. $\frac{32}{3}$ cm	3. 8 cm	4. 2	5. 2
6. (a)	7. (c)	8. (a)	9. (d)	10. (b)
11. (d)	12. (b)	13. (b)	14. (d)	15. (c)
16. (b)	17. (d)	18. (a)	19. (d)	20. (d)
21. (c)	22. (b)	23. (d)	24. (b)	25. (c)
26. (d)	27. (c)	28. (b)	29. (b)	30. (b)
31. (b)	32. (b)	33. (c)	34. (c)	35. (b)
36. (b)	37. (b)	38. (c)	39. (d)	40. (a)
41. (c)	42. (a)	43. (b)	44. (d)	45. (c)
46. (b)	47. (d)	48. (d)	49. (c)	

Level 2: Review Your Concepts

50. (c)	51. (d)	52. (b)	53. (b)	54. (d)
55. (b)	56. (b)	57. (c)	58. (b)	59. (c)
60. (d)	61. (b)	62. (d)	63. (c)	64. (b)
65. (b)	66. (d)	67. (c)	68. (b)	69. (c)
70. (c)	71. (d)	72. (b)	73. (d)	74. (a)
75. (d)	76. (a)	77. (c)		

Level 3: Assess Your Concepts

78. (d)	79. (c)	80. (d)	81. (c)	82. (c)
83. (c)	84. (c)	85. (d)	86. (b)	87. (d)
88. (a)	89. (b)	90. (d)	91. (d)	92. (b)
93. (c)	94. (a)	95. (d)	96. (c)	97. (c)
98. (a)	99. (c)	100. (a)	101. (d)	

JEE Special Wing

Multiple-Answer Type Questions

1. (a, c, d)	2. (b, c)	3. (a, d)	4. (a, d)	5. (a, b, c, d)

Match The Column

6. (e)	7. (f)	8. (a)	9. (b)

Comprehension-Based Questions

10. (a)	11. (b)	12. (c)	13. (d)	14. (c)

Assertion and Reason Type Questions

15. (a)	16. (b)	17. (c)	18. (d)

Hints and Explanations

Classroom Wing

Very Short Answer Type Questions

1. Given $r = 4$ cm, $R = 5$ cm, and $d = 10$ cm

   The length of direct common tangent $= \sqrt{d^2 - (R - r)^2}$

   $= \sqrt{10^2 - (5-4)^2} = \sqrt{99} = \sqrt[3]{11}$ cm

2. Given $r = 3$ cm, $R = 5$ cm, and $d = 8$ cm

   The length of direct common tangent

   $= \sqrt{d^2 - (R + r)^2} = \sqrt{8^2 - (3+5)^2} = 0$

3. Draw SQ and PR parallel to each other.

   $\angle RPQ = \angle TQS$ (Alternate angles)

   $\angle TSQ = \angle TRP$ (Alternate angles)

   $\angle RTP = \angle QTS$ (Alternate angles)

   $\therefore \Delta PTR = \Delta QTS$

   $\therefore \frac{PT}{QT} = \frac{RT}{TS}$

   $\frac{4}{6} = \frac{3}{x}$

   $x = \frac{3 \times \cancel{6}^{3}}{\cancel{4}_{2}} = \frac{9}{2}$ cm

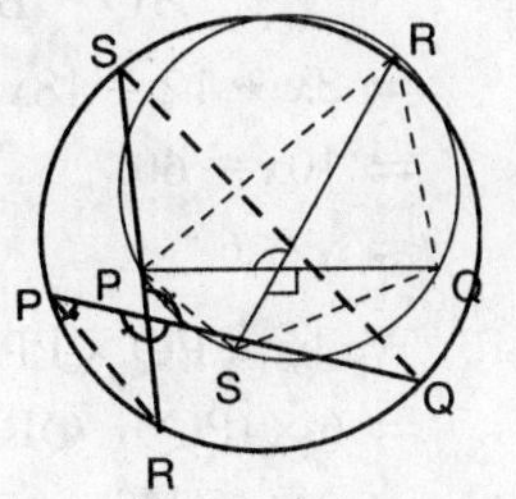

4. 1

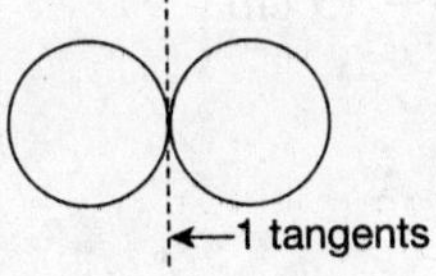

5. $\angle RPT$

   as $\angle RPT$ will signify that RP is diameter of circle and if RP is diameter then $\angle RQP = 90°$

6. $PQ = x$ cm

   Then

   $x^2 + 5^2 = (13)^2$

   $x^2 = 169 - 25$

   $x^2 = 144$

   $x = 12$ cm

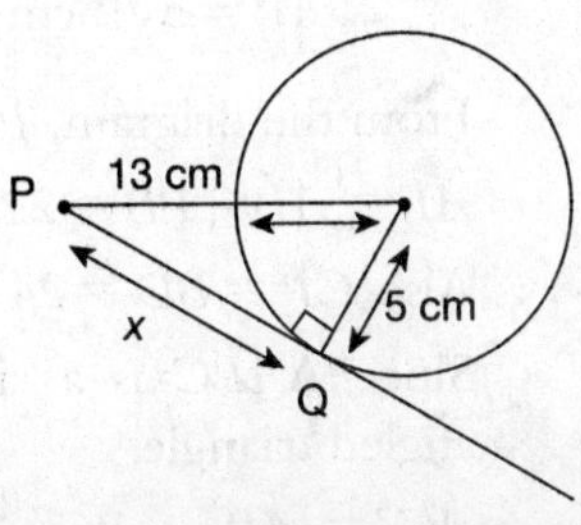

7. Intersect at 2 disjoint points

8. Draw $CD \,||\, AB$

   $AB \,||\, CD$

   $CE = r_1 - r_2$

   $DC^2 = ED^2 - CE^2$

   $= \sqrt{(r_1 + r_2)^2 - (r_1 - r_2)^2}$

   $= \sqrt{r_1^2 + r_2^2 + 2r_1r_2 - r_1^2 - r_2^2 + 2r_1r_2}$

   $= \sqrt{4r_1r_2}$

   $= 2\sqrt{r_1r_2}$

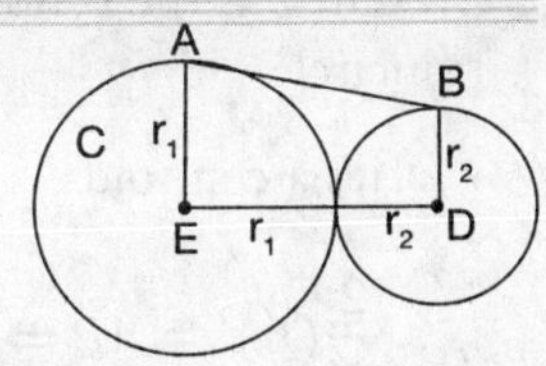

9. $\angle ADC = 2\angle ABC$

   $= 120°$

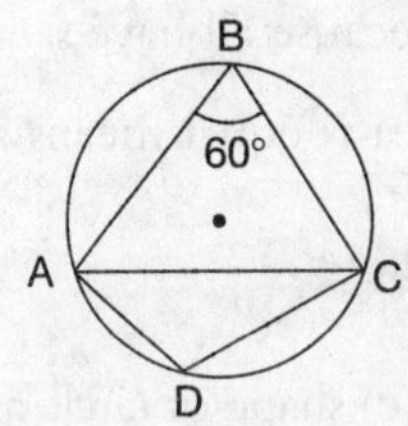

10. Oblique sides

11. Rectangle (chords bisect at 90°) and opposite sides are parallel as opposite angles are equal

12. Circle

13. $\frac{3}{2}x = 12$ cm

    $x = \frac{\cancel{12}^{4} \times 2}{\cancel{3}} = 8$ cm

14. Centroid divides median in the ratio of **2:1**

15. Equidistant

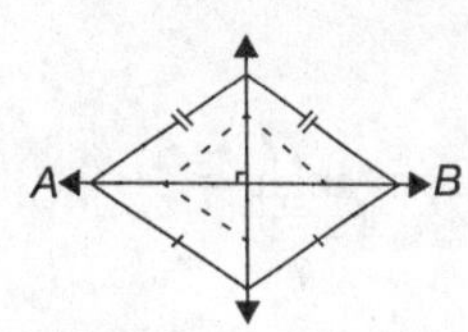

16. Locus will be another circle with radius $(p + q)$ or $(p - q)$ and will be concentric.

17. Locus will be a circle, whose diameter will be AB

18. Circum-center

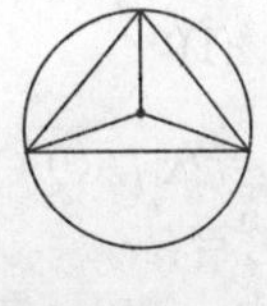

19. Angle bisectors of intersection angles

20. Median

21. Perpendicular Bisector

22. Point P is the centroid of triangle and centre of incircle

$\therefore$ it's a centroid

$\therefore \frac{2}{\cancel{3}}(\cancel{6})^2 = AP \Rightarrow 4$

$\therefore$ radius of circle $= 6 - 4 = 2$ units

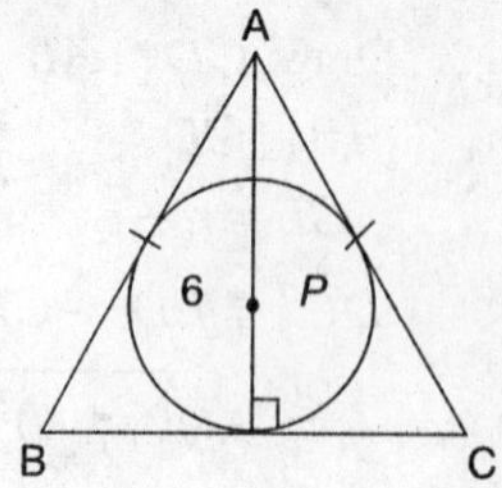

23. False, because every congruent figure will be similar.

24. Agree (same shape so they are similar)

25. True (because all have same shape)

26. Yes (Area is equal means along with shape, size is also same)

27. False

28. (b) and (c) shape of circle and square is always same.

29. False, equal chords can be on any side of circle. So not always parallel.

30. True, since $AD = DB$ and $DE \mid\mid BC$

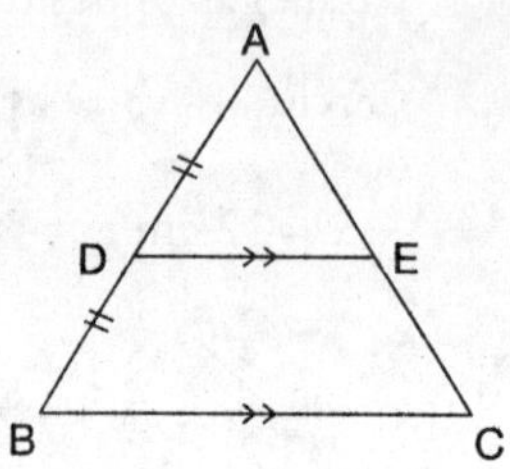

31. Yes as $\angle PST = \angle PQR$

$\angle PTS = \angle PRQ$

and $\angle P$ is common

32. False

33. True (As they from angle $= 90°$)

34. True

35. No, not always true

Short Answer Type Questions

36. We have $\Delta APQ \sim \Delta ABC$

$$\frac{PQ}{BC} = \frac{AQ}{AC} \qquad (1)$$

Let AQ = $3x$, QC = $2x$ (AQ:QC = 3:2)

$\therefore$ AC = AQ + QC = $5x$

$\therefore \frac{15}{BC} = \frac{3x}{5x}$ [From Eq. (1)]

$\Rightarrow$ BC = 25 cm

37. Let BD = x cm

$\Rightarrow$ CD = $(21 - x)$ cm (BC = 21 cm)

We have $\frac{AB}{AC} = \frac{BD}{CD}$

$\Rightarrow \frac{3}{4} = \frac{x}{21 - x}$

$\Rightarrow 63 - 3x = 4x$

$\Rightarrow x = 9$

38. We have $AC^2 = AB^2 + BC^2$

$= 15^2 + 36^2 = 39^2$

$\Rightarrow$ AC = 39

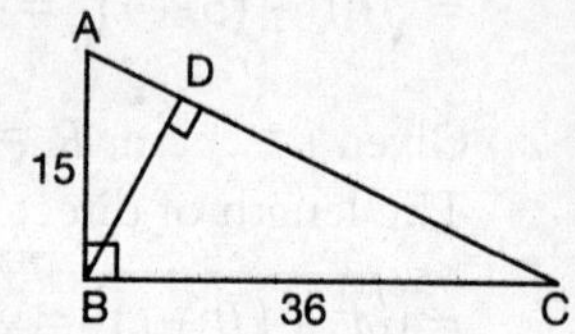

$\therefore \frac{1}{2} \times 36 \times 15 = \frac{1}{2} \times 39 \times BD \left(\text{Area} = \frac{1}{2}bh \right)$

$\Rightarrow BD = \frac{36 \times 15}{39} = \frac{180}{13}$ cm

39. We have $\frac{PA}{AQ} = \frac{PB}{BR} \Rightarrow \frac{2x+3}{6x-16} = \frac{3}{4}$

$\Rightarrow 8x + 12 = 18x - 48$

$\Rightarrow 10x = 60$

$\Rightarrow x = 6$

40. We have PQ × PR = PS × PT

$\Rightarrow$ 6 × (PQ + QR) = 5 × PT

$\Rightarrow$ 6 × (6 + 9) = 5 × PT

$\Rightarrow$ PT = 18 cm

$\therefore$ ST = PT – PS = 18 – 5 = 13 cm

41. $\frac{AT}{PQ} = \frac{5}{10} - \frac{1}{2} = \frac{AR}{QR}$

$\frac{AR}{PR + AQ} = \frac{1}{2}$

$2AR = AR + AQ$

$AR = AQ$

$\therefore AR = 5\sqrt{2}$ cm

42. From the diagram, $PB = CD = 12$ m

$AP = AB - PB = 22 - 12 = 10$ m

Also $CP = BD = 24$ m

Since ΔAPC is a right-angled triangle,

$AC^2 = AP^2 + PC^2$

$\Rightarrow AC^2 = 10^2 + 24^2$

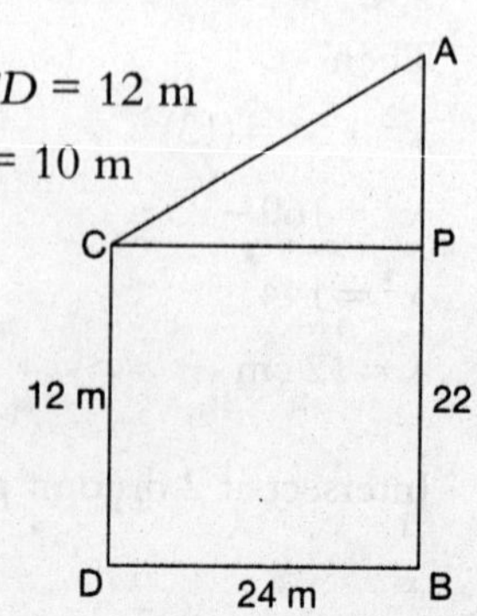

$\Rightarrow AC^2 = 676$

$AC = 26$ m

Hence, distance between their tops is 26 m.

43. Transverse common tangent

$= \sqrt{(\text{distance between centers})^2 - (R+r)^2}$

$301 = x^2 - 18^2$

$x^2 = 625$

$x = 25$ cm

44. $\angle DCA = 3\angle QCR$

$\angle DCA = 2\angle BDA$ (Angle made by arc)

In ΔCQR

$\angle QCR = \angle QRC$ (isosceles)

Similarly for arc QB,

$\angle QCR = 2\angle QDB$

$\angle QCR = 2\angle QDB$

Comparing them,

$\angle DCA = 3\angle QCR$

45. $3PQ^2 = SN^2 + NR^2 + QX^2 + XR^2 + PY^2 + YS^2$

Since PQ and RS are midpoints of quadrilateral $YMXN$

$\therefore \angle YPS = \angle YSP$ and similarly for all.

$SP^2 = SY^2 + YP^2$ (1)

$SR^2 = SN^2 + NR^2$ (2)

$QR^2 = RX^2 + QX^2$ (3)

Adding all 3

$SP^2 + SR^2 + QR^2$

$= SN^2 + NR^2 + QX^2 + XR^2 + PY^2 + YS^2$

$= 3PQ^2$

Hence proved

46. 5 units from $(-1, -2)$

Locus of a point will be the equation of a circle.

distance = 5 units

let points be x and y:

$$(x+1)^2 + (y+2)^2 = 5$$

$$x^2 + 1 + 2x + y^2 + 4 + 4y = 5$$

$$x^2 + y^2 + 2x + 4y = 0$$

47. Show: $\dfrac{TS+TR}{TS-TR} = \dfrac{x+y}{y-x}$

$\dfrac{y}{TR} = \dfrac{x}{TS}$

$yTS = xTR$

$TS = \dfrac{x}{y}TR$

$$\therefore \frac{TS+TR}{TS-TR} = \frac{\frac{x}{y}TR + TR}{\frac{x}{y}TR - TR} \Rightarrow \frac{TR\left[\frac{x+y}{y}\right]}{TR\left[\frac{x-y}{y}\right]}$$

$$= \frac{x+y}{-(x-y)} = \frac{x+y}{y-x}$$

48. $PF = ?$

Since length of tangents are equal.

$\therefore CE = DE = 4.5$

$DF = 9 - 4.5 = 4.5$

Similarly, $PA = PB = 13$ cm

and $DF = BF = 4.5$

$\therefore PF = 13 + 4.5 = 17.5$ cm

49. $a = \dfrac{1}{2} \times b \times h$

(a = area, b = base, h = height)

Since, h is only variable here, so, in order to make area constant, h cannot change.

H = Height will not change only when the vertex be on the line parallel to base

Hence, Locus will be line parallel to base.

50. Locus will be perpendicular bisector of AB, where midpoint of AB will not be included.

51. Let the locus of point P be (h, k),

Let coordinates of A and B be (x_1, y_1) and (x_2, y_2)

then, $PA^2 + PB^2 = AB^2$

Using distance formula,

$$(x_1 - h)^2 + (y_1 - k)^2 + (x_2 - h)^2 + (y_2 - k)^2 = AB^2$$

$$2h^2 + 2k^2 - 2(x_1 + x_2)h - 2(y_1 + y_2)k$$
$$+ (x_1^2 + y_1^2 + x_2^2 + y_2^2) = AB^2$$

$$h^2 + k^2 - (x_1 + x_2)h - (y_1 + y_2)k$$
$$+ \frac{\left[x_1^2 + y_1^2 + x_2^2 + y_2^2\right]}{2} = \frac{AB^2}{2}$$

Above equation represents equation of a circle, with center $\left[\dfrac{x_1 + x_2}{2}, \dfrac{y_1 + y_2}{2}\right]$ and diameter = AB

Hence, the required locus is the circle with diameter AB

52. Let (h, k) be the coordinates of P,

$$\frac{|TP|}{|MP|}=\frac{3}{2} \text{ using distance formula:}$$

$$\frac{\sqrt{(h+2)^2+(k-3)^2}}{\sqrt{(h-4)^2+(k+5)^2}}=\frac{3}{2}$$

Squaring and equating both sides,

$$4(h^2+4+2h+k^2+9-6k)=9(h^2+16-8k$$
$$+k^2+25+10k)$$

$$5h^2+5k^2-88h+114k+317=0$$

Replace (h, k) with (x, y) to get required locus:

$$5x^2+5y^2-88x+114y+317=0$$

53.

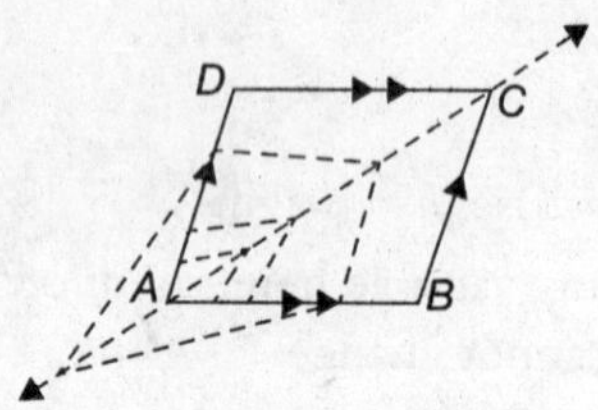

Required locus is the equation of diagonal AC

54. The required locus will be the, two equal cones of base radius BD and slant height AB or BC, in such a way that there bases touch each other

55. Let the 3 collinear points be A, B, C respectively, $(x_1, y_1), (x_2, y_2), (x_3, y_3)$

Let P (h, k) be an arbitrary point in plane, which is equidistant from A, B, C.

i.e., $PA = PB = PC$

Let consider $PA = PB$ and $PB = PC$

Applying distance formula on both equation we get:

$$\sqrt{(h-x_1)^2+(k-y_1)^2}=\sqrt{(h-x_2)^2+(k-y_2)^2}$$

$$h(x_2-x_1)+k(y_2-y_1)+C'=0 \quad (1)$$

(where C' is some constant)

$$\sqrt{(h-x_3)^2+(k-y_3)^2}=\sqrt{(h-x_2)^2+(k-y_2)^2}$$

$$h(x_2-x_3)+k(y_2-y_3)+C'=0 \quad (2)$$

(where C'' is some constant)

Since (1) and (2) are 2 different linear equation

$\Rightarrow$ locus of a point equidistant from 3 collinear points is not possible.

56. Same as $Q-23$

Locus will be the straight line, which will also be the angular bisector of $\angle A$

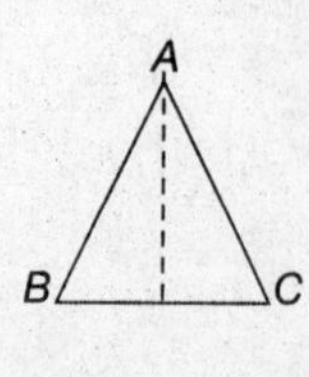

57. (A) Let us consider a point Z (h, k) which is equidistant from 2 point P (x_1, y_1) and Q (x_2, y_2)

Hence, ZPQ will form isosceles triangle

Now, $ZP = ZQ$

Using distance formula

$$\sqrt{(h-x_1)^2+(k-y_1)^2}=\sqrt{(h-x_2)^2+(k-y_2)^2}$$

$$2(x_1-x_2)h+2(y_2-y_1)k+C=0$$

(where c is the sum of all constant values)

The above equation represent a straight line. also, it is the locus of a point which is equidistant from 2 fixed points.

Hence, if Δ APQ, Δ BPQ, Δ CPQ are isosceles triangles on same base,

then, A, B, C will satisfy above equations

Hence, A, B, C are collinear points

(B) Given P, Q and R the midpoints of BC, AC and AB.

And given, $\angle BPR = \angle APR$.

$\Rightarrow \dfrac{BP}{AP}=\dfrac{BR}{AR}=1$ ($\because$ R is the midpoint of AB)

$\Rightarrow BP = AP \Rightarrow AP = 15$ cm ($\because$ $BP = 15$ cm)

$AC = 2$ $(CQ) = 24$ cm ($\because$ $CQ = 12$ cm)

$BC = 2$ $(PB) = 30$ cm ($\because$ $BP = 15$ cm)

By Appollonius theorem,

$AB^2 + AC^2 = 2$ $[AP^2 + BP^2]$

$AB^2 = 2[(15)^2 + (15)^2] - (24)^2$

$= 900 - 576 = 324 \Rightarrow AB = 18$ cm.

Essay Type Questions

58. We have AB $\|$ FC.

$\therefore \dfrac{\text{BC}}{\text{CE}}=\dfrac{\text{AF}}{\text{FE}} \Rightarrow \dfrac{12}{\text{CE}}=\dfrac{3}{2}$

$\Rightarrow$ CE = 8 cm

Let AF = $3x$ and FE = $2x$

(AF:FE = 3:2)

ΔFEC ~ ΔAEB (AB $\|$ FC)

$\Rightarrow \dfrac{\text{FE}}{\text{AE}}=\dfrac{\text{FC}}{\text{AB}} \Rightarrow \dfrac{\text{FE}}{\text{AF}+\text{FE}}=\dfrac{\text{FC}}{20}$

$\Rightarrow \dfrac{2x}{3x+2x}=\dfrac{\text{FC}}{20} \Rightarrow \text{FC}=8$ cm

$\therefore$ In ΔFCE, FE^2 = FC^2 + CE^2 ($\angle$FCE = 90°)

$\Rightarrow$ FE^2 = 8^2 + 8^2 = 128

$\Rightarrow$ FE = $\sqrt{128}=8\sqrt{2}$ cm.

59. Given, $\angle PAB = 40° \Rightarrow \angle OAP = 90° - 40° = 50°$

(Radius is perpendicular to the tangent at the point of contact, i.e., $\angle OAC = 90°$.)

$\angle OPA = \angle OAP = 50°$ (OA = OP = radius)

In ΔOAP, $\angle AOP = 180° - (50° + 50°) = 80°$

We have $\angle OPC = 90°$

$\therefore$ In quadrilateral OACP

$\angle ACP = 360° - (\angle OAC + \angle AOP + \angle OPC)$

$= 360° - (90° + 80° + 90°) = 100°$

Hence, the correct option is (a).

60. $\Delta FEC \sim \Delta AEB$ (FC $\|$ AB)

$\Rightarrow \frac{FC}{AB} = \frac{EC}{EB} \Rightarrow \frac{FC}{10} = \frac{15}{25}$ (EB = BC + CE = 10 + 15 = 25)

$\Rightarrow FC = 6$ cm

In ΔFCE, $FE^2 = FC^2 + CE^2 = 6^2 + 15^2$

$\Rightarrow FE^2 = 261 \Rightarrow FE = \sqrt{261} = \sqrt[3]{29}$ cm

61. AP = AS, BS = BR, CR = CQ, and DQ = DP

($\because$ Tangents drawn from an external point to a circle are equal.)

AB = AS + SB = AP + BR = 3 cm (1)

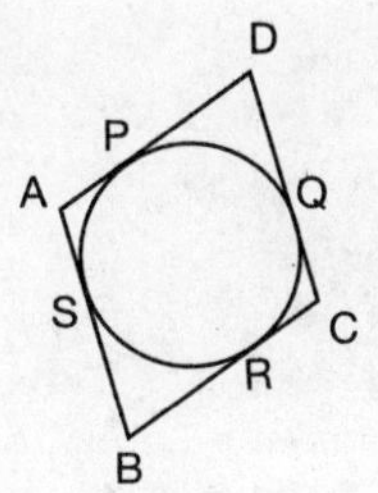

CD = DQ + QC = DP + CR = 4 cm (2)

Adding Eqs (1) and (2),

(AD + DP) + (BR + CR) = 7 cm

$\Rightarrow$ AD + BC = 7 cm

$\therefore$ The perimeter of ABCD = AB + CD + BC + AD = 3 + 4 + 7 = 14 cm

62. $\angle OAB = \angle OBA = 25°$ ($\because$ OA = OD = radius)

$\angle AOB = 180° - (\angle OAB + \angle OBA)$

$= 180° - (25° + 25°) = 130°$

$\angle OAP = \angle OBP = 90°$

($\because$ Radius is perpendicular to the tangent at the point of contact.)

In quadrilateral OAPB,

$\angle APB = 360° - (\angle OAP + \angle OBP + \angle AOB)$

$= 360° - (90° + 90° + 130°) = 50°$

63. $PC = QC$ (since P and Q are on circumference) radius $= PC = QC$

Using distance formula,

$$\sqrt{(x-5)^2 + (y-7)^2} = \sqrt{(5-1)^2 + (7-4)^2}$$

$$x^2 \cancel{+25} - 10x + y^2 + 49 - 14y = \cancel{25}$$

$\Rightarrow$ **$x^2 + y^2 - 10x - 14y + 49 = 0$**

It is the required equation of locus.

64. Let line 1 have slope = m,

since line 2 is perpendicular it will have slope = $\frac{-1}{m}$

Now, Using one point from of line,

$(y - y_1) = m(x - x_1)$ and $(y - y_2) = \frac{-1}{m}(x - x_2)$

$y - 1 = m(x - 1)$ and $y = \frac{-1}{m}(x - 1)$

$\Rightarrow \qquad \frac{1}{m} = \frac{x-1}{y-1}$ (1)

and $\qquad \frac{1}{m} = \frac{-y}{(x-1)}$ (2)

Equating equation (1) and (2),

$(x - 1)(x - 1) = -y(y - 1)$

$x^2 + 1 - 2x = -y^2 - y$

$x^2 + y^2 - 2x - y + 1 = 0$

It is the required equation of locus of point P

65. Let (h, k) be the coordinates of point P

A, B form the diameter

therefore applying mid-point formula to get coordinates of center

$$(x, y) = \left(\frac{0+2}{2}, \frac{2+4}{2}\right) = (1, 3)$$

also, radius $= \frac{\sqrt{(2-0)^2 + (4-2)^2}}{2} = \frac{2\sqrt{2}}{2} = \sqrt{2}$

equation of circle will become,

$$(x-1)^2 + (y-3)^2 = \left(\sqrt{2}\right)^2$$

Since, (h, k) is point on circle, it will satisfy the equation above

$$(h-1)^2 + (k-3)^2 = \left(\sqrt{2}\right)^2$$

$$h^2 + 1 - 2h + k^2 + 9 - 6k = 2$$

$$h^2 + k^2 - 2h - 6k + 8 = 0$$

replacing (h, k) with (x, y)

$x^2 + y^2 - 2x - 6y + 8 = 0$ is the required equation of locus.

66. We have, $KP^2 + PQ^2 = KQ^2$ (1)

KQM is an obtuse triangle and $KP \perp LM$

$KM^2 = KP^2 + PM^2$

$= KQ^2 - PQ^2 + PM^2$

$= KQ^2 - PQ^2 + (PQ + QM)^2$

$= KQ^2 - PQ^2 + PQ^2 + QM^2 + 2PQ\ QM$

$\therefore KM^2 = KQ^2 + QM^2 + 2PQ \times QM$

(from (1))

$\Rightarrow KM^2 > KQ^2 + QM^2$.

KLQ, $KP \perp LQ$

$KL^2 = KP^2 + LP^2$

$= KP^2 + (LQ - PQ)^2$

$= KP^2 + LQ^2 + PQ^2 - 2LQ \times PQ$

$= LQ^2 + KQ^2 - 2LQ \times PQ$ from (1)

$\Rightarrow KL^2 < LQ^2 + KQ^2$.

67. (i) AB is the direct common tangent of the circles

$\therefore AB = \sqrt{d^2 - (R-r)^2} = \sqrt{10^2 - (9-3)^2}$

$= \sqrt{10^2 - 6^2} = 8$ cm.

$PA = AB + BP$

$= 8 + 3 = 11$ cm

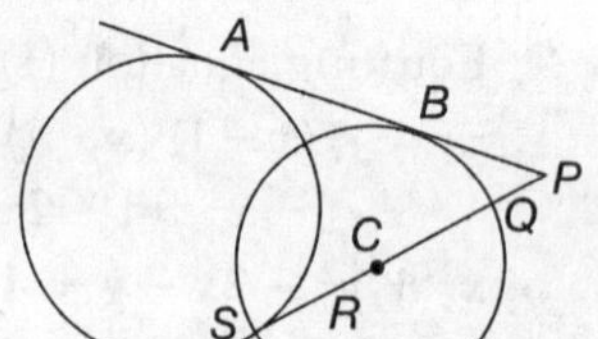

(ii) $PB^2 + BC^2 = PC^2$

$3^2 + 3^2 = PC^2$

$PC = 3\sqrt{2}$

$QP = PC - CQ = 3\sqrt{2} - 3 = 3(\sqrt{2} - 1)$ cm

68. Given $\overline{CQ} \,//\, \overline{BR}$ $PA = 8$ cm and $PQ = 12$ cm.

We know that $CQ \perp RP$.

Let $CA = x = CQ$ ($\because$ Radii)

In Δ CQP, $(x + 8)^2 = x^2 + 12^2$

$= x^2 + 64 + 16x = x^2 + 144 \Rightarrow 16x \Rightarrow 80 \Rightarrow x = 5$

$\therefore CA = CQ = 5$ cm.

$\Rightarrow PB = 10 + 8 = 18$ cm. and $CP = 5 + 8 = 13$ cm

$\Delta\, BRP \sim \Delta\, CQP$ ($\because CQ \parallel BR$)

$\frac{BP}{RP} = \frac{CP}{QP} = \frac{18}{12 + PR} = \frac{13}{12}$, $PR = \frac{216}{13}$.

and $\frac{BR}{CQ} = \frac{BP}{CP} = \frac{BR}{5} = \frac{18}{13}$, $BR = \frac{90}{13}$.

Perimeter of $\Delta\, PBR = BR + RP + PB$

Competition Wing

Level 1: Apply Your Concepts

1. Zero different circles cannot pass through all the same points.

2. $BD^2 + CD^2 = BC^2$

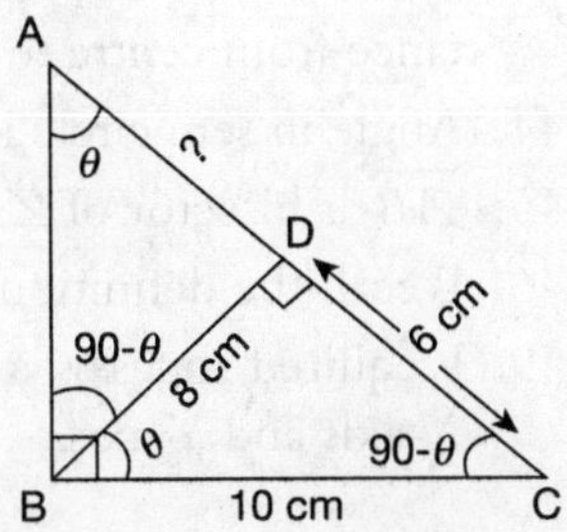

$BD^2 = 100 - 36 = 64$

$BD = 8$ cm

Since $BD \perp AC$

$\therefore AD = DC = \frac{1}{2} AC$

$\therefore AD = 6$ cm

Let $BAD = \theta$

$\therefore ABD = 90 - \theta$

$\therefore DBC = \theta$

$\therefore BCD = 90 - \theta$

$\therefore \Delta ABD \sim \Delta DCB$

In ΔACB

$\therefore \frac{AB}{8} = \frac{8}{6} \Rightarrow AB = \frac{64}{6} = \frac{32}{3}$ cm

3. 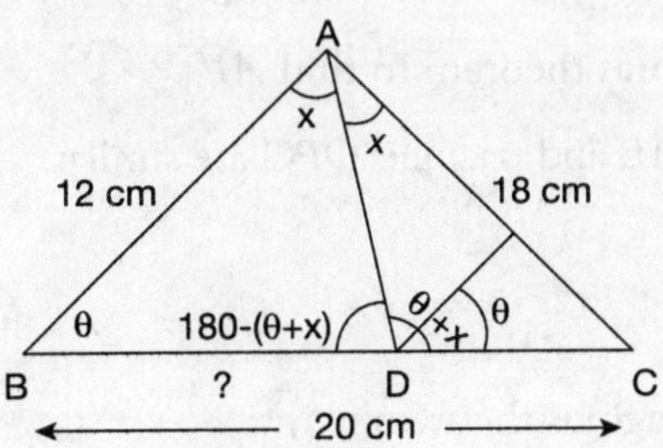

Let $\angle BAD = \angle DAC = x$

Let $\angle ABD = \theta$

$\therefore \angle BDA = 180 - (\theta + x)$

$\therefore \angle ADC = 180 - [(180) - (\theta + x)]$

$= \theta + x$

$\angle ACD = 180 - (\theta + x + x)$

4. The number of tangents drawn from an external point to a circle is = 2

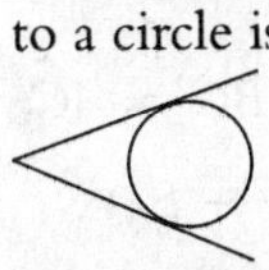

5. The number of common tangents = 2

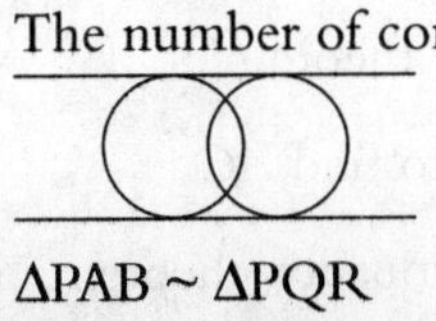

6. $\Delta PAB \sim \Delta PQR$

$\Rightarrow \frac{PA}{PQ} = \frac{AB}{QR}$ (1)

Given, PA:AQ = 1:3

Let PA = $x \Rightarrow$ AQ = $3x \Rightarrow$ PQ = PA + AQ = $4x$

$\therefore$ From Eq. (1), $\frac{x}{4x} = \frac{AB}{10}$ (Given QR = 10 cm)

$\Rightarrow AB = \frac{5}{2} = 2.5$ cm

Hence, the correct option is (a).

7. Let CD = $x \Rightarrow$ BD = $14 - x$ (BC = 14)

We have $\frac{AC}{AB} = \frac{CD}{BD} \Rightarrow \frac{12}{9} = \frac{x}{14 - x}$

$\Rightarrow 168 - 12x = 9x$

$\Rightarrow 21x = 168 \Rightarrow x = 8$

Hence, the correct option is (c).

8. In ΔABD, $AD^2 = AB^2 - BD^2$

$= 15^2 - 12^2 = 81 = 9^2$

$\Rightarrow$ AD = 9 cm

We have $BD^2 = AD \times CD$

$\Rightarrow 12^2 = 9 \times CD$

$\Rightarrow$ CD = 16 cm

In ΔBDC, $BC^2 = BD^2 + CD^2 = 12^2 + 16^2 = 400 = 20^2$

$\Rightarrow$ BC = 20 cm

Hence, the correct option is (a).

9. Option (d): We have $\frac{AP}{PB} = \frac{AQ}{QC}$

(By Basic Proportionality Theorem)

$\Rightarrow \frac{3x - 2}{2x + 7} = \frac{2}{3}$

$\Rightarrow 9x - 6 = 4x + 14 \Rightarrow x = 4$

Hence, the correct option is (d).

10. Let PQ = x cm

We have $PT^2 = PQ \times PR \Rightarrow PT^2 = PQ \times (PQ + QR)$

$\Rightarrow 12^2 = x(x + 7) \Rightarrow x^2 + 7x - 144 = 0$

$\Rightarrow (x - 9)(x + 16) = 0 \Rightarrow x = 9$ or $x = -16$

$\therefore$ PQ = 9 cm (-16 is not possible).

Hence, the correct option is (b).

11. Apply Pythagoras theorem.

12. $\angle BOC = 2\angle BAC$ and proceed.

13. Exterior angle of a cyclic quadrilateral is equal to its interior opposite angle, i.e., $\angle BAC = \angle DCA$ and proceed.

14. Radius of a circle is perpendicular to the tangent at the point of contact and tangents drawn to a circle from an external point are equal.

15. Tangents drawn to a circle from an external point are equal.

16. Recall the definition of locus. In the first or the second quadrant, y is positive.

17. Apply Pythagoras theorem.

18. Radius is perpendicular to the tangent at the point of contact.

In the quadrilateral $BOCP$, $\angle BOC + \angle BPC = 180°$.

19. Recall the properties of cyclic quadrilateral and also of tangents.

$\angle BOA + \angle BPA = 180°$ and $\angle BOA = 2\angle BQA$.

20. Apply 'alternate segment theorem'.

21. Tangents drawn to a circle from an external point are equal.

22. Length of the transverse common tangent $= \sqrt{d^2 - (R+r)^2}$.

23. Diagonals of a trapezium divide each other proportionally.

24. Recall the properties of cyclic quadrilateral.

$\angle PAB = \angle PBA$ and $\angle DAB = \angle DCE$.

25. Apply BPT and use componondo–dividendo after drawing the complete figure.

26. Diagonal of a square bisects the angle at the vertices.

$\angle FDC = 30°$ and $\angle FCD = 45°$.

27. Evaluate the solution from the options.

28. Apply 'alternate segment theorem'.

29. Recall 'alternate segment theorem'.

30. Radius is perpendicular to the tangent at the point of contact.

31. Apply 'alternate segment theorem'.

32. Apply 'alternate segment theorem'.

33. Recall the properties of a kite.

34. Apply Pythagoras theorem.

35. (i) $ADEF$ is a parallelogram.

(ii) $\angle FAD = 30°$ and

$\angle OAD = \angle OBA$

(angles opposite to equal sides).

36. Three points form a triangle.

37. Recall the definition.

38. Recall the properties of right triangle with respect to geometric centres.

41. Non-intersecting lines are parallel.

42. Equations of the lines which are k units from the Y-axis.

43. When a wheel is rolling on the straight path, the distance from centre to the path remains same.

44. Angle in semicircle is 90°.

45. AB is bisector of $\angle APB$.

46. Recall the definitions of geometric centres.

49. Required locus is a line which is in the midway of X-axis and Y-axis.

Level 2: Review Your Concepts

50. (i) In triangle PBS, $\angle B = 60°$.

$\therefore \angle P = 30°$ and $\angle S = 90°$.

(ii) The sides of the triangle PBS, i.e., BS, SP and PB are in the ratio $1 : \sqrt{3} : 2$.

(iii) Given $PS = 6$ cm.

51. (i) Use Pythagoras theorem to find AP.

(ii) Triangle QAB and triangle QPC are similar.

$\therefore \frac{QP}{PA} = \frac{QC}{CB}$

52. (i) Apply 'Pythagoras theorem'.

(ii) The tower is perpendicular to the surface of the ground.

53. (i) Apply 'angle bisector theorem'.

(ii) $AB : BC = AD : DC$.

(iii) Apply Pythagoras theorem, and find AB and BC.

54. (i) Apply 'Pythagoras theorem' for triangle ABC.

(ii) Let $AB = 3x$, $BD = x$ and $CD = 3x$.

(iii) First find AB and BC using $AB^2 + BC^2 = AC^2$.

(iv) Then find AD by using $AD^2 = AB^2 + BD^2$.

55. (i) Apply 'basic proportionality theorem'.

(ii) Apply Pythagoras theorem to find AC.

(iii) Then apply basic proportionality theorem, i.e., $CE/EB = CD/DA$.

56. (i) In triangle OBC, angles opposite to equal sides are equal.
(ii) $\angle ADB = \angle ACB = 90°$ (Since angle in a semi-circle is 90°).
(iii) $\angle OCB = \angle OBC$ and $\angle OAC = \angle OCA$ (Angles opposite to equal sides).

57. (i) $ACBD$ is a cyclic quadrilateral.
(ii) $\angle ACB$ and $\angle ADB$ are supplementary angles.
(iii) $\angle AOB = 2\angle ADB$.

58. (i) $APBC$ is a cyclic quadrilateral.
(ii) $\angle ABC$ is an angle in a semi-circle.
(iii) $ABQC$ is a cyclic quadrilateral.

59. (i) POQ and ROS are similar triangles.
(ii) SR and PQ are proportional to the square roots of the areas of similar triangles SOR and POQ.

60. (i) Triangles FEB and FDC are similar.
(ii) Triangles AED and EFB are similar.

61. (i) Triangle PDR, QDP, and QPR are similar.
(ii) Corresponding sides of similar triangles are proportional.
(iii) $\Delta PDQ \sim \Delta RDP$.

62. (i) Apply 'alternate segment theorem'.
(ii) Join QR and join PS.
$\angle PQR = \angle PSQ$ and
$\angle PRQ = \angle PSR$ (By alternate segment theorem)

63.

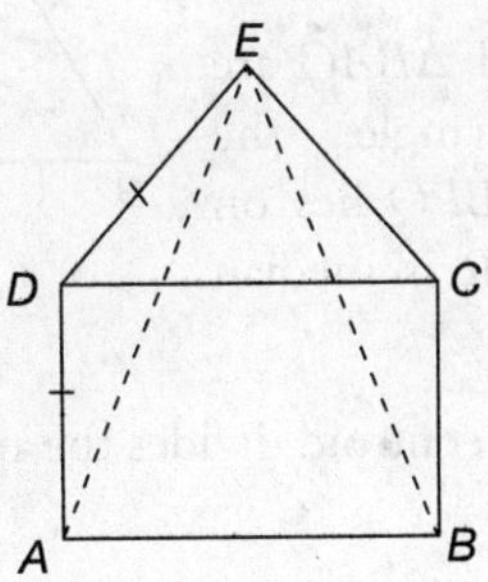

$\angle ADE = \angle ADC + \angle CDE = 90° + 60°$ ($\because$ Angles in a square and equilateral triangle) = 150°

In ΔADE, $AD = DE$

$\therefore \angle DAE = \angle DEA = \frac{1}{2}(180° - 150°)$

$= 15°$.

Similarly, $\angle CEB = 15°$

$\therefore \angle AEB = 60° - (\angle DEA + \angle CEB)$

$= 60° - (15° + 15°) = 30°$.

64. Given $PR = RQ$ and $\angle Q = 40°$

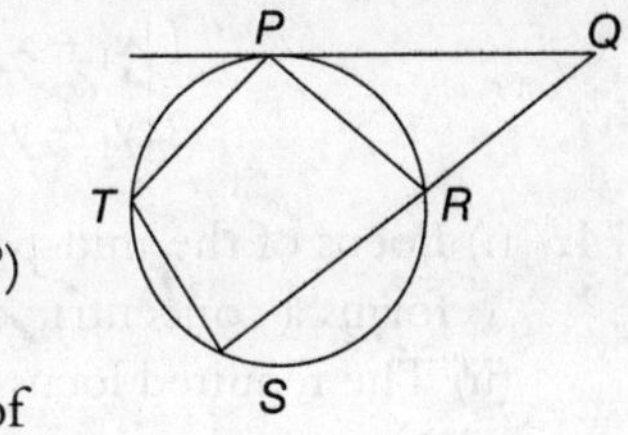

$\Rightarrow \angle RPQ = \angle Q$
$\therefore \angle RPQ = 40°$
In ΔPQR,
$\angle PRQ = 180° - (40° + 40°)$
$= 100°$.
We have, exterior angle of cyclic quadrilateralis equal to its interior opposite angle.
$\therefore \angle PTS = \angle PRQ$ ($\because PRST$ is a cyclic quadrilateral)
$\therefore \angle PTS = 100°$.

65. CDAB is the required sequential order.

67. (i) When a right triangle is rotated about one of its perpendicular sides, the other perpendicular side acts as radius of the base and the hypotenuse acts as the slant height of solid.
(ii) The top of a solid is a point (vertex).

68. $\Delta ADB \cong \Delta ADC$.

69. (i) Given, area of a triangle $ABC = 4$

$$\Rightarrow \frac{1}{2}\begin{vmatrix} x_1 - x_2 & x_2 - x_3 \\ y_1 - y_2 & y_2 - y_3 \end{vmatrix} = 4.$$

(ii) Substitute $(x_2, y_2) = (2, 5)$ and $(x_3, y_3) = (3, 4)$ and obtain the relation.

70. (i) The area of the given triangle will be half that of the given parallelogram.
(ii) Area of ΔPBC is half of the area of parallelogram $ABCD$.
(iii) Area of ΔPBC is given by

$$\frac{1}{2}\begin{vmatrix} x_1 - x_2 & x_2 - x_3 \\ y_1 - y_2 & y_2 - y_3 \end{vmatrix}.$$

and proceed same as above.

71. (i) Angle in a semi-circle is 90°.
(ii) Use, $(PA)^2 = (PB)^2 + (AB)^2$ and obtain the required locus.

72. (i) The perpendicular distance from $P(x_1, y_1)$ to the line $ax + by + c = 0$ is

$$\frac{|ax_1 + by_1 + c|}{\sqrt{a^2 + b^2}}.$$

(ii) The distance between P and X-axis is equal to thrice the distance between P and $x = 5$.

73. (i) As P is the centroid of ΔABC, area of ΔPAB is $\frac{1}{3}$ (area of ΔABC).

(ii) Area of ΔPAB is given by

$$\frac{1}{2}\begin{vmatrix} x_1 - x_2 & x_2 - x_3 \\ y_1 - y_2 & y_2 - y_3 \end{vmatrix}.$$

74. (i) Locus of the mid-points of equal chords in a circle forms a concentric circle with the given circle.

(ii) The required locus is a circle of radius 7 cm.

(iii) Now, find its area.

75. The required locus is a cylinder.

76. In a right triangle, the ortho-centre lies at the vertex which contains right angle.

$\therefore$ The given triangle is a right triangle, where $\angle B = 90°$. $\therefore AC^2 = AB^2 + BC^2$.

77. Given, in a ΔABC, $\angle A = \angle B + \angle C$

$\Rightarrow \angle A = 90°$, and BC is the hypotenuse.

The point equidistant from the vertices of a triangle is circum-centre of the triangle.

For a right triangle, circum-centre lies at the mid-point of the hypotenuse.

$\therefore$ The required point is the mid-point of BC.

Level 3: Assess Your Concepts

82. Given, $AB = 8$ cm and $BC = 6$ cm

$\therefore AC = \sqrt{8^2 + 6^2} = 10$ cm

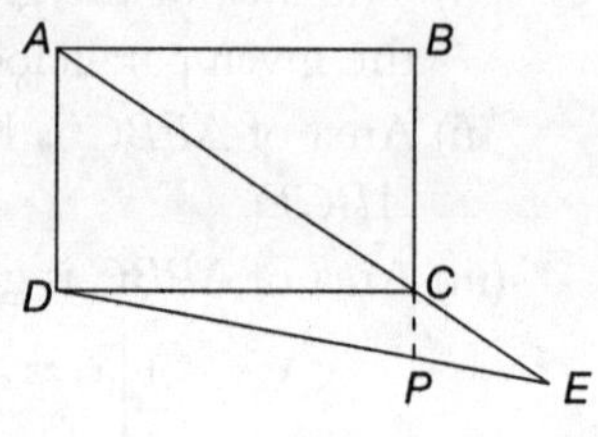

And also given $AC : CE = 2 : 1$

Produce BC to meet DE at the point P

As CP is parallel to AD,

$\Delta ECP \sim \Delta EAD$ (1)

$\therefore \frac{CP}{AD} = \frac{CE}{AE} = \frac{CP}{6} = \frac{1}{3}$

$\Rightarrow$ CP = 2 cm.

ΔCPD is a right triangle.

$\therefore DP = \sqrt{CD^2 + CP^2} = \sqrt{68} = 2\sqrt{17}$ cm

But $DP : PE = 2 : 1$ (from (1))

$PE = \sqrt{17}$ cm

$\therefore DE = DP + PE$

$= 2\sqrt{17} + \sqrt{17} = 3\sqrt{17}$ cm.

83.

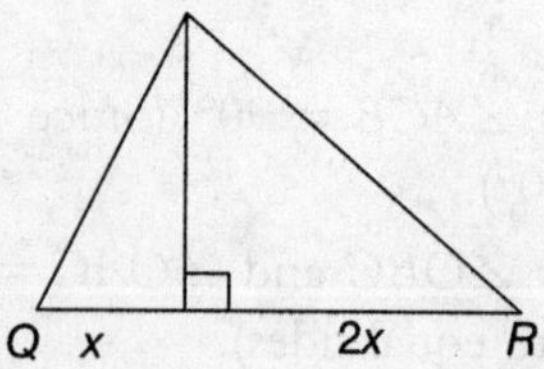

Given $PQ = 6$ cm, PR 9 cm and $QM : MR = x : 2x$

Let $QM = x$ and $MR = 2x$.

As PM is perpendicular QR, ΔPMQ and ΔPMR are right triangles.

$\therefore (PM)^2 = (OQ)^2 - (QM)^2$

$(PM)^2 = (PR)^2 - (MR)^2$ (2)

From Eqs. (1) and (2), we $(PQ)^2 - (QM)^2 = (PR)^2 - (MR)^2$

$(6)^2 - (x)^2 = (9)^2 - (2x)^2$

$\Rightarrow 3x^2 = 45 \Rightarrow x^2 = 15 \Rightarrow x = 15$ cm

$\therefore QR = 3\sqrt{15}$ cm.

84. $PQ = \frac{1}{3}(CD) + \frac{2}{3}(AB)$

$= \frac{1}{3}(12) + \frac{2}{3}(9) = 10$ cm.

85. Let $AB = BC = AC = 3x$

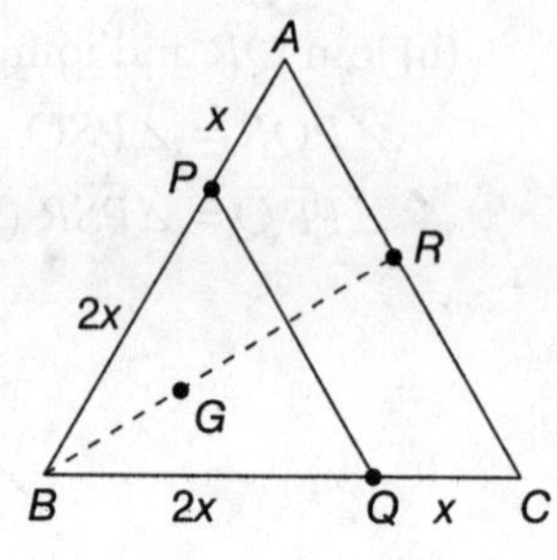

$\therefore BP = BQ = PQ = 2x$

($\because AP : BP = CQ : BQ = 1 : 2$)

As ΔBPQ and ΔBAC are equilateral triangle, the centroid of ΔBPQ lies on BR (where BR is median drawn on to AC)

We know that centroid divides the median in the ratio 2 : 1.

$\therefore BG = \frac{2\left[\frac{\sqrt{3}(2x)}{2}\right]}{3} = \frac{2\sqrt{3}x}{3}$

But $BR = \frac{\sqrt{3}(3x)}{2} = \frac{3\sqrt{3}x}{2}$

Now $GR = BR - BG$

$= \frac{3\sqrt{3}x}{2} - \frac{2\sqrt{3}x}{3} = \frac{5\sqrt{3}x}{6}$

Now $BG : GR = \frac{2\sqrt{3}x}{3} : \frac{5\sqrt{3}x}{6} = 4 : 5$.

86. Given $\angle NQR = 85°$

But $\angle NQR = \angle MQP$ ($\because$ Vertically opposite angles)

$\therefore \angle MQP = 85°$

By alternate segment theorem $\angle NQR = \angle QAB$

$\therefore \angle QAB = 85°$ and $\angle MQP = \angle QBA$

$\therefore \angle QBA = 85°$

In ΔAQB, $\angle AQB = 180° - (85° + 85°) = 10°$.

87. Two sides of *a* triangle 5 cm and 12 cm.

Let $a = 5$ cm and $b = 12$ cm

Let the third side be x cm

$\therefore 12 - 5 < x < 12 + 5$

$\Rightarrow 7 < x < 17$

$\therefore$ Possible integer values for x are 8, 9, 10, 11, 12, 13, 14, 15 and 16.

Case 1: If b is the longest side then $b^2 > a^2 + x^2$

$\Rightarrow 12^2 > 5^2 + x^2$

$\Rightarrow 144 - 25 > x^2$

$\Rightarrow x^2 < 119$

$\therefore x$ can be 8, 9 or 10.

Case 2: If x is the longest side, then $x^2 > a^2 + b^2$

$\Rightarrow x^2 > 5^2 + 12^2 \Rightarrow x^2 \Rightarrow 169$

$\therefore x$ can be 14, 15 or 16.

$\therefore$ Number of possible triangles

$= 6$ ($\because$ The measurement third side is an integer in cm).

88. Given $QR = QM = PM$ and $\angle MQR = 40°$

In ΔQMR, $QM = QR$

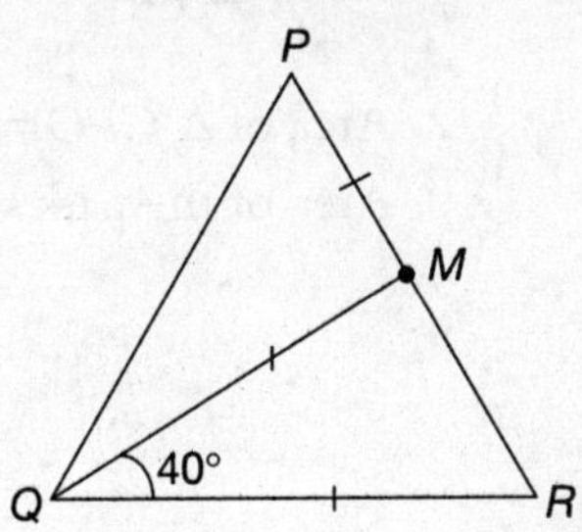

$\therefore \angle QRM = \angle QMR$

Now $\angle QRM = \angle QMR$

$= \frac{1}{2}(180° - 40°) = 70°$

In ΔMPQ, $PM = MQ$

$\angle PQM = \angle MPQ$ (1)

But $\angle PQM + \angle MPQ = \angle QMR = 70°$ (2)

From Eqs. (1) and (2),

$\angle MPQ = \frac{1}{2}(70°) = 35°$.

89.

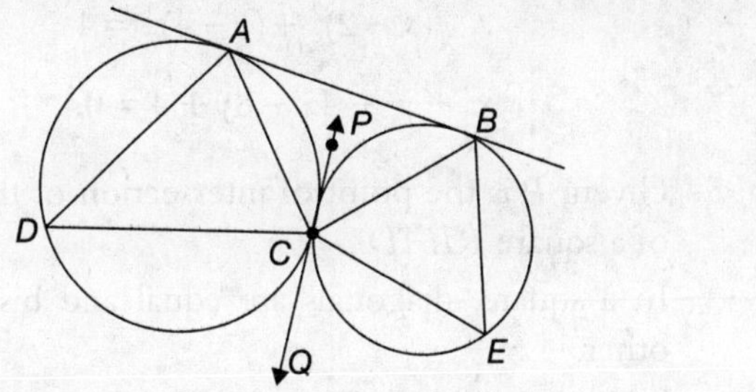

Join AC and BC

Draw a common tangent to the circles through the point C.

Let

$\angle ADC = x$ and $\angle BEC = y$ (1)

By alternate segment theorem, $\angle ADC = \angle BAC$,

$\angle ADC = \angle ACP$

$\therefore \angle BAC = \angle ACP = X$

and also $\angle BEC = \angle CBA$, $\angle BEC = \angle BCP$

$\therefore \angle CBA = \angle BCP = y$

In ΔABC, $\angle BAC + \angle CBA + \angle ACB = 180°$

$x + y + (x + y) = 180° \Rightarrow x + y = 90°$ (2)

From (1) and (2), we have

$\angle ADC + \angle BEC = 90°$.

90. (i) Area of triangle is given by

$$\frac{1}{2}\begin{vmatrix} x_1 - x_2 & x_2 - x_3 \\ y_1 - y_2 & y_2 - y_3 \end{vmatrix}.$$

(ii) Substitute $(x_2, y_2) = (1, 1)$, $(x_3, y_3) = (1, 0)$ and obtain the relation in terms of x_1 and y_1.

91. (i) If $xy > 0$, then $x > 0, y > 0$ (or) $x < 0, y < 0$.

(ii) Given, $OP = 2$, where $O = (0, 0)$ and $P = (x, y)$.

(iii) Substitute the values and obtain the locus.

93. Area of $A(2, 4)$, $B(4, 4)$, and $C(x, y)$ is 2 sq. units.

$$\frac{1}{2}\begin{vmatrix} 2-4 & 4-x \\ 4-4 & 4-y \end{vmatrix} = 2$$

$$\begin{vmatrix} -2 & 4-x \\ 0 & 4-y \end{vmatrix} = 4 \Rightarrow |2y - 8| = 4$$

$\Rightarrow |y - 4| = 2 \Rightarrow y - 4 = \pm 2$

$\Rightarrow y - 6 = 0$ or $y - 2 = 0$.

94. The required locus is a circle of radius 4 units and passing through point (2, 4).

Let $P(x, y)$ be any point on the locus.

$$\therefore \sqrt{(x-2)^2+(y-4)^2}=4$$

$$x^2+y^2-4x-8y+4=0.$$

95. Given, P is the point of intersection of the diagonals of a square $READ$.

In a square, diagonals are equal and bisect to each other.

$\therefore$ P is equidistant from the vertices.

As P lies on the diagonals, P is equidistant from any two adjacent sides.

$\therefore$ Hence, the correct answer is option (d).

96. When a coin is moving on the circumference of a square, the path of the center of the coin is a square.

$\therefore$ The required locus is a square of side (5 – 2) cm, i.e., 3 cm.

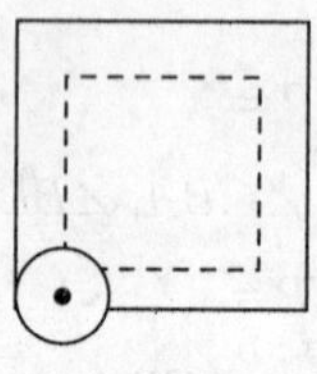

97. Given, $AB = 40$ cm, $BC = 41$ cm and $AC = 9$ cm.

$\therefore$ ABC is right triangle, right angled at A.

$\therefore$ Ortho-centre lies at A.

$\therefore$ Hence, the correct answer is option (c).

98. Given, O is equidistant from BC and CD.

$\therefore$ O lies on the bisector of $\angle BCD$, i.e., $\overline{AC}$.

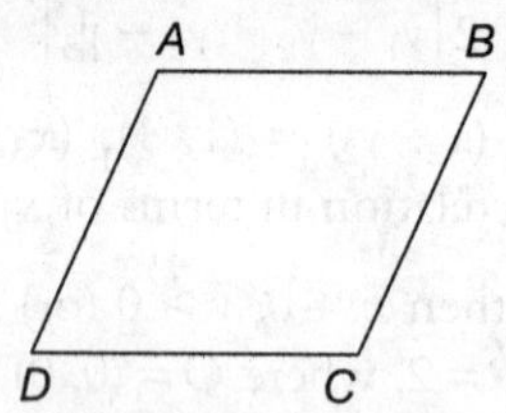

99. The required locus is the union of the locus passing through the origin and making angles of 45° and 135° with the X-axis in positive direction.

That is, $x = |y|$ or $y = |x|$.

100. Here, P is the point of intersection of bisectors of $\angle B$ and $\angle C$.

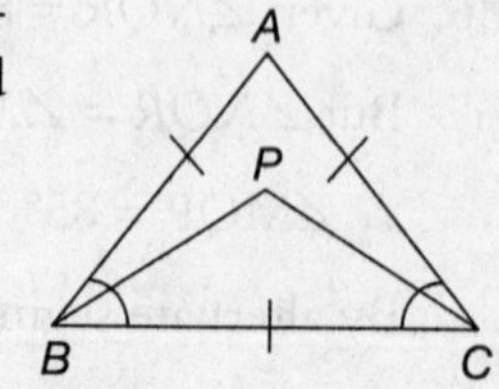

$\therefore \angle PBC = \angle PCB = 30°$

$\Rightarrow \angle BPC = 180° - (30° + 30°)$
$= 120°.$

101. The sides of the pentagon are in the ratio 20: 21. As shown in the figure, the pentagon can be divided into five congruent triangles.

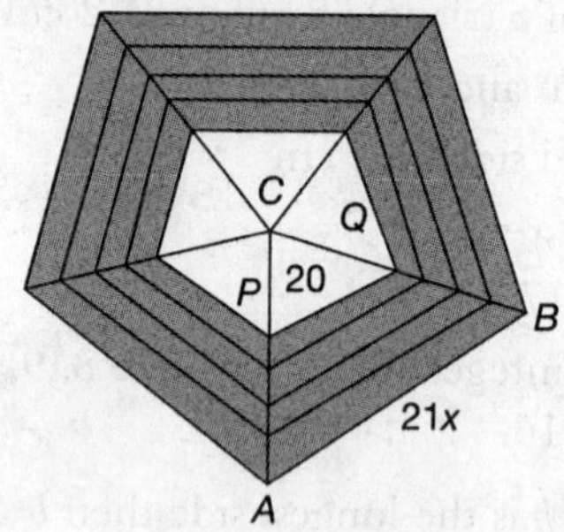

If $AB: PQ = 21: 20$

$$\frac{Ar\Delta ABC}{Ar\Delta CPQ}=\frac{(21x)^2}{(20x)^2}=\frac{441}{400}$$

Total area of the path 820 sq.m

$$\text{Area of } \Delta ABQP = \frac{820}{5} = 164 \text{ sq.m}$$

$Ar(\Delta CPQ) = 400y$ and $Ar(\Delta ABC) = 441y$

$\therefore$ Area of trapezium $PABQ$

$= 441y - 400y = 164$

$\Rightarrow 41y = 164$

$$y=\frac{164}{41}=4$$

$\therefore$ Area of Δ $CPQ = 400 \times 4 = 1600$ sq.m

$\therefore$ Area of the park $= 1600 \times 5 = 8000$ sq.m

JEE Special Wing

Multiple-Answer Type Questions

1. Given that two sides of an obtuse triangle are 21 cm and 29 cm.

Let the third side be x cm.

From the properties of triangles, $29 - 21 < x < 29 + 21$

i.e., $8 < x < 50$ (1)

In an obtuse triangle, the square of the longer side is greater than the sum of the squares of the shorter sides.

(i) If x is the measure of longer side, $x^2 > 29^2 + 21^2$.

$x^2 > 841 + 441$

$x^2 > 1282$

$x > \sqrt{1282}$

$x > 35.8$ (2)

From (1) and (2), $35.8 < x < 50$.

(ii) If 29 is the measure of longer side, $29^2 > x^2 + 21^2$.

$x^2 < 29^2 - 21^2$

$x^2 < 841 - 441$

$x^2 < 400$

$x < 20$ (3)

From (1) and (3), $8 < x < 20$.

Hence, the third side (x) of the obtuse triangle can be $8 < x < 20$ or $35.8 < x < 50$.

Hence, the choices (a, c, d) are correct.

2. Given that two sides of an acute triangle are 17 cm and 22 cm.

Let the third side be x cm.

From the properties of triangles, $22 - 17 < x < 22 + 17$

i.e., $5 < x < 39$ (1)

In an acute triangle, the square of the longer side is less than the sum of the squares of the shorter sides.

(i) If x is the measure of longer side, $x^2 < 22^2 + 17^2$.

$x^2 < 484 + 289$

$x^2 < 773$

$x < \sqrt{773}$

$x < 27.8$ (2)

Hence, $22 \le x < 27.8$ (3)

(ii) If 22 is the measure of longer side, $22^2 < x^2 + 17^2$.

$x^2 > 22^2 - 17^2$

$x^2 > 484 - 289$

$x^2 > 195$

$x > \sqrt{195}$

$x > 13.96$ (3)

Hence, $13.96 < x \le 22$ (4)

From (3) and (4), $13.96 < x < 27.8$

Hence, the choices (b and c) are correct.

3. Given that T, R, and S are three points lie on a circle.

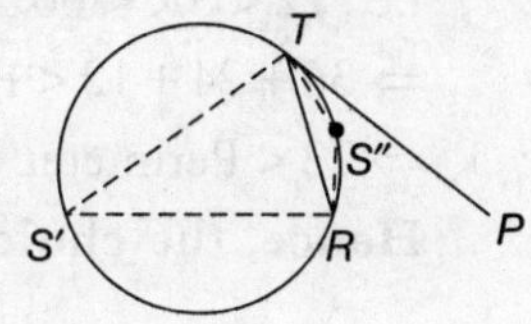

PT is a tangent drawn to the circle at T from an external point P.

$\angle PTR = 30°$.

As shown in the figure, point S can lie on major arc TR or minor arc TR. Let these points be S′ or S″ respectively.

$\angle TS'R = \angle PTR$ (By alternate segment theorem)

$\angle TS'R = 30°$.

Also, $\angle TS'R + \angle TS''R = 180°$

(Since $TS'RS''$ is a cyclic quadrilateral)

$30° + \angle TS''R = 180°$

$\angle TS''R = 150°$

So, $\angle TSR$ can be 30° or 150°.

Hence, the choices (a and d) are correct.

4. Given that the length of the direct common tangent of two circles of radii 12 cm and 3 cm is 12 cm.

The length of the direct common tangent

$= \sqrt{d^2 - (R - r)^2}$.

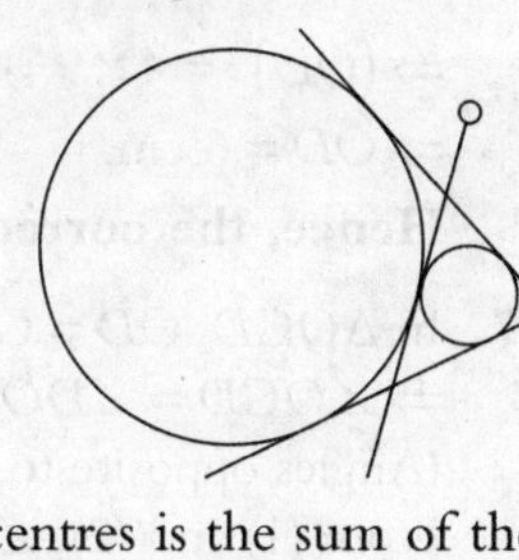

$\sqrt{d^2 - (12 - 3)^2} = 12$

$d^2 - 81 = 144$

$d^2 = 225$

$d = 15$

As the distance between the centres is the sum of the radii, the circles touch each other externally.

So, we can draw two direct common tangents and a transverse common tangent.

Hence, the choices (a and d) are correct.

5. Given that P is a point on the side RT of a triangle RST such that PR = 20 cm, PT = 16 cm, and $\angle TSR = \angle SPT$.

$TR = PR + PT = 20 + 16 = 36$ cm.

In ΔTSR and ΔTPS:

$\angle T = \angle T$ (Common Angle)

$\angle TSR = \angle TPS$ (Given)

By AA similarity, $\Delta TSR \sim \Delta TPS$.

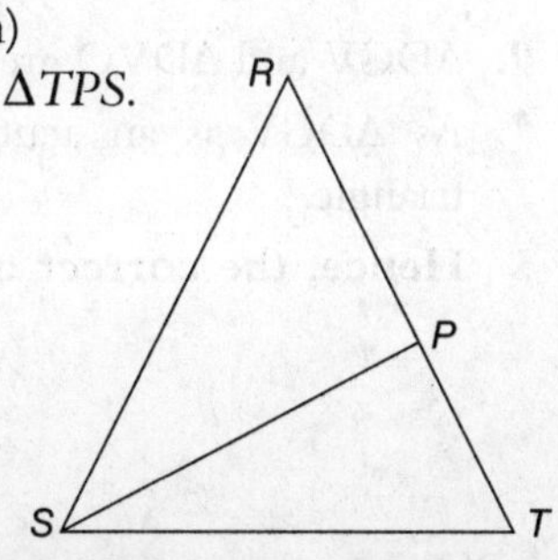

$\Rightarrow \frac{TS}{TP} = \frac{TR}{TS}$

$\Rightarrow \frac{TS}{16} = \frac{36}{TS}$

$\Rightarrow (TS)^2 = 4^2 \times 6^2$

$\Rightarrow TS = 4 \times 6 = 24$ cm.

From the properties of triangles, $36 - 24 < SR < 36 + 24$
i.e., $12 < SR < 60$ (1)
$\Rightarrow 36 + 24 + 12 <$ Perimeter of $\Delta RST < 36 + 24 + 60$
$\Rightarrow 72 <$ Perimeter of $\Delta RST < 120$
Hence, the choices (a, b, c, d) are correct.

Match The Column

Common Solutions for questions 6 to 9:
Given that OD is a tangent at D and OVG is a secant drawn to the circle.
$GV = 5$ cm, $VO = 4$ cm, and $DG = 6$ cm.
$OG = GV + VO = 5 + 4 = 9$ cm.

6. In ΔODV and ΔOGD:
$\angle O = \angle O$ (Common angle)
$\angle ODV = \angle OGD$
(By alternate segment theorem) (1)
By AA similarity, $\Delta ODV \sim \Delta OGD$.

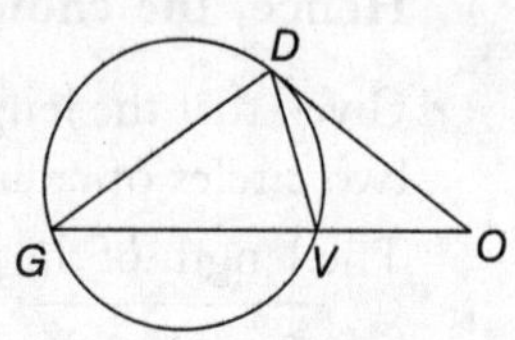

$\Rightarrow \dfrac{OD}{OG} = \dfrac{OV}{OD}$
$\Rightarrow \dfrac{OD}{9} = \dfrac{4}{OD}$
$\Rightarrow (OD)^2 = 4 \times 9$
$\Rightarrow OD = 6$ cm.
Hence, the correct option is (e).

7. In ΔOGD, $OD = GD = 6$ cm.
$\Rightarrow \angle OGD = \angle DOG$
(Angles opposite to equal sides) (2)
From (1) and (2), $\angle ODV = \angle DOG$.
$\Rightarrow \angle ODV = \angle DOV$
$\Rightarrow VO = DV$ (Sides opposite to equal angles)
$\Rightarrow DV = 4$ cm.
Hence, the correct option is (f).

8. In ΔDGV, $DG = 6$ cm, $GV = 5$ cm, and $DV = 4$ cm.
$\Rightarrow (6)^2 < (5)^2 + (4)^2$.
$\Rightarrow (DG)^2 < (GV)^2 + (DV)^2$.
Hence, ΔDGV is an acute triangle.
Hence, the correct option is (a).

9. ΔDGV and ΔDVO are sharing the side DV.
As ΔDGV is an acute triangle, ΔDVO an obtuse triangle.
Hence, the correct option is (b).

Comprehension-Based Questions

Common Solutions for questions 10 to 14:
Given that PQR is a tangent drawn to the circles with centres V and U at Q and R respectively.
PST is another tangent drawn to the circles with centres V and U at S and T respectively.
$VQ = VS = 20$ cm and $UR = UT = 45$ cm.

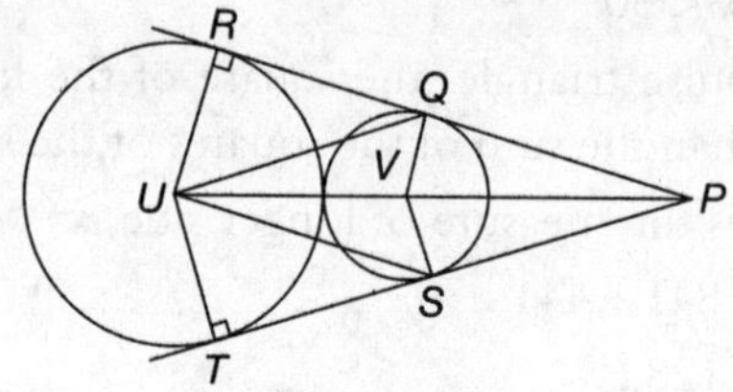

10. $RQ = \sqrt{(UV)^2 - (UR - VQ)^2}$
$= \sqrt{(45+20)^2 - (45-20)^2}$
$= \sqrt{(65)^2 - (25)^2}$
$= \sqrt{(90)(40)} = 60$ cm.
The perimeter of quadrilateral $RQVU$
$= RQ + QV + UV + RU$
$= 60 + 20 + 65 + 45 = 190$ cm.
Hence, the correct option is (a).

11. In ΔQRU, $\angle QRU = 90°$.
$QU = \sqrt{(QR)^2 + (UR)^2}$
$= \sqrt{(60)^2 + (45)^2}$
$= \sqrt{3600 + 2025}$
$= \sqrt{5625} = 75$ cm.
Hence, the correct option is (b).

12. In ΔPQV and ΔPRU, $QV \parallel RU$.
$\Rightarrow \angle PQV = \angle PRU$ and $\angle PVQ = \angle PUR$.
By AA similarity, $\Delta PQV \sim \Delta PRU$.
$\Rightarrow \dfrac{PQ}{PR} = \dfrac{QV}{RU} = \dfrac{PV}{PU}$
$\Rightarrow \dfrac{PQ}{PQ+60} = \dfrac{20}{45} = \dfrac{PV}{PV+65}$
$\Rightarrow \dfrac{PQ}{PQ+60} = \dfrac{4}{9} = \dfrac{PV}{PV+65}$
$\Rightarrow 9PQ = 4PQ + 240$ cm and $9PV = 4PV + 260$ cm.
$\Rightarrow 5PQ = 240$ cm and $5PV = 260$ cm.
$\Rightarrow PQ = 48$ cm and $PV = 52$ cm.
$\therefore PV - PQ = 52 - 48 = 4$ cm.
Hence, the correct option is (c).

13. Given that $\angle SPV = x$.
$\Rightarrow \angle SPV = \angle TPU = x$.
$\Rightarrow \angle TPR = 2\angle SPV = 2x$.
In quadrilateral $TPRU$, $\angle TPR + \angle RUT = 180°$.
$\Rightarrow 2x + \angle RUT = 180°$.
$\Rightarrow \angle RUT = 180° - 2x$.
$\Rightarrow$ Reflex $\angle RUT = 360° - (180° - 2x)$
$= 180° + 2x$
Hence, the correct option is (d).

14. Pairs of congruent triangles are as follows:
$\Delta PQV \cong \Delta PSV$
$\Delta PQU \cong \Delta PSU$
$\Delta VQU \cong \Delta VSU$
$\Delta QRU \cong \Delta STU$
$\Delta PRU \cong \Delta PTU$
Hence, there are five pairs of congruent triangles.
Hence, the correct option is (c).

Assertion and Reason Type Questions

15. **Assertion:** Given that $\Delta ABC \sim \Delta PQR$.
We know that the ratio of the areas of similar triangles is the square of the ratio of their perimeters.
$9 : 15 = (\text{Perimeter of } \Delta ABC)^2 : (\text{Perimeter of } \Delta PQR)^2$
$(\text{Perimeter of } \Delta ABC)^2 : (\text{Perimeter of } \Delta PQR)^2 = 3 : 5$
$(\text{Perimeter of } \Delta ABC) : \text{Perimeter of } \Delta PQR = \sqrt{3} : \sqrt{5}$.
So, **Assertion** is true.
Reason: The ratio of the areas of two similar triangles is the square of the ratio of their perimeters.
So, **Reason** is true and is the correct explanation to **Assertion**.
Hence, the correct option is (a).

16. **Assertion:** The tangents drawn to a circle from an eternal point are equal.
So, **Assertion** is true.
Reason: The tangent at any point on a circle is perpendicular to the radius through the point of contact.
So, **Reason** is true and not the correct explanation to **Assertion**.
Hence, the correct option is (b).

17. **Assertion:** If $ABCD$ is a cyclic quadrilateral and $\angle ABC = 60°$, then $\angle ADC = 120°$. It is a true statement since the opposite angles of a cyclic quadrilateral are supplementary.
Reason: In a cyclic quadrilateral, a pair of opposite angles are supplementary. One of them need not be twice the other.
So, **Reason** is false.
Hence, the correct option is (c).

18. **Assertion:** PT is a tangent at T and PAB is a secant drawn to a circle. If $PT = 24$ cm and $AB = 20$ cm, then $PA = 18$ cm.

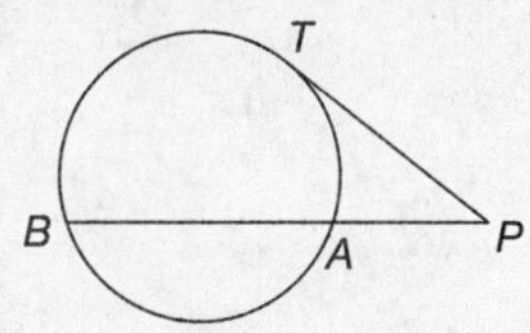

We have $(PT)^2 = PA \times PB$.
$(24)^2 = 18 \times 38$, which is false.
So, **Assertion** is false.
Reason: If PT is a tangent at T and PAB is a secant drawn to a circle, then $(PT)^2 = PA \times PB$.
Reason is a true statement.
Hence, the correct option is (d).

CHAPTER

8

Mensuration

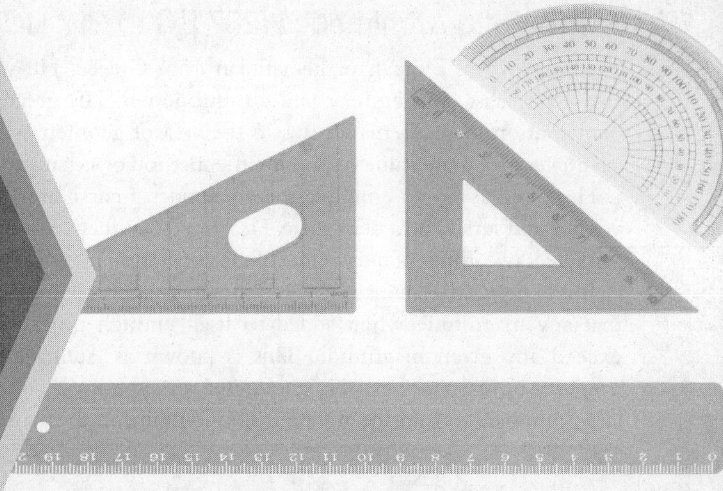

Remember

Before beginning this chapter, you should be able to:

- Explain polygons and their properties
- Use circles, circumference of a circle, sector of a circle in solving mathematical problems

Key Ideas

After completing this chapter, you should be able to:

- Calculate perimeters and areas of plane figures
- Study types of prisms, and pyramids and calculate lateral, total surface areas, and volumes of prisms and pyramids
- Compute curved, total surface area, and volume of cylinder and cone
- Obtain surface area and volume of sphere, hemisphere, and hollow sphere

Scientific Crypt

A Tribute to Archimedes (287 BC to 212 BC)

Archimedes was a great mathematician from Greece. He was also a physicist, an engineer and an astronomer. His greatest contribution to mathematics was in the area of geometry. He gave a very accurate value of pi using the method of exhaustion.

He found a way to compute the area under a curve and the volume and surface area of a sphere. He proved that the volume of a sphere is two-thirds of the volume of the circumscribing cylinder.

It is believed that he had invented integral calculus. He stated that any magnitude when added to itself enough times will exceed any given magnitude. This is known as Archimedes property of real numbers. He conducted an experiment using large numbers to find the number of sand grains in the world. In the process, he used powers of numbers like 101, 102, etc.

Other inventions/discoveries:

He invented a pump known as the Archimedean screw, which was used to draw and spray water directly from a low-lying water body to the fields. He discovered the buoyancy principle, which made it possible to compare the densities of metals. His theorem which gives the weight of a body immersed in a liquid, is known as Archimedes' principle.

He had a clear understanding of the functioning of a lever. He stated 'Give me a place to stand, and a lever long enough, I will move the world.'

FUN TIME

CROSSWORD

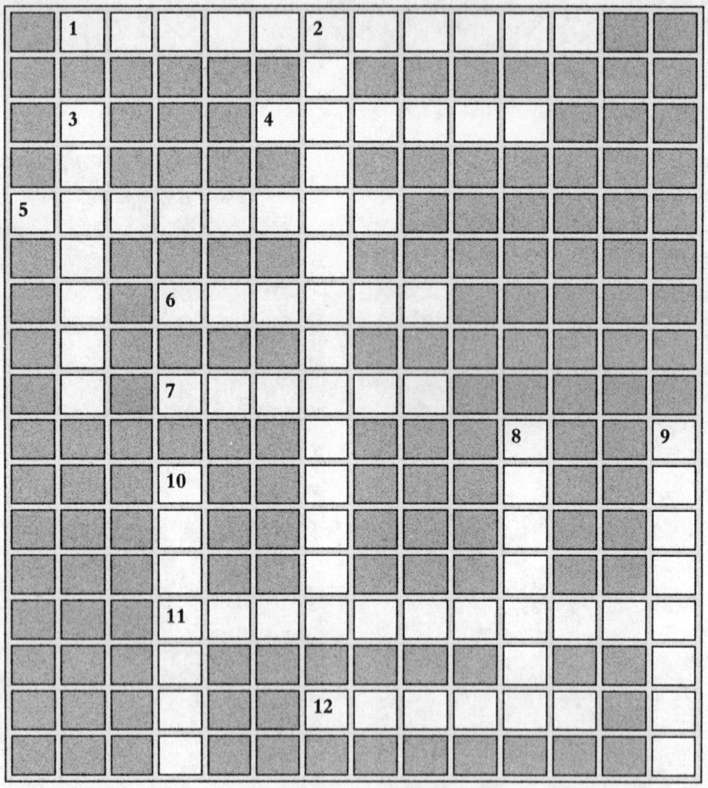

Across

1. Two equal pieces of a cricket ball
4. All the cubes and cuboids are
5. The vertical cross-section of a solid cone.
6. A solid but only one measure is enough to determine it.
7. A prism of rectangular base
11. A branch of mathematics that deals with the computation of geometric magnitudes.
12. A solid is melted and recast into another form, but one of its measures will not be changed.

Down

2. The lateral faces of a prism.
3. The vertices of a polygon are joined to a point in the space.
8. Conical bucket
9. Its volume will be 3 times to that of a cone whose base radii are equal and heights are equal.
10. It is a part of a circular region.

INTRODUCTION

Mensuration is a branch of mathematics that deals with the computation of geometric magnitudes, such as the length of a line, the area of a surface and the volume of a solid. In this chapter, we will deal with the areas and volumes of three dimensional figures like prisms, pyramids, cones, spheres, hemispheres, etc. However, some problems on plane figures like circles, sectors, segments, etc., as an exercise of revision.

Circle and Semi-Circle

1. Area of circle = πr^2 sq. units.
2. Area of the semicircle = $\dfrac{\pi r^2}{2}$ sq. units.
3. Circumference of the circle = $2\pi r$ units = πd units
4. Circumference of the semicircle = $(\pi + 2)r$ units

   $= \dfrac{36r}{7}$ units (Where r is radius and d is diameter)

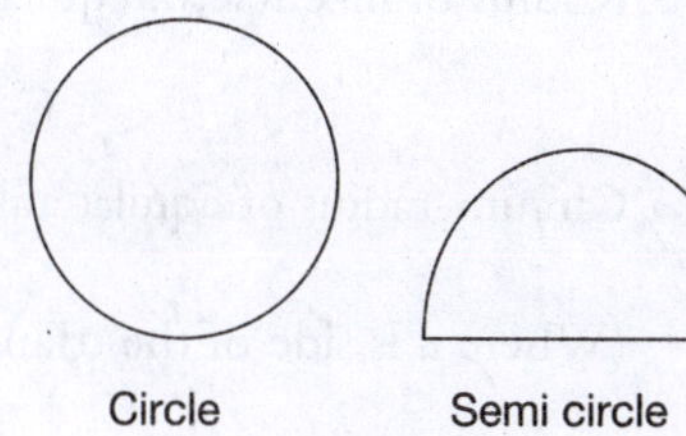

Figure 8.1

Circular Ring

Area of the ring = $\pi(R^2 - r^2) = \pi(R + r)(R - r)$

(Where R and r are outer radius and inner radius of a ring and $(R - r)$ is the width of the ring)

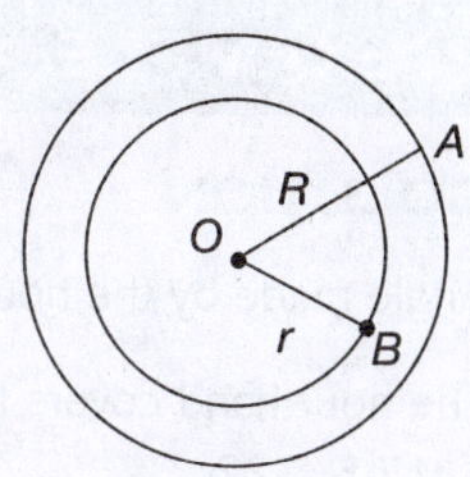

Figure 8.2

Sectors and Segements

1. Length of the arc ACB

   $l = \left(\dfrac{\theta}{360°}\right) 2\pi r$ units.

2. Area of the sector $AOBC$

   $A = \left(\dfrac{\theta}{360°}\right) \pi r^2$ sq. units.

3. Perimeter of the sector = $(l + 2r)$ units.
4. Area of the segment $ACB = (A -$ Area of the $\Delta AOB)$ sq. units.
5. Perimeter of the segment ACB = (Length of arc $ACB + AB$) units.
   (Where r is the radius of the circle and θ is sector angle)

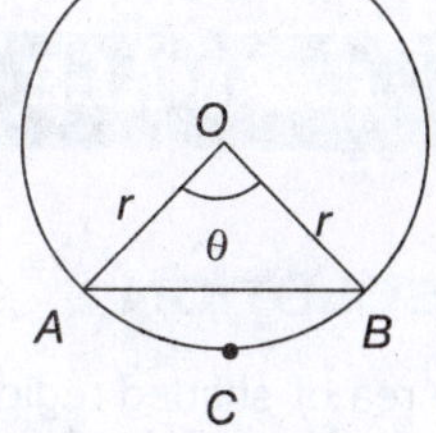

Figure 8.3

Rotations Made by a Wheel

1. Distance covered by a wheel in one revolution = Circumference of the wheel.
2. Number of rotations made by a wheel in unit time $= \dfrac{\text{Distance covered by it in unit time}}{\text{Circumference of the wheel}}$.
3. Angle made by minute hand in one minute $= \dfrac{360°}{60} = 6°$.
4. Angle made by hour hand in one minute $= \dfrac{30°}{60} = \left(\dfrac{1}{2}\right)^{\circ}$.

Equilateral Triangle

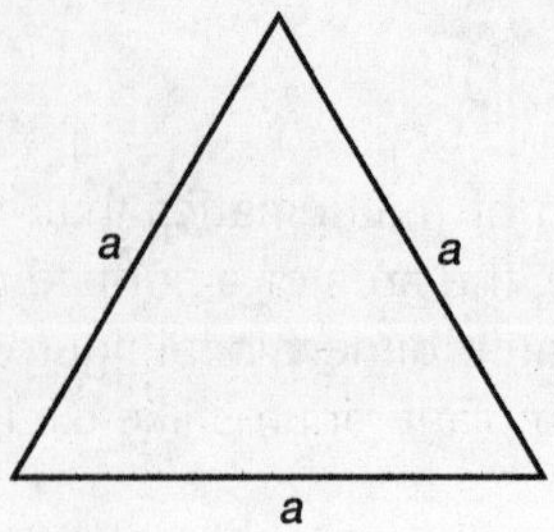

1. Circumference of an equilateral triangle = $3a$ units.
2. Area of the equilateral triangle $= \frac{\sqrt{3}a^2}{4}$ sq. units.
3. Height of the equilateral triangle $= \frac{\sqrt{3}a}{2}$ units.
4. Radius of in-circle of equilateral triangle $= \frac{1}{3}\left(\frac{\sqrt{3}a}{2}\right) = \frac{a}{2\sqrt{3}}$ units.
5. Circum-radius of equilateral triangle $= \frac{2}{3}\left(\frac{\sqrt{3}a}{2}\right) = \frac{a}{\sqrt{3}}$ units.

(Where a is side of the triangle)

Info Bytes!

The equilateral triangle is the only triangle where the triangle inequality (the sum of any two sides must be greater than or equal to the third side) becomes an equality.

EXAMPLE 8.1 The hour hand of a clock is 6 cm long. Find the area swept by it between 11:20 am and 11:55 am. (in cm^2)

SOLUTION

Angle made by the hours hand in 35 min = $35 \times \frac{1}{2} = 17.5°$.

The hour hand covers the area equal to the sector of radius 6 cm and angle 17.5°

$= \frac{17.5}{360} \times \frac{22}{7} \times (6)^2$

$= \frac{1}{10} \times \frac{35}{2} \times \frac{22}{7} = 5.5\,\text{cm}^2$

EXAMPLE 8.2 In the figure given below, *ABCD* is a square of side 7 cm. *BD* is an arc of a circle of radius *AB*. What is the area of the shaded region?

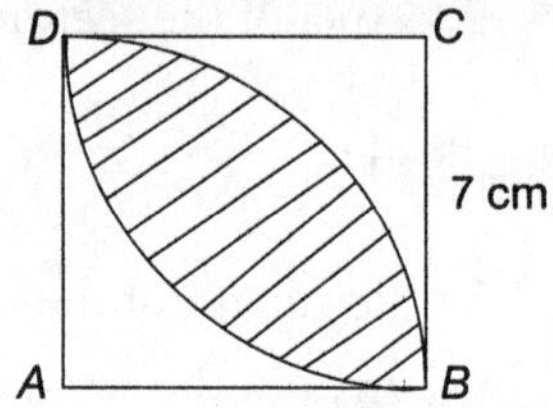

SOLUTION

Area of shaded region = $2(\text{Area of sector } \overline{BAD} - \text{Area of } \Delta ABD)$.

$= 2\left[\frac{90}{360} \times \frac{22}{7} \times 7^2 - \frac{1}{2} \times 7^2\right]$

$= 2\left[\frac{1}{4} \times 154 - \frac{49}{2}\right]$

$= \frac{2}{2}[77 - 49]$

= 28 sq cm.

Prisms

Prism is a solid in which two congruent and parallel polygons form the top and the bottom faces. The lateral faces are parallelograms. The line joining the centres of the two parallel polygons is called the axis of the prism and the length of the axis is referred to as the height of prism.

If two parallel and congruent polygons are regular and if the axis is perpendicular to the base, then the prism is called a right prism. The lateral surfaces of a right prism are rectangles.

Consider two congruent and parallel triangular planes ABC and PQR. If we join the corresponding vertices of both the planes, i.e., A to P, B to Q, and C to R, then the resultant solid formed is a triangular prism. A right prism, the base of which is a rectangle is called a cuboid and the one, the base of which is a pentagon is called a pentagonal prism. If all the faces of the solid are congruent, it is a cube. In case of a cube or a cuboid, any face may be the base of the prism. A prism whose base and top faces are squares but the lateral faces are rectangular is called a square prism.

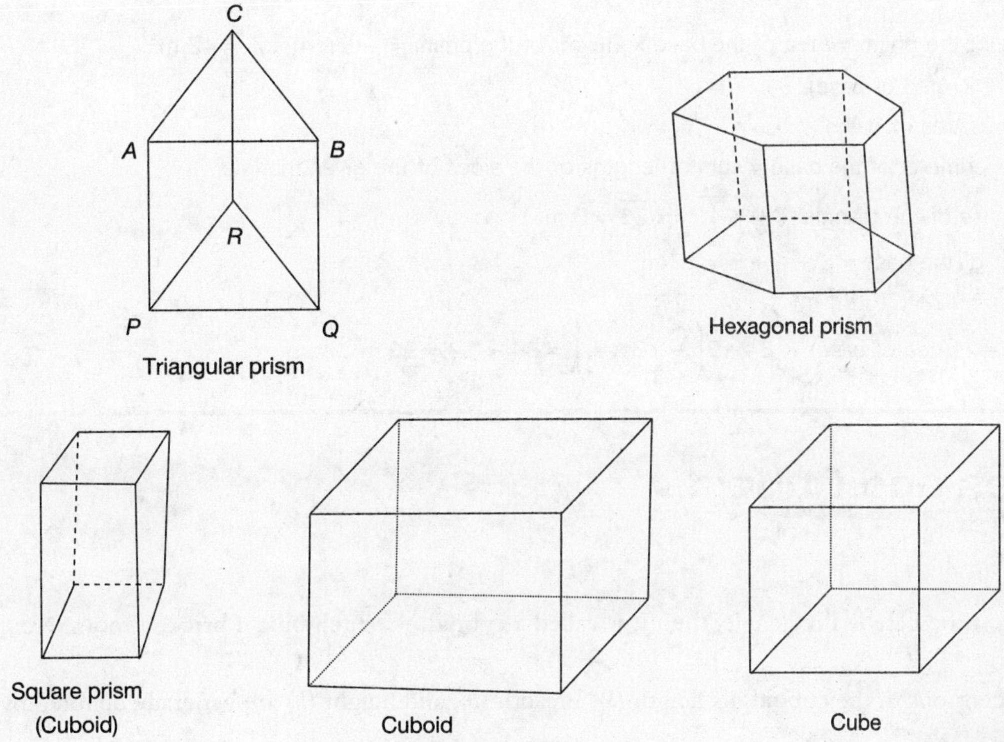

Figure 8.4

1. The number of lateral faces = The number of sides of the base.
2. The number of edges of a prism = Number of sides of the base × 3.
3. The sum of the lengths of the edges = 2(Perimeter of base) + Number of sides × Height.

Konnect

The following points hold good for all prisms.

Lateral Surface Area (LSA) of a Prism

LSA = Perimeter of base × Height = ph

Total Surface Area (TSA) of a Prism

TSA = LSA + 2(Area of base)

Volume of a Prism

Volume = Area of base × Height = Ah

Konnect

The volume of water flowing in a canal = The cross section area of the canal × The speed of water.

EXAMPLE 8.3 The base of a right prism is a right angled triangle. The measure of the base of the right-angled triangle is 3 m and its height 4 m. If the height of the prism is 7 m, then find,

(a) the number of edges of the prism.
(b) the volume of the prism.
(c) the total surface area of the prism.

SOLUTION

(a) The number of the edges = The number of sides of the base × 3 = 3 × 3 = 9.

(b) The volume of the prism = Area of the base × Height of the prism = $\frac{1}{2}(3 \times 4) \times 7 = 42$ m^3.

(c) TSA = LSA + 2(Area of base)

$= ph + 2(\text{Area of base})$

where, p = Perimeter of the base = sum of lengths of the sides of the given triangle.

As, hypotenuse of the triangle $\sqrt{3^2 + 4^2} = \sqrt{25} = 5$ m

∴ Perimeter of the base = 3 + 4 + 5 = 12 m

⇒ LSA = $ph = 12 \times 7 = 84$ m^2.

TSA = LSA + 2(Area of base) = $84 + 2\left(\frac{1}{2} \times 3 \times 4\right) = 84 + 12 = 96$ m^2.

Cubes and Cuboids

Cuboid

In a right prism, if the base is a rectangle, then it is called a cuboid. A match box, a brick, a room, etc., are in the shape of a cuboid.

The three dimensions of the cuboid, its length (l), breadth (b), and height (h) are generally denoted by $l \times b \times h$.

1. The lateral surface area of a cuboid = $ph = 2(l + b)h$ sq. units, where p is the perimeter of the base.
2. The total surface area of a cuboid = LSA + 2(Base area) = $2(l + b)h + 2lb = 2(lb + bh + lh)$ sq. units.
3. The volume of a cuboid = $Ah = (lb)h = lbh$ cubic units, where A is the area of the base.
4. Diagonal of cuboid $= \sqrt{l^2 + b^2 + h^2}$ units

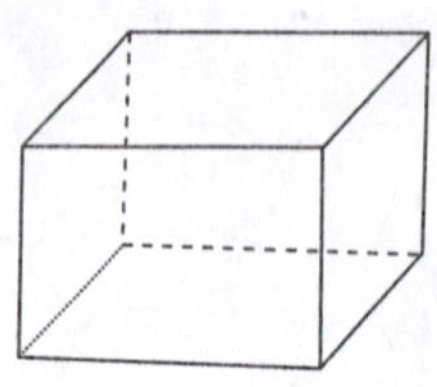

Figure 8.5 Cuboid

Konnect

If a box made of wood of thickness t has inner dimensions of l, b, and h, then

The outer length = $l + 2t$,

The outer breadth = $b + 2t$ and

The outer height = $h + 2t$.

Cube

In a cuboid, if all the dimensions, i.e., its length, breadth and height are equal, then the solid is called a cube.

All the edges of a cube are equal in length and each edge is called the side of the cube.

Thus, the size of a cube is completely determined by its side.

If the side of cube is 'a' units, then

1. The lateral surface area of a cube = $4a^2$ sq. units.
2. The total surface area of a cube = LSA + 2(Area of base) = $4a^2 + 2a^2 = 6a^2$ sq. units.
3. The volume of a cube = a^3 cubic units.
4. The diagonal of a cube = $\sqrt{a^2 + a^2 + a^2} = \sqrt{3}a$ units.

Konnect

If the inner edge of a cube made of wood of thickness 't' is 'a' units, then the outer edge of the cube is given by $(a + 2t)$ units.

EXAMPLE 8.4 The dimensions of a room are 12 m × 7 m × 5 m. Find:

(a) the diagonal of the room.
(b) the cost of flooring at the rate of ₹2 per m^2.
(c) the cost of whitewashing the room excluding the floor at the rate of ₹3 per m^2.

SOLUTION

(a) The diagonal of the room = $\sqrt{l^2 + b^2 + h^2} = \sqrt{12^2 + 7^2 + 5^2} = \sqrt{144 + 49 + 25} = \sqrt{218}$ m.

(b) To find the cost of the flooring, we should know the area of the base.

Base area = $lb = 12 \times 7 = 84\ m^2$

∴ The cost of flooring = 84 × 2 = ₹168.

(c) The total area that is to be whitewashed

$= \text{LSA} + \text{Area of roof} = 2(l + b)h + lb$

$= 2(12 + 7)5 + 12 \times 7 = 2(19)\ (5) + 84$

$= 190 + 84$

$= 274\ m^2$

∴ The cost of whitewashing = 274 × 3 = ₹822.

EXAMPLE 8.5 A box is in the form of a cube. Its edge is 5 m long. Find:

(a) the total length of the edges.
(b) the cost of painting the outside of the box, on all the surfaces, at the rate of ₹5 per m^2.
(c) the volume of liquid which the box can hold.

SOLUTION

(a) Length of edges = Number of edges of base × 3 × Length of each edge = 4 × 3 × 5 = 60 m.

(b) To find the cost of painting the box, we need to find the total surface area.

TSA = $6a^2 = 6 \times 5^2 = 6 \times 25 = 150\ m^2$

∴ Cost of painting = 150 × 5 = ₹750.

(c) Volume = $a^3 = 5^3 = 125\ m^3$. ∴ The cost of whitewashing = 274 × 3 = ₹822.

EXAMPLE 8.6 The areas of three different faces of a cuboidal box are 24 cm^2, 60 cm^2 and 90 cm^2. Find the longest edge of the cuboid (in cm).

SOLUTION

Let the length, breadth and height of a cuboid be l, b and h.

bh = 90 cm^2

bh = 60 cm^2

lb = 24 cm^2

$(lbh)^2 = 90 \times 60 \times 24$

$(lbh)^2 = 2 \times 3^2 \times 5 \times 2^2 \times 3 \times 5 \times 2^3 \times 3$

$(lbh)^2 = 2^6 \times 3^4 \times 5^2$

$lbh = 2^3 \times 3^2 \times 5$

$lbh = 360\ cm^3$

Greatest edge of the cuboid is $= \frac{lbh}{bh} = \frac{360}{24} = 15\text{cm}$

Right Circular Cylinder

A cylinder has two congruent and parallel circular planes which are connected by a curved surface. Each of the circular planes is called the base of the cylinder. A road roller, water pipe, power cables, round pillars are some of the objects which are in the shape of a cylinder.

In the Fig. 8.6, a right circular cylinder is shown. Let A be the centre of the top face and A' be the centre of the base. The line joining the centres (i.e., AA') is called the axis of cylinder. The length AA' is called the height of the cylinder. If the axis is perpendicular to the base, then it is a right circular cylinder. The radius r of the base of the cylinder and the height h, completely describe the cylinder.

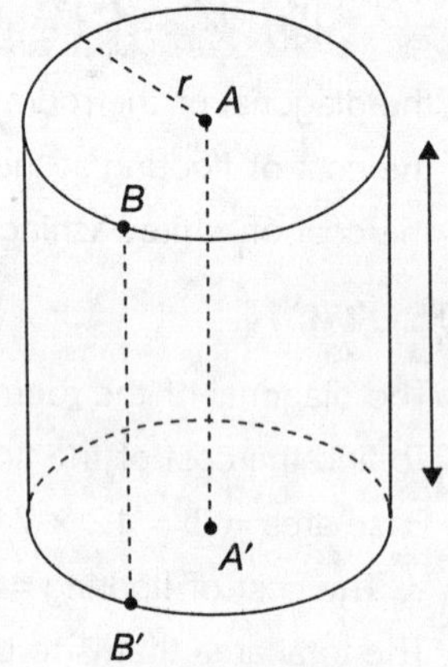

Figure 8.6

Lateral (curved) surface area = Perimeter of base × Height = $2\pi rh$ sq. units.

The total surface area = LSA + 2(Base area) = $2\pi rh + 2(\pi r^2) = 2\pi r(h + r)$ sq. units.

Volume = Area of base × Height = $\pi r^2 h$ cubic units.

Hollow Cylinder

The part of a cylinder from which a smaller cylinder of the same axis is cut out is a hollow cylinder. Let R and r be the external and internal radii of the hollow cylinder and h be the height.

Volume of the material used = $\pi R^2 h - \pi r^2 h = \pi h(R + r)(R - r)$ cubic units.

Curved surface area = $2\pi Rh + 2\pi rh = 2\pi h(R + r)$ sq. units.

Total surface area = Curved surface area + Area of the two ends.

$= 2\pi h(R + r) + 2\pi(R^2 - r^2) = 2\pi(R + r)(R - r + h)$ sq. units.

Konnect

If a plastic pipe of length l is such that its outer radius is R and the inner radius is r, then the volume of the plastic content of the pipe $= l\pi(R^2 - r^2)$ cubic units.

EXAMPLE 8.7 A rectangular piece of paper of length 11 cm and breadth 10 cm is rolled along its length to form a cylinder. Find the TSA of the cylinder (in cm^2).

SOLUTION

Base perimeter of the cylinder = length of the rectangular piece of paper = 11 cm

i.e. $2\pi r = 11$

$r = \frac{11}{2} \times \frac{7}{22}$

$r = \frac{7}{4}$ cm

Height of the cylinder = Breadth of the rectangular piece of paper = 10 cm

TSA of the cylinder $2\pi r(r + h) = 2 \times \frac{22}{7} \times \frac{7}{4}\left(\frac{7}{4} + 10\right) = 11\left(\frac{47}{4}\right) = 129\frac{1}{4}$ sq cm

EXAMPLE 8.8 A sphere and a cylinder are of a size such that the sphere can be placed exactly inside the cylinder as shown in the figure. The ratio of the CSA of the cylinder to the surface area of the sphere is ______. (Neglect the thickness of the cylinder)

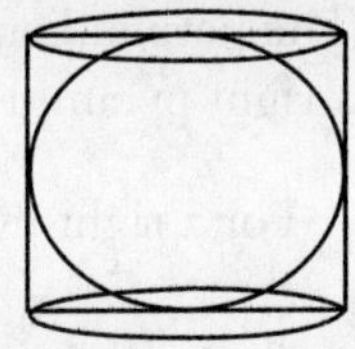

SOLUTION

Let the radius of the sphere be 'r'.

Radius of a cylinder = r

Height of the cylinder = $2r$

The ratio of CSA of the cylinder to the surface area of the sphere = $2\pi rh : 4\pi r^2$

$= 2\pi r\,(2r) : 4\pi r^2$

$= 4\pi r^2 : 4\pi r^2$

$= 1 : 1$

Pyramid

A pyramid is a solid obtained by joining the vertices of a polygon to a point in the space by straight lines. The base of the solid obtained is the polygon and lateral faces are triangles. The fixed point in space where all the triangles (i.e., lateral faces) meet is called its vertex.

In the Fig. 8.7, the base $ABCD$ is a quadrilateral. All the vertices of the base are joined to a fixed point O in space, by straight lines. The resultant solid obtained is called a pyramid.

The straight line joining the vertex and the centre of the base is called the axis of the pyramid. If the axis is not perpendicular to the base, it is an oblique pyramid.

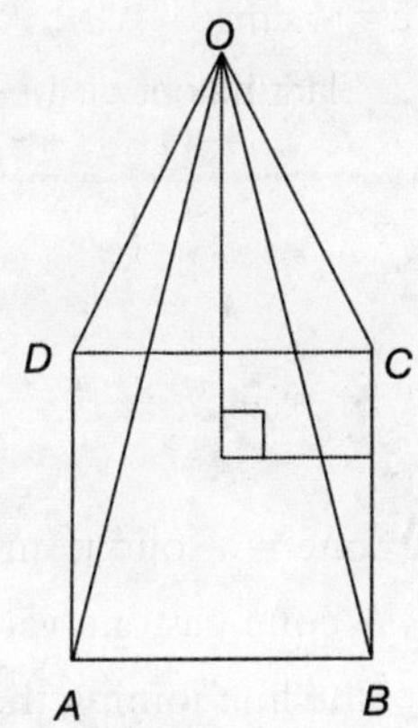

Figure 8.7

Right Pyramid

If the base of a pyramid is a regular polygon and if the line joining the vertex to the centre of the base is perpendicular to the base, then the pyramid is called a right pyramid.

The length of the line segment joining the vertex to the centre of the base of a right pyramid is called the height of the pyramid and is represented by 'h'.

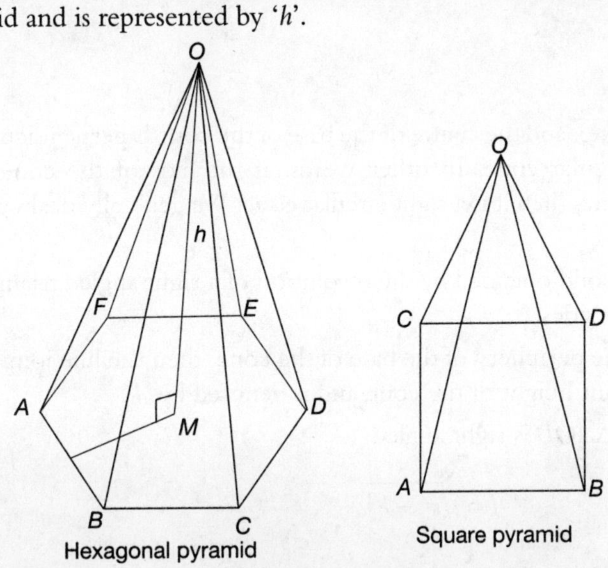

Figure 8.8

The perpendicular distance between the vertex and the mid-point of any of the sides of the base (i.e., regular polygon) of a right pyramid is called its slant height and is represented by '*l*'.

For a right pyramid with perimeter of base = p, Height = h and Slant height = l,

1. Lateral surface area = $\frac{1}{2}$ (Perimeter of base) × (Slant height) = $\frac{1}{2}pl$.
2. Total surface area = Lateral surface area + Area of base.
3. Volume of a pyramid = $\frac{1}{3}$ × Area of base × Height.

EXAMPLE 8.9 The base of a pyramid is an equilateral triangle of side 4 cm. The LSA of the pyramid is 24 cm. Find the slant height of the pyramid. (in cm).

SOLUTION

LSA of the pyramid= $\frac{1}{2}$ (Perimeter of the base × Slant height)

$\frac{1}{2} \times 3 \times 4 \times \ell = 24$

$\ell = 4$ cm

∴ Slant height of the pyramid = 4 cm

Cone

A cone is a solid pointed figure with a circular base. A cone is a kind of pyramid whose base is a circle.

A cone has one vertex, one plane surface (i.e., the base) and a curved surface (i.e., the lateral surface).

The line joining the vertex to the centre of base (i.e., AO) is called the axis of the cone. The length of the line segment AO is called the height or perpendicular height of the cone. An icecream cone and a conical tent are some of the examples of conical objects.

Right Circular Cone

In a cone, if the line joining the vertex and the centre of the base of the cone is perpendicular to the base, then it is a right circular cone. In other words, if the axis of the cone is perpendicular to the base of the cone, then it is a right circular cone. We generally deal with problems on right circular cones.

A cone is generally defined as a solid obtained by the revolution of a right angled triangle about one of its two perpendicular sides.

If we consider any point B on the periphery of the base of the cone, then the line joining B and the vertex A is called the slant height of the cone and is denoted by '*l*'.

From the figure, it is clear that ΔAOB is right angled.

∴ $$l = \sqrt{r^2 + h^2}.$$

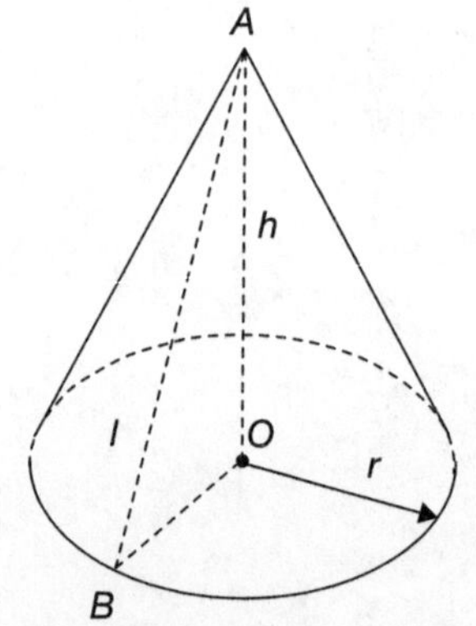

Figure 8.9 Cone

Hollow Cone

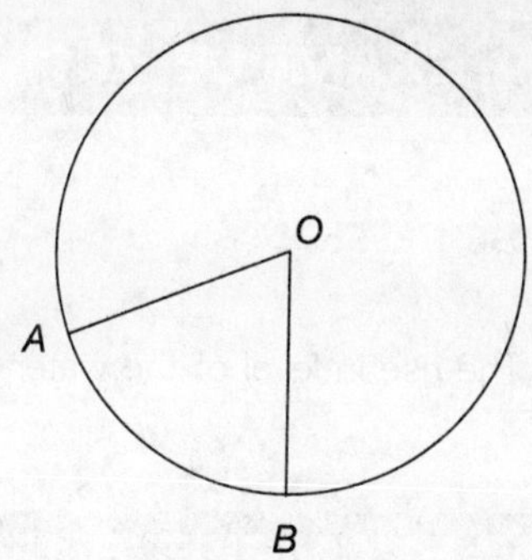

Figure 8.10

In earlier classes, we have studied about sector. We may recall that sector is an area bounded by an arc of a circle and its two radii. (as shown in Fig. 8.11)

Now consider the sector *AOB*. If we roll the sector up and bring (join) together the radii *OA* and *OB* such that they coincide, then the figure formed is called a hollow cone. The radius of the circle becomes the slant height of the cone and the length of the arc of the sector becomes the perimeter of the base of the cone.

For a cone of radius *r*, height *h* and slant height *l*,

1. Curved surface area of a cone = πrl sq. units.
2. Total surface area of a cone = Curved surface area + area of base = $\pi rl + \pi r^2$ $= \pi r(r + l)$ sq. units.
3. Volume of a cone = $\frac{1}{3}\pi r^2 h$ cubic units.

EXAMPLE 8.10 A salt heap is in the shape of a cone with the base radius of 1.5 m and slant height of 3.5 m. How much canvas is required to cover the heap? (in m^2)

SOLUTION

Canvas required to cover the salt heap = CSA of the cone.

$\pi rl = \frac{22}{7} \times 1.5 \times 3.5$

$= \frac{22}{7} \times \frac{15}{10} \times \frac{35}{10}$

$= 16.5 \text{ m}^2$

$\therefore$ Required canvas = 16.5 m^2

Cone Frustum (or a Conical Bucket)

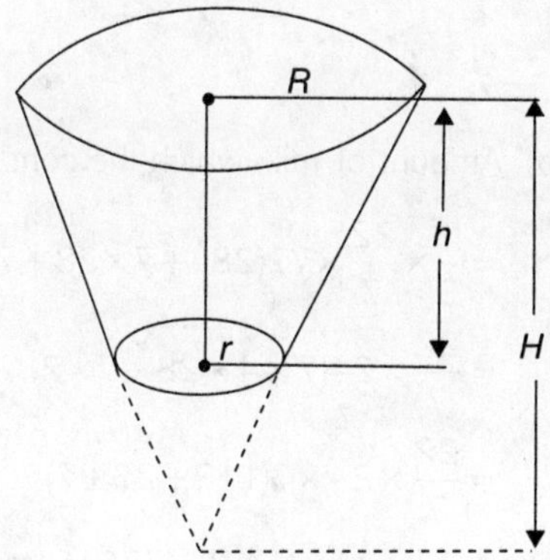

Figure 8.11

If a right circular cone is cut by a plane perpendicular to its axis (i.e., a plane parallel to the base), then the solid portion containing the base of the cone is called the frustum of the cone.

From the Fig. 8.12, we observe that a frustum is in the shape of a bucket.

Let,

Radius of upper base be *R*,

Radius of lower base = *r*,

Height of frustum = *h*,

Slant height of frustum = *l*

1. Curved surface area of a frustum = $\pi l(R + r)$ sq. units.
2. Total surface area of a frustum = Curved surface area + Area of upper base + Area of lower base $= \pi l(R + r) + \pi r^2 + \pi R^2$ sq. units.
3. Volume of a frustum = $\frac{1}{3}\pi h(R^2 + Rr + r^2)$ cubic units.
4. Slant height (l) of a frustum $= \sqrt{(R - r)^2 + h^2}$ units.

EXAMPLE 8.11 A cylindrical vessel of radius 3 cm has some water in it. A solid conical shaped iron piece of radius 1.5 cm and height 6 cm is dropped into the vessel such that it is totally immersed in the water. Find the rise in level of the water. (in cm)

SOLUTION

The rise in level of the water in the cylindrical vessel $= \dfrac{\text{Volume of the conical iron piece}}{\text{Base area of the cyclinder}} = \dfrac{\frac{1}{3}\pi \times 1.5 \times 1.5 \times 6}{\pi \times 3 \times 3} = 0.5\text{cm}$

EXAMPLE 8.12 The diameter of an icecream cone is 7 cm and its height is 12 cm. Find the volume of icecream that the cone can contain.

SOLUTION

Volume of icecream $= \dfrac{1}{3}\pi r^2 h = \dfrac{1}{3} \times \dfrac{22}{7} \times \left(\dfrac{7}{2}\right)^2 \times 12 = 22 \times 7 = 154 \text{ cm}^3.$

EXAMPLE 8.13 The diameters of top and bottom portions of a milk can are 56 cm and 14 cm respectively. The height of the can is 72 cm. Find the

(a) area of metal sheet required to make the can (without lid).

(b) volume of milk which the container can hold.

SOLUTION

The milk can is in the shape of a frustum with $R = 28$ cm, $r = 7$ cm and $h = 72$ cm.

(a) Area of metal sheet required = Curved surface area + Area of bottom base

$$= \pi l(R + r) + \pi r^2$$

Now, $l = \sqrt{(R - r^2) + h^2} = \sqrt{(28 - 7)^2 + 72^2} = \sqrt{21^2 + 72^2} = \sqrt{9(7^2 + 24^2)}$

$$= 3\sqrt{49 + 576} = 3 \times \sqrt{625} = 3 \times 25 = 75 \text{ cm}$$

$\therefore$ Area of metal sheet $= \dfrac{22}{7} \times 75(28 + 7) + \dfrac{22}{7} \times 7^2 = 22 \times 75 \times 5 + 22 \times 7$

$$= 22(375 + 7)$$

$$= 22(382) = 8404 \text{ cm}^2.$$

(b) Amount of milk which the container can hold $= \dfrac{1}{3}\pi h(R^2 + Rr + r^2)$

$$= \frac{1}{3} \times \frac{22}{7} \times 72(28^2 + 7 \times 28 + 7^2)$$

$$= \frac{22}{7} \times 24(7 \times 4 \times 28 + 7 \times 28 + 7 \times 7)$$

$$= \frac{22}{7} \times 24 \times 7(112 + 28 + 7)$$

$$= 22 \times 24 \times (147) = 77616 \text{ cm}^3.$$

EXAMPLE 8.14 From a circular canvas of diameter 56 m, a sector of 270° was cut out and a conical tent was formed by joining the straight ends of this piece. Find the radius and the height of the tent.

SOLUTION

As shown in the figure, when the free ends of the torn canvas are joined to form a cone, the radius of sector becomes slant height.

$\therefore l = \dfrac{56}{2} = 28$ m.

The length of the arc of the sector becomes the circumference of the base of the cone.

Let the radius of the base of the cone = r.

$$\Rightarrow 2\pi r = 2\times\frac{22}{7}\times\frac{56}{2}\times\left(\frac{270}{360}\right)$$

$$\Rightarrow 2\pi r = 2\times\frac{22}{7}\times 28\times\frac{3}{4}\Rightarrow r = 21\,\text{m}$$

$\therefore$ Height, $h=\sqrt{l^2-r^2}=\sqrt{28^2-21^2}=\sqrt{7^2(4^2-3^2)}=7\sqrt{16-9}=7\sqrt{7}$ m

$\therefore h = 7\sqrt{7}$ m and $r = 21$ m.

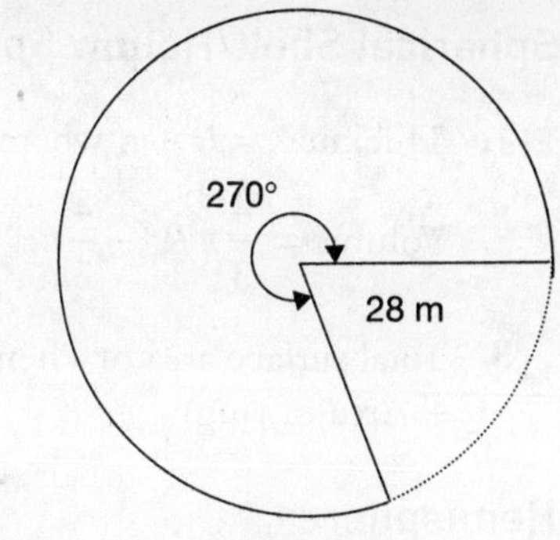

Figure 8.12

Sphere

Sphere is a set of points in the space which are equidistant from a fixed point. The fixed point is called the centre of the sphere and the distance is called the radius of the sphere. A lemon, a foot ball, the moon, globe, the Earth, small lead balls used in cycle bearings are some objects which are spherical in shape.

A line joining any two points on the surface of sphere and passing through the centre of the sphere is called its diameter.

The size of sphere can be completely determined by knowing its radius or diameter.

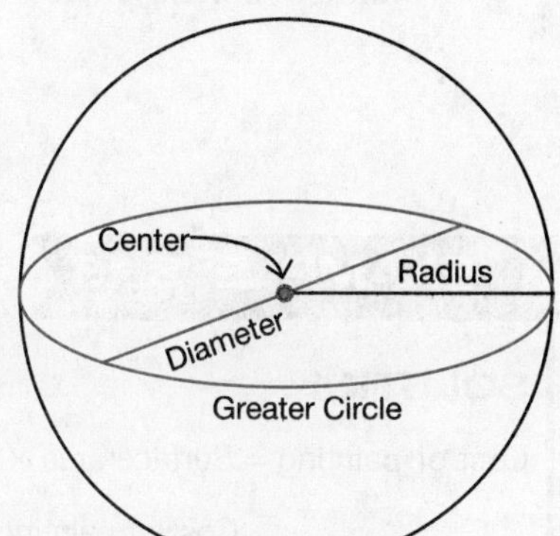

Solid Sphere

A solid sphere is the region in space bounded by a sphere. The centre of a sphere is also a part of solid sphere whereas the centre is not a part of hollow sphere. Marbles, lead shots, etc., are the examples of solid spheres while a tennis ball is a hollow sphere.

Hollow Sphere

From a solid sphere a smaller sphere having the same centre of the solid sphere, is cut off, then we obtain a hollow sphere. This can also be called a spherical shell.

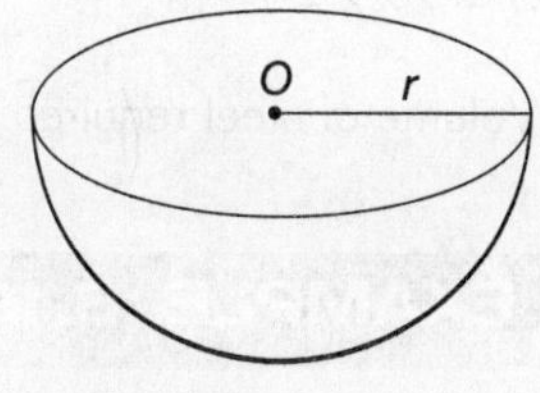

Figure 8.13 Hemisphere

Hemisphere

If a sphere is cut into two halves by a plane passing through the centre of sphere, then each of the halves is called a hemisphere.

Hemispherical Shell

A hemispherical shell is shown in the figure given.

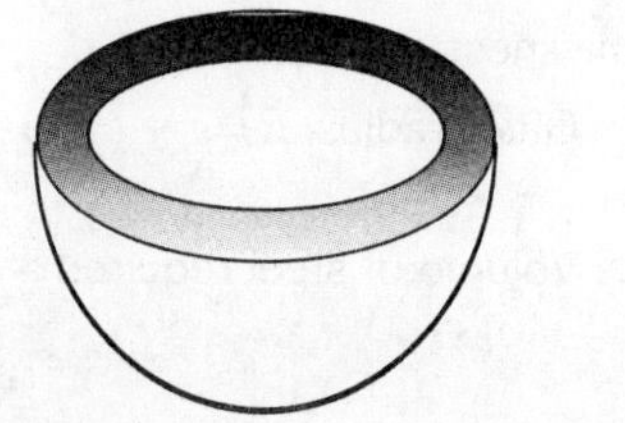

Figure 8.14 Hemispherical shell

Formulae to Memorize

Sphere

1. Surface area of a sphere = $4\pi r^2$ sq. units
2. Volume of a sphere = $\frac{4}{3}\pi r^3$ sq. units

Spherical Shell/Hollow Sphere

1. Thickness = $R - r$, where R = Outer radius, r = Inner radius
2. Volume = $\frac{4}{3}\pi R^3 - \frac{4}{3}\pi r^3$ cubic units
3. Total surface area of a hemispherical shell = $\frac{1}{2}$(Surface area of outer hemisphere + Surface area of inner hemisphere + Area of ring)

Hemisphere

1. Curved surface area of a hemisphere = $2\pi r^2$ sq. units
2. Total surface area of a hemisphere = $3\pi r^2$ sq. units
3. Volume of a hemisphere = $\frac{2}{3}\pi r^3$ cubic units

EXAMPLE 8.15 The cost of painting a solid sphere at the rate of 50 paise per square metre is ₹1232. Find the volume of steel required to make the sphere.

SOLUTION

Cost of painting = Surface area × Rate of painting

$\therefore$ Surface area = $\frac{\text{Cost of painting}}{\text{Rate of painting}} = \frac{1232}{0.5} = 2464 \text{ m}^2.$

$\Rightarrow 4\pi r^2 = 2464 \Rightarrow r^2 = \frac{2464}{4\pi} = \frac{616}{\left(\frac{22}{7}\right)} = \frac{616 \times 7}{22} = 28 \times 7$

$\Rightarrow r = 7 \times 2 = 14$ m

$\therefore$ Volume of steel required = $\frac{4}{3}\pi r^3 = \frac{4}{3} \times \frac{22}{7} \times 14 \times 14 \times 14 = \frac{34496}{3} \text{m}^3.$

EXAMPLE 8.16 A hollow hemispherical bowl of thickness 1 cm has an inner radius of 6 cm. Find the volume of metal required to make the bowl.

SOLUTION

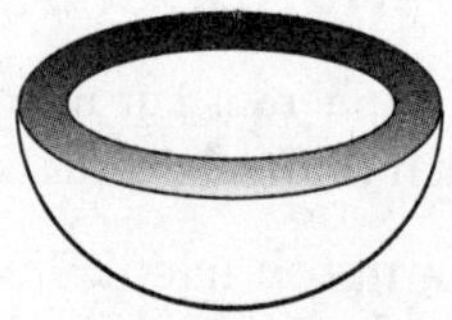

Figure 8.15

Inner radius, r = 6 cm

thickness, t = 1 cm

$\therefore$ Outer radius, $R = r + t = 6 + 1 = 7$ cm

$\therefore$ Volume of steel required $= \frac{2}{3}\pi R^3 - \frac{2}{3}\pi r^3$

$= \frac{2}{3} \times \frac{22}{7} \times 7^3 - \frac{2}{3} \times \frac{22}{7} \times 6^3 = \frac{44}{21}(7^3 - 6^3)$

$= \frac{44}{21}(343 - 216) = \frac{44}{21} \times 127 = \frac{5588}{21} \text{ cm}^2.$

EXAMPLE 8.17

A thin hollow hemispherical sailing vessel is made of metal covered by a conical canvas tent. The radius of the hemisphere is 14 m and total height of vessel (including the height of tent) is 28 m. Find area of metal sheet and the canvas required.

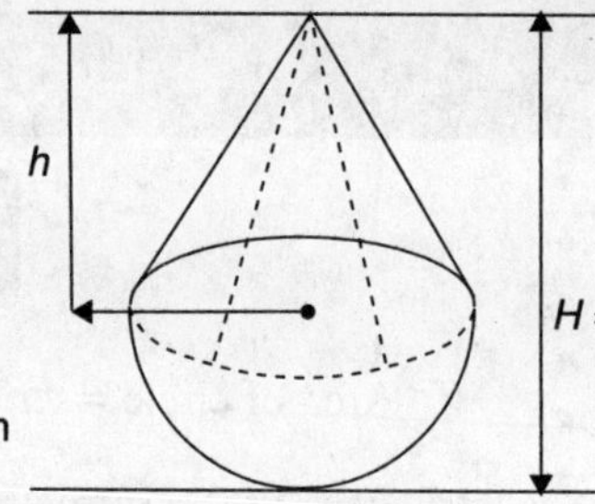

Figure 8.16

SOLUTION

The vessel (with the conical tent) is shown in figure.

Total height, $H = 28$ m

Radius of hemisphere $= r = 14$ m

$\therefore$ Height of conical tent $= h = H - r = 28 - 14 = 14$ m

We can observe that radius of base of cone = Radius of the hemisphere = 14 m

$\therefore$ Area of canvas required $= \pi r l = \frac{22}{7} \times 14 \times \sqrt{14^2 + 14^2} = 44 \times 14\sqrt{2} = 616\sqrt{2}\ \text{m}^2$

Area of metal sheet required = Surface area of hemisphere $= 2\pi r^2 = 2 \times \frac{22}{7} \times 14 \times 14 = 1232\ \text{m}^2$.

EXAMPLE 8.18

A wafer cone is completely filled with icecream forms a hemispherical scoop, just covering the cone. The radius of the top of the cone, as well as the height of the cone are 7 cm each. Find the volume of the icecream in it (in cm^3). (Take $\pi = 22/7$ and ignore the thickness of the cone)

SOLUTION

Required volume = Volume of the icecream forming the hemisphere + Volume of the icecream within the cone.

Radius of the hemispherical shape = Radius of the cone = 7 cm

$$\therefore \text{Required volume} = \frac{2}{3}\pi(7)^3 + \frac{1}{3}\pi(7)^3$$

$$= \pi(7)^3 = \frac{22}{7}(7)^3 = (22)(49)$$

$$= 1078\ \text{cm}^3.$$

POINTS TO REMEMBER

- ✔ Area of circle = πr^2 sq. units.
- ✔ Area of the semicircle = $\dfrac{\pi r^2}{2}$ sq. units.
- ✔ Circumference of the circle = $2\pi r$ units = πd units
- ✔ Circumference of the semicircle = $(\pi + 2)r$ units $= \dfrac{36r}{7}$ units (Where r is radius and d is diameter)
- ✔ Area of the ring = $\pi(R^2 - r^2) = \pi(R + r)(R - r)$
- ✔ Length of the arc ACB $l = \left(\dfrac{\theta}{360°}\right)2\pi r$ units.
- ✔ Area of the sector $AOBC$ $A = \left(\dfrac{\theta}{360°}\right)\pi r^2$ sq. units.
- ✔ (Where r is the radius of the circle and θ is sector angle)
- ✔ Perimeter of the sector = $(l + 2r)$ units.
- ✔ Area of the segment ACB = (A – Area of the ΔAOB) sq. units.
- ✔ Perimeter of the segment ACB = (Length of arc $ACB + AB$) units.
- ✔ Area of the equilateral triangle $= \dfrac{\sqrt{3}a^2}{4}$ sq. units.
- ✔ Height of the equilateral triangle $= \dfrac{\sqrt{3}a}{2}$ units.
- ✔ Radius of in-circle of equilateral triangle $= \dfrac{1}{3}\left(\dfrac{\sqrt{3}a}{2}\right) = \dfrac{a}{2\sqrt{3}}$ units.
- ✔ The number of lateral faces = The number of sides of the base.
- ✔ The number of edges of a prism = Number of sides of the base × 3.
- ✔ The sum of the lengths of the edges = 2(Perimeter of base) + Number of sides × Height.
- ✔ The lateral surface area of a cuboid = $ph = 2(l + b)h$ sq. units, where p is the perimeter of the base.
- ✔ The total surface area of a cuboid = LSA + 2(Base area) = $2(l + b)h + 2lb = 2(lb + bh + lh)$ sq. units.
- ✔ The volume of a cuboid = $Ah = (lb)h = lbh$ cubic units, where A is the area of the base.
- ✔ Diagonal of cuboid $= \sqrt{l^2 + b^2 + h^2}$ units
- ✔ The lateral surface area of a cube = $4a^2$ sq. units.
- ✔ The total surface area of a cube = LSA + 2(Area of base) = $4a^2 + 2a^2 = 6a^2$ sq. units.
- ✔ The volume of a cube = a^3 cubic units.
- ✔ The diagonal of a cube $= \sqrt{a^2 + a^2 + a^2} = \sqrt{3}\,a$ units.
- ✔ A cone is a solid pointed figure with a circular base. A cone is a kind of pyramid whose base is a circle. A cone has one vertex, one plane surface (i.e., the base) and a curved surface (i.e., the lateral surface).
- ✔ Curved surface area of a cone = πrl sq. units.
- ✔ Total surface area of a cone = Curved surface area + area of base = $\pi rl + \pi r^2 = \pi r(r + l)$ sq. units.
- ✔ Volume of a cone = $\dfrac{1}{3}\pi r^2 h$ cubic units.
- ✔ Curved surface area of a frustum = $\pi l(R + r)$ sq. units.
- ✔ Total surface area of a frustum = Curved surface area + Area of upper base + Area of lower base = $\pi l(R + r) + \pi r^2 + \pi R^2$ sq. units.
- ✔ Volume of a frustum = $\dfrac{1}{3}\pi h(R^2 + Rr + r^2)$ cubic units.
- ✔ Slant height (l) of a frustum $= \sqrt{(R - r)^2 + h^2}$ units.
- ✔ Curved surface area of a hemisphere = $2\pi r^2$ sq. units
- ✔ Total surface area of a hemisphere = $3\pi r^2$ sq. units
- ✔ Volume of a hemisphere = $\dfrac{2}{3}\pi r^3$ cubic units

PRACTICE QUESTIONS CLASSROOM WING

Very Short Answer Type Questions

Directions of questions from 1 to 7:
Fill in the blanks.

1. If the number of lateral surfaces of a right prism is equal to n, then the number of edges of the base of the prism is ______.
2. If f, e, and v represent the number of rectangular faces, number of edges and number of vertices, respectively, of a cuboid, then the values of f, e, and v, respectively, are ______.
3. If the ratio of the base radii of two cones having the same curved surface areas is 6 : 7, then the ratio of their slant heights is ______.
4. The heights of two cones are equal and the radii of their bases are R and r. The ratio of their volumes is ______.
5. If the heights of two cylinders are equal and their radii are in the ratio of 7 : 5, then the ratio of their volumes is ______.
6. The volumes of two cylinders of radii R, r and heights H, h, respectively, are equal. If $R : r = 2 : 3$, then $H : h =$ ______.
7. A sphere and the base of a cylinder have equal radii. The diameter of the sphere is equal to the height of the cylinder. The ratio of the curved surface area of the cylinder and surface area of the sphere is ______.

Directions of questions from 8 to 21:
Answer the following questions.

8. The total surface area of a hollow hemisphere, whose inner and outer radii are r and R, respectively.
9. The difference between the curved surface area of a sphere of radius R and that of cylinder of base radius r and height $2R$ can be
10. Find curved surface area of a frustum of a cone whose slant height is equal to the sum of radii (R, r) of the circular ends of the frustum.
11. The total surface area of a hollow cylinder open at both the ends and whose height is equal to twice its inner radius (r) and outer radius is R.
12. The volume of a hollow hemisphere whose thickness is equal to inner radius (r).
13. The volume of a cone whose height is seven times its base radius (r).
14. The radii of ends of a cone frustum are r and $2r$. The volume of the cone frustum of height $\left(2\frac{1}{2}\right)r$.
15. The volume of a hollow cylinder whose outer radius is twice the inner radius and height is $\frac{7}{18}$ times the inner radius (r).
16. A and B are the volumes of a pyramid and a right prism, respectively. If the pyramid and the prism have the same base area and the same height, then what is the relation between A and B?
17. A sector of a circle of radius 6 cm and central angle 30° is folded into a cone such that the radius of the sector becomes the slant height of the cone. What is the radius of the base of the cone thus formed?
18. What is the volume of a hollow cylinder with R, r and h as outer radius, inner radius and height, respectively?
19. The side of a cube is equal to the radius of the sphere. Find the ratio of their volumes.
20. What is the volume of sand to be spread uniformly over a ground of dimensions. $10x$ m × $8x$ m up to a height of $0.1x$ m?
21. The slant height, radii of upperend and of a cone frustum are $2a$ cm, $(a + b)$ cm and $(a - b)$ cm. What is its curved surface area?

Short Answer Type Questions

22. If a chord PQ of length 12 cm is making 120° at the centre 'O' of a circle, then find the area of ΔPOQ (in cm^2).
23. Three cubes having a face diagonal $6\sqrt{2}$ cm each are joined end to end. Find the total surface area of the resulting cuboid (in cm^2).

24. The volume of a square pyramid, 16 m high is 192 m^3. Find the side of its base.

25. A cylinder is formed by joining the lengths of a rectangular sheet of dimensions 35 cm × 22 cm. Find its volume (in cm^3).

26. The radius of a sphere is twice the base radius of a cone. If the height of the cone is twice the radius of the sphere, then find the ratio of the volumes of sphere and cone.

27. Find the number of cubes of side 2 m to be dropped in a cylindrical vessel of radius 14 m in order to increase the water level by 5 m.

28. Find the capacity of a closed cuboidal cistern whose length is 3 m, breadth is 2 m and height is 6 m. Also find the area of iron sheet required to make the cistern.

29. An open metallic conical tank is 6 m deep and its circular top has diameter of 16 m. Find the cost of tin plating its inner surface at the rate of ₹0.8 per 100 cm^2. (Take $\pi = 3.14$)

30. The total surface area of a hemisphere is 3768 cm^2. Find the radius of the hemisphere. (Take $\pi = 3.14$)

31. The base radius of a conical tent is 120 cm and its slant height is 750 cm. Find the area of the canvas required to make 10 such tents (in m^2). (Take $\pi = 3.14$)

32. From a cylindrical wooden log of length 30 cm and base radius $7\sqrt{2}$ cm, biggest cuboid of square base is made. Find the volume of wood wasted.

33. A right circular cone is such that the angle at its vertex is 90° and its base radius is 49 cm, then find the curved surface area of the cone.

34. The base of a right pyramid is an equilateral triangle, each side of which is $6\sqrt{3}$ cm long and its height is 4 cm. Find the total surface area of the pyramid in cm^2.

35. In the figure, $ABCD$ is an isosceles trapezium and AEB is an isosceles triangle. If $AB = \frac{5}{3}$ of CD. Area of the triangle AED is 12 sq cm, then find the area of the shaded region.

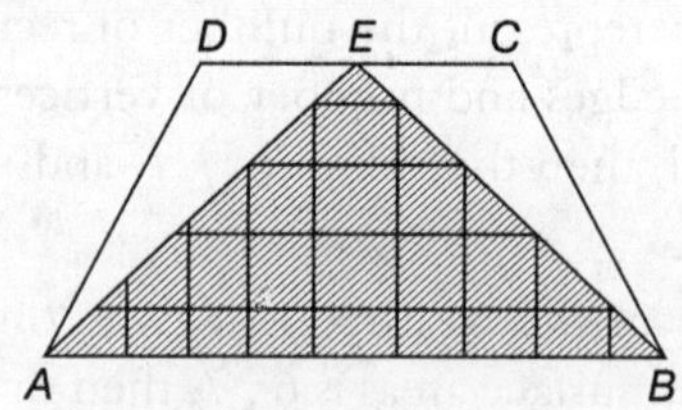

36. (A) A spherical piece of metal of diameter 6 cm is drawn into a wire of 4 mm in diameter. Find the length of the wire.

(B) In the given figure, ΔABC is a right isosceles triangle inscribed in a circle and $\Delta ABC = 90°$. 'O' is the centre of the circle. $\overline{OD} \perp \overline{AB}$ and $\overline{OEF} \perp \overline{BC}$. If the radius of the circle is 21 cm, then find the area of the shaded region.

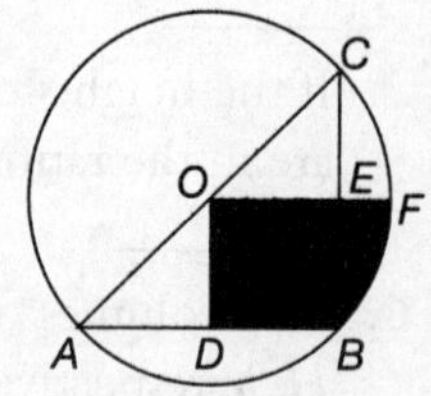

Essay Type Questions

37. A regular hexagonal pyramid is 15 m high, and the side of the base is 4 m. Find its volume (in m^3).

38. In the given figure, ABCD is a square of diagonal $14\sqrt{2}$ cm. With A as centre and AB as radius, the arc BD is drawn. Find the area of the shaded region (in cm^2).

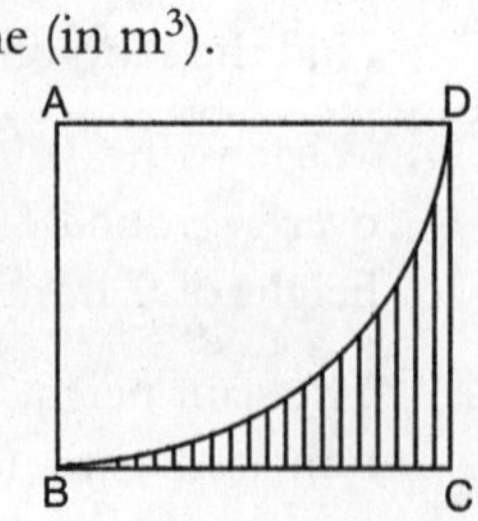

39. Find the volume of a cone whose base radius is 21 cm and angle at its vertex is 90° (in cm^3).

40. In the given figure, PQRS is a square of side $7\sqrt{2}$ cm. With P, R as centres and PQ as radius, the arcs QAS and QBS are drawn, respectively. Find the area of the shaded region (in cm^2).

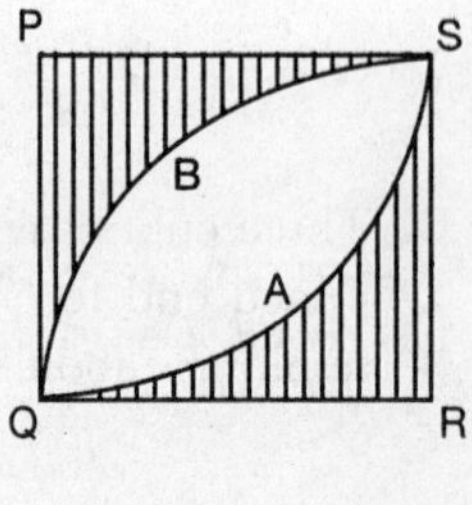

41. Find the curved surface of a cone whose base radius is 14 cm and angle at its vertex is 60° (in cm^2).

42. Chaco cream balls of a company are spherical in shape. Each Chaco ball contains cream as sphere inside with a radius equal to half the outer radius of the Chaco ball. If a box contains 24 Chaco balls and each ball has volume of 32 cm^3, then find the volume of the cream in each box.

PRACTICE QUESTIONS COMPETITION WING

Level 1: Apply Your Concepts

Directions of questions from 1 to 5:
Fill in the blanks.

1. A cone is formed by joining together the two straight edges of a sector, so that they coincide with each other. The length of the arc of the sector becomes the ______ of the circular base and radius of sector becomes the ______ of the cone.

2. The volume of a cube with diagonal d is ______.

3. Total number of faces in a prism which has 12 edges is ______.

4. W, P, H and A are whole surface area, perimeter of base, height and area of the base of a prism, respectively. The relation between W, P, H and A is ______.

5. If s is the perimeter of the base of a prism, n is the number of sides of the base, S is the total length of the edges and h is the height, then $S =$ ______.

Directions of questions from 6 to 31:
Select the correct alternative from the given choices.

6. The height of an equilateral triangle is 6 cm. Find its area (in cm^2).
(a) $12\sqrt{3}$ (b) $15\sqrt{3}$
(c) $16\sqrt{3}$ (d) $18\sqrt{3}$

7. If a chord AB of length 8 cm is making 90° at the centre 'O' of a circle, then find the area of ΔAOB (in cm^2).
(a) 10 (b) 14
(c) 16 (d) 18

8. A cylinder is formed by joining the breadths of a rectangular sheet of dimensions 44 cm × 32 cm. Find its curved surface area (in cm^2).
(a) 1467 (b) 1564
(c) 1752 (d) 1408

9. Radius and diameter of a sphere are, respectively, equal to the base radius and height of a cylinder. Find the ratio of their volumes.
(a) 1:2 (b) 2:3
(c) 4:3 (d) 2:1

10. The maximum possible sphere is carved out of a cube of edge 14 cm. Find its surface area (in cm^2).
(a) 576 (b) 592
(c) 616 (d) 634

11. A cylinder of volume 1056 cm^3 is melted and recast into a cone of base radius 6 cm. Find the height of the cone (in cm).
(a) 28 (b) 14
(c) 12 (d) 15

12. The area of an equilateral triangle is $18\sqrt{3}$ cm^2. Find its height (in cm).
(a) $6\sqrt{2}$ (b) $2\sqrt{6}$
(c) $3\sqrt{6}$ (d) $6\sqrt{3}$

13. Find the volume of the space covered by rotating a rectangular sheet of dimensions 16.1 cm × 7.5 cm along its length.
(a) 2846.25 cm^3 (b) 2664 cm^3
(c) 2864.25 cm^3 (d) 2684 cm^3

14. The base of a right prism is an equilateral triangle of edge 12 m. If the volume of the prism is $288\sqrt{3}$ m^3, then its height is ______.
(a) 6 m (b) 8 m
(c) 10 m (d) 12 m

15. A roller levelled an area of 165000 m^2 in 125 revolutions, whose length is 28 m. Find the radius of the roller.
(a) 7.5 m (b) 8.5 m
(c) 6.5 m (d) 7 m

16. A large sphere of radius 3.5 cm is carved from a cubical solid. Find the difference between their surface areas.
(a) 122 cm^2 (b) 80.5 cm^2
(c) 144.5 cm^2 (d) 140 cm^2

17. In the figure given below, $ABCD$ is a square of side 10 cm and a circle is inscribed in it. Find the area of the shaded part as shown in the figure.

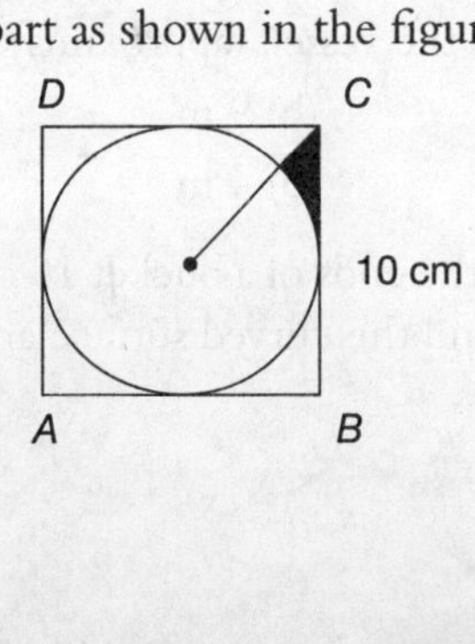

(a) $\left(\frac{100-36\pi}{41}\right)$ cm^2 (b) $\left(\frac{100-25\pi}{8}\right)$ cm^2

(c) $\left(\frac{100+25\pi}{8}\right)$ cm^2 (d) None of these

18. The outer curved surface area of a cylindrical metal pipe is 1100 m^2 and the length of the pipe is 25 m. The outer radius of the pipe is ______.

(a) 8 m (b) 9 m
(c) 7 m (d) 6 m

19. Find the area of the figure given below, in which AB = 100 m, CE = 30 m, C is mid-point of $\overline{AB}$ and D is mid-point of $\overline{AC}$ and $\overline{GF}$.

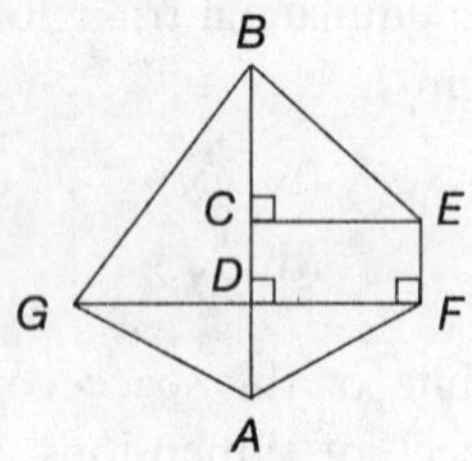

(a) 5250 m^2 (b) 3750 m^2
(c) 3375 m^2 (d) 3175 m^2

20. The area of the base of a right equilateral triangular prism is $16\sqrt{3}$ cm^2. If the height of the prism is 12 cm, then the lateral surface area and the total surface area of the prism, respectively, are

(a) 288 cm^2, $(288 + 32\sqrt{3})$ cm^2
(b) 388 cm^2, $(388 + 32\sqrt{3})$ cm^2
(c) 288 cm^2, $(288 + 24\sqrt{3})$ cm^2
(d) 388 cm^2, $(388 + 24\sqrt{3})$ cm^2

21. A metallic cone of diameter 32 cm and height 9 cm is melted and made into identical spheres, each of radius 2 cm. How many such spheres can be made?

(a) 72 (b) 64
(c) 52 (d) 48

22. A cylindrical vessel open at the top has a base radius of 28 cm. If the total cost of painting the outer part of the vessel is ₹357 at the rate of ₹0.2 per 100 cm^2, then find the height of the vessel. (approximately)

(a) 10 m (b) 9 m
(c) 8 m (d) 4 m

23. The radii of the ends of a bucket 16 cm high are 20 cm and 8 cm. Find the curved surface area of the bucket.

(a) 1760 cm^2 (b) 2240 cm^2
(c) 880 cm^2 (d) 3120 cm^2

24. A cylindrical vessel of radius 8 cm contains water. A solid sphere of radius 6 cm is lowered into the water until it is completely immersed. What is the rise in the water level in the vessel?

(a) 3 cm (b) 3.5 cm
(c) 4 cm (d) 4.5 cm

25. What is the difference in the areas of the regular hexagon circumscribing a circle of radius 10 cm and the regular hexagon inscribed in the circle?

(a) 50 cm^2 (b) $50\sqrt{3}$ cm^2
(c) $100\sqrt{3}$ cm^2 (d) $100\sqrt{3}$ cm^2

26. In the shown figure, two circles of radii of 7 cm each, are shown. $ABCD$ is rectangle and AD and BC are the radii. Find the area of the shaded region (in cm^2).

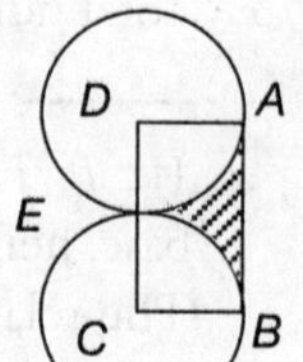

(a) 20 (b) 21
(c) 19 (d) 18

27. There is a closed rectangular shed of dimensions 10 m × 4 m inside a field. A cow is tied at one corner of outside of the shed with a 6 m long rope. What is the area that the cow can graze in the field?

(a) 66 m^2 (b) 88 m^2
(c) 0.8π m^2 (d) 27π m^2

28. The base of a right prism is a square of perimeter 20 cm and its height is 30 cm. What is the volume of the prism?

(a) 700 cm^3 (b) 750 cm^3
(c) 800 cm^3 (d) 850 cm^3

29. A conical cup when filled with icecream forms a hemispherical shape on its open end. Find the volume of icecream (approximately), if radius of the base of the cone is 3.5 cm, the vertical height of cone is 7 cm and width of the cone is negligible.

(a) 120 cm^3 (b) 150 cm^3
(c) 180 cm^3 (d) 210 cm^3

30. A hemispherical bowl of internal diameter 24 cm contains water. This water is to be filled in cylindrical bottles, each of radius 6 cm and height 8 cm. How many such bottles are required to empty the bowl?

(a) 3 (b) 4
(c) 5 (d) 6

31. A dome of a building is in the form of a hemisphere. The total cost of white washing it from inside, was ₹1330.56. The rate at which it was white washed is ₹3 per square metre. Find the volume of the dome approximately.
(a) 1150.53 m^3 (b) 1050 m^3
(c) 1241.9 m^3 (d) 1500 m^3

Level 2: Review Your Concepts

32. A circular garden of radius 15 m is surrounded by a circular path of width 7 m. If the path is to be covered with tiles at a rate of ₹10 per m^2, then find the total cost of the work. (in ₹)
(a) 8410 (b) 7140
(c) 8140 (d) 7410

33. Find the area of the shaded region, given that the radius of each circle is equal to 5 cm.

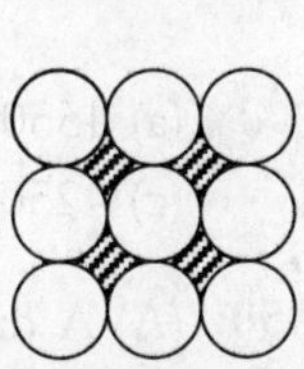

(a) $(400 - 100\pi)$ cm^2
(b) $(360 - 100\pi)$ cm^2
(c) 231 cm^2
(d) $(400 - 50\pi)$ cm^2

34. The volume of a right prism, whose base is an equilateral triangle, is $1500\sqrt{3}$ cm^3 and the height of the prism is 125 cm. Find the side of the base of the prism.
(a) $8\sqrt{3}$ cm (b) $4\sqrt{3}$ cm
(c) $16\sqrt{3}$ cm (d) $24\sqrt{3}$ cm

35. A right circular cylinder of volume 1386 cm^3 is cut from a right circular cylinder of radius 4 cm and height 49 cm, such that a hollow cylinder of uniform thickness, with a height of 49 cm and an outer raidus of 4 cm is left behind. Find the thickness of the hollow cylinder left behind.
(a) 0.5 cm (b) 2 cm
(c) 1.5 cm (d) 1 cm

36. The diagram shown above has four circles of 7 cm radius with centres at *A*, *B*, *C*, and *D*. If the quadrilateral *ABCD* represents a square, then find the area of the shaded region.

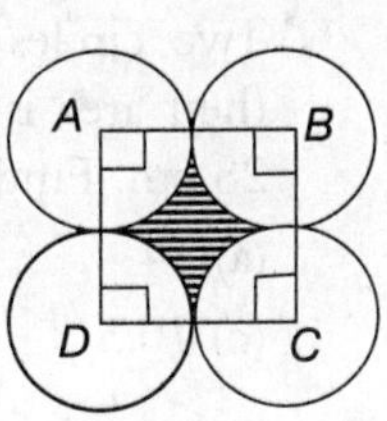

(a) 42 cm^2 (b) 21 cm^2
(c) 63 cm^2 (d) 84 cm^2

37. Find the total surface area of a hollow metallic hemisphere whose internal radius is 14 cm and the thickness of the metal is 7 cm.
(a) 4774 cm^2 (b) 4477 cm^2
(c) 4747 cm^2 (d) 7744 cm^2

38. A cylindrical drum 1.5 m in diameter and 3 m in height is full of water. The water is emptied into another cylindrical tank in which water rises by 2 m. Find the diameter of the second cylinder up to 2 decimal places.
(a) 1.74 m (b) 1.94 m
(c) 1.64 m (d) 1.84 m

39. Curved surface area of a conical cup is $154\sqrt{2}$ cm^2 and base radius is 7 cm. Find the angle at the vertex of the conical cup.
(a) 90° (b) 60°
(c) 45° (d) 30°

40. An equilateral triangle has a circle inscribed in it and is circumscribed by a circle. There is another equilateral triangle inscribed in the inner circle. Find the ratio of the areas of the outer circle and the inner equilateral triangle.
(a) $\frac{16\pi}{3\sqrt{3}}$ (b) $\frac{8\pi}{2\sqrt{3}}$
(c) $\frac{24\pi}{3\sqrt{3}}$ (d) None of these

41. A triangle has sides of 48 cm, 14 cm and 50 cm. Find its circum-radius (in cm).
(a) 25 (b) 12.5
(c) 20 (d) 17.5

42. The base of a pyramid is an *n*-sided regular polygon of area 360 cm^2. The total surface area of the pyramid is 900 cm^2. Each lateral face of the pyramid has an area of 30 cm^2. Find *n*.
(a) 20 (b) 18
(c) 16 (d) 24

43. In a right prism, the base is an equilateral triangle. Its volume is $80\sqrt{3}$ cm^3 and its lateral surface area is 240 cm^2. Find its height (in cm).
(a) 10 (b) 5
(c) 15 (d) 20

44. A right prism has a triangular base. If its perimeter is 24 cm and lateral surface area is 192 cm^2, find its height.

The following are the steps involved in solving the above problem. Arrange them in sequential order.

(A) $192 = 24 \times h$

(B) Given, LSA = 192 cm^2, Perimeter of the base = 24 cm

(C) $h = 8$ cm

(D) Lateral surface area of a prism = Perimeter of the base × Height

(a) BADC (b) BCAD

(c) DABC (d) BDAC

Level 3: Assess Your Concepts

45. An ink pen, with a cylindrical barrel of diameter 2 cm and height 10.5 cm, and completely filled with ink, can be used to write 4950 words. How many words can be written using 400 ml of ink?
(Take 1 litre = 1000 cm^3)

(a) 40000 (b) 60000

(c) 45000 (d) 80000

46. The diameters of the top and the bottom portions of a bucket are 42 cm and 28 cm. If the height of the bucket is 24 cm, then find the cost of painting its outer surface at the rate of 5 paise/cm^2.

(a) ₹158.25 (b) ₹172.45

(c) ₹168.30 (d) ₹164.20

47. In the following figure, a circle is inscribed in square *ABCD* and the square is circumscribed by a circle. If the radius of the smaller circle is *r* cm, then find the area of the shaded region (in cm^2).

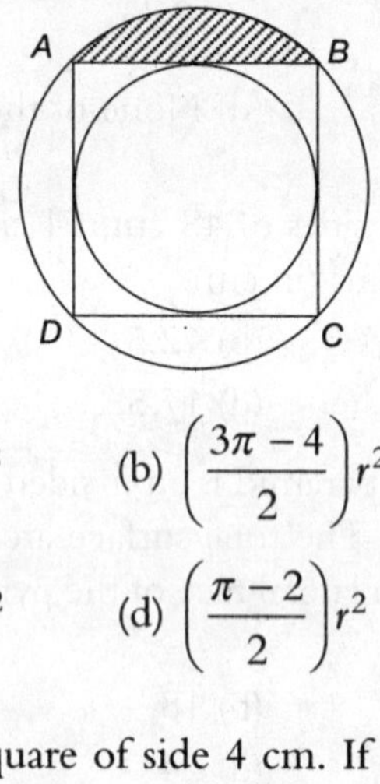

(a) $\left(\frac{\pi - 2}{4}\right)r^2$ (b) $\left(\frac{3\pi - 4}{2}\right)r^2$

(c) $\left(\frac{\pi + 2}{4}\right)r^2$ (d) $\left(\frac{\pi - 2}{2}\right)r^2$

48. *ABCD* is a square of side 4 cm. If *E* is a point in the interior of the square such that ΔCED is equilateral, then find the area of ΔACE (in cm^2).

(a) $2(\sqrt{3} - 1)$ (b) $4(\sqrt{3} - 1)$

(c) $6(\sqrt{3} - 1)$ (d) $8(\sqrt{3} - 1)$

49. In the given figure (not to scale), $QT = 90$ m and $UR = 50$ m. $QU : UT = UV : VT = 1 : 2$. $PV : VS = 4 : 5$. Find the area of the figure. (in m^2)

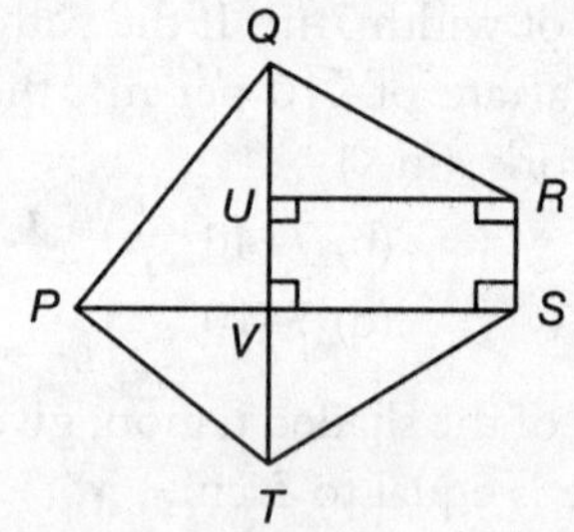

(a) 4550 (b) 4200

(c) 4250 (d) 4100

50. (A) A dish, in the shape of a frustum of a cone, has a height of 6 cm. Its top and its bottom have radii of 24 cm and 16 cm, respectively. Find its curved surface area (in cm^2).

(a) 240π (b) 400π

(c) 180π (d) 160π

(B) A pylon is in the form of a square based pyramid surmounted on a square based prism. Its base has sides 6 feet each and the height of the pylon is 79 feet. The height of the prism is 75 feet. If the cost of painting the pylon is ₹108 per sqm then find the cost of painting the pylon. (1 sqm = 10.8 sq feet approx.)

(a) 10800 (b) 18600

(c) 18000 (d) 1860

51. Two circles touch each other externally. The sum of their area is 490π cm^2. Their centres are separated by 28 cm. Find the difference of their radii (in cm).

(a) 14 (b) 7

(c) 10.5 (d) 3.5

52. A closed rectangular shed has dimensions 21 m × 14 m. It is inside a field. A cow is tied outside the shed at one of its corners with a 21 m rope. Find the area over which the cow can graze (in m^2).

(a) 342π (b) 294π

(c) 343π (d) 441π

53. In the given figure, $PQRS$ is a square of diagonal $7\sqrt{2}$ cm. With P as the centre, the arc QS is drawn. Find the area of the shaded region (in cm^2).

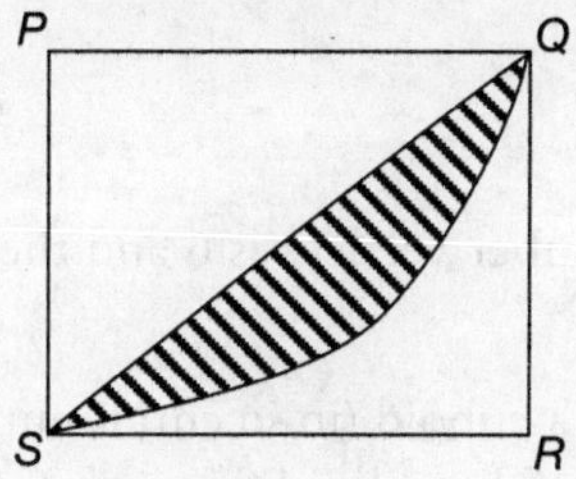

(a) $\frac{49}{4}(\pi - 2)$ (b) $\frac{49}{4}(\pi - 1)$

(c) $\frac{49}{4}(\pi - 3)$ (d) $\frac{49}{2}(\pi - 2)$

54. Three solid cubes have a face diagonal of $4\sqrt{2}$ cm each. Three other solid cubes have a face diagonal of $8\sqrt{2}$ cm each. All the cubes are melted together to form a cube. Find the side of the cube formed (in cm).

(a) $\sqrt[3]{324}$ (b) $\sqrt[3]{576}$

(c) 12 (d) 24

55. A rectangular sump has an inner length and breadth of 24 m and 20 m, respectively. Water flows through an inlet pipe at 180 m per minute. The cross-sectional area of the pipe is 0.5 m^2. The tank takes half an hour to get filled. Find the depth of the sump (in m).

(a) 4.625 (b) 6.125

(c) 5.625 (d) 5.125

56. To supply a river water to a city, 1000 identical cylindrical pipes of length 7 m and diameter 1.5 m each required. A tunnel of dimensions 7.1 km × 2 m × 2 m was dug, and pipes were placed in the tunnel. Find the volume soil to fill the tunnel after placing the pipes.

(a) 28400 (b) 28700

(c) 16000 (d) 16025

AT

PRACTICE QUESTIONS JEE SPECIAL WING

Multiple-Answer Type Questions

Directions for questions 1 to 5:
Each question has FOUR options (a), (b), (c), and (d). ONE OR MORE THAN ONE of these four option(s) is/are the correct answer(s).

1. The area of a rectangle is 72 sq cm. The length and the breadth of the rectangle are integers in cm, and each is more than 1 cm. Which of the following can be the perimeter of the rectangle?
   (a) 76 cm (b) 54 cm
   (c) 44 cm (d) 36 cm

2. A right solid has 12 edges. Which of the following can be true about the solid?
   (a) The number vertices is 8 and the number of faces is 6.
   (b) The number vertices is 7 and the number of faces is 7.
   (c) The number vertices is 10 and the number of faces is 4.
   (d) The number vertices is 6 and the number of faces is 8.

3. The LSA of a cuboid (in sq cm) is numerically equal to the volume of the cuboid (in cu cm). If the measures of the cuboid are integers in cm, which of the following can be the volume of the cuboid (in cu cm)?
   (a) 8 (b) 16
   (c) 32 (d) 48

4. The dimensions of a cuboid are 10 cm × 8 cm × 6 cm. A cylinder is carved out from the cuboid. Which of the following can be the volume of the cuboid (in cu cm)?
   (a) 72π (b) 90π
   (c) 108π (d) 126π

5. The dimensions of a cuboid are integers in cm. The areas of three mutually perpendicular faces are 90 sq cm, 72 sq cm and 80 sq cm. Which of the following of the cuboid can be found uniquely?
   (a) Volume (b) TSA
   (c) LSA (d) Longest diagonal

Match The Column

Directions for questions 6 to 9:
Read the paragraph given below and answer the questions.
The radius, vertical height and slant height of a solid cone are 12 cm, 16 cm, and 20 cm. The cone is cut by a plane parallel to the base of the cone such that a frustum of cone is formed with radii 3 cm (r) and 12 cm (R). The vertical and slant height of the frustum of the cone are h and l.

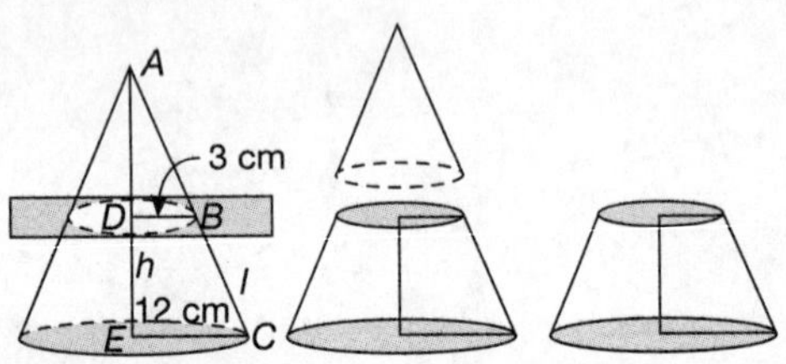

Column A	Column B
6. $(r+R):(h+l)$	(a) 1 : 6
7. Ratio of area of smaller base and CSA of the frustum	(b) 1 : 9
8. Ratio of TSA (in sq cm) and volume (in cu cm) of the frustum	(c) 5 : 9
9. Ratio of volumes of the frustum and the bigger cone	(d) 33 : 35
	(e) 63 : 64

Comprehension-Based Questions

Directions for questions 10 to 14:
Read the paragraph given below and answer the questions.
Master Arun is good at art. On the occasion of Ramanujan's day, he presented one of his art in the art gallery. The art is shown in the figure where a bigger circle is inscribed in an equilateral triangle of side $12\sqrt{3}$ cm. Also, three smaller congruent circles are inscribed in the triangle such that each smaller circle touches two sides of the triangle and the bigger circle. Also, he posed some interesting questions. Can you please help to answer the same? The questions are as follows.

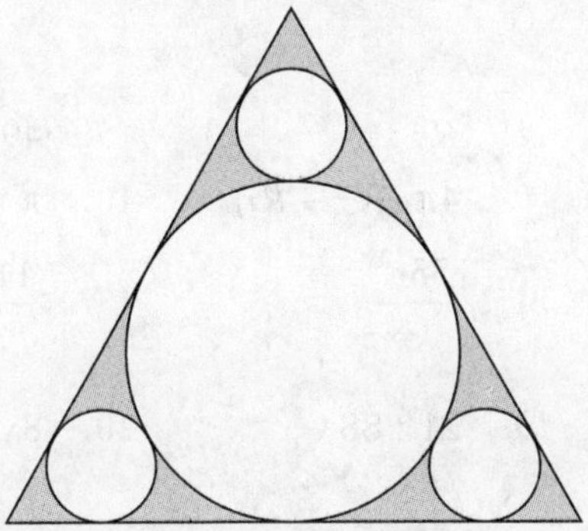

10. What is the measure of the radius of the bigger circle?
(a) 12 cm (b) 9 cm
(c) 6 cm (d) 3 cm

11. What is the distance between the centres of the bigger circle and the smaller circle?
(a) 4 cm (b) 8 cm
(c) 12 cm (d) 16 cm

12. By how many times the area of the bigger circle is the sum of the areas of the smaller circles?
(a) 1 (b) 2
(c) 3 (d) 4

13. What is the area (in cm^2) of the shaded region?
(a) $9(12\sqrt{3}-5\pi)$ (b) $12(9\sqrt{3}-4\pi)$
(c) $7(18\sqrt{3}-7\pi)$ (c) $18(7\sqrt{3}-3\pi)$

14. What is the area (in cm^2) of the triangle formed by joining the centres of the smaller circles?
(a) $12\sqrt{3}$ (b) $75\sqrt{3}$
(c) $36\sqrt{3}$ (d) $48\sqrt{3}$

Assertion and Reason Type Questions

Directions for questions 15 to 18:
Read the options given below and answer the questions.
In the light of the given statements, choose the most appropriate answer from the options given below.

(a) Both assertion (A) and reason (R) are true, and reason (R) is the correct explanation of assertion.
(b) Both assertion (A) and reason (R) are true, and reason (R) is not the correct explanation of assertion.
(c) Assertion (A) is true, but reason (R) is false.
(d) Assertion (A) is false, and reason (R) is true.

15. Assertion: The height of a pyramid whose base is a square of side 12 cm, is 15 cm. The volume of a pyramid is 720 cu cm.

Reason: The volume of a pyramid is the product of one-third of the area of the base and the vertical height of the pyramid.

16. Assertion: If the volume (in cu cm) of a sphere is numerically equal to the surface area (in sq cm) of the sphere, the radius of the sphere is 3 cm.

Reason: If the radius of the sphere is r cm, the volume of the corresponding hemisphere is $\frac{2\pi r^3}{3}$.

17. Assertion: The surface area of the largest sphere which is carved out of a cube of edge 14 cm, is 1728 sq cm.

Reason: If the largest sphere is carved out of a cube, then the diameter of the sphere is equal to the edge of the cube.

18. Assertion: The inner dimensions of a cuboidal box are 125 cm × 90 cm × 64 cm. The number of solid cuboids each of dimensions 25 cm × 22 cm × 21 cm that can be placed in the box is 60.

Reason: The number of solid cuboids is the ratio of the inner volume of the box and the volume of each solid cuboid.

ANSWER KEYS

Crossword

Across

1. Hemispheres 4. Prisms 5. Triangle 6. Sphere 7. Cuboid
11. Mensuration 12. Volume

Down

2. Parallelograms 3. Pyramid 8. Frustum 9. Cylinder 10. Segment

Classroom Wing

Very Short Answer Type Questions

1. n 2. 6, 12 and 8 3. 7 : 6 4. $R^2 : r^2$ 5. 49 : 25
6. 9 : 4 7. 1 : 1 8. $\pi\,(3R^2 + r^2)$ 9. $4\pi\,(R^2 - Rr)$ 10. $\pi\,(R + r)^2$
11. $2\pi\,(R + r)^2$ 12. $\frac{44}{3}r^3$ 13. $\frac{22r^3}{3}$ 14. $\frac{55r^3}{3}$ 15. $\frac{11r^3}{3}$
16. $A = \frac{B}{3}$ 17. $\frac{1}{2}$ cm 18. $\pi(R^2 - r^2)h$ 19. 21 : 88 20. $8x^3$ m^3
21. $4\pi a^2$ cm^2

Short Answer Type Questions

22. $12\sqrt{3}$ cm^2 23. 504 cm^2 24. 6 m 25. 1347.5 cm^3 26. 8:1
27. 385 28. 72 m^2 29. ₹28160 30. 20 cm 31. 282.85 m^2
32. 3360 cm^3 33. $7546\sqrt{2}$ cm^2 34. $657\sqrt{3}$ cm^2 35. 40 sq cm
36. (A) 900 cm (B) 283.5 sq cm

Essay Type Questions

37. $120\sqrt{3}$ cm^3 38. 42 cm^2 39. 9702 cm^3 40. 42 cm^2 41. 1232 cm^2
42. 96 cm^3

Competition Wing

Level 1: Apply Your Concepts

1. 0.5 cm 2. $\frac{d^3}{3\sqrt{3}}$ cu units. 3. 6 4. $W = P \times H + 2A$ 5. $nh + 2s$
6. (a) 7. (c) 8. (d) 9. (b) 10. (c)
11. (a) 12. (c) 13. (d) 14. (b) 15. (a)
16. (d) 17. (b) 18. (c) 19. (c) 20. (a)
21. (a) 22. (a) 23. (a) 24. (d) 25. (b)

26. (b)	27. (b)	28. (b)	29. (c)	30. (b)
31. (c)				

Level 2: Review Your Concepts

32. (c)	33. (a)	34. (b)	35. (d)	36. (a)
37. (a)	38. (d)	39. (a)	40. (a)	41. (a)
42. (b)	43. (d)	44. (d)		

Level 3: Assess Your Concepts

45. (b)	46. (c)	47. (d)	48. (b)	49. (a)
50. (A) (b)	(B) (b)	51. (a)	52. (c)	53. (a)
54. (c)	55. (c)	56. (d)		

JEE Special Wing

Multiple-Answer Type Questions

1. (a, b, c, d)	2. (a, b)	3. (b, c, d)	4. (a, b)	5. (a, b, d)

Match The Column

6. (c)	7. (b)	8. (a)	9. (e)

Comprehension-Based Questions

10. (c)	11. (b)	12. (c)	13. (b)	14. (d)

Assertion and Reason Type Questions

15. (a)	16. (b)	17. (d)	18. (c)

Hints and Explanations

Classroom Wing

Very Short Answer Type Questions

1. Lateral surface of right prism $= n$

Then no. of edges $= n$

2. $f \rightarrow$ rectangles faces $= 6$

$e \rightarrow$ no of edges $= 12$

$v \rightarrow$ no. of vertices $= 8$

3. Curved surface area is equal. i.e., πrl

$\therefore \frac{r_1}{r_2} = \frac{6}{7}$

$\pi r_1 l_1 = \pi r_2 l_2$

$\frac{6}{7} = \frac{l_2}{l_1}$

$\frac{l_1}{l_2} = \frac{7}{6}$

4. Volume of cone $= \frac{1}{3}\pi r^2 h$

$\frac{V_1}{V_2} = \frac{\frac{1}{3}\pi r_1^2 h_1}{\frac{1}{3}\pi r_2^2 h_2} \quad (h_1 = h_2)$

$\frac{V_1}{V_2} = \frac{R^2}{r^2}$

5. Volume of cylinder $= \pi r^2 h$

$h_1 = h_2$

$\frac{r_1}{r_2} = \frac{7}{5}$

$\frac{\pi r_1^2 h_1}{\pi r_2^2 h_2} = \frac{49}{25}$

6. $\pi R^2 H = \pi r^2 h$

$\frac{R^2}{r^2} = \frac{h}{H}$

$\frac{R}{r} = \sqrt{\frac{h}{H}}$

$\left(\frac{2}{3}\right)^2 = \frac{h}{H}$

$\frac{H}{h} = \frac{9}{4}$

7. Curved SA of cylinder $= 2\pi rh$

SA of sphere $= 4\pi r^2$

Diameter of sphere $= 2r = h$

Ratio $= \frac{2\pi r(2r)}{4\pi r^2} = \frac{1}{1}$

8. TSA $= 2\pi\ R^2 + 2\pi r^2 + \pi R^2 - \pi r^2$

$= \pi(3R^2 + r^2)$

9. The required difference

$= 4\pi R^2 - 2\pi(r)(2R)$

$= 4\pi R^2 - 4\pi Rr$

$= 4\pi(R^2 - Rr)$

10. CSA $= \pi l\ (R + r)$

$= \pi\ (R + r)^2\ (\because l = R + r)$

11. TSA $= 2\pi Rh + 2\pi rh + 2\pi(R^2 - r^2)$

$= 2\pi R(2r) + 2\pi r(2r) + 2\pi R^2 - 2\pi r^2$

$= 4\pi Rr + 4\pi r^2 + 2\pi R^2 - 2\pi r^2$

$= 2\pi(R^2 + 2Rr + r^2)$

$= 2\pi\ (R + r)^2$

12. The volume of hollow hemisphere $\frac{2}{3}\pi\left(R^3 - r^3\right)$

$= \frac{2}{3}\pi\left(8r^3 - r^3\right)(\therefore R = 2r)$

$= \frac{2}{3} \times \frac{22}{7} \times 7r^3 = \frac{44}{3}r^3$

13. The volume of a cone $= \frac{1}{3}\pi r^2 h$

$= \frac{1}{3} \times \frac{22}{7} \times r^2 \times 7r$

$= \frac{22r^3}{3}$

14. The volume of a cone frustum

$$= \frac{1}{3}\pi h\left(R^2 + Rr + r^2\right)$$

$$= \frac{1}{3}\pi \times \frac{5}{2}r\left[\left(2r^2\right) + \left(2r\right)r + r^2\right]\left(\therefore r = \frac{R}{2}\right)$$

$$= \frac{\pi \times 5r}{3\times 2}\left(7r^2\right) = \frac{55r^3}{3}$$

15. The volume of hollow cylinder

$$= \pi\,(R^2 - r^2)h$$

$$= \frac{22}{7}\left[\left(\left(2r^2\right) - r^2\right)\times\frac{7}{18}r\right]$$

$$= \frac{22}{7}\times 3r^2 \times \frac{7r}{18} = \frac{11r^3}{3}$$

16. $A \rightarrow$ vol of pyramid $= \dfrac{lb}{3}$

$B \rightarrow$ vol of right prism $= lb$

$$A = \frac{B}{3}$$

17. length of arc $= \dfrac{\cancel{30}^{\,1}}{\cancel{360}_{\,12}} = \dfrac{1}{12} =$ circumference of base of cone

Circumference of circle $= 2\pi r = 12\pi$

Length of arc $= \dfrac{1}{\cancel{12}}\times \cancel{12}\pi = \pi$

$\pi =$ Circumference of base of cone

$\cancel{\pi} = 2\cancel{\pi} r$

$r = \dfrac{1}{2}$ cm

18. Volume of hollow cylinder $= \pi h(R^2 - r^2)$

19. Volume of cube $= a^3$

Volume of sphere $= \dfrac{4}{3}\pi a^3$

$$\text{Ratio} = \frac{\cancel{a^3}}{\frac{4}{3}\pi \cancel{a^3}} = \frac{3}{4\pi} = \frac{3\times 7}{4\times 22} = \frac{21}{88}$$

20. Volume $= 10x \times 8x \times \dfrac{1}{10}x$

$= 8x^3$ m^3

Thickness $= (2 + x) - (2 - x)$

$= 2 + x - 2 + x$

$= 2x$ cm

21. CSA $= \pi l(R + r)$ sq units

$= \pi(2a)[(a + b)(a - b)]$

$= 2a\pi(a + b + a - b)$

$= 2a\pi(2a)$

$= 4a^2\pi$ cm^2

Short Answer Type Questions

22. OR is the perpendicular bisector of PQ.

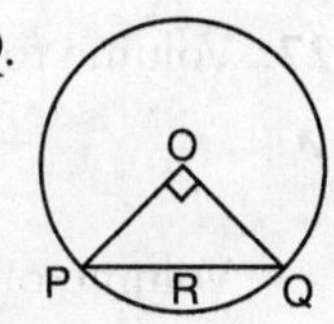

$\therefore RQ = \dfrac{PQ}{2} = \dfrac{12}{2} = 6$ cm

The angles of ΔORQ are 30°, 60°, and 90°.

$\therefore$ The ratio of its corresponding sides is $1 : \sqrt{3} : 2$.

$$\Rightarrow \frac{OR}{RQ} = \frac{1}{\sqrt{3}} \Rightarrow \frac{OR}{6} = \frac{1}{\sqrt{3}}$$

$\Rightarrow OR = 2\sqrt{3}$ cm

$\therefore$ Area of $\Delta POQ = \dfrac{1}{2}\times PQ \times OR$

$= \dfrac{1}{2}\times 12 \times 2\sqrt{3} = 12\sqrt{3}$ cm^2

23. The face diagonal of the cube $= 6\sqrt{2}$ cm

$\Rightarrow$ The edge of the cube $= \dfrac{6\sqrt{2}}{\sqrt{2}} = 6$ cm

$\therefore$ The dimensions of the resulting cuboid are:
$l = 6 \times 3 = 18$ cm, $b = 6$ cm, and $h = 6$ cm.

$\therefore$ Total surface area of the cuboid

$= 2(\text{lb} + \text{bh} + \text{lh})$

$= 2(18 \times 6 + 6 \times 6 + 18 \times 6) = 504$ cm^2

24. Given $\dfrac{1}{3}Ah = 192$ m^2

$\Rightarrow \dfrac{1}{3}\times A \times 16 = 192 \Rightarrow A = 36$ m^2

$\Rightarrow$ (side) (side) $= 36 \Rightarrow$ side $= 6$ m

Hence, the correct option is (b).

25. Here, $2\pi r = 22$ cm

$\Rightarrow 2\times\dfrac{22}{7}\times r = 22 \Rightarrow r = 3.5$ cm

$h =$ length $= 35$ cm

$\therefore$ Volume $= \pi r^2 h = \dfrac{22}{7}\times(3.5)^2\times 35$

$= 1347.5$ cm^3

26. Let the radius of the cone be r.

$\therefore$ Radius of the sphere = $2r$

Height of the cone = 2 (2r) = $4r$

$$\frac{\text{Volume of the sphere}}{\text{Volume of the Cone}} = \frac{\frac{4}{3}p(2r)^3}{\frac{1}{3}pr^2(4r)}$$

$$= \frac{4\times 8p^3}{4r^3} = 8:1$$

27. Volume to be increased $= \pi r^2 h$

$= \pi r^2(5)$

Volume of cubes $= 2\times 2\times 2$

$= 8\text{ m}^3$

No of cubes $= \frac{22}{7}\times\frac{14\times 14\times 5}{8}$

$= 385$

28. Volume of cistern $= lbh$

$= 3\times 2\times 6 = 36$

area of iron sheet $= 2(lb + bh + hl)$

$= 2(6+12+18)$

$= 36\times 2 = 72\text{ m}^2$

29. CSA of cone $= \pi r(l+r)$

$\pi\times 8\times(6+8) = 112\pi\text{ m}^2$

$1\text{ m}\rightarrow 100\text{ cm}$

$1\text{m}^2\rightarrow 10^4\text{ cm}^2$

$112\pi\text{ m}^2\rightarrow 112\pi\times 10^4\text{ cm}^2$

$100\text{ cm}^2\rightarrow ₹\,0.8$

$1\text{cm}^2\rightarrow\frac{0.8}{100}\times 112\pi\times 10^4$

$= \frac{0.8\times 112\pi\times 10^4}{100}$

$= ₹28160$

30. TSA $= 3\pi r^2$ sq units

$3768 = 3\times 3.14r^2$

$r^2 = 400$

$r = 20$ cm

31. $r = 120$ cm

$l = 750$ cm

CSA $= \pi rl$

$= \pi\times 120\times 750$

10 tents $= \frac{\pi\times 120\times 750\times 10}{10^4}\text{ m}^2$

$= 90\pi$

$= 282.85\text{ m}^2$

32. Volume of wodden leg $= \pi r^2 h$

$= \pi\times(7\sqrt{2})^2\times 30$

$= \pi\times 49\times 2\times 30$

$= \pi\times 49\times 60$

$= 2940\,\pi$

$= 9240\text{ cm}^3$

Volume of cuboid $= lbh$

$= 30\times r\sqrt{2}\times r\sqrt{2}$

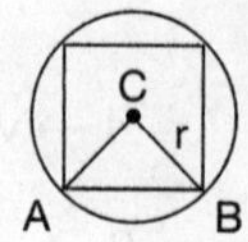

$AB^2 = AC^2 + BC^2$

$= r^2 + r^2$

$AB = \sqrt{2r^2} = r\sqrt{2}$

Volume of Cuboid $= 30\times r^2\times 2$

$= 30\times 49\times 2\times 2$

$= 5880\text{ cm}^3$

wood wasted $= 9240 - 5880$

$= 3360\text{ cm}^3$

33. Let slant height be x and $\perp$ will bisect vertex angle.

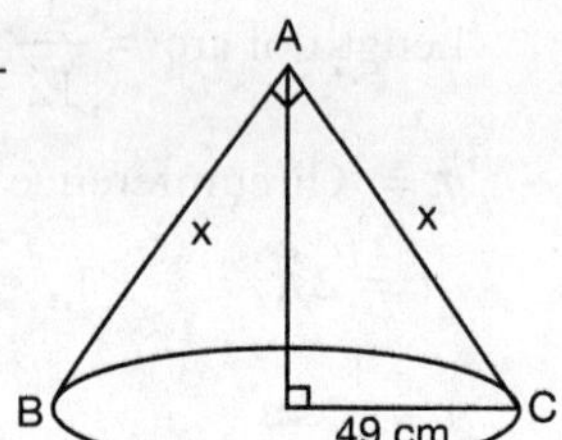

$\therefore\ \Delta ABC$ isisosright angle Δ

$\therefore x^2 + x^2 = (49\times 2)^2$

$x^2 = 4802$

C.S.A of Cone $= \pi rl$

$= \frac{22}{7}\times 49\times\sqrt{4802}$

$= 22\times 7\times 49\sqrt{2}$

$= 7546\sqrt{2}\text{ cm}^2$

34. $a = 6\sqrt{3}$ cm

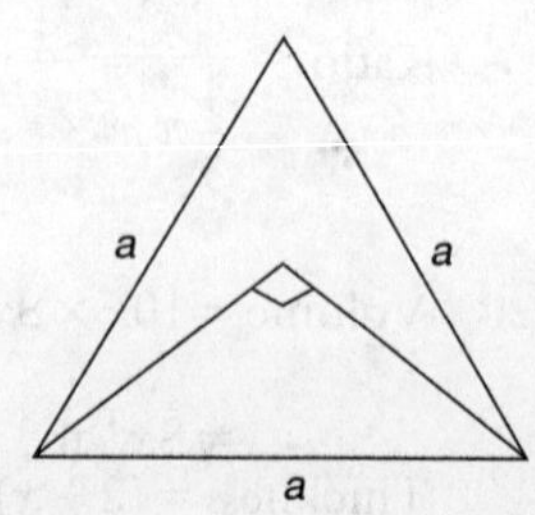

$h = 4$ cm

$x^2 + x^2 = a^2$

$x^2 = \frac{a^2}{2}$

$l^2 = h^2 + \frac{a^2}{2}$

TSA of pyramid $= \frac{1}{2} pl + \text{Area of base}$

Area of equilateral triangle $= \frac{\sqrt{3}a^2}{4}$

$$= \frac{1}{2} \times (3a)\left[4^2 + \left(\frac{36 \times 3}{2}\right)\right] + \frac{\sqrt{3}}{4}[36 \times 3]$$

$$= \frac{3}{2} \times 6\sqrt{3}[70] + 27\sqrt{3}$$

$$= 9\sqrt{3}(70) + 27\sqrt{3}$$

$$= 657\sqrt{3} \text{ cm}^2$$

35. $AB = \frac{5}{3}\ CD$; ΔAEB is isosceles.

$AB = \frac{5}{3}\ (2DE)$

(Since $ABCD$ is an isosceles trapezium and AEB is an isosceles triangle)

$AB = \frac{10}{3} \times DE$

Since the heights are equal to the ΔDEA and ΔABE,

Area of $\Delta ABE = \frac{10}{3} \times$ Area of ΔADE

$= \frac{10}{3} \times 12 = 40$ sq cm.

36. (A) Volume of sphere $= \frac{4}{3}\pi r^3$

$= \frac{4}{3}\pi(3)^3$

Volume of cylinder $= \pi r^2 h$

$= \pi \times \left(\frac{2}{10}\right)^2 \times h$

1 cm=10 mm

1 mm$=\frac{1}{10}$ cm

4 mm$=\frac{4}{10}$ cm

Equate both

$$\frac{4}{3}\pi(3)^3 = \pi \times \left(\frac{4}{100}\right)^2 \times h$$

$h = 3 \times 3 \times 100$

$= 900$ cm

(B) Given $AO = OC = 21$ cm

$\Rightarrow BC = AB = 21\sqrt{2} \Rightarrow BD = \frac{21\sqrt{2}}{2} = \frac{21}{\sqrt{2}}$

Clearly $BDEO$ is a square $\Rightarrow OD = DB = \frac{21\sqrt{2}}{2}$

Area of the shaded region

= Area of ΔOBD + Area of sector OBF

$$= \frac{1}{2} OD \times DB + \frac{\angle BOF}{360^\circ} \times \pi \times (OB)^2$$

$$\frac{1}{2}\left(\frac{21\sqrt{2}}{2} \times \frac{21\sqrt{2}}{2}\right) + \frac{45^\circ}{360^\circ} \times \frac{22}{7}(21)^2$$

$$= \frac{441}{4} + \frac{693}{4} = \frac{1134}{4}$$

$= 283.5$

$\therefore$ Area of shaded region = 283.5 sq cm.

Essay Type Questions

37. The area of the base of the pyramid (A) = the area of regular hexagon

$$= 6 \times \frac{\sqrt{3}}{4}a^2 = 6 \times \frac{\sqrt{3}}{4} \times 4^2 = 24\sqrt{3} \text{ cm}^2$$

$\therefore$ Volume $= \frac{1}{3}Ah$

$$= \frac{1}{3} \times 24\sqrt{3} \times 15 = 120\sqrt{3} \text{ cm}^2$$

38. Diagonal of the square $= 14\sqrt{2}$ cm

$\Rightarrow$ Side $= \frac{14\sqrt{2}}{\sqrt{2}} = 14$ cm

Area of the shaded region = area of the square – area of the sector ABD

$$= 14^2 - \frac{90^\circ}{360^\circ} \times \frac{22}{7} \times (14)^2 = 42 \text{ cm}^2$$

39.

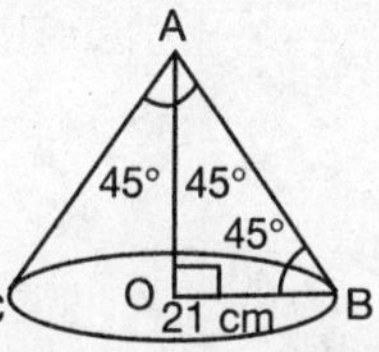

Given $r = 21$ cm and $\angle BAC = 90°$:

$\angle OAB = \frac{1}{2}\angle BAC = 45°$

In ΔAOB, OA = OB

$\Rightarrow$ Height (h) = OA = 21 cm

$\therefore$ Volume $= \frac{1}{3}\pi r^2 h = \frac{1}{3} \times \frac{22}{7} \times 21^2 \times 21$

$= 9702$ cm^3

40. The area of the shaded region QASR.

= The area of square PQRS – the area of sector PQAS

$= (7\sqrt{2})(7\sqrt{2}) - \frac{90°}{360°} \times \frac{22}{7} \times (7\sqrt{2})^2$

$= 98 - 77 = 21$ cm^2

Similarly, the area of the shaded region PQBS = 21 cm^2.

$\therefore$ The area of the shaded region = 21 + 21

= 42 cm^2

41.

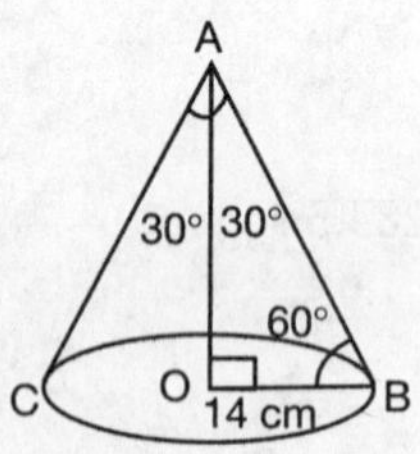

Given $r = 14$ cm

$\angle BAC = 60° \Rightarrow \angle OAB = \frac{1}{2}\angle BAC = 30°$

In ΔAOB, the angles are 30°, 60°, and 90°.

$\therefore$ The ratio of the corresponding sides is $1 : \sqrt{3} : 2$.

$\therefore$ Slant height of the cone = AB = 2 × OB = 28 cm

$\therefore$ Curved surface area of the cone = $\pi r l$

$= \frac{22}{7} \times 14 \times 28 = 1232$ cm^2

42. Let the radius of each Chaco ball is R and the radius of the spherical cream ball be r.

$r = \frac{R}{2}$ and $\frac{4}{3}\pi R^3 = 32$ cm^3

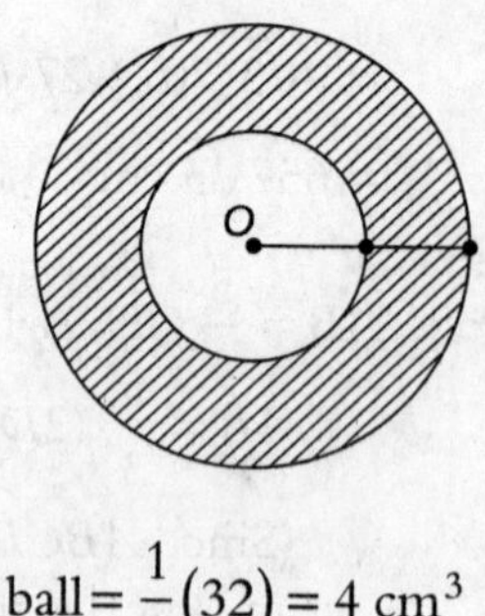

Volume of cream in each Chaco ball $= \frac{4}{3}\pi\left(\frac{R}{2}\right)^3$

$= \frac{4}{3}\left(\frac{\pi R^3}{8}\right) = \frac{1}{8}\left(\frac{4}{3}\pi R^3\right)$

$\therefore$ Volume of cream in each Chaco ball $= \frac{1}{8}(32) = 4$ cm^3

The volume of the cream in the box = 24(4) cm^3

= 96 cm^3

Competition Wing

Level 1: Apply Your Concepts

1. Circumference 0.5 cm

2. Diagonal of cube $= a\sqrt{3}$ units $= d$

$a = \frac{d}{\sqrt{3}}$ units

Volume of cube $= a^3 = \frac{d^3}{3\sqrt{3}}$ cu units

3. No. of faces in prism = ?

Edges = 12

With 12 edges we have 6 faces.

4. W = Lateral (LSA) surface area + 2 (Area of base)

LSA = Perimeter of base × Height

LSA = $P \times H$

$W = P \times H + 2A$

5. $s \rightarrow$ perimeter of base of prism

$n \rightarrow$ no. of side of base

$S \rightarrow$ total length of edges

$h \rightarrow$ height

$S = ?$

$S = 2s + n \times h$

$= nh + 2s$

6. Let the side of the equilateral triangle be a cm.

Given $\frac{\sqrt{3}}{2}a = 6 \Rightarrow a = \frac{12}{\sqrt{3}} \Rightarrow a = 4\sqrt{3}$

$\therefore$ Area $= \frac{\sqrt{3}}{4}a^2 = \frac{\sqrt{3}}{4}\left(4\sqrt{3}\right)^2 = 12\sqrt{3}$ cm^2

Hence, the correct option is (a).

7.

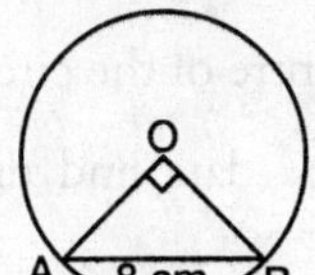

Given AB = 8 cm = hypotenuse of ΔOAB.

Area of a right isosceles triangle $= \frac{h^2}{4} = \frac{8^2}{4} = 16$ cm^2

Hence, the correct option is (c).

8. CSA of the cone = Area of the rectangle

= 44 × 32

= 1408 cm^2

Hence, the correct option is (d).

9. Let the radius of the sphere be r cm.

$\therefore$ Diameter = $2r$ cm

Base radius of the cylinder = r cm

Height = $2r$ cm (given)

$\therefore$ Required ratio $= \frac{\frac{4}{3}pr^3}{pr^2(2r)} (\because h = 2r)$

$= \frac{4}{6} = 2:3$

Hence, the correct option is (b).

10. Diameter of the sphere = the edge of the cube = 14 cm

$\Rightarrow 2r = 14$ cm $\Rightarrow r = 7$ cm

$\therefore$ Surface area $= 4\pi r^2 = 4 \times \frac{22}{7} \times 7^2$

$= 616$ cm^2

Hence, the correct option is (c).

11. Given $r = 6$ cm

$\frac{1}{3}\pi^2 h = 1056$ (given)

$\Rightarrow \frac{1}{3} \times \frac{22}{7} \times 6^2 \times h = 1056$

$\Rightarrow h = 28$ cm

Hence, the correct option is (a).

12. Given $\frac{\sqrt{3}}{4}a^2 = 18\sqrt{3}$

$\Rightarrow a^2 = 72 \Rightarrow a = 6\sqrt{2}$ cm

$\therefore$ Height$= \frac{\sqrt{3}}{2}a = \frac{\sqrt{3}}{2} \times 6\sqrt{2} = 3\sqrt{6}$ cm

Hence, the correct option is (c).

13. Find the volume of cylinder. Whose radius is breadth of rectangle and height is equal to length of the rectangle.

14. Volume of the prism = Area of the base × Height.

15. Area levelled by the roller in one revolution = CSA of the cylinder.

16. Diameter of the sphere = Length of the edge of a cube.

17. Draw $\overline{OP}$ from the centre to the midpoint of $\overline{BC}$.

18. CSA of a cylinder = $2\pi Rh$.

19. Find individual areas of different parts of the figure.

20. Find the edge of the prism.

21. Volume of the cone = Volume of all the spheres formed.

22. TSA of outer part $= 357 \times \frac{100}{0.2}$ cm^2.

23. CSA of bucket $= \pi l(R + r)$.

24. Equate the two volumes.

25. Find the area of two hexagon.

26. Required area is the difference of areas of rectangle and sum of areas of two sectors.

27. Draw the diagram and proceed.

28. Volume of the prism = Area of the base × Height.

29. Required volume = Volume of cone + Volume of sphere.

30. Volume of bowl = Volume of a bottle × Number of bottles.

31. Volume of a hemisphere $= \frac{3}{2}\pi r^3$ cubic units.

Level 2: Review Your Concepts

32. (i) Area of circular path = Area of ring.
 (ii) Area of path $= \pi(R^2 - r^2)$.
 (iii) Total cost = Area × cost/m^2.

33. (i) Find the area of the square formed by joining the centers of all outer circles.
 (ii) The required area = Area of the square − 16 $\left(\frac{1}{4} \times \text{Area of circle}\right)$.

34. (i) Volume of prism $= \frac{\sqrt{3}}{4} a^2 \times$ Height.
 (ii) Use the above formula and get the value of a.

35. Find the radius of the cylinder which is cut. (i.e., $\pi r^2 h = 1386$).

36. Area of shaded region = Area of square ABCD $-4\left(\frac{1}{4} \times \text{Area of circle}\right)$.

37. TSA $= 3\pi R^2 + \pi r^2$.

38. Volume of water in the cylindrical drum = Volume of the second cylinder up to the water risen.

39. Use, $\tan\left(\frac{\theta}{2}\right) = \frac{r}{h}$ and find θ.

40. (i) Circum radius $= \frac{a}{\sqrt{3}}$ and inradius $= \frac{a}{2\sqrt{3}}$, where a is the side of the outer equilateral triangle.
 (ii) For an equilateral triangle of side a, if an in-circle and circum circle are drawn whose radii are r and R then $r = \frac{a}{2\sqrt{3}}$ and $R = \frac{a}{\sqrt{3}}$.

41. $48^2 = 2304$
 $14^2 = 196$
 $50^2 = 2500$
 $48^2 + 14^2 = 50^2$
 ∴ The triangle is right angled and its hypotenuse is 50 cm. Its circum radius $= \frac{50}{2}$ cm = 25 cm.

42. Total area of the lateral faces = 900 − 360 = 540 cm^2.
 Number of lateral faces it has $\frac{540}{30} = 18$.

43. Let the side of the base be a cm. Let the height of the prism be h cm.
 $$\left(\frac{\sqrt{3}}{4}a^2\right)(h) = 80\sqrt{3} \quad (1)$$
 $$(3a)(h) = 240 \quad (2)$$
 $$\frac{(1)}{(2)} \Rightarrow \frac{\sqrt{3}}{12}a = \frac{\sqrt{3}}{3}$$
 $a = 4$
 From Eq. (2), $\Rightarrow h = 20$.

44. BDAC

Level 3: Assess Your Concepts

45. (i) 1 ml = 1 cm^3.
 (ii) Find the number of words per 1 ml of ink.

46. CSA of a bucket $= \pi l(R + r)$.

47. Diagonals of the square meet at the centre of the circles.

48. (i) Draw the figure according to the data and draw $\overline{EF} \parallel \overline{CD}$.
 (ii) Area of ΔACE = Area of the triangle ABC − {Area of ΔECD + Area of $ABED$}.

49. $QT = 90$ m
 $QU : UT = 1 : 2$
 ∴ $UT = 60$ m
 $UV : VT = 1 : 2$ and $QU = 30$ m
 ∴ $UV = 20$ m and $VT = 40$ m
 $URSV$ is a rectangle.
 ∴ $VS = UR = 50$ m.

$PV : VS = 4 : 5$

$\therefore PV = 40$ m.

Area of the figure = Area of ΔPQT + Area of $QRST$

$$= \frac{1}{2}(PV)(QT) + \frac{1}{2}(QT + RS)(UR)$$

$$= \frac{1}{2}(40)(90) + \frac{1}{2}(90 + 20)(50)$$

$(\because RS = UV = 20$ m)

$= 1800 + 2750 = 4550$ m^2.

50. (A) The bucket is in shape of a frustum. The slant height of a frustum

$= \sqrt{(\text{Top radius} - \text{Bottom Radius})^2 + (\text{Height})^2}$.

$\therefore$ Slant height of the bucket

$l = \sqrt{(24-16)^2 + 6^2} = 10$ m.

$\therefore$ Its curved surface area $= \pi l(R + r)$

$= \pi\,(10)(24 + 16) = 400\,\pi$ m^2.

(B) **Prism:**

$a = 6$ feet

H = 75 feet

Pyramid:

$a = \frac{7}{4}$ feet

$79 - 75 = 4$ feet.

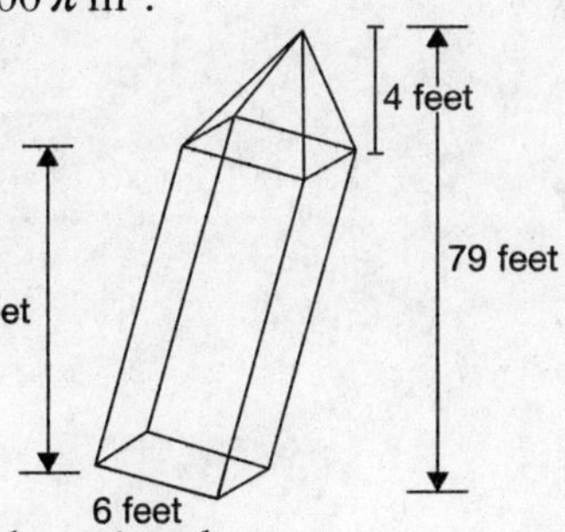

Area of the surface to be painted

= LSA of prism + LSA of pyramid.

$$= PH + \frac{1}{2}Pl = PH + \frac{1}{2}P\sqrt{h^2 + \left(\frac{a}{2}\right)^2}$$

$$= 4(6)\,(75) + \frac{1}{2}\,(4)(6)\,\sqrt{4^2 + 3^2}$$

$= 1800 + 12(5) = 1860$ sq ft

$= \frac{1860}{10.8}$ *sq m*

The cost painting

$= \frac{1860}{10.8} \times$ (₹108)

$= 1860 \times$ (₹10) = ₹18600

51. Let the radii of the circles be denoted by r_1 cm and r_2 cm where $r_1 \geq r_2$. As the circles touch each other externally, distance between their centres = Sum of their radii.

$\therefore r_1 + r_2 = 28$ (1)

Also $\pi(r_1)^2 + \pi(r_2)^2 = 490\,\pi$

$\therefore (r_1)^2 + (r_2)^2 = 490$ (2)

Squaring both sides of Eq. (1), we get

$(r_1)^2 + (r_2)^2 + 2(r_1)(r_2) = 784$

From Eq. (2), $490 + 2(r_1)(r_2) = 784$

$r_1 \cdot r_2 = 147$ (3)

Solving Eqs. (1) and (3), we get,

$r_1 = 21$ and $r_2 = 7$. ($\therefore\ r_1 \geq r_2$)

$\therefore$ Required difference = 14 cm.

52.

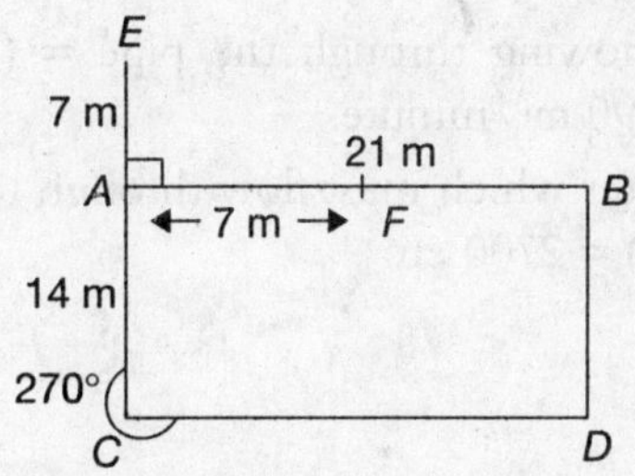

Suppose the cow was tied at C. Total area it can graze = Area of the sector ECD with central angle 270° and radius 21 m + Area of the sector EAF with central angle 90°

and radius 7 m $= \frac{270°}{360°}\pi(21)^2 + \frac{90°}{360°}\pi(7)^2$

$$= \frac{3}{4}\pi(441) + \frac{1}{4}\pi(49) = 343\pi \text{ m}^2.$$

53. Area of the shaded region

= Area of the sector PQS – Area of ΔPQS

$QS = \sqrt{2}$ (side) $= 7\sqrt{2}$ cm.

Side = 7 cm

$\therefore$ Area of sector PQS

$$= \frac{90°}{360°}\pi\,(7)^2 = \frac{49\pi}{4}\text{ cm}^2$$

Area of $\Delta PQS = \frac{1}{2}(PQ)(PS)$

$$= \frac{1}{2}(7)^2 = \frac{49}{2}\text{ cm}^2$$

$\therefore$ Required area $= \left(\frac{49\pi}{4} - \frac{49}{2}\right)$ cm^2

$$= \frac{49}{4}(\pi - 2)\text{ cm}^2.$$

54. Side of each of the first three cubes = $\dfrac{4\sqrt{2}}{\sqrt{2}}$ = 4 cm.

Side of each of the other three cubes = $\dfrac{8\sqrt{2}}{\sqrt{2}}$ = 8 cm.

Let the side of the cube formed be a cm.

Total volume of the six cubes = $3(4^3 + 8^3)$ = $3(64 + 512) = 1728$ cm^3.

$\therefore a^3 = 1728$

$a = 12$.

55. Let the depth of the sump be h m.

Volume of water flowing through the pipe = (180)(0.5) m^3/minute = 90 m^3/minute.

Total volume of water which must flow through to fill the sump = (90)(30) = 2700 cm^3.

$\therefore (24)(20)(h) = 2700$

$h = 5.625$.

56. 

Length of cylindrical pipe = 7 m, diameter = 1.5 m

Volume of the 1000 pipes

$= \dfrac{22}{7} \times \dfrac{1.5}{2} \times \dfrac{1.5}{2} \times 7 \times 1000$

= 12375 cu m.

Volume of the tunnel = 7100 × 2 × 2 = 28400 cu m.

The required volume = (28400 – 12375) = 16025 cm^3.

JEE Special Wing

Multiple-Answer Type Questions

1. Given that the area of a rectangle is 72 sq cm.
Let length and breadth of the rectangle be l cm and b cm.
$\Rightarrow l \times b = 72$, where l cm and b are integers more than 1.
$\Rightarrow (l, b)$ can be $(36, 2), (24, 3), (18, 4), (12, 6), (9, 8)$.
The perimeter of a rectangle $= 2(l + b)$.
The perimeter of the rectangle can be 76 cm, 54 cm, 44 cm, 36 cm, 34 cm.
Hence, choice (a, b, c, d) are correct.

2. A right solid has 12 edges.
So, the solid can be a prism whose base is a quadrilateral or a pyramid whose base is a hexagon.
A prism with quadrilateral base 6 faces and 8 vertices.
A pyramid with hexagonal base 7 faces and 7 vertices.
Hence, choice (a and b) are correct.

3. Given that the LSA of a cuboid (in sq cm) is numerically equal to the volume of the cuboid (in cu cm).
$\Rightarrow 2h(l + b) = lbh$
$\Rightarrow 2(l + b) = lb$
$\Rightarrow \frac{l+b}{lb} = \frac{1}{2}$
$\Rightarrow \frac{1}{l} + \frac{1}{b} = \frac{1}{2}$
$\Rightarrow l = 4$ and $b = 4$ (Since l and b are integers)
And h can be any integer.
Therefore, the volume of the cuboid (in cu cm) must be a multiple of 16.
Hence, choice (b, c, d) are correct.

4. The dimensions of a cuboid are 10 cm $\times$ 8 cm $\times$ 6 cm.
A cylinder is carved out from the cuboid.
(i) If the base of the cylinder lies on the face of dimensions 8 cm $\times$ 6 cm.
Radius $(r) = \frac{6}{2} = 3$ cm and height $(h) = 10$ cm.
The volume of the cuboid $= \pi r^2 h = 90\pi$ cu cm.
(ii) If the base of the cylinder lies on the face of dimensions 10 cm $\times$ 6 cm.
Radius $(r) = \frac{6}{2} = 3$ cm and height $(h) = 8$ cm.
The volume of the cuboid $= \pi r^2 h = 72\pi$ cu cm.
(iii) If the base of the cylinder lies on the face of dimensions 10 cm $\times$ 8 cm.
Radius $(r) = \frac{8}{2} = 4$ cm and height $(h) = 6$ cm.
The volume of the cuboid $= \pi r^2 h = 96\pi$ cu cm.
Hence, choice (a and b) are correct.

5. Let the dimensions of a cuboid be a cm, b cm, and c cm.
Here, the length of the cuboid can be a cm, b cm, or c cm.
From the given data, $a \times b = 90$ sq cm, $b \times c = 72$ sq cm and $a \times c = 80$ sq cm.
$(ab)(bc)(ac) = 90 \times 72 \times 80$
$(abc)^2 = 100 \times 72 \times 72$
$(abc)^2 = (720)^2$
$abc = 720.$
$\Rightarrow a = \frac{abc}{bc} = \frac{720}{72} = 10$
$b = \frac{abc}{ac} = \frac{720}{80} = 9$
$c = \frac{abc}{ab} = \frac{720}{90} = 8.$
The length, breadth, and height of the cuboid are 10 cm, 9 cm, and 8 cm, but need not be in the same order.
If the dimensions of a cuboid are l cm $\times$ b cm $\times$ h cm,
Volume of the cuboid $= lbh$
LSA $= 2h(l + b)$
TSA $= 2(lb + bh + lh)$
The longest diagonal of the cuboid $= \sqrt{l^2 + b^2 + h^2}$.
The length, breadth, and height of the cuboid have no fixed values.
Hence the volume, TSA and longest diagonal of the cuboid can be determined uniquely, but we cannot find the LSA uniquely.
For example, if $h = 8$ cm, LSA $= 2 \times 8(10 + 9) = 304$ sq cm.
If $h = 9$ cm, LSA $= 2 \times 9(10 + 8) = 324$ sq cm.
Hence, choice (a, b, d) are correct.

Match The Column

Common Solutions for questions 6 to 9:
Given that the radius, vertical height, and slant height of a solid cone are 12 cm, 16 cm, and 20 cm.

The cone is cut by a plane parallel to the base of the cone such that a frustum of cone is formed with radii 3 cm (r) and 12 cm (R).

The vertical and slant height of the frustum of the cone are h and l.

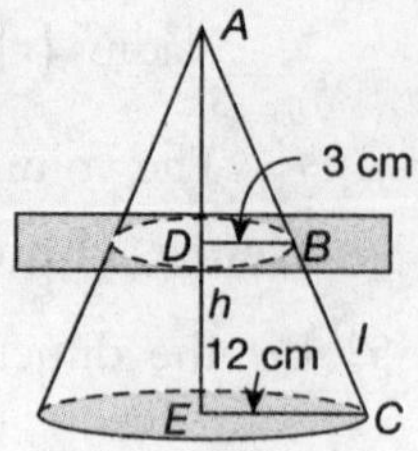

$\Rightarrow DB\ (r) = 3$ cm

$EC\ (R) = 12$ cm

$AE = 16$ cm and $AC = 20$ cm.

As DB is parallel to EC,

$\angle ADB = \angle AEC$ and $\angle ABD = \angle ACE$.

By AA similarity, $\Delta ADB \sim \Delta AEC$.

$$\Rightarrow \frac{AD}{AE} = \frac{DB}{EC} = \frac{AB}{AC}$$

$$\Rightarrow \frac{AD}{16} = \frac{3}{12} = \frac{AB}{20}$$

$$\Rightarrow \frac{AD}{16} = \frac{1}{4} = \frac{AB}{20}$$

$\Rightarrow AD = 4$ cm and $AB = 5$ cm.

$\Rightarrow h = DE = AE - AD = 16 - 4 = 12$ cm.

Also, $l = BC = AC - AB = 20 - 5 = 15$ cm.

6. $(r + R) : (h + l) = (3 + 12) : (12 + 15)$

$= 15 : 27 = 5 : 9$.

Hence, the correct option is (c).

7. The ratio of area of smaller base and CSA of the cone frustum $= \pi r^2 : \pi(r + R)l$

$= r^2 : (r + R)l$

$= 3^2 : (3 + 12)15 = 1 : 9$.

Hence, the correct option is (b).

8. The ratio of TSA (in sq cm) and volume (in sq cm) of the frustum

$= \left[\pi R^2 + \pi r^2 + \pi(r + R)l\right] : \pi\left[r^2 + R^2 + rR\right]h$

$= \left[R^2 + r^2 + (r + R)l\right] : \left[r^2 + R^2 + rR\right]h$

$= \left[(12)^2 + 3^2 + (3 + 12)15\right] : \left[(12)^2 + 3^2 + 3(12)\right]12$

$= [144 + 9 + 225] : [144 + 9 + 36]12$

$= 378 : [189]12 = 1 : 6$.

Hence, the correct option is (a).

9. Ratio of volumes of the frustum and the bigger cone

$= \pi\left[r^2 + R^2 + rR\right]h : \pi R^2(AE)$

$= \left[r^2 + R^2 + rR\right]h : R^2(AE)$

$= \left[(12)^2 + 3^2 + 3(12)\right]12 : (12)^2(16)$

$= [144 + 9 + 36] : 192$

$= 189 : 192 = 63 : 64$.

Hence, the correct option is (e).

Comprehension-Based Questions

Common Solutions for questions 10 to 14:

The bigger circle is inscribed in an equilateral triangle of side $12\sqrt{3}$ cm.

Also, three smaller congruent circles are inscribed in the triangle such that each smaller circle touches two sides of the triangle and the bigger circle.

Let the triangle be TSR.

Let A and C be centres of the bigger circle and smaller circle nearer to the point S respectively.

M and N be two points on SR such that $AM \perp SR$ and $CN \perp SR$.

Let B be the point of contact of the bigger circle and the smaller circle.

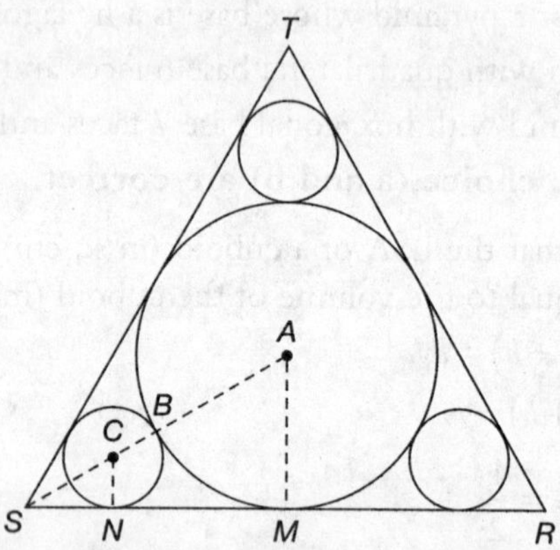

10. Given that $SR = 12\sqrt{3}$ cm.

$\Rightarrow SM = MR = 6\sqrt{3}$ cm.

$\angle MSA = \angle TSA = \frac{60°}{2} = 30°$.

$\angle AMS = 90°$.

$\Rightarrow \angle MAS = 180° - 90° - 30° = 60°$.

$\angle MSA : \angle MAS : \angle AMS = 30° : 60° : 90° = 1 : 2 : 3$.

$\Rightarrow AM : MS : AS = 1 : \sqrt{3} : 2$.

As $MS = 6\sqrt{3}$ cm, $AM = 6$ cm, and $AS = 12$ cm.

The radius of the bigger circle = 6 cm.

Hence, the correct option is (c).

11. $BS = AS - AB = 12 - 6 = 6$ cm.

$CS = 2(CN)$

$\Rightarrow BS = 3(CN)$

$\Rightarrow 6 = 3(CN)$

$\Rightarrow CN = 2$ cm $= BC$.

The distance between the centres of the bigger circle and the smaller circle $= AC$.

$= AB + BC = 6 + 2 = 8$ cm.

Hence, the correct option is (b).

12. $\dfrac{\text{The area of the bigger circle}}{\text{The sum of the areas of the smaller circles}}$

$= \dfrac{\pi(AM)^2}{3\times\pi(CN)^2}$

$= \dfrac{(AM)^2}{3\times(CN)^2}$

$= \dfrac{(6)^2}{3\times(2)^2} = 3.$

The area of the bigger circle is three times the sum of the areas of the smaller circles.

Hence, the correct option is (c).

13. The area of the shaded region = The area of the triangle TSR – The area of the four circles

$= \dfrac{\sqrt{3}(\text{SR})^2}{4} - \pi(\text{AM})^2 - 3\times\pi(\text{CN})^2$

$= \dfrac{\sqrt{3}\left(12\sqrt{3}\right)^2}{4} - \pi(6)^2 - 3\times\pi(2)^2$

$= 108\sqrt{3} - 48\pi$

$= 12\left(9\sqrt{3} - 4\pi\right)\text{ cm}^2$

Hence, the correct option is (b).

14. Let the triangle be CEF.

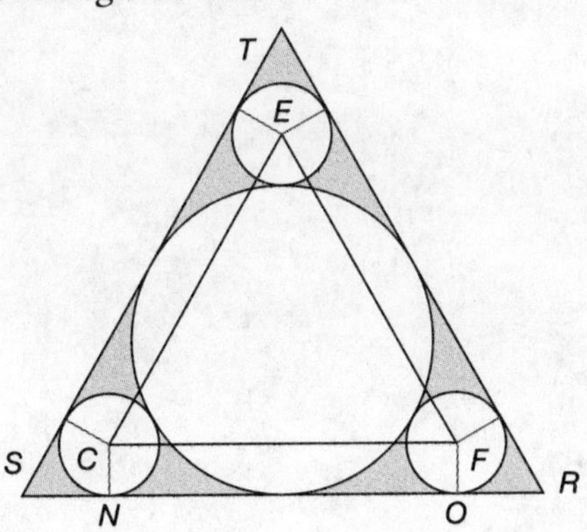

As $CN = 2$ cm, $\angle CSN = 30°$, and $\angle SCN = 60°$, $SN = 2\sqrt{3}$ cm.

$\Rightarrow SN = OR = 2\sqrt{3}$ cm.

Now $CF = NO = SR - SN - OR$

$= 12\sqrt{3} - 2\sqrt{3} - 2\sqrt{3} = 8\sqrt{3}$ cm.

Similarly, $CE = EF = 8\sqrt{3}$ cm.

CEF is an equilateral triangle.

The area of the equilateral triangle $CEF = \dfrac{\sqrt{3}(\text{CF})^2}{4}$

$= \dfrac{\sqrt{3}\left(8\sqrt{3}\right)^2}{4} = 48\sqrt{3}$ sq cm.

Hence, the correct option is (d).

Assertion and Reason Type Questions

15. **Assertion:** The side of the base (s) 12 cm.

The vertical height of the pyramid (h) = 15 cm.

The volume of a pyramid = $\dfrac{1}{3}$ × Area of the base × Vertical height

$= \dfrac{1}{3}\times s^2\times h$

$= \dfrac{1}{3}\times(12)^2\times 15$

= 720 cu cm.

So, **Assertion** is true.

Reason: The volume of a pyramid is the product of one-third of the area of the base and the vertical height of the pyramid.

So, **Reason** is true and is the correct explanation to **Assertion**.

Hence, the correct option is (a).

16. **Assertion:** The volume of a sphere is $\dfrac{4\pi r^3}{3}$.

The surface area of the sphere is $4\pi r^2$.

Given that $\dfrac{4\pi r^3}{3} = 4\pi r^2$.

$\Rightarrow r = 3$ cm.

So, **Assertion** is true.

Reason: If the radius of the sphere is r cm, the volume of the corresponding hemisphere is $\dfrac{2\pi r^3}{3}$.

So, **Reason** is true and not the correct explanation to **Assertion**.

Hence, the correct option is (b).

17. **Assertion:** The edge of cube (s) = 14 cm.

The diameter of the sphere is equal to the edge of the cube.

The radius of the sphere (r) = 7 cm.

The surface area of the sphere = $4\pi r^2$

$= 4\left(\dfrac{22}{7}\right)7^2 = 4(22)7 = 616$ sq cm.

So, **Assertion** is false.

Reason: If the largest sphere is carved out of a cube, then the diameter of the sphere is equal to the edge of the cube.

So, **Reason** is true.

Hence, the correct option is (d).

18. **Assertion:** The inner dimensions of a cuboidal box are 125 cm × 90 cm × 64 cm.

The inner dimensions of each solid are 25 cm × 22 cm × 21 cm.

The number of cuboids that can be placed along the length of the box is $\frac{125}{25} = 5$.

The number of cuboids that can be placed along the breadth of the box is $\frac{90}{22} \approx 4$.

The number of cuboids that can be placed along the breadth of the box is $\frac{64}{21} \approx 3$.

The number of cuboids that can be placed in the box $= 5 \times 4 \times 3 = 60$.

So, **Assertion** is true.

Reason: The ratio of the inner volume of the box and the volume of each solid cuboid may not give the number of solids as we may find some gap length-wise, breadth-wise or height-wise when the inner dimensions of the box are not the multiples of the dimensions of the solid cuboids.

So, **Reason** is false.

Hence, the correct option is (c).

CHAPTER 9

Coordinate Geometry

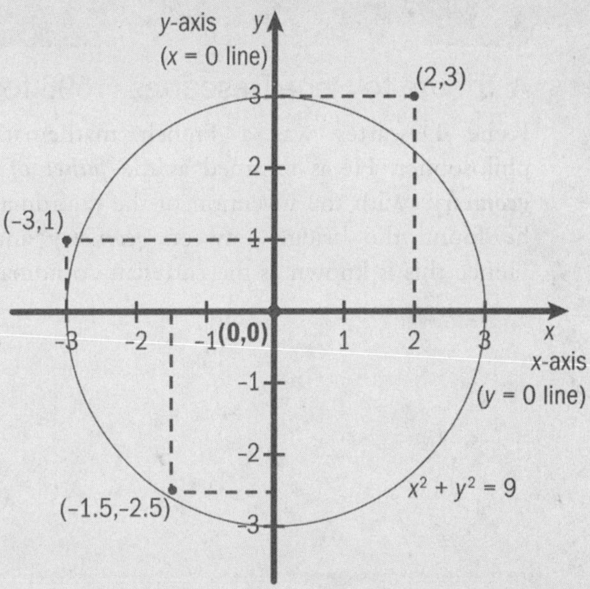

Remember

Before beginning this chapter, you should be able to:

- Label coordinates of a point and tell conversion of signs
- Show points on the plane, distance between the points

Key Ideas

After completing this chapter, you should be able to:

- Study distance between a point and the axes and apply the distance formula in solving word problems
- Explain signs of coordinates of a point in four quadrants
- Understand inclination and slope of a straight line
- Obtain equation of a line parallel or perpendicular to the given line
- Find out midpoint, centroid, median and altitude of a triangle
- Calculate areas of triangle and quadrilateral

Scientific Crypt

A Tribute to Rene Descartes (1596 to 1650)

Rene Descartes was a French mathematician and philosopher. He is regarded as the ***father of analytical geometry.*** With the invention of the coordinate system, he found the bridge between ***geometry*** and ***algebra***. Hence this is known as the cartesian coordinate system. He entered college at the age of eight and became a lawyer at the age of 20. His major contribution to the field of Mathematics is the Cartesian coordinate system. In philosophy, he is known for his work 'Meditation on First Philosophy'.

FUN TIME

CROSSWORD

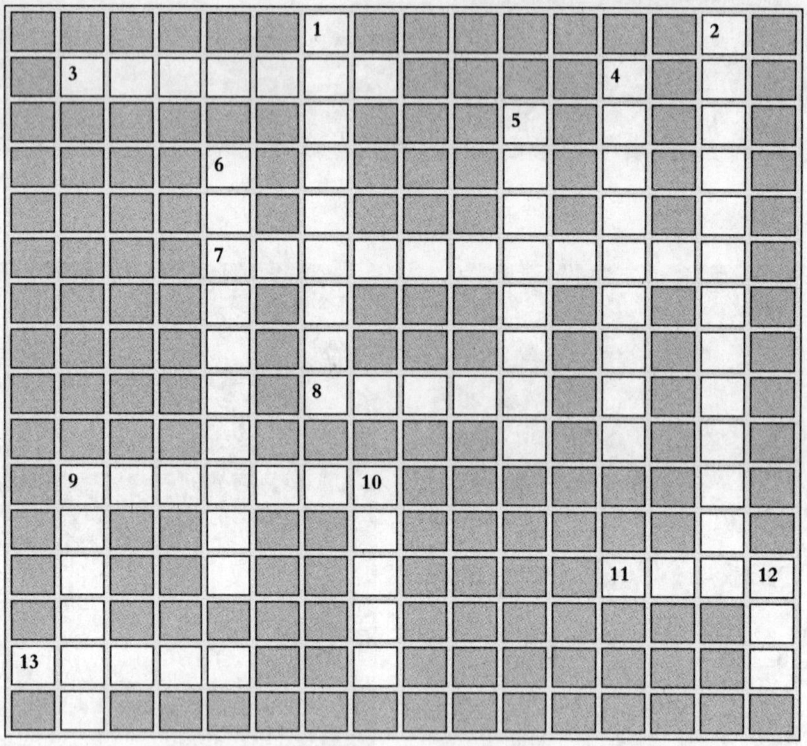

Across

3. The slope of a line is defined by the ____ of its inclination.
7. The angle made by a straight line with a positive direction.
8. The area of a triangle formed by $2x + 3y = 6$ with the coordinate axes is ____square units.
9. A straight line which is neither parallel to the x-axis nor parallel to the y-axis.
11. The slope of the x-axis.
13. The angle between the axes.

Down

1. $x/a + y/b = 1$ is ____form of a line.
2. $2x + 3y = 5$ and $3x - 2y = 10$ are ____lines.
4. If AB + BC = AC, then A, B and C are ____points.
5. $2x + 3y = 5$ and $2x + 3y = 10$ are ____lines.
6. If P, Q, R, S are collinear points in the same order and PQ = QR = RS, then Q and R are the points of
9. The point of intersection of the x-axis and the y-axis.
10. The slopes of non-vertical parallel lines are
12. The slope of a line whose inclination is 45 degrees.

INTRODUCTION

Let $X'OX$ and YOY' be two mutually perpendicular lines intersecting at the point O in a plane.

These two lines are called reference lines or coordinate axes. The horizontal reference line $X'OX$ is called X-axis and the vertical reference line YOY' is called Y-axis.

The point of intersection of these two axes, i.e., O is called the origin. The plane containing the coordinate axes is called coordinate plane or XY-plane.

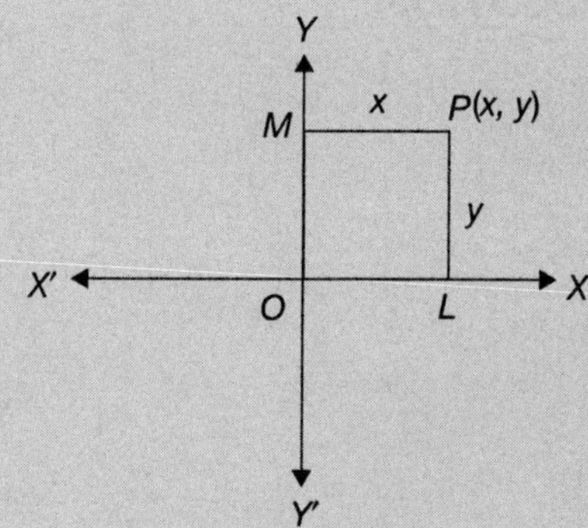

Coordinates of a Point

Let P be a point in the XY-plane. Draw perpendiculars PL and PM to X-axis and Y-axis, respectively.

Let $PL = y$ and $PM = x$. Then, the point P is taken as (x, y). Here x and y are called the rectangular Cartesian coordinates or simply coordinates of the point P. x is called x-coordinate or abscissa and y is called y-coordinate or ordinate of the point P. $P(x, y)$ is x units away from Y-axis and y units away from X-axis.

Convention of Signs

1. Towards the right side of the Y-axis, x-coordinate of any point on the graph paper is taken positive and towards the left side of the Y-axis, x-coordinate is taken negative.
2. Above the X-axis, the y-coordinate of any point on the graph paper is taken positive and below the X-axis, y-coordinate is taken negative.

If (x, y) is a point in the plane and Q_1, Q_2, Q_3, Q_4 are the four quadrants of rectangular coordinate system, then,

1. If $x > 0$ and $y > 0$, then $(x, y) \in Q_1$.
2. If $x < 0$ and $y > 0$, then $(x, y) \in Q_2$.
3. If $x < 0$ and $y < 0$, then $(x, y) \in Q_3$.
4. If $x > 0$ and $y < 0$, then $(x, y) \in Q_4$.

EXAMPLE 9.1 If $x < 0$ and $y > 0$, then $(-x, y)$ lies in which quadrant?

SOLUTION

$x < 0 \Rightarrow -x > 0$

$\therefore$ The point $(-x, y)$ lies in the first quadrant, i.e., Q_1.

EXAMPLE 9.2 If $(a, b) \in Q_3$, then $(-a, -b)$ belongs to which quadrant?

SOLUTION

Given $(a, b) \in Q_3 \Rightarrow a < 0, b < 0$ then $-a$ is positive and $-b$ is also positive, therefore $(-a, -b) \in Q_1$.

EXAMPLE 9.3 Plot the points $A(2, 3)$, $B(-1, 2)$, $C(-3, -2)$, and $D(4, -2)$ in the XY-plane.

SOLUTION

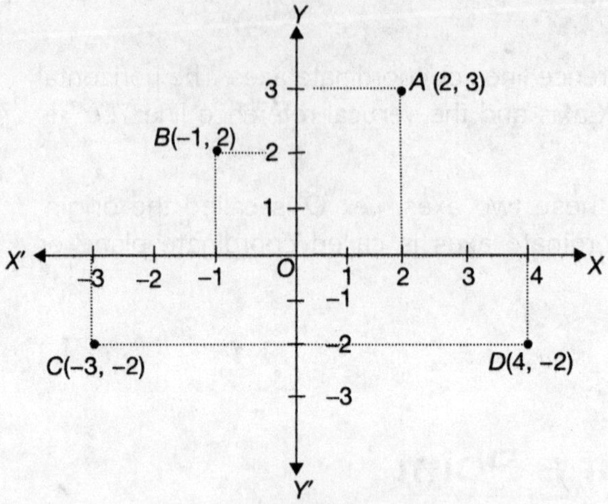

Figure 9.1

Points on the Plane

Point on X-axis and Y-axis

Let P be a point on X-axis, so that its distance from X-axis is zero. Hence, the point P can be taken as $(x, 0)$.

Let P' be a point on Y-axis, so that its distance from Y-axis is zero. Hence, the point P' can be taken as $(0, y)$.

Konnect

The distance of a point $A(x_1, y_1)$ from origin $O(0, 0)$ is $OA = \sqrt{x_1^2 + y_1^2}$.

Distance Between Two Points

Consider two points $A(x_1, y_1)$ and $B(x_2, y_2)$. Draw perpendiculars AL and BM from A and B to X-axis, AN is the perpendicular drawn from A on to BM.

From right triangle ABN, $AB = \sqrt{AN^2 + BN^2}$.

Here, $AN = x_2 - x_1$, and $BN = y_2 - y_1$

$$AB = \sqrt{(x_2 - x_1)^2 + (y_2 - y_1)^2}$$

Hence, the distance between two points $A(x_1, y_1)$ and $B(x_2, y_2)$ is:

$$AB = \sqrt{(x_2 - x_1)^2 + (y_2 - y_1)^2} \text{ units.}$$

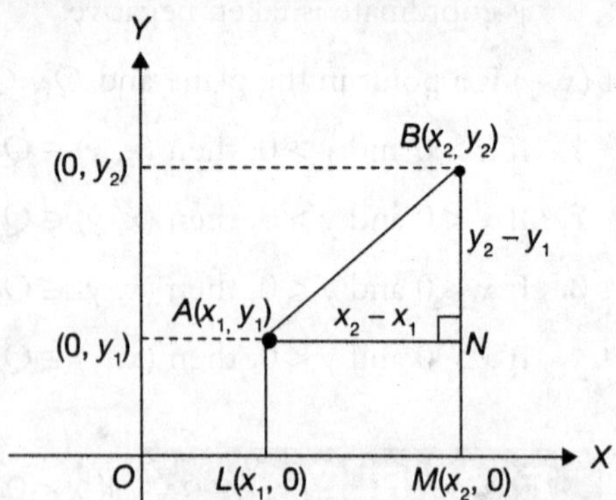

Figure 9.2

EXAMPLE 9.4 Find the distance between the points $(3, -5)$ and $(5, -1)$.

SOLUTION

Let the given points be $A(3, -5)$ and $B(5, -1)$.

$AB = \sqrt{(5-3)^2 + (-1-(-5))^2} = \sqrt{4+16} = \sqrt{20} = 2\sqrt{5}$ units.

EXAMPLE 9.5 Find a if the distance between the points $P(11, -2)$ and $Q(a, 1)$ is 5 units.

SOLUTION

Given, $PQ = 5$

$\Rightarrow \sqrt{(a-11)^2 + (1-(-2))^2} = 5$

Taking square on both sides, we get,

$(a - 11)^2 = 25 - 9 = 16$

$a - 11 = \pm 4$

$\therefore a = 15$ or 7.

EXAMPLE 9.6 Find the coordinates of a point on Y-axis which is equidistant from the points (13, 2) and (12, −3).

SOLUTION

Let $P(0, y)$ be the required point and the given points be $A(12,-3)$ and $B(13, 2)$.

Then $PA = PB$ (given)

$\sqrt{(12-0)^2 + (-3-y)^2} = \sqrt{(13-0)^2 + (2-y)^2} \Rightarrow \sqrt{144 + (y+3)^2} = \sqrt{169 + (2-y)^2}$

Taking square on both sides, we get,

$144 + 9 + y^2 + 6y = 169 + 4 + y^2 - 4y$

$\Rightarrow 10y = 20 \Rightarrow y = 2.$

$\therefore$ The required point on Y-axis is (0, 2).

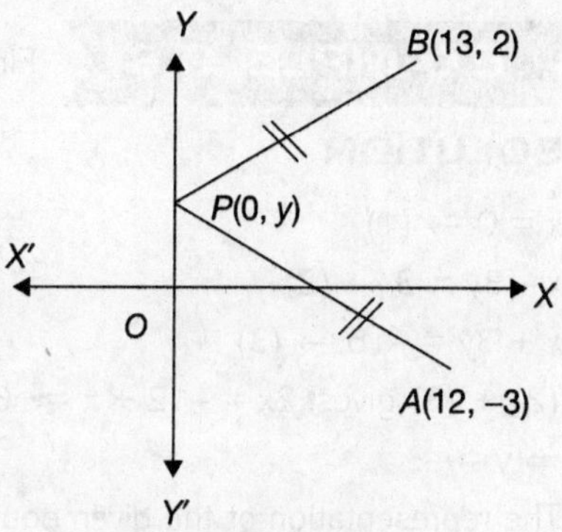

Figure 9.3

Applications of Distance Formula

Collinearity of Three Points Let A, B, and C be three given points. The distances AB, BC, and CA can be calculated using distance formula.

If the sum of any two of these distances is found to be equal to the third distance, then the points A, B, and C will be collinear.

Konnect

1. If AB + BC = AC, then the points A, B, and C are collinear.

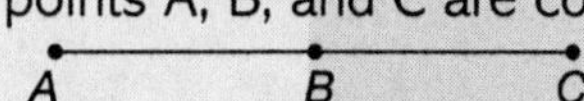

2. If AC + CB = AB, then the points A, C, and B are collinear.

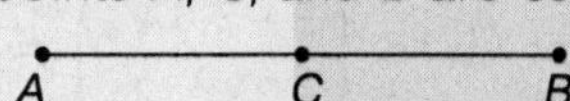

3. BA + AC = BC, then the points B, A, and C are collinear.

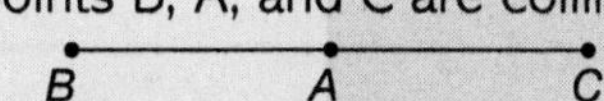

By notes (1), (2), and (3), we can find the position of points in collinearity.

EXAMPLE 9.7 Show that the points $A(2, 3)$, $B(3, 4)$, and $C(4, 5)$ are collinear.

SOLUTION

Given, $A = (2, 3)$, $B = (3, 4)$, and $C = (4, 5)$

$AB = \sqrt{(3-2)^2 + (4-3)^2} = \sqrt{2}$ units.

$BC = \sqrt{(4-3)^2 + (5-4)^2} = \sqrt{2}$ units.

$AC = \sqrt{(4-2)^2 + (5-3)^2} = \sqrt{4+4} = \sqrt{8} = 2\sqrt{2}$ units.

Now, $AB + BC = \sqrt{2} + \sqrt{2} = 2\sqrt{2} = AC$

That is, $AB + BC = AC$.

Hence, the points A, B, and C are collinear.

EXAMPLE 9.8 Find the area (in sq units) of a triangle formed by $x = 0$, $x - 3y = 3$ and $x + 3y + 15 = 0$.

SOLUTION

$x = 0 \rightarrow (1)$

$x - 3y = 3 \rightarrow (2)$

$x + 3y = -15 \rightarrow (3)$

(2) + (3) gives, $2x = -12 + x = 6$

$\Rightarrow y = -3$

The representation of the given equations are as follows

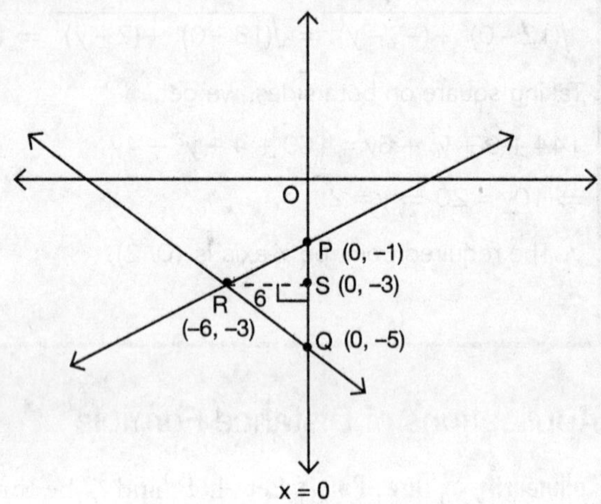

$\overline{RS} \perp \overline{PQ}$

$PQ = -1 - (-5) = 4$ units

$RS = 0 - (-6) = 6$ units

Area of $\Delta PQR = \dfrac{PQ \times RS}{2} = \dfrac{4 \times 6}{2} = 12$ sq. units

EXAMPLE 9.9 If A (3, 1) and B (7, 1) are the two vertices of an equilateral triangle ABC. If C is in quadrant I, then find the coordinates of C.

SOLUTION

ABC is an equilateral triangle where A (3, 1), B (7, 1)

AB is parallel to x – axis and AB = 7 – 3 = 4 units

$\therefore$ Height of the triangle $= \dfrac{\sqrt{3}}{2} \times 4 = 2\sqrt{3}$ units

The altitude from C passes through the mid point of AB i.e. $\left(\dfrac{3+7}{2}, \dfrac{1+1}{2}\right) = (5, 1)$

$\therefore$ The coordinates of C are $(5, 2\sqrt{3} + 1)$.

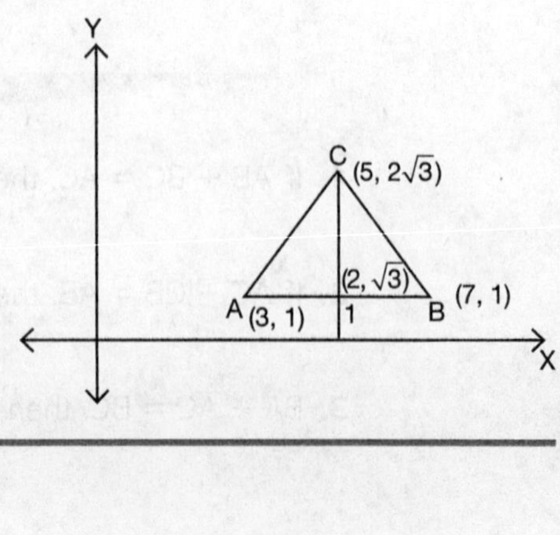

EXAMPLE 9.10 Find the area of a parallelogram ABCD whose three vertices are given as A (0, 9), B (3, 3), and C (1, –2).

SOLUTION

A (0, 9), B (3, 3), C (1, –2)

In the parallelogram ABCD, area of ΔABC is equal to area of ΔADC

∴ Area of parallelogram ABCD = 2 × Area of ΔABC

$= 2 \times \frac{1}{2} | x_1(y_2 - y_3) + x_2(y_3 - y_1) + x_3(y_1 - y_2) |$

$= |0(3 + 2) + 3(-2 - 9) + 1(9 - 3)|$

$= |-33 + 6|$

= 27 sq. units.

EXAMPLE 9.11 The vertices of a Δ*ABC* are *A*(1, 2), *B*(3, –4), and *C*(5, –6). Find its circum-centre and circum-radius.

SOLUTION

Let *S*(*x*, *y*) be the circum-centre of Δ*ABC*.

∴ $SA^2 = SB^2 = SC^2$.

Consider, $SA^2 = SB^2$

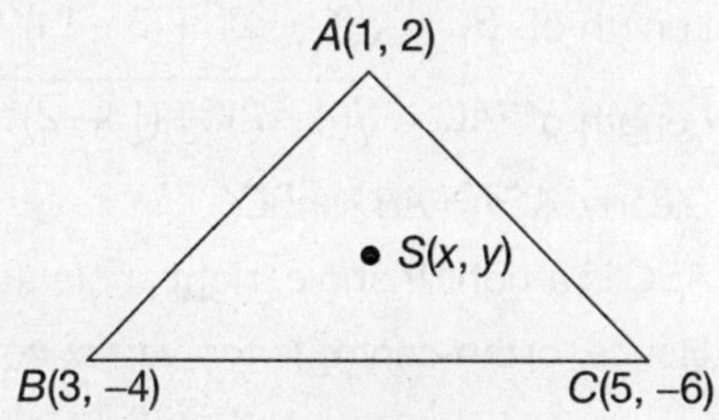

Figure 9.4

$\Rightarrow (x - 1)^2 + (y - 2)^2 = (x - 3)^2 + (y + 4)^2$

$\Rightarrow x^2 - 2x + 1 + y^2 - 4y + 4 = x^2 - 6x + 9 + y^2 + 8y + 16$

$\Rightarrow -2x - 4y + 1 + 4 = -6x + 9 + 8y + 16$

$\Rightarrow 4x - 12y - 20 = 0$

$\Rightarrow x - 3y = 5$ (1)

$SB^2 = SC^2$

$\Rightarrow (x - 3)^2 + (y + 4)^2 = (x - 5)^2 + (y + 6)^2$

$\Rightarrow x - y = 9$ (2)

Solving Eqs. (1) and (2), we have,

$x = 11$ and $y = 2$

∴ The required circum-centre of Δ*ABC* is (11, 2).

Circum-radius $= SA = \sqrt{(11-1)^2 + (2-2)^2} = 10$ units.

EXAMPLE 9.12 A circle intersects the *x* – axis at (4, 0), (9, 0) and the *y* – axis at (0, 12) and (*x*, *y*). The coordinates of (*x*, *y*) are ______.

SOLUTION

As (*x*, *y*) lies on the *y* – axis, *x* = 0 and

OA = 4, OB = 9,

OC = *y*, OD = 12

We have, OA × OB = OC × OD

4 × 9 = *y* × 12

y = 3

∴ C = (0, 3)

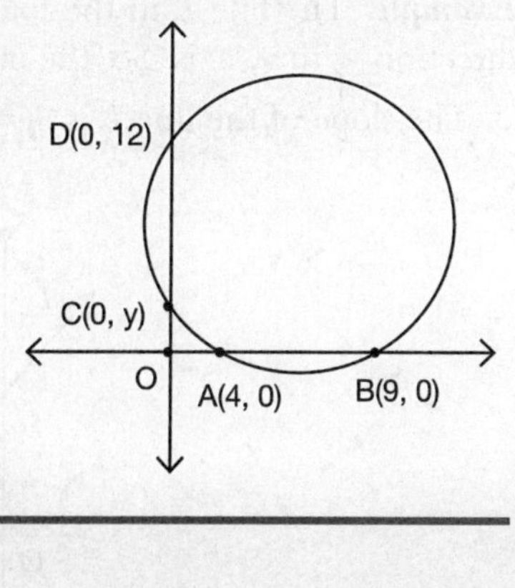

EXAMPLE 9.13 Find the area of a square whose one pair of the opposite vertices are (3, 4) and (5, 6).

SOLUTION

Let the given vertices be $A(3, 4)$ and $C(5, 6)$.

Length of $AC = \sqrt{(3-5)^2+(4-6)^2} = \sqrt{8}$ units.

Area of the square $= \dfrac{AC^2}{2} = \dfrac{(\sqrt{8})^2}{2} = 4$ sq. units.

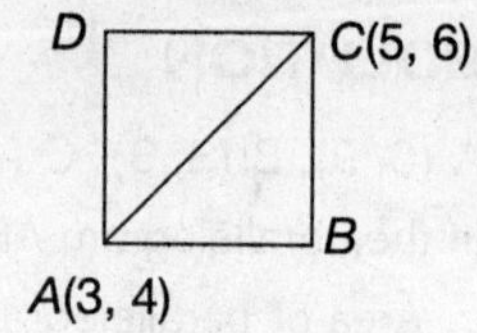

Figure 9.6

EXAMPLE 9.14 Find the ortho-centre of the ΔABC formed by the vertices $A(2, 2)$, $B(6, 3)$, and $C(4, 11)$.

SOLUTION

The given vertices of ΔABC are $A(2, 2)$, $B(6, 3)$ and $C(4, 11)$.

Length of $AB = \sqrt{(6-2)^2+(3-2)^2} = \sqrt{17}$ units

Length of $BC = \sqrt{(6-4)^2+(3-11)^2} = \sqrt{68}$ units

Length of $AC = \sqrt{(4-2)^2+(11-2)^2} = \sqrt{85}$ units

Clearly, $AC^2 = AB^2 + BC^2$

ABC is a right triangle, right angle at B.

Hence, ortho-centre is the vertex containing right angle, i.e., $B(6, 3)$.

Straight Lines

Inclination of a Line

The angle made by a straight line with positive direction of X-axis in the anti-clockwise direction is called its inclination.

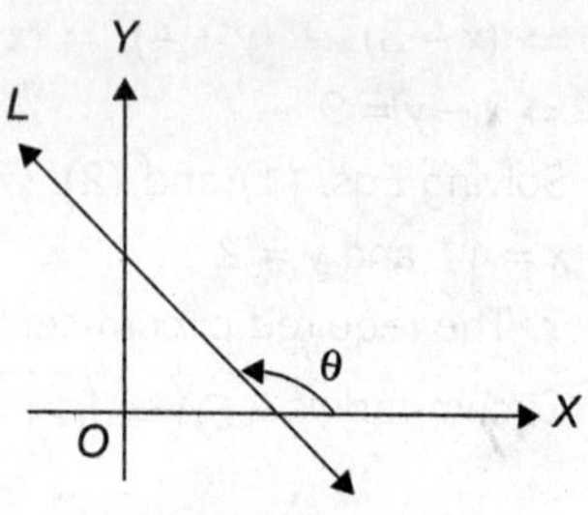

Figure 9.7

Slope or Gradient of a Line

If θ is the inclination of a line L, then its slope is denoted by m and is given by $m = \tan\theta$.

Example: The inclination of the line l in the Fig. 15.9 is 45°.

$\therefore$ The slope of the line is $m = \tan 45° = 1$.

Example: The line L in the following figure makes an angle of 45° in clockwise direction with X-axis. So, the inclination of the line L is $180° - 45° = 135°$.

$\therefore$ The slope of the line L is $m = \tan 135° = -1$.

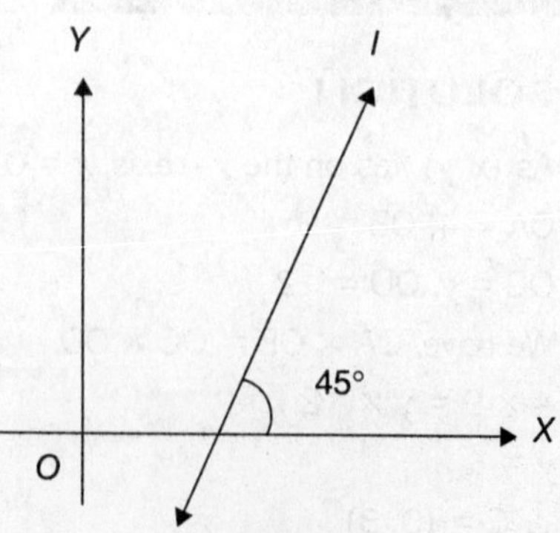

Figure 9.8

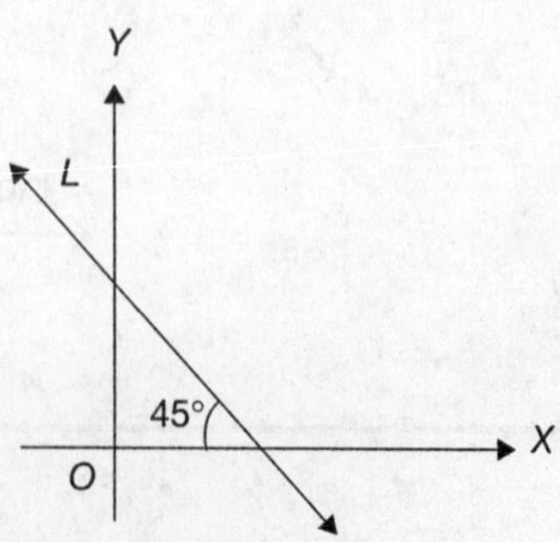

Figure 9.9

Some Results on the Slope of a Line

1. The slope of a horizontal line is zero. Hence,
   (i) Slope of X-axis is zero.
   (ii) Slope of any line parallel to X-axis is also zero.
2. The slope of a vertical line is not defined. Hence,
   (i) Slope of Y-axis is undefined.
   (ii) Slope of any line parallel to Y-axis is also undefined.

Theorem 1

Two non-vertical lines are parallel if and only if their slopes are equal.

Proof: Let L_1 and L_2 be two non-vertical lines with slopes m_1 and m_2, respectively.

If θ_1 and θ_2 are the inclinations of the lines, L_1 and L_2, respectively, then $m_1 = \tan\theta_1$ and $m_2 = \tan\theta_2$

Now, since $L_1 \parallel L_2$. Then, $\theta_1 = \theta_2$. (∵ They form a pair of corresponding angles)

$\Rightarrow \tan\theta_1 = \tan\theta_2$

$\Rightarrow m_1 = m_2$

Conversely, let $m_1 = m_2$

$\Rightarrow \tan\theta_1 = \tan\theta_2$

$\Rightarrow \theta_1 = \theta_2$

$\Rightarrow L_1 \parallel L_2$ (∵ θ_1 and θ_2 form a pair of corresponding angles)

Hence, two non-vertical lines are parallel if and only if their slopes are equal.

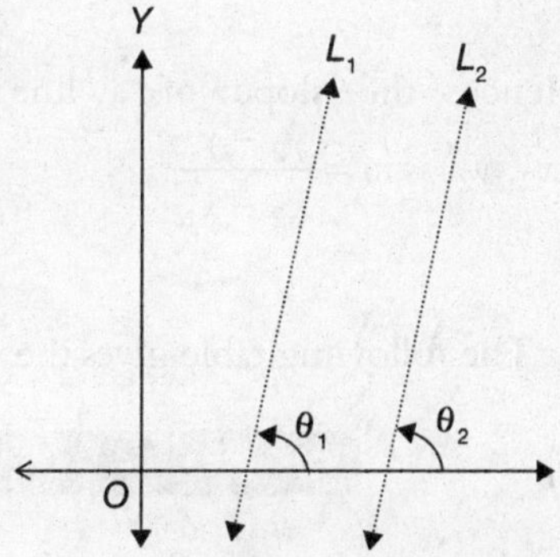

Figure 9.10

Theorem 2

Two non-vertical lines are perpendicular to each other if and only if the product of their slopes is –1.

Proof: Let L_1 and L_2 be two non-vertical lines with slopes, m_1 and m_2.

If θ_1 and θ_2 are the inclinations of the lines L_1 and L_2, respectively, then $m_1 = \tan\theta_1$ and $m_2 = \tan\theta_2$.

If $L_1 \perp L_2$, then,

$\theta_2 = 90° + \theta_1$ (∵ The exterior angle of a triangle is equal to the sum of two opposite interior angles)

$\Rightarrow \tan\theta_2 = \tan(90° + \theta_1)$

$\Rightarrow \tan\theta_2 = -\cot\theta_1$

$\Rightarrow \tan\theta_2 = \dfrac{-1}{\tan\theta_1}$ $[\because \theta_1 \neq 0]$

$\Rightarrow \tan\theta_1 \cdot \tan\theta_2 = -1$

$\therefore\ m_1 m_2 = -1$

Conversely, let $m_1 m_2 = -1$

$\Rightarrow \tan\theta_1 \tan\theta_2 = -1$

$\Rightarrow \tan\theta_2 = \dfrac{-1}{\tan\theta_1} [\because \theta_1 \neq 0]$

$\Rightarrow \tan\theta_2 = -\cot\theta_1$

$\Rightarrow \tan\theta_2 = \tan(90° + \theta_1)$

$\Rightarrow \theta_2 = 90° + \theta_1$

$\Rightarrow L_1 \perp L_2$.

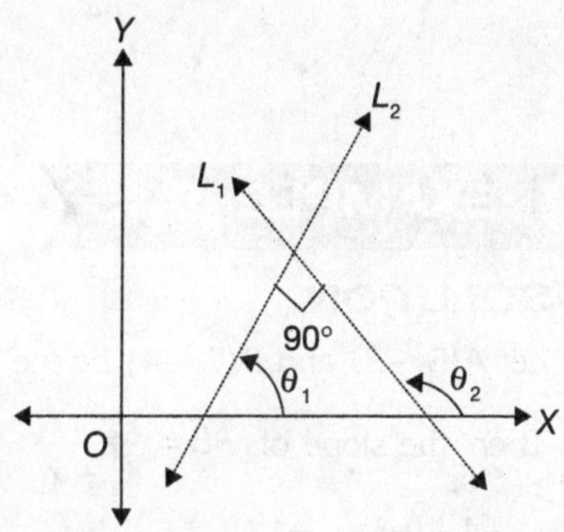

Figure 9.11

Hence, two non-vertical lines are perpendicular to each other if and only if the product of their slopes is –1.

The Slope of a Line Passing Through the Points (x_1, y_1) and (x_2, y_2)

Let $A(x_1, y_1)$ and $B(x_2, y_2)$ be two given points.

Let AB be the straight line passing through the points A and B.

Let θ be the inclination of the line $\overleftrightarrow{AB}$.

Draw the perpendiculars AL and BM on to X-axis from A and B, respectively.

Also draw $AN \perp BM$.

Then, $\angle NAB = \theta$

Also, $BN = BM - MN = BM - AL = y_2 - y_1$

$AN = LM = OM - OL = x_2 - x_1$

$\therefore$ The slope of the line L is, $m = \tan\theta = \dfrac{BN}{AN} = \dfrac{y_2 - y_1}{x_2 - x_1}$.

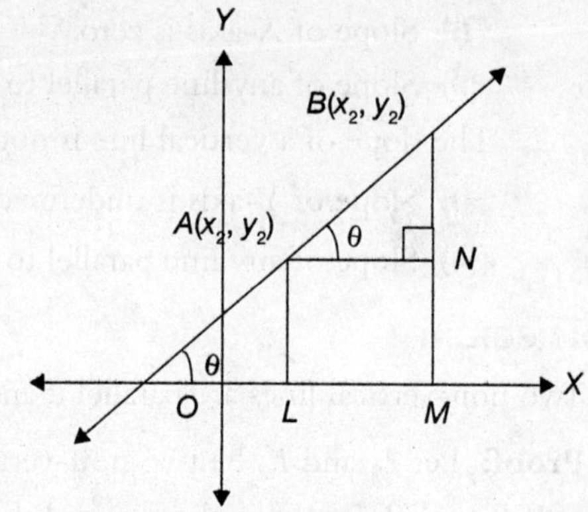

Figure 9.12

Hence, the slope of a line passing through the points (x_1, y_1) and (x_2, y_2) is $m = \dfrac{y_2 - y_1}{x_2 - x_1}$.

The following table gives the inclination (θ) of the line and its corresponding slope (m) for some particular values of θ.

θ	0°	30°	45°	60°	90°	120°	135°	150°
$m = \tan\theta$	0	$\dfrac{1}{\sqrt{3}}$	1	$\sqrt{3}$	∞	$-\sqrt{3}$	-1	$\dfrac{-1}{\sqrt{3}}$

That is, if $m_1 = m_2$, then A, B, and C are collinear.

Konnect

If the points A, B and C are collinear, then the slope of AB = the slope of BC.

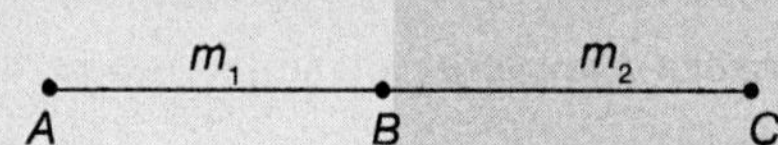

EXAMPLE 9.15 Find the slope of line joining the points (5, −3) and (7, −4).

SOLUTION

Let $A(5, -3)$ and $B(7, -4)$ be the given points.

Then, the slope of $\overleftrightarrow{AB} = \dfrac{y_2 - y_1}{x_2 - x_1}$

$= \dfrac{-4-(-3)}{7-5} = \dfrac{-1}{2}$.

EXAMPLE 9.16 Find the value of k if the slope of the line joining the points $(k, 4)$ and $(-3, -2)$ is $\frac{1}{2}$.

SOLUTION

Let the given points be $A(k, 4)$ and $B(-3, -2)$.

Given, the slope of $\overleftrightarrow{AB} = \frac{1}{2}$

$\frac{-2-4}{-3-k} = \frac{1}{2}$

$\Rightarrow -12 = -3 - k$

$\Rightarrow k = -3 + 12$

$\Rightarrow k = 9.$

EXAMPLE 9.17 The equation of the line passing through P (4, 3) and Q (6, –1) is $ax + by + c = 0$. Find the value of $5a + b + c$.

SOLUTION

P (4, 3), Q (6, –1)

$y - y_1 = \frac{(y_2 - y_1)}{(x_2 - x_1)}(x - x_1)$

$y - 3 = \frac{-1-3}{6-4}(x-4)$

$y - 3 = \frac{-4}{2}(x-4)$

$y - 3 = -2x + 8$

$2x + y = 11$

$2x + 1y + (-11) = 0$

Comparing with $ax + by + c = 0$

$a = 2, b = 1, c = -11$

$5a + b + c = 5 \times 2 + 1 - 11 = 0.$

EXAMPLE 9.18 If the points $(-3, 6)$, $(-9, a)$ and $(0, 15)$ are collinear, then find a.

SOLUTION

Let the given points be $A(-3, 6)$, $B(-9, a)$, and $C(0, 15)$.

The slope of $AB = \frac{a-6}{-9+3} = \frac{6-a}{6}$

The slope of $BC = \frac{a-15}{-9-0} = \frac{15-a}{9}$

Since the points A, B, and C are collinear.

The slope of $\overleftrightarrow{AB}$ = the slope of $\overleftrightarrow{BC}$

$\Rightarrow \frac{6-a}{6} = \frac{15-a}{9}$

$\Rightarrow 18 - 3a = 30 - 2a$

$\Rightarrow a = -12$

Hence, $a = -12$.

Intercepts of a Straight Line

Say a straight line L meets X-axis in A and Y-axis in B.
Then, OA is called the x-intercept and OB is called the y-intercept.

Example: The line L in the given figure meets X-axis at $A(4, 0)$ and Y-axis at $B(0, -5)$.

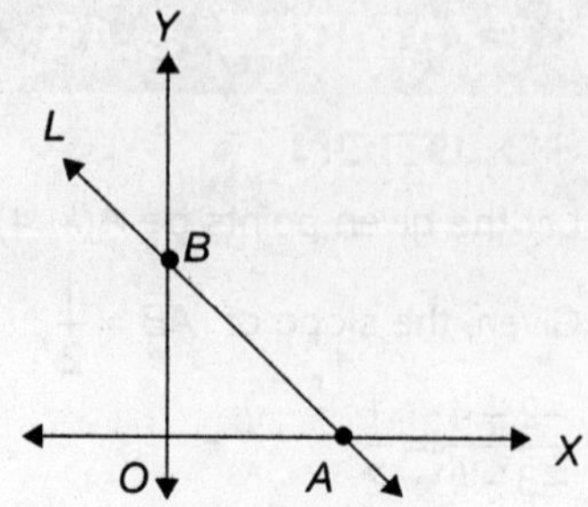

Figure 9.13

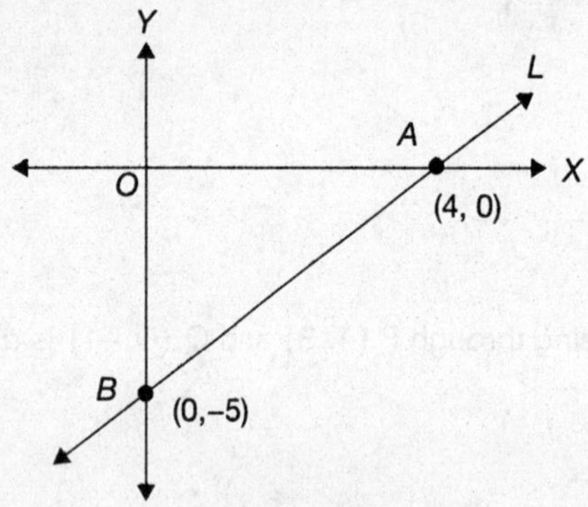

Figure 9.14

Konnect

OA and OB are taken as positive or negative based on whether the line meets positive or negative axes.

Hence, the x-intercept = 4 and y-intercept = –5.

Equation of a Line in General Form

An equation of the form, $ax + by + c = 0$. (where $a + b \neq 0$, i.e., a and b are not simultaneously equal to zero), which is satisfied by every point on a line and not by any point outside the line, is called the equation of a line.

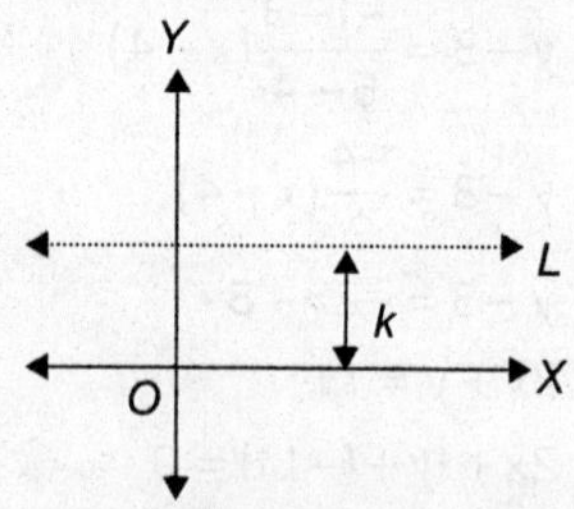

Figure 9.15

Equations of Some Standard Lines

Equation of X-axis We know that the y-coordinate of every point on X-axis is zero so, if $P(x, y)$ is any point on X-axis, then $y = 0$.

Hence, the equation of X-axis is $y = 0$.

Equation of Y-axis We know that the x-coordinate of every point on Y-axis is zero. So, if $P(x, y)$ is any point on Y-axis, then $x = 0$, hence, the equation of Y-axis is $x = 0$.

Equation of a Line Parallel to X-axis Let L be a line parallel to X-axis and at a distance of k units away from X-axis.

Then, the y-coordinate of every point on the line L is k.

So, if $P(x, y)$ is any point on the line L, then $y = k$.

Hence, the equation of a line parallel to X-axis at a distance of k units from it is $y = k$.

Konnect

For the lines lying below X-axis, k is taken as negative. problems.

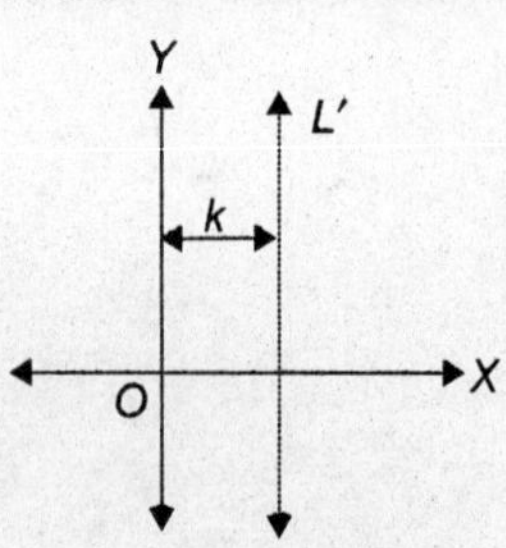

Figure 9.16

Konnect

For the lines lying towards the left side of Y-axis, k is taken as negative.

Equation of a Line Parallel to *Y*-axis Let L' be a line parallel to Y-axis and at a distance of k units away from it.

Then the x-coordinate of every point on the line L' is k.

So, if $P(x, y)$ is any point on the line L', then $x = k$.

Hence, the equation of a line parallel to Y-axis and at a distance of k units from it is $x = k$.

Oblique Line

A straight line which is neither parallel to X-axis nor parallel to Y-axis is called an oblique line or an inclined line.

Different Forms of Equations of Oblique Lines

Gradiant Form (or) Slope Form The equation of a straight line with slope m and passing through origin is given by $y = mx$.

Point-Slope Form The equation of a straight line passing through the point (x_1, y_1) and with slope m is given by $y - y_1 = m(x - x_1)$.

Slope-intercept Form The equation of a straight line with slope m and having y-intercept c is given by $y = mx + c$.

Two-point Form The equation of a straight line passing through the points (x_1, y_1) and (x_2, y_2) is given by,

$$y - y_1 = \frac{y_2 - y_1}{x_2 - x_1}(x - x_1) \quad \text{or} \quad \frac{y - y_1}{y_2 - y_1} = \frac{x - x_1}{x_2 - x_1}.$$

Intercept Form The equation of a straight line with x-intercept as a and y-intercept as b is given by $\frac{x}{a} + \frac{y}{b} = 1$.

> **Konnect**
>
> Area of triangle formed by the line $\frac{x}{a} + \frac{y}{b} = 1$ with the coordinate axes is $\frac{1}{2}|ab|$ sq. units.

EXAMPLE 9.19 Find the equation of a line parallel to X-axis and passing through the point $(3, -4)$.

SOLUTION

We know that the equation of a line parallel to X-axis can be taken as $y = k$.

Given, the line passes through the point $(3, -4)$

$\Rightarrow k = -4$

Hence, the equation of the required line is $y = -4$, i.e., $y + 4 = 0$.

EXAMPLE 9.20 Find the equation of a line having a slope of $-\frac{3}{4}$ and passing through the point $(3, -4)$.

SOLUTION

We know that, the equation of a line passing through the point (x_1, y_1) and having a slope m is given by $y - y_1 = m(x - x_1)$.

Hence, the equation of the required line is:

$y - (-4) = -\frac{3}{4}(x - 3)$

$\Rightarrow 4(y + 4) = -3(x - 3)$

$\Rightarrow 3x + 4y + 7 = 0.$

EXAMPLE 9.21 Find the equation of a line making intercepts 3 and –4 on the coordinate axes, respectively.

SOLUTION

Given,

x-intercept (*a*) = 3

y-intercept (*b*) = –4

∴ The equation of the required line is:

$$\frac{x}{a}+\frac{y}{b}=1$$

i.e., $\frac{x}{3}+\frac{y}{-4}=1$

$4x-3y=12$ (or) $4x-3y-12=0$.

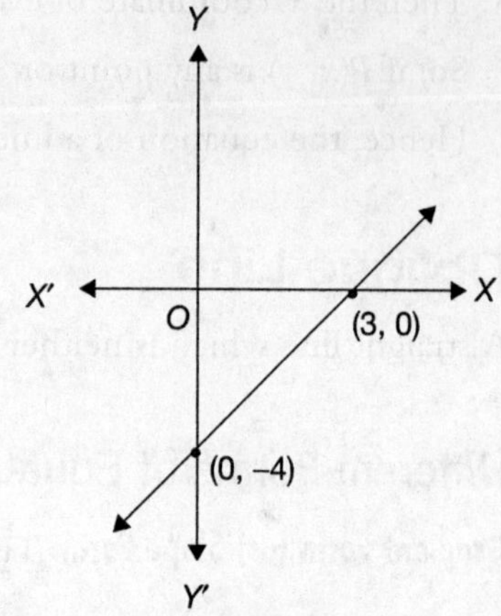

Figure 9.17

Area of Triangle

Consider $A(x_1, y_1)$, $B(x_2, y_2)$ and $C(x_3, y_3)$ as the vertices of ΔABC. Draw perpendiculars *AP*, *BQ*, and *CR* on to *X*-axis.

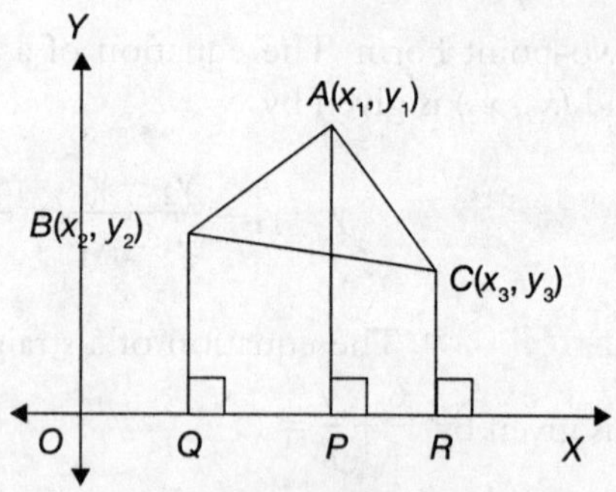

Figure 9.18

Area of ΔABC = Area of trapezium *APQB* + Area of trapezium *APRC* – Area of trapezium *BCRQ*

$$=\frac{1}{2}QP(AP+BQ)+\frac{1}{2}PR(AP+CR)-\frac{1}{2}QR(BQ+CR)$$

Here $QP=x_1-x_2$, $PR=x_3-x_1$, $QR=x_3-x_2$,

$AP=y_1$, $BQ=y_2$, $CR=y_3$

$$=\frac{1}{2}(x_1-x_2)(y_1+y_2)+\frac{1}{2}(x_3-x_1)(y_1+y_3)-\frac{1}{2}(x_3-x_2)(y_2+y_3)$$

$$=\frac{1}{2}(x_1y_2-x_1y_3-x_2y_1+x_2y_3+x_3y_1-x_3y_2)$$

$$=\frac{1}{2}[x_1(y_2-y_3)+x_2(y_3-y_1)+x_3(y_1-y_2)]$$

As the area is always positive,

∴ Area of ΔABC, $\Delta=\frac{1}{2}|x_1(y_2-y_3)+x_2(y_3-y_1)+x_3(y_1-y_2)|$ sq. units

or

$$\Delta=\frac{1}{2}\begin{vmatrix}x_1-x_2 & y_1-y_2\\ x_2-x_3 & y_2-y_3\end{vmatrix}\text{ sq. units.}$$

Konnect

1. Area of a triangle with vertices (x_1, y_1), (x_2, y_2) and (0, 0) is, $\Delta = \frac{1}{2}|x_1y_2 - x_2y_1|$
2. Area of ΔABC is zero, if the points A, B, and C are collinear.
3. Area of triangle DEF formed by the mid-points of the sides of the ΔABC is $\frac{1}{4}$ of the area of ΔABC, i.e., area of $\Delta ABC = 4$(Area of ΔDEF).
4. If G is the centroid of ΔABC, then area of $\Delta ABC = 3$(area of ΔAGB) $= 3$(area of ΔBGC) $= 3$(area of ΔACG).

Area of a Quadrilateral

Area of a quadrilateral with vertices (x_1, y_1), (x_2, y_2), (x_3, y_3), and (x_4, y_4) is given by $\frac{1}{2}\begin{vmatrix} x_1 - x_3 & y_1 - y_3 \\ x_2 - x_4 & y_2 - y_4 \end{vmatrix}$.

EXAMPLE 9.22 Find the area of the triangle whose vertices are $A(1, -2)$, $B(3, 4)$, and $C(2, 3)$.

SOLUTION

Area of $\Delta ABC = \frac{1}{2}\begin{vmatrix} 1-3 & -2-4 \\ 3-2 & 4-3 \end{vmatrix} = \frac{1}{2}\begin{vmatrix} -2 & -6 \\ 1 & 1 \end{vmatrix} = \frac{1}{2}|-2-(-6)| = 2$ sq. units.

EXAMPLE 9.23 Find the value of p, if the points $A(2, 3)$, $B(-1, 6)$, and $C(p, 4)$ are collinear.

SOLUTION

Given, the points $A(2, 3)$, $B(-1, 6)$, and $C(p, 4)$ are collinear.

$\therefore$ Area of $\Delta ABC = 0$

$$\Rightarrow \frac{1}{2}\begin{vmatrix} 2-(-1) & 3-6 \\ -1-p & 6-4 \end{vmatrix} = 0$$

$$\Rightarrow \begin{vmatrix} 3 & -3 \\ -1-p & 2 \end{vmatrix} = 0$$

$\Rightarrow 6 - 3(1 + p) = 0 \Rightarrow p = 1$

Hence, $p = 1$.

Straight Lines

Consider two points $A(x_1, y_1)$ and $B(x_2, y_2)$. Let $C(x, y)$ be any point on AB that divide AB in the ratio $m : n$.

Draw perpendiculars AL, CN, and BM to X-axis.

AP and CQ are perpendiculars drawn to CN and BM.

Now it is clear that ΔAPC and ΔCQB are similar.

$$\therefore \frac{AC}{CB} = \frac{AP}{CQ} = \frac{CP}{BQ} \qquad (1)$$

Here, $LN = x - x_1$ and $NM = x_2 - x$.

From Eq. (1), we have,

$$\frac{m}{n} = \frac{x - x_1}{x_2 - x}, \quad (AP = LN \text{ and } CQ = NM)$$

$$\Rightarrow mx_2 - mx = nx - nx_1.$$

$$\Rightarrow mx_2 + nx_1 = mx + nx.$$

$$\therefore x = \frac{mx_2 + nx_1}{m + n}.$$

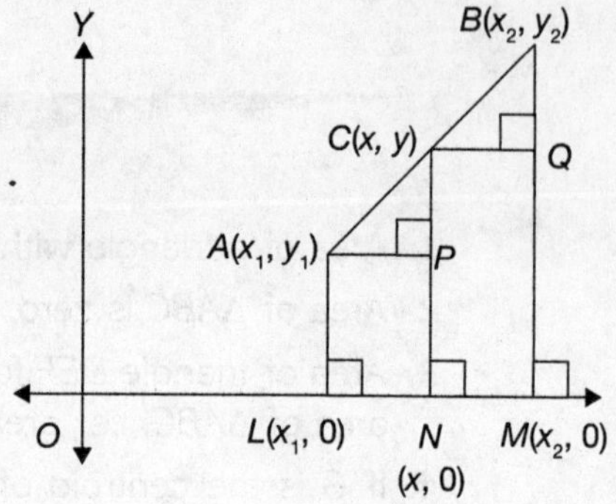

Figure 9.19

Similarly we can obtain, $\dfrac{m}{n} = \dfrac{y - y_1}{y_2 - y} \Rightarrow y = \dfrac{my_2 + ny_1}{m + n}$.

Hence, the coordinates of 'C' are $\left(\dfrac{mx_2 + nx_1}{m + n}, \dfrac{my_2 + ny_1}{m + n}\right)$.

In this case we notice that point C lies in between A and B. So we say that C divides AB in the ratio $m : n$ internally.

Konnect

1. When C does not lie between A and B, i.e., as shown below, then we say that C divides AB in $m : n$ ratio externally, then the coordinates of C are $\left(\dfrac{mx_2 - nx_1}{m - n}, \dfrac{my_2 - ny_1}{m - n}\right)$

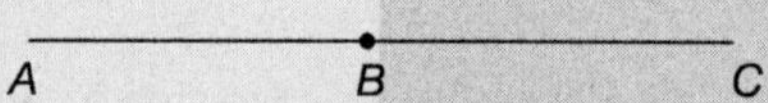

2. Let $P(x, y)$ divides the line segment joining the points $A(x_1, y_1)$ and $B(x_2, y_2)$ in the ratio $m : n$, then, $\dfrac{m}{n} = \dfrac{x - x_1}{x_2 - x}$ (or) $\dfrac{y - y_1}{y_2 - y}$.
3. X-axis divides the line joining the points (x_1, y_1) and (x_2, y_2) in the ratio $-y_1 : y_2$ (or) $y_1 : -y_2$.
4. Y-axis divides the line joining the points (x_1, y_1) and (x_2, y_2) in the ratio $-x_1 : x_2$.

EXAMPLE 9.24 Find the coordinates of the point P which divides the line segment joining the points $A(3, -2)$ and $B(2, 6)$ internally in the ratio 2 : 3.

SOLUTION

Given, $P(x, y)$ divides AB internally in the ratio 2 : 3.

So, $P = \left(\dfrac{mx_2 + nx_1}{m + n}, \dfrac{my_2 + ny_1}{m + n}\right)$

Here, $(x_1, y_1) = (3, -2)$, $(x_2, y_2) = (2, 6)$ and $m : n = 2 : 3$

$$\therefore P = \left(\frac{2(2) + 3(3)}{2 + 3}, \frac{2(6) + 3(-2)}{2 + 3}\right) = \left(\frac{13}{5}, \frac{6}{5}\right).$$

Hence, $P\left(\dfrac{13}{5}, \dfrac{6}{5}\right)$ is the required point.

EXAMPLE 9.25 Find the coordinates of a point P which divides the line segment joining the points $A(1, 3)$ and $B(3, 4)$ externally in the ratio 3 : 4.

SOLUTION

Given, P divides AB externally in the ratio 3 : 4.

So, $P = \left(\frac{mx_2 - nx_1}{m-n}, \frac{my_2 - ny_1}{m-n}\right)$

Here, $(x_1, y_1) = (1, 3)$, $(x_2, y_2) = (3, 4)$ and $m : n = 3 : 4$.

$\therefore P = \left(\frac{3(3)-4(1)}{3-4}, \frac{3(4)-4(3)}{3-4}\right) = (-5, 0)$

Hence, $P = (-5, 0)$.

EXAMPLE 9.26 Find the ratio in which the point $P(3, -2)$ divides the line segment joining the points $A(1, 2)$ and $B(-1, 6)$.

SOLUTION

The ratio in which P divides AB is $AP : PB = (x - x_1) : (x_2 - x)$ $(3 - 1) : (-1 - 3) = 2 : -4 = -1 : 2$.

Hence, P divides AB externally in the ratio 1 : 2.

EXAMPLE 9.27 Find the ratio in which the line joining the points (2, –3) and (3, 1) is divided by X-axis and Y-axis.

SOLUTION

The ratio in which X-axis divides is $-y_1 : y_2$,

i.e., $-(-3) : 1 = 3 : 1$

The ratio in which Y-axis divides is $-x_1 : x_2$

$= (-2) : 3$

That is, 2 : 3 externally.

Mid-point

Let $A(x_1, y_1)$ and $B(x_2, y_2)$ be two given points and M be the mid-point of AB.

Then, M divides AB in the ratio 1 : 1 internally.

So, $M = \left(\frac{1 \cdot x_2 + 1 \cdot x_1}{1+1}, \frac{1 \cdot y_2 + 1 \cdot y_1}{1+1}\right) = \left(\frac{x_1 + x_2}{2}, \frac{y_1 + y_2}{2}\right)$

Hence, the coordinates of the mid-point of the line segment joining the points (x_1, y_1) and (x_2, y_2) are given by $\left(\frac{x_1 + x_2}{2}, \frac{y_1 + y_2}{2}\right)$.

Points of Trisection

Let $A(x_1, y_1)$ and $B(x_2, y_2)$ be two given points. Then, the two points which divide AB in the ratio 1 : 2 and 2 : 1 internally are called the points of trisection of AB.

Further, if P and Q are the points of trisection of AB, respectively,

$$P = \left(\frac{2x_1 + x_2}{3}, \frac{2y_1 + y_2}{3}\right) \text{ and } Q = \left(\frac{x_1 + 2x_2}{3}, \frac{y_1 + 2y_2}{3}\right).$$

Konnect

1. If the mid-points of ΔABC are $P(x_1, y_1)$, $Q(x_2, y_2)$ and $R(x_3, y_3)$, then its vertices are $A(-x_1 + x_2 + x_3, -y_1 + y_2 + y_3)$, $B(x_1 - x_2 + x_3, y_1 - y_2 + y_3)$, and $C(x_1 + x_2 - x_3, y_1 + y_2 - y_3)$.
2. The fourth vertex of a parallelogram whose three vertices (x_1, y_1), (x_2, y_2) and (x_3, y_3) in order is $(x_1 - x_2 + x_3, y_1 - y_2 + y_3)$.

EXAMPLE 9.28 Find the mid-point of the line segment joining the points (1, −3) and (6, 5).

SOLUTION

Let $A(1, -3)$ and $B(6, 5)$ be the given points and M be the mid-point of AB.

Then, $M = \left(\frac{x_1 + x_2}{2}, \frac{y_1 + y_2}{2}\right) = \left(\frac{1+6}{2}, \frac{-3+5}{2}\right) = \left(\frac{7}{2}, 1\right)$

Hence, the mid-point of AB is $\left(\frac{7}{2}, 1\right)$.

EXAMPLE 9.29 Find the points of trisection of the line segment joining the points (3, −2) and (4, 1).

SOLUTION

Let $A(3, -2)$ and $B(4, 1)$ be the given points.

Let P and Q be the points of trisection of AB respectively.

Then, $P = \left(\frac{2(3)+4}{3}, \frac{2(-2)+1}{3}\right)$ and $Q = \left(\frac{3+2(4)}{3}, \frac{-2+2(1)}{3}\right)$

$\Rightarrow P = \left(\frac{10}{3}, -1\right)$ and $Q = \left(\frac{11}{3}, 0\right)$.

Hence, the points of trisection are $\left(\frac{10}{3}, -1\right)$ and $\left(\frac{11}{3}, 0\right)$.

EXAMPLE 9.30 Find the fourth vertex of the rhombus formed by (−1, −1), (6, 1), and (8, 8).

SOLUTION

Let the three vertices of rhombus be $A(-1, -1)$, $B(6, 1)$, and $C(8, 8)$, then fourth vertex $D(x, y)$ is given by,

$D(x, y) = (x_1 - x_2 + x_3, y_1 - y_2 + y_3)$

$= (-1 - 6 + 8, -1 - 1 + 8)$

$= (1, 6)$

Hence, the required fourth vertex is $D(1, 6)$.

EXAMPLE 9.31 Find the area of the triangle formed by the mid-points of the sides of ΔABC, where $A(3, 2)$, $B(-5, 6)$, and $C = (8, 3)$.

SOLUTION

$$\text{Area of } \Delta ABC = \frac{1}{2}\begin{vmatrix} 3-(-5) & 2-6 \\ -5-8 & 6-3 \end{vmatrix} = \frac{1}{2}\begin{vmatrix} 8 & -4 \\ -13 & 3 \end{vmatrix} = \frac{1}{2}|8(3)-4(13)|$$

$$= \frac{1}{2}|24-52|$$

$$= \frac{1}{2}|-28| = 14 \text{ sq. units.}$$

Hence, the area of triangle formed by the mid-points of the sides of $\Delta ABC = \frac{1}{4}$(Area of ΔABC)

$= \frac{1}{4}(14) = 3.5$ sq. units.

Centroid

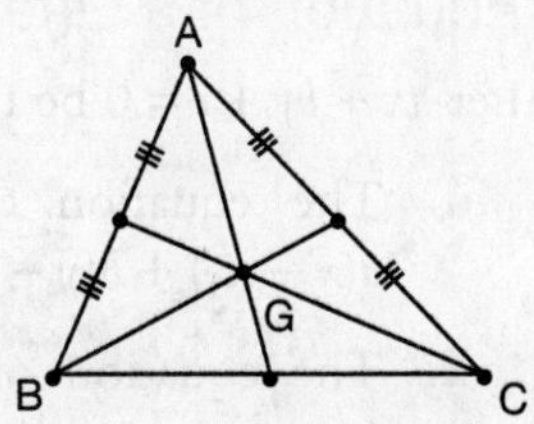

Let $A(x_1, y_1)$, $B(x_2, y_2)$, and $C(x_3, y_3)$ be the vertices of ΔABC and G be its centroid.

Then, the coordinates of G are given by, $G = \left(\frac{x_1 + x_2 + x_3}{3}, \frac{y_1 + y_2 + y_3}{3}\right)$.

EXAMPLE 9.32 Find the centroid of ΔABC whose vertices, are $A(1, -3)$, $B(-3, 6)$, and $C(-4, 3)$.

SOLUTION

Given, $A(1, -3)$, $B(-3, 6)$, and $C(-4, 3)$.

So, centroid of $\Delta ABC = \left(\frac{x_1 + x_2 + x_3}{3}, \frac{y_1 + y_2 + y_3}{3}\right) = \left(\frac{1-3-4}{3}, \frac{-3+6+3}{3}\right) = (-2, 2)$.

Hence, $(-2, 2)$ is the centroid of ΔABC.

EXAMPLE 9.33 Find the centroid of the triangle formed by the lines $x = 0$, $y = 0$, and $x + y = 10$ as sides.

SOLUTION

Let OAB be the triangle formed by the given lines.

O is the point of intersections of $x = 0$ and $y = 0$, i.e., origin $\Rightarrow O(0, 0)$.

A is the point of intersection of $x = 0$ and $x + y = 10$, i.e., $A(0, 10)$ and B is the point of intersection of $y = 0$ and $x + y = 10$, i.e., $B(10, 0)$.

$\therefore$ Centroid of ΔOAB is,

$$G = \left(\frac{x_1 + x_2 + x_3}{3}, \frac{y_1 + y_2 + y_3}{3}\right)$$

$$= \left(\frac{0+0+10}{3}, \frac{0+10+0}{3}\right)$$

$$= \left(\frac{10}{3}, \frac{10}{3}\right).$$

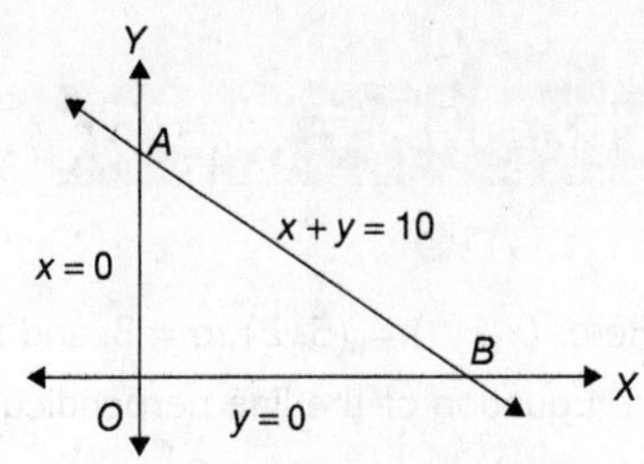

Figure 9.20

EXAMPLE 9.34 Find the third vertex of ΔABC if two of its vertices are $A(-3, 2)$, $B(1, 5)$, and its centroid is $G(3, -4)$.

SOLUTION

Let $C(x, y)$ be the third vertex.

Given, centroid of $\Delta ABC = (3, -4)$

$$\Rightarrow \left(\frac{-3+1+x}{3}, \frac{2+5+y}{3}\right) = (3, -4)$$

$$\Rightarrow \frac{-2+x}{3} = 3, \frac{7+y}{3} = -4$$

$\Rightarrow x = 11, y = -19$

$\therefore$ The third vertex is $(11, -19)$.

Equation of a Line Parallel or Perpendicular to the Given Line

Let $ax + by + c = 0$ be the equation of a straight line, then,

1. The equation of a line passing through the point (x_1, y_1) and parallel to the given line is given by $a(x - x_1) + b(y - y_1) = 0$.
2. The equation of a line passing through the point (x_1, y_1) and perpendicular to the given line is given by $b(x - x_1) - a(y - y_1) = 0$.

EXAMPLE 9.35 Find the equation of a line passing through the point $A(2, -3)$ and parallel to the line $2x - 3y + 6 = 0$.

SOLUTION

Here, $(x_1, y_1) = (2, -3)$, $a = 2$ and $b = -3$.

$\therefore$ Equation of the line passing through $A(2, -3)$ and parallel to the line $2x - 3y + 6 = 0$ is $a(x - x_1) + b(y - y_1) = 0$, i.e.,

$2(x - 2) - 3(y + 3) = 0$

$\Rightarrow 2x - 3y - 13 = 0$

Hence, the equation of the required line is $2x - 3y - 13 = 0$.

EXAMPLE 9.36 Find the equation of a line passing through the point (5, 2) and perpendicular to the line $3x - y + 6 = 0$.

SOLUTION

Here, $(x_1, y_1) = (5, 2)$, $a = 3$, and $b = -1$.

$\therefore$ Equation of the line perpendicular to $3x - y + 6 = 0$ and passing through the point (5, 2) is

$b(x - x_1) - a(y - y_1) = 0$, i.e.,

$-1(x - 5) - 3(y - 2) = 0$

$\Rightarrow (x - 5) + 3(y - 2) = 0$

$\Rightarrow x + 3y - 11 = 0$

Hence, the equation of the required line is $x + 3y - 11 = 0$.

EXAMPLE 9.37 The line $(5x - 8y + 11)\lambda + (8x - 3y + 4) = 0$ is parallel to X-axis. Find λ.

SOLUTION

The given line is,

$(5x - 8y + 11)\lambda + (8x - 3y + 4) = 0$

That is, $x(5\lambda + 8) - y(8\lambda + 3) + (11\lambda + 4) = 0$.

As the given line is parallel to X-axis, its slope = 0, i.e., the coefficient $x = 0$

$\Rightarrow 5\lambda + 8 = 0.$

Hence, $\lambda = \frac{-8}{5}$.

Median of the Triangle

A line drawn from the vertex, which bisects the opposite side is called a median of the triangle.

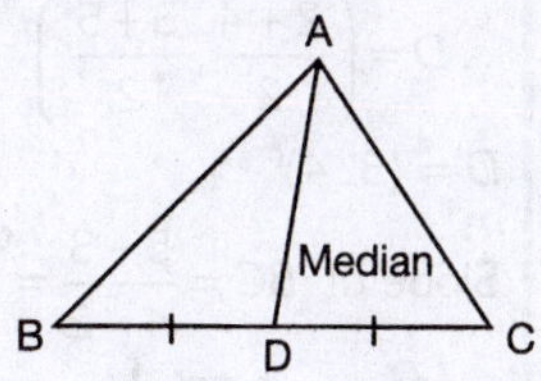

EXAMPLE 9.38 Find the median to the side BC of the triangle whose vertices are $A(-2, 1)$, $B(2, 3)$, and $C(4, 5)$.

SOLUTION

Let E be the mid-point of side BC.

$\therefore E = \left(\frac{2+4}{2}, \frac{3+5}{2}\right) = (3, 4)$

Equation of line AE is,

$$y - y_1 = \frac{y_2 - y_1}{x_2 - x_1}(x - x_1)$$

$$\Rightarrow y - 1 = \frac{4-1}{3-(-2)}(x+2)$$

$$y - 1 = \frac{3}{5}(x+2)$$

$5y - 5 = 3x + 6$

$\therefore$ The required equation of the median is $3x - 5y + 11 = 0$.

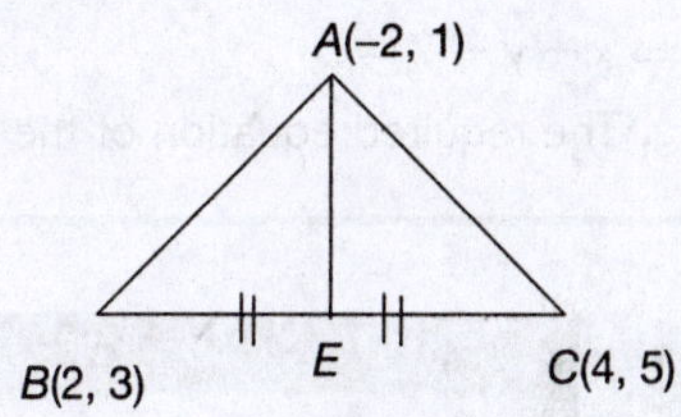

Figure 9.21

Altitude of the Triangle

A perpendicular dropped from the vertex to the opposite side in a triangle is called an altitude.

EXAMPLE 9.39 Find the equation of the altitude drawn to side BC of ΔABC, whose vertices are $A(-2, 1)$, $B(2, 3)$, and $C(4, 5)$.

SOLUTION

Let AD be the altitude drawn to side BC.

Slope of $BC = \frac{y_2 - y_1}{x_2 - x_1} = \frac{5-3}{4-2} = 1$

$\therefore$ Slope of $AD = -1$ ($\because AD \perp BC$)

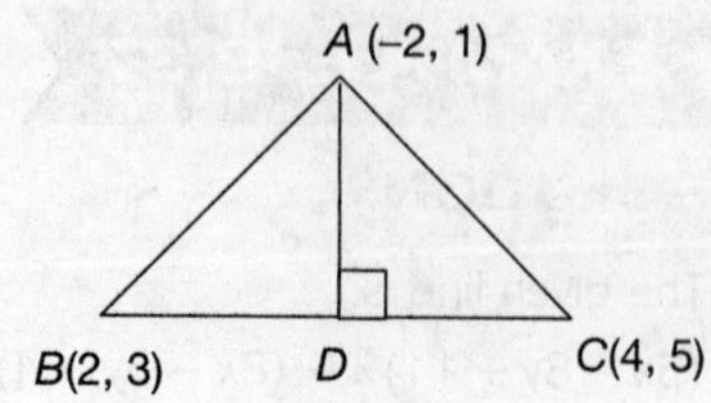

Figure 9.22

Equation of AD is,

$\Rightarrow y - y_1 = m(x - x_1)$

$\Rightarrow y - 1 = -1\,(x + 2)$

$\Rightarrow y - 1 = -x - 2$

$\Rightarrow x + y + 1 = 0.$

$\therefore$ The required equation of altitude is $x + y + 1 = 0$.

EXAMPLE 9.40 Find the equation of the perpendicular bisector drawn to the side BC of ΔABC, whose vertices are $A(-2, 1)$, $B(2, 3)$, and $C(4, 5)$.

SOLUTION

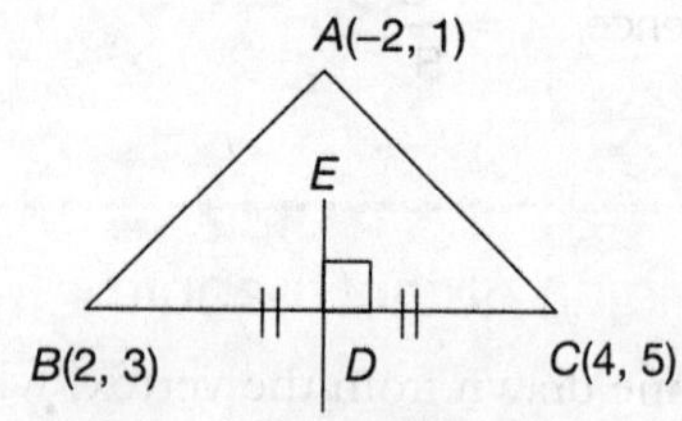

Figure 9.23

Let D be the mid-point of side BC.

$$\therefore D = \left(\frac{2+4}{2}, \frac{3+5}{2}\right)$$

$D = (3, 4)$

Slope of $BC = \dfrac{5-3}{4-2} = 1$

$\Rightarrow$ Slope of $ED = -1$ ($\because ED \perp BC$)

Equation of ED is $y - y_1 = m(x - x_1)$

$\Rightarrow y - 4 = -1(x - 3)$

$\Rightarrow y - 4 = -x + 3$

$\Rightarrow x + y - 7 = 0$

$\therefore$ The required equation of the perpendicular bisector is $x + y - 7 = 0$.

POINTS TO REMEMBER

- ✔ The distance between two points $A(x_1, y_1)$ and $B(x_2, y_2)$ is:

  $AB = \sqrt{(x_2 - x_1)^2 + (y_2 - y_1)^2}$ units.

- ✔ The distance of a point $A(x_1, y_1)$ from origin $O(0, 0)$ is $OA = \sqrt{x_1^2 + y_1^2}$.

- ✔ The slope of the line L is, $m = \tan\theta = \dfrac{y_2 - y_1}{x_2 - x_1}$.

- ✔ The equation of a straight line passing through the points (x_1, y_1) and (x_2, y_2) is given by,

$$y - y_1 = \frac{y_2 - y_1}{x_2 - x_1}(x - x_1) \quad \text{or} \quad \frac{y - y_1}{y_2 - y_1} = \frac{x - x_1}{x_2 - x_1}.$$

- ✔ Area of a triangle with vertices (x_1, y_1), (x_2, y_2) and $(0, 0)$ is, $\Delta = \frac{1}{2}|x_1y_2 - x_2y_1|$.

- ✔ Area of a quadrilateral with vertices (x_1, y_1), (x_2, y_2), (x_3, y_3), and (x_4, y_4) is given by $\frac{1}{2}\begin{vmatrix} x_1 - x_3 & y_1 - y_3 \\ x_2 - x_4 & y_2 - y_4 \end{vmatrix}$.

- ✔ The coordinates of the mid-point of the line segment joining the points (x_1, y_1) and (x_2, y_2) are given by $\left(\dfrac{x_1 + x_2}{2}, \dfrac{y_1 + y_2}{2}\right)$.

DW

PRACTICE QUESTIONS CLASSROOM WING

Very Short Answer Type Questions

Directions of questions from 1 to 20:
Fill in the blanks.

1. The distance of a point (2, 3) from Y-axis is ______.
2. The slope of the line perpendicular to $5x + 3y + 1 = 0$ is ______.
3. If (x, y) represents a point and $|x| > 0$ and $y > 0$ then in ______ quadrants can the point lie.
4. The line $4x + 7y + 9 = 0$ meet the X-axis at ______ and Y-axis at ______.
5. The area of the triangle, with vertices A(2, 0), B(0, −4) and origin is ______.
6. The area of the triangle formed by the points (0, 0), $(0, a)$, $(b, 0)$ is ______.
7. The area of the triangle formed by the line $ax + by + c = 0$ with coordinate axes is ______.
8. If the points (5, 5), (7, 7), and (a, 8) are collinear, then the value of a is ______.
9. The end vertices of one diagonal of a parallelogram are (1, 3) and (5, 7), then the mid-point of the other diagonal is ______.
10. The ortho-centre of the triangle formed by the points (0, 1), (1, 2) and (0, 2) is ______.
11. If A(4, 0), B(0, −6) are the two vertices of a triangle OAB where O is origin, then the circum-centre of the triangle OAB is ______.
12. If the centre and radius of a circle is (3, 4) and 7, then the position of the point (5, 3) w.r.t the circle is ______.
13. If A(2, 3), B(x, y), and C(4, 3) are the vertices of a right triangle, right angled at A, then x = ______.
14. The coordinates of the points P which divides (1, 0) and (0, 0) in 1 : 2 ratio are ______.
15. If (5, 7) and (9, 3) are the ends of the diameter of a circle, then the centre of the circle is ______.
16. The centroid of the triangle formed by the lines $x = 0$, $y = 0$, and $x + y = 6$ is ______.
17. The line $ax + by + c = 0$ is such that $a = 0$ and $bc \neq 0$, then the line is perpendicular to ______ axis.
18. If A is one of the points of trisection of the line joining B and C, then A divides BC in the ratio ______ (or) ______.
19. The ratio that the line joining points (3, −6) and (4, 9) is divided by X-axis is ______.
20. If (1, 2), (3, 4), and (0, 6) are the three vertices of a parallelogram taken in that order, then the fourth vertex is ______.

Short Answer Type Questions

Directions of questions from 21 to 34:
Answer the following questions.

21. The following steps are involved in finding the equation of a line passing through the point (5, −6) and parallel to the line $3x - 5y + 11 = 0$.
    Arrange the steps in sequential order.
    (A) This line passes through (5, −6).
    (B) $3(5) - 5(-6) + k = 0$
    (C) $3x - 5y + k = 0$
    (D) $3x - 5y - 45 = 0$
22. Find the slope of the line perpendicular to $\overleftrightarrow{AB}$ where $A(5, -6)$ and $B(2, -7)$.
23. If $A(-2, -1)$, $B(-4, 5)$ and $C(2, 3)$ are three vertices of the parallelogram $ABCD$, then find the vertex D.
24. Find the equation of the line parallel to Y-axis and passing through the point (3, −5).
25. Find the equation of a line, whose inclination is 30° and making an intercept of $\frac{-3}{5}$ on Y-axis.
26. Find the equation of a straight line whose slope is −5 and making an intercept 3 on the Y-axis.

27. Find the centroid of a triangle whose vertices are (3, −1), (2, 4), and (−8, 6).

28. Find the equation of a line passing through the point (2, −3) and parallel to the line $2x - 3y + 8 = 0$.

29. If $A(2, -2)$, $B(3, 4)$, and $C(7, 2)$ are the mid points of the sides PQ, QR, and RP, respectively, of ΔPQR, then find its vertices.

30. Let (−3, 2) be one end of a diameter of a circle with centre (4, 6). Find the other end of the diameter.

31. Let $A(-1, 2)$ and $D(3, 4)$ be the end points of the median AD of ΔABC. Find the co-ordinates of the point of intersection.

32. Find the point of intersection of the lines $3x + 5y + 2 = 0$ and $4x + 7y + 3 = 0$.

33. Find the coordinates of the point which divides the line joining the points $A(-3, 2)$ and $B(2, 6)$ internally in the ratio 3 : 2.

34. Find the point on Y-axis which is equidistant from $A(3, -6)$ and $B(-2, 5)$.

Essay Type Questions

35. (A) Find the equation of a line parallel to the line $2x + 3y - 6 = 0$ and whose sum of intercepts is 10.

(B) Find the ratio in which the Y-axis divides the line segment joining the points (3, 9) and (−4, 2). Also find a point on the X-axis which meets the line segment when it is produced.

36. What will be the equation of a line passing through (8, 5) and perpendicular to the line $3x - 7y + 5 = 0$?

37. If C(−3, 6) divides the line segment joining A(−9, −12) and B(0, 15) internally, then find the value of $\frac{AB}{AC}$.

38. What will be the radius of the circle which passes through (0, 0), (6, 0), and (0, 8)?

39. What will be the equation of the altitude of a triangle PQR which divides the base PQ in the ratio 2:3 where P(4, 7), and Q(6, 9)?

40. The center of a circle is at (3, 4). Find the points on both the coordinate axes through which the circle is passing / touching such that the radius of the circle is the minimum.

41. Prove that the centroid of a triangle ABC is the same as the centroid of the triangle formed by the midpoints of the sides of the triangle.

PRACTICE QUESTIONS COMPETITION WING

Level 1: Apply Your Concepts

Directions of questions from 1 to 5:
Fill in the blanks.

1. If the inclination of a line is 45°, then the slope of the line is ______.
2. If the point (x, y) lies in the third quadrant, then x is ______ and y is ______.
3. The point of intersection of the lines $x = 2$ and $y = 3$ is ______.
4. The point of intersection of medians of triangle is called its ______.
5. The line $y + 7 = 0$ is parallel to ______ axis.

Directions of questions from 6 to 33:
Select the correct alternative from the given choices.

6. Find the area of the triangle formed by the line $5x + 4y - 20 = 0$ with the coordinate axes (in square units).
   (a) 10 (b) 12
   (c) 15 (d) 20
7. Find the equation of a line passing through (–2, 3) and making x–intercept 5 units.
   (a) $3x + 4y - 6 = 0$
   (b) $5x + 7y - 11 = 0$
   (c) $2x + 5y - 10 = 0$
   (d) $3x + 7y - 15 = 0$
8. What will be the area of the triangle formed by the line $8x - 3y - 12 = 0$ with the coordinate axes (in square units)?
   (a) 3 (b) 3.5
   (c) 4 (d) 4.5
9. Find the equation of a line making y–intercept 3 units and passing through (–3, –5).
   (a) $8x - 3y + 9 = 0$
   (b) $3x + 5y - 15 = 0$
   (c) $2x - 5y - 19 = 0$
   (d) $6x + y - 23 = 0$
10. Find the perimeter of the triangle whose vertices are (2, 4), (6, 8), and (2, 8).
   (a) $4\left(\sqrt{2}+1\right)$ units (b) $4\left(2+\sqrt{2}\right)$ units
   (c) $12\sqrt{2}$ units (d) $16\sqrt{2}$ units
11. Find a point on the x–axis which is equidistant from A(3, –6) and (–2, 5).
   (a) $\left(\frac{3}{5},0\right)$ (b) $\left(\frac{8}{5},0\right)$
   (c) $\left(\frac{9}{5},0\right)$ (d) $\left(\frac{6}{8},0\right)$
12. Find the equation of a line passing through the point P(2, 3) and parallel to $2x + 3y + 5 = 0$.
   (a) $2x + 3y + 9 = 0$
   (b) $3x + 2y - 13 = 0$
   (c) $2x + 3y - 13 = 0$
   (d) $2y + 3x + 13 = 0$
13. Calculate the area of a triangle whose vertices are A(1, 2), B(3, 5), and C(–2, 2).
   (a) 5.5 (b) 4.5
   (c) 6.5 (d) 7.5
14. Find λ, if the line $3x - \lambda y + 6 = 0$ passes through the point (–3, 4).
   (a) $\frac{3}{4}$ (b) $\frac{-3}{4}$
   (c) $\frac{4}{3}$ (d) $\frac{-4}{3}$
15. If $A(-2, 3)$ and $B(2, 3)$ are two vertices of ΔABC and $G(0, 0)$ is its centroid, then the coordinates of C are ______.
   (a) (0, –6) (b) (–4, 0)
   (c) (4, 0) (d) (0, 6)
16. Let ΔABC be a right triangle in which $A(0, 2)$ and $B(2, 0)$. Then the coordinates of C can be ______.
   (a) (0, 0) (b) (2, 2)
   (c) Either (a) or (b) (d) None of these
17. If $A(4, 7)$, $B(2, 5)$, $C(1, 3)$, and $D(-1, 1)$ are the four points, then the lines AC and BD are ______.
   (a) perpendicular to each other
   (b) parallel to each other
   (c) neither parallel nor perpendicular to each other
   (d) None of these

18. Find the area of the triangle formed by the line $5x - 3y + 15 = 0$ with coordinate axes.
(a) 15 cm^2 (b) 5 cm^2
(c) 8 cm^2 (d) $\frac{15}{2}$ cm^2

19. Equation of a line whose inclination is 45° and making an intercept of 3 units on X-axis is:
(a) $x + y - 3 = 0$. (b) $x - y - 3 = 0$.
(c) $x - y + 3 = 0$. (d) $x + y + 3 = 0$.

20. The centre of a circle is $C(2, k)$. If $A(2, 1)$ and $B(5, 2)$ are two points on its circumference, then the value of k is ______.
(a) 6 (b) 2
(c) –6 (d) –2

21. The distance between the points $(2k + 4, 5k)$ and $(2k, -3 + 5k)$ in units is ______.
(a) 1 (b) 2
(c) 4 (d) 5

22. The equation of the line with inclination 45° and passing through the point (–1, 2) is ______.
(a) $x + y + 3 = 0$ (b) $x - y + 3 = 0$
(c) $x - y - 3 = 0$ (d) $x + y - 3 = 0$

23. The distance between the points $(3k + 1, -3k)$ and $(3k - 2, -4 - 3k)$ (in units) is ______.
(a) $3k$ (b) $5k$
(c) 5 (d) 3

24. The angle made by the line $x - \sqrt{3}y + 1 = 0$ with the positive Y-axis is ______.
(a) 60° (b) 30°
(c) 45° (d) 90°

25. If ΔABC is a right triangle in which $A(3, 0)$ and $B(0, 5)$, then the coordinates of C can be ______.
(a) (5, 3) (b) (3, 5)
(c) (0, 0) (d) Both (b) and (c)

26. If the roots of the quadratic equation $2x^2 - 5x + 2 = 0$ are the intercepts made by a line on the coordinate axes, then the equation of the line can be
(a) $4x + y = 2$. (b) $2x + 5y + 2$.
(c) $x + 4y = 2$. (d) Both (a) and (c)

27. The inclination of the line $\sqrt{3}x - y + 5 = 0$ with X-axis is ______.
(a) 90° (b) 45°
(c) 60° (d) 30°

28. The equation of the line parallel to $3x - 2y + 7 = 0$ and making an intercept –4 on X-axis is:
(a) $3x - 2y + 12 = 0$
(b) $3x - 2y - 12 = 0$
(c) $3x + 2y - 12 = 0$
(d) $3x + 2y + 12 = 0$

29. A triangle is formed by the lines $x + y = 8$, X-axis and Y-axis. Find its centroid.
(a) $\left(\frac{8}{3}, \frac{8}{3}\right)$ (b) (8, 8)
(c) (4, 4) (d) (0, 0)

30. The point which divides the line joining the points $A(1, 2)$ and $B(-1, 1)$ internally in the ratio 1 : 2 is ______.
(a) $\left(\frac{-1}{3}, \frac{5}{3}\right)$ (b) $\left(\frac{1}{3}, \frac{5}{3}\right)$
(c) (–1, 5) (d) (1, 5)

31. Find the area of the triangle formed by the line $3x - 4y + 12 = 0$ with the coordinate axes.
(a) 6 $units^2$ (b) 12 $units^2$
(c) 1 $units^2$ (d) 36 $units^2$

32. The equation of a line whose sum of intercepts is 5 and the area of the triangle formed by the line with positive coordinate axis is 2 sq. units can be
(a) $x + y = 4$. (b) $x + 4y = 4$.
(c) $y + 4x + 4 = 0$. (d) $y = x + 4$.

33. Find the equation of a line which divides the line segment joining the points (1, 1) and (2, 3) in the ratio 2 : 3 perpendicularly.
(a) $5x - 5y + 2 = 0$ (b) $5x + 5y + 2 = 0$
(c) $x + 2y - 5 = 0$ (d) $x + 2y + 7 = 0$

Level 2: Review Your Concepts

34. The equation of the line making an angle of 45° with X-axis in positive direction and having y-intercept as –3 is ______.
(a) $3x - y + 1 = 0$
(b) $3x + y - 1 = 0$
(c) $x - y + 3 = 0$
(d) $x - y = 3$

35. Which of the following lines is perpendicular to $x + 2y + 3 = 0$?

(a) $\sqrt{2x} - y + 3 = 0$

(b) $\sqrt{2x} + \sqrt{2y} - 5 = 0$

(c) $2\sqrt{2x} - \sqrt{2y} + 3 = 0$

(d) $x + \sqrt{2y} + 4 = 0$

36. The ortho-centre of the triangle formed by the points (0, 3), (0, 0) and (1, 0) is ______.

(a) $\left(\frac{1}{3}, 1\right)$ (b) $\left(\frac{1}{2}, \frac{3}{2}\right)$

(c) (0, 0) (d) $\left(0, \frac{3}{2}\right)$

37. The equation of the line passing through the point of intersection of the lines $x + 2y + 3 = 0$ and $2x - y + 5 = 0$ and parallel to X-axis is ______.

(a) $5y + 1 = 0$ (b) $5x - 13 = 0$

(c) $5x + 13 = 0$ (d) $5y - 1 = 0$

38. Find the equation of a line which divides the line segment joining the points (1, –2) and (3, –1) in the ratio 3 : 1 perpendicularly.

(a) $x - 2y - 5 = 0$

(b) $6x + 4y - 5 = 0$

(c) $3x + 2y - 5 = 0$

(d) $8x + 4y - 15 = 0$

39. If $x + p = 0$, $y + 4 = 0$ and $x + 2y + 4 = 0$ are concurrent, then p = ______.

(a) 4 (b) –2

(c) –4 (d) 2

40. The perpendicular bisector of the side PQ is

(a) $x - y = 0$. (b) $x + y - 2 = 0$.

(c) $3x - 2y - 2 = 0$. (d) $x + 2y - 6 = 0$.

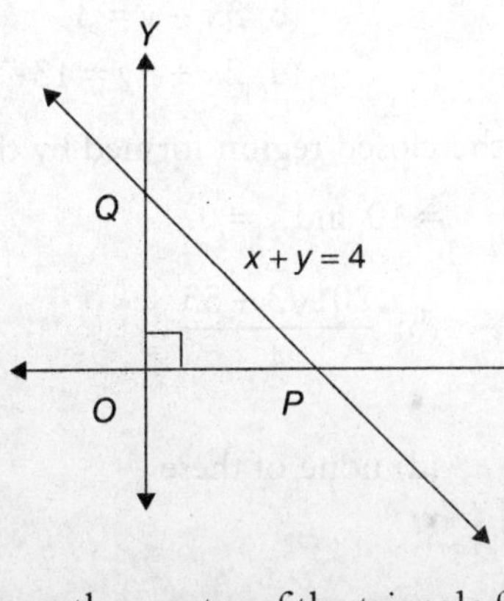

41. The ortho-centre of the triangle formed by the vertices $A(4, 6)$, $B(4, 3)$ and $C(2, 3)$ is ______.

(a) (2, 3) (b) (4, 3)

(c) (4, 6) (d) (3, 4)

42. The circum-centre and the ortho-centre of the triangle formed by the sides $y = 0$, $x = 0$ and $2x + 3y = 6$ are respectively ______.

(a) (3, 2), (0, 0) (b) $\left(\frac{3}{2}, 1\right)$, (0, 0)

(c) (–3, 1), (0, 0) (d) $\left(-\frac{3}{2}, 1\right)$, (0, 0)

43. The equation of median drawn to the side BC of ΔABC whose vertices are $A(1, -2)$, $B(3, 6)$ and $C(5, 0)$ is ______.

(a) $5x - 3y - 11 = 0$

(b) $5x + 3y - 11 = 0$

(c) $3x - 5y + 11 = 0$

(d) $3x - 5y - 11 = 0$

44. Find the equation of the line passing through (1, 1) and forming an area of 2 sq. units with positive coordinate axis.

(a) $2x + 3y = 5$ (b) $x - y + 2 = 0$

(c) $x + y - 2 = 0$ (d) $x - y + 1 = 0$

45. If the vertices of a triangle are $A(3, -3)$, $B(-3, 3)$ and $C(-3\sqrt{3}, -3\sqrt{3})$, then the distance between the ortho-centre and the circum-centre is ______.

(a) $6\sqrt{2}$ units (b) $6\sqrt{3}$ units

(c) 0 unit (d) None of these

46. The circum-centre of the triangle formed by the lines $x + 4y = 7$, $5x + 3y = 1$ and $3x - 5y = 21$ is ______.

(a) (–3, 2) (b) (3, 1)

(c) (3, –1) (d) (–3, –2)

47. Find the equation of the median of the triangle, formed by the line $8x + 5y = 40$ with the coordinate axes. Given that the median is passing through the origin.

(a) $5x - 8y = 0$ (b) $5x + 8y = 0$

(c) $8x - 5y = 0$ (d) $8x + 5y = 0$

48. Find the area of a triangle formed by the lines $4x - y - 8 = 0$, $2x + y - 10 = 0$ and $y = 0$ (in sq units).

(a) 5 (b) 6

(c) 4 (d) 3

49. Find the length of the longest side of the triangle formed by the line $3x + 4y = 12$ with the coordinate axes.

(a) 9 (b) 16

(c) 5 (d) 7

50. The following are the steps involved in finding the centroid of the triangle with vertices (5, 4), (6,7) and (1, 1). Arrange them in sequential order from first to last.
(A) The required centroid (4, 4)
(B) The centroid of the triangle with the vertices (x_1, y_1), (x_2, y_2) and (x_3, y_3) is $\left(\frac{x_1+x_2+x_3}{3}, \frac{y_1+y_2+y_3}{3}\right)$
(C) The centroid is $\left(\frac{5+6+1}{3}, \frac{4+7+1}{3}\right)$
(a) ABC (b) CBA
(c) BAC (d) BCA

Level 3: Assess Your Concepts

51. In what ratio does the line $4x + 3y - 13 = 0$ divide the line segment joining the points (2, 1) and (1, 4)?
(a) 3 : 2 internally
(b) 2 : 3 externally
(c) 2 : 3 internally
(d) 3 : 2 externally

52. If $A(3, 4)$, $B(1, -2)$ are the two vertices of triangle ABC and $G(3, 5)$ is the centroid of the triangle, then the equation of AC is ______.
(a) $4x - 5y - 7 = 0$
(b) $4x - 5y + 8 = 0$
(c) $9x - 2y - 23 = 0$
(d) $9x - 2y - 19 = 0$

53. If $ax + 4y + 3 = 0$, $bx + 5y + 3 = 0$ and $cx + 6y + 3 = 0$ are concurrent lines, then $a + c =$ ______.
(a) $3b$ (b) $2b$
(c) b (d) $4b$

54. If (5, 3), (4, 2) and (1, –2) are the mid points of sides of triangle ABC, then the area of ΔABC is
(a) 2 sq. units (b) 3 sq. units
(c) 1 sq. unit (d) 4 sq. units

55. Find the distance between the ortho-centre and circum-centre of the triangle formed by joining the points (5, 7), (4, 10), and (6, 9).
(a) $\sqrt{\frac{5}{4}}$ units (b) $\sqrt{\frac{5}{2}}$ units
(c) $\sqrt{10}$ units (d) $\sqrt{5}$ units

56. (A) Area of the region formed by $4|x| + 3|y| = 12$ is ______.
(a) 18 sq. units (b) 20 sq. units
(c) 24 sq. units (d) 36 sq. units

(B) If $2y = 5$, $y = 0$ and $\left(0, \frac{5}{2}\right)$ are one of the longest diagonals, one of the sides and one of the vertices of a regular hexagon respectively and the hexagon completely lies in the first quadrant, then find the equations the other longest diagonals of the hexagon.
(a) $2\sqrt{3}x + 2y = 0$ (b) $2\sqrt{3}x + 2y = 15$
(c) $4x + 3y = 15$ (d) None

57. Find the radius of the circle which passes through the origin, (0, 4) and (4, 0).
(a) 2 (b) $4\sqrt{2}$
(c) $\sqrt{8}$ (d) $3\sqrt{2}$

58. Find the circum-centre of the triangle whose vertices are (0, 0), $(3, \sqrt{3})$, and $(0, 2\sqrt{3})$.
(a) $(1, \sqrt{3})$ (b) $(\sqrt{3}, \sqrt{3})$
(c) $(2\sqrt{3}, 1)$ (d) $(2, \sqrt{3})$

59. Find the ortho-centre of the triangle formed by the lines $3x - 4y = 10$, $8x + 6y = 15$ and Y-axis.
(a) $\left(\frac{3}{5}, \frac{7}{5}\right)$ (b) $\left(\frac{12}{5}, \frac{-7}{10}\right)$
(c) $\left(\frac{3}{5}, \frac{12}{5}\right)$ (d) $\left(\frac{12}{5}, \frac{-3}{10}\right)$

60. The equation of a line which passes through (2, 3) and the product of whose intercepts on the coordinate axis is 27, can be ______.
(a) $5x + 4y = 22$ (b) $3x - y = 3$
(c) $3x + 4y = 18$ (d) $2x + 3y = 13$

61. Find the area of the closed region formed by the lines $y = \sqrt{3}x + 9$, $x + y = 10$ and $y = 0$.
(a) $\frac{251 + 50\sqrt{3}}{2}$ (b) $\frac{201\sqrt{3} + 53}{4}$
(c) $\frac{201 + 53\sqrt{3}}{4}$ (d) none of these

PRACTICE QUESTIONS JEE SPECIAL WING

Multiple-Answer Type Questions

Directions for questions 1 to 5:
Each question has FOUR options (a), (b), (c), and (d). ONE OR MORE THAN ONE of these four option(s) is/are the correct answer(s).

1. Which of the following is equidistant from (3, –8) and (–7, 4)?
   (a) (–2, –2) (b) (4, 3)
   (c) (–8, –7) (d) (10, 8)

2. If a line $ax + by + c = 0$ is perpendicular to both the lines $4x - ky + 17 = 0$ and $kx - 9y + 13 = 0$, find the value of k.
   (a) –6 (b) –3
   (c) 3 (d) 6

3. Three vertices of parallelogram are (–3, 9), (–5, –7) and (6, –4). Find the fourth vertex of the parallelogram.
   (a) (8, 12) (b) (4, –15)
   (c) (4, –20) (d) (–14, 6)

4. A circle intersects the y –axis at (0, 5) and (0, 15). If the circle touches the x –axis at a point, find the coordinates of the point.
   (a) $(5\sqrt{3}, 0)$ (b) $(5\sqrt{2}, 0)$
   (c) $(-5\sqrt{2}, 0)$ (d) $(-5\sqrt{3}, 0)$

5. Find the point of trisection of the line segment joining (–9, 15) and (21, –36).
   (a) $(1,-2)$ (b) $(11,-19)$.
   (c) $(6,-21)$ (d) $(4,-7)$

Match The Column

Directions for questions 6 to 9:
Read the paragraph given below and answer the questions.

In the given figure AB and CD represent the x-axis and the y-axis respectively.

A circle is drawn with P as centre and AB as diameter.

$A = (-2, 0)$ and $B = (8, 0)$.

$Q\ (x, 3)$ is a point on the circle, and it lies in the first quadrant.

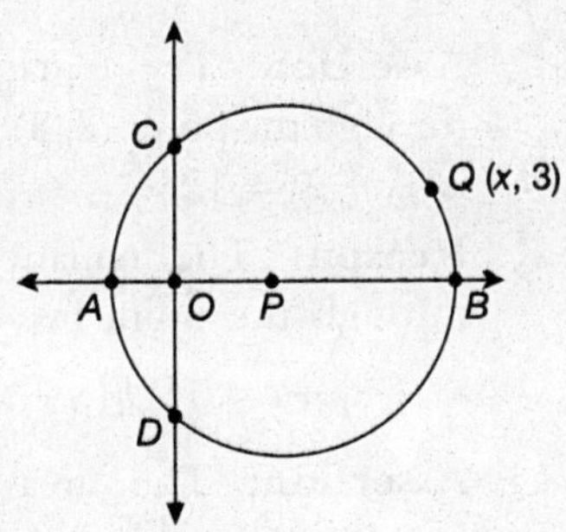

Column A	Column B
6. CD	(a) 28
7. BC	(b) $\sqrt{80}$
8. QD	(c) 18
9. Perimeter of ΔPCD	(d) $\sqrt{60}$
	(e) 8
	(f) $\sqrt{98}$

Comprehension-Based Questions

Directions for questions 10 to 14:
Read the paragraph given below and answer the questions.

On a Sunday, Dhathri and her companions decided to go on a day's excursion. They met at their school, Mahavidyalaya, at 12 noon. From school, they went to a restaurant, Bakasura, and had a sumptuous lunch. They left the restaurant to watch the movie RRR at Feast, an Imax theatre. From the theatre, they went to a park for recreation and played some games. The same day, at 8:00 pm, they returned from the park to school. The school, restaurant, theatre, and park are represented by the coordinate points $M(8, 7)$, $B(-1, 6)$, $F(-2, -3)$, and $R(7, -2)$.

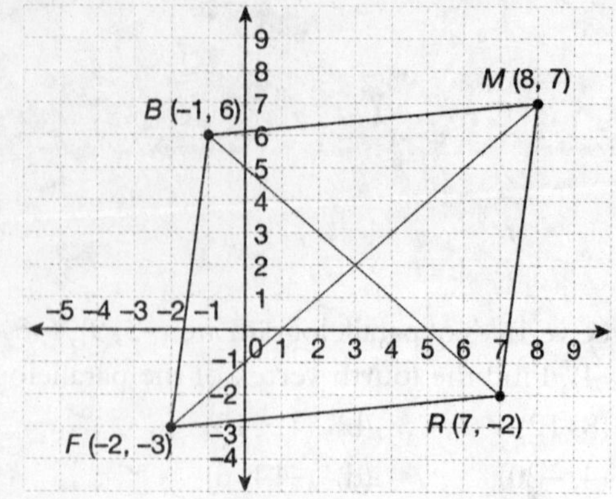

10. By how many units is the distance between the school and the theatre more/less than that between the hotel and the park?

(a) $2\sqrt{2}$ (b) $4\sqrt{2}$
(c) $8\sqrt{2}$ (d) $10\sqrt{2}$

11. What is the measure of the angle between the lines joining the school and the theatre, and the hotel and the park?

(a) 120° (b) 90°
(c) 45° (d) 30°

12. What is the perimeter (in units) of the quadrilateral formed by *M*, *B*, *F* and *R*?

(a) $8\sqrt{82}$ (b) $4\sqrt{82}$
(c) 36 (d) 48

13. Which of the following is the true statement about the quadrilateral *MBFR*?

(a) A parallelogram but not a rhombus
(b) A rectangle but not a square.
(c) A rhombus but not a square.
(d) A trapezium but not isosceles trapezium.

14. What is the area (in sq units) of the quadrilateral *MBFR*?

(a) 150 (b) 120
(c) 100 (d) 80

Assertion and Reason Type Questions

Directions for questions 15 to 18:
Read the options given below and answer the questions.
In the light of the given statements, choose the most appropriate answer from the options given below.

(a) Both assertion (A) and reason (R) are true, and reason (R) is the correct explanation of assertion.
(b) Both assertion (A) and reason (R) are true, and reason (R) is not the correct explanation of assertion.
(c) Assertion (A) is true, but reason (R) is false.
(d) Assertion (A) is false, and reason (R) is true.

15. **Assertion:** The triangle formed by *A*(2, 3), *B*(2, 7) and *C*(6, 7) is an isosceles triangle.

Reason: For any three non-collinear points *A*, *B*, and *C*, if *AB* = *BC*, *BC* = *AC* or *AB* = *AC*, then *ABC* is an isosceles triangle.

16. **Assertion:** If the end points of a diameter are *P*(12, –31) and *Q*(–24, 13), the centre of the circle is *O*(–6, –22).

Reason: The midpoint of a diameter of a circle is the centre of the circle. The midpoint of the line segment joining (x_1, y_1), and (x_2, y_2) is $\left(\frac{x_1+x_2}{2}, \frac{y_1+y_2}{2}\right)$.

17. **Assertion:** The equation of a straight line passing through the point (2, 3) and parallel to $3x + 2y + 12 = 0$ is $3x + 2y = 12$.

Reason: The equation of a straight line passing through the point (x_1, y_1) and perpendicular to line $ax + by + c = 0$ is $b(x - x_1) - a(y - y_1) = 0$.

18. **Assertion:** The area of the triangle formed by $5x + 4y = 40$ with the coordinate axes is 40 sq units.

Reason: The area of the triangle formed by $\frac{x}{a} + \frac{y}{b} = 1$ with the coordinate axes is $\frac{|ab|}{2}$ sq units.

ANSWER KEYS

Crossword

Across

3. Tangent 7. Inclination 8. Three 9. Oblique 11. Zero
13. Right

Down

1. Intercept 2. Perpendicular 4. Collinear 5. Parallel 6. Trisection
9. Origin 10. Equal 12. One

Classroom Wing

Very Short Answer Type Questions

1. 2 units 2. $\frac{3}{5}$ 3. first quadrant or second quadrant
4. $\left(-\frac{9}{4}, 0\right)$ and $\left(0, -\frac{9}{7}\right)$ 5. 4 sq. units 6. $\frac{1}{2}|ab|$ sq. units 7. $\frac{1}{2}\left|\frac{c^2}{ab}\right|$
8. 8 9. (3, 5) 10. (0, 2) 11. (2, –3)
12. inside the circle 13. 2 14. $\left(\frac{2}{3}, 0\right)$ 15. (7, 5) 16. (2, 2)
17. Y-axis 18. 2 : 1 or 1 : 2 19. 2 : 3 or 3 : 2 20. (–2, 4)

Short Answer Type Questions

21. CADB 22. –3 23. (4, –3) 24. $x = 3$
25. $5\sqrt{3}y - 5x + 3\sqrt{3} = 0$. 26. $5x + y - 3 = 0$ 27. (–1, 3)
28. $2x - 3y - 13 = 0$ 29. $P(6, -4)$, $Q(-2, 0)$ and $R(8, 8)$ 30. (11, 10) 31. $\left(\frac{5}{3}, \frac{10}{3}\right)$
32. (1 – 1) 33. $\left(0, \frac{22}{5}\right)$ 34. $\left(0, \frac{-8}{11}\right)$

Essay Type Questions

35. (A) $2x + 3y - 24 = 0$ (B) (–6, 0) 36. $7x + 3y - 71 = 0$ 37. $\frac{3}{2}$ 38. 5 units
39. $5x + 5y - 63 = 0$ 40. $A(3, 0)$, $B(0, 4 - \sqrt{7})$ and $D(0, 4 + \sqrt{7})$.

Competition Wing

Level 1: Apply Your Concepts

1. 1 2. negative, negative 3. (2, 3) 4. centroid 5. X-axis
6. (a) 7. (d) 8. (a) 9. (a) 10. (b)

11. (b)	12. (c)	13. (b)	14. (b)	15. (a)
16. (c)	17. (b)	18. (d)	19. (b)	20. (a)
21. (d)	22. (b)	23. (c)	24. (a)	25. (d)
26. (d)	27. (c)	28. (a)	29. (a)	30. (b)
31. (a)	32. (b)	33. (c)		

Level 2: Review Your Concepts

34. (d)	35. (c)	36. (c)	37. (a)	38. (d)
39. (c)	40. (a)	41. (b)	42. (b)	43. (a)
44. (c)	45. (c)	46. (b)	47. (c)	48. (b)
49. (c)	50. (d)			

Level 3: Assess Your Concepts

51. (c)	52. (d)	53. (b)	54. (a)	55. (b)
56. (A) (c) (B) (b)	57. (c)	58. (a)	59. (b)	60. (c)
61. (c)				

JEE Special Wing

Multiple-Answer Type Questions

1. (a, b, c, d)	2. (a, d)	3. (a, c, d)	4. (a, d)	5. (a, b)

Match The Column

6. (e)	7. (b)	8. (f)	9. (c)

Comprehension-Based Questions

10. (a)	11. (b)	12. (b)	13. (c)	14. (d)

Assertion and Reason Type Questions

15. (a)	16. (d)	17. (b)	18. (a)

Hints and Explanations

Classroom Wing

Very Short Answer Type Questions

1. 2

2. $3y+1=-5x$

$3y=-5x-1$

$y=\frac{-5}{3}x-\frac{1}{3}$

Slope of line perpendicular $=\frac{3}{5}$

3. 1st quadrant or second quadrant

4. Take $x=0$

$7y+9=0$

$y=-\frac{9}{7}$

Take $y=0$

$4x+9=0$

$x=\frac{-9}{4}$

$\left(-\frac{9}{4},0\right)$ and $\left(0,-\frac{9}{7}\right)$

5. Area $=\frac{1}{2}(2)(4)$

$=4$ sq.units

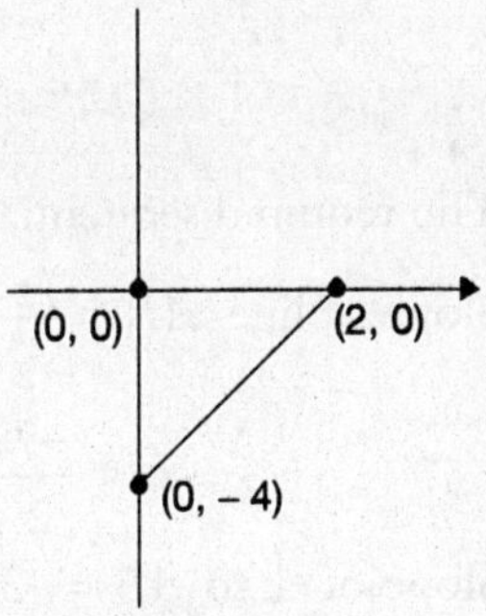

6. $\frac{1}{2}|ab|$ sq. units

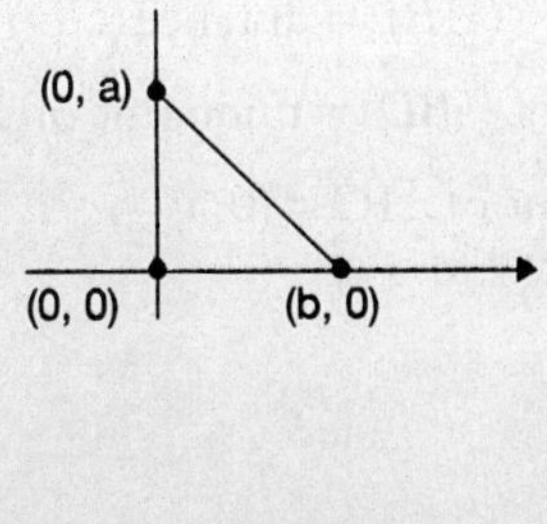

7. Take $x=0$

$ax+by+c=0$

$by=-c$

$y=\frac{-c}{b}$

Take $y=0$

$ax+by+c=0$

$ax=-c$

$x=\frac{-c}{a}$

$\therefore$ Area $=\frac{1}{2}\times\left|\frac{c}{a}\times\frac{c}{b}\right|=\frac{1}{2}\left|\frac{c^2}{ab}\right|$

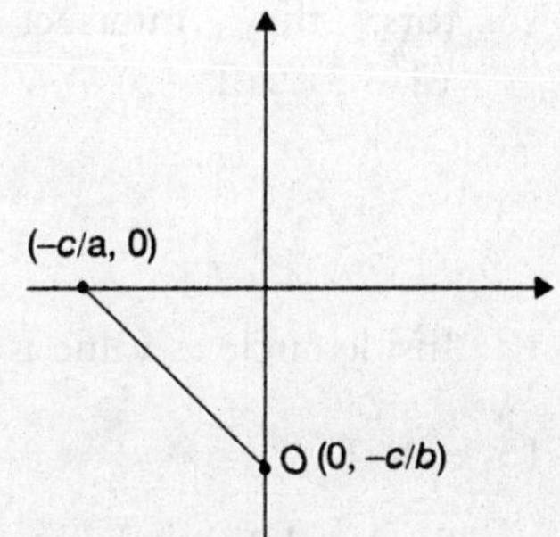

8. 8 for points to be collinear

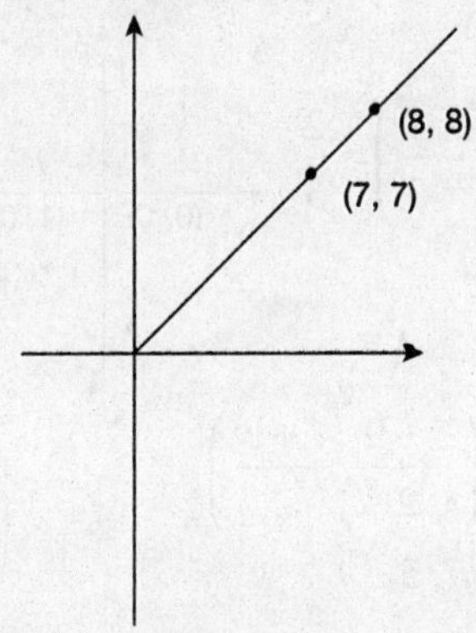

9. Midpoint of other diagonal is same as midpoint of this diagonal as diagonals of parallelogram bisect each other

$\therefore\left(\frac{1+5}{2},\frac{3+7}{2}\right)=(3,5)$

10. (0, 2) as orthocenter is the point of intersection of altitudes drawn from each vertex.

$\therefore$ Altitude from vertex (1, 2) will coincide with others at (0, 2)

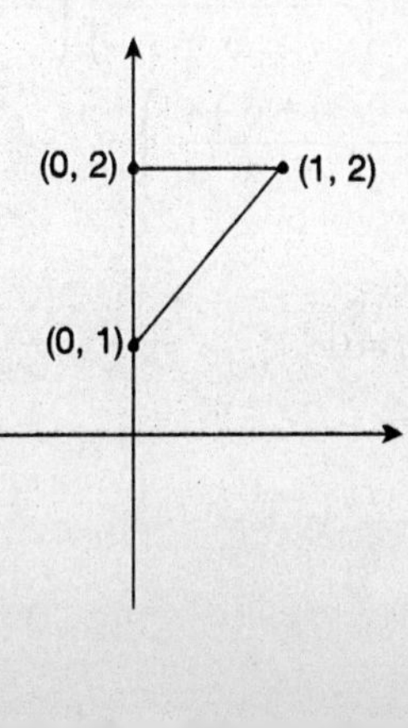

11. Midpoint of $AB = (2, -3)$

Midpoint of $OB = (0, -3)$

Midpoint of $OA = (2, 0)$

After drawing $\perp$ bisectors, they intersect at $(2, -3) \therefore (2, -3)$

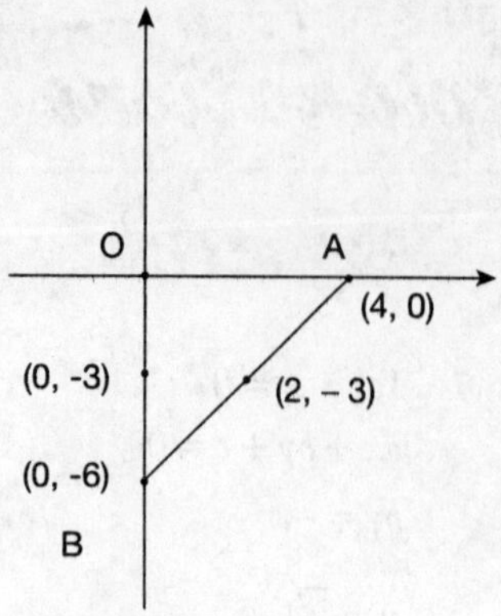

12. Inside circle as value is less than radius.

13. $x = 2$

Since AB is a line parallel to y-axis.

$\therefore$ x-coordinate of both would be same.

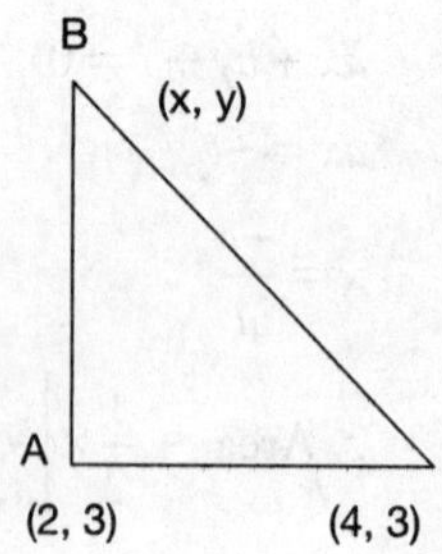

14. $\dfrac{(1, 0)}{(0, 0)} = \dfrac{1x}{2x}$

$\therefore \dfrac{1x}{3x} = \left(1 - \dfrac{1}{3}\right) = \dfrac{2}{3}$

$\therefore \left(\dfrac{2}{3}, 0\right)$

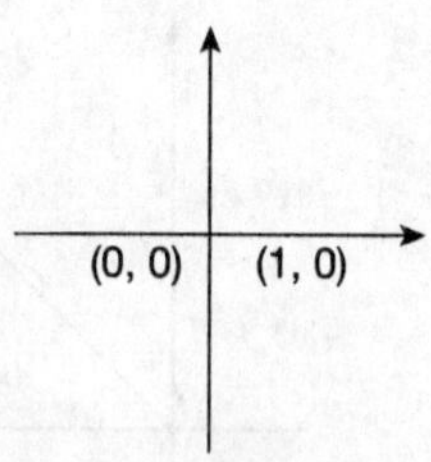

15. Center $= \left(\dfrac{5+9}{2}, \dfrac{7+3}{2}\right)$

$= (7, 5)$

16.

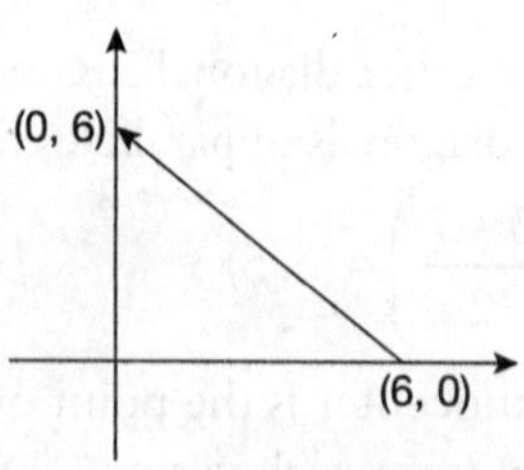

Centroid $= \left(\dfrac{x_1 + x_2 + x_3}{3}\right), \left(\dfrac{y_1 + y_2 + y_3}{3}\right)$

$\therefore \left(\dfrac{0+6+0}{3}, \dfrac{0+6+0}{3}\right)$

$= (2, 2)$

17. $ax + by + c = 0$

$by = -ax - c$

$y = -\dfrac{a}{b}x - \dfrac{c}{b}$

Since, $a = 0$

$\therefore y = -\dfrac{c}{b}$

Perpendicular to y-axis

18. A will divide the trisection line BC in ratio $1:2$ or $2:1$

19. Total distance between points $= 9 + 6 = 15$

Value below x-axis $= \dfrac{6}{15} = \dfrac{2}{5}$

And above x-axis $= \dfrac{9}{15} = \dfrac{3}{5}$

$\therefore$ line is divided in ratio of $2:3$ or $3:2$

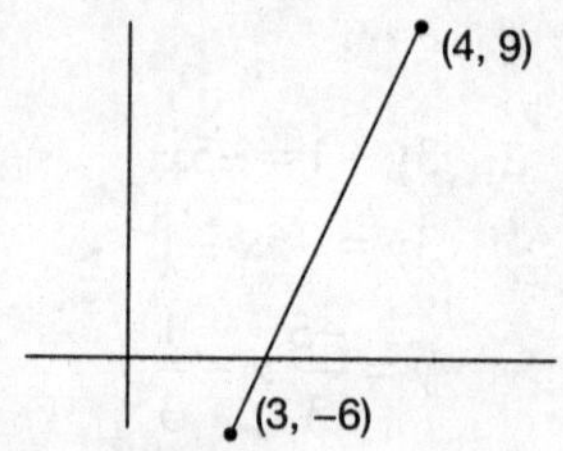

20. Since AD and BC are parallel,

$\therefore$ Distance between them will be same at all points.

$\therefore \text{dist}(x)_{AB} = 2$

$\text{dist}(y)_{AB} = 2$

$\therefore D$ should be either $(-2, 4)$ or $(2, 8)$

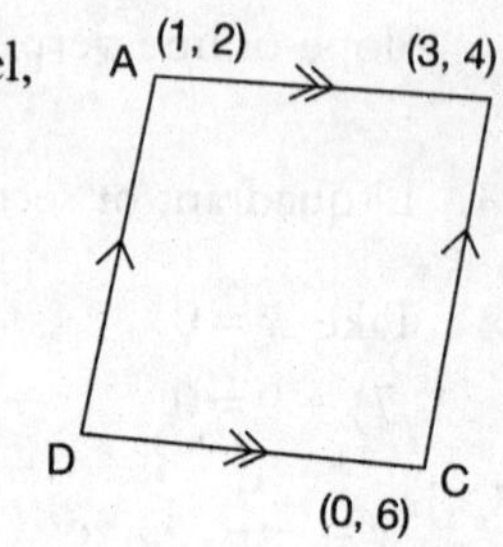

Now, for AB and DC

$\text{dist}(x)_{BC} = 3$

$\text{dist}(y)_{BC} = 2$

$\therefore D$ should be $= (4, 4)$ or $(-2, 0)$

Now D will be $(-2, 4)$ {Taking common values of all 4}.

Short Answer Type Questions

21. The required sequential order is CABD.

22. Slope of line $AB = \dfrac{y_2 - y_1}{x_2 - x_1}$

$= \dfrac{-7+6}{2-5} = \dfrac{-1}{-3} = \dfrac{1}{3}$

Slope of $\perp$ to $AB = -3$

23. $AD \,||\, BC$ and $AB \,||\, CD$

$\therefore$ Distance (AB) = distance (CD)

Midpoint of BD = midpoint of AC

$\therefore$ Midpoint of $AC = (0, 1)$

$\therefore$ Vertex D

$0 = \frac{x-4}{2}$

$x = 4$

$1 = \frac{y+5}{2}$

$y = 2 - 5 = -3$

$(4, -3)$

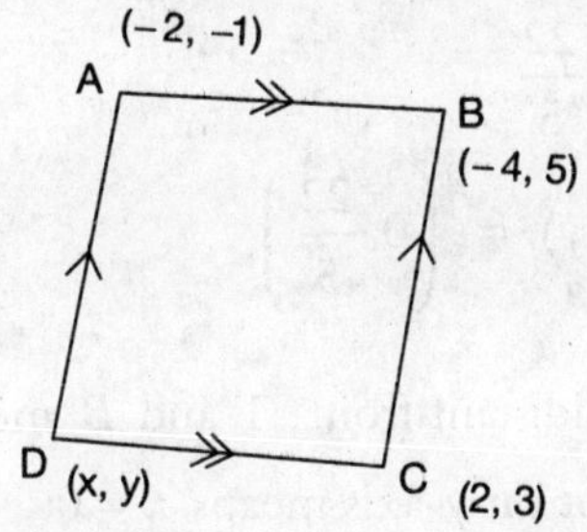

24. Equation of line $\Rightarrow x = a$

$(x = a) \Rightarrow$ should be satisfied by $(3, -5)$

$3 = a$

$\therefore x = 3$

25. $m = \tan 30 = \frac{1}{\sqrt{3}}$

$c = \frac{-3}{5}$

$y = mx + c$

$y = \frac{1}{\sqrt{3}}x - \frac{3}{5}$

$5\sqrt{3}y = 5x - 3\sqrt{3}$

$5\sqrt{3}y - 5x + 3\sqrt{3} = 0$

26. $y = mx + c$

$y = -5x + 3$

$5x + y - 3 = 0$

27. Centroid $= \left(\frac{3+2-8}{3}, \frac{-1+4+6}{3}\right)$

$= \left(\frac{-3}{3}, \frac{9}{3}\right)$

$= (-1, 3)$

28. Slope of line $2x - 3y + 8 = 0$

$3y = 2x + 8$

$y = \frac{2}{3}x + \frac{8}{3}$

Slope of new line $= \frac{2}{3}$ and should pass through $(2, -3)$.

$y = mx + c$

$-3 = \frac{2}{3}(2) + c$

$c = -3 - \frac{4}{3} = \frac{-9-4}{3} = -\frac{13}{3}$

$\therefore y = \frac{2}{3}x - \frac{13}{3}$

$3y = 2x - 13$

$2x - 3y - 13 = 0$

29.

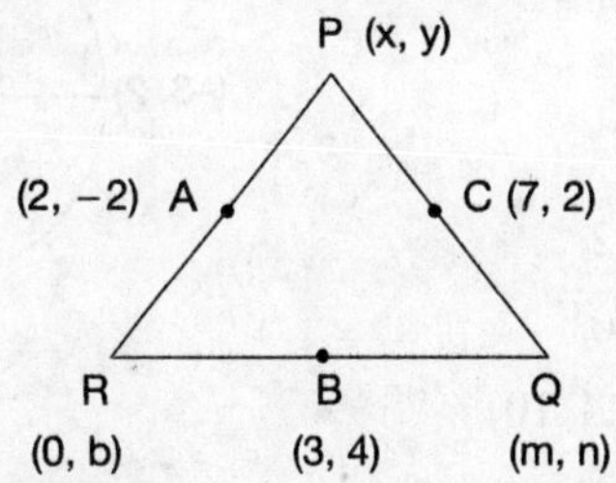

Let $P = (x, y)$

$Q = (a, b)$

$R = (m, n)$

$x + a = 4$ (1)

$y + b = -4$ (2)

$x + m = 14$ (3)

$y + n = 4$ (4)

$a + m = 6$ (5)

$b + n = 8$ (6)

Adding (1) + (3) + (5),

$2x + 2a + 2m = 24$

Adding (2) + (4) + (6),

$2y + 2b + 2n = 8$

$x + a + m = 12$ (7)

$y + b + n = 4$ (8)

Subtract (1) from (7)

$m = 8$

Subtract (3) from (7)

$a = -2$

Subtract (5) from (7)

$x = 6$

Subtract (2) from (8)

$n = +8$

Subtract (4) from (8)

$b = 0$

Subtract (6) from (8)

$y = -4$

Vertices are $(x, y), (m, n), (a, b)$

$P(6, -4), R(8, +8), Q(-2, 0)$

30. Center is midpoint of diameter of circle.

$$\therefore \frac{-3+x}{2} = 4$$

$$x - 3 = 8$$

$$x = 11$$

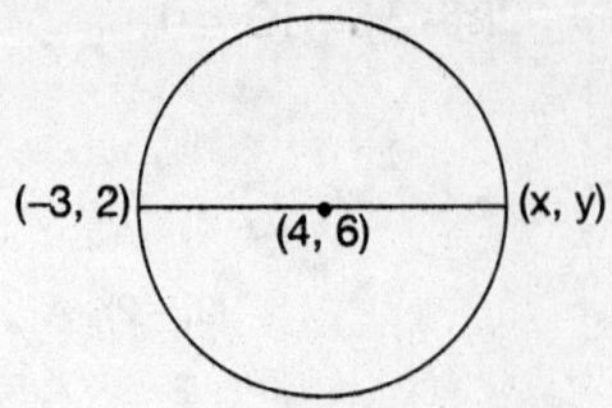

$$\frac{2+y}{2} = 6$$

$$2 + y = 12$$

$$y = 10$$

$$(x, y) = (11, 10)$$

31. Centroid divides median in ratio 2:1.

The coordinates of the centroid G of the triangle ABC = [2(3)+1(-1)/3, 2(4)+1(2)/3] = [5/3, 10/3]

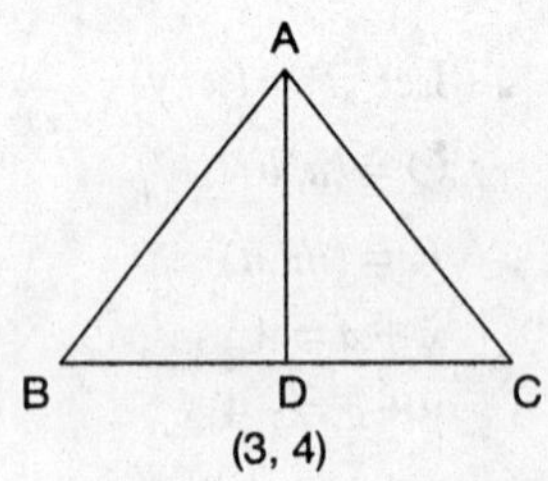

32. Point of intersection

$$3x + 5y + 2 = 0 \quad \times 4 \qquad (1)$$

$$4x + 7y + 3 = 0 \times 3$$

$$12x + 20y + 8 = 0$$

$$12x + 21y + 9 = 0$$

$$(-) \quad (-) \quad (-)$$

$$-y = 1$$

$$y = -1$$

Substitute in (1)

$$3x + 5(-1) + 2 = 0$$

$$3x = 5 - 2 = 3$$

$$x = 1$$

$$(x, y) = (1, -1)$$

33. $x = \dfrac{m_1x_2 + m_2x_1}{m_1 + m_2}$

$$x = \frac{3(2) + 2(-3)}{5}$$

$$= \frac{6-6}{5} = 0$$

$$x = 0$$

$$y = \frac{m_1y_2 + m_2y_1}{m_1 + m_2}$$

$$y = \frac{3(6) + 2(2)}{5}$$

$$y = \frac{18+4}{5}$$

$$y = \frac{22}{5}$$

$$(x, y) = \left(0, \frac{22}{5}\right)$$

34. Equidistant from A and B means ratio is 1:1.

Point on y-axis means $x = 0$

$\therefore (0, a)$

For AC

$$AC = \sqrt{(0+2)^2 + (a-5)^2}$$

$$= \sqrt{4 + a^2 + 25 - 10a}$$

$$= \sqrt{a^2 + 29 - 10a}$$

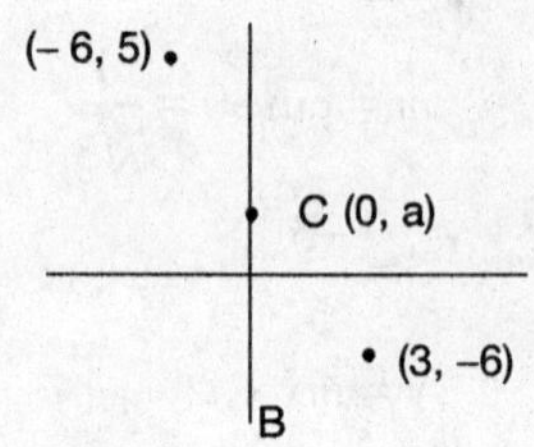

For CB

$$= \sqrt{(3-0)^2 + (-6-a)^2}$$

$$= \sqrt{9 + 36 + a^2 + 12a}$$

$$= \sqrt{45 + a^2 + 12a}$$

Equate AC and CB and squaring both sides

$$a^2 + 29 - 10a = 45 + a^2 + 12a$$

$$-22a = 45 - 29 = 16$$

$$a = \frac{-16}{22} = \frac{-8}{11}$$

$$\left(0, -\frac{8}{11}\right)$$

Essay Type Questions

35. (A) $2x + 3y - 6 = 0$

$$3y = -2x + 6$$

$$y = -\frac{2}{3}x + \frac{6}{3}$$

$$= \frac{-2}{3}x + 2$$

$$m = -\frac{2}{3}$$

Slope of line parallel to this line $= \dfrac{-2}{3}$

Intercept of new line $= 10 - 2 = 8$

$$y = mx + c \Rightarrow y = \frac{-2}{3}x + 8$$

$$3y = -2x + 24$$

$$2x + 3y - 24 = 0$$

(B) Let (0, y) be the point on the Y – axis which divides the join of (3, 9) and (–4, 2) in the ratio $m : n$.

$(0, y) = \left(\frac{-4m+3n}{m+n}, \frac{2m+9n}{m+n}\right)$

$\Rightarrow \frac{-4m+3n}{m+n} = 0$

$\Rightarrow -4m + 3n = 0$

$\Rightarrow 4m = 3n$

$\Rightarrow m/n = ¾ \Rightarrow m : n = 3 : 4$

Let (x, 0) be the point on the X-axis which divides the join of (3, 9) and (-4, 2) is the ratio $m : n$ externally.

$(x, 0) = \left(\frac{m(-4)-3n}{m-n}, \frac{2m-9n}{m-n}\right)$

$\Rightarrow \frac{2m-9n}{m-n} = 0$

$\Rightarrow 2m - 9n = 0$

$2m = 9n$

$\frac{m}{n} = \frac{9}{2} \Rightarrow m : n = 9: 2$

$x = \frac{-4m-3n}{m-n}$

$x = \frac{-4(9)-3(2)}{9-2} = \frac{-36-6}{7}$

$x = -6$

$\therefore$ The required print on the X – axis is (–6, 0).

36. Let the equation of a line perpendicular to $3x - 7y + 5 = 0$ is $7x + 3y + k = 0$.

And it is passing through (8, 5).

$\Rightarrow 7(8) + 3(5) + k = 0$

$56 + 15 + k = 0 \therefore k = -71$

$\therefore$ The required line is $7x + 3y - 71 = 0$.

37. Let C(–3, 6) divides A(–9, –12) and B(0, 15) in the ratio m:n internally.

$\therefore (-3,6) = \left(\frac{0-9n}{m+n}, \frac{15m-12n}{m+n}\right)$

$\Rightarrow \frac{-9n}{m+n} = -3 \Rightarrow -9n = -3m - 3n$

$\Rightarrow -3m = -6n \Rightarrow \frac{m}{n} = \frac{2}{1}$

$\Rightarrow \frac{AB}{BC} = \frac{2}{1}$

Let AC = $2x$ and BC = x

$\therefore \frac{AB}{AC} = \frac{AC+BC}{AC} = \frac{2x+x}{2} = \frac{3}{2}$

38.

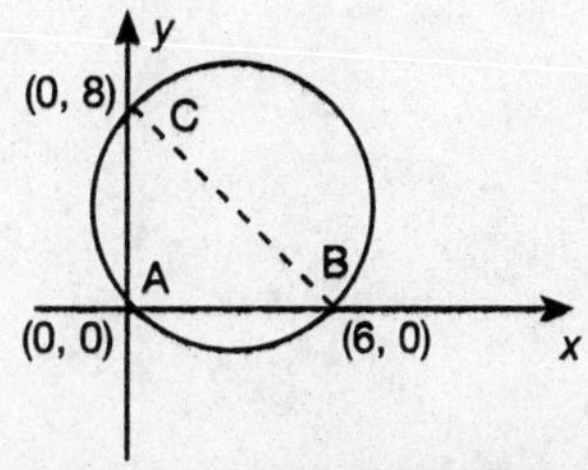

Since $\Rightarrow$ CAB = 90°, BC is the diameter.

$\Rightarrow BC = \sqrt{6^2+8^2} = \sqrt{100} = 10$ units

$\therefore$ radius = 5 units

39. Given P(4, 7), Q(6, 9)

Let M divides PQ in the ratio 2:3.

$\Rightarrow M(x,y) = \left(\frac{2\times6+3\times4}{2+3}, \frac{2\times9+3\times7}{2+3}\right)$

$= \left(\frac{24}{5}, \frac{39}{5}\right)$

Slope of $\overline{PQ} = \frac{9-7}{6-4} = \frac{2}{2} = 1$

Slope of its altitude = –1

$\therefore$ Equation of the altitude is $y - \frac{39}{5} = -1\left(x - \frac{24}{5}\right)$

$\Rightarrow 5y - 39 = -5x + 24$

$\Rightarrow 5x + 5y - 63 = 0$

40. The center is at (3, 4) which is 4 units away from the x – axis.

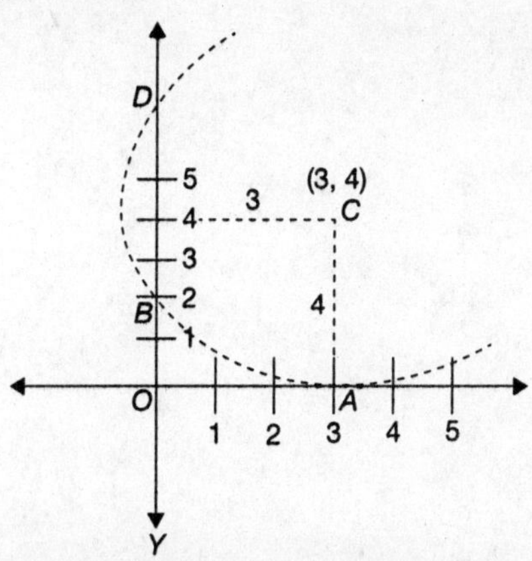

$\therefore$ The minimum radius of the circle should be 4 units, since the circle has to intersects / touches the axes.

$\Rightarrow$ The circle touches the x – axis at $A(3, 0)$.

Since $AC \perp OA$ and $OA = 3$ units

Let the circle intersect the Y axis at $B(0, y)$ $BC = 4$ units

$$\sqrt{(3-0)^2+(4-y)^2}=4$$

$$\sqrt{9+(4-y)^2}=4$$

$$9 + (4 - y)^2 = 16$$

$$(4 - y)^2 = 7$$

$$4 - y = \pm\sqrt{7}$$

$$4 \pm \sqrt{7} = y$$

$\therefore$ The points on the coordinate axes are $A(3, 0)$, $B(0, 4 - \sqrt{7})$ and $D(0, 4 + \sqrt{7})$.

41. Let $P(a, b)$ $Q(c, d)$, and $R(e, f)$ be the vertices of the triangle PQR and L, M, N are the midpoints of PQ, QR and RS respectively.

Centroid of the triangle PQR is

$$G\left(\frac{a+c+e}{3}, \frac{b+d+f}{3}\right).$$

L is the midpoint of PQ

$$=\left(\frac{a+c}{2}, \frac{b+d}{2}\right)$$

M is the midpoint of QR

$$=\left(\frac{c+e}{2}, \frac{d+f}{2}\right)$$

N is the midpoint of RS

$$=\left(\frac{e+a}{2}, \frac{f+b}{2}\right)$$

$\therefore$ Centroid of the triangle

$$LMN \text{ is } \left(\frac{\frac{a+c}{2}+\frac{c+e}{2}+\frac{e+a}{2}}{3}, \frac{\frac{b+d}{2}+\frac{b+d}{2}+\frac{f+b}{2}}{3}\right)$$

$$=\left(\frac{2(a+c+e)}{2\times 3}, \frac{2(b+d+f)}{2\times 3}\right)$$

$$=\left(\frac{a+c+e}{3}, \frac{b+d+f}{3}\right) = \text{centroid of } \Delta PQR.$$

Competition Wing

Level 1: Apply Your Concepts

1. $\tan 45° = 1$
2. −ve, − ve
3. (2, 3)
4. Centroid
5. X-axis
6. $5x + 4y - 20 = 0 \Rightarrow 5x + 4y = 20$

$\Rightarrow \frac{5x+4y}{20} = 1 \Rightarrow \frac{x}{4} + \frac{y}{5} = 1$

$\therefore$ Required area $= \frac{1}{2}|ab| = \frac{1}{2}|4 \times 5| = 10$ sq. units.

Hence, the correct option is (a).

7. x–intercepts $= 5 \Rightarrow$

The line passes through (5, 0).

$\therefore$ The equation of line passing through (–2, 3) and (5, 0) is

$\frac{x-x_1}{x_2-x_1} = \frac{y-y_1}{y_2-y_1} \Rightarrow \frac{x+2}{5+2} = \frac{y-3}{0-3}$

$\Rightarrow \frac{x+2}{7} = \frac{y-3}{-3} \Rightarrow 3x - 6 = 7y - 21$

$\Rightarrow 3x + 7y - 15 = 0$

Hence, the correct option is (d).

8. Given line is $8x - 3y - 12 = 0$

If $y = 0 \Rightarrow 8x - 12 = 0 \Rightarrow x = \frac{3}{2}$

If $x = 0 \Rightarrow -3y - 12 = 0 \Rightarrow y = -4$

$\therefore$ x–intercept $(a) = \frac{3}{2}$ and y–intercept (b) $= -4$

$\therefore$ Required area of the triangle $= \frac{1}{2}|ab|$

$= \frac{1}{2}\left|\frac{3}{2} \times -4\right| = 3$ sq. units

Hence, the correct option is (a).

9. y–intercept $= 3 \Rightarrow$ The line passes through (0, 3).

$\therefore$ The equation of the line passing through (0, 3) and (–3, –5) is

$\frac{x-x_1}{x_2-x_1} = \frac{y-y_1}{y_2-y_1} \Rightarrow \frac{x-0}{-3-0} = \frac{y-3}{-5-3}$.

$\Rightarrow -8x = -3y + 9 \Rightarrow 8x - 3y + 9 = 0$

Hence, the correct option is (a).

10. Let A(2, 4), B(6, 8), and C(2, 8).

$\therefore \text{AB} = \sqrt{(6-2)^2 + (8-4)^2}$

$= \sqrt{16+16} = \sqrt{32}$ m

$\text{BC} = \sqrt{(2-6)^2 + (8-8)^2}$

$= \sqrt{4^2} = 4$ m

$\text{AC} = \sqrt{(2-2)^2 + (8-4)^2}$

$= \sqrt{4^2} = 4$ m

$\therefore$ Perimeter of the triangle ABC $= \sqrt{32} + 4 + 4$

$= 4\sqrt{2} + 8 = 4\left(2 + \sqrt{2}\right)$m

Hence, the correct option is (b).

11. Let P(x, 0) be a point on the x–axis, such that AP = BP.

$\Rightarrow AP^2 = BP^2$

$(3 - x)^2 + (-6 - 0)^2 = (-2 - x)^2 + (5 - 0)^2$

$\Rightarrow 9 - 6x + x^2 + 36 = 4 + 4x + x^2 + 25$

$45 - 29 = 10x$

$16 = 10x$

$\Rightarrow x = \frac{8}{5}$

$\therefore$ The required point is $\left(\frac{8}{5}, 0\right)$.

Hence, the correct option is (b).

12. Let the equation of a line parallel to $2x + 3y + 5 = 0$ be $2x + 3y + k = 0$.

This line is passing through (2, 3).

$\Rightarrow 2(2) + 3(3) + k = 0$

$4 + 9 + k = 0$

$k = -13$

$\therefore$ The required line is $2x + 3y - 13 = 0$.

Hence, the correct option is (c).

13. A(1, 2), B(3, 5), C(–2, 2)

$\therefore$ Area of triangle ABC

$= \frac{1}{2}|1(5-2) + 3(2-2) + (-2)(2-5)|$

$= \frac{1}{2}|3 + 0 + 6|$

$= \frac{9}{2}$

$= 4.5$ sq. units

Hence, the correct option is (b).

14. Substitute the given point in the line.

15. Use the centroid formula.

16. Use right triangle properties.

17. Find the slopes of AC and BD.

18. Find the intercepts made on X-axis and Y-axis. Then, area $= \frac{1}{2}|ab|$.

19. Slope = $\tan\theta$ and intercept on X-axis = 3.

20. Radius of any circle is constant.

21. Use the distance formula.

22. Find slope and use point slope form of the line.

23. Use distance formula.

24. Slope $m = \tan\theta$ and the angle between positive X-axis and Y-axis is 90°.

25. Use $AC^2 = AB^2 + BC^2$.

26. Find the roots and substitute in $\frac{x}{a}+\frac{y}{b}=1$.

27. The inclination of a line with the positive X-axis is called the slope.

28. (i) If two lines are parallel, then their slopes are equal.

(ii) The equation of any line parallel to $ax + by + c = 0$ can be taken as $ax + by + k = 0$.

(iii) Find the X-intercept of the line and equate it to the given x-intercept then get the value of k.

29. (i) Evaluate the vertices of the triangle and proceed.

(ii) Find the point, where the line cuts X-axis and Y-axis.

(iii) These two points and the origin are the vertices of the triangle.

(iv) Then use the formula centroid

$$= \left(\frac{x_1 + x_2 + x_3}{3}, \frac{y_1 + y_2 + y_3}{3}\right).$$

30. Use the section formula.

31. Area of the triangle formed by the line $\frac{1}{2}|ab|$, a, b are intercepts of the line.

32. (i) $a + b = 5$ and $\frac{1}{2}|ab| = 2$.

(ii) The equation of a line in the intercept form is $\frac{x}{a}+\frac{y}{b}=1 \Rightarrow a+b=5$.

(iii) Then use the formula to find the area of the triangle formed by a line with coordinate axis, is

$$A = \frac{1}{2}|ab| \Rightarrow |ab| = 4.$$

33. (i) Evaluate the point using section formula then proceed.

(ii) Find the point on the required line that divides the line joining the points in the ratio 2 : 3.

(iii) If two lines are perpendicular then $m_1 \times m_2 = -1$.

(iv) Find the slope of the required line.

(v) Hence, find the equation of the line by using slope-point formula.

Level 2: Review Your Concepts

34. (i) Use $y = mx + c$ where $m = \tan\theta$.

(ii) Slope of the required line is tan 45°.

(iii) Use the slope and y-intercept form.

35. (i) Find the slope of the given line.

(ii) Use the concept, if two lines are perpendicular to each other, then $m_1 \times m_2 = -1$.

36. First prove the given triangle is a right triangle. In a right triangle, ortho-centre is the vertex containing right angle.

37. First find the point of intersection(x_1, y_1) of first two lines. The equation of the line parallel to X-axis is $y = y_1$.

38. (i) Find the point diving in the ratio 3 : 1.

(ii) Find the equation of line by using point-slope form.

39. (i) Solve Eqs. (2) and (3).

(ii) If three lines are concurrent then the point of intersection of any two lines, always lie on the third line.

40. (i) Find the coordinates of the points P and Q.

(ii) Then find the mid point of PQ say M.

(iii) Now the required line is perpendicular to PQ and passes through M.

41. (i) Prove the given vertices form a right triangle.

(ii) In a right-angled triangle, the vertex containing right angle is the ortho-centre.

42. Clearly the given lines forms a right triangle. In a right triangle circum-centre is the mid point of hypotenuse and ortho-centre is the vertex containing 90°.

43. Find the equation of the line passing through A and mid point of BC.

44. The area of triangle formed by $\frac{x}{a}+\frac{y}{b}=1$ with the coordinate axes is $\frac{1}{2}|ab|$.

45. (i) ABC forms an equilateral triangle.

(ii) In an equilateral triangle all the geometric centres except ex-centre coincide.

46. Prove that the given lines form a right triangle, then find the ends of the hypotenuse there by find the mid-point of them.

47. The vertices of the triangle formed by $8x + 5y = 40$ with the coordinate axes are O(0, 0), A(5, 0), B(0, 8).

Mid point of AB is $\left(\frac{5}{2}, 4\right)$.

Required median is in the form of $y = mx$ and it is passing through $\left(\frac{5}{2}, 4\right)$.

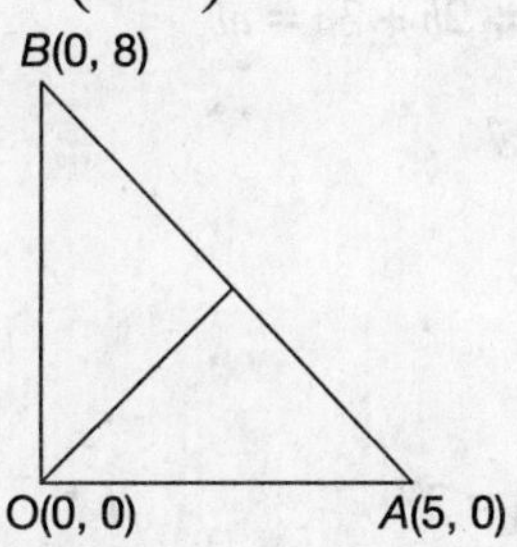

$\Rightarrow 4 = m\left(\frac{5}{2}\right) \Rightarrow m = \frac{8}{5}$

$\therefore y = \frac{8}{5}x \Rightarrow 8x - 5y = 0.$

48. $4x - y - 8 = 0$ and $2x + y - 10 = 0$ intersect at (3, 4) and intersect $y = 0$ at (2, 0) and (5, 0), respectively

Since the base is X-axis

Its height = 4 units

$\Rightarrow$ Area $= \frac{1}{2}\times(5-2)\times 4 = 6$ sq. units

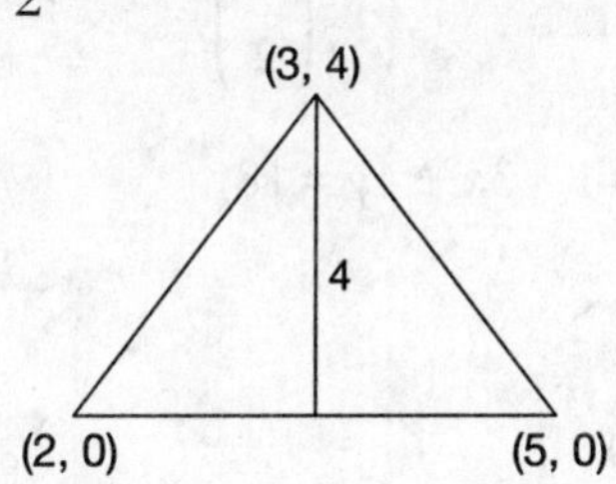

49. $3x + 4y = 12$

$\Rightarrow \frac{x}{4}+\frac{y}{3}=1$

Vertices of the triangle formed are (4, 0), (0, 3) and (0, 0).

$\Rightarrow$ The longest side is the hypotenuse joining (4, 0) and (0, 3)

$\therefore$ Its length = 5 units.

50. BCA are in sequential order from first to last.

Level 3: Assess Your Concepts

56. (A) $4|x| + 3|y| = 12 \quad \Rightarrow 4x - 3y = 12$

$4x + 3y = 12 - 4x - 3y = 12 - 4x + 3y = 12$

These lines form a rhombus.

Area $= \frac{1}{2}d_1d_2 = \frac{1}{2}\times 6\times 8 = 24$ sq. units.

(B) $ABCDEF$ is a regular polygon.

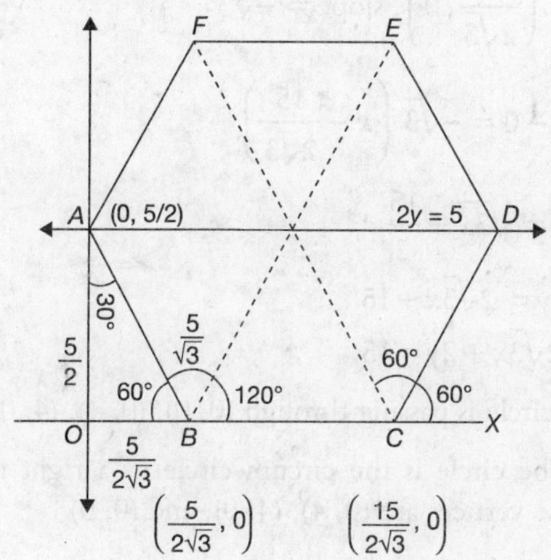

Let $A\left(0, \frac{5}{2}\right)$ and $B(x, 0)$ on $X-$ axis.

Since $OA \perp OB$ and $\angle ABC = 120°$, $\angle OBA = 60°$

$OA = \frac{5}{2}$, $OB = \frac{5}{2\sqrt{3}}$

$\Rightarrow AB = \frac{5}{\sqrt{3}} = BC$

$B = \left(\frac{5}{2\sqrt{3}}, 0\right)$ and $C = \left(\frac{5}{2\sqrt{3}} + \frac{5}{\sqrt{3}}, 0\right)$

i.e., $C = \left(\frac{15}{2\sqrt{3}}, 0\right)$

Required lines are BE and CF.

BE makes 60° with the $X-$ axis and CF makes 120° with $X-$ axis.

$\therefore$ Slope of BE is $\tan 60° = \sqrt{3}$.

And the slope of CF is $\tan 120°$

$= -\cot 30°$

$= -\sqrt{3}$

Equation of BE:

$B\left(\frac{5}{2\sqrt{3}}, 0\right)$, slope $= \sqrt{3}$

$y - 0 = \sqrt{3}\left(x - \frac{5}{2\sqrt{3}}\right)$

$y = \sqrt{3}x - \frac{5}{2}$

$2y = 2\sqrt{3}x - 5$

$2\sqrt{3}x - 2y = 5$

Equation of CF

$C\left(\frac{15}{2\sqrt{3}}, 0\right)$, slope $= -\sqrt{3}$

$y - 0 = -\sqrt{3}\left(x - \frac{15}{2\sqrt{3}}\right)$

$y = \sqrt{3}x + \frac{15}{2}$

$2y = 2\sqrt{3}x + 15$

$2\sqrt{3}x + 2y = 15$

57. The circle is passing through (0, 0), (0, 4), (4, 0)

$\Rightarrow$ The circle is the circum-circle of a right triangle whose vertices are (0, 4), (4, 0), and (0, 0)

$\therefore$ Length of the diameter

$\Rightarrow \sqrt{4^2 + 4^2} = \sqrt{32}$

Radius $= \frac{\sqrt{32}}{2} = \sqrt{8}$.

58. Let $O(0, 0)$, $A(3, \sqrt{3})$, $B(0, 2\sqrt{3})$

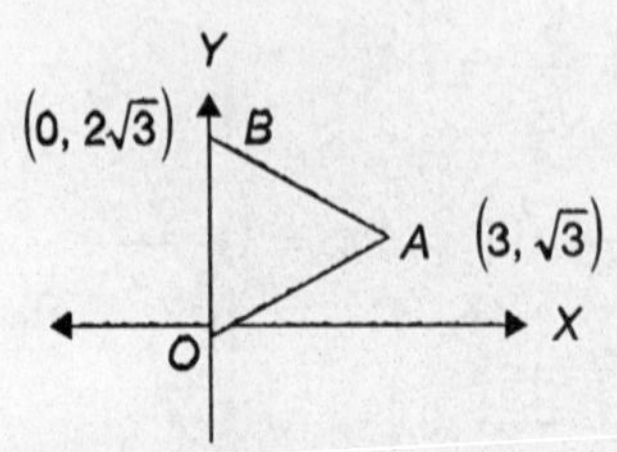

$OB = \sqrt{(2\sqrt{3})^2} = \sqrt{12}$

$AO = \sqrt{3^2 + (\sqrt{3})^2} = \sqrt{12}$

$AB = \sqrt{3^2 + (\sqrt{3} - 2\sqrt{3})^2} = \sqrt{12}$

$\therefore$ ΔABC is an equilateral triangle

$\Rightarrow \left(\frac{0+3+0}{3}, \frac{0+\sqrt{3}+2\sqrt{3}}{3}\right) = (1, \sqrt{3})$, is the centroid as well as circum-centre.

59. $3x - 4y = 10$ (1)

$8x + 6y = 15$

$4x + 3y = \frac{15}{2}$

Eqs. (1) and (2) are perpendicular lines, their intersecting point is the ortho-centre.

On solving Eqs. (1) and (2), we get the ortho- centre as $\left(\frac{12}{5}, \frac{-7}{10}\right)$.

60. Let the equation of the line is $\frac{x}{a} + \frac{y}{b} = 1$

$\Rightarrow \frac{2}{a} + \frac{3}{b} = 1 \Rightarrow 2b + 3a = ab$

$\Rightarrow 3a + 2b = 27$

$ab = 27$

$b = \frac{27}{a}$

$\Rightarrow 3a + 2 \times \frac{27}{a} = 27$

$3a^2 + 54 = 27a$

$3a^2 - 27a + 54 = 0$

$3a^2 - 27a + 54 = 0$

$a^2 - 9a + 18 = 0$

$a^2 - 6a - 3a + 18 = 0$

$a(a - 6) - 3(a - 6) = 0$

$\Rightarrow a = 6, 3 \Rightarrow b = \frac{9}{2}$ or 9

Required equation is $\frac{x}{6} + \frac{y}{\left(\frac{9}{2}\right)} = 1$

$\Rightarrow \frac{3x + 4y}{18} = 1 \quad 3x + 4y = 18$

or $\frac{x}{3} + \frac{y}{9} = 1$

$\Rightarrow 3x + y = 9$

61. Let $\overline{AB}: y = \sqrt{3}x + 9$

$\overline{BC}: x + y = 10$ and

$\overline{CA}: y = 0$

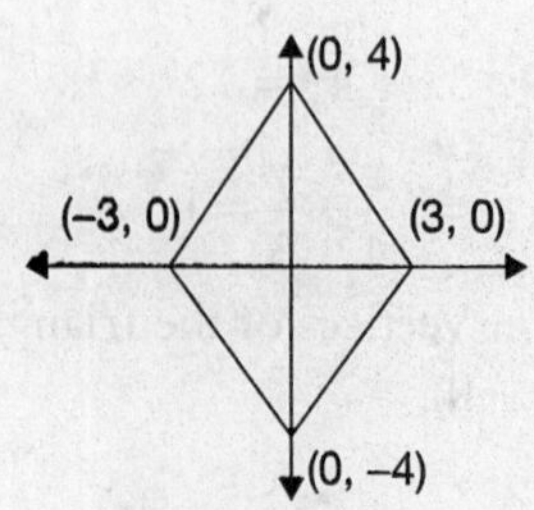

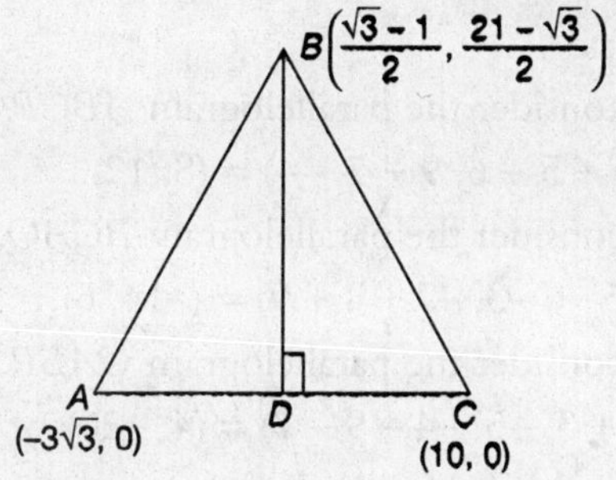

From BC and CA, $C(10, 0)$.

From AB and CA, $A\left(-3\sqrt{3}, 0\right)$

Form AB and BC, $10 - x = \sqrt{3}x + 9$

$\Rightarrow 1 = x\left(1+\sqrt{3}\right)$

$$x = \frac{1}{\left(1+\sqrt{3}\right)}$$

$$x = \frac{\sqrt{3}-1}{2}$$

$$\therefore y = 10 - \left(\frac{\sqrt{3}-1}{2}\right)$$

$$= \frac{20-\sqrt{3}+1}{2}$$

$$= \frac{21-\sqrt{3}}{2}$$

$$B\left(\frac{\sqrt{3}-1}{2}, \frac{21-\sqrt{3}}{2}\right)$$

$\therefore$ Area of the triangle

$$= \frac{1}{2}AC \times BD$$

$$= \frac{1}{2}\left(10+3\sqrt{3}\right) \times \left(\frac{21-\sqrt{3}}{2}\right)$$

$$= \frac{\left(10+3\sqrt{3}\right)\left(21-\sqrt{3}\right)}{4}$$

$$= \frac{210-10\sqrt{3}+63\sqrt{3}-9}{4} = \frac{201+53\sqrt{3}}{4}.$$

JEE Special Wing

Multiple-Answer Type Questions

1. Let (x, y) be the point equidistant from (3, –8) and (–7, 4)?

$\Rightarrow \sqrt{(x-3)^2+(y+8)^2}=\sqrt{(x+7)^2+(y-4)^2}$

$\Rightarrow (x-3)^2+(y+8)^2=(x+7)^2+(y-4)^2$

$\Rightarrow x^2-6x+9+y^2+16y+64$

$=x^2+14x+49+y^2-8y+16$

$\Rightarrow 20x-24y=8$

$\Rightarrow 5x-6y=2$

All the given points (–2, –2), (4, 3), (–8, –7), and (10, 8) satisfy the above equation.

Hence, choice (a, b, c, d) are correct.

Note: The line $5x-6y=2$ is the right bisector of the line joining (3, –8) and (–7, 4).

2. Given that the line $ax+by+c=0$ is perpendicular to both the lines $4x-ky+17=0$ and $kx-9y+13=0$.

Hence, the lines $4x-ky+17=0$ and $kx-9y+13=0$ are parallel.

The slope of $4x-ky+17=0$ is $\frac{-4}{k}$.

The slope of $kx-9y+13=0$ is $\frac{k}{9}$.

We know that the slopes of parallel lines are equal.

$\Rightarrow \frac{4}{k}=\frac{k}{9}$

$\Rightarrow k^2=36.$

$\Rightarrow k=\pm 6.$

Hence, choice (a and d) are correct.

3.

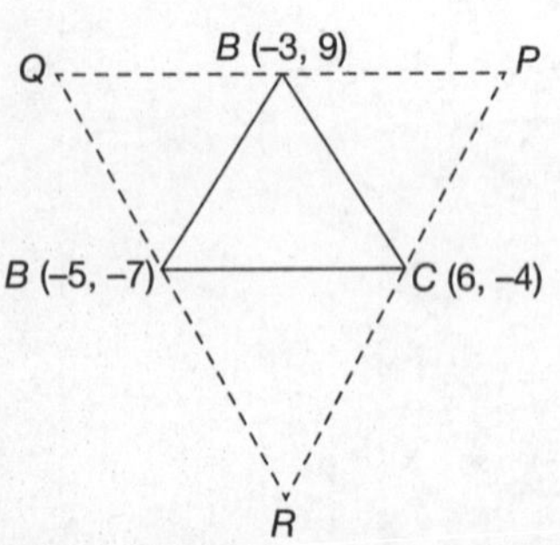

Let the three vertices of parallelogram are $A(-3, 9)$, $B(-5, -7)$ and $C(6, -4)$.

As shown in the figure, the fourth vertex of the parallelogram can be P, Q, or R.

If $D(x_1, y_1), E(x_2, y_2), F(x_3, y_3)$ are three vertices of a parallelogram $DEFGH$, then the fourth vertex $G=(x_1-x_2+x_3, y_1-y_2+y_3)$.

Let us consider the parallelogram $ABCP$.

$P = (-3+5+6, 9+7-4) = (8, 12)$.

Let us consider the parallelogram $BCAQ$.

$Q = (-5-6-3, -7+4+9) = (-14, 6)$.

Let us consider the parallelogram $CABR$.

$R = (6+3-5, -4-9-7) = (4, -20)$.

Hence, choice (a, c, d) are correct.

4.

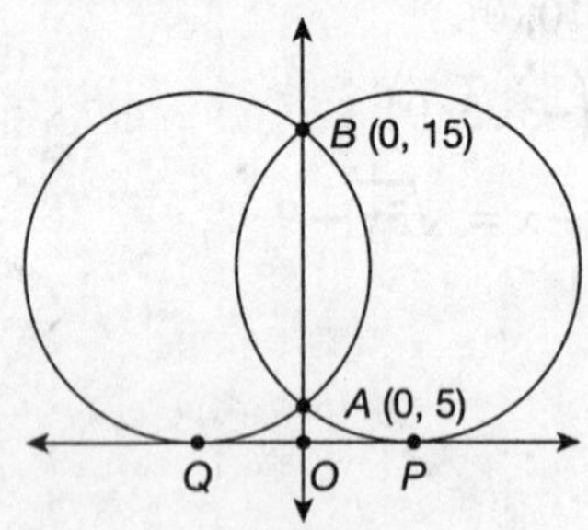

A circle intersects the y-axis at (0, 5) and (0, 15).

Let $A = (0, 5)$ and $B = (0, 15)$.

$\Rightarrow OA = 5$ and $OB = 15$.

The circle touches the x-axis at a point. As shown in the figure, it may touch the positive x-axis or the negative x-axis. Let these points be P and Q.

OP is a tangent and OAB is a secant.

We have $(\text{OP})^2=\text{OA}\times\text{OB}$.

$\Rightarrow (\text{OP})^2=5\times 15$

$\Rightarrow (\text{OP})^2=75.$

$\Rightarrow OP=\pm 5\sqrt{3}.$

$\Rightarrow OP=\pm\sqrt{75}.$

Hence, the circle may touch the x axis at $(5\sqrt{3}, 0)$ or $(-5\sqrt{3}, 0)$.

Hence, choice (a and d) are correct.

5. The point of trisection of line segment joining two points is a point which divides the line segment in the ratio 1 : 2 or 2 : 1.

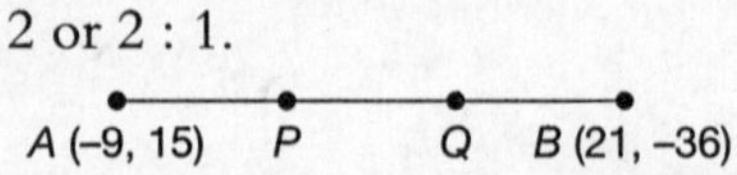

Let the points of trisection of the line segment joining $A(-9, 15)$ and $B(21, -36)$ be P and Q, where P divides AB in the ratio 1 : 2 and Q divides AB in the ratio 2 : 1.

So, $P=\left(\frac{1\times 21+2\times(-9)}{1+2}, \frac{1\times(-36)+2\times 15}{1+2}\right)$

$=\left(\frac{3}{3}, \frac{-6}{3}\right)=(1, -2).$

$$\text{So, } Q = \left(\frac{2\times21+1\times(-9)}{2+1}, \frac{2\times(-36)+1\times15}{2+1}\right)$$

$$= \left(\frac{33}{3}, \frac{-57}{3}\right) = (11, -19).$$

Hence, choice (a and b) are correct.

Match The Column

Common Solutions for questions 6 to 9:

Given that a circle is drawn with P as centre and AB as diameter.

$A = (-2, 0)$ and $B = (8, 0)$.

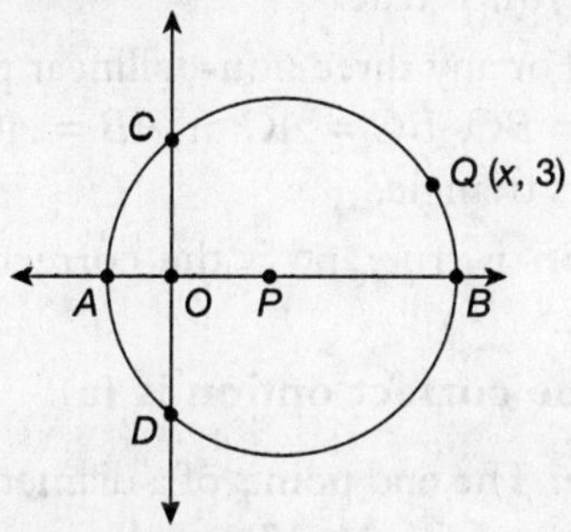

$\Rightarrow OA = 2$ and $OB = 8$.

$$\Rightarrow P = \left(\frac{-2+8}{2}, \frac{0+0}{2}\right) = (3, 0).$$

$Q\ (x, 3)$ is a point on the circle, and it lies in the first quadrant.

We have $OA \times OB = OC \times OD$.

$\Rightarrow 2\times8 = (OC)^2$ (Since $OC = OD$)

$\Rightarrow (OC)^2 = 16$

$\Rightarrow OC = \pm4$.

Hence, $C = (0, 4)$ and $D = (0, -4)$.

6. We have $C = (0, 4)$ and $D = (0, -4)$.

$CD = 4 - (-4) = 8$.

Hence, the correct option is (e).

7. We have $B = (8, 0)$ and $C = (0, 4)$.

The distance between two points

$= \sqrt{(x_2-x_1)^2+(y_2-y_1)^2}$

$BC = \sqrt{(0-8)^2+(4-0)^2}$

$= \sqrt{64+16}$

$= \sqrt{80}$.

Hence, the correct option is (b).

8. We have $Q(x, 3)$, $B = (8, 0)$ and $P(3, 0)$.

$PQ = PB$ (Since radii of a circle are equal)

$\sqrt{(3-x)^2+(0-3)^2} = 8 - 3$

$9 + x^2 - 6x + 9 = 25$

$x^2 - 6x - 7 = 0$

$(x-7)(x+1) = 0$

$x = 7$ or $x = -1$

As $Q(x, 3)$ lies in the first quadrant, $x = 7$.

Hence, $Q = (7, 3)$.

We have $Q = (7, 3)$ and $D = (0, -4)$.

$QD = \sqrt{(0-7)^2+(-4-3)^2}$

$= \sqrt{98}$.

Hence, the correct option is (f).

9. We have $P(3, 0)$, $C = (0, 4)$ and $D = (0, -4)$.

$PC = PD = 5$ (Since radii of a circle are equal)

$CD = 4 - (-4) = 8$.

Perimeter of $\Delta\ PCD = PC + PD + CD$

$= 5 + 5 + 8 = 18$.

Hence, the correct option is (c).

Comprehension-Based Questions

Common Solutions for questions 10 to 14:

The school, restaurant, theatre, and park are represented by the coordinate points $M(8, 7)$, $B(-1, 6)$, $F(-2, -3)$, and $R(7, -2)$ respectively.

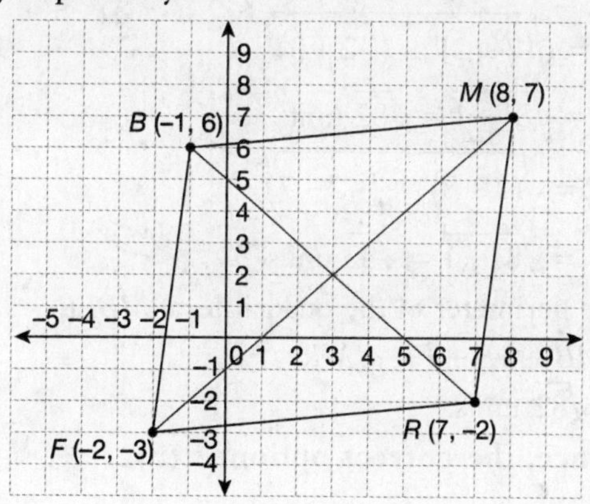

10. The distance between two points

$= \sqrt{(x_2-x_1)^2+(y_2-y_1)^2}$

$MF = \sqrt{(-2-8)^2+(-3-7)^2}$

$= \sqrt{2(100)} = 10\sqrt{2}$ units.

$BR = \sqrt{(7+1)^2+(-2-6)^2}$

$= \sqrt{2(64)} = 8\sqrt{2}$ units.

Hence, the distance between the school and theatre is $2\sqrt{2}$ units more than that between the hotel and park.

Hence, the correct option is (a).

11. The slope of a line $= \frac{y_2 - y_1}{x_2 - x_1}$.
The slope of the line joining the school, $M(8, 7)$ and theatre $F(-2, -3) = \frac{-3-7}{-2-8} = \frac{-10}{-10} = 1$.
The slope of the line joining the school, $B(-1, 6)$ and theatre $R(7, -2) = \frac{-2-6}{7+1} = \frac{-8}{8} = -1$.
The product of the slopes $= 1 \times (-1) = -1$.
So, the lines are perpendicular to each other.
Hence, the measure of the angle between the lines joining the school and theatre, and the hotel and park is 90°.
Hence, the correct option is (b).

12. The distance between two points
$= \sqrt{(x_2 - x_1)^2 + (y_2 - y_1)^2}$.
$M(8, 7)$, $B(-1, 6)$, $F(-2, -3)$, and $R(7, -2)$
$MB = \sqrt{(-1-8)^2 + (6-7)^2}$
$= \sqrt{81+1} = \sqrt{82}$ units.
$FB = \sqrt{(-2+1)^2 + (-3-6)^2}$
$= \sqrt{81+1} = \sqrt{82}$ units.
$FR = \sqrt{(7+2)^2 + (-2+3)^2}$
$= \sqrt{81+1} = \sqrt{82}$ units.
$MR = \sqrt{(7-8)^2 + (-2-7)^2}$
$= \sqrt{81+1} = \sqrt{82}$ units.
The perimeter of the quadrilateral $MBFR$
$= MB + FB + FR + MR$
$= 4\sqrt{82}$ units.
Hence, the correct option is (b).

13. We have $MB = FB = FR = MR$.
Also, MF and FB are unequal and perpendicular to each other.
In the quadrilateral $MBFR$, the sides are equal, the diagonals are unequal and perpendicular to each other.
Hence, $MBFR$ is a rhombus but not the square.
Hence, the correct option is (c).

14. The quadrilateral $MBFR$ is a rhombus.
The area of a rhombus is half of the product of the diagonals.
Hence, the area of $MBFR = \frac{MF \times BR}{2}$.
$= \frac{10\sqrt{2} \times 8\sqrt{2}}{2} = 80$ sq units.
Hence, the correct option is (d).

Assertion and Reason Type Questions

15. **Assertion:** Given that $A(2, 3)$, $B(2, 7)$ and $C(6, 7)$.
$AB = 7 - 3 = 4$ units.
(Since the x-coordinates are same)
$BC = 6 - 2 = 4$ units.
(Since the y-coordinates are same)
Hence, ABC is an isosceles triangle.
So, **Assertion** is true.
Reason: For any three non-collinear points A, B, and C, if $AB = BC$, $BC = AC$ or $AB = AC$, then ABC is an isosceles triangle.
So, **Reason** is true and is the correct explanation to **Assertion**.
Hence, the correct option is (a).

16. **Assertion:** The end points of a diameter of a circle are $P(12, -31)$ and $Q(-24, 13)$.
The centre of the circle is the midpoint of a diameter.
The midpoint of the line segment joining (x_1, y_1) and (x_2, y_2) is $\left(\frac{x_1 + x_2}{2}, \frac{y_1 + y_2}{2}\right)$.
The centre of the circle $= \left(\frac{12-24}{2}, \frac{-31+13}{2}\right) = (-6, -9)$.
So, **Assertion** is false.
Reason: The midpoint of a diameter of a circle is the centre of the circle. The midpoint of the line segment joining (x_1, y_1), and (x_2, y_2) is $\left(\frac{x_1 + x_2}{2}, \frac{y_1 + y_2}{2}\right)$.
So, **Reason** is true.
Hence, the correct option is (d).

17. **Assertion:** The equation of a straight line passing through the point (x_1, y_1) and parallel to line $ax + by + c = 0$ is to $a(x - x_1) + b(y - y_1) = 0$.
So, the equation of a straight line passing through the point (2, 3) and parallel to $3x + 2y + 12 = 0$ is $3(x - 2) + 2(y - 3) = 0$.
$\Rightarrow 3x - 6 + 2y - 6 = 0$
$\Rightarrow 3x + 2y = 12$
So, **Assertion** is true.
Reason: The equation of a straight line passing through the point (x_1, y_1) and perpendicular to line $ax + by + c = 0$ is to $b(x - x_1) - a(y - y_1) = 0$.

So, **Reason** is true and not the correct explanation to **Assertion**.

Hence, the correct option is (b).

18. **Assertion:** Given that $5x + 4y = 40$.

$$\Rightarrow \frac{5x}{40} + \frac{4y}{40} = \frac{40}{40}$$

$$\Rightarrow \frac{x}{8} + \frac{y}{10} = 1$$

The area of the triangle formed by $\frac{x}{a} + \frac{y}{b} = 1$ with the coordinate axes is $\frac{|ab|}{2}$ sq units.

The area of the triangle formed by $\frac{x}{8} + \frac{y}{10} = 1$ with the coordinate axes

$$= \frac{|8 \times 10|}{2} = 40 \text{ sq units.}$$

So, **Assertion** is true.

Reason: The area of the triangle formed by $\frac{x}{a} + \frac{y}{b} = 1$ with the coordinate axes is $\frac{|ab|}{2}$ sq units.

So, **Reason** is true and is the correct explanation to **Assertion**.

Hence, the correct option is (a).

Unit IV

Trigonometry

In this Unit

CHAPTER

10

Trigonometry

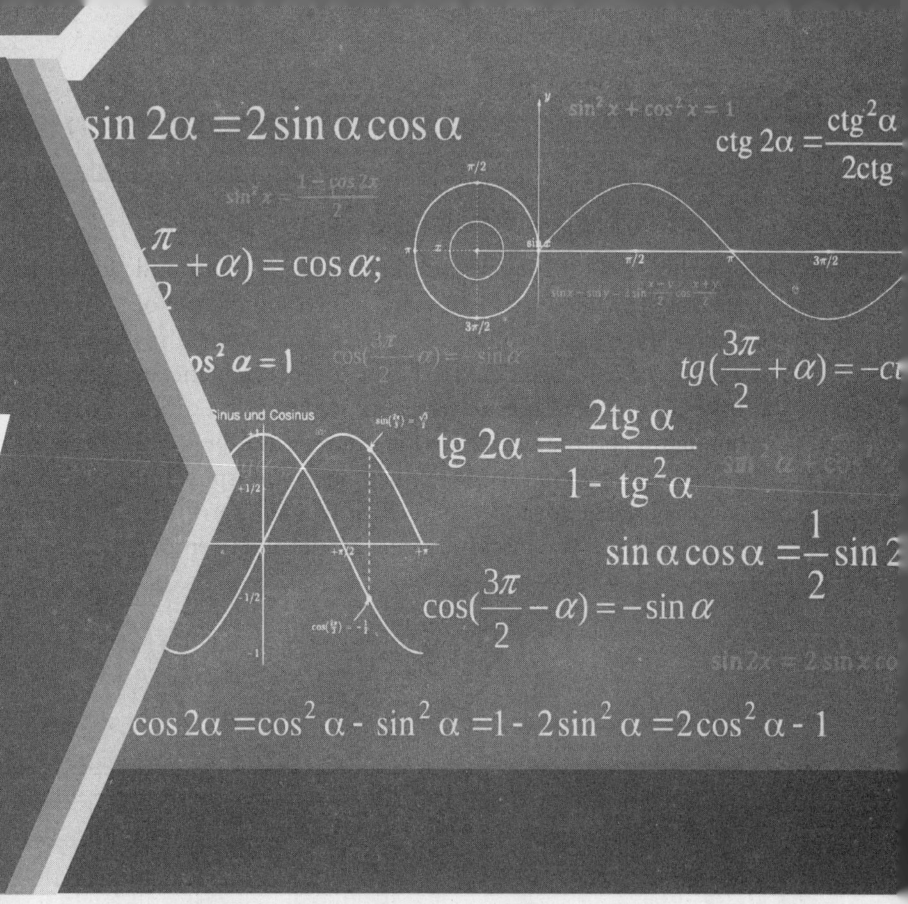

Remember

Before beginning this chapter, you should be able to:

- Basic trigonometric identities
- Know systems of measurement of angle

Key Ideas

After completing this chapter, you should be able to:

- Convert angles using three systems of measurements of angles
- Study trigonometric identities and solve numerical problems using them
- Understand trigonometric ratios of specific and compound angles
- Learn signs of trigonometric ratios in different quadrants and how to use trigonometric table
- Calculate heights of poles, longer distances, etc., using trigonometric identities

Scientific Crypt

A Tribute to Hipparchos (190 BC to 120 BC)

Hipparchos was a Greek astrologer, astronomer and mathematician. He made extensive and systematic use of the knowledge and techniques of the Babylonians in his own studies. He is considered to be the first mathematician to have used trigonometric tables to compute the orbits of the moon and the sun. For a long time, it was believed that Ptolemy (2 century AD) had invented spherical trigonometry (an advanced branch of trigonometry). In the last century, it was discovered that Menelaus (1 century AD) had also used the results of spherical trigonometry. Today, there are many reasons to believe that Hipparchos and, possibly even earlier mathematicians, were aware of this branch of mathematics. While earlier mathematicians may have used isolated results, Hipparchos consolidated known results, discovered many new results and applied them to generate new knowledge. Therefore, he is considered to be the founder of **trigonometry**.

FUN TIME

CROSSWORD

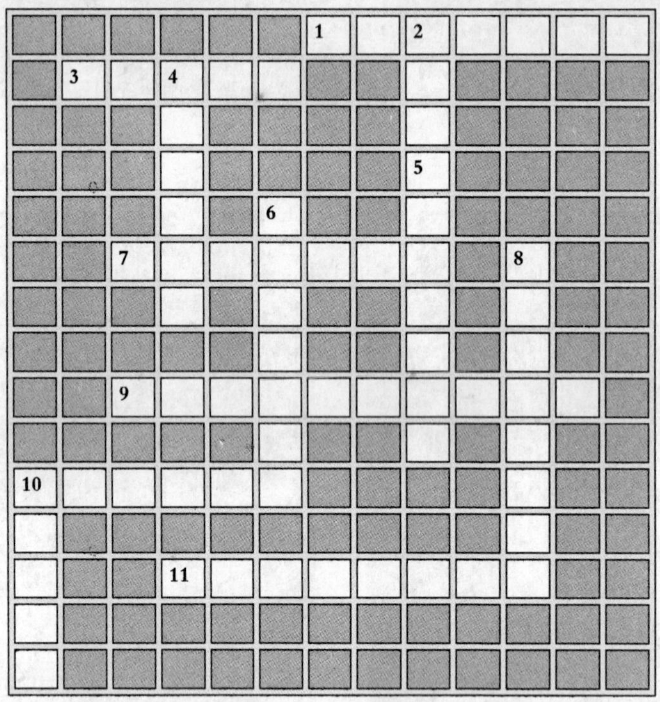

Across

1. In a circular system, the units of the measure of an angle.
3. The measure formed between two rays having a common initial point.
5. The measure of an angle is a _______ number.
7. In the sexagesimal system, the units of the measure of an angle.
9. tan x and cot x are _______ to each other, x is neither 0 nor 90 degrees.
10. The centesimal system is also called as _______ system.
11. The secant of an angle in the fourth quadrant.

Down

2. The angle of elevation is always equal to the angle of
4. In the centesimal system, the units of the measure of an angle.
6. The sexagesimal system is also called as _______ system.
8. The cosine of an angle in the third quadrant.
10. The quadrant in which all the trigonometric ratios are positive.

INTRODUCTION

The word trigonometry is originated from the Greek word 'tri' means three, 'gonia' means angle and 'metron' means measure. Hence, the word trigonometry means three angle measure, i.e., it is the study of geometrical figures which have three angles, i.e., triangles.

The great Greek mathematician Hipparchus of 140 BCE gave relation between the angles and sides of a triangle. Further trigonometry is developed by Indian (Hindu) mathematicians. This was migrated to Europe via Arabs.

Trigonometry plays an important role in the study of Astronomy, Surveying, Navigation, and Engineering. Nowadays it is used to predict stock market trends.

Angle

A measure formed between two rays having a common initial point is called an angle. The two rays are called the arms or sides of the angle and the common initial point is called the vertex of the angle.

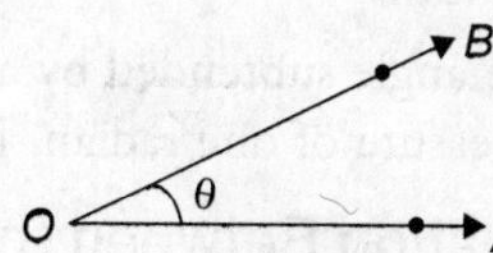

Figure 10.1

In the Fig. 10.1, OA is said to be the initial side and the other ray OB is said to be the terminal side of the angle.

The angle is taken positive when measured in anti-clockwise direction and is taken negative when measured in clockwise direction (see Fig. 10.2).

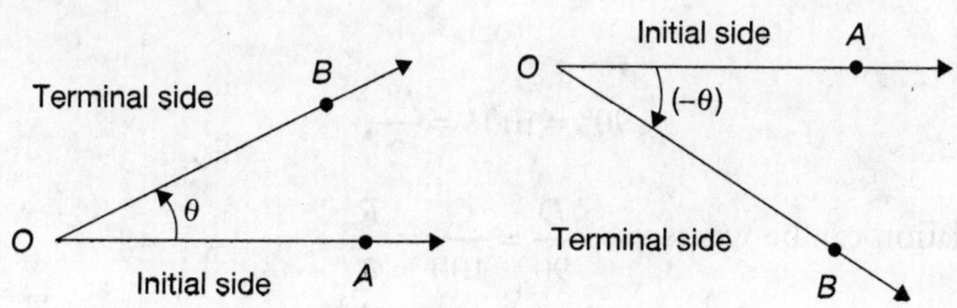

Figure 10.2

Systems of Measurement of Angle

We have the following systems of the measurement of angle.

Sexagesimal System

In this system, the angle is measured in degrees(°).

Degree

When the initial ray is rotated through $\left(\frac{1}{360}\right)$ of one revolution, we say that an angle of one degree (1°) is formed at the initial point. A degree is divided into 60 equal parts and each part is called one minute (1′). Further, a minute is divided into 60 equal parts called seconds (″).

So, 1 right angle = 90°

1° = 60′ (minutes)

1′ = 60″ (seconds).

> **Info Bytes!**
> This system is also called the British system.

Centesimal System

In this system, the angle is measured in grades.

Grade

When the initial ray is rotated through $\left(\frac{1}{400}\right)$ of one revolution, an angle of one grade is said to be formed at the initial point. It is written as 1^g.

Further, one grade is divided into 100 equal parts called minutes and one minute is further divided into 100 equal parts called seconds.

So, 1 right angle $= 100^g$

$1^g = 100'$ (minutes)

$1' = 100''$ (seconds).

Konnect

This system is also called the French system.

Circular System

In this system, the angle is measured in radians.

Radian

The angle subtended by an arc of length equal to the radius of a circle at its centre is said to have a measure of one radian. It is written as 1^c (see Fig. 10.3).

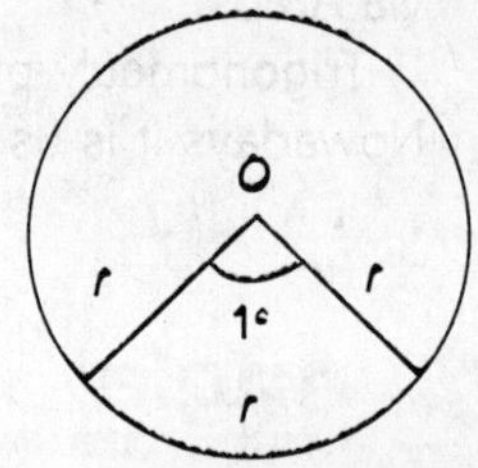

Figure 10.3

Relation Between the Units of the Three Systems

When a rotating ray completes one revolution, the measure of angle formed about the vertex is $360°$ or 400^g or $2\pi^c$.

So,

$$360° = 400^g = 2\pi^c$$

(or)

$$90° = 100^g = \frac{\pi^c}{2}.$$

Info Bytes!

This measure is also known as radian measure.

For convenience, the above relation can be written as, $\frac{D}{90} = \frac{G}{100} = \frac{R}{\frac{\pi}{2}}$.

Where D denotes degrees, G grades, and R radians.

Remember

1. $1° = \frac{\pi}{180}$ radians $= 0.0175$ radians (approximately)

Konnect

1. The measure of an angle is a real number.
2. If no unit of measurement is indicated for any angle, it is considered as radian measure.

EXAMPLE 10.1 Which of the following is equivalent to $72° - 30^g$?

(a) $\frac{\pi^\circ}{4}$ (b) $\frac{\pi^\circ}{3}$ (c) $\frac{\pi^\circ}{2}$ (d) None of these

SOLUTION

We have, $90° = 100^g$

$\Rightarrow 72° = \frac{100^g}{90°} \times 72° = 80^g$

Now, $72° - 30^g = 80^g - 30^g = 50^g$

$= \frac{200^g}{4} = \frac{\pi^\circ}{4}$

Therefore, option (a) is correct.

EXAMPLE 10.2 Convert 150^g into sexagesimal measure.

SOLUTION

Given, $G = 150^g$

We have, $\frac{D}{90} = \frac{G}{100}$

So, $\frac{D}{90} = \frac{150}{100}$ or, $D = \frac{3}{2} \times 90 = 135.$

Hence, sexagesimal measure of 150^g is 135°.

Alternate Method

$$1^g = \frac{9^\circ}{10}$$

$$\Rightarrow 150^\circ = 150 \times \frac{9}{10}$$

$$= 135^\circ$$

EXAMPLE 10.3 What is the sexagesimal measure of angle measuring $\frac{\pi^c}{3}$.

SOLUTION

Given, $R = \frac{\pi^c}{3}$

We have, $\frac{D}{90} = \frac{R}{\frac{\pi}{2}}$

So, $\frac{D}{90} = \frac{\frac{\pi}{3}}{\frac{\pi}{2}}$

$$\Rightarrow D = \frac{2}{3} \times 90 = 60^\circ.$$

Hence, the sexagesimal measure of $\frac{\pi^c}{3}$ is 60°.

Alternate Method

$$\pi^\circ = 180^\circ$$

$$\frac{\pi^\circ}{3} = \frac{180^\circ}{3} = 60^\circ$$

Trigonometric Ratios

Let AOB be a right triangle with $\angle AOB$ as 90°. Let $\angle OAB$ be θ. Notice that $0^\circ < \theta < 90^\circ$, i.e., θ is an acute angle (see Fig. 10.4).

We can define six possible ratios among the three sides of the triangle AOB, known as trigonometric ratios. They are defined as follows.

1. Sine of the angle θ (or) simply $\sin\theta$:

$$\sin\theta = \frac{\text{Side opposite to angle } \theta}{\text{Hypotenuse}} = \frac{OB}{AB}.$$

2. Cosine of the angle θ or simply $\cos\theta$:

$$\cos\theta = \frac{\text{Side adjacent to angle } \theta}{\text{Hypotenuse}} = \frac{OA}{AB}.$$

3. Tangent of the angle θ or simply $\tan\theta$:

$$\tan\theta = \frac{\text{Side opposite to } \theta}{\text{Side adjacent to } \theta} = \frac{OB}{OA}.$$

4. Cotangent of the angle θ or simply $\cot\theta$:

$$\cot\theta = \frac{\text{Side adjacent to } \theta}{\text{Side opposite to } \theta} = \frac{OA}{OB}.$$

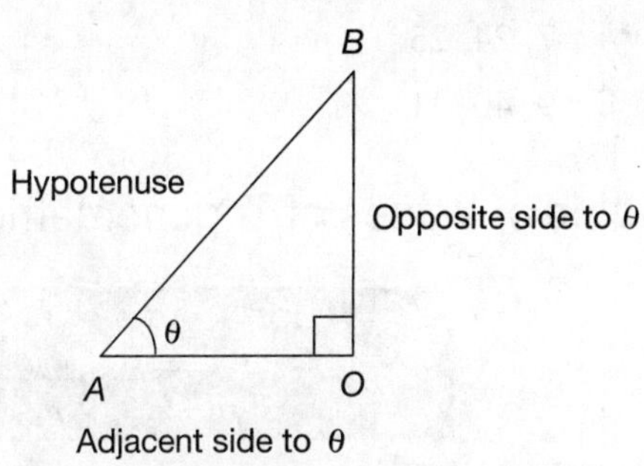

Figure 10.4

5. Cosecant of the angle θ or simply cosec θ:

$$\operatorname{cosec}\theta = \frac{\text{Hypotenuse}}{\text{Side opposite to }\theta} = \frac{AB}{OB}.$$

6. Secant of the angle θ or simply sec θ:

$$\sec\theta = \frac{\text{Hypotenuse}}{\text{Side adjacent to }\theta} = \frac{AB}{OA}.$$

Observe that,

1. $\operatorname{cosec}\theta = \frac{1}{\sin\theta}$, $\sec\theta = \frac{1}{\cos\theta}$ and $\cot\theta = \frac{1}{\tan\theta}$.
2. $\tan\theta = \frac{\sin\theta}{\cos\theta}$ and $\cot\theta = \frac{1}{\tan\theta} = \frac{\cos\theta}{\sin\theta}$.

Info Bytes!

Pythagorean Triplets and Trigonometry are related through the fundamental concept of the Pythagorean Theorem, which is a cornerstone in Trigonometry.

EXAMPLE 10.4 If $\sin\theta = \frac{3}{5}$, then find the values of $\tan\theta$ and $\sec\theta$.

SOLUTION

Given, $\sin\theta = \frac{3}{5}$.

Let AOB be the right triangle such that, $\angle OAB = \theta$.

Assume that $OB = 3$ and $AB = 5$ (see Fig. 10.5).

Then, $OA = \sqrt{AB^2 - OB^2} = \sqrt{25-9} = 4$.

So, $\tan\theta = \frac{\text{Side opposite to }\theta}{\text{Side adjacent to }\theta} = \frac{OB}{OA} = \frac{3}{4}$ and

$\sec\theta = \frac{\text{Hypotenuse}}{\text{Side adjacent to }\theta} = \frac{AB}{OA} = \frac{5}{4}$.

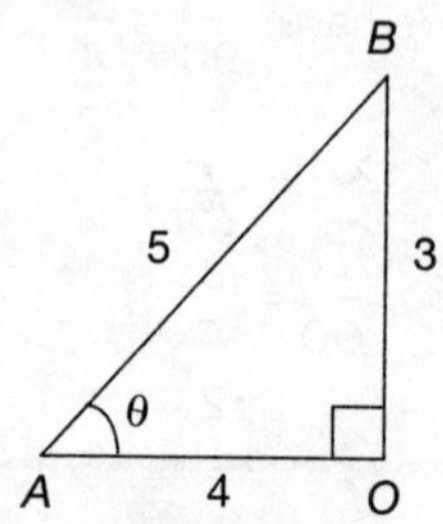

Figure 10.5

Some Pythagorean Triplets

1. 3, 4, 5
2. 5, 12, 13
3. 8, 15, 17
4. 7, 24, 25
5. 9, 40, 41

Trigonometric Identities

1. $\sin^2\theta + \cos^2\theta = 1$
2. $\sec^2\theta - \tan^2\theta = 1$
3. $\operatorname{cosec}^2\theta - \cot^2\theta = 1$

Table of Values of Trigonometric Ratios for Specific Angles

Trigonometric Ratios \ Angles	0°	30°	45°	60°	90°
$\sin\theta$	0	$\frac{1}{2}$	$\frac{1}{\sqrt{2}}$	$\frac{\sqrt{3}}{2}$	1
$\cos\theta$	1	$\frac{\sqrt{3}}{2}$	$\frac{1}{\sqrt{2}}$	$\frac{1}{2}$	0

$\tan\theta$	0	$\frac{1}{\sqrt{3}}$	1	$\sqrt{3}$	∞
$\text{cosec}\,\theta$	∞	2	$\sqrt{2}$	$\frac{2}{\sqrt{3}}$	1
$\sec\theta$	1	$\frac{2}{\sqrt{3}}$	$\sqrt{2}$	2	∞
$\cot\theta$	∞	$\sqrt{3}$	1	$\frac{1}{\sqrt{3}}$	0

From the above table, we observe that:

1. $\sin\theta = \cos\theta$, $\tan\theta = \cot\theta$ and $\sec\theta = \text{cosec}\,\theta$, if $\theta = 45°$.
2. $\sin\theta$ and $\tan\theta$ are increasing functions, when $0° \le \theta \le 90°$.
3. $\cos\theta$ is a decreasing function, when $0° \le \theta \le 90°$.

EXAMPLE 10.5 Find the value of tan 420° + tan 480°.

SOLUTION

tan 420° + tan 480°= tan (360° + 60°) + tan (450° + 30°)

= tan 60° – cot 30°

$= \sqrt{3} - \sqrt{3} = 0$

EXAMPLE 10.6
(a) 3. Solve for θ: $4\sin^2 3\theta - 3 = 0$, where $0° < 3\theta < 90°$
(b) 6. If $\sec(3\theta + 30°) = \text{cosec}\,(5\theta + 20°)$ and $5\theta < 70°$, then $\tan 6\theta =$ ______.

SOLUTION

(a) Given $0° < 3\theta < 90°$ and $4\sin^2 3\theta - 3 = 0$.

$\Rightarrow 4\sin^2 3\theta = 3$

$\Rightarrow \sin^2 3\theta = \frac{3}{4}$

$\Rightarrow \sin 3\theta = \frac{\sqrt{3}}{2} = \sin 60°$

$\Rightarrow 3\theta = 60°$

$\Rightarrow \theta = 5°$

(b) Given $5\theta < 70°$

$\sec(3\theta + 30°) = \text{cosec}\,(5\theta + 20°)$

$\Rightarrow 3\theta + 30° + 5\theta + 20° = 90°$

$\Rightarrow 8\theta = 40°$

$\Rightarrow \theta = 5°$

$\therefore \tan 6\theta = \tan 30° = \frac{1}{\sqrt{3}}$

EXAMPLE 10.7 Find the values of $\frac{\tan 60° - \tan 30°}{1 + \tan 60° \tan 30°}$ and tan30°. What do you observe?

SOLUTION

$$\frac{\tan 60° - \tan 30°}{1 + \tan 60° \tan 30°} = \frac{\sqrt{3} - \frac{1}{\sqrt{3}}}{1 + \sqrt{3}.\frac{1}{\sqrt{3}}} = \frac{\frac{(3-1)}{\sqrt{3}}}{2} = \frac{1}{\sqrt{3}} \text{ and } \tan 30° = \frac{1}{\sqrt{3}}.$$

Hence, $\frac{\tan 60° - \tan 30°}{1 + \tan 60° \tan 30°} = \tan 30°$.

Trigonometric Ratios of Compound Angles

1. $\sin(A+B) = \sin A \cos B + \cos A \sin B$ and $\sin(A-B) = \sin A \cos B - \cos A \sin B$
2. $\cos(A+B) = \cos A \cos B - \sin A \sin B$ and $\cos(A-B) = \cos A \cos B + \sin A \sin B$
3. $\tan(A+B) = \dfrac{\tan A + \tan B}{1 - \tan A \tan B}$ and $\tan(A-B) = \dfrac{\tan A - \tan B}{1 + \tan A \tan B}$

Also, by taking $A = B$ in the above relations, we get,

1. $\sin 2A = 2\sin A\cos A$
2. $\cos 2A = \cos^2 A - \sin^2 A = 2\cos^2 A - 1 = 1 - 2\sin^2 A$
3. $\tan 2A = \dfrac{2\tan A}{1-\tan^2 A}$

EXAMPLE 10.8 Find the value of sin 75°.

SOLUTION

We have, $\sin 75° = \sin(45° + 30°) = \sin 45° \cos 30° + \cos 45° \sin 30° = \frac{1}{\sqrt{2}}\cdot\frac{\sqrt{3}}{2} + \frac{1}{\sqrt{2}}\cdot\frac{1}{2} = \frac{\sqrt{3}+1}{2\sqrt{2}}$.

$\therefore \sin 75° = \dfrac{\sqrt{3}+1}{2\sqrt{2}}$.

EXAMPLE 10.9 Find the value of tan 15°.

SOLUTION

We have, $\tan 15° = \tan(45° - 30°) = \dfrac{\tan 45° - \tan 30°}{1 + \tan 45° \tan 30°} = \dfrac{1-\frac{1}{\sqrt{3}}}{1+\frac{1}{\sqrt{3}}} = \dfrac{\sqrt{3}-1}{\sqrt{3}+1}$

$$= \frac{(\sqrt{3}-1)}{(\sqrt{3}+1)} \times \frac{(\sqrt{3}-1)}{(\sqrt{3}-1)}$$

$$= \frac{(\sqrt{3}-1)^2}{3-1} = \frac{3+1-2\sqrt{3}}{2} = \frac{4-2\sqrt{3}}{2} = 2-\sqrt{3}.$$

$\therefore \tan 15° = \dfrac{\sqrt{3}-1}{\sqrt{3}+1}$ or $2-\sqrt{3}$.

EXAMPLE 10.10 Eliminate θ from the equations $x = p \sin\theta$ and $y = q \cos\theta$.

SOLUTION

We know that trigonometric ratios are meaningful when they are associated with some θ, i.e., we cannot imagine any trigonometric ratio without θ. Eliminate θ means, eliminating the trigonometric ratio itself by suitable identities.

Given, $x = p \sin\theta$ and $y = q \cos\theta$

$\Rightarrow \dfrac{x}{p} = \sin\theta$ and $\dfrac{y}{q} = \cos\theta$

We know that, $\sin^2\theta + \cos^2\theta = 1$.

So, $\left(\frac{x}{p}\right)^2 + \left(\frac{y}{q}\right)^2 = 1$

Hence, the required equation is $\frac{x^2}{p^2} + \frac{y^2}{q^2} = 1$.

EXAMPLE 10.11 Find the relation obtained by eliminating θ from the equations $x = r\cos\theta + s\sin\theta$ and $y = r\sin\theta - s\cos\theta$.

SOLUTION

Given, $x = r\cos\theta + s\sin\theta$

$\Rightarrow x^2 = (r\cos\theta + s\sin\theta)^2$

$= r^2\cos^2\theta + 2rs\cos\theta\cdot\sin\theta + s^2\sin^2\theta.$

Also, $y = r\sin\theta - s\cos\theta$.

or $y^2 = r^2\sin^2\theta + s^2\cos^2\theta - 2rs\sin\theta\cdot\cos\theta$

or, $x^2 + y^2 = r^2(\cos^2\theta + \sin^2\theta) + s^2(\sin^2\theta + \cos^2\theta)$

or, $= r^2(1) + s^2(1)$ $[\because \sin^2\theta + \cos^2\theta = 1]$

$= r^2 + s^2.$

Hence, the required relation is $x^2 + y^2 = r^2 + s^2$.

EXAMPLE 10.12 Eliminate θ from the equations.

$x = \operatorname{cosec}\theta + \cot\theta$ $\quad y = \operatorname{cosec}\theta - \cot\theta$.

SOLUTION

Given, $x = \operatorname{cosec}\theta + \cot\theta$ and $y = \operatorname{cosec}\theta - \cot\theta$.

Multiplying these equations, we get

$xy = (\operatorname{cosec}\theta + \cot\theta)(\operatorname{cosec}\theta - \cot\theta)$

$= \operatorname{cosec}^2\theta - \cot^2\theta = 1.$

Hence, the required relation is $xy = 1$.

EXAMPLE 10.13 Eliminate θ from the equations $m = \tan\theta + \cot\theta$ and $n = \tan\theta - \cot\theta$.

SOLUTION

Given,

$m = \tan\theta + \cot\theta$ (1)

$n = \tan\theta - \cot\theta$ (2)

Adding Eqs. (1) and (2), we get,

$m + n = 2\tan\theta$

$\Rightarrow \tan\theta = \frac{m+n}{2}$

Subtracting Eq. (2) from Eq. (1), we get,

$m - n = 2\cot\theta$

$\Rightarrow \cot\theta = \frac{m-n}{2}$

$\therefore \tan\theta\cdot\cot\theta = \left(\frac{m+n}{2}\right)\cdot\left(\frac{m-n}{2}\right)$

$$\Rightarrow \tan\theta \cdot \frac{1}{\tan\theta} = \frac{m^2 - n^2}{4}$$

$$\Rightarrow 1 = \frac{m^2 - n^2}{4} \quad \text{or} \quad m^2 - n^2 = 4.$$

Hence, by eliminating 'θ', we obtain the relation $m^2 - n^2 = 4$.

EXAMPLE 10.14

If $\cos(A+B) = \frac{1}{2}$ and $\sec B = \sqrt{2}$, then find A and B.

SOLUTION

Given,

$$\cos(A+B) = \frac{1}{2}$$

$$\cos(A+B) = \cos 60°$$

$$A + B = 60° \qquad (1)$$

$$\sec B = \sqrt{2} = \sec 45°$$

$$B = 45° \qquad (2)$$

From Eqs. (1) and (2), we have

$\therefore A = 15°$ and $B = 45°$.

EXAMPLE 10.15

Find the length of the chord which subtends an angle of 120° at the centre 'O' and which is at a distance of 5 cm from the centre.

SOLUTION

Let the chord be AB and OD be the distance of chord from the centre of circle.

Given $\angle AOB = 120°$ and $OD = 5$ cm, clearly, $\Delta OAD \cong \Delta OBD$, by SSS axiom

$$\angle AOD = \angle BOD = \frac{1}{2}(\angle AOB) = 60° \text{ in } \Delta AOD$$

$$\tan 60° = \frac{AD}{OD}$$

$$\Rightarrow \sqrt{3} = \frac{AD}{5} \Rightarrow AD = 5\sqrt{3}.$$

$\therefore$ The length of the chord, $AB = 2AD = 10\sqrt{3}$ cm.

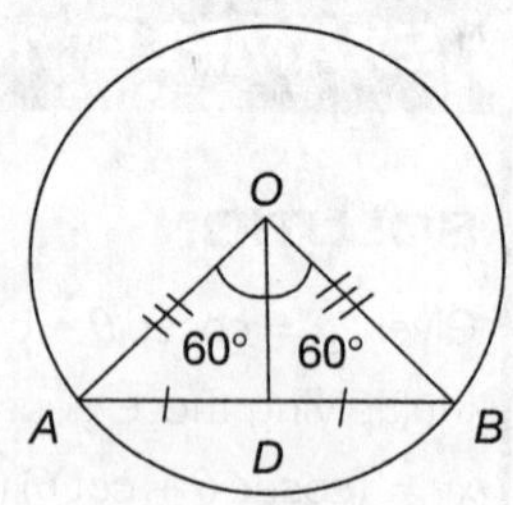

Figure 10.6

EXAMPLE 10.16

Evaluate: $\sqrt{\frac{1-\sin\theta}{1+\sin\theta}}$.

SOLUTION

Given, $\sqrt{\frac{1-\sin\theta}{1+\sin\theta}}$

Rationalize the denominator, i.e.,

$$\sqrt{\frac{1-\sin\theta}{1+\sin\theta} \cdot \frac{1-\sin\theta}{1-\sin\theta}}$$

$$= \sqrt{\frac{(1-\sin\theta)^2}{(1)^2 - \sin^2\theta}} = \sqrt{\frac{(1-\sin\theta)^2}{1-\sin^2\theta}} = \sqrt{\frac{(1-\sin\theta)^2}{\cos^2\theta}} \qquad (\because \sin^2\theta + \cos^2\theta = 1)$$

$$= \sqrt{\left(\frac{1-\sin\theta}{\cos\theta}\right)^2} = \frac{1-\sin\theta}{\cos\theta}$$

$$= \frac{1}{\cos\theta} - \frac{\sin\theta}{\cos\theta} = \sec\theta - \tan\theta \qquad \left(\because \sec\theta = \frac{1}{\cos\theta}, \tan\theta = \frac{\sin\theta}{\cos\theta}\right)$$

$$\therefore \sqrt{\frac{1-\sin\theta}{1+\sin\theta}} = \sec\theta - \tan\theta.$$

Standard Position of the Angle

The angle is said to be in its standard position if its initial side coincides with the positive X-axis (see Fig. 10.7).

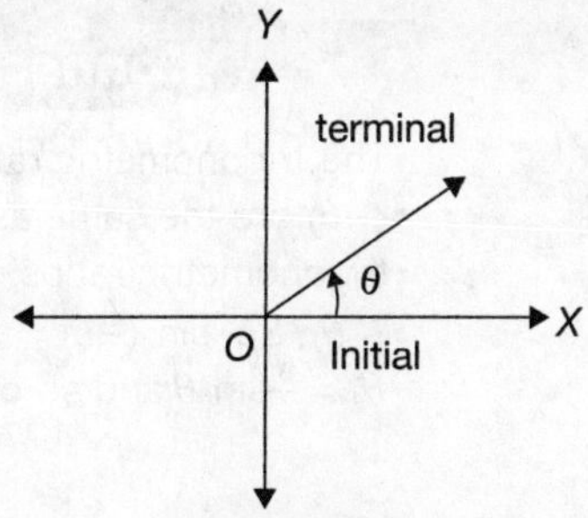

Figure 10.7

Konnect

1. The rotation of terminal side in anti-clockwise direction we consider the angle formed is positive and rotation in clockwise direction the angle formed is negative.
2. Depending upon the position of terminal side we decide the angle in different quadrants.

Co-terminal Angles

The angles that differ by either 360° or the integral multiples of 360° are called co-terminal angles (see Fig. 10.8).

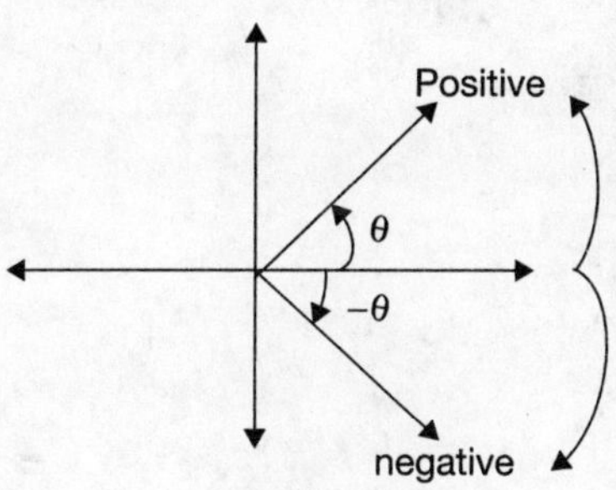

Figure 10.8

Example: 60°, 360° + 60° = 420°, 2 · 360° + 60° = 780° are co-terminal angles.

Konnect

1. If θ is an angle then its co-terminal angle is in the form of $(n \cdot 360° + \theta)$.
2. The terminal side of co-terminal angles in their standard position coincides (see Fig. 10.9).

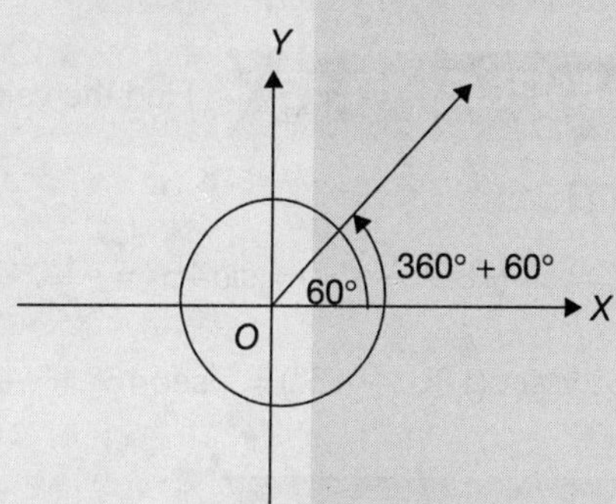

Figure 10.9

Signs of Trigonometric Ratios

1. If θ lies in the first quadrant, i.e., $0 < \theta < \dfrac{\pi}{2}$, then all the trigonometric ratios are taken positive.
2. If θ lies in the second quadrant, i.e., $\dfrac{\pi}{2} < \theta < \pi$, then only $\sin\theta$ and $\operatorname{cosec}\theta$ are taken positive and all the other trigonometric ratios are taken negative.
3. If θ lies in the third quadrant, i.e., $\pi < \theta < \dfrac{3\pi}{2}$, then only $\tan\theta$ and $\cot\theta$ are taken positive and all the other trigonometric ratios are taken negative.
4. If θ lies in the fourth quadrant, i.e., $\dfrac{3\pi}{2} < \theta < 2\pi$, then only $\cos\theta$ and $\sec\theta$ are taken positive and all the other trigonometric ratios are taken negative.

Trigonometric Ratios of (90° – θ)

$\sin(90° - \theta) = \cos\theta$ $\quad$ $\cos(90° - \theta) = \sin\theta$

$\tan(90° - \theta) = \cot\theta$ $\quad$ $\cot(90° - \theta) = \tan\theta$

$\operatorname{cosec}(90° - \theta) = \sec\theta$ $\quad$ $\sec(90° - \theta) = \operatorname{cosec}\theta$

Trigonometric Ratios of $(90° + \theta)$

$\sin(90° + \theta) = \cos\theta$ $\quad$ $\cos(90° + \theta) = -\sin\theta$
$\tan(90° + \theta) = -\cot\theta$ $\quad$ $\cot(90° + \theta) = -\tan\theta$
$\text{cosec}(90° + \theta) = \sec\theta$ $\quad$ $\sec(90° + \theta) = -\text{cosec}\,\theta$

Trigonometric Ratios of $(180° - \theta)$

$\sin(180° - \theta) = \sin\theta$ $\quad$ $\cos(180° - \theta) = -\cos\theta$
$\tan(180° - \theta) = -\tan\theta$ $\quad$ $\cot(180° - \theta) = -\cot\theta$
$\text{cosec}(180° - \theta) = \text{cosec}\,\theta$ $\quad$ $\sec(180° - \theta) = -\sec\theta$

Trigonometric Ratios of $(180° + \theta)$

$\sin(180° + \theta) = -\sin\theta$ $\quad$ $\cos(180° + \theta) = -\cos\theta$
$\tan(180° + \theta) = \tan\theta$ $\quad$ $\cot(180° + \theta) = \cot\theta$
$\text{cosec}(180° + \theta) = -\text{cosec}\,\theta$ $\quad$ $\sec(180° + \theta) = -\sec\theta$

Similarly, the trigonometric ratios of $270° \pm \theta$ and $360° \pm \theta$ can be written.

Konnect

The trigonometric ratios of $(-\theta)$ are the same as the trigonometric ratios of $(360° - \theta)$. So, $\sin(-\theta) = \sin(360° - \theta) = -\sin\theta$ and so on.

EXAMPLE 10.17 What is the value of tan 315°?

SOLUTION

$\tan 315° = \tan(360° - 45°) = -\tan 45° = -1$

$\therefore \tan 315° = -1.$

EXAMPLE 10.18 Find the value of $\sin^2 135° + \sec^2 135°$.

SOLUTION

$\sin 135° = \sin(180° - 45°) = \sin 45° = \dfrac{1}{\sqrt{2}}.$

$\sec 135° = \sec(180° - 45°) = -\sec 45° = -\sqrt{2}.$

$\therefore \sin^2 135° + \sec^2 135° = \left(\dfrac{1}{\sqrt{2}}\right)^2 + \left(-\sqrt{2}\right)^2 = \dfrac{1}{2} + 2 = \dfrac{5}{2}.$

EXAMPLE 10.19 If $\cos A = \dfrac{5}{13}$ and A is not in first quadrant, then find the value of $\dfrac{\sin A - \cos A}{\tan A + 1}$.

SOLUTION

Given that $\cos A = \dfrac{5}{13}$ and A is not in first quadrant

$\Rightarrow A$ is in fourth quadrant.

$\sin A = \dfrac{-12}{13}$ and $\tan A = \dfrac{-12}{5}$

Now, $\dfrac{\sin A - \cos A}{\tan A + 1} = \dfrac{\dfrac{-12}{13} - \dfrac{5}{13}}{\dfrac{-12}{5} + 1} = \dfrac{-17}{13} \times \dfrac{-5}{7} = \dfrac{85}{91}.$

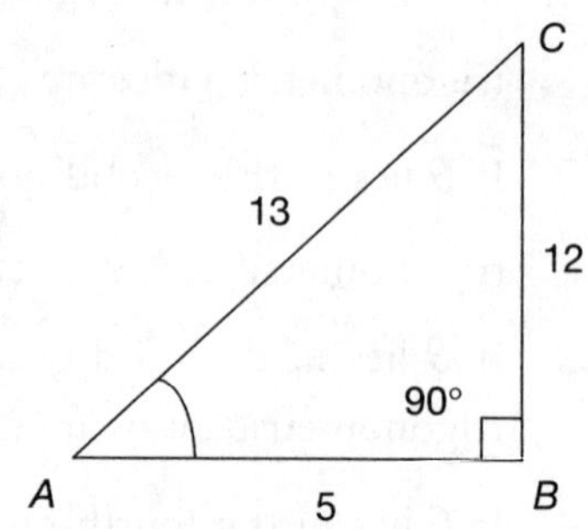

Figure 10.10

EXAMPLE 10.20 If $ABCD$ is a cyclic quadrilateral, then find the value of $\cos A \cos B - \cos C \cos D$.

SOLUTION

Given, $ABCD$ is a cyclic quadrilateral

$A + C = 180°$ and $B + D = 180°$

Now, $\cos A \cos B - \cos C \cos D$

$= \cos A \cos B - \cos(180° - A) \cos(180° - B) = \cos A \cos B - (-\cos A)(-\cos B)$

$= \cos A \cos B - \cos A \cos B = 0.$

EXAMPLE 10.21 If $\operatorname{cosec}\theta - \cot\theta = m - 1$, then the value of $\frac{1-\cos\theta}{1+\cos\theta} =$ ______.

SOLUTION

$$\operatorname{cosec}\theta - \cot\theta = m - 1$$

$$\frac{1}{\sin\theta} - \frac{\cos\theta}{\sin\theta} = m - 1$$

$$\frac{1-\cos\theta}{\sin\theta} = m - 1$$

$$\frac{(1-\cos\theta)^2}{\sin^2\theta} = (m-1)^2$$

$$\frac{(1-\cos\theta)(1-\cos\theta)}{1-\cos^2\theta} = (m-1)^2$$

$$\frac{(1-\cos\theta)(1-\cos\theta)}{(1-\cos\theta)(1+\cos\theta)} = (m-1)^2$$

$$\Rightarrow \frac{1-\cos\theta}{1+\cos\theta} = (m-1)^2$$

$$\frac{1-\cos\theta}{1+\cos\theta} = m^2 - 2m + 1.$$

EXAMPLE 10.22 If $\sin\theta$ and $\cos\theta$ are the roots of the equation $mx^2 + nx + 1 = 0$, then find the relation between m and n.

SOLUTION

The given equation is $mx^2 + nx + 1 = 0$

Here, $a = m$, $b = n$ and $c = 1$

$$\sin\theta + \cos\theta = \frac{-b}{a} = \frac{-n}{m}$$

$$\sin\theta x \cos\theta = \frac{c}{a} = \frac{1}{m}$$

Consider,

$$\sin\theta + \cos\theta = \frac{-n}{m}$$

$$\text{or } (\sin\theta + \cos\theta)^2 = \left(\frac{-n}{m}\right)^2$$

$$\text{or, } \sin^2\theta + \cos^2\theta + 2\sin\theta\cos\theta = \frac{n^2}{m^2}$$

$$\Rightarrow 1 + 2\sin\theta\cos\theta = \frac{n^2}{m^2} \qquad (\because \sin^2\theta + \cos^2\theta = 1)$$

$$1 + 2\left(\frac{1}{m}\right) = \frac{n^2}{m^2} \qquad \left(\because \sin\theta\cos\theta = \frac{1}{m}\right)$$

$$1 + \frac{2}{m} = \frac{n^2}{m^2}$$

$$\Rightarrow n^2 - m^2 = 2m.$$

EXAMPLE 10.23

In ΔPQR, $\angle PQR = 90°$, $\angle SRQ = \beta$ and $\angle PRQ = \alpha$. If $SQ = 3$ cm, $PS = 4$ cm and $QR = 5$ cm, then $\tan(\alpha - \beta) =$ _____.

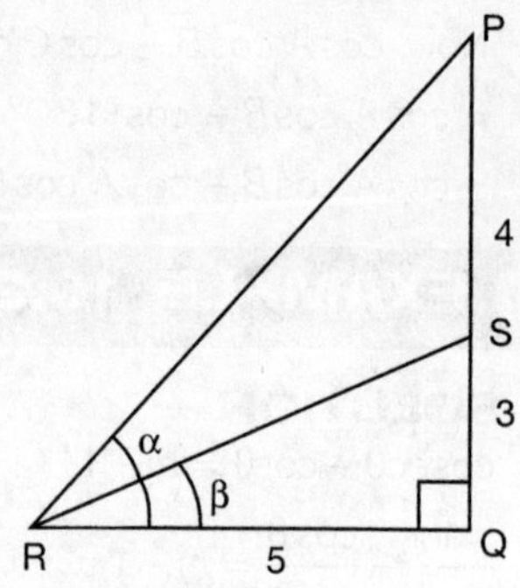

Figure 10.11

SOLUTION

$\tan\alpha = \frac{7}{5}$ and $\tan\beta = \frac{3}{5}$

$$\tan(\alpha-\beta) = \frac{\tan\alpha - \tan\beta}{1+\tan\alpha\tan\beta} = \frac{\left(\frac{7}{5}-\frac{3}{5}\right)}{1+\left(\frac{7}{5}\right)\left(\frac{3}{5}\right)} = \frac{(4/5)}{1+\left(\frac{21}{25}\right)} = \frac{(4/5)}{(46/25)} = \frac{2/1}{23/5} = \frac{10}{23}$$

EXAMPLE 10.24

Express the following as a single trigonometric ratio:
(a) $\sqrt{3}\cos\theta - \sin\theta$ (b) $\sin\theta - \cos\theta$.

SOLUTION

(a) Given, $\sqrt{3}\cos\theta - \sin\theta = 2\left(\frac{\sqrt{3}}{2}\cos\theta - \frac{1}{2}\sin\theta\right)$

$$= 2(\cos\theta \cdot \cos 30° - \sin\theta \cdot \sin 30°) = 2(\cos(\theta + 30°))$$

$\Rightarrow \sqrt{3}\cos\theta - \sin\theta = 2\cos(\theta + 30°)$.

(b) $\sin\theta - \cos\theta = \sqrt{2}\left(\frac{\sin\theta - \cos\theta}{\sqrt{2}}\right)$

$$= \sqrt{2}\left(\frac{1}{\sqrt{2}}\sin\theta - \frac{1}{\sqrt{2}}\cos\theta\right) = \sqrt{2}\left[\sin\theta\cos\left(\frac{\pi}{4}\right) - \cos\theta\sin\left(\frac{\pi}{4}\right)\right]$$

$= \sqrt{2}\sin\left(\theta - \frac{\pi}{4}\right)$ [$\because \sin(A-B) = \sin A\cos B - \cos A\sin B$]

EXAMPLE 10.25

If $A + B = 90°$, then prove that,
(a) $\sin^2 A + \sin^2 B = 1$ (b) $\tan^2 A - \cot^2 B = 0$.

SOLUTION

Given, $A + B = 90°$
$\Rightarrow B = 90° - A$.

(a) $\sin^2 A + \sin^2 B = \sin^2 A + \sin^2(90° - A) = \sin^2 A + \cos^2 A$ ($\therefore \sin(90° - \theta) = \cos\theta$)
$= 1$.

(b) $\tan^2 A - \cot^2 B = \tan^2 A - \cot^2(90° - A) = \tan^2 A - \tan^2 A$ ($\because \tan\theta = \cot(90° - \theta) = 0$ $\tan^2 A - \cot^2 B = 0$.

EXAMPLE 10.26

Simplify the following:

(a) $\begin{vmatrix} \cos A & \sin A \\ \sin A & -\cos A \end{vmatrix}$

(b) $\log(\cot 1°) + \log\cot 2° + \log(\cot 3°) + \ldots + \log(\cot 89°)$

(c) $\sin 1° \cdot \sin 2° \ldots \sin 181°$.

SOLUTION

(a) $\begin{vmatrix} \cos A & \sin A \\ \sin A & -\cos A \end{vmatrix} = \cos A(-\cos A) - \sin A\sin A = -\cos^2 A - \sin^2 A$

$= -(\sin^2 A + \cos^2 A) = -1$

$\therefore \begin{vmatrix} \cos A & \sin A \\ \sin A & -\cos A \end{vmatrix} = -1.$

(b) log (cot 1°) + log (cot 2°) + ⋯ + log (cot 89°)

= log (cot 1° · cot 2° ⋯ cot 89°). [∵ log a + log b + ⋯ + log n = log (abc … n)]

We know that,

cot 1° = tan 89°, cot 2° = tan 88° and so on

cot 1° · cot 89° = cot 1° · tan 1° = 1 and so on

cot 1° · cot 2° … cot 89° = 1

⇒ log (cot 1° cot 2° ⋯ cot 89°) = log (1) = 0.

(c) sin 1° · sin 2° · sin 3° ⋯ sin 181°.

We know that, sin 180° = 0

sin 1° · sin 2° ⋯ sin 180° · sin 181° = 0.

Trigonometric Tables

The values of trigonometric ratios of different angles can be found by using natural sines, natural cosines, natural tangents, etc. These tabular values are approximate and tally upto three decimal places.

The following example gives an idea how to find any value of trigonometric ratios.

EXAMPLE 10.27 Find the value of sin 65°28′.

SOLUTION

Step 1: We have to refer the table of natural sines in order to find the value of sin 65°28′.

Step 2: We have to slide our view from left to right in the row containing 65° until we reach the intersection with 28′ and directly minutes table, so as to locate the nearest approximation in the minutes, i.e., in this problem 24′ and note down the value.

Step 3: We locate the difference of minutes (i.e., here 4′) in the mean difference and add it to the value in step 2.

To get the value of sin 65°28′, consider the following procedure.

0′	6′	12′	18′	24′	…	54′	Mean Differences				
							1	2	3	4	5
0.9063	9070	9078	9085	9092	…	9128	1	2	4	5	6

Now,

sin 65° 28′ = sin 65° · 24′ + 4′

= 0.9092 + 0.0005

= 0.9097.

Hence, sin 65°28′ = 0.9097.

EXAMPLE 10.28 Find the area of the right angle triangle with one of the acute angles being 65° and hypotenuse 6 cm.

SOLUTION

Let the right triangle be ABC, $\angle B = 90°$, $\angle A = 65°$ and $AC = 6$ cm.

From ΔABC,

$$\cos 65° = \frac{AB}{AC}$$

$$0.4226 = \frac{AB}{6}$$

$$AB = 2.5356$$

$$\sin 65° = \frac{BC}{AC} \Rightarrow 0.9063 = \frac{BC}{6}$$

$$BC = 5.4378$$

$$\text{Area of } \Delta ABC = \frac{1}{2} AB \times BC = \frac{1}{2}(2.5356)(5.4378)$$

$$= 6.8940 \text{ cm}^2 \text{ (approximately)}$$

Hence, the area of the ΔABC is 6.8940 cm^2.

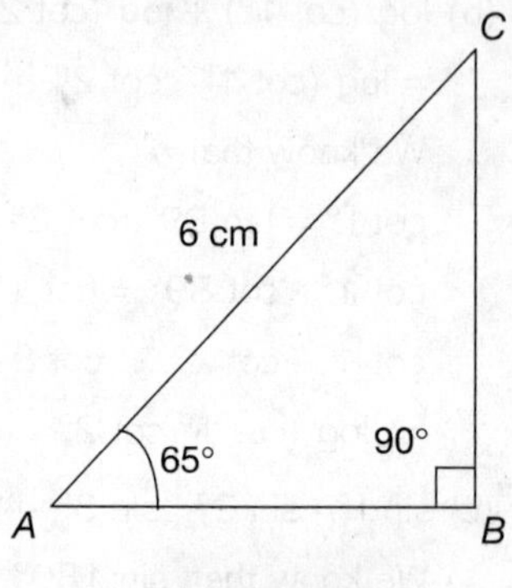

Figure 10.12

EXAMPLE 10.29 Find the length of the chord which subtends an angle of 110° at the centre of the circle of radius 7 cm. (Take sin 55° = 0.8192)

SOLUTION

Let the chord be AB. O be the centre of the circle and OD is shortest distance of the chord from the centre of circle.

Given $OA = OB = 7$ cm, $\angle AOB = 110°$.

Clearly, $\Delta AOD \cong \Delta BOD$ by SSS axiom

$$\angle AOD = \angle BOD = \frac{1}{2} \angle AOB = 55°.$$

In ΔAOD,

$$\sin 55° = \frac{AD}{AO}$$

$$0.8192 = \frac{AD}{7}$$

$AD = 5.7344$.

The length of the chord $= 2AD$

$= 2(5.7344)$

$= 11.4688$ cm.

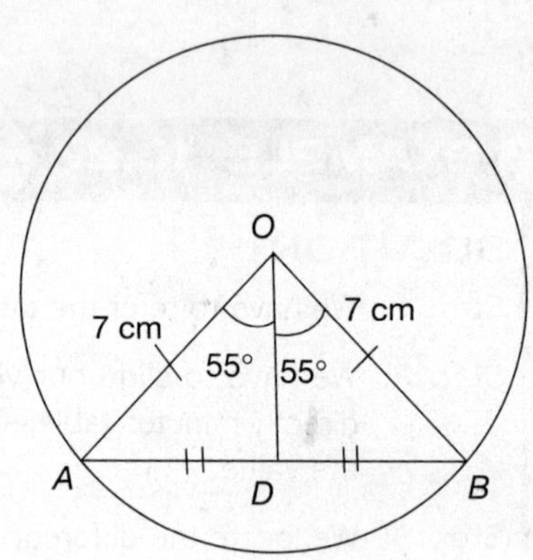

Figure 10.13

Heights and Distances

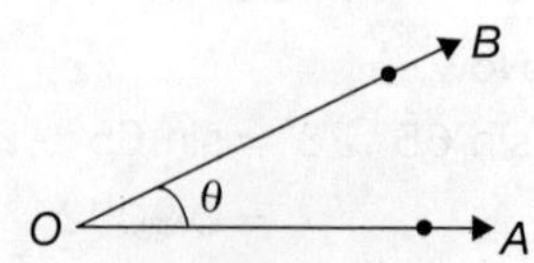

Figure 10.14

1. Let AB be a vertical line and PA and $P'B$ be two horizontal lines as shown in the Fig. 10.15.
2. Let $\angle APB = \alpha$ and $\angle PBP' = \beta$. Then,
   (i) α is called the angle of elevation of the point B as seen from the point P and
   (ii) β is called the angle of depression of the point P as seen from the point B.

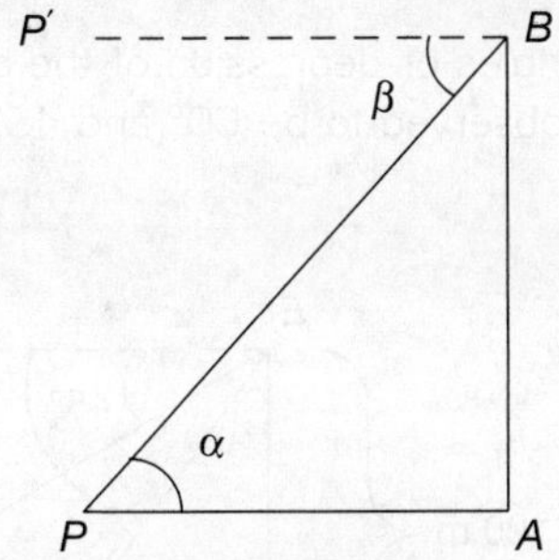

Figure 10.15

Konnect

Angle of elevation is always equal to the angle of depression.

EXAMPLE 10.30

Find the length of the chord which subtends an angle of 110° at the centre of the circle of radius 7 cm. (Take sin 55° = 0.8192)

SOLUTION

Let the height of the tower be h m.

From ΔPAB, $\tan 30^\circ = \frac{AB}{PA}$

$$\Rightarrow \frac{1}{\sqrt{3}} = \frac{h}{50} \Rightarrow h = \frac{50}{\sqrt{3}} \text{ (or) } \frac{50\sqrt{3}}{3}.$$

Hence, the height of the tower is $\frac{50\sqrt{3}}{3}$ m.

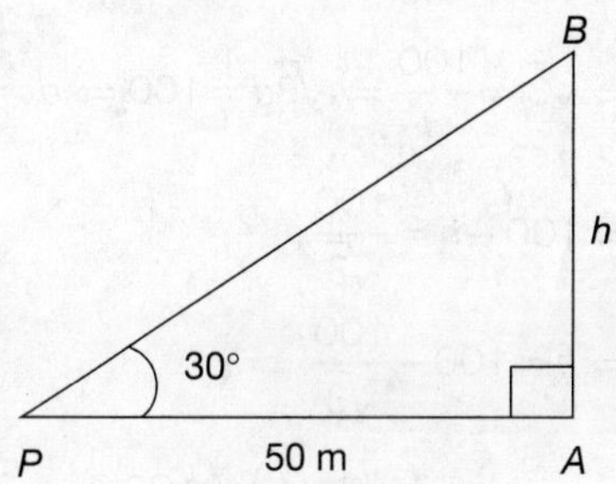

Figure 10.16

EXAMPLE 10.31

The angle of elevation of the top of a tower is 45°. On walking 20 m towards the tower along the line joining the foot of the observer and foot of the tower, the angle of elevation is found to be 60°. Find the height of the tower.

SOLUTION

Let the height of the tower be h m.

Let $QA = x$ m

In ΔPAB,

$$\tan 45^\circ = \frac{AB}{PA} \Rightarrow 1 = \frac{h}{20 + x} \Rightarrow 20 + x = h$$

$$\Rightarrow x = h - 20 \qquad (1)$$

From $\Delta\, QAB$,

$$\tan 60^\circ = \frac{AB}{QA}$$

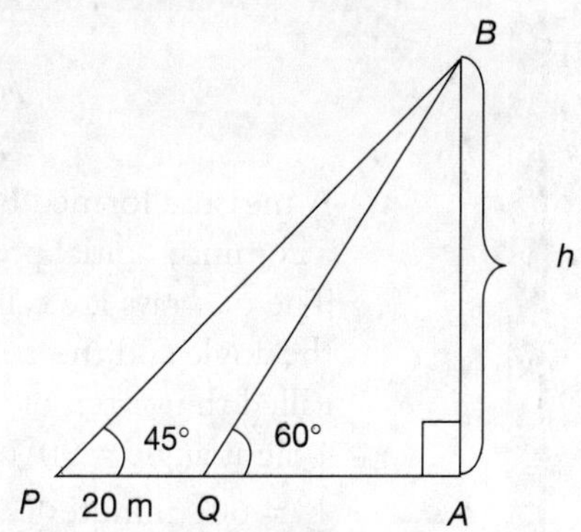

Figure 10.17

$$\Rightarrow \sqrt{3} = \frac{h}{x} \Rightarrow h = \sqrt{3}\, x \Rightarrow h = \sqrt{3}(h - 20), \qquad \text{(using Eq. (1))}$$

$$\Rightarrow (\sqrt{3} - 1)\, h = 20\sqrt{3} \Rightarrow h = \frac{20\sqrt{3}}{\sqrt{3} - 1} = \frac{20\sqrt{3}(\sqrt{3} + 1)}{(\sqrt{3} - 1)(\sqrt{3} + 1)} = \frac{20(3 + \sqrt{3})}{3 - 1} = 10(3 + \sqrt{3})$$

Hence, the height of the tower is $10(3 + \sqrt{3})$ m.

EXAMPLE 10.32 From the top of a building 100 m high, the angles of depression of the bottom and the top of an another building just opposite to it are observed to be 60° and 45° respectively. Find the height of the building.

SOLUTION

Let the height of the building be h m

Let $AC = BD = d$ m

From ΔBDE,

$$\tan 45° = \frac{ED}{BD} \Rightarrow 1 = \frac{100-h}{d}$$

$$\Rightarrow d = 100 - h \qquad (1)$$

From $\Delta\ ACE$,

$$\tan 60° = \frac{CE}{AC}$$

$$\Rightarrow \sqrt{3} = \frac{100}{d} \Rightarrow \sqrt{3}d = 100 \Rightarrow d = \frac{100}{\sqrt{3}}$$

$$\Rightarrow 100 - h = \frac{100}{\sqrt{3}} \qquad \text{(using Eq. (1))}$$

$$\Rightarrow h = 100 - \frac{100}{\sqrt{3}}$$

$$= 100\left(\frac{\sqrt{3}-1}{\sqrt{3}}\right) = \frac{100(3-\sqrt{3})}{3}.$$

Hence, the height of the tower is $\frac{100(3-\sqrt{3})}{3}$ m.

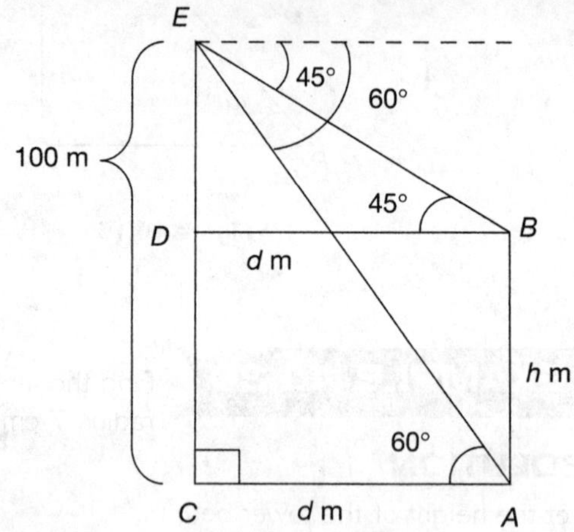

Figure 10.18

POINTS TO REMEMBER

- ✔ A measure formed between two rays having a common initial point is called an angle. The two rays are called the arms or sides of the angle and the common initial point is called the vertex of the angle.
- ✔ 1 right angle = 90°
  1° = 60′ (minutes)
  1′ = 60″ (seconds).
- ✔ 1 right angle = 100^g
  1^g = 100′ (minutes)
  1′ = 100″ (seconds).
- ✔ $\sin(A + B) = \sin A \cos B + \cos A \sin B$ and $\sin(A - B) = \sin A \cos B - \cos A \sin B$
- ✔ $\cos(A + B) = \cos A \cos B - \sin A \sin B$ and $\cos(A - B) = \cos A \cos B + \sin A \sin B$
- ✔ $\tan(A + B) = \frac{\tan A + \tan B}{1 - \tan A \tan B}$ and $\tan(A - B) = \frac{\tan A - \tan B}{1 + \tan A \tan B}$
- ✔ Also, by taking $A = B$ in the above relations, we get,
- ✔ $\sin 2A = 2\sin A \cos A$
- ✔ $\cos 2A = \cos^2 A - \sin^2 A = 2\cos^2 A - 1 = 1 - 2\sin^2 A$
- ✔ $\tan 2A = \frac{2\tan A}{1 - \tan^2 A}$

PRACTICE QUESTIONS CLASSROOM WING

Very Short Answer Type Questions

***Directions of questions from 1 to 15:* Fill in the blanks.**

1. If sec θ + cosec θ = 0, then tan θ = ______.
2. cos 1° · cos 2° · cos 3° ··· cos 120° = ______.
3. The $\dfrac{3\pi}{2}$ is equivalent to ______ in centesimal system.
4. If $A + B = 360°$, then $\dfrac{\tan A + \tan B}{1 - \tan A \tan B}$ = ______.
5. If tan θ + cot θ = 2, then $\tan^{10}\theta + \cot^{10}\theta$ = ______ (where $0 < \theta < 90°$).
6. $\sin(180 + \theta) + \cos(270 + \theta) + \cos(90 + \theta) + \sin(360 + \theta)$ = ______.
7. If sin θ + cos θ = 1 and $0° \le \theta \le 90°$, then the possible values of θ are ______.
8. cosec$(7\pi + \theta)$ · sin $(8\pi + \theta)$ = ______.
9. If $\sin(A+B) = \cos(A-B) = \dfrac{\sqrt{3}}{2}$, then cot 2$A$ = ______.
10. If ΔABC is an isosceles triangle and right angled at B, then $\dfrac{\tan A + \tan C}{\cot A + \cot C}$ = ______.
11. tan(A + B) tan (A – B) = ______.
12. The angles of a quadrilateral are in the ratio 1 : 2 : 3 : 4. Then the smallest angle in the centesimal system is ______.
13. If $\alpha + \beta = 90°$ and $\alpha = \dfrac{\beta}{2}$ then tan α · tan β = ______.
14. $[\sin\alpha + \sin(180 - \alpha) + \sin(180 + \alpha)]$ cosec α = ______.
15. If $\cot\theta = \dfrac{4}{3}$ where $180 < \theta < 270$, then sin θ + cos θ = ______.

***Directions of questions from 16 to 22:* Answer the following questions.**

16. Convert 250^g into other two measures.
17. Evaluate $\sin^2 45° + \cos^2 60° + \text{cosec}^2 30°$.
18. If $ABCD$ is a cyclic quadrilateral, then find the value of cos$A$ + cos B + cos C + cos D.
19. If $\sin\theta_1 = \dfrac{7}{25}$ and $\cos\theta_2 = \dfrac{24}{25}$, then find the relation between θ_1 and θ_2.
20. Find the value of tan 1140°.
21. Express $\dfrac{\tan\theta + 1}{\tan\theta - 1}$ as a single trigonometric ratio.
22. If cosec θ + cot θ = 3, then find cos θ.

Short Answer Type Questions

23. Find the relation obtained by eliminating 'θ' from the equations $x = a$ sec θ and $y = b$ tan θ.
24. If cosec θ – cot θ = 0, then what will be the value of sec θ ?
25. Find the relation obtained by eliminating 'θ' from the equations a = b cosec θ and $x = y$ tan θ.
26. If x = a cosθ + b sinθ and y = a sinθ – b cosθ, then which of the following relations is correct?
27. (A) Simplify sin(A + 45°) · sin(A – 45°).
    (B) If $A + B = 225°$, then find the value of (tan A + 1) (tan B + 1).
28. Eliminate θ from the following equations: $x = a \sin\theta$, $y = b\cos\theta$ and $z = a\sin^2\theta + b\cos^2\theta$.
29. If $\sin A = \dfrac{3}{5}$ and A is not in the first quadrant, then find $\dfrac{\cos A + \sin 2A}{\tan A + \sec A}$.
30. If $\cos(A - B) = \dfrac{5}{13}$ and $\sin(A + B) = \dfrac{4}{5}$, then find sin 2$B$.
31. (A) If cosec θ – cot θ = 2, then find the value of $\text{cosec}^2\theta + \cot^2\theta$.

(B) If $\sin\theta + \operatorname{cosec}\theta = 2$, then find
(i) $\sin^{2015}\theta + \cos^{2015}\theta$ and (ii) $\sin^{2016}\theta - \operatorname{cosec}^{2017}\theta$.

32. Prove that $\dfrac{1+\cos A}{1-\cos A} = (\operatorname{cosec} A + \cot A)^2$.

33. From a steamer moving towards a lighthouse at a constant velocity, the angle of elevation of the top of the lighthouse is observed to be 30°. Ten minutes from that instant, the angle of elevation changes to 60°. If the steamer reaches the light house at 12:00 noon, then find the time at which the first observation was made.

34. If $3\sin A + 4\cos A = 4$, then find $4\sin A - 3\cos A$.

35. A ladder of length 50 m rests against a vertical wall, at a height of 30 m from the ground. Find the inclination of the ladder with the horizontal. Also find the distance between the foot of the ladder and the wall.

36. Eliminate θ from the following equations:
$x \sin\alpha + y \cos\alpha = p$ and $x \cos\alpha - y \sin\alpha = q$.

37. Prove that $\left(\dfrac{1-\sin\alpha}{\cos\alpha} + \dfrac{\cos\alpha}{1+\sin\alpha}\right)\left(\sec\alpha + \dfrac{1}{\cot\alpha}\right) = 2.$

Essay Type Questions

38. Find the value of $\cos^2 10° + \cos^2 20° + \cos^2 30° + \ldots + \cos^2 90°$.

39. From the top of a tower 150 m high, the angles of depression of the top and bottom of a building are observed to be 45° and 60°, respectively. Find the height of the building (in m).

40. Find the value of $\sin^2 5° + \sin^2 15° + \sin^2 25° + \ldots + \sin^2 85°$.

41. From the top and the bottom of a building 50 m high, the angles of elevation are 30° and 45°, respectively. Find the height of the tower (in m).

42. The angle of elevation of the top of a tower is 45°. On walking 24 m towards the tower along the line joining the foot of the observer and foot of the tower, the angle of elevation is found to be 60°. Find the height of the tower (use $= \sqrt{3} = 1.732$).

43. A flag staff *EP* is situated at *E*, the midpoint of side *AB* of a square shaped field *ABCD*. If the *PE* subtends an angle of 30° at C, then find the height of the flag staff, given side of the square is 6 m.

PRACTICE QUESTIONS COMPETITION WING

Level 1: Apply Your Concepts

Directions of questions from 1 to 5:
Fill in the blanks.

1. If $\sin\theta = \frac{1}{2}$ where $0° \le \theta \le 180°$, then the possible values of θ are ______.

2. $\cot\theta$ in terms of $\sin\theta =$ ______ $(0 \le \theta \le 90°)$.

3. If A and B are two complementary angles, then $\sin A \cdot \cos B + \cos A \cdot \sin B =$ ______.

4. If the angle of a sector is 45° and the radius of the sector is 28 cm then the length of the arc is ______.

5. If $ABCD$ is a cyclic quadrilateral, then $\tan A + \tan C =$ ______.

Directions of questions from 6 to 35:
Select the correct alternative from the given choices.

6. If $\tan A = \frac{5}{12}$ and A is not in the first quadrant, then find $\frac{\sin A + \cos A}{\sin A - \cos A}$.

   (a) $\frac{-12}{5}$ (b) $\frac{-17}{7}$
   (c) $\frac{12}{5}$ (d) $\frac{-15}{7}$

7. If $\frac{1 + \tan A}{1 - \tan A} = \tan 75°$, then A = ______.

   (a) 30° (b) 45°
   (c) 15° (d) 60°

8. If $5\cot^2 A = \sin^2 60° + \sec^2 30°$, then what will be the value of $\text{cosec}^2 A$?

   (a) $\frac{5}{12}$ (b) $\frac{11}{12}$
   (c) $\frac{17}{12}$ (d) $\frac{7}{12}$

9. If $\cos A = \frac{8}{17}$ and A is not in the first quadrant, then find the value of $\frac{\text{cosec } A + \cot A}{\text{cosec } A - \cot A}$.

   (a) $\frac{31}{15}$ (b) $\frac{18}{11}$
   (c) $\frac{25}{9}$ (d) $\frac{27}{13}$

10. If $\frac{1 - \tan q}{1 + \tan q} = \tan 30°$, then $\theta =$ ______.

    (a) 15° (b) 30°
    (c) 45° (d) 60°

11. If $\sec^2 A = \cot^2 30° + 2\cos^2 45°$, then find the value of $\sin^2 A$.

    (a) $\frac{1}{4}$ (b) $\frac{1}{2}$
    (c) $\frac{3}{4}$ (d) 1

12. A wheel makes 20 revolutions per hour. The radians it turns through 25 minutes is ______.

    (a) $\frac{50\pi^c}{7}$ (b) $\frac{250\pi^c}{3}$
    (c) $\frac{150\pi^c}{7}$ (d) $\frac{50\pi^c}{3}$

13. $\frac{\sin^4\theta - \cos^4\theta}{\sin^2\theta - \cos^2\theta} =$ ______.

    (a) −1 (b) 2
    (c) 0 (d) 1

14. Simplified expression of $(\sec\theta + \tan\theta)(1 - \sin\theta)$ is ______.

    (a) $\sin^2\theta$ (b) $\cos^2\theta$
    (c) $\tan^2\theta$ (d) $\cos\theta$

15. If $a = \sec\theta - \tan\theta$ and $b = \sec\theta + \tan\theta$, then

    (a) $a = b$. (b) $\frac{1}{a} = \frac{-1}{b}$.
    (c) $a = \frac{1}{b}$. (d) $a - b = 1$.

16. If $\sec\alpha + \tan\alpha = m$, then $\sec^4\alpha - \tan^4\alpha - 2\sec\alpha\tan\alpha$ is ______.

    (a) m^2 (b) $-m^2$
    (c) $\frac{1}{m^2}$ (d) $\frac{-1}{m^2}$

17. If $\sin^4 A - \cos^4 A = 1$, then $(A/2)$ is ______. $(0 < A \le 90°)$.

    (a) 45° (b) 60°
    (c) 30° (d) 40°

18. The value of tan 15° tan 20° tan 70° tan 75° is

    (a) −1 (b) 2
    (c) 0 (d) 1

19. In a ΔABC, $\tan\left(\frac{A+C}{2}\right) =$ ______.

(a) $\tan\frac{B}{2}$ (b) $\cot\frac{B}{2}$
(c) $-\tan B$ (d) $\cot B$

20. If $\tan(A-30°) = 2-\sqrt{3}$, then find A.

(a) $\frac{\pi^c}{2}$ (b) $\frac{\pi^c}{4}$
(c) $\frac{\pi^c}{6}$ (d) $\frac{\pi^c}{3}$

21. If $\sin^4\theta - \cos^4\theta = K^4$, then $\sin^2\theta - \cos^2\theta$ is ______.

(a) K^4 (b) K^3
(c) K^2 (d) K

22. $\frac{\tan^3\theta - 1}{\tan\theta - 1} =$ ______.

(a) $\sec^2\theta + \tan\theta$ (b) $\sec^2\theta - \tan\theta$
(c) 0 (d) $\tan\theta - \sec^2\theta$

23. For all values of θ, $1 + \cos\theta$ can be ______.

(a) positive (b) negative
(c) non-positive (d) non-negative

24. If $\sin 3\theta = \cos(\theta - 6°)$, where 3θ and $(\theta - 6°)$ are acute angles then the value of θ is ______.

(a) 42° (b) 24°
(c) 12° (d) 26°

25. $(\operatorname{cosec} A - \sin A)(\sec A - \cos A)(\tan A + \cot A) =$ ______.

(a) −1 (b) 2
(c) 0 (d) 1

26. If $x = a(\operatorname{cosec}\theta + \cot\theta)$ and $y = b(\cot\theta - \operatorname{cosec}\theta)$, then

(a) $xy - ab = 0$. (b) $xy + ab = 0$.
(c) $\frac{x}{a} + \frac{y}{b} = 1$. (d) $x^2 y^2 = ab$.

27. The value of $\frac{\cos^4 x + \cos^2 x \sin^2 x + \sin^2 x}{\cos^2 x + \sin^2 x \cos^2 x + \sin^4 x}$ is ______.

(a) 2 (b) 1
(c) 3 (d) 0

28. $\frac{1}{1+\sin\theta} + \frac{1}{1-\sin\theta}$ is equal to ______.

(a) $2\sec^2\theta$ (b) $2\cos^2\theta$
(c) 0 (d) 1

29. If $\tan(\alpha+\beta) = \frac{1}{2}$ and $\tan\alpha = \frac{1}{3}$, then $\tan\beta =$ ______.

(a) $\frac{1}{6}$ (b) $\frac{1}{7}$
(c) 1 (d) $\frac{7}{6}$

30. The value of $\log\sin 0° + \log\sin 1° + \log\sin 2° + \cdots + \log\sin 90°$ is ______.

(a) 0 (b) 1
(c) −1 (d) undefined

31. Which of the following is not possible?

(a) $\sin\theta = \frac{3}{5}$ (b) $\sec\theta = 100$
(c) $\operatorname{cosec}\theta = 0.14$ (d) None of these

32. $\sin^2 20° + \cos^2 160° - \tan^2 45° =$ ______.

(a) 2 (b) 0
(c) 1 (d) −2

33. $\frac{\sin\theta + \cos\theta}{\sin\theta - \cos\theta} + \frac{\sin\theta - \cos\theta}{\sin\theta + \cos\theta} =$ ______.

(a) $\frac{2}{1-2\cos^2\theta}$ (b) $\frac{2}{2\sin^2\theta - 1}$
(c) Both (a) and (b) (d) None of these

34. The length of the side (in cm) of an equilateral triangle inscribed in a circle of radius 8 cm is ______.

(a) $16\sqrt{3}$ (b) $12\sqrt{3}$
(c) $8\sqrt{3}$ (d) $10\sqrt{3}$

35. Which among the following is true?

(a) $\sin 1° > \sin 1^c$ (b) $\sin 1° < \sin 1^c$
(c) $\sin 1° = \sin 1^c$ (d) None of these

Level 2: Review Your Concepts

36. If $2\sin\alpha + 3\cos\alpha = 2$, then $3\sin\alpha - 2\cos\alpha =$ ______.

(a) ±3 (b) ±1
(c) 0 (d) ±2

37. If $\frac{\sin^2\alpha - 3\sin\alpha + 2}{\cos^2\alpha} = 1$, then α can be ______.

(a) 60° (b) 45°
(c) 0° (d) 30°

38. If $\cot A = \frac{5}{12}$ and A is not in the first quadrant, then $\frac{\sin A - \cos A}{1 + \cot A}$ is ______.

(a) $\frac{-74}{25}$ (b) $\frac{-84}{221}$

(c) $\frac{-87}{223}$ (d) None of these

39. If $\frac{1+\sin\alpha}{1-\sin\alpha} = \frac{m^2}{n^2}$, then $\sin\alpha$ is ______.

(a) $\frac{m^2+n^2}{m^2-n^2}$ (b) $\frac{m^2-n^2}{m^2+n^2}$

(c) $\frac{m^2+n^2}{n^2-m^2}$ (d) $\frac{n^2-m^2}{m^2+n^2}$

40. If $\sin\theta - \cos\theta = \frac{3}{5}$, then $\sin\theta\cos\theta =$ ______.

(a) $\frac{16}{25}$ (b) $\frac{9}{16}$

(c) $\frac{9}{25}$ (d) $\frac{8}{25}$

41. If $ABCD$ is a cyclic quadrilateral, then the value of $\cos^2 A - \cos^2 B - \cos^2 C + \cos^2 D$ is ______.

(a) 0 (b) 1

(c) −1 (d) 2

42. The length of minute hand of a wall clock is 12 cm. Find the distance covered by the tip of the minute hand in 25 minutes.

(a) $\frac{220}{7}$ cm (b) $\frac{110}{7}$ cm

(c) $\frac{120}{7}$ cm (d) $\frac{240}{7}$ cm

43. $\sin^2 2° + \sin^2 4° + \sin^2 6° + \cdots + \sin^2 90° =$ ______.

(a) 22 (b) 23

(c) 44 (d) 45

44. A straight highway leads to the foot of a tower of height 50 m. From the top of the tower, the angles of depression of two cars standing on the highway are 30° and 60°. What is the distance between the two cars? (in metres)

(a) $\frac{100}{\sqrt{3}}$ (b) $50\sqrt{3}$

(c) $\frac{50}{\sqrt{3}}$ (d) $100\sqrt{3}$

45. The angle of elevation of the top of a hill from the foot of a tower is 60° and the angle of elevation of the top of the tower from the foot of the hill is 30°. If the tower is 50 m high, then what is the height of the hill?

(a) 180 m (b) 150 m

(c) 100 m (d) 120 m

46. $\tan 38° - \cot 22° =$ ______.

(a) $\frac{1}{2}\operatorname{cosec} 38° \sec 22°$ (b) $2 \sin 22° \cos 38°$

(c) $-\frac{1}{2}\operatorname{cosec} 22° \sec 38°$ (d) None of these

47. $\frac{1-\cos\theta}{\sin\theta} + \frac{\sin\theta}{1-\cos\theta} =$ ______.

(a) $2\sin\theta$ (b) $2\cos\theta$

(c) $2\operatorname{cosec}\theta$ (d) $2\sec\theta$

48. $\sqrt{-4+\sqrt{8+16\operatorname{cosec}^4\alpha\sin^4\alpha}} =$ ______.

(a) $\operatorname{cosec}\alpha - \sin\alpha$ (b) $2\operatorname{cosec}\alpha + \sin\alpha$

(c) $2\operatorname{cosec}\alpha - \sin\alpha$ (d) $\operatorname{cosec}\alpha - 2\sin\alpha$

49. The angles of depression of the top and the bottom of a 7 m tall building from the top of a tower are 45° and 60°, respectively. Find the height of the tower in metres.

(a) $7(3+\sqrt{3})$ (b) $\frac{7}{2}(3-\sqrt{3})$

(c) $\frac{7}{2}(3+\sqrt{3})$ (d) $7(3-\sqrt{3})$

50. If $\tan 86° = m$, then $\frac{\tan 176° + \cot 4°}{m + \tan 4°}$ is ______.

(a) $\frac{m^2-1}{m^2+1}$. (b) $\frac{m^2+1}{1-m^2}$.

(c) $\frac{1-m^2}{1+m^2}$. (d) $\frac{m^2+1}{m^2-1}$.

51. The following sentences are the steps involved in proving the result $\frac{\cos x}{1-\tan x} + \frac{\sin x}{1-\cot x} = \cos x + \sin x$. Arrange them in sequential order from first to last.

(A) $\frac{\cos^2 x}{\cos x - \sin x} + \frac{\sin^2 x}{\sin x - \cos x}$

(B) $\frac{\cos^2 x - \sin^2 x}{\cos x - \sin x}$

(C) $\frac{\cos x}{1-\frac{\sin x}{\cos x}} + \frac{\sin x}{1-\frac{\cos x}{\sin x}}$

(a) (A), (B), and (C) (b) (C), (A), and (B)

(c) (C), (B), and (A) (d) None of these

Level 3: Assess Your Concepts

52. There is a small island in the river which is 100 m wide and a tall tree stands on the island. P and Q are points directly opposite each other on the two banks and in line with the tree. If the angles of elevation of the top of the tree from P and Q are, respectively, are 30° and 45°, find the height of the tree (in metres).
(a) $50(\sqrt{3}-1)$ (b) $50(\sqrt{3}+1)$
(c) $100(\sqrt{3}+1)$ (d) $100(\sqrt{3}-1)$

53. A balloon is connected to a meteorological ground station by a cable of length 215 m inclined at 60° to the horizontal. Determine the height of the balloon from the ground. Assume that there is no slack in the cable.
(a) $107.5\sqrt{3}$ m (b) $100\sqrt{3}$ m
(c) $215\sqrt{3}$ m (d) $215/\sqrt{3}$ m

54. If $\sqrt{2}\cos\theta - \sqrt{6}\sin\theta = 2\sqrt{2}$, then the value of θ can be ______.
(a) 0° (b) −45°
(c) 30° (d) −60°

55. A circus artist climbs from the ground along a rope which is stretched from the top of a vertical pole and tied at the ground at a certain distance from the foot of the pole. The height of the pole is 12 m and the angle made by the rope with the ground is 30°. Calculate the distance covered by the artist in reaching the top of the pole.
(a) 24 m (b) 6 m
(c) 12 m (d) None of these

56. Find the value of $\sin^2 5° + \sin^2 10° + \sin^2 15° + \cdots + \sin^2 90°$.
(a) 8 (b) 9
(c) $\frac{17}{2}$ (d) $\frac{19}{2}$

57. If $\sec\theta + \tan\theta = 2$, then find the value of $\sin\theta$.
(a) $\frac{3}{5}$ (b) $\frac{2}{5}$
(c) $-\frac{3}{5}$ (d) $-\frac{2}{5}$

58. If $\cos\theta + \left(\frac{1}{\sqrt{3}}\right)\sin\theta = \frac{2}{\sqrt{3}}$, then find θ in circular measure.
(a) $\frac{\pi^c}{10}$ (b) $\frac{\pi^c}{9}$
(c) $\frac{\pi^c}{6}$ (d) $\frac{\pi^c}{3}$

59. $\sqrt{\frac{1+\sin\theta}{1-\sin\theta}} =$ ______.
(a) $\sec\theta + \tan\theta$ (b) $\sec\theta - \cot\theta$
(c) $\operatorname{cosec}\theta + \tan\theta$ (d) $\operatorname{cosec}\theta - \tan\theta$

60. If $\frac{\sin^2\theta - 5\sin\theta + 3}{\cos^2\theta} = 1$, then θ can be ______.
(a) 30° (b) 45°
(c) 60° (d) 0°

61. If $\cot\theta = \frac{24}{7}$ and θ is not in the first quadrant, then find the value of $\tan\theta - \sec\theta$.
(a) 1 (b) $\frac{4}{3}$
(c) $\frac{3}{2}$ (d) $\frac{5}{4}$

62. If $\sin 20° = p$, then find the value of $\left(\frac{\sin 380° - \sin 340°}{\cos 380° + \cos 340°}\right)$.
(a) $\sqrt{1-p^2}$ (b) $\sqrt{\frac{1-p^2}{p}}$
(c) $\frac{p}{\sqrt{1-p^2}}$ (d) None of these

63. Find the value $\tan\left(22\frac{1°}{2}\right)$.
(a) $\sqrt{2}-1$ (b) $1+\sqrt{2}$
(c) $2+\sqrt{3}$ (d) $2-\sqrt{3}$

64. If the sun ray's inclination increases from 45° to 60°, the length of the shadow of a tower decreases by 50 m. Find the height of the tower (in m).
(a) $50(\sqrt{3}-1)$ (b) $75(3-\sqrt{3})$
(c) $100(\sqrt{3}+1)$ (d) $25(3+\sqrt{3})$

65. The angles of depression of two points from the top of the tower are 30° and 60°. If the height of the tower is 30 m, then find the maximum possible distance between the two points.

(a) $40\sqrt{3}$ m (b) $30\sqrt{3}$ m

(c) $20\sqrt{3}$ m (d) $10\sqrt{3}$ m

66. From a point on the ground, the angle of elevation of an aeroplane flying at an altitude of 500 m changes from 45° to 30° in 5 seconds. Find the speed of the aeroplane (in kmph).

(a) $720(\sqrt{3}-1)$ (b) $720(\sqrt{3}+1)$

(c) $360(\sqrt{3}-1)$ (d) $360(\sqrt{3}+1)$

67. From the top of a building, the angles of elevation and depression of top and bottom of a tower are 60° and 30°, respectively. If the height of the building is 5 m, then find the height of the tower.

(a) $10\sqrt{3}$ m (b) 15 m

(c) $15\sqrt{3}$ m (d) 20 m

68. In the figure given below (not to scale), *ABCD*, *BEFC* and *EGHF* are three squares. Find $\angle FAE + \angle HAG$.

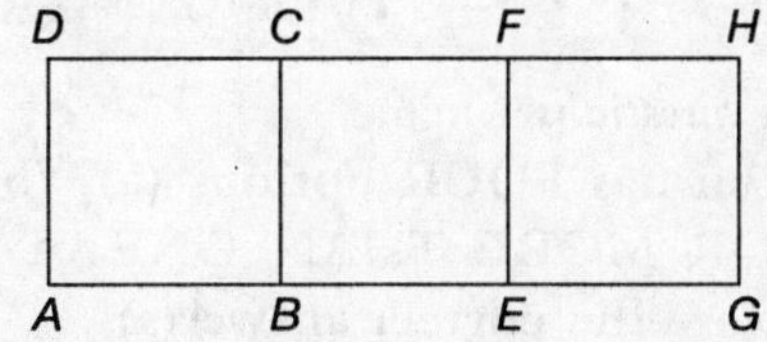

(a) 30° (b) 45°

(c) 60° (c) 120°

AT

PRACTICE QUESTIONS JEE SPECIAL WING

Multiple-Answer Type Questions

Directions for questions 1 to 6:
Each question has FOUR options (a), (b), (c), and (d). ONE OR MORE THAN ONE of these four option(s) is/are the correct answer(s).

1. Which of the following is equivalent to 100^g?

(a) $\frac{\pi^c}{4} + 45°$ (b) $54° + \frac{\pi^c}{5}$

(c) $108° - \frac{\pi^c}{10}$ (d) $\frac{4\pi^c}{5} - 54°$

2. Which of the following is equivalent to $\frac{2}{\sqrt{3}}$?

(a) sec 30° (b) cosec 120°

(c) sec 330° (d) cosec 420°

3. Which of the following is equivalent to sin 30°.cos 60° + sin 60°.cos 30° ?

(a) sin 90° (b) tan 225°

(c) sec 360° (d) cosec 270°

4. If $\cos\theta + \sec\theta = 2$, then which of the following is equal to $\cos\theta + \sec\theta$?

(a) $\cos^{2025}\theta + \sec^{2025}\theta$ (b) $\cos^{2026}\theta - \sec^{2026}\theta$

(c) $\cos^{2026}\theta + \sec^{2027}\theta$ (d) $\cos^{2028}\theta - \sec^{2029}\theta$

5. If $\frac{2\tan^2\theta - 3\tan\theta - 3}{\sec^2\theta} = 1$, find the value of $\tan\theta$.

(a) −1 (b) −2

(c) 2 (d) 4

6. Which of the following trigonometric ratios will take the values $(-\infty, -1)$?

(a) $\sec\theta$ (b) $\sin\theta$

(c) $\text{cosec}\theta$ (d) $\cot\theta$

Match The Column

Directions for questions 7 to 10:
Read the paragraph given below and answer the questions.

In the given figure, *AB*, *QP* and *CD* represent three towers placed on a plane ground. The distance between the towers *AB* and *CD* is 600 m. From the top of the tower, the angles of elevation of the tops of the towers *AB* and *CD* are 45° and 60° respectively. Also, the top of the tower, the angles of depressions of the bottoms of the towers *AB* and *CD* are 30° and 45° respectively.

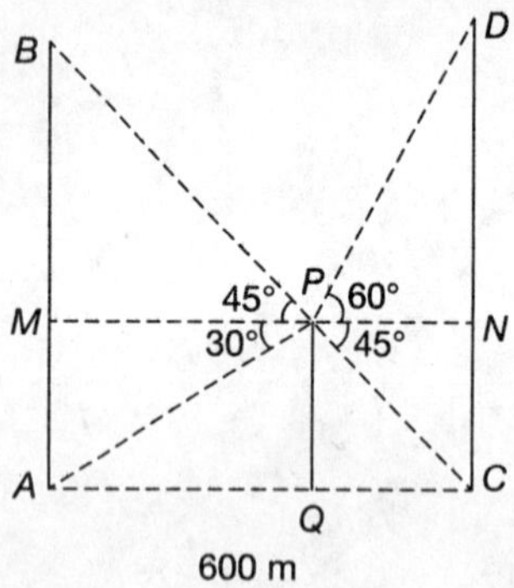

Column A	Column B (in m)
7. *AB* – *PQ*	(a) 0
8. *AP* – *PD*	(b) $600(\sqrt{3}-1)$
9. *CD*	(c) $300(3-\sqrt{3})$
10. *AD*	(d) 600
	(e) $600\sqrt{2}$

Comprehension-Based Questions

Directions for questions 11 to 14:

Read the paragraph given below and answer the questions.

From a point 150 m above a lake, the angle of elevation of a bird is 30° and the angle of the depression of the reflection of the bird in the lake is 60°.

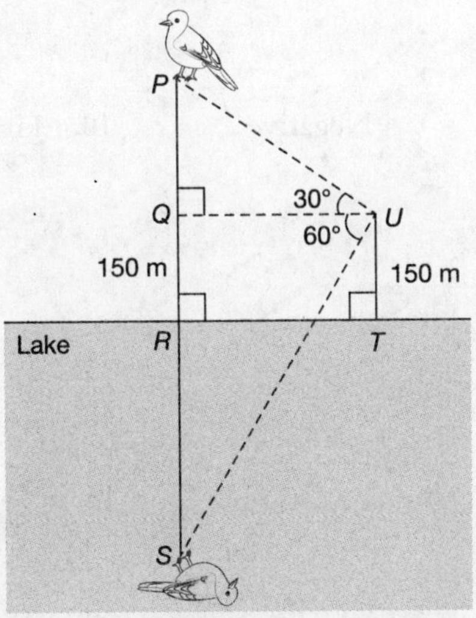

11. At what height is the bird?
    (a) 250 m (b) 300 m
    (c) 350 m (d) 450 m

12. What is the distance of the bird from the point of observation?
    (a) 300 m (b) 400 m
    (c) 500 m (d) 600 m

13. What is the distance of the reflection of the bird from the point of observation?
    (a) $150\sqrt{3}$ m (b) $200\sqrt{3}$ m
    (c) $250\sqrt{3}$ m (d) $300\sqrt{3}$ m

14. What is the horizontal distance of the bird from the point of observation?
    (a) $150\sqrt{3}$ m (b) $200\sqrt{3}$ m
    (c) $250\sqrt{3}$ m (d) $300\sqrt{3}$ m

Assertion and Reason Type Questions

Directions for questions 15 to 18:

Read the options given below and answer the questions.

In the light of the given statements, choose the most appropriate answer from the options given below.

(a) Both assertion (A) and reason (R) are true, and reason (R) is the correct explanation of assertion.
(b) Both assertion (A) and reason (R) are true, and reason (R) is not the correct explanation of assertion.
(c) Assertion (A) is true, but reason (R) is false.
(d) Assertion (A) is false, and reason (R) is true.

15. **Assertion:** $\sec^2(2026°) = 1 + \tan^2(2026°)$.
    Reason: For any angle 6, $\sec^2\theta - \tan^2\theta = 1$.

16. **Assertion:** If $\sin\alpha + \sin\beta + \sin\gamma = 3$, then $\sin\alpha = 1$.
    Reason: The value of $\sin 90°$ is 1.

17. **Assertion:** *PQRS* is a trapezium in which $PQ \parallel RS$. $\tan P + \tan Q = 0$.
    Reason: A trapezium is a cyclic quadrilateral.

18. **Assertion:** $\cot 179° \times \cot 178° \times \cot 177° \times \cot 176° \times \ldots \times \cot 1° = 1$.
    Reason: $\cot 90° = 0$.

ANSWER KEYS

Crossword

Across

1. Radians 3. Angle 5. Real 7. Degrees 9. Reciprocal
10. French 11. Positive

Down

2. Depression 4. Grades 6. British 8. Negative 10. First

Classroom Wing

Very Short Answer Type Questions

1. –1 2. 0 3. 300^g 4. 0 5. 2
6. 0 7. 0° and 90° 8. –1 9. 0 10. 1
11. $\frac{\tan^2 A - \tan^2 B}{1-\tan^2 A \tan^2 B}$. 12. 36° 13. 1 14. 1 15. $\frac{-7}{5}$
16. $\frac{5\pi^c}{4}$ 17. $\frac{19}{4}$ 18. 0 19. $\theta_1 + \theta_2 = 90°$ 20. $\sqrt{3}$
21. $-\tan\left(\theta + \frac{\pi}{4}\right)$ 22. $\frac{4}{5}$

Short Answer Type Questions

23. 1 24. 1 25. 1 26. $x^2 + y^2 = a^2 + b^2$
27. (A) $-\frac{1}{2}\cos 2A$ (B) 2 28. $bx^2 + ay^2 = abz$ 29. $\frac{22}{25}$ 30. $\frac{-16}{65}$
31. (A) $\frac{17}{8}$ (B) (i) 1; (ii)0 33. 11: 45 a.m. 34. ±3 35. 40 m
36. $x^2 + y^2 = p^2 + q^2$

Essay Type Questions

38. 4 39. $50(3-\sqrt{3})$m 40. $4\frac{1}{2}$ 41. $25(\sqrt{3}+3)$ 42. 56.784 m
43. $\sqrt{15}$ m

Competition Wing

Level 1: Apply Your Concepts

1. 30° or 150° 2. $\frac{\sqrt{1-\sin^2\theta}}{\sin\theta}$ 3. 1 4. 22 cm 5. 0
6. (b) 7. (a) 8. (c) 9. (c) 10. (a)
11. (c) 12. (d) 13. (d) 14. (d) 15. (c)

16. (c)	17. (a)	18. (d)	19. (b)	20. (b)
21. (a)	22. (a)	23. (d)	24. (b)	25. (d)
26. (b)	27. (b)	28. (a)	29. (b)	30. (d)
31. (b)	32. (d)	33. (b)	34. (b)	35. (b)

Level 2: Review Your Concepts

36. (b)	37. (d)	38. (b)	39. (b)	40. (d)
41. (a)	42. (a)	43. (b)	44. (a)	45. (b)
46. (c)	47. (c)	48. (c)	49. (c)	50. (a)
51. (b)				

Level 3: Assess Your Concepts

52. (a)	53. (a)	54. (d)	55. (a)	56. (d)
57. (a)	58. (c)	59. (a)	60. (a)	61. (b)
62. (c)	63. (a)	64. (d)	65. (a)	66. (c)
67. (d)	68. (b)			

JEE Special Wing

Multiple-Answer Type Questions

1. (a, b, c, d)	2. (a, b, c, d)	3. (a, b, c)	4. (a, c)	5. (a, d)
6. (a, c, d)				

Match The Column

7. (c)	8. (a)	9. (d)	10. (e)

Comprehension-Based Questions

11. (b)	12. (a)	13. (d)	14. (a)

Assertion and Reason Type Questions

15. (a)	16. (b)	17. (c)	18. (d)

Hints and Explanations

Classroom Wing

Very Short Answer Type Questions

1. $\sec \theta + \operatorname{cosec} \theta = 0 \Rightarrow \sec \theta = -\operatorname{cosec} \theta$

$\Rightarrow \dfrac{\operatorname{cosec}}{\sec q} = -1 \Rightarrow \tan \theta = -1$

2. $\cos 1° \cdot \cos 2° \cdot \cos 3° \cdots \cos 120°$

Value of $\cos 90° = 0$

Therefore, all becomes 0.

3. $\pi^c = 200^g$

$1^c = \dfrac{200^g}{\pi}$

$\left(\dfrac{3\pi}{2}\right)^c = \dfrac{200}{\pi} \times \dfrac{3\pi}{2}$

$= 300^g$

4. $A + B = 360°, \dfrac{\tan A + \tan B}{1 - \tan A \cdot \tan B}$

$\tan(A+B) = \dfrac{\tan A + \tan B}{1 - \tan A \cdot \tan B}$

$\tan(360°) = 0$

5. $\tan\theta + \cot\theta = 2$

This value can occur only at $\tan\theta = 1$ and $\cot\theta = 1$

$(\tan\theta)^{10} + (\cot\theta)^{10} = 2$

6. $\sin(180+\theta) + \cos(270+\theta) + \cos(90+\theta) + \sin(360+\theta)$

$= -\sin\theta + \sin\theta + (-\sin\theta) + \sin\theta$

$= 0$

7. $\sin\theta + \cos\theta = 1$

either $\sin\theta = 1$ or $\cos\theta = 1$

$0°$ and $90°$

8. $\operatorname{cosec}(7\pi + \theta) \cdot \sin(8\pi + \theta)$

$= -\operatorname{cosec}(\theta) \cdot \sin(\theta)$

$= -\dfrac{1}{\sin\theta} . \sin\theta$

$= -1$

9. $\sin(A+B) = \cos(A-B) = \dfrac{\sqrt{3}}{2}$

$A + B = \sin^{-1}\left(\dfrac{\sqrt{3}}{2}\right)$

$A + B = \dfrac{\pi}{3}$ (1)

$A - B = \cos^{-1}\left(\dfrac{\sqrt{3}}{2}\right)$

$A - B = \dfrac{\pi}{6}$ (2)

On solving (1) and (2),

$A + B = \dfrac{\pi}{3}$

$A - B = \dfrac{\pi}{6}$

$2A = \dfrac{\pi}{2}$

$A = \dfrac{\pi}{4}$

$\cot(2A) = \cot\left(2 \cdot \dfrac{\pi}{4}\right)$

$= \cot\left(\dfrac{\pi}{2}\right)$

$= 0$

10. $A + B + C = 180°$

$A + C = 90°$, $A = C$ because isoceles $A = C = \dfrac{\pi}{4}$

$\dfrac{\tan(A) + \tan C}{\cot A + \cot C}$

$\dfrac{\tan\left(\dfrac{\pi}{4}\right) + \tan\left(\dfrac{\pi}{4}\right)}{\cot\left(\dfrac{\pi}{4}\right) + \cot\left(\dfrac{\pi}{4}\right)}$

$\dfrac{1+1}{1+1} = 1.$

11. $\tan(A+B) \cdot \tan(A-B)$

$= \dfrac{\tan A + \tan B}{1 - \tan A \cdot \tan B} \cdot \dfrac{\tan A - \tan B}{1 + \tan A \cdot \tan B}$

$= \dfrac{\tan^2 A - \tan^2 B}{1 - \tan^2 A \cdot \tan^2 B}$

12. $A+B+C+D=360^\circ$

Let smallest angle be x

$x+2x+3x+4x=360^\circ$

$10x=360^\circ$

$x=36^\circ$

in centesimal system.

13. $\alpha+\beta=90^\circ$

$\frac{\beta}{2}+\beta=90^\circ$

$\frac{3\beta}{2}=90^\circ$

$\beta=90^\circ$

$\alpha=30^\circ$

$\tan\alpha\cdot\tan\beta=\frac{1}{\sqrt{3}}\cdot\sqrt{3}$

$=1$

14. $[\sin\alpha+\sin(180-\alpha)+\sin(180+\alpha)]\operatorname{cosec}\alpha$

$=[\sin\alpha+\sin\alpha-\sin\alpha]\cdot\cos ec\alpha$

$=\sin\alpha\cdot\frac{1}{\sin\alpha}$

$=1$

15. $\cot\theta=\frac{3}{4}$

$\frac{\cos\theta}{\sin\theta}=\frac{3}{4}$

$\sqrt{3^2+4^2}=\sqrt{5^2}=5$

$\sin\theta=\frac{-4}{5}$

$\cos\theta=-\frac{3}{5}$

$\sin\theta+\cos\theta=-\frac{4}{5}+\left(-\frac{3}{5}\right)$

$=\frac{-7}{5}$

16. $250^g=\frac{5\pi^c}{4}$

17. $\sin^2 45^\circ+\cos^2 60^\circ+\operatorname{cosec}^2 30^\circ$

$\left(\frac{1}{\sqrt{2}}\right)^2+\left(\frac{1}{2}\right)^2+(2)^2$

$=\frac{2+1+16}{4}$

$=\frac{19}{4}$

18. ABCD cyclic quadrilateral.

$A+C=180^\circ$

$B+D=180^\circ$

$\cos A+\cos B+\cos C+\cos D$

$\cos A+\cos B+\cos(180-A)+\cos(180-B)$

$\cos A+\cos B-\cos A-\cos B$

$=0$

19. $\theta_1=\frac{7}{25},\ \theta_2=\frac{24}{25}$

$\sqrt{7^2+24^2}=\sqrt{25^2}$

$=25$

Therefore, right-angled triangle

$\theta_1+\theta_2=90^\circ$

20. $\tan(1140^\circ)$

$=\tan(780+360^\circ)$

$=\tan(780^\circ)$

$=\tan(420+360^\circ)$

$=\tan(420^\circ)$

$=\tan(360+60^\circ)$

$=\tan(60^\circ)$

$=\sqrt{3}$

21. $\dfrac{\tan\theta+\tan\left(\frac{\pi}{4}\right)}{\tan\theta-\tan\left(\frac{\pi}{4}\right)}$

$=\dfrac{\left(\tan\theta+\tan\left(\frac{\pi}{4}\right)\right)^2}{\tan^2\theta-1}$

On solving, we get, $-\tan\left(\theta+\frac{\pi}{4}\right)$

22. $\operatorname{cosec}\theta+\cot\theta=3$

$\frac{1}{\sin\theta}+\frac{\cos\theta}{\sin\theta}=3$

$\frac{1+\cos\theta}{\sin\theta}=3$

$\frac{1+\cos\theta}{\sqrt{1-\cos^2\theta}}=3$

$= (1+\cos\theta)^2 = 9(1-\cos^2\theta)$

$= 1+\cos^2\theta + 2\cos\theta - 9 + 9\cos^2\theta = 0$

$= 10\cos^2\theta + 2\cos\theta - 8 = 0$

$= 5\cos^2\theta + \cos\theta - 4 = 0$

$= 5\cos^2\theta + 5\cos\theta - 4\cos\theta - 4 = 0$

$= 5\cos\theta(\cos\theta+1) - 4(\cos\theta+1) = 0$

$= (5\cos\theta - 4)(\cos\theta+1) = 0$

$= \cos\theta = \frac{4}{5}, \cos\theta = -1$

Short Answer Type Questions

23. $x = a\sec\theta \Rightarrow \sec\theta = \frac{x}{a}$

$y = b\tan\theta \Rightarrow \tan\theta = \frac{y}{b}$

$\sec^2\theta - \tan^2\theta = 1$

$\Rightarrow \left(\frac{x}{a}\right)^2 - \left(\frac{y}{b}\right)^2 = 1$

$\Rightarrow \frac{x^2}{a^2} - \frac{y^2}{b^2} = 1$

24. $\operatorname{cosec}\theta - \cot\theta = 0$

$\Rightarrow \operatorname{cosec}\theta = \cot\theta$

$\Rightarrow \frac{1}{\sin q} = \frac{\cos q}{\sin q}$

$\Rightarrow \cos\theta = 1 \Rightarrow \sec\theta = 1$

25. $a = b\operatorname{cosec}\theta \Rightarrow \operatorname{cosec}\theta = \frac{a}{b}$

$x = y\tan\theta \Rightarrow \tan\theta = \frac{x}{y} \Rightarrow \cot\theta = \frac{y}{x}$

$\operatorname{cosec}^2\theta - \cot^2\theta = 1 \Rightarrow \left(\frac{a}{b}\right)^2 - \left(\frac{y}{x}\right)^2 = 1$

$\Rightarrow \frac{a^2}{b^2} - \frac{y^2}{x^2} = 1$

26. $x = a\cos\theta + b\sin\theta$

$y = a\sin\theta - b\cos\theta$

$x^2 + y^2 = a^2(\cos^2\theta + \sin^2\theta) + b^2(\sin^2\theta + \cos^2\theta)$

$x^2 + y^2 = a^2 + b^2$

27. (A) $\sin(A+45°)\cdot\sin(A-45°)$

$= \left(\frac{\sin A}{\sqrt{2}} + \frac{\cos A}{\sqrt{2}}\right)\left(\frac{\sin A}{\sqrt{2}} - \frac{\cos A}{\sqrt{2}}\right)$

$= \frac{\sin^2 A}{2} - \frac{\cos^2 A}{2}$

$= \frac{-(\cos^2 A - \sin^2 A)}{2}$

$= \frac{-\cos 2A}{2}$

$= -\frac{1}{2}\cos 2A$

(B) Given that $A + B = 225°$

$\tan(A + B) = \tan 225°$

$\frac{\tan A + \tan B}{1-\tan A\tan B} = \tan(180° + 45°).$

$\frac{\tan A + \tan B}{1-\tan A\tan B} = \tan 45°$

$\frac{\tan A + \tan B}{1-\tan A\tan B} = 1$

$\tan A + \tan B = 1 - \tan A\tan B$

$\tan A + \tan B + \tan A\tan B = 1$

$\tan A(1 + \tan B) + (\tan B + 1) = 1 + 1$

$(1 + \tan B)(\tan A + 1) = 2$

28. $x = a\sin\theta$

$y = b\cos\theta$

$z = a\sin^2\theta + b\cos^2\theta$

$z = a\left(\frac{x^2}{a^2}\right) + b\left(\frac{y^2}{b^2}\right)$

$z = \frac{x^2}{a} + \frac{y^2}{b}$

$zab = bx^2 + ay^2$

29. (A) $\sin A = \frac{3}{5}$

$\cos A = \frac{-4}{5}$

$\tan A = \frac{-3}{4}$

$= \frac{\cos A - \sin 2A}{\tan A + \sec A}$

$= \frac{\frac{-4}{5} + 2\sin A\cos A}{\frac{-3}{4} + \left(\frac{-5}{4}\right)}$

$$= \frac{-\frac{4}{5} - 2 \times \frac{3}{5} \times \left(\frac{-4}{5}\right)}{\frac{-8}{4}}$$

$$= \frac{\frac{4}{5} + \frac{24}{25}}{2} = \frac{44}{25 \times 2}$$

$$= \frac{22}{25}$$

30. $\cos(\alpha - \beta) = \frac{5}{13}$

$\sin(\alpha + \beta) = \frac{4}{5}$

$\sin 2\beta = \sin[\alpha + \beta - \alpha + \beta]$

$= \sin(\alpha + \beta) \cdot \cos(\alpha - \beta) + \cos(\alpha + \beta) \cdot \sin(\alpha - \beta)$

$= \frac{5}{13} \times \frac{4}{5} - \frac{12}{13} \times \frac{3}{5}$

$= \frac{20}{65} - \frac{36}{65}$

$= -\frac{16}{65}$

31. (A) $\frac{1}{\sin\theta} - \frac{\cos\theta}{\sin\theta} = 2$

$1 - \cos\theta = 2\sin\theta$

$1 - \cos\theta = 2\sqrt{1 - \cos^2\theta}$

Squaring both sides,

$(1 - \cos\theta)^2 = 4(1 - \cos^2\theta)$

$1 + \cos^2\theta - 2\cos\theta = 4 - 4\cos^2\theta$

$1 + \cos^2\theta - 2\cos\theta - 4 + 4\cos^2\theta = 0$

$5\cos^2\theta - 2\cos\theta - 3 = 0$

$5\cos^2\theta - 5\cos\theta + 3\cos\theta - 3 = 0$

$5\cos\theta(5\cos\theta - 1) + 3(\cos\theta - 1) = 0$

$(5\cos\theta + 3)(5\cos\theta - 1) = 0$

$\cos\theta = \frac{1}{5}$

$\cos\theta = \frac{-3}{5}$

$\Rightarrow \operatorname{cosec}^2\theta + \cot^2\theta$

$\Rightarrow \frac{1}{\sin^2\theta} + \frac{\cos^2\theta}{\sin^2\theta}$

$= \frac{1 + \cos^2\theta}{1 - \cos^2\theta}$

$= \frac{1 + \frac{9}{25}}{1 - \frac{9}{25}}$

$= \frac{34}{16}$

$= \frac{17}{8}$

(B) Given, $\sin\theta + \frac{1}{\sin\theta} = 2$

$\frac{\sin^2\theta + 1}{\sin\theta} = 2$

$\sin^2\theta + 1 = 2\sin\theta$

$\sin^2\theta + 1 - 2\sin\theta = 0$

$(\sin\theta - 1)^2 = 0$

$\sin\theta - 1 = 0$

$\sin\theta = 1$

$\sin\theta = \sin 90°$

$\theta = 90°$

(i) $\sin^{2015}\theta + \cos^{2015}\theta = \sin^{2015} 90° + \cos^{2015} 90°$

$= (1)^{2015} + (0)^{2015} = 1$

(ii) $\sin^{2016}\theta - \operatorname{cosec}^{2017}\theta$

$= (1)^{2016} - \left(\frac{1}{1}\right)^{2017} = 1 - 1 = 0$

32. $(\operatorname{cosec} A + \cot A)^2 = \left(\frac{1}{\sin A} + \frac{\cos A}{\sin A}\right)^2$

$= \left(\frac{\cos A + 1}{\sin A}\right)^2$

$= \frac{(\cos A + 1)^2}{(\sqrt{1 - \cos^2 A})^2}$

$= \frac{(\cos A + 1)^2}{1 - \cos^2 A}$

$= \frac{(1 + \cos A)^2}{(1 + \cos A)(1 - \cos A)}$

$= \frac{1 + \cos A}{1 - \cos A}$

Hence proved.

33.

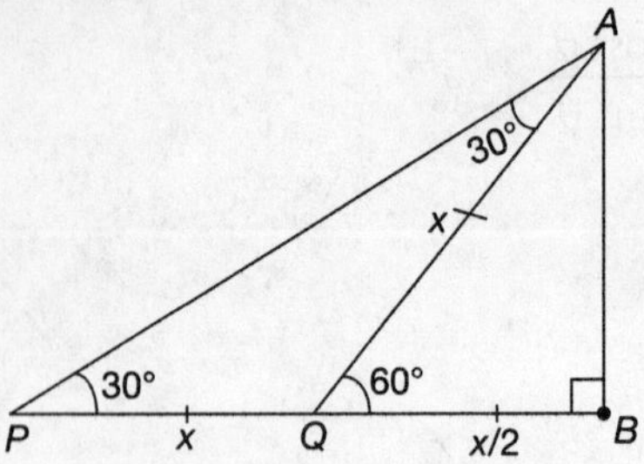

Let AB represent the lighthouse, P and Q be the points of observation. In ΔAPQ,

$\angle APQ = \angle PAQ = 30°$

$\Rightarrow AQ = PQ = x$

In ΔAQB, $\cos 60° = \dfrac{BQ}{x}$.

$\Rightarrow BQ = \dfrac{x}{2}$.

The steamer takes 10 minutes to travel from P to Q (i.e., a distance of x), then it will take $\dfrac{10}{2}$ i.e., 5 minutes to travel QB $(x/2)$.

$\therefore$ It takes 15 minutes for the steamer to travel from P to B. Hence, at the instant when the steamer is at P, the time is 11: 45 a.m.

34. $3\sin A = 4 - 4\cos A$

Squaring both sides,

$9\sin^2 A = 16 + 16\cos^2 A - 32\cos A$

$9(1-\cos^2 A) = 16 + 16\cos^2 A - 32\cos A$

$16\cos^2 A + 9\cos^2 A + 16 - 9 - 32\cos A = 0$

$25\cos^2 A - 32\cos A + 7 = 0$

$25\cos^2 A - 25\cos A - 7\cos A + 7 = 0$

$25\cos A(\cos A - 1) - 7(\cos A - 1) = 0$

$\cos A = 1$

$\cos A = \dfrac{7}{25}$

$\cos A = 1,\ \sin A = 0$

(i) $4\sin A - 3\cos A = 4(0) - 3(1)$

$= -3$

(ii) $\cos A = \dfrac{7}{25},\ \sin A = \dfrac{24}{25}$

$= 4\left(\dfrac{24}{25}\right) - 3\left(\dfrac{7}{25}\right)$

$= \dfrac{75}{25}$

$= 3$

so, ± 3.

35. $\sin\theta = \dfrac{30}{50}$

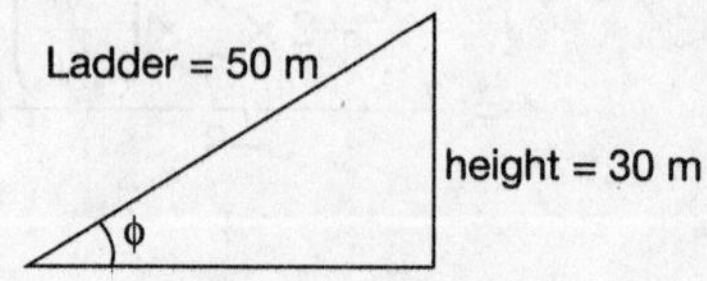

$\sin\theta = \dfrac{3}{5}$

$\theta = \sin^{-1}\left(\dfrac{3}{5}\right)$

Distance $= (50)^2 = (30)^2 + x^2$

$2500 = 900 + x^2$

$x^2 = 1600$

$x = 40$ m

36. $x\sin\alpha - y\cos\alpha = p \qquad \times\cos\alpha$

$x\cos\alpha - y\sin\alpha = q \qquad \times\sin\alpha$

$x\sin\alpha\cos\alpha - y\cos^2\alpha = p\cos\alpha$

$x\cos\alpha\sin\alpha - y\sin^2\alpha = q\sin\alpha$

$(-) \qquad (+) \qquad (-)$

$y(\sin^2\alpha + \cos^2\alpha) = p\cos\alpha - q\sin\alpha$

$y = p\cos\alpha - q\sin\alpha$

$x\sin\alpha + (p\cos\alpha - q\sin\alpha)y = p$

$x\sin\alpha + py\cos\alpha - qy\sin\alpha = p$

$x\sin\alpha = p - py\cos\alpha + qy\sin\alpha$

$\sin\alpha = \dfrac{p - py\cos\alpha + qy\sin\alpha}{x}$

On solving $x^2 + y^2 = p^2 + q^2$

37. $\left(\left(\dfrac{1-\sin\alpha}{\cos\alpha}\right) + \dfrac{\cos\alpha}{(1+\sin\alpha)}\right)\left(\sec\alpha + \dfrac{1}{\cot\alpha}\right)$

$= \left(\dfrac{1-\sin^2\alpha+\cos^2\alpha}{(1+\sin\alpha)\cos\alpha}\right)\left(\dfrac{1}{\cos\alpha} + \dfrac{\sin\alpha}{\cos\alpha}\right)$

$= \dfrac{2\cos^2\alpha}{(1+\sin\alpha)\cos\alpha}\left(\dfrac{1+\sin\alpha}{\cos\alpha}\right)$

$= 2$

Hence proved.

Essay Type Questions

38. $\cos^2 10° + \cos^2 20° + \cos^2 30° + \ldots + \cos^2 90°$

$= (\cos^2 10° + \cos^2 80°) + (\cos^2 20° + \cos^2 70°)$

$+ (\cos^2 30° + \cos^2 60°) + (\cos^2 40° + \cos^2 50°)$

$+ \cos^2 90°$

$= (\cos^2 10° + \sin^2 10°) + (\cos^2 20° + \sin^2 20°)$

$+ (\cos^2 30° + \sin^2 30°) + (\cos^2 40° + \sin^2 40°) + 0^2$

$[\because \cos(90° - \theta) = \sin\theta]$

$= 1 + 1 + 1 + 1 + 0 = 4.$

39. Let AB be the tower and PQ be the building.

Let PQ = h m.

$\therefore$ AC = h m and BC

= AB – AC = (150 – h) m

(Given AB = 150 m)

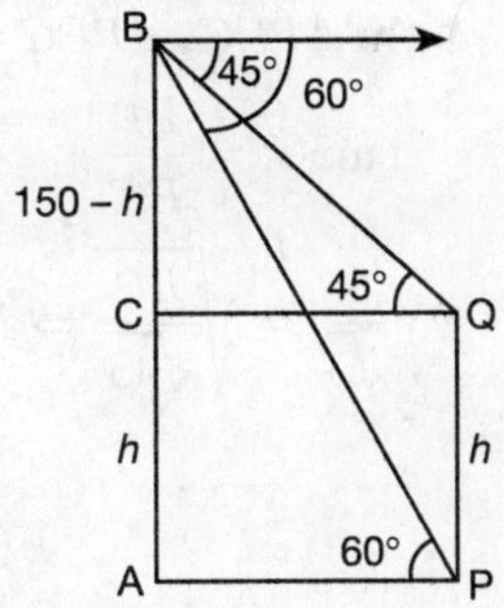

In $\Delta BCQ, \tan 45° \frac{BC}{CQ}$

$\Rightarrow 1 = \frac{150-h}{CQ} \Rightarrow CQ$

$= 150 - h$

$\therefore$ AP = CQ = 150 – h

In ΔBAP, $\tan 60° \frac{AB}{AP} \Rightarrow \sqrt{3} = \frac{150}{150-h}$

$\Rightarrow 150 - h = \frac{150}{\sqrt{3}} \times \frac{\sqrt{3}}{\sqrt{3}} \Rightarrow 150 - h = 50\sqrt{3}$

$\Rightarrow h = 50\left(3-\sqrt{3}\right)$ m

40. $\sin^2 5° + \sin^2 15° + \sin^2 25° + ... + \sin^2 85°$

$= (\sin^2 5° + \sin^2 85°) + (\sin^2 15° + \sin^2 75°)$

$+ (\sin^2 25° + \sin^2 65°) + (\sin^2 35° + \sin^2 55°)$

$+ \sin^2 45°$

$= (\sin^2 5° + \cos^2 5°) + (\sin^2 15° + \cos^2 15°)$

$+ (\sin^2 25° + \cos^2 25°) + (\sin^2 35° + \cos^2 35°)$

$+\left(\frac{1}{\sqrt{2}}\right)^2$

[$\because \sin (90° – \theta) = \cos \theta$]

$= 1+1+1+1+\frac{1}{2} = 4\frac{1}{2}$

41. Let AB and PQ be the building and towers, respectively.

Let QR = x m and BR = AP = y m

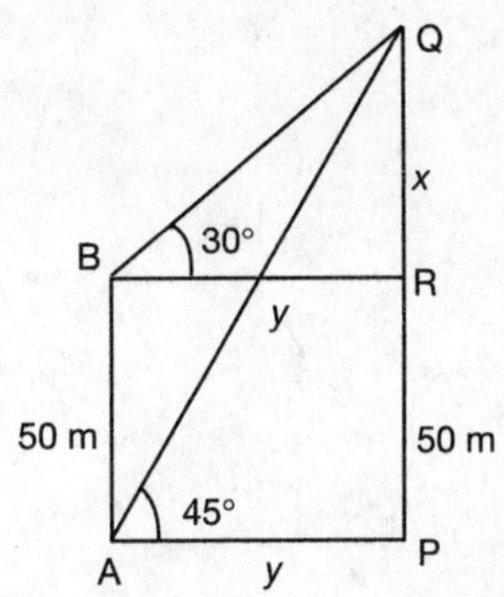

In ΔBQR, $\tan 30° = \frac{x}{y}$

$\Rightarrow \frac{1}{\sqrt{3}} = \frac{x}{y} \Rightarrow y = \sqrt{3}x$ ...(1)

In ΔAQP, $\tan 45° = \frac{PQ}{AP}$

$\Rightarrow 1 = \frac{50+x}{y} \Rightarrow y = 50 + x \Rightarrow \sqrt{3}x = 50 + x$ [From Eq. (1)]

$\Rightarrow x\left(\sqrt{3}-1\right) = 50$

$\Rightarrow x = \frac{50}{\sqrt{3}-1} \times \frac{\sqrt{3}+1}{\sqrt{3}+1} = \frac{50\left(\sqrt{3}+1\right)}{2} = 25\left(\sqrt{3}+1\right)$ m

Height of the tower = x + 50 = $25\sqrt{3} + 25 + 50$

$= 25\sqrt{3} + 75 = 25(\sqrt{3} + 3)$

42.

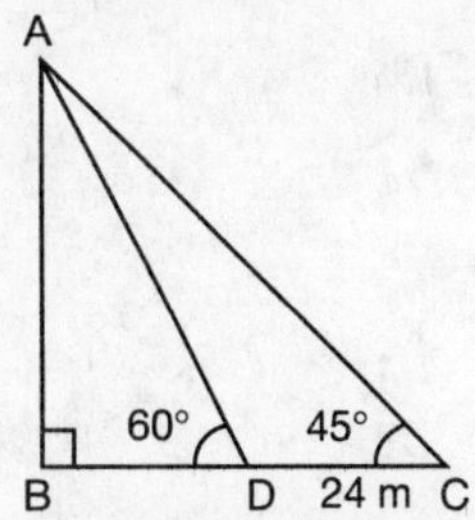

Let AB is a tower.

In $\Delta ABC, \tan 45° = \frac{AB}{AC}$

$1 = \frac{AB}{BD + DC}$

BD + CD = AB

BD + 24 = AB (1)

In ΔABD, $\tan 60° = \frac{AB}{BD}$

$\sqrt{3} = \frac{AB}{BD}$

$BD = \frac{AB}{\sqrt{3}}$ (2)

From Eqs (1) and (2) $\Rightarrow \frac{AB}{\sqrt{3}} + 24 = AB$

$24 = AB - \frac{AB}{\sqrt{3}}$

$24 = AB\frac{\left(\sqrt{3}-1\right)}{\sqrt{3}}$

$\Rightarrow AB = \frac{24\left(\sqrt{3}\right)}{\left(\sqrt{3}-1\right)} = \frac{24\sqrt{3} \times \left(\sqrt{3}+1\right)}{2}$

$= 12\sqrt{3}\left(\sqrt{3}+1\right) = 36 + 12\sqrt{3}$ m

= 36 + 12 × 1.732

= 36 + 20.784

= 56.784 m

43. Given $AB = BC = CD = AD = 6\text{m}$

In ΔABC, $\angle EBC = 90°$

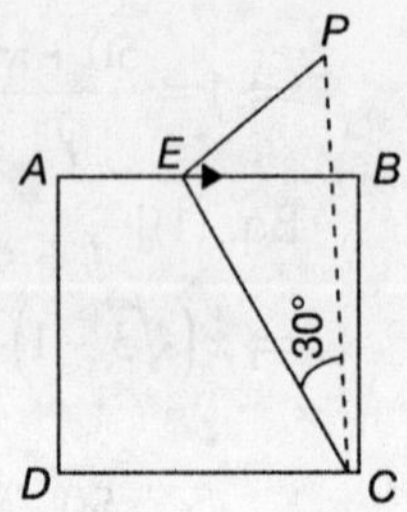

$$EC = \sqrt{BC^2 + EB^2}$$

$$= \sqrt{BC^2 + \left(\frac{AB}{2}\right)^2}$$

$$= \sqrt{36+9}$$

$$= \sqrt{45}\ \text{m}.$$

In ΔPEC, $\angle PEC = 90°$ and $\angle ECP = 30°$.

$$\tan 30° = \frac{EP}{EC}$$

$$\frac{1}{\sqrt{3}} = \sqrt{\frac{EP}{\sqrt{45}}} \Rightarrow EP = \frac{\sqrt{45}}{\sqrt{3}} = \sqrt{15}\ \text{m}$$

Competition Wing

Level 1: Apply Your Concepts

1. $\sin\theta = \dfrac{1}{2}$

30°, or 150°

2. $\cot\theta = \dfrac{\cos\theta}{\sin\theta}$

$\sin^2\theta + \cos^2\theta = 1$

$\dfrac{\sqrt{1-\sin^2\theta}}{\sin\theta}$

3. $\sin A \cdot \cos B + \cos A \sin B$

$\sin A \cdot \cos(90 - A) + \cos A \sin(90 - A)$

$\sin^2 A + \cos^2 B = 1$

4. Length of arc $= \dfrac{\text{(angle of sector)}}{360} \cdot 2\pi r$

$= \left(\dfrac{45}{360}\right) 2\pi(28)$

$= 7\pi$

$= 7 \times 3.14$

$= 22$ cm.

5. ABCD cyclic quadrilateral

$A + C = 90°$

$\tan(A+C) = \dfrac{\tan A + \tan C}{1 - \tan A \cdot \tan C}$

$\tan(90°)\cdot(1 - \tan A \tan C) = \tan(A) + \tan(C)$

$\tan(A) + \tan(C) = 0°$

6. Given $\tan A = \dfrac{5}{12}$ and A is not in the quadrant I.

$\Rightarrow$ A is in the quadrant III

$AC^2 = AB^2 + BC^2 = 5^2 + 12^2$

$\Rightarrow AC^2 = 13^2 \Rightarrow AC = 13$

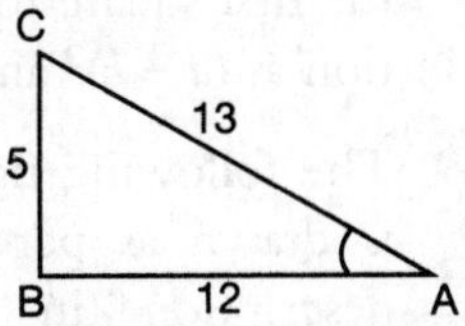

$\sin A = \dfrac{-5}{13}$ and $\cos A = \dfrac{-12}{13}$

($\because$ A is in the quadrant III.)

$\therefore \dfrac{\sin A + \cos A}{\sin A - \cos A} = \dfrac{\dfrac{-5}{13} - \dfrac{12}{13}}{\dfrac{-5}{13} + \dfrac{12}{13}} = \dfrac{-17}{7}$

Hence, the correct option is (b).

7. $\dfrac{1 + \tan A}{1 - \tan A} = \tan 75°$

$\Rightarrow \dfrac{\tan 45° + \tan A}{1 - \tan 45° \tan A} = \tan 75°$

$\Rightarrow \tan(45° + A) = \tan 75° \Rightarrow 45° + A = 75°$

$\Rightarrow A = 30°$

Hence, the correct option is (a).

8. $5\cot^2 A = \sin^2 60° + \sec^2 30° = \left(\dfrac{\sqrt{3}}{2}\right)^2 + \left(\dfrac{2}{\sqrt{3}}\right)^2$

$\Rightarrow 5\cot^2 A = \dfrac{3}{4} + \dfrac{4}{3} = \dfrac{25}{12} \Rightarrow \cot^2 A = \dfrac{5}{12}$

$\therefore \text{cosec}^2 A = 1 + \cot^2 A = 1 + \dfrac{5}{12} = \dfrac{17}{12}$

Hence, the correct option is (c).

9. Given $\cos A = \dfrac{8}{17}$ and A is not in 1st quadrant.

$\Rightarrow$ A is in the 4th quadrant.

$AC^2 = AB^2 + BC^2 \Rightarrow 17^2 = 8^2 + BC^2$

$\Rightarrow BC^2 = 225 \Rightarrow BC = 15$

$\text{cosec } A = \dfrac{-17}{15}, \cot A = \dfrac{-8}{15}$

($\because$ A is in the 4th quadrant)

$\dfrac{\text{cosec } A + \cot A}{\text{cosec } A - \cot A} = \dfrac{\dfrac{-17}{15} - \dfrac{8}{15}}{\dfrac{-17}{15} + \dfrac{8}{15}} = \dfrac{25}{9}$

Hence, the correct option is (c).

10. $\dfrac{1 - \tan q}{1 + \tan q} = \tan 30°$

$\Rightarrow \dfrac{\tan 45° - \tan q}{1 + \tan 45° \tan q} = \tan 30°$

$\Rightarrow \tan(45° - \theta) = \tan 30°$

$\Rightarrow 45° - \theta = 30° \Rightarrow \theta = 15°$

Hence, the correct option is (a).

11. $\sec^2 A = \cot^2 30° + 2\cos^2 45° = \left(\sqrt{3}\right)^2 + 2 \times \left(\dfrac{1}{\sqrt{2}}\right)^2 = 4$

$\Rightarrow \cos^2 A = \dfrac{1}{4}$

$\therefore \sin^2 A = 1 - \cos^2 A = 1 - \dfrac{1}{4} = \dfrac{3}{4}$

Hence, the correct option is (c).

12. Find the angle covered in one hour.

13. $a^4 - b^4 = (a^2 - b^2)(a^2 + b^2)$.

14. Write $\sec\theta$ and $\tan\theta$ in terms of $\sin\theta$ and $\cos\theta$.

15. Use the identity $\sec^2\theta - \tan^2\theta = 1$.

16. Simplify the given expression and find $\sec\alpha - \tan\alpha$.

17. $a^4 - b^4 = (a^2 - b^2)(a^2 + b^2)$.

18. $\tan\theta = \cot(90 - \theta)$ and $\tan\theta \cdot \cot\theta = 1$.

19. $A + B + C = 180°$.

20. Use the identity $\tan(A - B) = \dfrac{\tan A - \tan B}{1 + \tan A \tan B}$.

21. $a^4 - b^4 = (a^2 - b^2)(a^2 + b^2)$.

22. Use $a^3 - b^3 = (a - b)(a^2 + ab + b^2)$.

23. Recall the range of $\cos\theta$.

24. Use complementary angles.

25. Replace $\operatorname{cosec} A$ by $\dfrac{1}{\sin A}$ and $\sec A$ by $\dfrac{1}{\cos A}$.

26. Use $\operatorname{cosec}^2\theta - \cot^2\theta = 1$.

27. Simplify the numerator and denominator by taking common terms appropriately.

28. Take LCM and simplify.

29. $\tan(\alpha + \beta) = \dfrac{\tan\alpha + \tan\beta}{1 - \tan\alpha \tan\beta}$.

30. $\log a + \log b + \log c + \cdots = \log(a \cdot b \cdot c \cdots)$.

31. Recall the ranges of $\sin\theta$ and $\cos\theta$.

32. $\sin(180 - \theta) = \sin\theta$.

33. Simplify the expression.

34. Equal chords subtend equal angles at the centre ($2r\sin 60°$).

35. (i) $1°$ is always less than 1^c.

(ii) The value $\sin\theta$ increases from $0°$ to $90°$.

Level 2: Review Your Concepts

36. Put $2\sin\alpha - 3\cos\alpha = k$, square the two equations and add.

37. Use the identity $\cos^2\alpha + \sin^2\alpha = 1$ and convert the equation into quadratic form in terms of $\sin\alpha$ and then solve.

38. (i) $\cot\theta$ is positive in the first and the third quadrants. As A is not in first quadrant, A is in the third quadrant.

(ii) Using the right angle triangle find the values of $\sin A$, $\cos A$ and $\cot A$ in third quadrant.

39. Apply componendo–dividendo rule, i.e., if $\dfrac{a}{b} = \dfrac{c}{d}$, then $\dfrac{a+b}{a-b} = \dfrac{c+d}{c-d}$.

40. Square the given equation, then use the identity $\cos^2\theta + \sin^2\theta = 1$ to evaluate the value of $\sin\theta\cos\theta$.

41. (i) In a cyclic quadrilateral, sum of the opposite angles is 180°.

(ii) Use the result, $\cos(180 - \theta) = -\cos\theta$ and simplify.

42. $l = r\theta$, where l = length, r = radians and θ = angle in radians.

43. Use the results $\sin^2 88 = \cos^2 2$ and $\sin^2\theta + \cos^2\theta = 1$ to simplify the given expression.

44. Use $\tan\theta$ = opposite side/adjacent side in the triangles so formed.

45.

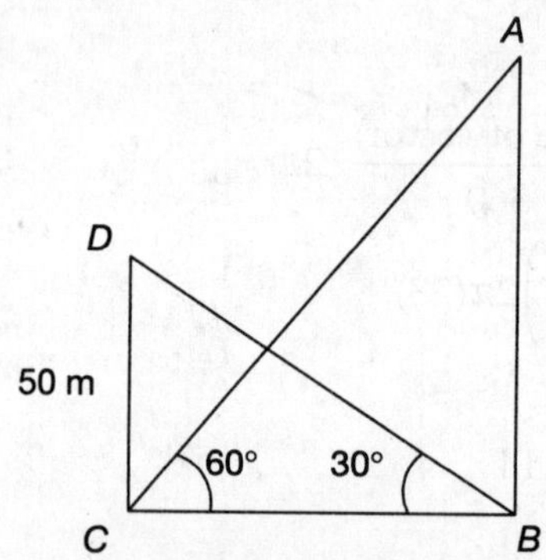

Use the figure, by taking the values of $\tan 30°$ from ΔBCD and $\tan 60°$ from ΔABC, find CD.

46. (i) Convert the given trigonometric values in terms of $\sin\theta$, $\cos\theta$, then simplify to obtain the required value.

(ii) Use the formula, cost $(A + B) = \cos A \cdot \cos B - \sin A \cdot \sin B$.

47. Take LCM and use the identity $\sin^2\theta + \cos^2\theta = 1$ to simplify the given equation.

48. Express the square root function as $(a + b)^2$ and remove the first square root. Again express the obtained function as $(a - b)^2$ and then simplify.

49. The following figure is drawn as per the description in the problem.

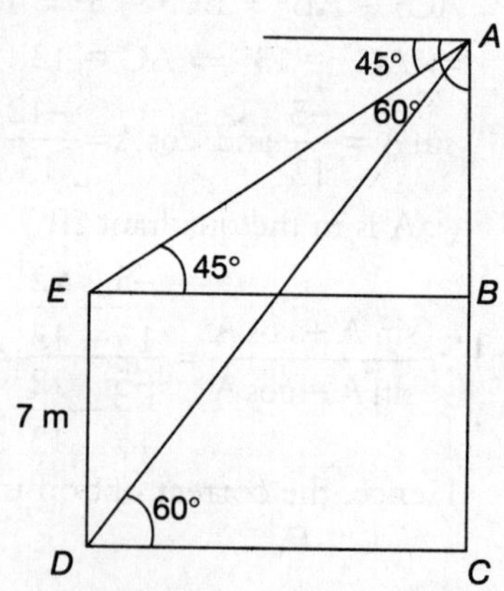

Use the figure, to find DC from ΔADC and AB from ΔAEB as $DC = BE$.

50. Express $\tan 176° = -\cot 86°$, $\cot 4° = \tan 86°$ and $\tan 4° = \cot 86°$. Then substitute these values to simplify the given expression.

51. (C), (A), and (D) are in sequential order from first to last.

Level 3: Assess Your Concepts

52. Draw the figure as per the description given in the problem. Two right triangles are formed. Use appropriate trigonometric ratios by considering each of the triangle and find the height of the tree.

53. Draw a right triangle according to the data and take the ratio of $\sin\theta$ to evaluate the height of the balloon from the ground.

54. (i) Divide the equation with $2\sqrt{2}$.

Then substitute $\frac{1}{2} = \cos 60°$ and $\frac{\sqrt{3}}{2} = \sin 60°$.

(ii) Now apply the formula,

$\cos(A + B) = \cos A \cos B - \sin A \sin B$ then obtain the value of θ.

55. (i) Draw a figure as per the situation described then use the concept, $\sin\theta = \frac{\text{Opposite side to } \theta}{\text{Hypotenuse}}$.

(ii) Given θ and opposite side, find hypotenuse which is the required length of the rope.

56. $\sin^2 5° + \sin^2 10° + \sin^2 15° + \cdots + \sin^2 90°$

$= (\sin^2 5° + \sin^2 85°) + (\sin^2 10° + \sin^2 80°) + \cdots +$

$\sin^2 45 + \sin^2 90° \, (\sin 85° = \cos 5°)$

$= 8 + \left(\frac{1}{\sqrt{2}}\right)^2 + 1 = 9 + \frac{1}{2} = \frac{19}{2}.$

57. Given,

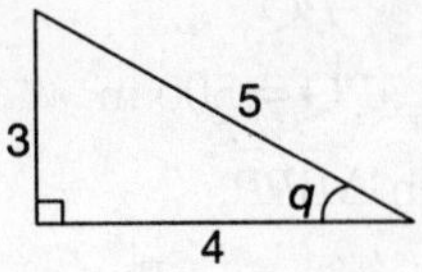

$\sec\theta + \tan\theta = 2$ (1)

$\sec\theta - \tan\theta = \frac{1}{2}$ (2)

Adding Eqs. (1) and (2), we get,

$2\sec\theta = \frac{5}{2}$

$\Rightarrow \sec\theta = \frac{5}{4}$

$\Rightarrow \cos\theta = \frac{4}{5}$

$\sin\theta = \frac{3}{5}.$

58. Given,

$\cos\theta + \left(\frac{1}{\sqrt{3}}\right)\sin\theta = \frac{2}{\sqrt{3}}$

$\Rightarrow \left(\frac{\sqrt{3}}{2}\right)\cos\theta + \left(\frac{1}{2}\right)\sin\theta = 1$

$\Rightarrow \sin 60° \cos\theta + \sin\theta \cos 60° = 1$

$\Rightarrow \sin(60° + \theta) = \sin 90°$

$\Rightarrow 60° + \theta = 90°$

$\Rightarrow \theta = 30° = \frac{\pi^c}{6}.$

59. $\sqrt{\frac{1+\sin\theta}{1-\sin\theta}} = \sqrt{\frac{(1+\sin\theta)(1+\sin\theta)}{(1-\sin\theta)(1+\sin\theta)}}$

$= \sqrt{\frac{(1+\sin\theta)^2}{1-\sin^2\theta}}$

$= \frac{1+\sin\theta}{\cos\theta} = \sec\theta + \tan\theta.$

60. $\sin^2\theta - 5\sin\theta + 3 = \cos^2\theta$

$\Rightarrow \sin^2\theta - 5\sin\theta + 3 = 1 - \sin^2\theta$

$\Rightarrow 2\sin^2\theta - 5\sin\theta + 2 = 0$

$\Rightarrow (2\sin\theta - 1)(\sin\theta - 2) = 0$

$\sin\theta = 2$ or $\frac{1}{2}$.

But $\sin\theta = 2$ is not possible

$\therefore \sin\theta = \frac{1}{2} \Rightarrow \theta = 30°.$

61. Given, $\cot\theta = \frac{24}{7}$

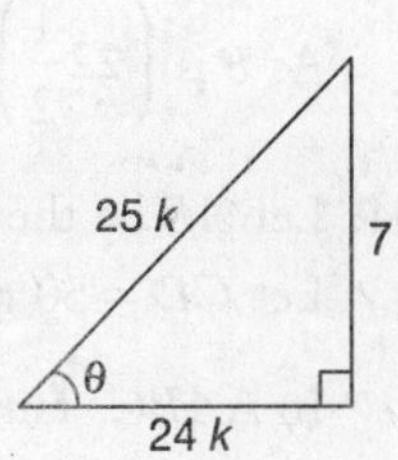

As $\tan\theta$ is positive and $\theta \notin Q_1$,

$\theta \in Q_3$.

$\therefore \sec\theta = -\frac{25}{24}$

$\tan\theta = \frac{7}{24}$

Now $\tan\theta - \sec\theta = \frac{7}{24} + \frac{25}{24}$

$= \frac{32}{24} = \frac{4}{3}.$

62. Given, $\sin 20° = p$

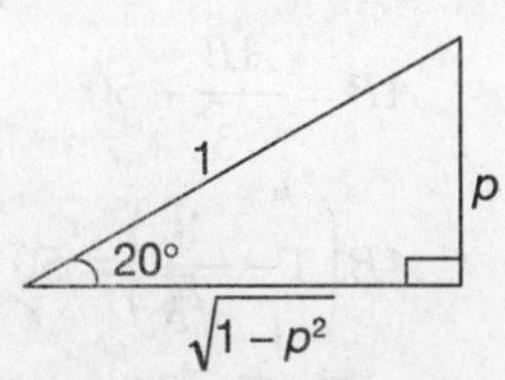

$\sin 380° = \sin(360° + 20°)$

$= \sin 20°$

$\sin 340° = \sin(360° - 20°)$

$= -\sin 20°$

$\cos 380° = \cos(360° + 20°)$

$= \cos 20°$

$\cos 340° = \cos(360° - 20°)$

$= \cos 20°$

$$\therefore \left(\frac{\sin 380 - \sin 340}{\cos 380 + \cos 340}\right) = \frac{\sin 20 - (-\sin 20)}{\cos 20 + \cos 20}$$

$$= \frac{2\sin 20°}{2\cos 20°}$$

$$= \tan 20° = \frac{p}{\sqrt{1-p^2}}.$$

63. We have, $\tan 2\theta = \dfrac{2\tan\theta}{1-\tan^2\theta}$

Let $\theta = \left(22\frac{1}{2}\right)^\circ \Rightarrow 2\theta = 45°$

$$\therefore \tan 45° = \frac{2\tan\theta}{1-\tan^2\theta}.$$

$$1 = \frac{2\tan\theta}{1-\tan^2\theta}$$

$\Rightarrow 1 - \tan^2\theta = 2\tan\theta$

$\Rightarrow \tan^2\theta + 2\tan\theta - 1 = 0$

$$\tan\theta = \frac{-2 \pm \sqrt{2^2 - 4(1)(-1)}}{2(1)}$$

$$= \frac{-2 \pm \sqrt{8}}{2} = -1 \pm \sqrt{2}.$$

As θ is $\left(22\frac{1}{2}\right)^\circ$, $\tan\left(22\frac{1}{2}\right)^\circ = \sqrt{2} - 1$.

64. Let AB be the height of the tower.

Let $CD = 50$ m (given)

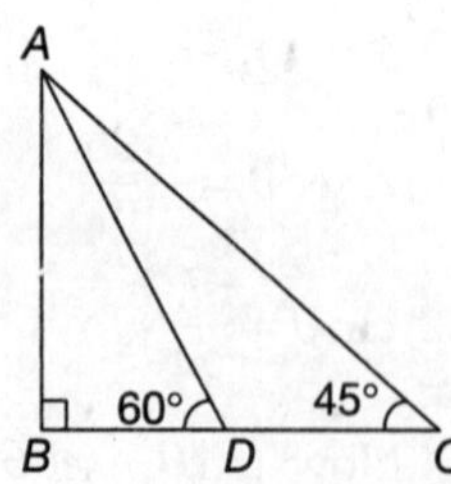

In ΔABC, $\tan 45° = \dfrac{AB}{BC}$

$\Rightarrow 1 = \dfrac{AB}{BD + CD}$ (1)

$\Rightarrow AB = BD + 50$

In ΔABD,

$\tan 60° = \dfrac{AB}{BD} \Rightarrow \sqrt{3} = \dfrac{AB}{BD}$

$\Rightarrow BD = \dfrac{AB}{\sqrt{3}}$ (substitute BD in Eq. (1))

$$AB = \frac{AB}{\sqrt{3}} + 50$$

$$AB\left(1 - \frac{1}{\sqrt{3}}\right) = 50$$

$$AB\left(\frac{\sqrt{3}-1}{\sqrt{3}}\right) = 50$$

$$AB = \frac{50\sqrt{3}}{\sqrt{3}-1} = \frac{50\sqrt{3}(\sqrt{3}+1)}{3-1}$$

$$= 25(3+\sqrt{3}) \text{ m.}$$

65. For the maximum possible distance, two points lie on either side of the tower.

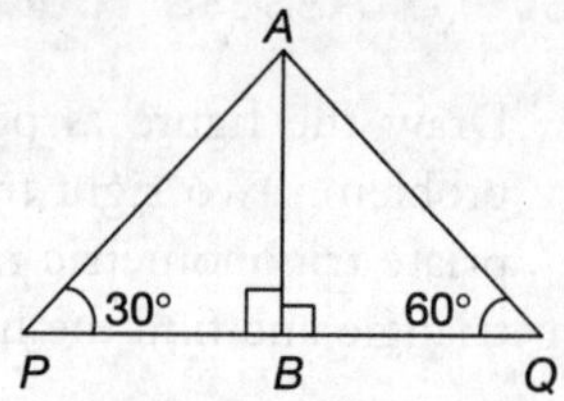

Let AB be the height of the tower.

$AB = 30$ m (given)

Let P and Q be the given points.

In ΔABP,

$$\tan 30° = \frac{AB}{PB} \Rightarrow \frac{1}{\sqrt{3}} = \frac{30}{PB} \Rightarrow PB = 30\sqrt{3}.$$

In ΔABQ, $\tan 60° = \dfrac{AB}{BQ}$

$$\Rightarrow \sqrt{3} = \frac{30}{BQ} \Rightarrow BQ = \frac{30}{\sqrt{3}} \text{ m.}$$

Now, $PQ = PB + BQ$

$$= 30\sqrt{3} + \frac{30}{\sqrt{3}} = 30\left(\sqrt{3} + \frac{1}{\sqrt{3}}\right)$$

$$= 30\left(\frac{4}{\sqrt{3}}\right) = 40\sqrt{3} \text{ m.}$$

66. Let A and B be the initial and final positions of the plane.

Given, $AQ = 500$ m

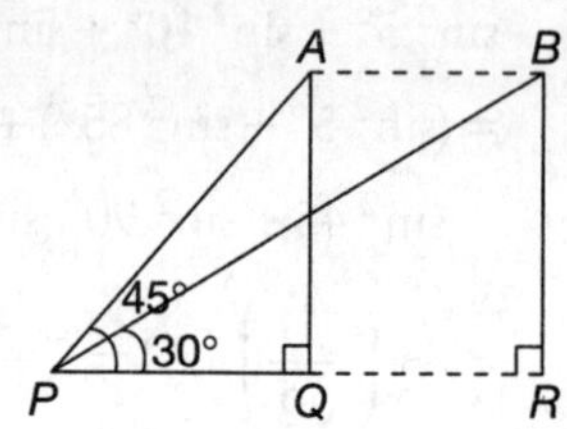

$\therefore BR = 500$ m ($AQ = BR$)

In ΔAPQ,

$$\tan 45° = \frac{AQ}{PQ}$$

$$1 = \frac{500}{PQ}$$

$\therefore PQ = 500$ m.

In ΔBPR,

$$\tan 30° = \frac{BR}{PR}$$

$$\frac{1}{\sqrt{3}} = \frac{500}{PQ + QR} \Rightarrow 500 + QR = 500\sqrt{3}$$

$QR = 500(\sqrt{3} - 1)$ m

$\therefore AB = 500(\sqrt{3} - 1)$ m.

$$\text{Speed of the plane} = \frac{AB}{\text{Time}}$$

$$= \left(\frac{500(\sqrt{3}-1)}{5}\right) \text{m/s}$$

$= 100(\sqrt{3}-1)$ m/s

$= 100(\sqrt{3}-1)\left(\frac{18}{5}\right)$ kmph

$= 360(\sqrt{3}-1)$ kmph.

67. AB be the height of the building.

$\therefore AB = 5$ m (given)

Let PQ be the height of the tower.

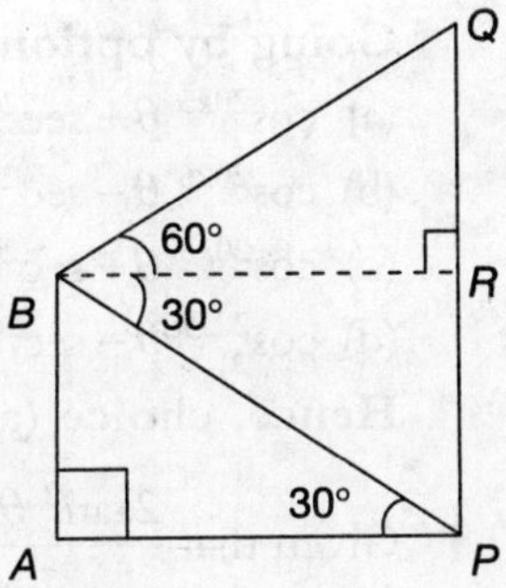

In ΔABP,

$\tan 30° = \frac{AB}{AP} \Rightarrow \frac{1}{\sqrt{3}} = \frac{5}{AP}$.

$\therefore AP = 5\sqrt{3} \Rightarrow \therefore BR = 5\sqrt{3}$ m

In ΔBQR, $\tan 60° = \frac{QR}{BR}$

$\sqrt{3} = \frac{QR}{5\sqrt{3}} \Rightarrow QR = 15$ m.

From the figure, $PQ = PR + QR$

$= 5 + 15 = 20$ m.

68. Let $\angle FAE = \theta_1$, and $\angle HAG = \theta_2$

$\tan \theta_1 = \frac{FE}{AE} = \frac{1}{2}$

$\tan \theta_2 = \frac{HG}{AG} = \frac{1}{3}$

$\tan(\theta_1 + \theta_2) = \frac{\tan\theta_1 + \tan\theta_2}{1 - \tan\theta_1 \tan\theta_2}$

$= \frac{\frac{1}{2}+\frac{1}{3}}{1-\left(\frac{1}{2}\right)\left(\frac{1}{3}\right)}$

$= \frac{\frac{5}{6}}{\frac{5}{6}} = 1$

$\tan(\theta_1 + \theta_2) = \tan 45°$

$\Rightarrow \theta_1 + \theta_2 = 45°$

$\angle FAE + \angle HAG = 45°$.

JEE Special Wing

Multiple-Answer Type Questions

1. **Going by options:**

(a) $\frac{\pi^c}{4}+45^\circ=\frac{200^g}{4}+\frac{45^\circ}{180^\circ}\times 200^g$

$=50^g+50^g=100^g$

(b) $54^\circ+\frac{\pi^c}{5}=\frac{54^\circ}{180^\circ}\times 200^g+\frac{200^g}{5}$

$=60^g+40^g=100^g$

(c) $108^\circ-\frac{\pi^c}{10}=\frac{108^\circ}{180^\circ}\times 200^g-\frac{200^g}{10}$

$=120^g-20^g=100^g$

(d) $\frac{4\pi^c}{5}-54^\circ=\frac{4\times 200^g}{5}-\frac{54^\circ}{180^\circ}\times 200^g$

$=160^g-60^g=100^g$

Hence, all the given options are equivalent to 100^g.

Hence, choice (a, b, c, d) are correct.

2. **Going by options:**

(a) $\sec 30^\circ=\frac{2}{\sqrt{3}}$.

(b) $\text{cosec}120^\circ=\text{cosec}(180^\circ-60^\circ)=\text{cosec}60^\circ=\frac{2}{\sqrt{3}}$.

(c) $\sec 330^\circ=\sec(360^\circ-30^\circ)=\sec 30^\circ=\frac{2}{\sqrt{3}}$.

(d) $\text{cosec}420^\circ=\text{cosec}(360^\circ+60)=\text{cosec}60^\circ=\frac{2}{\sqrt{3}}$.

Hence, all the given options are equivalent to $\frac{2}{\sqrt{3}}$.

Hence, choice (a, b, c, d) are correct.

3. $\sin 30^\circ.\cos 60^\circ+\sin 60^\circ.\cos 30^\circ=\sin(30^\circ+60^\circ)$
$=\sin 90^\circ=1.$

Going by options:

(a) $\sin 90^\circ=1.$

(b) $\tan 225^\circ=\tan(180^\circ+45^\circ)=\tan 45^\circ=1.$

(c) $\sec 360^\circ=\sec(360^\circ+0^\circ)=\sec 0^\circ=1.$

(d) $\text{cosec } 270^\circ=\text{cosec}(270^\circ-0^\circ)=-\text{cosec } 0^\circ$, which is undefined.

Hence, choice (a, b, c) are correct.

4. Given that $\cos\theta+\sec\theta=2.$

$\Rightarrow \cos\theta+\frac{1}{\cos\theta}=2$

$\Rightarrow \cos^2\theta+1=2\cos\theta$

$\Rightarrow \cos^2\theta-2\cos\theta+1=0$

$\Rightarrow (\cos\theta-1)^2=0$

$\Rightarrow \cos\theta-1=0$

$\Rightarrow \cos\theta=1 \Rightarrow \sec\theta=1.$

Going by options:

(a) $\cos^{2025}\theta+\sec^{2025}\theta=1^{2025}+1^{2025}=1+1=2.$

(b) $\cos^{2026}\theta-\sec^{2026}\theta=1^{2026}-1^{2026}=1-1=0.$

(c) $\cos^{2026}\theta+\sec^{2027}\theta=1^{2026}+1^{2027}=1+1=2.$

(d) $\cos^{2028}\theta-\sec^{2029}\theta=1^{2028}-1^{2029}=1-1=0.$

Hence, choice (a and c) are correct.

5. Given that $\frac{2\tan^2\theta-3\tan\theta-3}{\sec^2\theta}=1.$

$\Rightarrow \frac{2\tan^2\theta-3\tan\theta-3}{1+\tan^2\theta}=1$

$\Rightarrow 2\tan^2\theta-3\tan\theta-3=1+\tan^2\theta$

$\Rightarrow \tan^2\theta-3\tan\theta-4=0$

$\Rightarrow \tan^2\theta-4\tan\theta+\tan\theta-4=0$

$\Rightarrow \tan\theta(\tan\theta-4)+1(\tan\theta-4)=0$

$\Rightarrow (\tan\theta-4)(\tan\theta+1)=0$

$\Rightarrow \tan\theta=4$ or $\tan\theta=-1.$

Hence, choice (a and d) are correct.

6. Given set of values is $(-\infty,-1)$.

The range of the values satisfied by $\sin\theta$ (or) $\cos\theta$ is $[-1,1]$.

The range of the values satisfied by $\tan\theta$ (or) $\cot\theta$ is $(-\infty,\infty)$.

The range of the values satisfied by $\sec\theta$ (or) $\text{cosec}\theta$ is $(-\infty,1]\cup[1,\infty)$.

Hence, choice (a, c, d) are correct.

Match The Column

Common Solutions for questions 7 to 10:

$AC=MN=600$ m.

$\angle MPB=45^\circ$ and $\angle NPD=60^\circ$

$\angle MPA=30^\circ$ and $\angle NPC=45^\circ$

$\Rightarrow \angle MPA=\angle QAP=30^\circ$ and $\angle NPC=\angle QCP=45^\circ$.

Let QC be x m.

$\therefore AQ=(600-x)$ m.

$\Rightarrow QC=PN=x\ m$ and $AQ=MP=(600-x)$ m.

In ΔAQP, $\tan 30^\circ=\frac{PQ}{AQ}$.

$\frac{1}{\sqrt{3}}=\frac{PQ}{600-x}$

$\Rightarrow PQ = \dfrac{600 - x}{\sqrt{3}}$ (1)

In ΔCQP, $\tan 45° = \dfrac{PQ}{QC}$.

$1 = \dfrac{PQ}{x}$

$\Rightarrow PQ = x$ (2)

From (1) and (2), $x = \dfrac{600 - x}{\sqrt{3}}$.

$\Rightarrow \sqrt{3}x = 600 - x$

$\Rightarrow \sqrt{3}x + x = 600$

$\Rightarrow \left(\sqrt{3} + 1\right)x = 600$

$\Rightarrow x = \dfrac{600}{\left(\sqrt{3} + 1\right)}$

$\Rightarrow x = 300\left(\sqrt{3} - 1\right)$

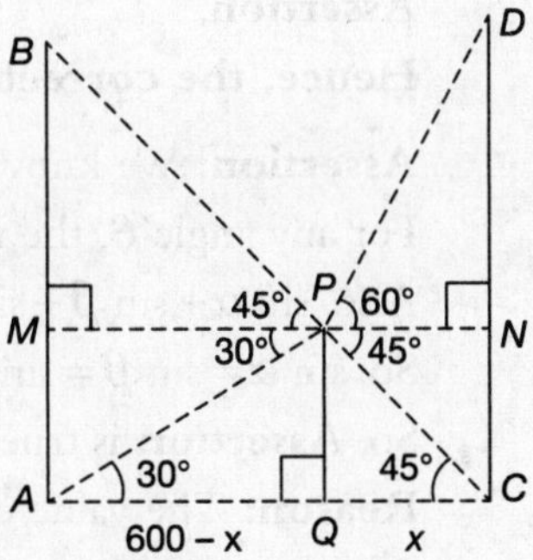

Hence, $PQ = AM = NC = PN = 300\left(\sqrt{3} - 1\right)$ m.

In ΔCAB, $\tan 45° = \dfrac{AB}{AC}$.

$1 = \dfrac{AB}{600}$

$\Rightarrow$ AB = 600 m.

7. $AB - PQ = 600 - 300\left(\sqrt{3} - 1\right)$

$= 300\left(2 - \sqrt{3} + 1\right) = 300\left(3 - \sqrt{3}\right)$ m.

Hence, the correct option is (c).

8. In ΔAQP, $\sin 30° = \dfrac{PQ}{AP}$.

$\dfrac{1}{2} = \dfrac{300\left(\sqrt{3} - 1\right)}{AP}$

$\Rightarrow AP = 600\left(\sqrt{3} - 1\right)$ m.

In ΔDNP, $\sin 60° = \dfrac{DN}{PD}$

$\Rightarrow \dfrac{\sqrt{3}}{2} = \dfrac{300\left(\sqrt{3} - 1\right)\sqrt{3}}{PD}$

$\Rightarrow \dfrac{1}{2} = \dfrac{300\left(\sqrt{3} - 1\right)}{PD}$

$\Rightarrow$ PD $= 600\left(\sqrt{3} - 1\right)$ m.

$\Rightarrow AP = PD$

$\Rightarrow AP - PD = 0$.

Hence, the correct option is (a).

9. In ΔDNP, $\tan 60° = \dfrac{DN}{PN}$.

$\Rightarrow \sqrt{3} = \dfrac{DN}{300\left(\sqrt{3} - 1\right)}$

$\Rightarrow DN = 300\left(\sqrt{3} - 1\right)\sqrt{3} = 300\left(3 - \sqrt{3}\right)$

Now, $CD = NC + DN$.

$= 300\left(\sqrt{3} - 1\right) + 300\left(3 - \sqrt{3}\right) = 600$ m.

Hence, the correct option is (d).

10. As $AB = CD = AC$, and AB and CD are perpendicular to AC, $ACBD$ is a square.

Hence, $AD = \sqrt{2}\,AC = 600\sqrt{2}$ m.

Hence, the correct option is (e).

Comprehension-Based Questions

Common Solutions for questions 11 to 14:

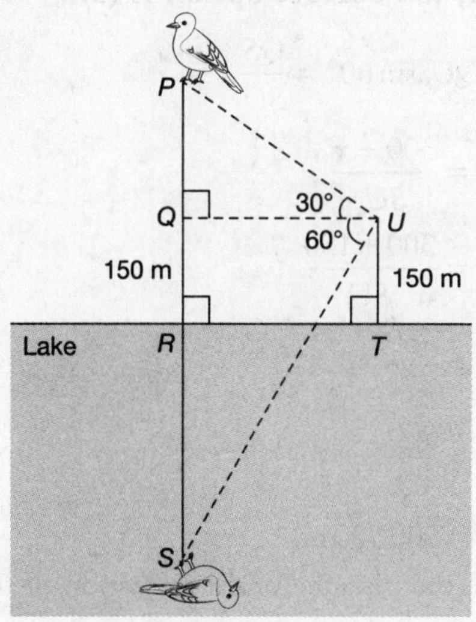

Given that $UT + QR = 150$ m.

$\angle PUQ = 30°$ and $\angle SUQ = 60°$.

Let PQ be x m.

As $PR = RS$, $RS = (150 + x)$ m.

$\Rightarrow QS = QR + RS$

$= (150 + 150 + x) = (300 + x)$ m.

11. In ΔPQU, $\tan 30° = \dfrac{PQ}{QU}$.

$\Rightarrow \dfrac{1}{\sqrt{3}} = \dfrac{x}{QU}$

$\Rightarrow QU = x\sqrt{3}$ (1)

In ΔSQU, $\tan 60° = \dfrac{QS}{QU}$.

$\Rightarrow \sqrt{3} = \dfrac{300 + x}{QU}$

$\Rightarrow QU = \dfrac{300 + x}{\sqrt{3}}$ (2)

From (1) and (2), $x\sqrt{3} = \dfrac{300 + x}{\sqrt{3}}$

$\Rightarrow 3x = 300 + x$

$\Rightarrow 2x = 300$

$\Rightarrow x = 150$

$PR = PQ + QR = 150 + 150 = 300$ m.

The height at which the bird flies = 300 m.

Hence, the correct option is (b).

12. In ΔPQU, $\sin 30° = \dfrac{PQ}{PU}$.

$\Rightarrow \dfrac{1}{2} = \dfrac{150}{PU}$

$\Rightarrow PU = 300$

Hence, the distance of the bird from the point of observation = 300 m.

Hence, the correct option is (a).

13. In ΔSQU, $\sin 60° = \dfrac{QS}{SU}$.

$\Rightarrow \dfrac{\sqrt{3}}{2} = \dfrac{300 + x}{SU}$

$\Rightarrow \dfrac{\sqrt{3}}{2} = \dfrac{300 + 150}{SU}$

$\Rightarrow \dfrac{\sqrt{3}}{2} = \dfrac{450}{SU}$

$\Rightarrow SU = \dfrac{900}{\sqrt{3}}$

$\Rightarrow SU = 300\sqrt{3}$ m.

Hence, the distance of the reflection of the bird from the point of observation = $300\sqrt{3}$ m.

Hence, the correct option is (d).

14. The horizontal distance of the bird from the point of observation = QU.

$= 150\sqrt{3}$ m.

Hence, the correct option is (a).

Assertion and Reason Type Questions

15. **Assertion:** We know that for any angle θ, $\sec^2\theta - \tan^2\theta = 1$.

$\sec^2(2026°) = 1 + \tan^2(2026°)$

$\Rightarrow \sec^2(2026°) - \tan^2(2026°) = 1.$

So, **Assertion** is true.

Reason: For any angle θ, $\sec^2\theta - \tan^2\theta = 1$.

Reason is true and is the correct explanation to **Assertion.**

Hence, the correct option is (a).

16. **Assertion:** We know that the range of $\sin\theta$ is $[-1, 1]$.

For any angle θ, the maximum value of $\sin\theta$ is 1.

Also, $\sin\alpha + \sin\beta + \sin\gamma = 3$.

So, $\sin\alpha = \sin\beta = \sin\gamma = 1$.

So, **Assertion** is true.

Reason: The value of $\sin 90°$ is 1.

Reason is true but not the correct explanation of **Reason.**

Hence, the correct option is (b).

17. **Assertion:** Given that $PQRS$ is a trapezium in which $PQ \parallel RS$.

$\Rightarrow \angle P + \angle Q = 180°$.

$\tan P + \tan Q = \tan P + \tan(180° - P)$

$= \tan P - \tan P = 0.$

So, **Assertion** is true.

Reason: A trapezium is a cyclic quadrilateral.

A trapezium need not be a cyclic a cyclic quadrilateral.

So, **Reason** is false.

Hence, the correct option is (c).

18. **Assertion:** We know that $\cot 90° = 0$.

$\cot 179° \times \cot 178° \times \cot 177° \times \ldots \times \cot 1°$

$= \cot 179° \times \cot 178° \times \cot 177° \times \ldots \times \cot 90°$

$\times \ldots \times \cot 1° = 0.$

$\cot 179° \times \cot 178° \times \cot 177° \times \ldots \times \cot 1° = 1$ is a false statement.

Reason: $\cot 90° = 0$ is true.

Hence, the correct option is (d).

Unit V

Statistics and Probability

In this Unit

CHAPTER

11

Statistics

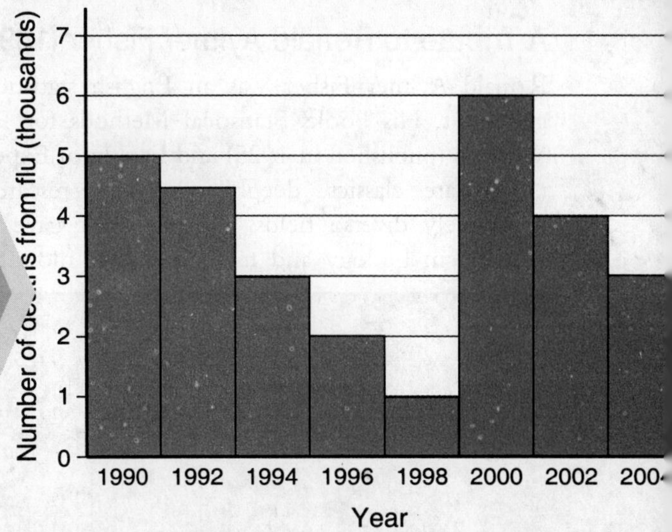

Remember

Before beginning this chapter, you should be able to:

- Define data, types of data, tabulation of data, and statistical graphs
- Understand range, quartiles, deviation, etc.

Key Ideas

After completing this chapter, you should be able to:

- Explain types of data and statistical groups
- Study measures of central tendencies for grouped and ungrouped data—mean, median, and mode
- Evaluate empirical relation between mean, median, and mode
- Learn about standard deviation, coefficient of variation, quartiles, estimation of median and quartiles from ogives, estimation of mode from histogram

Scientific Crypt

A Tribute to Ronald Aylmer Fisher (1890 AD – 1962 AD)

Ronald Aylmer Fisher was an English statistician and geneticist. His books Statistical Methods for Research Workers (published in 1925) and Design of Experiments (1935) are classics, deeply valued by researchers in completely diverse fields. Fisher's work gave research workers in biology and medicine their most powerful tools. In theoretical statistics, he worked on the analysis of variance and developed a method to estimate maximum likelihood. He conceived the ideas of sufficiency, ancillary, Fisher's linear discriminator and Fisher information. His paper on gene frequency clines (forms of species) marked the first application of computers to biology.

FUN TIME

CROSSWORD

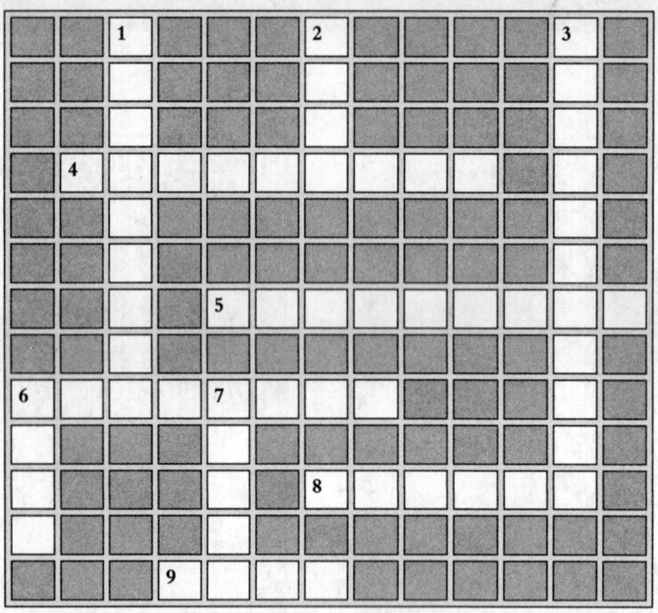

Across

4. The number of times a particular observation occurs
5. It is a graph which is drawn for a classified frequency distribution.
6. A series formulated from raw data.
8. It is the middlemost term of a raw data.
9. It depends on all the observations.

Down

1. These are the observations which divide the data into four equal parts.
2. The most frequently found value in data.
3. Each numerical figure in data.
6. A numerical information
7. How is 4 related to: 5, 6, 7, 8, 9?

INTRODUCTION

The word 'statistics' is derived from the Latin word 'status' which means political state. Political states had to collect information about their citizens to facilitate governance and plan for development. Then, in course of time, statistics came to mean a branch of mathematics which deals with collection, classification, presentation and analysis of numerical data. In this chapter, we shall learn about the classification of data, i.e., grouped data and ungrouped data, measures of central tendency, and their properties.

Data

The word 'data' means, information in the form of numerical figures or a set of given facts.

For example, the percentage of marks scored by 10 students of a class in a test are:

36, 80, 65, 75, 94, 48, 12, 64, 88 and 98.

The set of these figures is the data related to the marks scored by the 10 students in a class test.

Info Bytes!

Humans create over 2.5 quintillion bytes of data each day, with internet usage, social media, and company databases being the primary contributors.

Types of Data

Statistics is basically the study of numerical data. It includes methods of collection, classification, presentation, analysis of data and inferences from data. Data can be qualitative or quantitative in nature. If one speaks of honesty, beauty, Color, etc., the data is qualitative, while height, weight, distance, marks, etc., are quantitative. Data can also be classified as raw data and grouped data.

Raw Data

Data obtained from direct observation is called raw data. The marks obtained by 10 students in a monthly test is an example of raw data or ungrouped data.

In fact, little can be inferred from this data. So, to make this data clearer and more meaningful, we group it into ordered intervals.

Grouped Data

To present the data in a more meaningful way, we condense the data into convenient number of classes or groups, generally not exceeding 10 and not less than 5. This helps us in perceiving at a glance, certain salient features of data.

Some Basic Definitions

Before getting into the details of tabular representation of data, let us review some basic definitions:

Observation Each numerical figure in a data is called an observation.

Frequency The number of times a particular observation occurs is called its frequency.

Tabulation or Presentation of Data

A systematical arrangement of the data in a tabular form is called 'tabulation' or 'presentation' of the data. This grouping results in a table called 'frequency table' that indicates the number of scores within each group.

Many conclusions about the characteristics of the data, the behaviour of variables, etc., can be drawn from this table.

The quantitative data that is to be analyzed statistically can be divided into three categories:

Info Bytes!

Statistical methods were crucial for cryptanalysts in deciphering coded messages.

1. **Individual Series:** Any raw data that is collected, forms an individual series.

Examples:

(i) The weights of 5 students:
32, 40, 65, 48 and 54 (in kg).

(ii) Percentage of marks scored by 10 students in a test:
48, 59, 63, 72, 48, 72, 84, 98, 90 and 60.

2. **Discrete Series:** A discrete series is formulated from raw data. Here, the frequency of the observations are taken into consideration.

Example:
Given below is the data showing the number of computers in 12 families of a locality:

1, 1, 2, 3, 2, 1, 4, 3, 2, 2, 1, 1.

Arranging the data in ascending order, we have

1, 1, 1, 1, 1, 2, 2, 2, 2, 3, 3, 4.

To count, we can use tallymarks. We record tallymarks in bunches of five, the fifth one crossing the other four diagonally, i.e., ~~||||~~.

Thus, we may prepare the following frequency table:

Number of Computers	Tally Marks	Number of Families (Frequency)
1	~~||||~~	5
2						4
3				2
4			1

3. **Continuous Series:** When the data contains large number of observations, we put them into different groups called 'class intervals', such as 1–10, 11–20, 21–30.

Here, 1–10 means data whose values lie between 1 and 10 including both 1 and 10.
This form is known as 'inclusive form'. Also, 1 is called the 'lower limit' and 10 is called the 'upper limit'.

Example:
Given below are the marks (out of 50) obtained by 30 students in an examination:

43	19	25	32	48
17	29	9	15	50
7	24	20	37	44
22	2	50	27	25
18	42	16	1	33
25	35	45	35	28

Taking class intervals 1–10, 11–20, 21–30, 31–40 and 41–50, we prepare a frequency distribution table for the above data.

First, we write the marks in ascending order as:

1	2	7	9	15	16	17	18	19	20
22	24	25	25	25	27	28	29	32	33
35	35	37	42	43	44	45	48	50	50

Now, we can prepare the following frequency distribution table:

Class Interval	Tally Marks	Frequency
1–10	||||	4
11–20	~~||||~~ |	6
21–30	~~||||~~ |||	8
31–40	~~||||~~	5
41–50	~~||||~~ ||	7

Now, with this idea, let us review some more concepts about tabulation.

Class Interval

A group into which the raw data is condensed is called a class interval.

Each class is bounded by two figures which are called the class limits. The figure on the L.H.S is called lower limit and the figure on the R.HS is called upper limit of the class. Thus, 0–10 is a class with lower limit being '0' and the upper limit being '10'.

Class Boundaries

In an exclusive form, the lower and upper limits are known as class boundaries or true lower limit and true upper limit of the class. Thus, the boundaries of 15–25 in exclusive form are 15 and 25.

The boundaries in an inclusive form are obtained by subtracting 0.5 from the lower limit and adding 0.5 to the upper limit.

Thus, the boundaries of 15–25 in the inclusive form are 14.5–25.5.

Class Size

The difference between the true upper limit and the true lower limit is called 'class size'.

Hence, in the above example, the class size = 25 − 15 = 10.

Class Mark or Mid-value

$$\text{Class mark} = \frac{1}{2}(\text{upper limit} + \text{lower limit})$$

Thus, the class mark of 15–25 is, $\frac{1}{2}(25+15) = 20$.

Statistical Graphs

Information provided by a numerical frequency distribution is easily understood when represented by diagrams or graphs. Diagrams act as visual aids and leave a lasting impression on the mind. This enables the investigator to make quick conclusions about the distribution.

There are different types of graphs or diagrams to represent statistical data. Some of them are:

1. Bar chart or bar graph (for unclassified frequency distribution)
2. Histogram (for classified frequency distribution)
3. Frequency polygon (for classified frequency distribution)
4. Frequency curve (for classified frequency distribution)
5. Cumulative frequency curve (for classified frequency distribution).
   (i) Less than cumulative frequency curve.
   (ii) Greater than cumulative frequency curve.

Bar Graph

The important features of bar graphs are:

(i) Bar graphs are used to represent unclassified frequency distributions.

(ii) Frequency of a value of a variable is represented by a bar (rectangle) whose length (i.e., height) is equal (or proportional) to the frequency.

(iii) The breadth of the bar is arbitrary and the breadths of all the bars are equal. The bars may or may not touch each other.

EXAMPLE 11.1 Represent the following frequency distribution by a bar graph:

Value of variable	2	4	6	8	10
Frequency	5	8	4	2	7

SOLUTION

Either of the following bar graphs [Figs. 11.1 (a) or (b)] may be used to represent the above frequency distribution. The first graph takes value of the variable along the X-axis and the frequency along the Y-axis, whereas the second one takes the frequency along the X-axis and the value of the variable on the Y-axis.

All the rectangles (i.e., bars) should be of same width and uniform spaces should be left between any two consecutive bars.

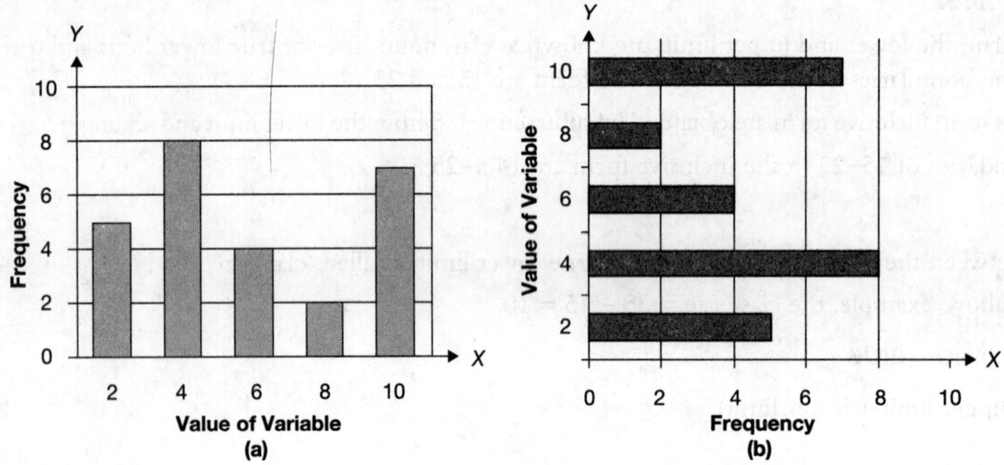

Figure 11.1

Histograms

Classified or grouped data is represented graphically by histograms. A histogram consists of rectangles each of which has its breadth proportional to the size of concerned class interval and its height proportional to the corresponding frequency. In a histogram, two consecutive rectangles have a common side.

Hence, in a histogram, we do the following:

1 We represent class boundaries along the X-axis.

2. Along the Y-axis, we represent class frequencies.

3. We construct rectangles with bases along the X-axis and heights along the Y-axis.

EXAMPLE 11.2 Construct a histogram for the following frequency distribution:

Class Interval	20–30	30–40	40–50	50–60	60–70
Frequency	5	8	3	7	4

SOLUTION

Here, the class intervals are continuous.

The following histogram is drawn according to the method described above:

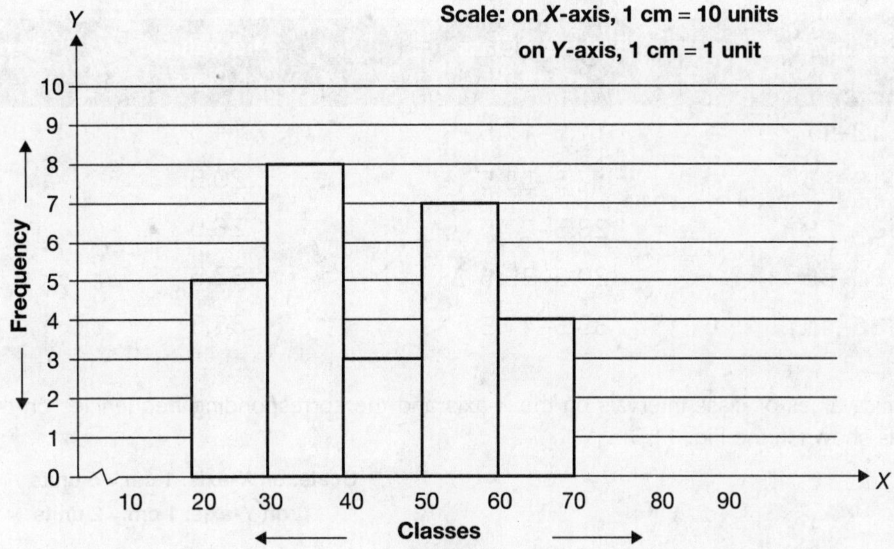

Histogram

Figure 11.2

Remarks

The following points may be noted:

1. A link mark (—⁄\/—) made on the horizontal axis, between the vertical axis and first vertical rectangle, if there is a gap between 0 and the lower boundary of first class interval.
2. We may shade all rectangles. A heading for the histogram may also be given.

Important Observations

1. If the class intervals are discontinuous, the distribution has to be changed into continuous intervals, and then the histogram has to be drawn.
2. Bar graphs are used for unclassified frequency distributions, whereas histograms are used for classified frequency distribution. The breadths of rectangles in a bar graph are arbitary, while those in histogram are determined by class size.

Frequency Polygon

Frequency polygons are used to represent classified or grouped data graphically. It is a polygon whose vertices are the mid-points of the top sides of the rectangles, forming the histogram of the frequency distribution.

To draw a frequency polygon for a given frequency distribution, the mid-values of the class intervals are taken on *X*-axis and the corresponding frequencies on *Y*-axis and the points are plotted on a graph sheet.

These points are joined by straight line segments which form the frequency polygon.

EXAMPLE 11.3

Construct a frequency polygon for the following data:

Class Interval	12–17	18–23	24–29	30–35	36–41	Total
Frequency	10	7	12	8	13	50

SOLUTION

Here, the class intervals are discontinuous.

Hence, first we convert the class intervals to continuous class intervals, and then find the mid-points of each class intervals. We do this by adding 0.5 to each upper limit and subtracting 0.5 from each lower limit.

Class Interval	Exclusive Class Interval	Mid-value of Class	Frequency
12–17	11.5–17.5	14.5	10
18–23	17.5–23.5	20.5	7
24–29	23.5–29.5	26.5	12
30–35	29.5–35.5	32.5	8
36–41	35.5–41.5	38.5	13

Now, taking the mid-values of class intervals on the *X*-axis and the corresponding frequencies on the *Y*-axis, we draw the frequency polygon as shown in the Fig. 11.3.

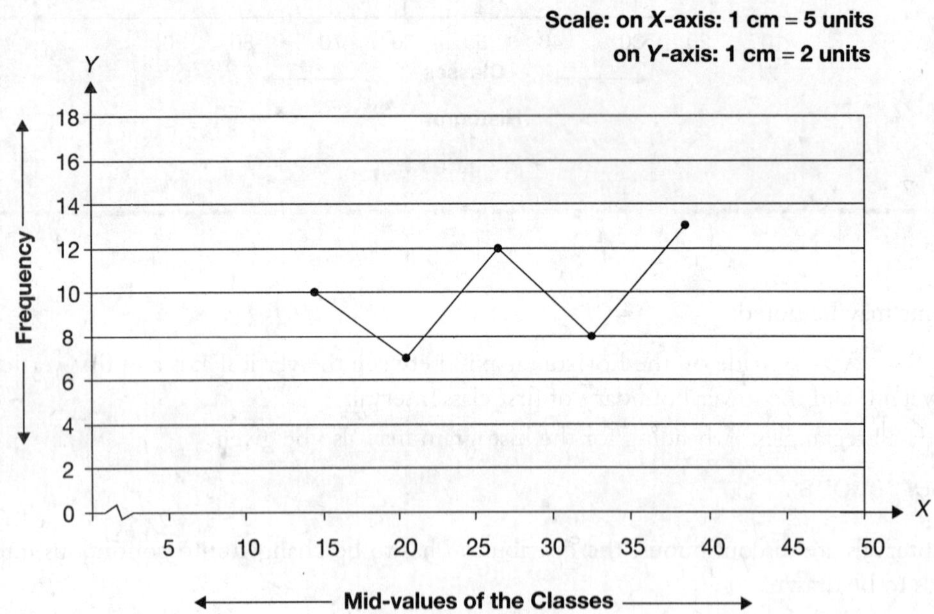

Frequency Polygon

Figure 11.3

Frequency Curve

Frequency curves are used to graphically represent classified or grouped data.

As the class-interval in a frequency distribution decreases, the points of the frequency polygon become closer and closer, and then the frequency polygon tends to become a frequency curve. So, when the number of scores in the data is sufficiently large and the class-intervals become smaller (ultimately tending to zero), the limiting form of frequency polygon becomes frequency curve.

EXAMPLE 11.4 Draw a frequency curve for the following data:

Mid-values	5	10	15	20	25	30	35	40
Frequency	2	4	7	5	10	12	6	4

SOLUTION

For the given (i.e., a table) showing the mid-values of classes and frequencies is made.

Mid-value of Classes	Frequency
5	2
10	4
15	7
20	5
25	10
30	12
35	6
40	4

Now, taking the mid-values of the classes along the *X*-axis and the corresponding frequency along the *Y*-axis, we mark the points obtained from the above table in a graph sheet and join them with a smooth curve, which gives the following frequency curve:

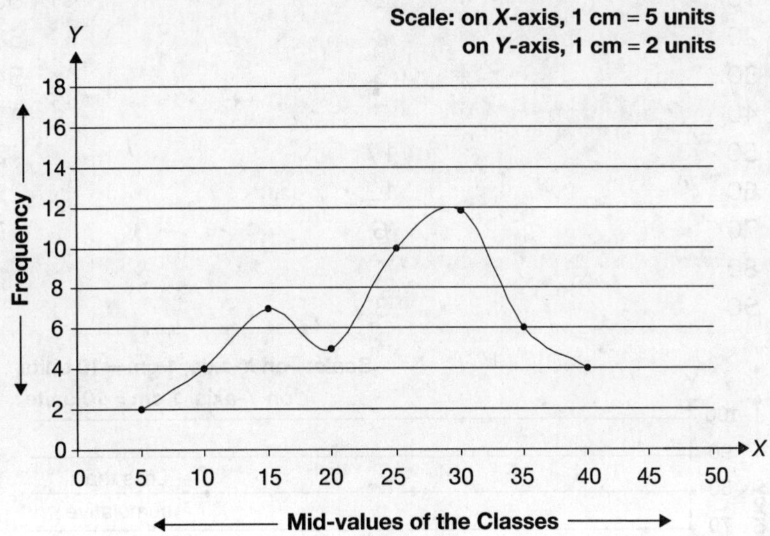

Figure 11.4

Cumulative Frequency Curves

The curves drawn for cumulative frequencies less than or more than the true limits of the classes of a frequency distribution are called 'cumulative frequency curves'. The curve drawn for the 'less than cumulative frequency distribution' is called the 'less than cumulative frequency curve' and the curve drawn for the greater than cumulative frequency distribution is called the 'greater than cumulative frequency curve'.

From these curves, we can find the total frequency above or below a particular value of the variable.

EXAMPLE 11.5 For the given distribution, draw the less than and greater than cumulative frequency curves.

Class	10–20	20–30	30–40	40–50	50–60	60–70	70–80	80–90	90–100
Frequency	2	4	5	7	17	12	6	4	3

SOLUTION

Less than cumulative frequency distribution:

Upper Boundaries of the Classes	Frequency	Less than Cumulative Frequency
20	2	2
30	4	6
40	5	11
50	7	18
60	17	35
70	12	47
80	6	53
90	4	57
100	3	60

Greater than cumulative frequency distribution:

Lower Boundaries of the Classes	Frequency	Greater than Cumulative Frequency
10	2	60
20	4	58
30	5	54
40	7	49
50	17	42
60	12	25
70	6	13
80	4	7
90	3	3

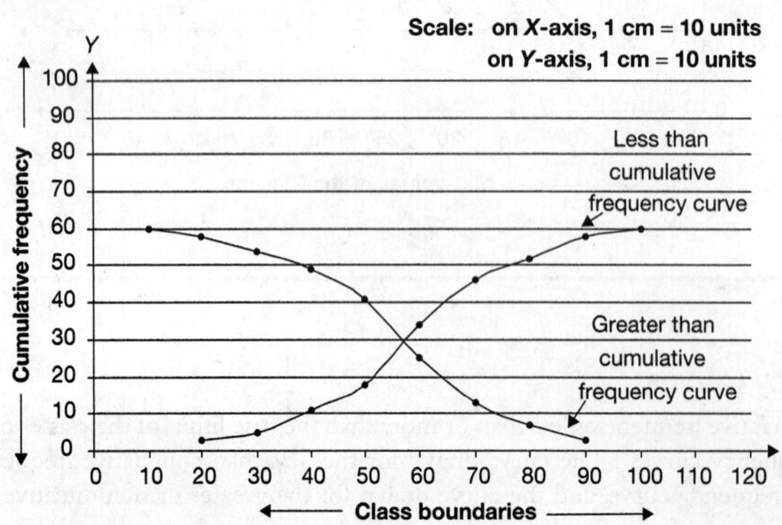

Figure 11.5

Measures of Central Tendencies for Ungrouped Data

Till now, we have observed that data collected in statistical enquiry or investigation happens in the form of raw data. If data is very large, users cannot get much information. For this reason, data is grouped together to obtain some conclusions.

The measure of central tendency is a value which represents the total data, that is, it is the value in a data around which the values of all the other observations tend to concentrate.

The most commonly used measures of central tendency are the:

1. Arithmetic mean
2. Median
3. Mode

These measures give an idea about how the data is clustered or concentrated.

Arithmetic Mean or Mean (AM)

The arithmetic mean (or simply the mean) is the most commonly used measure of central tendency.

Arithmetic Mean for Raw Data

The arithmetic mean of a statistical data is defined as the quotient obtained when the sum of all the observations or entries is divided by the total number of items.

If $x_1, x_2, ..., x_n$ are the n items, then:

$$\text{AM} = \frac{x_1 + x_2 + \cdots + x_n}{n} = \frac{\sum_{i=1}^{n} x_i}{n}, \text{ or briefly } \frac{\sum x}{n}.$$

AM is usually denoted by $\overline{x}$.

EXAMPLE 11.6 Find the mean of the first 10 natural numbers.

SOLUTION

Given data is 1, 2, 3, ..., 10

$$\therefore \text{Arithmetic mean (AM)} = \frac{\text{Sum of observations}}{\text{Total number of observations}} = \frac{1+2+3+\cdots+10}{10} = \frac{55}{10} = 5.5.$$

Mean of Discrete Series

Let $x_1, x_2, x_3, \ldots, x_n$ be n observations with respective frequencies $f_1, f_2, \ldots, f_n$.

This can be considered as a special case of raw data where the observation x_1 occurs f_1 times, x_2 occurs f_2 times, and so on.

$$\therefore \text{The mean of the above data} = \frac{f_1x_1 + f_2x_2 + \cdots + f_nx_n}{f_1 + f_2 + \cdots + f_n}.$$

It can also be represented by, $\overline{x} = \dfrac{\sum_{i=1}^{n} f_i x_i}{\sum_{i=1}^{n} f_i}$

Weighted Arithmetic Mean

When the variables $x_1, x_2, ..., x_n$ do not have same importance, and the weights $w_1, w_2, ..., w_n$ are given to each of the variables, the weighted arithmetic mean is given by, $\overline{X}_w = \dfrac{\sum x_i w_i}{\sum w_i}$.

EXAMPLE 11.7 The salaries of 100 workers of a factory are given below:

Salary (in ₹)	Number of Workers
6,000	40
8,000	25
10,000	12
12,000	10
15,000	8
20,000	4
25,000	1
Total	**100**

Find the mean salaries of the workers of the factory.

SOLUTION

The mean $\overline{x}$ is given by:

$$\overline{x} = \frac{(6000\times 40)+(8000\times 25)+(10000\times 12)+(12000\times 10)+(15000\times 8)+(20000\times 4)+(25000\times 1)}{40+25+12+10+8+4+1}$$

$\Rightarrow \overline{x} = ₹9050$

∴ The mean salary of the workers is ₹9050.

Some Important Results About AM

1. The algebraic sum of deviations taken about the mean is zero. That is, $\sum_{i=1}^{n}(x_i - \overline{x}) = 0$.
2. The value of the mean depends on all the observations.
3. The AM of two numbers a and b is $\frac{a+b}{2}$.
4. **Combined mean:** If $\overline{x}_1$ and $\overline{x}_2$ are the arithmetic means of two series with n_1 and n_2 observations, respectively, then the combined mean is:

$$\overline{x}_c = \frac{n_1\overline{x}_1 + n_2\overline{x}_2}{n_1 + n_2}$$

The above result can be extended to any number of groups of data.

5. If $\overline{x}$ is the mean of $x_1, x_2, \ldots, x_n$, then the mean of $x_1 + a, x_2 + a, x_3 + a, \ldots, x_n + a$ is $\overline{x} + a$, for all values of a.
6. If $\overline{x}$ is the mean of $x_1, x_2, \ldots, x_n$, then the mean of $ax_1, ax_2, \ldots, ax_n$ is $a\overline{x}$ and that of $\frac{x_1}{a}, \frac{x_2}{a}, \ldots, \frac{x_n}{a}$ is $\frac{\overline{x}}{a}$.
7. The mean of the first n natural numbers is $\left(\frac{n+1}{2}\right)$.
8. The mean of the squares of the first n natural numbers $= \frac{(n+1)(2n+1)}{6}$.
9. The mean of the cubes of the first n natural numbers $= \frac{n(n+1)^2}{4}$.

EXAMPLE 11.8 If the average wage of 50 workers is ₹100 and the average wage of 30 of them is ₹120, then find the average wage of the remaining workers.

SOLUTION

We know that,

$$\text{Average} = \frac{\text{Sum of the quantities}}{\text{Number of the quantities}}$$

$$\therefore \frac{\text{Wage of 50 workers}}{50} = 100$$

$$\Rightarrow \text{Wage}_{50} = 50 \times 100 = ₹5000$$

Similarly,

$$\frac{\text{Wage}_{30}}{30} = 120 \Rightarrow \text{Wage}_{30} = 30 \times 120 = ₹3600$$

Now,

$$\text{Wage of 20 workers} = \text{Wage}_{50} - \text{Wage}_{30}$$

$$= 5000 - 3600$$

$$= ₹1{,}400$$

$$\Rightarrow \text{Average wage}_{20} = \frac{1400}{20} = ₹70$$

EXAMPLE 11.9

x	2	4	6	8
f	3	5	6	y

The mean of the above data is 5.5. Find the missing frequency (y) in the above distribution.

SOLUTION

Given AM = 5.5

$$\Sigma f \cdot x = 2 \times 3 + 4 \times 5 + 6 \times 6 + 8 \times y$$

$$= 6 + 20 + 36 + 8y$$

$$\Sigma f \cdot x = 62 + 8y \quad (1)$$

$$\text{Now } \Sigma f = 3 + 5 + 6 + y$$

$$\Sigma f = 14 + y \quad (2)$$

Using Eqs. (1) and (2),

$$\text{AM} = \frac{\sum f \cdot x}{\sum f} \Rightarrow 5.5 = \frac{62 + 8y}{14 + y}$$

$$\Rightarrow 5.5(14 + y) = 62 + 8y$$

$$\Rightarrow 77 + 5.5y = 62 + 8y$$

$$\Rightarrow 8y - 5.5y = 77 - 62$$

$$\Rightarrow 2.5y = 15$$

$$\Rightarrow y = 6$$

Median

Another measure of central tendency of a given data is the median.

Definition

If the values x_i in the raw data are arranged either in the increasing or decreasing order of magnitude, then the middle-most value in this arrangement is called the median.

Thus, for the raw (i.e., ungrouped) data, the median is computed as follows:

1. The values of the observations are arranged in order of magnitude.
2. The middle-most value is taken as the median. Hence, depending on the number of observations (odd or even), we determine median as follows.

   (i) When the number of observations(n) is odd, then the median is the value of $\left(\frac{n+1}{2}\right)$th observation.

   (ii) If the number of observations(n) is even, then the median is the mean of $\left(\frac{n}{2}\right)$th observation and $\left(\frac{n}{2}+1\right)$th observation.

EXAMPLE 11.10 Find the median of the following data: 2, 7, 3, 15, 12, 17, and 5.

SOLUTION

Arranging the given numbers in the ascending order, we have 2, 3, 5, 7, 12, 15, 17.

Here, the middle term is 7.

∴ Median = 7.

EXAMPLE 11.11 Find the median of the data 5, 8, 4, 12, 16, and 10.

SOLUTION

Arranging the given data in ascending order, we have 4, 5, 8, 10, 12, 16.

As the given number of values is even, we have two middle values. Those are $\left(\frac{n}{2}\right)$th and $\left(\frac{n}{2}+1\right)$th observations. Those are 8 and 10.

∴ Median of the data = Average of 8 and 10.

$$= \frac{8+10}{2} = 9.$$

Some Important Facts About Median

1. The median does not take into consideration all the items.
2. The sum of absolute deviations taken about the median is the least.
3. The median can be calculated graphically, but not the mean.
4. The median is not effected by extreme values.
5. The sum of deviations taken about median is less than the sum of absolute deviations taken from any other observation in the data.

EXAMPLE 11.12 The median of a set of positive integers is 32. If each integer of the set is multiplied by 4 and then 9 is added to each of the resulting numbers, the median of the new set of numbers thus obtained is _______.

SOLUTION

Given, median = 32

The median of the new numbers will be obtained by applying the same pattern.

Therefore, the median of the new numbers = $4 \times 32 + 9 = 137$.

Mode

The third measure of central tendency of a data is the mode.

The most frequently found value in the data is called the mode.

This is the measure which can be identified in the simplest way.

EXAMPLE 11.13 Find the mode of 0, 5, 2, 7, 2, 1, 1, 3, 2, 4, 5, 7, 5, 1, and 2.

SOLUTION

Among the given observations, the most frequently found observation is 2. It occurs 4 times.

$\therefore$ Mode = 2.

Properties of Mode

1. It can be graphically calculated.
2. It is not effected by extreme values.
3. It can be used for open-ended distribution and qualitative data.

Empirical Relationship Among Mean, Median, and Mode

For a moderately symmetric data, the above three measures of central tendency can be related by the formula, Mode = 3 × Median – 2 × Mean.

Konnect

1. For a given data, the mode may or may not exist. In a series of observations, if no item occurs more than once, then the mode is said to be ill-defined.
2. If the mode exists for a given data, it may or may not be unique.
3. Data having unique mode is uni-model, while data having two modes is bi-model.

EXAMPLE 11.14 If the ratio of the mode and the median of a data is 5 : 4, then what is the ratio of the median and the mean of the data?

SOLUTION

Mode : Median = 5 : 4

Let the mode be $5x$ and the median be $4x$.

Mode = 3(Median) – 2 (Mean)

$$5x = 3(4x) - 2(\text{Mean})$$

$$2(\text{Mean}) = 12x - 5x$$

$$\text{Mean} = \frac{7x}{2}$$

$$\text{Median : Mean} = 4x : \frac{7x}{2} = 8 : 7$$

Observations

1. For a symmetric distribution,

$$\text{Mean} = \text{Median} = \text{Mode}.$$

2. Given any two of the mean, median and mode, the third can be calculated.
3. This formula is to be applied in the absence of sufficient data.

Measure of Central Tendencies for Grouped Data

We studied the measure of central tendencies of ungrouped or raw data. Now, we study the measures of central tendencies (i,e., mean, median, and mode) for grouped data.

Mean of Grouped Data

If the frequency distribution of 'n' observations of a variable x has k classes, x_i is the mid-value, and f_i is the frequency of ith class, then the mean $\overline{x}$ of grouped data is defined as:

$$\overline{x} = \frac{f_1x_1 + f_2x_2 + \cdots + f_kx_k}{f_1 + f_2 + \cdots + f_k} = \frac{\sum_{i=1}^{k} f_ix_i}{\sum_{i=1}^{k} f_i}$$

(or) simply, $\overline{x} = \frac{\sum f_ix_i}{N}$; where $N = \sum_{i=1}^{k} f_i$.

In grouped data, it is assumed that the frequency of each class is concentrated at its mid-value.

EXAMPLE 11.15 Calculate the arithmetic mean (AM) of the following data:

Percentage of Marks	0–20	20–40	40–60	60–80	80–100
Number of Students	2	12	13	15	8

SOLUTION

Let us write the tabular form as given below:

Percentage of Marks	Number of Students (fi)	Midpoints of Classes (xi)	fixi
0–20	2	10	20
20–40	12	30	360
40–60	13	50	650
60–80	15	70	1050
80–100	8	90	720
	$\Sigma f_i = N = \mathbf{50}$		$\Sigma f x_i = \mathbf{2800}$

$\therefore$ Mean $= \overline{x} = \frac{\sum fx}{N} = \frac{2800}{50} = 56.$

Short-cut Method for Finding the Mean of Group Data (Deviation Method)

Sometimes, when the frequencies are large in number, the calculation of mean using the given formula is cumbersome. This can be simplified if the class interval of each class of grouped data is the same. Under the assumption of equal class interval, we get the following formula for the mean of grouped data:

$$\overline{x} = A + \frac{1}{N}\left(\sum_{i=1}^{k} f_i u_i\right) \times C$$

Where, A = Assumed value from among mid-values

C = Length of class interval

k = Number of classes of the frequency distribution

N = Sum of frequencies $= \sum_{i=1}^{k} f_i$

$u_i = \frac{x_i - A}{C}$, $i = 1, 2, 3, \ldots, k$ and

x_i = mid-value of the ith class

u_i is called the deviation or difference of the mid-value of the ith class from the assumed value, divided by the class interval.

Using this method, the previous example can be worked out as follows:

Percentage of Marks	Number of Students (fi)	Mid-values (xi)	Deviation $u_i = \frac{x_i - A}{C}$	fiui
0–20	2	10	−3	−6
20–40	12	30	−2	−24
40–60	13	50	−1	−13
60–80	15	70 (*A*)	0	0
80–100	8	90	1	8
	N = 50			**$\Sigma f_i u_i = -35$**

Here, $A = 70$; $N = 50$; $C = 20$; $\Sigma f_i u_i = -35$

$\therefore$ AM $= A + \frac{1}{N}(\Sigma f_i u_i) \times c = 70 + \frac{1}{50}(-35) \times 20 = 70 - 14 = 56.$

Median of Grouped Data

Before finding out how to obtain the median of grouped data, first we review what a median class is.

If 'n' is the number of observations, then from the cumulative frequency distribution, the class in which $\left(\frac{n}{2}\right)$th observation lies is called the median class.

Formula for calculating median:

$$\text{Median } (M) = L + \frac{\frac{n}{2} - F}{f}(C)$$

Where, L = Lower boundary of the median class, i.e., class in which $\left(\frac{n}{2}\right)$th observation lies.

n = Sum of frequencies

F = Cumulative frequency of the class just preceding the median class

f = Frequency of median class

C = Length of class interval

EXAMPLE 11.16

Following is the data showing weights of 40 students in a class. Find its median.

Weight	45	46	47	48	49	50	51	52	53
Number of Students	6	2	3	4	7	4	7	4	3

SOLUTION

To find the median, we prepare less than cumulative frequency table as given below:

Weight in kgs	Number of Students	Cumulative Frequency (*F*)
45	6	6
46	2	8
47	3	11
48	4	15
49	7	22
50	4	26
51	7	33
52	4	37
53	3	40

Here, $n = 40$ which is even.

$\therefore$ Median = Value of $\frac{40}{2}$, or the 20th observation.

From the column of cumulative frequency, the value of 20th observation is 49.

$\therefore$ Median = 49 kg.

EXAMPLE 11.17

Find the median of the following data:

Class Interval	0–10	10–20	20–30	30–40	40–50
Frequency	7	6	5	8	9

Konnect

In the above example, we do not have any class interval. As there is no class interval, we cannot use the formula.

SOLUTION

To find the median, we prepare the following table:

Class Interval	Frequency	Cumulative Frequency
0–10	7	7
10–20	6	13 (*F*)
20–30	5 (*f*)	18
30–40	8	26
40–50	9	35
Total	**35**	

$$\text{Median} = L + \frac{\left(\frac{n}{2} - F\right)}{f} \times C$$

Here, $n = 35 \Rightarrow \frac{n}{2} = \frac{35}{2} = 17.5$

This value appears in the class 20–30.

L = Lower boundary of median class = (20–30) = 20

$F = 13$; $f = 5$ and $C = 10$ (class length)

$$\therefore \text{Median} = 20 + \frac{\left(\frac{35}{2} - 13\right)}{5} \times 10 = 20 + \frac{9}{2 \times 5} \times 10 = 29.$$

Mode of Grouped Data

The formula for determining the mode of grouped data is $L_1 + \dfrac{\Delta_1 C}{\Delta_1 + \Delta_2}$.

Where, L_1 = Lower boundary of model class (class with highest frequency).

$\Delta_1 = f - f_1$ and $\Delta_2 = f - f_2$, where f is the frequency of model class

f_1 = Frequency of the previous class of the model class

f_2 = Frequency of the next class of the model class.

Rewriting the formula:

$$\text{Mode} = L_1 + \frac{(f - f_1)C}{(f - f_1) + (f - f_2)}$$

$$\text{Mode} = L_1 + \frac{(f - f_1)C}{2f - (f_1 + f_2)}$$

EXAMPLE 11.18 The following information gives the monthly salaries of 100 employees. Find the mode of the data.

Salary (₹)	2000–3499	3500–4999	5000–6499	6500–7999	8000–9499
Number of Persons	35	37	21	12	5

SOLUTION

Here, the given classes are not continuous.

Hence, we first rewrite it as follows:

Salary	Adjusted Salary (₹)	Number of Persons
2000–3499	1999.5–3499.5	35 (f_1)
3500–4999	3499.5–4999.5	37 (f)
5000–6499	4999.5–6499.5	21 (f_2)
6500–7999	6499.5–7999.5	12
8000–9499	7999.5–9499.5	5

From the above table, it can be known that the maximum frequency occurs in the class interval 3500–4999.

$\therefore f = 37; f_1 = 35; f_2 = 29;$

$L_1 = 3499 \cdot 5; C = 1500$

$$\therefore \text{Mode} = L_1 + \frac{(f - f_1)C}{(f - f_1) + (f - f_2)} = 3499.5 + \frac{1500(2)}{2+8} = 3499.5 + 300 = 3799.5.$$

EXAMPLE 11.19 Mode for the following distribution is 22 and $10 > y > x$. Find y.

Class Interval	0–10	10–20	20–30	30–40	40–50	Total
Frequency	5	8	10	x	y	30

SOLUTION

Class	Frequency
0–10	5
10–20	$8 - f_1$
20–30	$10 - f$
30–40	$x - f_2$
40–50	y
Total	**30**

Since $10 > y > x$,

The model class is 20 – 30.

$L_1 = 20.$

and $5 + 8 + 10 + x + y = 30$

$x + y = 30 - 23$

$x + y = 7$ (1)

$$\text{Mode} = L_1 + \frac{(f - f_1) \times c}{(f - f_1) + (f - f_2)}$$

$$\Rightarrow 20 + \frac{(10-8) \times 10}{(10-8) + (10 - x)} = 22$$

$$\Rightarrow 20 + \frac{20}{12 - x} = 22$$

$$\frac{20}{12 - x} = 2 \Rightarrow 2x = 4$$

$x = 2$ (2)

from (1) & (2) $y = 5$.

Range

The difference between the maximum and the minimum values of the given observations is called the range of the data.

Given $x_1, x_2, \ldots, x_n$ (n individual observations)

$$\text{Range} = (\text{Maximum value}) - (\text{Minimum value}).$$

EXAMPLE 11.20 Find the range of {2, 7, 6, 4, 3, 8, 5, 12}.

SOLUTION

By arranging the given data in the ascending order.

We have, {2, 3, 4, 5, 6, 7, 8, 12}

∴ Range = (Maximum value) − (Minimum value) = 12 − 2 = 10.

> **Info Bytes!**
>
> The range of the class interval is the difference of the actual limits of the class.

Calculation of Variance and Standard Deviation for Raw Data

Standard deviation (SD) is referred to as the root mean squared deviation about the mean. It is denoted by the symbol σ and read as sigma.

Variance is denoted by σ^2, which is the square of the standard deviation.

$\therefore$ Variance = $(\text{SD})^2$, or SD $= \sqrt{\text{Variance}}$

$$\text{SD }(\sigma) = \sqrt{\frac{(x_1-\bar{x})^2+(x_2-\bar{x})^2+\cdots+(x_n-\bar{x})^2}{n}}$$

where, $x_1, x_2, \ldots, x_n$ are n observations with mean as $\bar{x}$.

Alternatively, the above formula can also be written as:

$$\text{SD }(\sigma) = \sqrt{\frac{\sum_{i=1}^{n}(x_i-\bar{x})^2}{n}}.$$

> **Info Bytes!**
>
> Unlike standard deviation, the coefficient of variation can be used to compare variability between datasets with different units and scales.

EXAMPLE 11.21 Find the standard deviation of 3, 5, 7, 11 and 14.

SOLUTION

The arithmetic mean of 3, 5, 7, 11 and 14 $= \dfrac{3+5+7+11+14}{5} = 8$

$$\text{Variance} = \frac{(8-3)^2+(8-5)^2+(8-7)^2+(8-11)^2+(8-14)^2}{5} = \frac{25+9+1+9+36}{5} = 16$$

S.D. $= \sqrt{\text{variance}} = \sqrt{16} = 4$

The standard deviation of 3, 5, 7, 11 and 14 is 4

Calculation of Variance and SD for a Grouped Data

1. $N = \Sigma f =$ The sum of the frequencies
2. AM $(\bar{x}) = \dfrac{\sum fx}{N}$
3. $D =$ Deviation from the AM $(x-\bar{x})$
4. Standard deviation (SD) $= \sigma = \sqrt{\dfrac{\sum fD^2}{N}}$

EXAMPLE 11.22 The range of first 30 even multiples of 9 is ______.

SOLUTION

The first 30 even multiples of 9 are 9 × 2, 9 × 4, 9 × 6, ..., 9 × 60. i.e., 18, 36, 54, ..., 540.

Hence, the range of first 30 even multiples of 9 is = 540 – 18 = 522.

EXAMPLE 11.23 Find the SD for the given data:

CI	0–10	10–20	20–30	30–40
Frequency	4	3	2	1

SOLUTION

CI	f	x Mid-point	fx	$D = x - \overline{x}$	D^2	fD^2
0–10	4	5	20	–10	100	400
10–20	3	15	45	0	0	0
20–30	2	25	50	10	100	200
30–40	1	35	35	20	400	400
	$\Sigma f = 10$		$\Sigma fx = 150$			$\Sigma fD^2 = 1000$

$$\text{AM} = \overline{x} = \frac{\sum fx}{\sum f} = \frac{150}{10} = 15$$

$$\text{SD} = \sigma = \sqrt{\frac{\sum fD^2}{N}} = \sqrt{\frac{1000}{10}} = \sqrt{100} = 10.$$

EXAMPLE 11.24 If the standard deviation of $2x_i + 3$ is 8, then the variance of $\frac{3x_i}{2}$.

SOLUTION

SD $(2x_i) + 3 = 8$

SD of $2x_i = 8$ ($\because$ SD dose not alter when term is decreased by fixed constant.)

SD of $x_i = 4$

Variance of $x_i = \text{SD}^2 = 16$

Variance of $\frac{3x_i}{2} = \left(\frac{9}{4}\right) \times$ Variance of x_i ($\because \text{Var}(ax + b) = a^2 \text{ Var}(x)$)

$$= \left(\frac{9}{4}\right)(16) = 36$$

Coefficient of Variation (CV)

For any given data, let SD be the standard deviation and AM be the arithmetic mean, then coefficient of variation (CV) of the data is defined as:

$$\text{CV} = \frac{\text{SD}}{\text{AM}} \times 100$$

This is a relative measure and helps in measuring the consistency. Smaller the CV, greater is the consistency.

EXAMPLE 11.25 In a series of observations, find the coefficient of variation given S.D. = 17.5 and A.M. = 350.

SOLUTION

Coefficient of variation $= \frac{\text{S.D.}}{\text{A.M.}} \times 100 = \frac{17.5}{350} \times 100 = 5.$

Quartiles

In a given data, the observations that divide the given set of observations into four equal parts are called quartiles.

First Quartile or Lower Quartile

When the given observations are arranged in ascending order, the observation which lies mid-way between the lower extreme and the median is called the first quartile, or the lower quartile, and is denoted as Q_1.

Third Quartile or Upper Quartile

Of the data when the given observations are arranged in ascending order, the observation that lies in mid-way between the median and the upper extreme observation is called the third quartile, or the upper quartile, and is denoted by Q_3.

We can find Q_1 and Q_3 for an ungrouped data containing n observations as follows:

We arrange the given n observations or items in ascending order, then,

Lower or first quartile, Q_1 is $\left(\frac{n}{4}\right)$th item or observation if n is even and $\left(\frac{n+1}{4}\right)$th item or observation when n is odd.

EXAMPLE 11.26 Find Q_1 for 8, 12, 7, 5, 16, 10, 21, and 19.

SOLUTION

Arranging the given observations in ascending order.

We have, 5, 7, 8, 10, 12, 16,19, 21

Here, $n = 8$ (n is even)

$\therefore$ First quartile, $Q_1 = \left(\frac{n}{4}\right)$th item $= \left(\frac{8}{4}\right)$th item = 2nd item of the data, i.e., 7.

$\therefore Q_1 = 7.$

EXAMPLE 11.27 Find Q_1 of the observations 21, 12, 9, 6, 18, 16, and 5.

SOLUTION

Arranging the observations in ascending order, we have 5, 6, 9, 12, 16, 18, 21.

Here, $n = 7$ (odd)

$\therefore Q_1 = \left(\frac{n+1}{4}\right)$th item, i.e., $\left(\frac{7+1}{4}\right)$th item = 2nd item.

$\therefore Q_1 = 6.$

EXAMPLE 11.28 The marks of 10 students in a class are 38, 24, 16, 40, 25, 27, 17, 32, 22, and 26. Find Q_1.

SOLUTION

The given observations, when arranged in ascending order, we have 16, 17, 22, 24, 25, 26, 27, 32, 38, 40.
Here, $n = 10$ (even)

$$\therefore Q_1 = \left(\frac{n}{4}\right) \text{th item} = \left(2\frac{1}{2}\right) \text{th item of the data}$$

$$\therefore Q_1 = \text{2nd item} + \frac{1}{2}(\text{3rd} - \text{2nd}) \text{ item} = 17 + \frac{1}{2}(22-17) = 17 + \frac{5}{2} = 19.5$$

$\therefore Q_1 = 19.5$

Q_3 is $\left(\frac{3n}{4}\right)$th item, when n is even and $3\left(\frac{n+1}{4}\right)$th item when n is odd.

EXAMPLE 11.29 Find Q_3 for 7, 16, 19, 10, 21, and 12.

SOLUTION

By arranging the data in ascending order, we have 7, 10, 12, 16, 19, 21.
Here, $n = 6$ (even)

$$\therefore Q_3 = 3\left(\frac{n}{4}\right) \text{th item} = 4\frac{1}{2} \text{ th item}$$

$$\Rightarrow Q_3 = \left[\text{4th} + \frac{1}{2}(\text{5th} - \text{4th})\right] \text{item} = 16 + \frac{1}{2}(19-16)$$

$Q_3 = 17.5.$

Semi-inter Quartile Range or Quartile Deviation (QD)

Quartile deviation is given by the formula, $QD = \frac{Q_3 - Q_1}{2}$.

EXAMPLE 11.30 Find semi-inter quartile range of the following data:

X	2	5	6	8	9	10	12
Frequency	1	8	12	16	11	9	3

SOLUTION

X	Frequency	Cumulative Frequency
2	1	1
5	8	9
6	12	21
8	16	37
9	11	48
10	9	57
12	3	60
	$N = 60$	

Here, $N = 60$

$\therefore Q_1 = \left(\frac{N}{4}\right)$th item $= \left(\frac{60}{4}\right)$th item = 15th item

$\therefore Q_1 = 6$ (as the 15th item lies in 21 in the cumulative frequency)

$Q_3 = 3\left(\frac{N}{4}\right)$th item = 45th item

$\therefore Q_3 = 9$ (as 45th item lies in 48 in the cumulative frequency)

Semi-inter quartile range (QD) $= \frac{Q_3 - Q_1}{2} = \frac{9-6}{2} = 1.5.$

Konnect

For an individual data, the second quartile Q_2 coincides with median.

$\Rightarrow Q_2$ = Median of the data.

EXAMPLE 11.31 The heights of 31 students in a class are given below:

Height (in cm)	126	127	128	129	130	131	132
Number of Students	7	3	4	2	5	6	4

1. Find the median of the above frequency distribution.
2. Find the semi-interquartile range of the above frequency distribution.

SOLUTION

Height (in cm)	Number of Students	Cumulative Frequency
126	7	7
127	3	10
128	4	14
129	2	16
130	5	21
131	6	27
132	4	31
Total	**31**	

Median $= \left(\frac{n+1}{2}\right)^{th}$ observation

$= \left(\frac{31+1}{2}\right) = 16^{th}$ observation

$= 129$

$Q_1 = \left(\frac{n+1}{4}\right)^{th}$ observation

$= \left(\frac{31+1}{4}\right)^{th} = 8^{th}$ observation

$\Rightarrow Q_1 = t_8 = 127$

$Q_3 = 3\left(\frac{n+1}{4}\right)^{th}$ observation

$= 3\times\left(\frac{31+1}{4}\right)^{th}$

$= 24^{th}$ observation

$Q_3 = 131$

Semi-interquartile range

$= \frac{Q_3 - Q_1}{2}$

$= \frac{131-127}{2}$

$= 2.$

Estimation of Median and Quartiles from Ogive

1. Prepare the cumulative frequency table with the given data.
2. Draw ogive.
3. Let total number of observations = Sum of all frequencies = N.
4. Mark the points A, B and C on Y-axis, corresponding to $\frac{N}{4}, \frac{N}{2}$, and $\frac{3N}{4}$.
5. Mark three points (P, Q, R) on ogive corresponding to $\frac{3N}{4}, \frac{N}{2}$, and $\frac{N}{4}$.
6. Draw vertical lines from the points R, Q and P to meet X-axis Q_1, M, and Q_3.
7. Then, the abscissas of Q_1, M, and Q_3 gives lower quartile, median and upper-quartile.

Info Bytes!

Musicians use ogives in a way too. The term 'ogive' in music represents a piece composed of 2 or more segments, reminding us that ogives, median, and quartiles in statistics are also about combining and analysing different data segments.

EXAMPLE 11.32 The following table shows the distribution of the weights of a group of students:

Weight in Kg	30–35	35–40	40–45	45–50	50–55	55–60	60–65
No. of students	5	6	7	5	4	3	2

SOLUTION

Class Interval	Number of Students (Frequency)	Cumulative Frequency
30–35	5	5
35–40	6	11
40–45	7	18
45–50	5	23
50–55	4	27
55–60	3	30
60–65	2	32
	$N = 32$	

$N = 32$

$\Rightarrow \frac{N}{4} = 8, \frac{N}{2} = 16$, and $\frac{3N}{4} = 24$

From the graph:

Lower quartile (Q_1) = 38

Upper quartile (Q_3) = 52

Median (M) = 44

Scale: on X-axis; 1 cm = 5 units
on Y-axis; 1 cm = 4 units

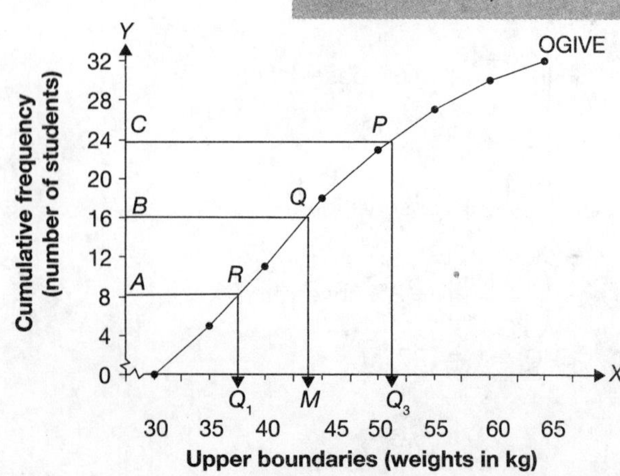

Figure 11.6

Estimation of Mode from Histogram

1. Draw a histogram to represent the given data.
2. From the upper corners of the highest rectangle, draw segments to meet the opposite corners of adjacent rectangles, diagonally as shown in the given example. Mark the intersecting point as P.
3. Draw PM perpendicular to X-axis, to meet X-axis at M.
4. Abscissa of M gives the mode of the data.

EXAMPLE 11.33 Estimate mode of the following data from the histogram:

CI	0–10	10–20	20–30	30–40	40–50	50–60	60–70
Frequency	10	16	17	20	15	13	12

SOLUTION

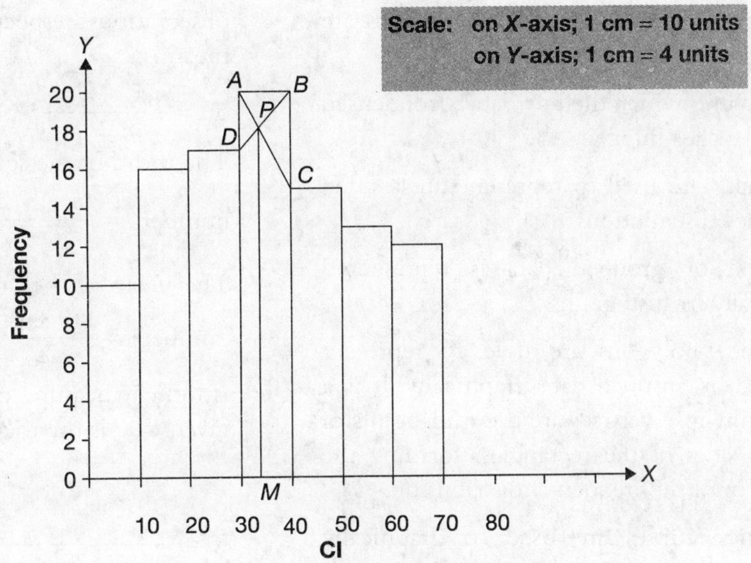

Figure 11.7

From the graph, mode (M) = 34

POINTS TO REMEMBER

- ✔ The word 'data' means, information in the form of numerical figures or a set of given facts.
- ✔ Data obtained from direct observation is called raw data.
- ✔ A systematically arrangement of the data in a tabular form is called 'tabulation' or 'presentation' of the data.
- ✔ Any raw data that is collected, forms an individual series.
- ✔ A discrete series is formulated from raw data. Here, the frequency of the observations are taken into consideration.
- ✔ A group into which the raw data is condensed is called a class interval.
- ✔ Bar graphs are used to represent unclassified frequency distributions.
- ✔ Classified or grouped data is represented graphically by histograms.
- ✔ Frequency polygons are used to represent classified or grouped data graphically. It is a polygon whose vertices are the mid-points of the top sides of the rectangles, forming the histogram of the frequency distribution.
- ✔ Frequency curves are used to graphically represent classified or grouped data.
- ✔ The arithmetic mean (or simply the mean) is the most commonly used measure of central tendency.
- ✔ If $x_1, x_2, ..., x_n$ are the n items, then:

$$\text{AM} = \frac{x_1 + x_2 + \cdots + x_n}{n} = \frac{\sum_{i=1}^{n} x_i}{n}, \text{ or briefly } \frac{\sum x}{n}.$$

AM is usually denoted by $\overline{x}$.

- ✔ When the variables $x_1, x_2, ..., x_n$ do not have same importance, and the weights $w_1, w_2, ..., w_n$ are given to each of the variables, the weighted arithmetic mean is given by, $\overline{X}_w = \dfrac{\sum x_i w_i}{\sum w_i}$.
- ✔ The algebraic sum of deviations taken about the mean is zero. That is, $\sum_{i=1}^{n} (x_i - \overline{x}) = 0$.
- ✔ **Combined mean:** If $\overline{x}_1$ and $\overline{x}_2$ are the arithmetic means of two series with n_1 and n_2 observations, respectively, then the combined mean is:
- ✔ $\overline{x}_c = \dfrac{n_1\overline{x}_1 + n_2\overline{x}_2}{n_1 + n_2}$
- ✔ The mean of the squares of the first n natural numbers $= \dfrac{(n+1)(2n+1)}{6}$.
- ✔ The mean of the cubes of the first n natural numbers $= \dfrac{n(n+1)^2}{4}$.
- ✔ Another measure of central tendency of a given data is the median.
- ✔ $\overline{x} = \dfrac{f_1x_1 + f_2x_2 + \cdots + f_kx_k}{f_1 + f_2 + \cdots + f_k} = \dfrac{\sum_{i=1}^{k} f_i x_i}{\sum_{i=1}^{k} f_i}$
- ✔ The mode of grouped data is $L_1 + \dfrac{\Delta_1 C}{\Delta_1 + \Delta_2}$.
- ✔ $\text{SD}(\sigma) = \sqrt{\dfrac{(x_1 - \overline{x})^2 + (x_2 - \overline{x})^2 + \cdots + (x_n - \overline{x})^2}{n}}$
- ✔ $\text{QD} = \dfrac{Q_3 - Q_1}{2}$.

PRACTICE QUESTIONS CLASSROOM WING

Very Short Answer Type Questions

Directions of questions from 1 to 10:
Fill in the blanks.

1. If 1–5, 6–10, 11–15, ..., are the classes of a frequency distribution, then the size of the class is ______.
2. A class interval of a data has 15 as the lower limit and 25 as the size. Then, the class mark is ______.
3. In a histogram, the ______ of all rectangles are equal.
4. The sum of 12 observations is 600, then their mean is ______.
5. If the lower boundary of the class is 25 and the size of the class is 9, then the upper boundary of the same class ______.
6. Arithmetic mean of first n natural numbers is ______.
7. Range of the scores 25, 33, 44, 26, 17 is ______.
8. Upper quartile of the data 4, 6, 7, 8, 9 is ______.
9. Lower quartile of the data 5, 7, 8, 9, 10 is ______.
10. Consider the data: 2, x, 3, 4, 5, 2, 4, 6, 4, where $x > 2$. The mode of the data is ______.

Directions of questions from 11 to 14:
State whether the following statements are true or false.

11. The width of a rectangle in a histrogram represents frequency of the class. (True/False)
12. If 16 observations are arranged in ascending order, then the median is $\frac{(\text{8th observation } + \text{9th observation})}{2}$. (True/False)
13. The mean of x, y, z is y, then $x + z = 2y$. (True/False)
14. 2(Median – Mean) = Mode – Mean. (True/False)

Directions of questions from 15 to 23:
Answer the following questions.

15. Find the arithmetic mean of the series 13, 15, 17, 19, 21, ... 57.
16. Find the arithmetic mean of the series 28, 30, 32, 34, ... 66.
17. Find the median of the data 123, 134, 145, 156, ... 343.
18. Find the mode of the following data.

Observation	5	15	25	35	45
Frequency	6	8	12	9	5

19. Calculate the variance of the data 4, 8, 9, 11, 13.
20. Observations of the certain data are $\frac{x}{8}, \frac{x}{4}, \frac{x}{2}, x, \frac{x}{16}$ where $x > 0$. If median of the given data is 8, then find the mean of the given data.
21. The mean of 12 observations is 14. By an error, one observation is registered as 24 instead of −24. Find the actual mean.
22. The mean weight of 20 students is 25 kg and the mean weight of another 10 students is 40 kg. Find the mean weight of the 30 students.
23. Find the variance and standard deviation of the scores 7, 8, 9, 10 and 16.

Short Answer Type Questions

24. Tabulate the given data by taking
    Class intervals: 1–10, 11–20, 21–30, 31–40
    Data: 9, 10, 8, 6, 7, 4, 3, 2, 16, 28, 22, 36, 24, 18, 27, 35, 19, 29, 23, 34.
25. If the mean and the median of a unimodel data are 34.5 and 32.5, then find the mode of the data.

26. (A) The heights of 100 students in primary classes is classified as follows. Find the median.

Height (in cm)	Number of Students
81	22
82	14
83	26
84	23
85	15

27. The weight (in kg) of 25 children of 9th class is given. Find the mean weight of the children.

Weight (in kg)	Number of Children
40	3
41	4
42	6
43	2
44	5
45	5

28. If the mean of the following data is 5.3, then find the missing frequency y of the following distribution:

x	f
4	11
8	2
6	3
7	y

29. (A) The mean of the data is 15. If each observation is divided by 5 and 2 is added to each result, then find the mean of the observations so obtained.

(B) Discuss about the mode of the data: 2, 3, 1, 4, 3, 2, 4, 1, 2, 5, 6, 3 and x.

30. Draw the histogram for the following distribution:

Marks	Number of Students
0–10	3
10–20	4
20–30	8
30–40	9
40–50	6

31. Find the mode of the following data:

Class Interval	Frequency
1–5	3
6–10	4
11–15	10
16–20	6
21–25	7

32. A six-faced balanced dice is rolled 20 times, and the frequency distribution of the integers obtained is given below. Find the inter quartile range.

Integer	Frequency
1	3
2	4
3	2
4	5
5	4
6	2

33. Construct a less than cumulative frequency curve and a greater than cumulative frequency curve and answer the following:

Daily Wages (in ₹)	Number of Persons
20–30	5
30–40	12
40–50	17
50–60	36
60–70	20
70–80	10
80–90	8
90–100	2

(i) Find the number of persons who received ₹60 and more than ₹60.

(ii) Find the number of persons who received ₹90 and less than ₹90.

34. Draw the frequency polygon for the following distribution:

Class Interval	Frequency
0–5	8
5–10	12
10–15	20
15–20	16
20–25	4

35. Find the median of the following data:

Class Interval	Frequency
0–20	8
20–40	10
40–60	12
60–80	9
80–100	9

36. Construct a greater than cumulative frequency curve.

Class Interval	Frequency
5–9	1
10–14	5
15–19	10
20–24	19
25–29	25
30–34	21
35–39	15
40–44	3
45–49	1

37. (A) Draw a histogram of the following data on a graph paper and estimate the mode.

Percentage of Marks	Number of Students
0–20	10
20–40	12
40–60	16
60–80	14
80–100	8

(B) Find the median of the following data:
2, 6, 18, ...4374

38. If the variance of $7x_1 - 14, 7x_2 - 14, 7x_3 - 14, \ldots 7x_{10} - 14$ is 2401, find SD of $14x_1 + 7, 14x_2 + 7, \ldots 14x_{10} + 7$.

Essay Type Questions

39. Find the arithmetic mean of the first 20 terms of the series 2, 4, 8, 16, …

40. The observations of a certain data are $\frac{x}{3}, \frac{x}{6}, \frac{2x}{7}, \frac{3x}{8}, \frac{x}{4}, \frac{2x}{3}$, and $\frac{x}{7}$ where $x > 0$. If the median of the data is 12, then what will be the value of x?

41. The observations of a certain data are $\frac{x}{2}, \frac{2x}{3}, \frac{3x}{5}, \frac{4x}{7}, \frac{5x}{12}$, and $\frac{6x}{13}$, where $x > 0$. If the median of the data is 60, then find the value of x.

42. If A = 1 + 2 + 3 … + 50
B = 1 + 3 + 5 + … + 75
C = 2 + 4 + 6 + … + 76
Find the median of the data A, B, and C.

43. Find the variance and SD for the given frequency distribution.

Class Interval	Frequency
1–5	4
6–10	1
11–15	2
16–20	3

44. The mean of the following data is 2. Find the values of m and n if they exist.

x_i	4	3	2	1
f_i	1	m	n	4

PRACTICE QUESTIONS COMPETITION WING

Level 1: Apply Your Concepts

Directions of questions from 1 to 5:
Fill in the blanks.

1. The class mark of a class is 25 and if the upper limit of that class is 40, then its lower limit is ______.
2. Consider the data: 2, 3, 2, 4, 5, 6, 4, 2, 3, 3, 7, 8, 2, 2. The frequency of 2 is ______.
3. 1–5, 6–10, 11–15, …, are the classes of a distribution, the upper boundary of the class 1–5 is ______.
4. 0–10, 10–20, 20–30, …, are the classes, the lower boundary of the class 20–30 is ______.
5. The mid-value of 20–30 is ______.

Directions of questions from 6 to 18:
Select the correct alternative from the given choices.

6. The mode of the data 5, 4, x, 3, 2, 5, 3, 5, 2, 3, 5, where $x > 3$, is ______.
(a) 2 (b) 4
(c) 5 (d) 3

7. Calculate standard deviation of the data 2005, 2009, 2008, 2007, and 2011.
(a) 2 (b) 3
(c) 4 (d) 5

8. The mode of the observations 3, 6, 3, 7, 7, 9, 3, 9, 7, 6, 3, 6, 7, x, and 6 cannot be ______.
(a) 3 (b) 6
(c) 7 (d) 9

9. Calculate the variance of the data 5012, 5013, 5015, 5018, and 5022.
(a) 13.2 (b) 12.7
(c) 15.5 (d) 16.4

10. If the less than cumulative frequency of a class is 50 and that of the previous class is 30, then the frequency of that class is ______.
(a) 10 (b) 20
(c) 40 (d) 30

11. The mode of the data 6, 4, 3, 6, 4, 3, 4, 6, 5, and x can be:
(a) Only 5 (b) Both 4 and 6
(c) Both 3 and 6 (d) 3, 4 or 6

12. If the greater than cumulative frequency of a class is 60 and that of the next class is 40, then find the frequency of that class.
(a) 10 (b) 20
(c) 50 (d) 30

13. If the difference between the mode and median is 2, then the difference between the median and mean is ______ (in the given order).
(a) 2 (b) 4
(c) 1 (d) 0

14. In a series of observations, SD is 7 and mean is 28. Find the coefficient of variation.
(a) 4 (b) $\frac{1}{4}$
(c) 25 (d) 12.5

15. If the SD of $x_1, x_2, x_3, \ldots, x_n$ is 5, then find SD of $x_1 + 5, x_2 + 5, x_3 + 5, \ldots, x_n + 5$.
(a) 0 (b) 10
(c) 5 (d) 2

16. In a series of observations, coefficient of variation is 16 and mean is 25. Find the variance.
(a) 4 (b) 8
(c) 12 (d) 16

17. If the SD of $y_1, y_2, y_3, \ldots, y_n$ is 6, then variance of $(y_1 - 3), (y_2 - 3), (y_3 - 3), \ldots, (y_n - 3)$ is ______.
(a) 6 (b) 36
(c) 3 (d) 27

18. Lower quartile, upper quartile, and interquartile range are Q_1, Q_3, and Q. If the average of Q, Q_1, and Q_3 is 40 and semi-interquartile range is 6, then find the lower quartile.
(a) 24 (b) 36
(c) 48 (d) 60

Direction for questions 19 and 30: These questions are based on the following data.
The weights of 20 students in a class are given below.

Weight (In kg)	Number of Students
31	6
32	3
33	5
34	2
35	4

19. Find the median of the above frequency distribution.
(a) 32.5 (b) 33
(c) 33.5 (d) 32

20. The interquartile range of the above frequency distribution is ______.
(a) 4 (b) 3
(c) 2 (d) 1

21. Find the interquartile range of the data 3, 6, 5, 4, 2, 1 and 7.
(a) 4 (b) 3
(c) 2 (d) 1

22. If the mean of the lower quartile and upper quartile is 10 and the semi-interquartile range is 5, then the lower quartile and the upper quartile are ______ and ______.
(a) 2, 12 (b) 3, 13
(c) 4, 14 (d) 5, 15

23. The lower quartile of the data 5, 3, 4, 6, 7, 11, 9 is ______.
(a) 4 (b) 3
(c) 5 (d) 6

24. Find the arithmetic mean of the first 567 natural numbers.
(a) 284 (b) 283.5
(c) 283 (d) 285

25. If $a < b < c < d$ and a, b, c, d are non-zero integers, the mean and median of a, b, c, d is 0, then which of the following is correct?
(a) $b = -c$ (b) $a = -d$
(c) Both (a) and (b) (d) None of these

26. The mean of 16 observations is 16. If one observation 16 is deleted and three observations 5, 5 and 6 are included, then find the mean of the final observations.
(a) 16 (b) 15.5
(c) 13.5 (d) None of these

27. If $L = 44.5$, $N = 50$, $F = 15$, $f = 5$ and $C = 20$, then find the median from of given data.
(a) 84.5 (b) 74.5
(c) 64.5 (d) 54.5

28. If $L = 39.5$, $\Delta_1 = 6$, $\Delta_2 = 9$, and $c = 10$, then find the mode of the data.
(a) 45.5 (b) 43.5
(c) 46.5 (d) 44.5

29. The average weight of 55 students is 55 kg, and the average weight of another 45 students is 45 kg. Find the average weight of all the students.
(a) 48 kg (b) 50 kg
(c) 50.5 kg (d) 52.25 kg

30. If the mean of 26, 19, 15, 24, and x is x, then find the median of the data.
(a) 23 (b) 22
(c) 20 (d) 21

Level 2: Review Your Concepts

31. The mean and median of the data a, b and c are 50 and 35, where $a < b < c$. If $c - a = 55$, then find $(b - a)$.
(a) 8 (b) 7
(c) 3 (d) 5

32. If $a < b < 2a$, and the mean and the median of a, b and $2a$ are 15 and 12, then find a.
(a) 7 (b) 11
(c) 10 (d) 8

33. The variance of $6x_i + 3$ is 30, find the standard deviation of x_i.
(a) $\frac{5}{\sqrt{6}}$ (b) $\sqrt{\frac{5}{6}}$
(c) 30 (d) $\sqrt{30}$

34. The frequency distribution of the marks obtained by 28 students in a test carrying 40 marks is given below:

Marks	Number of Students
0–10	6
10–20	x
20–30	y
30–40	6

If the mean of the above data is 20, then find the difference between x and y.
(a) 3 (b) 2
(c) 1 (d) 0

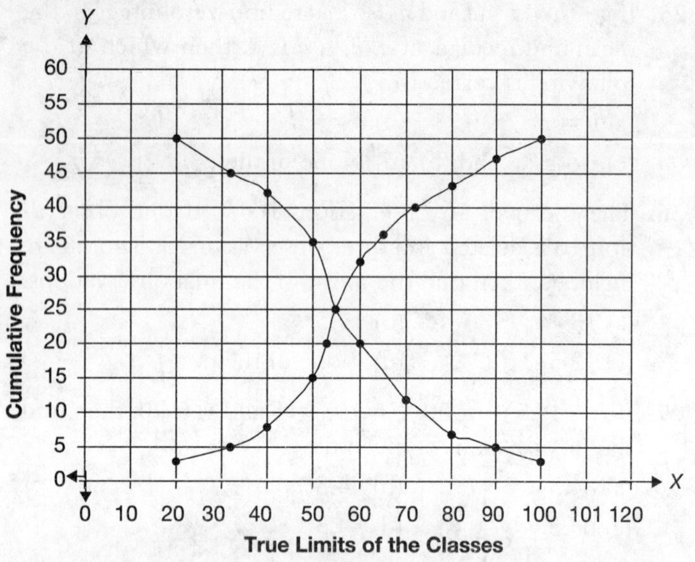

Figure 11.8

Direction for questions 35 and 39: These question are based on the following data above (figure)
The given figure represents the percentage of marks on the X-axis and the number of students on Y-axis.

35. Find the number of students who scored less than or equal to 50% of marks.

(a) 35 (b) 15
(c) 20 (d) 30

36. Find the number of students who scored greater than or equal to 90% of marks.

(a) 47 (b) 45
(c) 5 (d) 10

37. Find the variance of the scores 2, 4, 6, 8, and 10.

(a) 2 (b) 4
(c) 6 (d) 8

38. If $A = 55.5$, $N = 100$, $C = 20$, and $\Sigma f_i d_i = 60$, then find the mean from the given data.

(a) 67.5 (b) 57.5
(c) 77.5 (d) 47.5

39. Mode for the following distribution is 17.5 and x is less than 6. Find x.

Class Interval	Frequency
0–5	5
5–10	2
10–15	3
15–20	6
20–25	x

(a) 3 (b) 2
(c) 4 (d) 5

Direction for questions 40 and 41: These questions are based on the following data: consider the following distribution table.

Class Interval	Frequency
0–6	2
6–12	4
12–18	6

40. Find the coefficient of variation for the given distribution.

(a) $\frac{200\sqrt{6}}{11}$ (b) $\frac{200\sqrt{3}}{11}$
(c) $\frac{500}{11}$ (d) $\frac{200\sqrt{5}}{11}$

41. Find the variance for the given distribution:

(a) 24 (b) 12
(c) 20 (d) 25

Directions for questions 42 to 44:
Select the correct alternative from the given choices.

42. Find the mean of the quartiles Q_1, Q_2, and Q_3 of the data 5, 9, 8, 12, 7, 13, 10, 14.

(a) 9 (b) 10
(c) 9.5 (d) 11.5

43. Which of the following cannot be determined?
(A) Range of the factors of 64
(B) Range of the first 10 positive integers

(a) A
(b) B
(c) Both (A) and (B)
(d) None of these

44. Find the mean of the following data.
Range of first n natural numbers, range of negative integers from $-n$ to -1 (where $-n < -1$), range of first n positive even integers and range of first n positive odd integers.

(a) $\frac{3}{2}(n-1)$ (b) $\frac{3n-2}{2}$
(c) $\frac{3}{2}(n-2)$ (d) $\frac{4n-3}{2}$

Level 3: Assess Your Concepts

45. The arithmetic mean of the following data is 7. Find $(a + b)$.

x	f
4	a
6	4
7	b
9	5

(a) 4 (b) 2
(c) 3 (d) Cannot be determined

Direction for questions 46 and 57: The questions are based on the following data.
The performance of four students in annual report is given below.

Name of Student	Mean Score ($\bar{x}$)	SD (σ)
Dheeraja	75	11.25
Nishitha	65	5.98
Sindhuja	48	8.88
Akshitha	44	5.28

46. Who is more consistent than the others?
(a) Dheeraja (b) Nishitha
(c) Sindhuja (d) Akshitha

47. Who is less consistent than the others?
(a) Dheeraja (b) Nishitha
(c) Sindhuja (d) Akshitha

48. If the mean of the squares of first n natural numbers is 105, then find the median of the first n natural numbers.
(a) 8 (b) 9
(c) 10 (d) 11

49. Range of the scores 18, 13, 14, 42, 22, 26 and x is 44 $(x > 0)$. Find the sum of the digits of x.
(a) 16 (b) 14
(c) 12 (d) 18

50. Find the arithmetic mean of the series 1, 3, 5, ..., $(2n - 1)$.
(a) $\frac{2n-1}{n}$ (b) $\frac{2n+1}{n}$
(c) n (d) $n + 2$

51. The arithmetic mean of the squares of first n natural numbers is ______.
(a) $\frac{(n+1)(2n+1)}{6}$ (b) $\frac{n+1}{6}$
(c) $\frac{n^2-1}{6}$ (d) $\frac{n-1}{6}$

52. If X, M, Z are denoting mean, median and mode of a data and $X : M = 9 : 8$, then find the ratio $M : Z$.
(a) 8 : 9 (b) 4 : 3
(c) 7 : 6 (d) 5 : 4

53. The arithmetic mean of the series 1, 3, 3^2, ..., 3^{n-1} is ______.
(a) $\frac{3^n}{2n}$ (b) $\frac{3^n-1}{2n}$
(c) $\frac{3^{n-1}}{n+1}$ (d) $\frac{3^n+1}{2n}$

54. The mean of the data x, $x + a$, $x + 2a$, $x + 3a$, ..., ($2n + 1$ terms) is ______.
(a) $x + (n - 1)a$ (b) $x + (n + 1)a$
(c) $x + (n + 2)a$ (d) $x + an$

55. The mean height of 25 boys in a class is 150 cm, and the mean height of 35 girls in the same class is 145 cm. The combined mean height of 60 students in the class is ______ (approximately).
(a) 143 cm (b) 146 cm
(c) 147 cm (d) 145 cm

56. The sum of 15 observations of a data is $(434 + x)$. If the mean of the data is x, then find x.
(a) 25 (b) 27
(c) 31 (d) 33

57. The mean weight of 9 students is 25 kg. If one more student is joined in the group the mean is unaltered, then the weight of the 10th student is ______ (in kg).
(a) 25 (b) 24
(c) 26 (d) 23

PRACTICE QUESTIONS JEE SPECIAL WING

Multiple-Answer Type Questions

Directions for questions 1 to 6:

Each question has FOUR options (a), (b), (c), and (d). ONE OR MORE THAN ONE of these four option(s) is/are the correct answer(s).

1. An observation x is included in the following data, where $100 \le x \le 102$.

Observation	100	101	102	103	104
Frequency	14	13	13	12	11

Which of the following can be the mode(s) of the data?

(a) 100 (b) 101
(c) 102 (d) 103

2. Read the following table and answer the question that follows.

Observation	1	2	3	4	5
Frequency	1	2	3	2	1

Which of the following is equal to 3?

(a) Mean (b) Median
(c) Mode (d) Range

3. If the range of 101, 103, 211, 223, 307, 311, 409, 419, and y is 402, then what is the value of y?

(a) 13 (b) 17
(c) 379 (d) 503

4. Read the following table and answer the question that follows.

Marks	No. of Students
0 – 10	1
10 – 20	2
20 – 30	4
30 – 40	2
40 – 50	1

Which of the following is true about the given data.

(a) The average of the mean and the mode is equal to the median of the data.
(b) The difference of the mean and the median is equal to the difference of the mode and the median.
(c) The sum of the mean and the median is equal to the sum of the mode and the median.
(d) Mean ≥ Median ≥ Mode

5. If the median of 3, 13, 23, 33, 43, p, 63, 73, 83, 93, 103 is p, then which of the following can be the value of p?

(a) 63 (b) 53
(c) 47 (d) 43

6. The standard deviation of the sequence $5x_i - 6$ is 30. Which of the following sequences whose standard deviation is equivalent to that of $5x_i - 6$?

(a) $5x_i$ (b) $5x_i + 6$
(c) $6x_i + 5$ (d) None of these

Match The Column

Directions for questions 7 to 10:

Read the paragraph given below and answer the questions.

A: 1, 2, 3, 4, 5, … 2025
B: 1, 4, 9, 16, 25, … 2025
C: 1, 2, 2, 3, 3, 3, 4, 4, 4, 4, … (The last element is 10)
D: 1, 3, 5, 7, 9, … 2025

Column A	Column B (in m)
7. The average of the mean of the sequence *A* and the median of the sequence *B*	(a) 510
8. The sum of the median of the sequence *B* and the mode of the sequence *C*	(b) 539
9. The mean of the median of the sequence *C* and the mean of the sequence *D*	(c) 667
10. The range of the medians of the sequences *A*, *B*, *C* and *D*	(d) 771
	(e) 1000
	(f) 1006

Comprehension-Based Questions

Directions for questions 11 to 14:

Read the paragraph given below and answer the questions.

The health minister of a state requested that the concerned team gather information on the age, height, weight, and BMI of adult residents in his state in honour of the program **The Healthy Mind resides in a Healthy Body**.

The following table shows the BMIs of adult residents of the state.

BMI	No. of Men (in lakhs)	No. of Women (in lakhs)	Remarks
15 – 20	4	6	Underweight
20 – 25	10	8	Ideal Weight
25 – 30	2	4	Overweight
30 – 35	4	2	Obese

11. What is the median BMI of men residents of the state?

(a) 20 (b) 21
(c) 22 (d) 23

12. What is the mean BMI of women residents of the state?

(a) 21 (b) 23
(c) 25 (d) 27

13. What is the total adult residents (in lakhs) who are neither overweight nor obese?

(a) 28 (b) 26
(c) 24 (d) 22

14. What is the mode BMI of adult residents of the state?

(a) 26 (b) 24
(c) 22 (d) 20

Assertion and Reason Type Questions

Directions for questions 15 to 18:

In the light of the given statements, choose the most appropriate answer from the options given below.

(a) Both assertion (A) and reason (R) are true, and reason (R) is the correct explanation of assertion.
(b) Both assertion (A) and reason (R) are true, and reason (R) is not the correct explanation of assertion.
(c) Assertion (A) is true, but reason (R) is false.
(d) Assertion (A) is false, and reason (R) is true.

15. Assertion: The quartile deviation of prime numbers less than 20 is 5.

Reason: If x and y are the lower and upper quartiles of a data, then the quartile deviation of the data is $\frac{y-x}{2}$.

16. Assertion: The coefficient of variation of 17, 18, 19, 20, 21, 22, 23 is 20.

Reason: If the arithmetic mean (AM) and the standard deviation (SD) of a data are x and y respectively, then the coefficient of variation of the data is $\frac{y}{x} \times 100$.

17. Assertion: For a given data, if mean > median > mode and the difference between the mean and mode is 9, then the difference between mean and median is 3.

Reason: For a given data, the difference between the mean and mode is three times the difference between mean and median.

18. Assertion: The mean of 1, 3, 5, 7, … 99 is 50.

Reason: The mean of the first n natural numbers is given by $\frac{n+1}{2}$.

ANSWER KEYS

Crossword

Across

4. Frequency 5. Histogram 6. Discrete 8. Median 9. Mean

Down

1. Quartiles 2. Mode 3. Observation 6. Data 7. Range

Classroom Wing

Very Short Answer Type Questions

1. 5
2. 27.5
3. width
4. 50
5. 34
6. $\frac{(n+1)}{2}$
7. 27
8. 8.5
9. 6
10. 4
11. False
12. True
13. True
14. False
15. 35
16. 47
17. 233
18. 25
19. 9.2
20. 12.4
21. 10
22. 30 kg
23. Variance = 10, SD $= \sqrt{10}$

Short Answer Type Questions

24.

Class Interval	Tally Marks	Frequency
1–10	~~||||~~ |||	8
11–20	|||	3
21–30	~~||||~~ |	6
31–40	|||	3

25. 28.5
26. 83 cm
27. 42.68 kg
29. (A) 5
30. 5
31. 13.5
32. 3
33. (i) 40 (ii) 108
35. 50
37. (A) 53 (B) 108
38. 98

Essay Type Questions

39. $\frac{2^{20}-1}{10}$
40. 42
41. 112
42. 1444
43. Variance = 41 SD $= \sqrt{41}$
44. $m = 2$; n = any whole no.

Competition Wing

Level 1: Apply Your Concepts

1. 10	2. 5	3. 5.5	4. 20	5. 25
6. (c)	7. (a)	8. (d)	9. (a)	
10. (b)	11. (d)	12. (b)	13. (c)	
14. (c)	15. (c)	16. (d)	17. (b)	18. (c)
19. (b)	20. (b)	21. (a)	22. (d)	
23. (a)	24. (a)	25. (c)	26. (d)	27. (a)
28. (b)	29. (c)	30. (d)		

Level 2: Review Your Concepts

31. (d)	32. (b)	33. (b)	34. (d)	35. (b)
36. (c)	37. (d)	38. (a)	39. (a)	40. (d)
41. (c)	42. (c)	43. (d)	44. (a)	

Level 3: Assess Your Concepts

45. (d)	46. (d)	47. (a)	48. (b)	49. (c)
50. (c)	51. (a)	52. (b)	53. (b)	54. (d)
55. (c)	56. (c)	57. (a)		

JEE Special Wing

Multiple-Answer Type Questions

1. (a, b, c)	2. (b, c)	3. (b, d)	4. (a, b, c, d)	5. (a, b, c, d)
6. (a, b)				

Match The Column

7. (d)	8. (b)	9. (a)	10. (f)

Comprehension-Based Questions

11. (d)	12. (b)	13. (a)	14. (c)

Assertion and Reason Type Questions

15. (a)	16. (d)	17. (a)	18. (b)

Hints and Explanations

Classroom Wing

Very Short Answer Type Questions

1. Classes given clearly show the difference between lower and upper limit
So 5

2. Class mark = mean
Upper limit = 15 + 25 = 40

$$\text{Mean} = \frac{15+40}{2} = \frac{55}{2} = 27.5$$

3. Width

4. Sum = 600

$$\text{Mean} = \frac{600}{12} = 50$$

5. 34 = (25 + 9)

6. Sum of first n natural nos $= \frac{n(n+1)}{2}$

$$\text{mean} = \frac{\not{n}(n+1)}{2\times \not{n}} = \left(\frac{n+1}{2}\right)$$

7. Range = max – min
= 44 – 17
27

8. n = odd

$$\therefore \frac{3(n+1)\text{th}}{4}$$

$n = 5$

$$= 3\left(\frac{\not{6}\,3}{\not{4}\,2}\right) = \frac{9}{2} = 4.5\text{ th term}$$

$$\therefore 4\text{th term} + \frac{1}{2}(5\text{th} - 4\text{th term})$$

$$= 8 + \frac{1}{2}(9-8)$$

$$= 8.5$$

9. Lower quartile $= \frac{1}{4}(n+1)$th term when n is odd.
$n = 5$

$$\frac{1}{\not{4}\,2}(\not{6}^{\,3})\text{th term} = 1.5\text{th term}$$

$$= 5 + \frac{1}{2}(7-5) = 6$$

10. Mode = 4
Mode is max no. of times a term has occurred.

11. False, width is similar for each rectangles so it does not signify anything.

12. True ∴ formula of median

13. $$\text{mean} = \frac{x+y+x}{3} = y$$

$$x + y + z = 3y$$

$$x + z = 2$$

∴ True

14. False

15. 13, 15, 17, 19, 21,..., 7 are the consecutive odd numbers that form an arithmetic progression.
Arithmetic mean

$$= \frac{13+57}{2} = \frac{70}{2} = 35$$

16. 28, 30, 32, 34, ..., 66
∴ Observations are in arithmetic progression.

$$\text{Arithmetic mean} = \frac{\text{First term+last term}}{2}$$

$$= \frac{28+66}{2} = \frac{94}{2} = 47$$

17. 123, 134, 145, 156, ..., 343 are in A.P.

$$\text{Median} = \text{mean} = \frac{123+343}{2} = 233$$

18. As 25 has highest frequency, the mode is 25.

19. Arithmetic mean of the data

$$\frac{4+8+9+11+13}{5} = \frac{45}{5} = 9$$

$$\text{Variance} = \frac{25+1+0+4+16}{5}$$

$$= \frac{46}{5} = 9.2$$

Variance = 9.2

20. Ascending order

$$\frac{x}{16}, \frac{x}{8}, \frac{x}{4}, \frac{x}{2}, x$$

$$\text{Median} = \left(\frac{n+1}{2}\right)\text{th term} = \frac{6}{2} = 3\text{rd term}$$

$$= \frac{x}{4} = 8 \Rightarrow x = 32$$

$$\text{Mean} = \frac{4+8+16+32+2}{5}$$

$$= \frac{62}{5} = 12.4$$

21. $\text{Sum} = 14 \times 12 = 168$

$$\text{Corrections} = 168 - 24 - 24$$

$$= 120$$

$$\text{Mean} = \frac{120}{12} = 10$$

22. $\text{Sum of 20 students} = 25 \times 20$

$$\text{Sum of 10 students} = 40 \times 10$$

$$\text{Total sum} = 500 + 400 = 900 \text{ units}$$

$$\text{Mean weight} = \frac{900}{30} = 30 \text{ kg}$$

23. $\text{Mean} = \dfrac{7+8+9+10+16}{5} = 10$

Variance

$$= \frac{(7-10)^2 + (8-10)^2 + (9-10)^2 + (10-10)^2 + (16-10)^2}{5}$$

$$= \frac{9+4+1+0+36}{5} = 10$$

$$\text{SD} = \sqrt{\text{Variance}} = \sqrt{10}$$

Short Answer Type Questions

24.

Class-Interval	Frequency
1–10	8
11–20	3
21–30	6
31–40	3

25. 2(median – mean) = mode – median

⇒ 3 median = mode + 2 mean

3(32.5) = mode + 2(34.5)

Mode = 97.5 – 69

= 28.5

26.

Height (cm)	No. of students	Cf
81	22	22
82	14	36
83	26	62
84	23	85
85	15	100

$$n = 100$$

$$\text{Median} = \left(\frac{n}{2}\right)\text{th observation}$$

$$= 50\text{th}$$

$$= 83 \text{ cm}$$

27.

Weight (kg)	No. of children (f_i)	$f_i x_i$
40	3	120
41	4	164
42	6	252
43	2	86
44	5	220
45	5	225
	$\Sigma f_i = 25$	$\Sigma f_i x_i = 1067$

$$\text{Mean} = \frac{\Sigma f_i x_i}{\Sigma f_i} = \frac{1067}{25}$$

$$= 42.68 \text{ kg}$$

28.

x_i	f_i	x_if_i
4	11	44
8	2	16
6	3	18
7	y	$7y$
	$\Sigma f_i = 16 + y$	$\Sigma f_ix_i = 78 + 7y$

$$\text{Mean} = 5.3 = \frac{78+7y}{16+y}$$
$$84.8+5.3y = 78+7y$$
$$6.8 = 1.7y$$
$$y = 4$$

29. (A) Since mean = 15 and for each observation similar changes are made.

$$\therefore \left(\frac{\cancel{15}^{3}}{\cancel{5}}\right)+2=3+2=5$$

(B)

Observation	Frequency
1	2
2	3
3	3
4	2
5	1
6	1
x	1

If $x = 1$, then modes are 1, 2, 3.
If $x = 2$, then mode is 2.
If $x = 3$, then mode is 3.
If $x = 4$, then modes are 2, 3, 4.
If $x = 5$, 6, or >6, then modes are 2 and 3.

30.

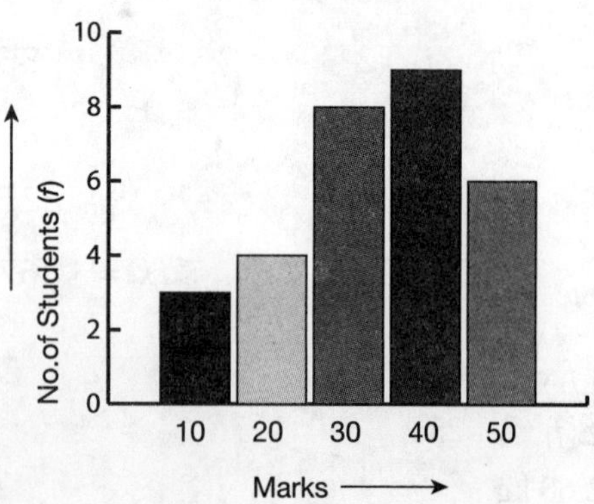

31.

CI	Frequency	Adjusted Interval
1 – 5	3	0.5 – 5.5
6 – 10	4	5.5 – 10.5
11 – 15	10	10.5 – 15.5
16 – 20	6	15.5 – 20.5
21 – 25	7	20.5 – 25.5

Maximum frequency (10) for interval = 11 – 15

$$\therefore \quad f = 10,\ f_1 = 4,\ f_2 = 6$$
$$L_1 = 10.5,\ C = 5$$
$$\therefore \text{mode} = L_1 + \frac{(f-f_1)C}{(f-f_1)+(f-f_2)}$$
$$= 10.5 + \frac{(10-4)5}{6+4}$$
$$= 10.5 + \frac{30}{10} = 13.5$$

32.

Integer	f	Cf
1	3	3
2	4	7
3	2	9
4	5	14
5	4	18
6	2	20
	N = 20	

$$Q_1 = \left(\frac{N}{4}\right)\text{th item} = \frac{20}{4} = 5\text{th term} = 2$$
$$Q_3 = 3\left(\frac{N}{4}\right)\text{th item} = \frac{20}{4}\times 3 = 15\text{th term} = 5$$
$$\text{Interquartile range} = Q_3 - Q_1$$
$$= 5 - 2 = 3$$

33.

Daily wage (Rs.)	No. of person	Cf
20–30	5	5
30–40	12	17
40–50	17	34
50–60	36	70
60–70	20	90
70–80	10	100
80–90	8	108
90–100	2	110

(i) Received 60 and >60
= 4 classes, each of interval 10
$\therefore 20+10+8+2=40$

(ii) Received 90 and <90
Then 108 (from Cf)

34.

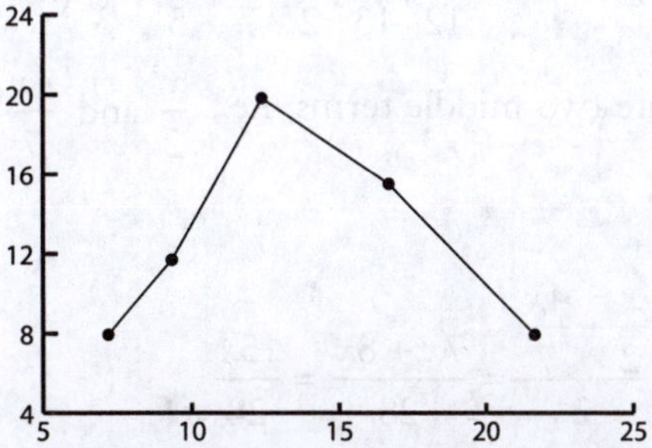

35.

CI	f	Cf
0–20	8	8
20–40	10	18
40–60	12	30
60–80	9	39
80–100	9	48
	$\Sigma f = 48$	

$$\text{Median} = L + \frac{\left(\frac{m}{2} - F\right)}{f} \times C$$

$$n = 48 \therefore \frac{n}{2} = \frac{48}{2} = 24$$

Class = 40 – 60
Lower = 40
$F = 18$

$$\text{Median} = 40 + \frac{\left(\frac{48}{2} - 18\right)}{12} \times 20$$

$$= 40 + \frac{(24-18)\times 20}{12}$$

$$= 40 + \frac{6\times 20}{12}$$

$$= 50$$

36.

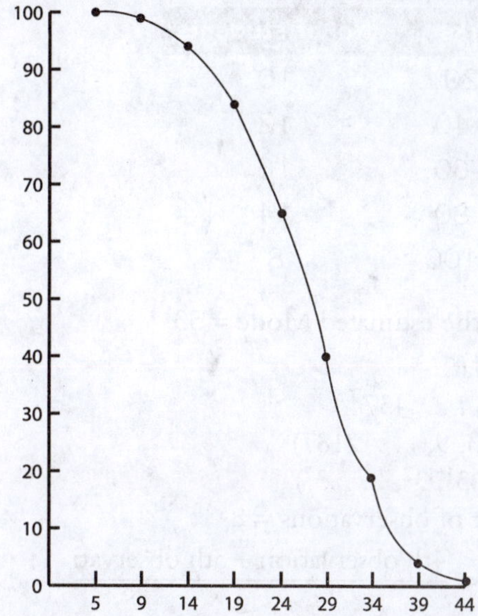

CI	F	Cf	More than Cf
5–9	1	1	100
10–14	5	6	99
15–19	10	16	94
20–24	19	35	84
25–29	25	60	65
30–34	21	81	40
35–39	15	96	19
40–44	3	99	4
45–49	1	100	1

37. (A)

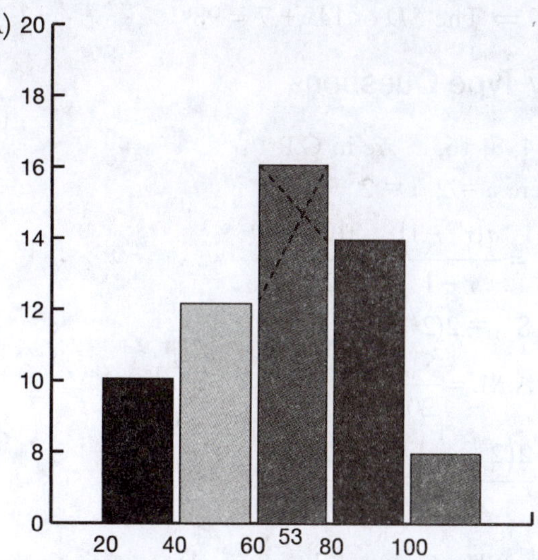

Marks	No. of students
0–20	10
20–40	12
40–60	16
60–80	14
80–100	8

Hence, the estimated Mode = 53

(B) Given data:

2, 6, 18, ...4374

$\Rightarrow 2(1, 3, 9, \ldots .2187)$

$\Rightarrow 2(1^0, 3^1, 3^2, \ldots .3^7)$

Number of observations = 8

$$\text{Median} = \frac{\text{4th observation} + \text{5th observati}}{2}$$

$$= \frac{2(3^3) + 2(3^4)}{2}$$

= 27 + 81 = 108.

38. The variance of $7x_i - 14$ is 2401.

$\Rightarrow$ The *SD* of $7x_i - 14$

$= \sqrt{\text{Variance}}$

$= \sqrt{2401} = 49$

$\Rightarrow$ The *SD* of $7x_i = 49$

$\Rightarrow$ The *SD* of $x_i = \frac{49}{7} = 7$

$\Rightarrow$ The *SD* of $14x_i = 14(7) = 98$.

$\Rightarrow$ The *SD* of $14x_i + 7 = 98$

Essay Type Questions

39. 2, 4, 8, 16, ... are in G.P.

Here $a = 2$, $r = 2$

$$S_n = \frac{a(r^n - 1)}{r - 1} = \frac{2(2^n - 1)}{2 - 1}$$

$\therefore S_{20} = 2(2^{20} - 1)$

$\therefore \text{A.M.} = \frac{S_{20}}{20}$

$$= \frac{2(2^{20} - 1)}{20} = \frac{2^{20} - 1}{10}$$

40. Ascending order of the given observations is

$\frac{2x}{3}, \frac{3x}{8}, \frac{x}{3}, \frac{2x}{7}, \frac{x}{4}, \frac{x}{6},$ and $\frac{x}{7} (\because x > 0)$

$$\text{Median} = \frac{2x}{7} = 12(\textit{given})$$

$$\Rightarrow x = \frac{7 \times 12}{2} = 42$$

41. The ascending order is $\frac{5x}{12}, \frac{6x}{13}, \frac{x}{2}, \frac{4x}{7}, \frac{3x}{5}, \frac{2x}{3} (x > 0)$.

Here, there are two middle terms, i.e., $\frac{x}{2}$ and $\frac{4x}{7}$.

$\frac{x}{2}$ and $\frac{4x}{7}$

$$\therefore \text{Median} = \frac{\frac{x}{2} + \frac{4x}{7}}{2} = \frac{7x + 8x}{28} = \frac{15x}{28}$$

Given $\frac{15x}{28} = 60 \Rightarrow x = 112$

42. $A = \frac{50 \times 51}{2}$

$= \frac{2550}{2}$

= 1275

B = 38^2 = 1444

C = 38(39)

= 1482

$\Rightarrow$ A < B < C

$\therefore$ Median = B = 1444.

43.

CI	Frequency	Corrected	Mid-point (x)	fx	D = $x - \bar{x}$
1–5	4	0.5–5.5	3	12	-7
6–10	1	5.5–10.5	8	8	-2
11–15	2	10.5–15.5	13	26	3
16–20	3	15.5–20.5	18	54	8
	Σf = 10			Σfx = 100	

$$\bar{x} = \frac{\sum fx}{\sum f} = \frac{100}{10} = 10$$

D^2	fD^2
49	196
4	4
9	18
64	192
	$\Sigma fD^2 = 410$

$$SD = \sigma = \sqrt{\frac{\sum fD^2}{N}}$$

$$= \sqrt{\frac{410}{10}}$$

$$= \sqrt{41}$$

Variance = $(SD)^2 = 41$

44.

x_i	f_i	$f_i x_i$
4	1	4
3	m	$3m$
2	n	$2n$
1	4	4

$\Sigma f_i = 5 + m + n$

$\Sigma f_i x_i = 8 + 3m + 2n$

$$\text{Mean} = \frac{\sum f_i x_i}{\sum f_i}$$

$$2 = \frac{8 + 3m + 2n}{5 + m + n}$$

$\Rightarrow 10 + 2m + 2n = 8 + 3m + 2n$

$\Rightarrow m = 2$

The value of n is any whole number.

Competition Wing

Level 1: Apply Your Concepts

1. Mean = 25

   Lower limit = x

   $$\frac{x+4}{2} = 25$$

   $$x = 50 - 40 = 10$$

2. Count the no of times '2' is occurring $= 5$

3. Upper boundary = 5.5

4. Lower boundary = 20

5. Mid value is the middle number of the interval, i.e., 25.

6. $x \neq 3$ as $x > 3$

   $\therefore$ The most frequently found observation is 5.

   $\therefore$ mode = 5

   Hence, the correct option is (c).

7. The SD of 2005, 2009, 2008, 2007, and 2011 is same as the SD of (2005 – 2000), (2009 – 2000), (2008 – 2000), (2007 – 2000), and (2011 – 2000), i.e., 5, 9, 8, 7, and 11.

   $$\text{A.M.} = \frac{5+9+8+7+11}{5} = 8$$

   $$\text{Variance} = \frac{(5-8)^2+(9-8)^2+(8-8)^2+(7-8)^2+(11-8)^2}{5}$$

   $$= \frac{9+1+0+1+9}{5} = 4$$

   $$\therefore \text{S.D.} = \sqrt{\text{Variance}} = \sqrt{4} = 2$$

   Hence, the correct option is (a).

8. If $x = 3$, then mode is 3 ($\because$ 3 occurs 5 times).

   If $x = 6$, then mode is 6 ($\because$ 6 occurs 5 times).

   If $x = 7$, then mode is 7 ($\because$ 7 occurs 5 times).

   If $x = 9$, then mode cannot be 9 as 9 occurs 3 times and other observations occur 4 times each.

   Hence, the correct option is (d).

9. The variance of 5012, 5013, 5015, 5018, and 5022 is same as the variance of 12, 13, 15, 18, and 22.

   $$\text{Mean} = \frac{12+13+15+18+22}{5} = \frac{80}{5} = 16$$

   $\therefore$ Variance =

   $$\frac{(12-16)^2+(13-16)^2+(15-16)^2+(18-16)^2+(22-16)^2}{5}$$

   $$= \frac{16+9+1+4+36}{5} = \frac{66}{5} = 13.2$$

   Hence, the correct option is (a).

10. Frequency of a particular class = Cumulative frequency of that class – Cumulative frequency of the previous class.

11. An observation which has more frequency in the data is called the mode of the data.

12. Frequency of a particular Class = (cumulative frequency of that class) – (Cumulative frequency of the next class).

13. Use the empirical formula.

14. Coefficient of variation $= \frac{\text{Standard deviation}}{\text{Mean}} \times 100$.

15. SD does not alter when each term is increased by fixed constant.

16. Coefficient of variation $= \frac{\text{Standard deviation}}{\text{Mean}} \times 100$.

17. SD does not alter when each term is decreased by fixed constant.

18. Semi-interquartile range $= \frac{Q_3 - Q_1}{2}$.

19. Find the less than cumulative frequency, then find the median by using formulae.

20. Find the less than cumulative frequency, then find inter-quartile range by using formulae.

21. $Q = Q_3 - Q_1$.

22. Semi-interquartile range $= \frac{Q_3 - Q_1}{2}$.

23. Write the data in the ascending order.

    Lower quartile is $\left(\frac{n+1}{4}\right)$observation.

24. Arithmetic mean of first 'n' natural numbers is $\frac{n+1}{2}$.

25. Average $= \frac{\text{Sum of the quantities}}{\text{Number of the quantities}}$.

26. Mean $= \frac{\text{Sum of the observations}}{\text{Number of the observations}}$.

27. Median $= L + \left[\frac{\left(\frac{N}{2} - F\right)C}{f}\right]$.

28. Mode $= L_1 + \left[\dfrac{(f - f_1)C}{2f - (f_1 - f_2)}\right]$.

29. Average $= \dfrac{\text{Sum of the quantities}}{\text{Number of the quantities}}$.

30. Arithmatic mean $= \dfrac{\text{Sum of the quantities}}{\text{Number of the quantities}}$.

Level 2: Review Your Concepts

31. (i) Since, a, b, c are in ascending order, b is the median.

(ii) AM $= \dfrac{\text{Sum of all observations}}{\text{Total number of observations}}$.

(iii) Using the above relation, write the relation between c and a, and find the value of a and c. Finally, find the values of b and a.

32. (i) Since, $a < b < 2a$, Median $= b = 12$.

(ii) Mean $= \dfrac{\text{Sum of all observations}}{\text{Total number of observations}}$.

33. (i) If the variance of $(ax_i + b)$ is k, then SD of $(ax_i + b) = \sqrt{k}$.

(ii) SD of $x_i = \dfrac{\sqrt{k}}{a}$.

34. (i) Find the mid-values (x_i) of class intervals.

(ii) Find $\dfrac{\sum fx}{\sum f}$.

(iii) Equate $\dfrac{\sum fx}{\sum f}$ with mean, and find the values of x and y.

35. In the given graph, one curve represents the less than cumulative frequency, another curve represents the greater than cumulative frequency.

36. Apply the greater than cumulative frequency concept.

37. (i) SD of AP with common difference 'd' is $d\sqrt{\dfrac{n^2-1}{12}}$.

(ii) Variance $= (\text{SD})^2$.

38. (i) Use arithmetic mean formula for grouped data.

(ii) Mean of grouped data

$$= A + \frac{\Sigma f_i d_i}{N} \times C.$$

40. Find mode of the given data in terms of x and form an equation to find x.

41. (i) First calculate the mean.

(ii) Find deviations about the mean $(x_i - \overline{x})$.

$D = x_i - \overline{x}$, $N =$ Sum of all the frequencies, SD $= \sqrt{\dfrac{\Sigma f D^2}{N}}$.

42. The increasing order of given the observations:

5, 7, 8, 9, 10, 12, 13, 14

$Q_1 = \left(\dfrac{n}{4}\right)$th observation

$Q_1 =$ 2nd observation

$\therefore Q_1 = 7$

$Q_2 =$ Mean of $\left(\dfrac{n}{2}\right)$th, $\left(\dfrac{n}{2}+1\right)$th observation

$=$ Mean of 4 th, 5 th items $= \dfrac{9+10}{2} = 9.5$

$Q_3 = \left(\dfrac{3n}{4}\right)$th $= \left(3\times\dfrac{8}{4}\right)$th 6th observation

$Q_3 = 12$

Mean of Q_1, Q_2, $Q_3 = \dfrac{7+9.5+12}{3} = \dfrac{28.5}{3} = 9.5$.

43. (a) Range of the factors of 64 is $64 - 1 = 63$.

(b) Range of the first ten-positive integers is 9.

44. Range of the first 'n' natural numbers $= n - 1$.

Range of the last n negative integers $= -1 - (-n)$ $= n - 1$.

Range of the first 'n' positive even integers $= 2n - 2$.

Range of first 'n' positive odd integers $= (2n - 1) - (1)$ $= 2n - 2$.

$\therefore$ Mean of the given data is

$$\frac{(n-1)+(n-1)+(2n-2)+(2n-2)}{4}$$

$$= \frac{6n-6}{4} = \frac{3n-3}{2}$$

$$= \frac{3}{2}(n-1).$$

Level 3: Assess Your Concepts

45. Use the arithmetic mean formulae for descreate series.

46. (i) Coefficient of variation $= \dfrac{\text{SD}}{\text{Mean}} \times 100$.

(ii) Using the above, find CV of all the four members.

(iii) The member whose CV is least is more consistent.

47. (i) Find coefficient of variation then decide.

(ii) The one with highest CV is less consistent.

48. The mean of the squares of n natural numbers $\frac{(n+1)(2n+1)}{6}$.

49. Range is the maximum value – minimum value.

50. $1 + 3 + 5 + \cdots + (2n - 1) = n^2$

$\therefore$ AM $= \frac{n^2}{n} = n$.

51. $\Sigma n^2 = \frac{n(n+1)(2n+1)}{6}$

$AM = \frac{n(n+1)(2n+1)}{6n} = \frac{(n+1)(2n+1)}{6}$

52. Mode = 3 × Median – 2 × Mean

$Z = 3M - 2X$

Given, $X : M = 9 : 8$

$\Rightarrow \frac{X}{M} = \frac{9}{8}$

$X = \frac{9M}{8}$

$\therefore Z = 3M - 2\times\frac{9M}{8} = 3M - \frac{9M}{4}$

$Z = \frac{3M}{4} \quad \therefore \frac{M}{Z} = \frac{4}{3}$

$\Rightarrow M : Z = 4 : 3.$

53. $\bar{x} = \frac{1 + 3 + 3^2 + \cdots + 3^{n-1}}{n}$

$= \frac{1\left(\frac{3^n - 1}{3 - 1}\right)}{n} = \frac{3^n - 1}{2n}$

54. Sum of the given observations $S_n = x + x + a + x + 2a + \ldots$ for $(2n + 1)$ terms

$\therefore$ The total number of terms in the given series is $(2n + 1)$ and first term = x and common difference = a

$= \frac{2n+1}{2}[2\cdot x + (2n + 1 - 1)a]$

$= \frac{2n+1}{2}[2x + 2an] = (2n + 1)(x + an)$

$AM = \frac{S_n}{2n+1} = \frac{(2n+1)(x+an)}{2n+1}$

AM = $x + an$.

55. Given $n_1 = 25$, $n_2 = 35$

$\bar{x}_1 = 150$ and $\bar{x}_2 = 145$

Combined mean, $\bar{x} = \frac{n_1\bar{x}_1 + n_2\bar{x}_2}{n_1 + n_2}$

$\bar{x} = \frac{25\times150 + 35\times145}{25 + 35} = \frac{3750 + 5075}{60}$

$= \frac{8825}{60} = 147$ (approximately).

56. Given sum of all observations = 434 + x and $n = 15$, $\bar{x} = x$.

$\therefore \quad \frac{434 + x}{15} = x$

$434 + x = 15x$

$x = \frac{434}{14} \Rightarrow x = 31$.

57. The sum of the weights of the 9 students = 25 × 9 = 225 kg.

If one more student is joined in the group, then total number of students is 10, and the mean is 25.

The sum of the weights of the 10 students is 25 × 10 = 250 kg.

The weight of the 10th student is 250 – 225 = 25 kg.

JEE Special Wing

Multiple-Answer Type Questions

1. Given that $100 \leq x \leq 102$.

Observation	100	101	102	103	104
Frequency	14	13	13	12	11

If $x = 100$, the frequency of 100 is 15 which is the highest. So, mode of the data is 100.

If $x = 101$, the frequency of each of 100 and 101 is 14 which is the highest. So, modes of the data are 100 and 101.

If $x = 102$, the frequency of each of 100 and 102 is 14 which is the highest. So, modes of the data are 100 and 102.

Hence, choice (a, b, c) are correct.

2. Given data:

Observation	1	2	3	4	5
Frequency	1	2	3	2	1

(a) $\text{Mean} = \dfrac{1\times2+2\times2+3\times3+4\times2+5\times1}{2+2+3+2+1}$

$= \dfrac{28}{10} = 2.8.$

(b) As the number of observations is 10, the median

$= \dfrac{5^{th}\text{ Observation} + 6^{th}\text{ Observation}}{2} = \dfrac{3+3}{2} = 3.$

(c) The highest frequency is 3 and the corresponding observation is 3.

So, the mode is 3.

(d) Range = Highest Score – Lowest Score

$= 5 - 1 = 4.$

Hence, choice (b and c) are correct.

3. Given that the range of 101, 103, 211, 223, 307, 311, 409, 419, and y is 402.

We have the range = highest score – lowest score.

(i) If the highest score is 419, the lowest score is not 101 since 402 is the range of the data.

So, the lease score is y.

$419 - y = 402.$

$y = 419 - 402 = 17.$

(ii) If the highest score is y, the lowest score is 101.

$y - 101 = 402.$

$y = 402 + 101 = 503.$

Hence, choice (b and d) are correct.

4. Given data:

Marks	Mid-values (x_i)	No. of Students (f_i)	$f_i \times x_i$
0 – 10	5	1	5
10 – 20	15	2	30
20 – 30	25	4	100
30 – 40	35	2	70
40 – 50	45	1	45
Total		10	250

$$\text{Mean} = \frac{\sum f_i \times x_i}{\sum f_i}$$

$$= \frac{250}{10} = 25.$$

Marks	No. of Students (f_i)	Cumulative Frequencies
0 – 10	1	1
10 – 20	2	3 (cf)
20 – 30	4 (f)	7
30 – 40	2	9
40 – 50	1	10

$n = 10,\ h = 10,$ and $L = 20.$

$$\text{Median} = L + \frac{\left(\frac{n}{2} - cf\right)h}{f}$$

$$= 20 + \frac{\left(\frac{10}{2} - 3\right)10}{4}$$

$$= 20 + 5 = 25.$$

Marks	No. of Students (f_i)
0 – 10	1
10 – 20	2(f_1)
20 – 30	4 (f)
30 – 40	2 (f_2)
40 – 50	1

$h = 10,$ and $L = 20.$

$$\text{Mode} = L + \frac{(f - f_1)h}{2f - f_1 - f_2}$$

$= 20 + \frac{(4-2)10}{8-2-2}$

$= 20 + 5 = 25.$

As mean = median = mode, **choice (a, b, c, d) are correct.**

5. Given that the median of 3, 13, 23, 33, 43, p, 63, 73, 83, 93, 103 is p.

$\Rightarrow$ 3, 13, 23, 33, 43, p, 63, 73, 83, 93, 103 are in ascending order.

$\Rightarrow 43 \le p \le 63$

Hence, choice (a, b, c, d) are correct.

6. Given that the standard deviation (SD) of the sequence $5x_i - 6$ is 30.

$\Rightarrow$ The SD of the sequence $5x_i = 30$.

$\Rightarrow$ The SD of the sequence $5x_i + 6 = 30$.

$\Rightarrow$ The SD of the sequence $x_i = \frac{30}{5} = 6$.

$\Rightarrow$ The SD of the sequence $6x_i = 6 \times 6 = 36$.

$\Rightarrow$ The SD of the sequence $6x_i + 5 = 36$.

Hence, choice (a and b) are correct.

Match The Column

Common Solutions for questions 7 to 10:

Given that

A: 1, 2, 3, 4, 5, … 2025 are in AP.

Mean = Median $= \frac{1+2025}{2} = 1013.$

As the frequency of each observation is 1, the mode is ill-defined.

B: 1, 4, 9, 16, 25, … 2025

$\Rightarrow$ B: $1^2, 2^2, 3^2, 4^2, 5^2, \ldots 45^2$

Median $= 23^2 = 529.$

C: 1, 2, 2, 3, 3, 3, 4, 4, 4, 4, … (The last element is 10)

$$\text{Mean} = \frac{1^2+2^2+3^2+4^2+\ldots+10^2}{10} = \frac{10(10+1)(20+1)}{6\times 10}$$

$$= \frac{(11)(21)}{6} = 38.5$$

Observation	Frequency	Cumulative Frequency
1	1	1
2	2	3
3	3	6
4	4	10
5	5	15
6	6	21
7	7	28
8	8	36
9	9	45
10	10	55

Total number of observations = 55.

Median = 28th Observation = 7.

Mode = 10.

D: 1, 3, 5, 7, 9, … 2025 are in AP.

Mean = Median $= \frac{1+2025}{2} = 1013.$

As the frequency of each observation is 1, the mode is ill-defined.

7. The average of the mean of the sequence A and the median of the sequence $B = \frac{1013+529}{2} = 771.$

Hence, the correct option is (d).

8. The sum of the median of the sequence B and the mode of the sequence $C = 529 + 10 = 539.$

Hence, the correct option is (b).

9. The mean of the median of the sequence C and the mean of the sequence $D = \frac{7+1013}{2} = 510.$

Hence, the correct option is (a).

10. The range of the medians of the sequences A, B, C and $D = 1013 - 7 = 1006.$

Hence, the correct option is (f).

Comprehension-Based Questions

Common Solutions for questions 11 to 14:

Given that:

BMI	No. of men (in lakhs)	No. of women (in lakhs)	Remarks
15 – 20	4	6	Underweight
20 – 25	10	8	Ideal Weight
25 – 30	2	4	Overweight
30 – 35	4	2	Obese

11.

BMI	No. of men (in lakhs) (f_i)	Cumulative Frequencies
15 – 20	4	4 (cf)
20 – 25	10 (f)	14
25 – 30	2	16
30 – 35	4	20

$n = 20$, $h = 5$, and $L = 20$.

$$\text{Median} = L + \frac{\left(\frac{n}{2} - cf\right)h}{f}$$

$$= 20 + \frac{\left(\frac{20}{2} - 4\right)5}{10}$$

$$= 20 + 3 = 23.$$

Hence, the correct option is (d).

12.

BMI	No. of women (in lakhs) (f_i)	Mid-values (x_i)	$f_i \times x_i$
15 – 20	6	17.5	105
20 – 25	8	22.5	180
25 – 30	4	27.5	110
30 – 35	2	32.5	65
Total	20		460

$$\text{Mean} = \frac{\sum f_i \times x_i}{\sum f_i}$$

$$= \frac{460}{20} = 23.$$

Hence, the correct option is (b).

13. The total adult residents (in lakhs) who are neither overweight nor obese = (4 + 6) + (10 + 8) = 28.

Hence, the correct option is (a).

14.

BMI	No. of adult (in lakhs) (f_i)
15 – 20	10 (f_1)
20 – 25	18 (f)
25 – 30	6 (f_2)
30 – 35	6

$h = 5$ and $L = 20$.

$$\text{Mode} = L + \frac{(f - f_1)h}{2f - f_1 - f_2}$$

$$= 20 + \frac{(18 - 10)5}{36 - 10 - 6}$$

$$= 20 + \frac{40}{20}$$

$$= 20 + 2 = 22.$$

Hence, the correct option is (c).

Assertion and Reason Type Questions

Solutions for questions 15 to 18:

15. **Assertion:** The prime numbers less than 20 are: 2, 3, 5, 7, 11, 13, 17, 19.

The number of terms (n) = 8.

The lower quartile (Q_1) = $\left(\frac{n}{4}\right)^{th}$ observation

= 2nd observation

= 3.

The lower quartile (Q_3) = $\left(\frac{3n}{4}\right)^{th}$ observation

= 6th observation

=13.

We have the quartile deviation = $\frac{Q_3 - Q_1}{2} = \frac{13 - 3}{2}$

= 5.

So, **Assertion** is true.

Reason: We have the quartile deviation = $\frac{Q_3 - Q_1}{2}$.

Given that x and y are the lower and upper quartiles of a data, then the quartile deviation of the data is $\frac{y - x}{2}$.

Reason is true and is the correct explanation to **Assertion**.

Hence, the correct option is (a).

16. **Assertion:** Given data: 17, 18, 19, 20, 21, 22, 23 are in AP with the common difference (d) is 1.

The number of terms (n) = 7.

Arithmetic mean (AM) = $\left(\frac{n+1}{2}\right)^{th}$ observation

= 4th observation

=20.

$$\text{Standard deviation (SD)} = d\sqrt{\frac{n^2 - 1}{12}}$$

$$= 1 \times \sqrt{\frac{7^2 - 1}{12}} = \sqrt{4} = 2.$$

$$\text{The coefficient of variation} = \frac{\text{SD}}{\text{AM}} \times 100$$

$$= \frac{2}{20} \times 100 = 10.$$

So, **Assertion** is false.

Reason: If the arithmetic mean (AM) and the standard deviation (SD) of a data are x and y respectively, then the coefficient of variation of the data is $\frac{y}{x}\times 100$, which is a true statement.

Hence, the correct option is (d).

17. **Assertion:** Given that mean > median > mode.

Also, mean – mode = 9.

We have, mode = 3 median – 2 mean.

$\Rightarrow$ mode – mean = 3 median – 2 mean – mean

$\Rightarrow$ mode – mean = 3 median – 3 mean

$\Rightarrow$ mode – mean = 3(median – mean)

$\Rightarrow$ mean – mode = 3(mean – median) (1)

$\Rightarrow$ 9 = 3(mean – median)

$\Rightarrow$ mean – median = 3.

So, **Assertion** is true.

Reason: For a given data, the difference between the mean and mode is three times the difference between mean and median.

From (1), we can see that the **Reason** is true and is the correct explanation to **Assertion**.

Hence, the correct option is (a).

18. **Assertion:** Given data: 1, 3, 5, 7, ... 99.

The given sequence has the first 50 odd natural numbers.

The sum of the first 50 odd natural numbers = $(50)^2$.

The mean of the first 50 odd natural numbers

$= \frac{(50)^2}{50} = 50.$

So, **Assertion** is true.

Reason: The sum of the first n natural numbers

$= \frac{n(n+1)}{2}$

The mean of the first n natural numbers is given by

$\frac{\frac{n(n+1)}{2}}{n} = \frac{n(n+1)}{2}.$

So, **Reason** is true but not the correct explanation to **Assertion**.

Hence, the correct option is (b).

CHAPTER 12

Probability

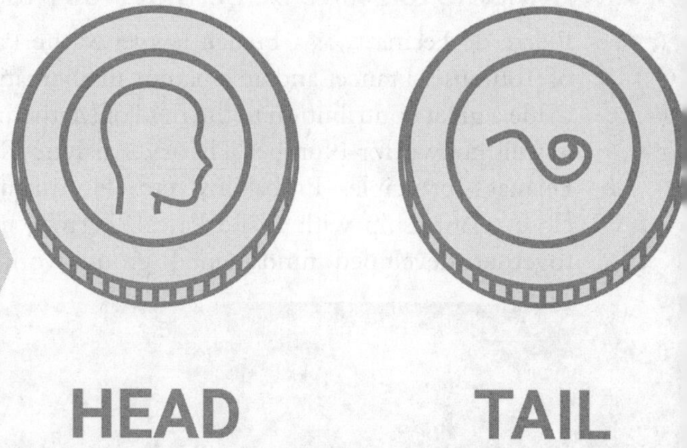

Remember

Before beginning this chapter, you should be able to:

- Recall some basic concepts related to probability
- Apply the concept in daily life and solve problems

Key Ideas

After completing this chapter, you should be able to:

- Understand about random experiments and events occurring
- Learn probability of an event and probability of non-occurrence of an event

Scientific Crypt

A Tribute to Pierre de Fermat (1601 to 1665)

Pierre de Fermat was a French lawyer at the Parliament of Toulouse, France, and an amateur mathematician. He made a great contribution to the field of Mathematics. He is well known for Number Theory, Analytic Geometry, Fermat's principle, Probability etc. He maintained a close relationship with Blaise Pascal. Fermat and Pascal together developed fundamental groundwork for the theory of probability. They are now honoured as founders of probability theory. Fermat is credited with carrying out the first rigorous probability calculations. In response to a query from a professional gambler, he showed that throwing at least one six in four throws of a die was more probable than throwing a double six in 24 throws of two dice.

FUN TIME

CROSSWORD

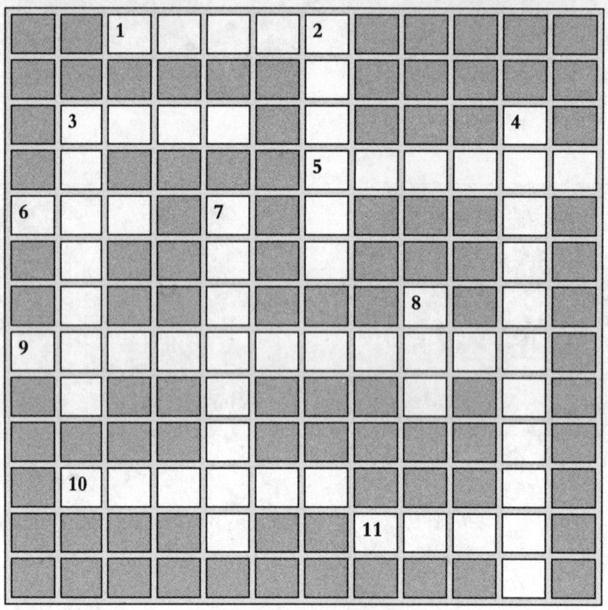

Across

1. It is an outcome.
3. When a coin is tossed, the probability of getting a HEAD.
5. Experiment of tossing a coin
6. When a dice is rolled, the probability of getting a number which is less than 7.
9. Arrangement
10. In these many ways, five students can be selected for two places.
11. One is the factorial of

Down

2. Number of two-digit numbers that can be formed by using 9, 7, 5, 3, 1 and 0
3. Number of outfits from 20 shirts and 5 trousers
4. Selection
7. In these many ways, 3 letters can be posted in 10 letterboxes.
8. Number of words formed by using the letters of the word 'TRY'

INTRODUCTION

In nature, there are two kinds of phenomena—deterministic and in-deterministic. Examples of deterministic phenomena are:

1. The sun rises in the east.
2. If an object is dropped, it falls to the ground.
3. Every organism which takes birth dies.

Examples of in-deterministic phenomena are:

1. The next vehicle that we see on a road going west to east may be headed east or west.
2. If a gas molecule is released in a container, it may head in any direction.
3. A person selected from a population may die before attaining the age of 75 years, when he attains the age of 75 or after he attains the age of 75.

Probability theory is the study of in-deterministic phenomena. While the theory has widespread applications in all walks of life, it is best to confine ourselves to certain simple kind of in-deterministic phenomena in the initial stage. Examples are tossing of coins, rolling dice, picking cards from well-shuffled decks and drawing objects from different containers, containing different objects. All these are examples of **random experiments**—situations in which we do something and we are not sure of the outcome, because there is more than one possible outcome. Tossing a coin, rolling a dice or drawing a card from a deck.

Sample Space

The set of all possible outcomes of an experiment is called its sample space. It is usually denoted by S.

Examples:

1. Consider a cubical dice with numbers 1, 2, 3, 4, 5 and 6 on its faces.

When we roll the dice, it can fall with any of its faces facing up. So, the number on each of its faces is a possible outcome.

Hence, the sample space (S) = $\{1, 2, 3, 4, 5, 6\}$.

2. When we toss an unbiased coin, the result can be a head(H) or a tail(T). So the sample space (S) = $\{H, T\}$.

Event

The outcomes or a combination of the outcomes is called an event. The probability of an event (E) is a measure of our belief that the event will occur. This may be zero, i.e., we do not expect the event to occur at all. For example, if two dice are rolled, the probability that the sum of the numbers which will come up 1 is zero. The probability may be 1, i.e., we are absolutely certain that the event will occur. For Example, If a coin is tossed the probability that we get a head or a tail is 1. But in general, we may believe that the event may occur but we are not absolutely certain, i.e., $0 < p < 1$.

Examples:

1. In rolling a dice, getting an even number is an event.

2. In tossing a coin, getting a head (H) is an event.

In the general case, when we are not sure of either the occurrence or non-occurrence of an event, how do we assign a number to the strength of our belief?

Consider the case of rolling a dice. It will show up one of the numbers-1, 2, 3, 4, 5, or 6. Each of these outcomes is equally likely, if the dice is an unbiased dice, i.e., well-balanced. So, when a dice is rolled once, there is only one way of getting the outcome 5, out of the six possible outcomes 1, 2, 3, 4, 5, or 6. Therefore, the probability of the number 5 showing up is 1 in 6. In other words, we say that the probability of getting 5 is $\frac{1}{6}$.

We write this as, $P(5) = \frac{1}{6}$.

Also, the probability of getting each of the other numbers is equal to $\frac{1}{6}$.

Similarly, in tossing an unbiased coin, we can say that the probability of getting a head or the probability of getting a tail is $\frac{1}{2}$.

Probability of an Event

Let E be an event of a certain experiment whose outcomes are equally likely. Then, the probability of the event E, denoted by $P(E)$, is defined as

$$P(E) = \frac{\text{Number of outcomes favourable to } E}{\text{Total number of possible outcomes}}.$$

Konnect

1. For any event E, $0 \le P(E) \le 1$.
2. If $P(E) = 0$, then E is said to be an impossible event.
3. If $P(E) = 1$, then E is said to be a certain or a sure event.

EXAMPLE 12.1 Find the probability of getting an even number when an unbiased dice is rolled once.

SOLUTION

When a dice is rolled, the total number of possible outcomes is 6.

Let E be the event of getting an even number. Then, the outcomes favourable to E are 2, 4, and 6, i.e., 3 outcomes are favourable.

Hence, $P(E) = \frac{3}{6} = \frac{1}{2}$.

EXAMPLE 12.2 When an unbiased dice is rolled once, what is the probability of getting a multiple of 3?

SOLUTION

When an unbiased dice is rolled, the total number of possible outcomes is 6.

Let E be the event of getting a multiple of 3.

Then, the outcomes favourable to E are 3 and 6, i.e., 2 outcomes are favourable.

Hence, $P(E) = \frac{2}{6} = \frac{1}{3}$.

Probability of Non-occurrence of an Event *E*

Let a random experiment have n possible outcomes – all equally likely. Say m of these are favourable for an event E. Then, there are $(n - m)$ outcomes which are not favourable to the event E.

Let $\bar{E}$ denote the non-occurrence of E.

Then, $P(\bar{E}) = \frac{n - m}{n}$,

That is, $P(\text{non-occurrence of } E) = \dfrac{n-m}{n}$.

Now, $P(E) + P(\bar{E})$

$$= \frac{m}{n} + \frac{n-m}{n} = \frac{m+(n-m)}{n} = \frac{n}{n} = 1.$$

That is, $P(E) + P(\bar{E}) = 1$.

Classification of a Pack (or Deck) of Cards

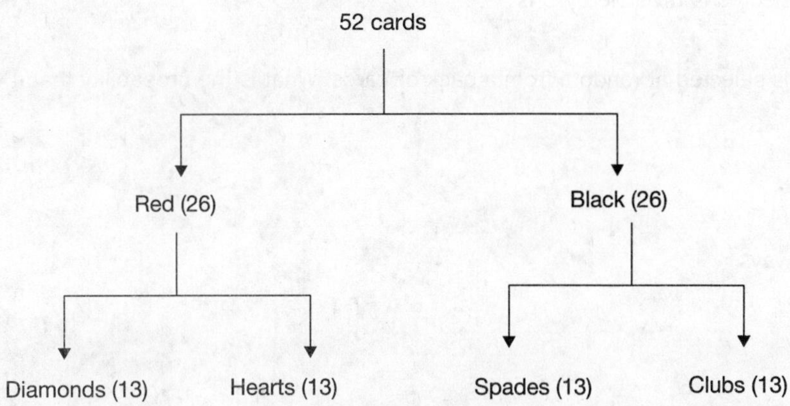

Figure 12.1

> **Info Bytes!**
>
> **Smallest Deck Ever Created:** The smallest deck of playable cards was created by B.D. Tyagi of India and measures only 5 mm × 3.5 mm × 1.5 mm. It's a fully playable deck with 52 cards.

The cards in each suit are Ace (A), King (K), Queen (Q), Jack (J), 10, 9, 8, 7, 6, 5, 4, 3, and 2.

The cards A, J, Q and K are called honours and the cards 2, 3, 4, 5, 6, 7, 8, 9, and 10 are called numbered cards. The cards J, Q, and K are called face cards.

EXAMPLE 12.3 When a fair dice is rolled, what is the probability of getting a number less than 5?

SOLUTION

When a fair dice is rolled, the total number of possible outcomes is 6.

Let E be the required event. Then, the outcomes favourable to E are 1, 2, 3 and 4, i.e., 4 favourable outcomes.

$\Rightarrow P(E) = \dfrac{4}{6} = \dfrac{2}{3}$.

Hence, the probability of getting a number less than 5 is $\dfrac{2}{3}$.

EXAMPLE 12.4 When a dice is rolled, what is the probability of getting a number 2 or 3?

SOLUTION

Total number of possible outcomes = 6.

Favourable outcomes are 2 and 3.

That is, 2 favourable outcomes.

$\therefore$ Required probability $= \dfrac{2}{6} = \dfrac{1}{3}$.

EXAMPLE 12.5 A number is chosen randomly from the set of integers from 1 to 20. What is the probability that it will be divisible by 5?

SOLUTION

There are 20 integers from 1 to 20.

So, an integer can be selected from 1 to 20 in 20 ways.

Let E be the required event. Then, the numbers favourable to E are 5, 10, 15, and 20, i.e., 4 favourable numbers.

$\Rightarrow P(E) = \frac{4}{20} = \frac{1}{5}$.

Hence, the probability that the number selected is divisible by 5 is $\frac{1}{5}$.

EXAMPLE 12.6 A card is selected at random from a pack of cards. What is the probability that it will be a red card?

SOLUTION

There are 52 cards in a pack of cards.

So, a card can be selected from it in 52 ways.

Out of the 52 cards, 26 cards are red coloured.

So, a red card can be selected in 26 ways.

Hence, required probability $= \frac{26}{52} = \frac{1}{2}$.

EXAMPLE 12.7 When a card is selected at random from a pack of cards, find the probability that it is a king.

SOLUTION

There are 52 cards in a pack of cards.

So, a card can be selected in 52 ways.

Now, there are 4 kings (one in each suit) in the pack.

So, a king can be selected in 4 ways.

$\therefore$ The required probability $= \frac{4}{52} = \frac{1}{13}$.

EXAMPLE 12.8 A number is selected from the numbers 1 to 20. What is the probability that it will be a prime number?

SOLUTION

Total number of ways of selecting a number from 1 to 20 is 20.

Let E be the event that the number selected is a prime number.

Then the numbers favourable to E are 2, 3, 5, 7, 11, 13, 17 and 19.

That is, 8 favourable numbers.

$\therefore P(E) = \frac{8}{20} = \frac{2}{5}$.

Hence, the probability that the number selected will be a prime number is $\frac{2}{5}$.

EXAMPLE 12.9

A bag contains 3 blue and 7 red balls. Find the probability that a ball selected at random from the bag will be a blue ball.

SOLUTION

Total number of balls in the bag = 3 + 7 = 10.

So, a ball can be selected from the bag in 10 ways.

Now, there are 3 blue balls in the bag.

So, a blue ball can be selected from the bag in 3 ways.

Hence, the required probability $= \frac{3}{10}$.

EXAMPLE 12.10

Find the probability of a card that is selected at random from a pack of cards will be a red honour.

SOLUTION

Total number of ways of selecting a card = 52.

There are 8 honours in the 26 red cards.

So, a red honour can be selected in 8 ways.

$\therefore$ The required probability $= \frac{8}{52} = \frac{2}{13}$.

EXAMPLE 12.11

There is a bunch of 10 keys out of which any one of the 4 keys can unlock a door. If a key is selected at random from the bunch and tried on the door, find the probability that the door will be unlocked.

SOLUTION

Total number of ways of selecting a key = 10.

4 keys can unlock the door.

$\Rightarrow$ Favourable outcomes = 4

$\therefore$ The required probability $= \frac{4}{10} = \frac{2}{5}$.

EXAMPLE 12.12

When two unbiased coins are tossed, what is the probability that both will show a head?

SOLUTION

When two coins are tossed together, the possible outcomes are HH, HT, TH, or TT,

That is, 4 possible outcomes.

Also, there is only one case where both the coins show heads.

$\therefore$ The required probability $= \frac{1}{4}$.

POINTS TO REMEMBER

- ✔ The set of all possible outcomes of an experiment is called its sample space.
- ✔ The outcomes or a combination of the outcomes is called an event.
- ✔ $P(E) = \dfrac{\text{Number of outcomes favorable to } E}{\text{Total number of possible outcomes}}$.
- ✔ $P(\bar{E}) = \dfrac{n-m}{n}$,
- ✔ $P(E) + P(\bar{E}) = 1$.

DW

PRACTICE QUESTIONS CLASSROOM WING

Very Short Answer Type Questions

Directions of questions from 1 to 7:
Fill in the blanks.

1. The set of all possible outcomes of an experiment is called the ______.
2. When a dice is thrown, the probability of getting any one of the numbers from 1 to 6 on the upper face is called ______ event.
3. The probability of any event of a random experiment cannot exceed ______.
4. If the probability of an event of a random experiment is $P(E) = 0$, then the event is called ______.
5. The probability of getting multiples of 3 when a dice is thrown is ______.
6. The range of probability of any event of a random experiment is ______.
7. The probability of getting 5 when a fair dice is thrown is ______.

Directions of questions from 8 to 22:
Answer the following questions.

8. The probability of getting all heads when three coins are tossed.
9. If two numbers are selected from the set {1, 2, 5, 7}, then the probability that the sum of the numbers is even.
10. The probability that a non-leap year has 53 Sundays.
11. When two dice are rolled, the probability that numbers coming up on both the dice are same.
12. The probability of getting two heads when three coins are tossed.
13. The probability that a card selected at random from a pack of cards is a numbered card.
14. Two numbers are chosen from 1 to 10. The probability that they are consecutive.
15. If a coin is tossed three times, find the probability that no two successive tosses will show the same face.
16. If two dice are rolled, find the probability that numbers coming up on both the dice will be multiples of 3.
17. Each of two persons a single throw with a dice. What is the probability of getting the same number on both the dice?
18. A cubical die is rolled. Find the probability of getting a composite number.
19. A set contains numbers from 40 to 60. Krishna chooses a number from the set. Find the probability that the number chosen is a prime number.
20. If n coins are tossed, then find the probability of getting either all heads or all tails.
21. If 8 boys are arranged in a row, what is the probability that 3 particular boys always sit together?
22. If a 5-digit number is formed by using the digits 1, 2, …, 9 (without repetitions), then what is the probability that it will be an even number?

Short Answer Type Questions

23. A bag contains 30 balls out of which 15 are red balls, w are white balls and g are green balls. The probability of getting a white ball is two times that of getting a green ball. Find the number of white balls and green balls.
24. A card is selected at random from a pack of cards. What is the probability that it will be an ace?
25. A number is selected from the set of integers from 1 to 20. What is the probability that it will be divisible by both 2 and 3?
26. A number is selected at random from the set of integers 1 to 100. What is the probability that it will be a multiple of 10?
27. (A) What is the probability of arranging the letters of the word CHEMISTRY such that the arrangements start with C and end with Y?

    (B) There are four boys and four girls. In how many ways these can be seated in a row such that

    (a) boys and girls alternate to each other

    (b) no two girls are adjacent to each other.

28. When two cards are drawn from a pack of cards, find the probability that both will be diamonds.

29. A number is selected at random from the set {1, 2, 3, 4, 5, 6, 7, 8, 9, 10}. What is the probability that it will be a root of the equation $x^2 - 2x + 1 = 0$?

30. A speaks truth in 70% cases. What is the probability that *A* will lie in stating a fact?

31. An urn contains 5 red, 3 blue and 2 green balls. What is the probability of selecting a green or a red ball?

32. A card is selected at random from a pack of cards. What is the probability that it is a numbered card?

33. When a die is rolled, what is the probability of getting a number which is a multiple of both 2 and 3?

34. 50 cards marked with numbers 1 to 50 are placed in a box. If a card is selected randomly from the box, then the probability that the number on the card selected will be a perfect cube is ________.

35. The probability of A winning a game is 0.7. Then the probability of A losing the game is ________.

36. For a cricket team, 11 persons have to be selected out of 20 aspirants. If 6 of the aspirants are definitely selected, and the other are selected at random, then what is the probability that 5 particular aspirants of the remaining 14 will be selected?

37. (A) When two dice are rolled together, what is the probability of getting the same faces on them?
(B) A cricket team of eleven members is to be formed from 9 batsmen and 6 bowlers. What is the probability that the team contains at least 5 bowlers?

Essay Type Questions

38. How many 5-digit odd numbers can be formed using the digits 2, 3, 5, 7, 8, and 9 if every digit can occur at most once in any number?

39. Fifteen points are marked on a plane so that no three points are collinear except 5 points. How many different lines can be drawn through these points?

40. If ${}^nP_r = 2730$ and ${}^nC_r = 455$ then, find the value of *r*.

41. Find the number of different codes that can be formed using all the digits 0, 1, 3, 7 without repeating any digit.

42. Of the six faces of a dice, two of the faces are painted white, two of the faces are painted green and the other two faces are painted yellow. Two of such dice are rolled. The probability that both the dice show different colours is ________.

43. If a number is chosen at random from five-digit numbers, then what is the probability that the number being palindrome?

PRACTICE QUESTIONS COMPETITION WING

Level 1: Apply Your Concepts

Directions of questions from 1 to 5:
Fill in the blanks.

1. An experiment in which all the outcomes of the experiment are known in advance and the exact outcome is not known in advance is called a ________.

2. A set of events which have no pair in common are called ________.

3. When a coin is tossed, the probability of getting neither head nor tail is called ________ event.

4. When a dice is thrown, the events {1}, {2}, {3}, {4}, {5} and {6} are called ________ events.

5. When a number is selected from a set of natural numbers, the probability of getting a number which is a multiple of 1 is ________.

Directions of questions from 6 to 33:
Select the correct alternative from the given choices.

6. From 9 gentlemen and 6 ladies, a committee of 5 members is to be formed. In how many ways this committee consists of at least 3 gentlemen?
(a) 1834 (b) 1962
(c) 2142 (d) 2206

7. A password of 4 letters is to be formed with *a*, *b*, *c*, *d* and *e*. How many passwords are possible if repetition of letters is not allowed?
(a) 625 (b) 120
(c) 140 (d) 150

8. How many words can be formed by using the letters of the word "TRAPEZIUM" which begin with A and end with Z?
(a) 5040 (b) 720
(c) 2450 (d) 120

9. A four-digit number is formed by using the digits 3, 5, 6, 8 and 9 with repetition. If one number is selected from those numbers, then what is the probability that it will be an odd number?
(a) $\frac{2}{3}$ (b) $\frac{2}{5}$
(c) $\frac{1}{3}$ (d) $\frac{3}{5}$

10. From 10 gentlemen and 7 ladies, a committee of 5 members is to be formed. In how many ways, the committee consists of at most 2 ladies?
(a) 2880 (b) 3990
(c) 2660 (d) 4242

11. A password of 4 letters is to be formed with vowels alone. How many passwords are possible if repetition of letters is allowed?
(a) 120 (b) 256
(c) 625 (d) 1024

12. How many words by using the letters of the word "MATHS" can be formed that begin with A and do not end with T?
(a) 18 (b) 21
(c) 24 (d) 27

13. A four-digit number is formed by using the digits 4, 5, 7, and 8 without repetition. If one number is selected from those numbers, then what is the probability that it is divisible by 3?
(a) 0 (b) 1
(c) $\frac{1}{2}$ (d) $\frac{1}{3}$

14. When two coins are tossed together, what is the probability that neither of them shows up head?
(a) $\frac{1}{3}$ (b) $\frac{1}{2}$
(c) 0 (d) $\frac{1}{4}$

15. When two cards are drawn from a well-shuffled pack of cards, what is the probability that both will be aces?
(a) $\frac{1}{221}$ (b) $\frac{2}{221}$
(c) $\frac{1}{13}$ (d) $\frac{1}{231}$

16. Two cards are drawn from a pack of cards one after another so that the first card is replaced before drawing the second card. What is the probability that the first card is an ace and the second is a number card?

(a) $\frac{9}{169}$ (b) $\frac{1}{52}$

(c) $\frac{1}{4}$ (d) $\frac{17}{52}$

17. Two numbers '*a*' and '*b*' are selected (successively without replacement in that order) from the integers 1 to 10. What is the probability that $\frac{a}{b}$ will be an integer?

(a) $\frac{17}{45}$ (b) $\frac{1}{5}$

(c) $\frac{19}{90}$ (d) $\frac{8}{45}$

18. There are 4 different mathematics books, 5 different physical science books and 3 different biological science books on a shelf. What is the probability of selecting a mathematics book from the shelf?

(a) $\frac{1}{3}$ (b) $\frac{1}{2}$

(c) $\frac{1}{4}$ (d) $\frac{5}{12}$

19. A number is selected at random from the integers 1 to 100. What is the probability that it is an even number?

(a) $\frac{1}{2}$ (b) $\frac{1}{50}$

(c) $\frac{1}{3}$ (d) $\frac{49}{100}$

20. A 3-digit number is to be formed using the digits 3, 4, 7, 8, and 2 without repetition. What is the probability that it is an odd number?

(a) $\frac{2}{5}$ (b) $\frac{1}{5}$

(c) $\frac{4}{5}$ (d) $\frac{3}{5}$

21. Two cards are drawn from a pack, what is the probability that the two cards are of different colors?

(a) $\frac{8}{17}$ (b) $\frac{1}{12}$

(c) $\frac{26}{51}$ (d) $\frac{27}{52}$

22. Two numbers '*a*' and '*b*' are selected successively one after another without replacement from the integers 1 to 15. What is the probability that $\frac{a}{b}$ will be an integer?

(a) $\frac{5}{7}$ (b) $\frac{3}{7}$

(c) $\frac{2}{7}$ (d) $\frac{1}{7}$

23. A card is drawn at random from a pack of cards. What is the probability that it is a face card of spades?

(a) $\frac{1}{13}$ (b) $\frac{1}{26}$

(c) $\frac{3}{52}$ (d) $\frac{3}{13}$

24. Two numbers are selected simultaneously from the first 20 natural numbers. What is the probability that the sum of the numbers is odd?

(a) $\frac{10}{19}$ (b) $\frac{1}{19}$

(c) $\frac{1}{10}$ (d) $\frac{19}{20}$

25. Two dice are rolled together, what is the probability that the total score on the two dice is greater than 10?

(a) $\frac{5}{6}$ (b) $\frac{1}{4}$

(c) $\frac{1}{6}$ (d) $\frac{1}{12}$

26. Two numbers are selected simultaneously from the first 25 natural numbers, what is the probability that the sum of the numbers is even?

(a) $\frac{6}{25}$ (b) $\frac{12}{25}$

(c) $\frac{4}{25}$ (d) $\frac{8}{25}$

27. A bag contains 7 red and 7 black coloured balls. A person drawn two balls from the bag, what is the probability that the two balls are the same in color?

(a) $\frac{6}{13}$ (b) $\frac{2}{7}$

(c) $\frac{4}{13}$ (d) $\frac{1}{13}$

28. Two dice are rolled together, what is the probability that the total score on the two dice is a prime number?

(a) $\frac{5}{12}$ (b) $\frac{1}{3}$

(c) $\frac{1}{2}$ (d) $\frac{13}{36}$

29. A committee of 4 persons is to be formed from 6 men and 4 women. What is the probability that the committee consists of equal number of men and women?

(a) $\frac{4}{7}$ (b) $\frac{3}{7}$

(c) $\frac{1}{7}$ (d) $\frac{6}{7}$

30. All the cards in an ordinary deck of 52 cards are numbered from 1 to 52. If a card is drawn at random from the deck, then what is the probability that it will have a prime number?

(a) $\frac{7}{26}$ (b) $\frac{15}{52}$

(c) $\frac{5}{17}$ (d) $\frac{4}{13}$

31. An urn contains 5 red, 3 black and 2 white. If three balls are chosen at random, then what is the probability that they will be of different colors?

(a) $\frac{1}{4}$ (b) $\frac{3}{4}$

(c) $\frac{1}{2}$ (d) $\frac{5}{6}$

32. What is the probability that a leap year has 52 Mondays?

(a) $\frac{2}{7}$ (b) $\frac{4}{7}$

(c) $\frac{5}{7}$ (d) $\frac{6}{7}$

33. If a letter is selected at random from the letters of the word FOUNDATION, what is the probability of the letter selected being a repeated letter?

(a) $\frac{1}{10}$ (b) $\frac{1}{5}$

(c) $\frac{2}{5}$ (d) $\frac{1}{2}$

Level 2: Review Your Concepts

34. Sunny and Bunny go to an icecream parlour where they find 5 different varieties of icecreams. If they order one icecream each, what is the probability that they both order the same variety of icecreams?

(a) $\frac{1}{5}$ (b) $\frac{4}{5}$

(c) $\frac{1}{2}$ (d) $\frac{1}{10}$

35. There are five ₹1 coins, two ₹2 coins and three ₹5 coins. If two coins are selected simultaneously at random, what is the probability of yielding the maximum amount?

(a) $\frac{3}{10}$ (b) $\frac{1}{5}$

(c) $\frac{1}{15}$ (d) $\frac{3}{10}$

36. A dice is rolled twice, what is the probability that the two dice show a different number?

(a) $\frac{2}{3}$ (b) $\frac{1}{6}$

(c) $\frac{5}{6}$ (d) $\frac{1}{2}$

37. A bag contains 3 red, 5 blue, and 7 green coloured balls. Find the probability of selecting a blue ball from the bag.

(a) $\frac{3}{15}$ (b) $\frac{1}{3}$

(c) $\frac{1}{4}$ (d) $\frac{2}{3}$

38. 7 coins are tossed simultaneously, what is the probability of getting at least two heads?

(a) $\frac{3}{18}$ (b) $\frac{15}{16}$

(c) $\frac{1}{16}$ (d) $\frac{3}{16}$

39. A bag contains 5 white balls and 6 green balls. Two balls are drawn from the bag one after another, what is the probability that both the balls are white? (the first ball is replaced before drawing the second ball)

(a) $\frac{2}{11}$ (b) $\frac{1}{11}$

(c) $\frac{3}{121}$ (d) $\frac{25}{121}$

40. A basket contains 12 fruits, of which 7 are not rotten. When one fruit is drawn at random, the probability that it is a rotten fruit is ________.

(a) $\frac{1}{3}$ (b) $\frac{7}{12}$

(c) $\frac{5}{12}$ (d) $\frac{2}{3}$

41. One card is selected from a well shuffled pack of cards, what is the probability that it is a red honoured card?

(a) $\frac{2}{13}$ (b) $\frac{3}{13}$

(c) $\frac{11}{13}$ (d) $\frac{9}{13}$

42. The probability that the month of April has exactly 5 Mondays is ________.

(a) $\frac{4}{7}$ (b) $\frac{5}{7}$

(c) $\frac{3}{7}$ (d) $\frac{2}{7}$

43. Hundred cards marked with numbers 1 to 100 are placed in a box. If a card is selected randomly from the box, then the probability that the number on the card selected will be a perfect square is ______.

(a) $\frac{1}{100}$ (b) $\frac{1}{25}$

(c) $\frac{1}{10}$ (d) $\frac{9}{10}$

44. 20 cards are numbered 1 to 20. If a card is selected at random, then what is the probability that the selected number will be an odd prime?

(a) $\frac{2}{5}$ (b) $\frac{3}{5}$

(c) $\frac{3}{10}$ (d) $\frac{7}{20}$

45. A 4-digit number is formed by using the digits 1, 2, 5, 6, and 8 without repetition. What is the probability that it will be an even number?

(a) $\frac{3}{5}$ (b) $\frac{2}{5}$

(c) $\frac{1}{2}$ (d) $\frac{3}{10}$

46. A basket contains 10 fruits of which 3 are rotten. If one fruit is drawn from the basket, then the probability that the fruit drawn is not rotten is ______.

(a) $\frac{4}{5}$ (b) $\frac{4}{5}$

(c) $\frac{7}{10}$ (d) $\frac{3}{10}$

47. An urn contains 6 blue and '*a*' green balls. If the probability of drawing a green ball is double that of drawing a blue ball, then '*a*' is equal to ______.

(a) 6 (b) 18

(c) 24 (d) 12

48. A card is drawn from a well shuffled pack of cards. What is the probability that it will be a black queen?

(a) $\frac{1}{52}$ (b) $\frac{1}{13}$

(c) $\frac{1}{26}$ (d) $\frac{1}{32}$

49. A box contains 30 balls. Among them 10 are black, 12 are blue, and the rest are orange. What is the probability that a ball drawn from the box will not be blue?

(a) $\frac{1}{3}$ (b) $\frac{3}{5}$

(c) $\frac{5}{6}$ (d) $\frac{1}{6}$

50. When an unbiased dice is thrown, the probability of getting a prime number is ______.

(a) $\frac{1}{3}$ (b) $\frac{1}{2}$

(c) $\frac{1}{4}$ (d) $\frac{2}{3}$

51. If a letter is selected at random from the letters of the word TRIANGLE, then what is the probability that it will be a consonant?

(a) $\frac{2}{7}$ (b) $\frac{3}{8}$

(c) $\frac{5}{8}$ (d) $\frac{1}{8}$

52. If a letter is selected at random from the letters of the word LOGARITHMS, then what is the probability that it will be a consonant?

(a) $\frac{3}{10}$ (b) $\frac{7}{10}$

(c) $\frac{1}{10}$ (d) $\frac{4}{10}$

Level 3: Assess Your Concepts

53. If one number is selected from the first 70 natural numbers, the probability that the number is a solution of $x^2 + 2x > 4$ is ______.

(a) $\frac{69}{70}$ (b) $\frac{1}{70}$

(c) 1 (d) 0

54. A man's pocket has seven ₹1 coins, three ₹2 coins and four ₹5 coins. If two coins are selected simultaneously, what is the probability of yielding the minimum amount?

(a) $\frac{3}{13}$ (b) $\frac{6}{13}$

(c) $\frac{3}{26}$ (d) $\frac{6}{43}$

55. Mr Balaram picked a prime number between the integers 1 and 20. What is the probability that it will be number 13?

(a) $\frac{7}{8}$ (b) $\frac{1}{20}$

(c) $\frac{1}{8}$ (d) $\frac{13}{20}$

56. Chandu picks up a letter from the English alphabet and finds it to be a vowel. Find the probability that it is either e or i.

(a) $\frac{2}{5}$ (b) $\frac{3}{5}$

(c) $\frac{1}{5}$ (d) $\frac{4}{5}$

57. A committee of 5 persons is to be formed from 7 men and 3 women. What is the probability that the committee contains 3 men?

(a) $\frac{5}{36}$ (b) $\frac{7}{12}$

(c) $\frac{5}{12}$ (d) $\frac{1}{3}$

58. A purse contains four fifty-paise coins, three two-rupee coins and three five-rupee coins. If three coins are selected at random, then what is the probability of getting the minimum amount?

(a) $\frac{1}{15}$ (b) $\frac{1}{10}$

(c) $\frac{1}{30}$ (d) $\frac{1}{5}$

59. A number is selected from the set {1, 2, 3, 4, 5, 6, 7, 8}. What is the probability that it will be a root of the equation $x^2 - 6x + 8 = 0$?

(a) $\frac{1}{3}$ (b) $\frac{2}{3}$

(c) $\frac{3}{4}$ (d) $\frac{1}{4}$

60. An urn contains 9 red balls and p green balls. If the probability of picking a red ball is thrice that of picking a green ball, then p is equal to ________.

(a) 6 (b) 7

(c) 2 (d) 3

61. If two dice are thrown, then find the probability that the total score on the two dice is 5.

(a) $\frac{2}{9}$ (b) $\frac{3}{8}$

(c) $\frac{1}{6}$ (d) $\frac{1}{9}$

62. A bag contains 8 balls numbered 1 to 8. If 2 balls are picked at random, then find the probability of the two balls being 2 and 3.

(a) $\frac{1}{28}$ (b) $\frac{2}{27}$

(c) $\frac{1}{14}$ (d) $\frac{1}{7}$

63. A 4-digit number is formed by using the digits 1, 2, 4, 8, and 9 without repetition. If one number is selected from those numbers, then what is the probability that it will be an odd number?

(a) $\frac{1}{5}$ (b) $\frac{2}{5}$

(c) $\frac{3}{5}$ (d) $\frac{4}{5}$

64. If two dice are rolled together, then find the probability that the sum of the numbers on the two dice is less than or equal to 10.

(a) $\frac{11}{12}$ (b) $\frac{1}{12}$

(c) $\frac{7}{12}$ (d) $\frac{1}{9}$

65. Three numbers are chosen from 1 to 15. Find the probability that they are consecutive.

(a) $\frac{1}{35}$ (b) $\frac{1}{13}$

(c) $\frac{2}{13}$ (d) $\frac{3}{35}$

66. One ticket is drawn from a bag containing 70 tickets numbered 1 to 70. Find the probability that it is a multiple of 5 or 7.

(a) $\frac{1}{10}$ (b) $\frac{1}{70}$

(c) $\frac{6}{70}$ (d) $\frac{11}{35}$

67. If a coin is tossed two times, then what is the probability of getting a head at least once?

(a) $\frac{1}{4}$ (b) $\frac{3}{4}$

(c) $\frac{1}{2}$ (d) 1

68. A, B, C are three points with co-ordinates $A(2, 0)$, $B(0, 0)$, $C(0, 2)$. D is the point in the plane of the triangle ABC such that $\angle ADC = 90°$. Find the probability that $ABCD$ is a simple closed figure.

(a) $\frac{1}{4}$ (b) $\frac{1}{6}$

(c) $\frac{1}{5}$ (d) $\frac{1}{2}$

AT

PRACTICE QUESTIONS JEE SPECIAL WING

Multiple-Answer Type Questions

Directions for questions 1 to 5:
Each question has FOUR options (a), (b), (c), and (d). ONE OR MORE THAN ONE of these four option(s) is/are the correct answer(s).

1. Which of the following can be the probability of an event?
   (a) 0.009 (b) 0.09
   (c) 0.9 (d) 9
2. Four coins are tossed simultaneously. The probability of getting an event is 0.25. Which of the following can be the event?
   (a) Exactly one head (b) Exactly three heads
   (c) At most two tails (d) At least two tails
3. Madhu has ten slips. He wrote only one number from zero to nine (in words) on each slip without repeating the number. If a slip is picked at random, the probability of occurrence of an event is 0.4. Which of the following can be the event?
   (a) Number which has exactly three distinct letters
   (b) Number which has exactly four distinct letters
   (c) Number which has exactly one distinct vowel
   (d) Number which has two distinct vowels
4. Which of the following are numerically equal to "The probability of getting head when a coin is tossed"?
   (a) The probability of getting a consonant when a letter is chosen at random from the word authorised.
   (b) The probability of getting an odd number when a dice is rolled.
   (c) The probability of getting a black card when a card is picked from a deck of cards.
   (d) The probability of getting an even numbered day when a day is chosen at random from the days of the year 1968.
5. Which of the following are impossible events?
   (a) If a month is selected at random from the year 1986, then the month consists of 29 days.
   (b) If two numbers are chosen at random from the set of even natural numbers, then both the numbers are prime.
   (c) If two dice are rolled, the sum of the numbers on the dice is a two-digit multiple of 7.
   (d) If a day is selected from the days of a week, then the day starts with the letter W.

Match The Column

Directions for questions 6 to 10:
Read the paragraph given below and answer the questions.
A deck of cards has 52 in which 36 are numbered cards. The cards *A*, *J*, *Q*, and *K* are called honours. *J*, *Q*, and *K* are face cards. A card is picked randomly from the deck.

Column A (Outcome)	Probability
6. An odd numbered card or a face card	(a) $\frac{9}{13}$
7. An honours card or an even numbered card	(b) $\frac{7}{13}$
8. An odd numbered black card or an honours card but not face card	(c) $\frac{5}{13}$
9. A black king or a red queen	(d) $\frac{4}{13}$
10. An even numbered red card or a composite numbered black card	(e) $\frac{3}{13}$
	(f) $\frac{1}{13}$

Comprehension-Based Questions

Directions for questions 11 to 15:

Read the paragraph given below and answer the questions.

A dice has 6 faces and the numbers on the dice are 1, 2, 3, 4, 5, and 6. When a dice is rolled, we need to consider the number which appears on the top face of the dice as the outcome. Two such dice are rolled.

11. What is the probability of getting the sum of the numbers as a prime number?

(a) $\frac{7}{36}$ (b) $\frac{5}{18}$

(c) $\frac{5}{12}$ (d) $\frac{7}{9}$

12. What is the probability of getting the sum of the numbers as a composite number?

(a) $\frac{7}{9}$ (b) $\frac{7}{12}$

(c) $\frac{7}{18}$ (d) $\frac{7}{36}$

13. What is the probability of getting one of them as a perfect square and the other as a multiple of 3?

(a) $\frac{7}{36}$ (b) $\frac{1}{3}$

(c) $\frac{5}{18}$ (d) $\frac{2}{9}$

14. What is the probability of getting a prime number on one dice and a composite number on the other dice?

(a) $\frac{1}{3}$ (b) $\frac{2}{9}$

(c) $\frac{5}{12}$ (d) $\frac{7}{18}$

15. What is the probability of getting the difference of the numbers as a prime number?

(a) $\frac{1}{2}$ (b) $\frac{4}{9}$

(c) $\frac{5}{12}$ (d) $\frac{7}{18}$

Directions for questions 16 to 20:

There are two straight lines l and m. Ten points are marked on l, and the points are (2, 1), (4, 1), (6, 1), (8, 1) … (20, 1). Thirteen points are marked on m and the points are (2, 6), (4, 6), (6, 6), (8, 6) … (26, 6). By joining a point on l and a point on m, a straight line is formed. By joining two points on a line and a point on other line, a triangles is formed. All the possible straight lines and triangles have been drawn.

16. If a straight line is selected at random, what is the probability of getting a line parallel to the y-axis?

(a) $\frac{1}{13}$ (b) $\frac{5}{13}$

(c) $\frac{9}{13}$ (d) $\frac{12}{13}$

17. If a straight line is selected at random, what is the probability of getting a slant line?

(a) $\frac{1}{13}$ (b) $\frac{5}{13}$

(c) $\frac{9}{13}$ (d) $\frac{12}{13}$

18. If a triangle is selected at random, what is the probability of getting a triangle whose two vertices lie on the line l?

(a) $\frac{117}{273}$ (b) $\frac{135}{273}$

(c) $\frac{156}{273}$ (d) $\frac{161}{273}$

19. If a triangle is selected at random, what is the probability of getting a triangle whose two vertices lie on the line m?

(a) $\frac{117}{273}$ (b) $\frac{135}{273}$

(c) $\frac{156}{273}$ (d) $\frac{161}{273}$

20. If a triangle is selected at random, what is the probability of getting a triangle whose area is 5 sq units?

(a) $\frac{83}{455}$ (b) $\frac{81}{455}$

(c) $\frac{79}{455}$ (d) $\frac{76}{455}$

Directions for questions 21 to 25:

In the given figure, $APQD$ is a rectangle and $ABCD$ is a square. A circle is inscribed in the square. MNR is an equilateral triangle inscribed in the circle. $BPQC$ is another rectangle.

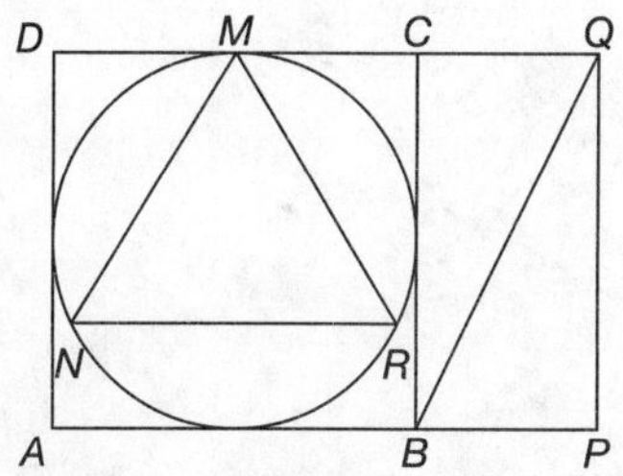

$AB = 14$ cm.

$AP = 21$ cm.

A point is marked interior of rectangle $APQD$.

21. What is the probability that the point lies interior of ΔPBQ?

(a) $\frac{1}{6}$ (b) $\frac{1}{7}$

(c) $\frac{3}{14}$ (d) $\frac{5}{21}$

22. What is the probability that the point lies interior of ΔMNR?

(a) $\frac{7\sqrt{3}}{64}$ (b) $\frac{5\sqrt{3}}{32}$

(c) $\frac{3\sqrt{3}}{16}$ (d) $\frac{\sqrt{3}}{8}$

23. What is the probability that the point lies interior of the circle but not interior of ΔMNR?

(a) $\frac{88-21\sqrt{3}}{168}$ (b) $\frac{66-14\sqrt{3}}{155}$

(c) $\frac{44-7\sqrt{3}}{143}$ (d) $\frac{22-6\sqrt{3}}{121}$

24. What is the probability that the point lies interior of square *ABCD* but not interior of the circle?

(a) $\frac{1}{6}$ (b) $\frac{3}{14}$

(c) $\frac{1}{7}$ (d) $\frac{5}{12}$

25. What is the probability that the point lies interior of rectangle *BPQC*?

(a) $\frac{1}{2}$ (b) $\frac{1}{3}$

(c) $\frac{1}{4}$ (d) $\frac{1}{5}$

Assertion and Reason Type Questions

Directions for questions 26 to 30:
In the light of the given statements, choose the most appropriate answer from the options given below.

(a) Both assertion (A) and reason (R) are true, and reason (R) is the correct explanation of assertion.
(b) Both assertion (A) and reason (R) are true, and reason (R) is not the correct explanation of assertion.
(c) Assertion (A) is true, but reason (R) is false.
(d) Assertion (A) is false, and reason (R) is true.

26. Assertion: In a random experiment, the probability of an event can be $\frac{11}{10}$.

Reason: The probability of an event lies between 0 and 1.

27. Assertion: If a coin is tossed, the sum of the probability of getting head and the probability of not getting head is 1.

Reason: The sum of the probabilities of complementary events is 1.

28. Assertion: If a dice is rolled, the probability of getting a natural number less than 7 is greater than that of getting a natural number more than 7.

Reason: The probabilities of an impossible event and a sure event are 1 and 0 respectively.

29. Assertion: A coin is tossed 9 times; the number of possible outcomes is 512.

Reason: A coin is tossed n times; the number of possible outcomes is 2^n.

30. Assertion: The probability that a day of the week selected at random will be Monday, is $\frac{1}{7}$.

Reason: The sum of the probabilities of all the elementary events of an experiment is 1.

ANSWER KEYS

Crossword

Across

1. Event 3. Half 5. Random 6. One 9. Permutation
10. Twenty 11. Zero

Down

2. Thirty 3. Hundred 4. Combination 7. Thousand 8. Six

Classroom Wing

Very Short Answer Type Questions

1. Sample space 2. Sure event 3. 1 4. Impossible event
5. $\frac{1}{3}$ 6. [0, 1] 7. $\frac{1}{6}$ 8. $\frac{1}{8}$ 9. $\frac{1}{2}$
10. $\frac{1}{7}$ 11. $\frac{1}{6}$ 12. $\frac{3}{8}$ 13. $\frac{9}{13}$ 14. $\frac{1}{5}$
15. $\frac{1}{4}$ 16. $\frac{1}{9}$ 17. $\frac{1}{6}$ 18. $\frac{1}{3}$ 19. $\frac{5}{21}$
20. $\frac{1}{2n-1}$ 21. $\frac{3}{28}$ 22. $\frac{4}{9}$

Short Answer Type Questions

23. $\frac{1}{3}, \frac{1}{6}$ 24. (A) $\frac{1}{13}$ 25. $\frac{3}{20}$ 26. $\frac{1}{10}$
27. (A) $\frac{1}{72}$ (B) (a) 1152 (b) 120(4!) 28. $\frac{1}{17}$ 29. $\frac{1}{10}$ 30. $\frac{3}{10}$
31. $\frac{7}{10}$ 32. $\frac{9}{13}$ 33. $\frac{1}{6}$ 34. $\frac{3}{50}$ 35. 0.3
36. $\frac{1}{2002}$ 37. (A) $\frac{1}{6}$ (B) $\frac{6}{13}$

Essay Type Questions

38. 480 39. 96 40. 3 41. 24 42. 2/3
43. $\frac{1}{100}$

Competition Wing

Level 1: Apply Your Concepts

1. Random experiment
2. Mutually exclusive
3. Impossible event
4. Equally likely
5. 1
6. (c)
7. (b)
8. (a)
9. (d)
10. (d)
11. (c)
12. (a)
13. (b)
14. (d)
15. (a)
16. (a)
17. (c)
18. (a)
19. (a)
20. (a)
21. (c)
22. (d)
23. (c)
24. (a)
25. (d)
26. (b)
27. (a)
28. (a)
29. (b)
30. (b)
31. (a)
32. (c)
33. (b)

Level 2: Review Your Concepts

34. (a)
35. (c)
36. (c)
37. (b)
38. (b)
39. (d)
40. (c)
41. (a)
42. (d)
43. (c)
44. (d)
45. (a)
46. (c)
47. (d)
48. (c)
49. (b)
50. (b)
51. (c)
52. (b)

Level 3: Assess Your Concepts

53. (a)
54. (a)
55. (c)
56. (a)
57. (c)
58. (c)
59. (d)
60. (d)
61. (d)
62. (a)
63. (b)
64. (a)
65. (a)
66. (d)
67. (b)
68. (d)

JEE Special Wing

Multiple-Answer Type Questions

1. (a, b, c)
2. (a, b)
3. (a, c)
4. (a, b, c, d)
5. (a, b, c)

Match The Column

6. (b)
7. (a)
8. (e)
9. (f)
10. (c)

Comprehension-Based Questions

11. (c)
12. (b)
13. (d)
14. (a)
15. (b)
16. (a)
17. (d)
18. (c)
19. (a)
20. (c)
21. (a)
22. (d)
23. (a)
24. (c)
25. (b)

Assertion and Reason Type Questions

26. (d)
27. (a)
28. (c)
29. (a)
30. (b)

Hints and Explanations

Classroom Wing

Very Short Answer Type Questions

1. Sample space
2. Sure event
3. 1 (1 is the maximum probability)
4. Impossible event (since probability = 0; thus event will never happen)
5. $\frac{2}{6} = \frac{1}{3}$ (3 and 6) are multiple of 3.
6. [0, 1]
7. $\frac{1}{6}$, 6 is the number of events in sample space
8. Total outcomes = $2^3 = 8$
   Favourable outcomes = 1
   Required probability = $\frac{1}{8}$
9. Total outcomes = ${}^4C_2 = 6$
   Favourable outcomes are (1, 5), (1, 7), and (5, 7).
   $\therefore$ Required probability $= \frac{3}{6} = \frac{1}{2}$
10. There are 52 Sundays in the first 364 days. The probability that the 365th day is Sunday can be $\frac{1}{7}$.
11. Total outcomes = $6^2 = 36$
    Favourable outcomes are (1, 1), (2, 2), (3, 3), (4, 4), (5, 5) and (6, 6).
    $\therefore$ Required probability $= \frac{6}{36} = \frac{1}{6}$
12. Total number of outcomes = $2^3 = 8$
    Favourable outcomes are HHT, HTH, and THH.
    $\therefore$ The required probability = $\frac{3}{8}$
13. The number of numbered cards (2 to 10) = 9
    Total numbered cards in a pack of cards are 9×4, i.e., 36.
    $\therefore$ The required probability $= \frac{36}{52} = \frac{9}{13}$
14. Options (a): Total number of outcomes = ${}^{10}C_2 = 45$
    Favourable outcomes are (1, 2); (2, 3); (3, 4); (4, 5); (5, 6); (6, 7); (7, 8); (8, 9); (9, 10).
    $\therefore$ The required probability $= \frac{9}{45} = \frac{1}{5}$
15. HHH, HTH
    HHT, TTH
    HTT, THH
    TTT, THT
    $\therefore P = \frac{2}{8} = \frac{1}{4}$
    (HTH, THT)
16. No. of both dice is multiples of 3.
    $\therefore (3,3), (3,6), (6,3), (6,6)$
    $= \frac{4}{36} = \frac{1}{9}$
17. Same no. of both dice $= \frac{6}{36} = \frac{1}{6}$
18. Composite = 4, 6
    $\therefore P = \frac{2}{6} = \frac{1}{3}$
19. Prime no between 40 – 60 are
    41, 43, 47, 53, 59
    $\therefore$ Probability $= \frac{5}{21}$
20. When 3 coins tossed $= \frac{2}{2^3} = \frac{1}{2^{3-1}}$
    $\therefore$ When n coins are tossed
    P (either all head or all tail) $= \frac{2}{2^n}$
    $= \frac{1}{2^{n-1}}$
21. — — — — — — —

    Since 3 always sit together so consider them as 1
    $\therefore$ These 6 can be arranged in 6! and in the pair of 3 also, shuffling will be there so 3!
    $\therefore P = \frac{6! \times 3!}{8!} = \frac{6! \times 3 \times 2}{8 \times 7 \times 6!} = \frac{3}{28}$

22. For even no, last digit should be a multiple of 2.

$\underline{8}\times\underline{7}\times\underline{6}\times\underline{5}\times\underline{4}$
↓
(2, 4, 6, 8)

Total possibility $= 9\times 8\times 7\times 6\times 5$

$\therefore$ Probability $= \dfrac{8\times 7\times 6\times 5\times 4}{9\times 8\times 7\times 6\times 5} = \dfrac{4}{9}$

Short Answer Type Questions

23. Red balls = 15

White balls = w

Green balls = g

P (white) $= 2P(G)$

$\dfrac{w}{30} = \dfrac{2g}{30}$

$w = 2g$ (1)

and $15 + w + g = 30$ (2)

Substitute (1) in (2)

$15 + 2g + g = 30$

$3g = 15$

$g = 5$

$w = 10$

$\therefore$ 10, 5

P (white) $= \dfrac{10}{30} = \dfrac{1}{3}$

P (green) $= \dfrac{5}{30} = \dfrac{1}{6}$

24. Ace cards = 4

P(Ace-card) $= \dfrac{4}{52} = \dfrac{1}{13}$

25. Divisible by 2 and 3 = 6, 12, 18

$\therefore P = \dfrac{3}{20}$

26. Multiple of 10 = {10, 20, 30, 40, 50, 60, 70, 80, 90, 100}

$\therefore$ Probability for multiple of 10 $= \dfrac{10}{100} = \dfrac{1}{10}$

27. (A) C $\underline{7}\times\underline{6}\times\underline{5}\times\underline{4}\times\underline{3}\times\underline{2}\times\underline{1}$ Y

Total arrangement = 9!

Required array $= \dfrac{7!}{9!} = \dfrac{7!}{9\times 8\times 7!} = \dfrac{1}{72}$

(B) (a) The arrangement must be as follows, where b's refers boys and g's refers girls.

$\underline{b}\ \underline{g}\ \underline{b}\ \underline{g}\ \underline{b}\ \underline{g}\ \underline{b}\ \underline{g}$

$\underline{g}\ \underline{b}\ \underline{g}\ \underline{b}\ \underline{g}\ \underline{b}\ \underline{g}\ \underline{b}$

Number of arrangements

$= (4!((4!) + (4!)(4!)$

$= 2(4!)^2 = 1152$

(b) $- b - b - b - b -$

The required number of ways

$= [(4!)(5\times 4\times 3\times 2)]$

$= 120(4!)$

28. Probability (both are diamond)

$= \dfrac{13\times 12}{52\times 51} = \dfrac{1}{17}$

29. Roots of equation:

$x^2 - 2x + 1 = 0$

$x^2 - x - x + 1 = 0$

$x(x-1) - 1(x-1) = 0$

$(x-1)(x-1) = 0$

$x = 1$

Since n (roots) = 1

Probability $= \dfrac{1}{n(s)} = \dfrac{1}{10}$

30. P(A will lie) $= \dfrac{100-70}{100} = \dfrac{30}{100} = \dfrac{3}{10}$

31. Red = 5

Blue = 3

Green = 2

P (Selecting green or red) $= \dfrac{7}{10}$

n (green or red) $= 5 + 2 = 7$

n (Total) $= 5 + 3 + 2 = 10$

32. Total numbered cards $= 9\times 4$

P (numbered card) $= \dfrac{4\times 9}{52} = \dfrac{9}{13}$

33. Number multiple of 2 and 3 = 6

n (multiple 2 and 3) = 1

Probability $= \dfrac{1}{6}$

34. Perfect cube between 1 to 50 = {8, 27, 1}

P (perfect cube) $= \dfrac{n(\text{perfect cube})}{n\ (\text{total})} = \dfrac{3}{50}$

35. P(winning) + P(loosing) = 1

$\therefore$ P(loosing) $= 1 - 0.7 = 0.3$

36. Since 6 has already been selected,we can choose 5 among 14 by ${}^{14}C_5$ ways.

Required Probability becomes $1/{}^{14}C_5 = 1/2002$

37. (A) $P(\text{same faces}) = \frac{n(\text{same face})}{\text{Total}} = \frac{6}{36} = \frac{1}{6}$

(B)

Number of Batsmen	Number of Bowlers	Total
9	6	15

Number of members to be selected = 11

$n(S) = 15_{C_{11}}$

Among 11 members, number of bowlers can be 5 or 6.

Number of ways to select the team = ${}^6C_5\left({}^9C_6\right) + {}^6C_6\left({}^9C_5\right)$

$$P(E) = \frac{n(E)}{n(S)}$$

$$= \frac{{}^6C_5\left({}^9C_6\right) + {}^6C_6\left({}^9C_5\right)}{{}^{15}C_{11}}$$

$$= \frac{6\left(\frac{9\times8\times7}{1\times2\times3}\right)+1\left(\frac{9\times8\times7\times6}{1\times2\times3\times4}\right)}{\frac{15\times14\times13\times12}{1\times2\times3\times4}}$$

$$= \frac{(9\times8\times7)+(9\times7\times2)}{15\times7\times13}$$

$$= \frac{(3\times8)+(3\times2)}{5\times13} = \frac{30}{65} = \frac{6}{13}$$

Essay Type Questions

38. Given digits are 2, 3, 5, 7, 8, and 9.

Since we require only odd numbers, the units place can be filled by either 3, 5, 7, or 9 in 4 ways.

The other places in order can be filled in 5 ways, 4 ways, 3 ways, and 2 ways, respectively. since repetition is not allowed.

Total number of 5-digit number can be formed = $4 \times 5 \times 4 \times 3 \times 2 = 480$.

39. For every different line, two points should be selected. The number of possible ways = ${}^{15}C_2$.

However, there are 5 points that are collinear, which give only one line.

Total number of distinct lines = ${}^{15}C_2 - {}^5C_2 + 1$

$$= \frac{15\times14}{2} - \frac{5\times4}{2} + 1$$

$= 105 - 10 + 1 = 96$

40. ${}^nP_r = 2730$ and ${}^nC_r = 455$

$$\frac{n!}{(n-r)!} = 2730 \text{ and } \frac{n!}{(n-r)!r!} = 455$$

$$\frac{2730}{r!} = 455$$

$$\frac{2730}{455} = r!$$

$r! = 6$

$\Rightarrow r! = 3 \times 2 \times 1$

$r! = 3!$

$r = 3$

41. Given digits are 0, 1, 3, and 7.

First place of the code can be one any of the digit of the given digits. It can be done in 4 ways.

Hence, the 2nd, 3rd, and 4th place can be filled in 3 ways, 2 ways, and 1 way, respectively.

Total number of codes that can be formed

$= 4 \times 3 \times 2 \times 1 = 24$

42. When a dice is rolled, it shows white or green or yellow.

When two dice are rolled, total number of possible cases is $3 \times 3 = 9$.

First dice shows any three colours and second dice shows remaining two colours.

The favourable cases = $3 \times 2 = 6$

Required probability $= \frac{6}{9} = 2/3$

43. 0 cannot be taken in ten thousand place.

Number of five-digit numbers = 9(10) (10) (10) (10) = $n(S)$

A palindrome number is a number which reads the same backward or forward.

TTh	Th	H	T	U

$\Rightarrow$ The digits in ten thousand and 'units' places are the same

Similarly, the digits in 'thousands' and 'tens' places are the same.

$\therefore$ Number of palindrome numbers, $n(E) = 9(10)(10)(1)(1)$

Now, $P(E) = \frac{n(E)}{n(S)} = \frac{9(10)(10)}{9(10)(10)(10)(10)}$

$$= \frac{1}{100}.$$

Competition Wing

Level 1: Apply Your Concepts

1. Random experiment
2. Mutually exclusive
3. Impossible event
4. Equally likely
5. 1 (as all no are multiple of one so probability becomes 1)
6. The committee is to contain at least three gentlemen, i.e., it may contain either 3, 4, or 5 gentlemen.
   $\therefore$ The total number of ways
   $= {}^9C_3 \times {}^6C_2 \times {}^9C_4 \times {}^6C_1 + {}^9C_5$
   $= 84 \times 15 + 126 \times 6 + 126 = 2142.$
   Hence, the correct option is (c).
7. The number of 4 letter passwords that can be formed with *a*, *b*, *c*, *d*, and *e* (without repetition) is ${}^5P_4$, i.e., 120.
   Hence, the correct option is (b).
8. The number of words which begin with A and end with Z is 7!, i.e., 5040.
   ($\because$ The 7 places between A and Z are filled in 7! ways.)
   Hence, the correct option is (a).
9. The number of four-digit numbers formed by using the digits 3, 5, 6, 8, and 9 with repetition is $5 \times 5 \times 5 \times 5$ is 625.
   The number of four-digit odd numbers is $5 \times 5 \times 5 \times 3$, i.e., 375. ($\because$ The last digit is filled in 3 ways, i.e., 3, 5, or 9.)
   $\therefore$ The required probability $= \frac{375}{625} = \frac{3}{5}$
   Alternative method:
   A four-digit number can end with 3, 5, 6, 8, or 9. Out of the five possibilities, three are odd digits (3, 5, 9).
   $\therefore$ The required probability $= \frac{3}{5}$
   Hence, the correct option is (d).
10. The committee is to contain at most two ladies, i.e., it may contain 0, 1 or 2 ladies.
   $\therefore$ The total number of ways
   $= {}^{10}C_5 + {}^{10}C_4 \times {}^7C_1 + {}^{10}C_3 \times {}^7C_2$
   $= 252 + 210 \times 7 + 120 \times 21$
   $= 4242$
   Hence, the correct option is (d).
11. The number of 4-letter passwords that can be formed with a, e, i, o, and u with repetition is $5 \times 5 \times 5 \times 5$, i.e., 625.
   Hence, the correct option is (c).
12. The number of words that begin with A and do not end with *T* is $1 \times 2 \times 3 \times 3 = 18$.
   Hence, the correct option is (a).
13. Any four-digit number formed from the digits 4, 5, 7, and 8 (without repetition) is divisible by 3, since the sum of the digits is 24, i.e., divisible by 3.
14. Both coins should show up tail.
15. There are 4 ace cards in pack of cards.
16. (i) There are 4 ace cards and 36 numbered cards.
   (ii) *P*(ace and number card) = *P*(ace card) × *P* (number card).
17. $b = 1, a = 2, 3, \ldots, 10.$
   $b = 2, a = 4, 6, \ldots, 10.$
   In this way, find the number of favourable events such that a/b is an in integer.
18. (i) Number of favourable outcomes = 4.
   (ii) Required probability
   $= \frac{\text{Number of mathematics books}}{\text{Total number of books in the shelf}}.$
19. There are 50 even numbers from 1 to 100.
20. (i) If a number ends with an odd number then it is odd number.
   (ii) Find the number of 3-digit odd numbers formed by using the digits 3, 4, 7, 8, and 2.
   (iii) Find the total number of 3-digit numbers formed by using the digits 3, 4, 7, 8, and 2.
21. (i) There are 26 red color and 26 black color cards.
   (ii) Select one red card and one black card.
   (iii) Total number of outcomes = ${}^{52}C_2$
22. Let $b = 1$, then $a = 2$ to 15.
   Let $b = 2$, then $a = 4, 6, \ldots, 14$.
   In this way, find numbers *a* and *b* such that $\frac{a}{b}$ is the integer.
23. Jack, Queen, and King are the face cards.
24. (i) One number is odd and other is even then sum is odd.

(ii) Two numbers from 20 can be selected in $^{20}C_2$ ways.

(iii) There are 10 even numbers and 10 odd numbers.

25. P(greater than 10) = P(sum be 11) + P(sum be 12).

26. (i) (Odd + Odd) = (Even + Even) = Even.

(ii) There are a total of 13 odd numbers and 12 even numbers.

(iii) P(sum even) = P(selecting 2 odd numbers) + P(selecting 2 even numbers).

27. (i) Number of ways of drawing 2 red balls = $^7C_2$, similarly number of ways of drawing 2 blackballs = $^7C_2$.

(ii) Total number of ways of drawing 2 balls out of 14 balls = $^{14}C_2$.

28. P(sum is prime) = P(sum 2) + P(sum 3) + P(sum 5) + P(sum 7) + P(sum 11).

29. (i) Committee should be formed with 2 men and 2 women.

(ii) Total number of ways in which the committee be selected is $^{(6+4)}C_4$ ways.

30. (i) Find the numbers which are prime from 1 to 52.

(ii) In total we have to select 1 card out of 52 cards.

31. (i) Choose one ball from each color.

(ii) In total, we have to select 3 out of 10 balls.

32. (i) Leap year contains 52 weeks and 2 odd days.

(ii) Find the probability that the odd days should not be Monday.

33. Find the number of repeated letters in the given word.

Level 2: Review Your Concepts

34. (i) Let the five different icecreams be a, b, c, d, and e.

(ii) favourable outcomes are (a, a), (b, b), (c, c), (d, d) and (e, e).

(iii) Total number of outcomes = 25.

35. (i) Maximum amount will be yielded, if the selected two coins are of ₹5.

(ii) Required probability

$$= \frac{\text{Number of ways of selecting two ₹5 coins}}{\text{Total number of ways of selecting two coins}}.$$

43. Find the number of favourable outcomes.

44. (i) Find the numbers which are odd primes from 1 to 20.

(ii) In total, we have to select 1 card out of 20.

45. (i) Find the number of 4-digit even numbers by filling the units digit by 2, 6, and 8.

(ii) Find the total number of 4 digit numbers. Required probability

$$= \frac{\text{Number of 4-digit even numbers}}{\text{Total number of 4-digit numbers}}.$$

46. (i) To yield minimum amount, select ₹1 coins.

(ii) Required probability

$$= \frac{\text{Number of ways of selecting two ₹1 coins}}{\text{Total number of ways of selecting two coins}}.$$

47. (i) Total number of balls in the urn = 6 + a.

(ii) P(Drawing a green ball) = 2P(Drawing a blue ball).

(iii) Using above condition find the value of a.

48. The total number of cards is 52.

There are two queen cards which are black.

Required probability $= \frac{2}{52} = \frac{1}{26}$.

49. The total number of balls is 30, of them 10 are black, 12 are blue, and 8 are orange.

There are 18 balls, which are not blue.

The required probability $= \frac{18}{30} = \frac{3}{5}$.

50. The sample space = {1, 2, 3, 4, 5, 6}.

The favourable outcomes = {2, 3, 5}.

Required probability $= \frac{3}{6} = \frac{1}{2}$.

51. There are 8 letters in the word TRIANGLE, of these 5 are consonants.

Required probability $= \frac{5}{8}$.

52. The total number of letters is 10.

The number of consonants = 7

Required probability $= \frac{7}{10}$.

Level 3: Assess Your Concepts

53. P(blue ball) =

$$\frac{\text{Number of blue balls in the bag}}{\text{Total number of balls in the bag}}.$$

55. (i) Number of favourable events = 1.

(ii) There are 8 prime numbers from 1 to 20.

56. (i) P(either e or i) = $P(e)$ + $P(i)$.

(ii) Total outcomes = 5, i.e., (a, e, i, o, u).

57. (i) Committee should consists of 3 men and 2 women.
(ii) P(committee of 5 persons) = Number of ways of selecting 3 men and 2 women to the number of ways of selecting 5 persons.

58. Total number of coins in the purse = 4 + 3 + 3 = 10.
The total number of ways of selecting 3 coins from 10 coins is ${}^{10}C_3 = 120$.
To get the minimum amount, these three coins must be 50 paise coins. This can be done in ${}^4C_3$ ways = 4 ways.

Required probability $= \frac{4}{120} = \frac{1}{30}$.

59. There are 8 numbers.
The roots of the equation $x^2 - 6x + 8 = 0$ are 2 and 4.
The number of favourable outcomes is 2.

The required probability $= \frac{2}{8} = \frac{1}{4}$.

60. Probability of picking a red ball $= \frac{9}{9+p}$

Probability of picking a green ball $= \frac{p}{9+p}$

Given, $\frac{9}{9+p} = \frac{3p}{9+p}$

$\Rightarrow 3p = 9 \Rightarrow p = 3$.

61. If two dice are rolled together, then the total number of outcomes = $6^2 = 36$.
Favourable outcomes that the sum of the numbers is 5: (4, 1), (1, 4), (2, 3), (3, 2).

The required probability $= \frac{4}{36} = \frac{1}{9}$.

62. The total number of ways of selecting two balls from 8 balls = ${}^8C_2 = 28$.
Number of favourable cases that one ball is 2 and other is 3, is 1.

Required probability $= \frac{1}{28}$.

63. Total number of outcomes = 5 × 4 × 3 × 2 = 120
The number of favourable cases = 2(4 × 3 × 2) = 48 (i.e., odd numbers)

The required probability $= \frac{48}{120} = \frac{2}{5}$.

64. If two dice are rolled together, then total number of outcomes = $6^2 = 36$.
Required probability = 1 – (the probability of getting the sum of the numbers on the two dice is greater than 10)

Favourable cases to get the sum greater than 10: (5, 6), (6, 5) and (6, 6).
Probability of getting the sum of the numbers on the two dice is greater than 10 $= \frac{3}{36} = \frac{1}{12}$.

The required probability $= 1 - \frac{1}{12} = \frac{11}{12}$.

65. The total number of ways of selecting three numbers from 15 numbers is = ${}^{15}C_3 = 455$.
The favourable outcomes are
(1, 2, 3), (2, 3, 4)... (13, 14, 15).

The required probability $= \frac{13}{455} = \frac{1}{35}$.

66. Total number of tickets are 70.
Multiples of 5 are 5, 10, 15, ..., 70.
There are 14 numbers, which are multiples of 5.
Multiples of 7 are 7, 14, ..., 70, i.e.,
There are 10 numbers, which are multiples of 7.
There are two numbers, which are multiple of both 7 and 5. Total number of numbers which are multiples of 5 or 7 = 14 + 10 – 2.

The required probability $= \frac{22}{70} = \frac{11}{35}$.

67. If two coins are tossed, then the total outcomes: {HH, HT, TH, TT}
The favourable outcomes of getting at least one head: {HH, HT, TH}
The required probability $= \frac{3}{4}$.

68.

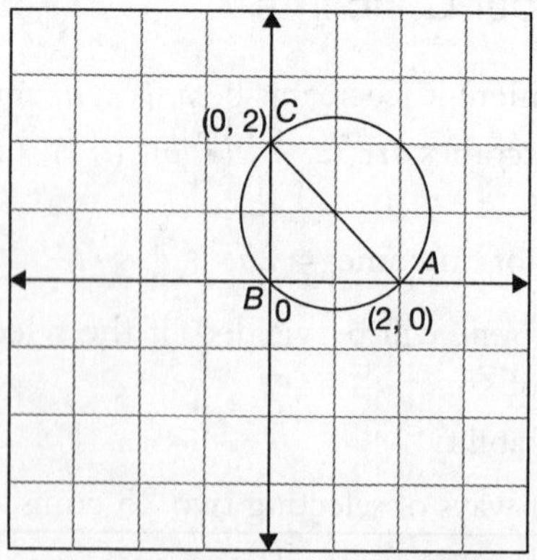

For $ABCD$ to be a convex quadrilateral, D should lie on the semicircle because it is given that $\angle ADC = 90°$

Required probability $= \frac{\pi r}{2\pi r} = \frac{1}{2}$

JEE Special Wing

Multiple-Answer Type Questions

1. We know that the probability of an event always lies between 0 and 1.

   Hence, choice (a, b, c) are correct.

2. Four coins are tossed simultaneously.

   $n(S) = 2^4 = 16.$

   The probability of an event is 0.25.

   Going by options:

   (a) Exactly one head:

   The favourable outcomes are: HTTT, THTT, TTHT, and TTTH.

   $\Rightarrow n(E) = 4.$

   $$P(E) = \frac{n(E)}{n(S)} = \frac{4}{16} = \frac{1}{4} = 0.25.$$

   (b) Exactly three heads:

   The favourable outcomes are: HHHT, HHTH, HTHH, and THHH.

   $\Rightarrow n(E) = 4.$

   $$P(E) = \frac{n(E)}{n(S)} = \frac{4}{16} = \frac{1}{4} = 0.25.$$

   (c) At most two tails:

   $$\Rightarrow n(E) = 4_{C_2} + 4_{C_1} + 4_{C_0} = \frac{4 \times 3}{1 \times 2} + 4 + 1.$$

   $$= 6 + 4 + 1 = 11$$

   $$P(E) = \frac{n(E)}{n(S)} = \frac{11}{16} = 0.6875.$$

   (d) At least two tails:

   $$\Rightarrow n(E) = 4_{C_2} + 4_{C_3} + 4_{C_4} = \frac{4 \times 3}{1 \times 2} + 4 + 1.$$

   $$= 6 + 4 + 1 = 11$$

   $$P(E) = \frac{n(E)}{n(S)} = \frac{11}{16} = 0.6875\,.$$

   Hence, choice (a and b) are correct.

3. Madhu has ten slips.

   He wrote only one number from zero to nine on each slip without repeating the number.

   $n(S) = 10.$

   The probability of an event is 0.5.

Number	No. of Distinct Letters	No. of Distinct Vowels
ZERO	4	2
ONE	3	2
TWO	3	1
THREE	4	1
FOUR	4	2
FIVE	4	2
SIX	3	1
SEVEN	4	1
EIGHT	5	2
NINE	3	2

   Going by options:

   (a) **Number which has exactly three distinct letters:**

   The favourable outcomes are: ONE, TWO, SIX, NINE

   $\Rightarrow n(E) = 4.$

   $$P(E) = \frac{n(E)}{n(S)} = \frac{4}{10} = 0.4.$$

   (b) **Number which has exactly four distinct letters:**

   The favourable outcomes are: ZERO, THREE, FOUR, FIVE, SEVEN

   $\Rightarrow n(E) = 5.$

   $$P(E) = \frac{n(E)}{n(S)} = \frac{5}{10} = 0.5.$$

   (c) **Number which has exactly one vowel:**

   The favourable outcomes are: TWO, THREE, SIX, SEVEN

   $\Rightarrow n(E) = 4.$

   $$P(E) = \frac{n(E)}{n(S)} = \frac{4}{10} = 0.4.$$

   (d) **Number which has exactly two distinct vowels:**

   The favourable outcomes are: ZERO, ONE, FOUR, FIVE, NINE, EIGHT

   $\Rightarrow n(E) = 6.$

   $$P(E) = \frac{n(E)}{n(S)} = \frac{5}{10} = 0.6\,.$$

   Hence, choice (a and c) are correct.

4. The probability of getting head when a coin is tossed is $\frac{1}{2}$.

Going by options:

(a) The number of letters in the word **authorised** $[n(S)]$ is 10.
The number of consonants $[n(E)]$ is 5.
The probability of getting a consonant,

$$P(E)=\frac{n(E)}{n(S)}=\frac{5}{10}=\frac{1}{2}.$$

(b) $S=\{1, 2, 3, 4, 5, 6\}$
$n(S) = 6.$
$E=\{1, 3, 5\}$
$n(E) = 3.$
The probability of getting an odd number when a dice is rolled, $P(E)=\frac{n(E)}{n(S)}=\frac{3}{6}=\frac{1}{2}.$

(c) The total number of cards, $[n(S)]$ is 52.
The number of black cards, $[n(E)]$ is 26.
The probability of getting a black card,

$$P(E)=\frac{n(E)}{n(S)}=\frac{26}{52}=\frac{1}{2}.$$

(d) As 1968 is a leap year, the total number of days, $[n(S)]$ is 366.
The number of even numbered days, $[n(E)]$ is 183.
The probability of getting an even numbered day,

$$P(E)=\frac{n(E)}{n(S)}=\frac{183}{366}=\frac{1}{2}.$$

Hence, choice (a, b, c, d) are correct.

5. **Going by options:**

(a) As 1986 is a non-leap year, the month February has 28 days. So, getting a month which consists of 29 days is an impossible event.

(b) There is one and only even prime, i.e., 2. If two numbers are chosen at random from the set of even natural numbers, getting both the numbers are prime is an impossible event.

(c) If two dice are rolled, the maximum sum of the numbers on the dice is 12. So, getting a two-digit multiple of 7, i.e., 14, 21, 28 … is an impossible event.

(d) As one of the days of the week may start with W (Wednesday), the given event is not an impossible event.

Hence, choice (a, b, c) are correct.

Match The Column

Common Solutions for questions 6 to 10:

Given that a deck of cards has 52 of which 36 are numbered cards.

The cards $A, J, Q,$ and K are called honours.

The cards $J, Q,$ and K are face cards.

A card is picked randomly from the deck.

$\Rightarrow n(S) = 52.$

There are four suits in a deck of cards. Each suit has the following cards:

2, 3, 4, 5, 6, 7, 8, 9, 10, A, J, Q, K.

6. The number of odd numbered cards $= 4\times4 = 16.$
The number of face cards $= 3\times4 = 12.$
$\Rightarrow n(E) = 16 + 12 = 28.$
The probability of getting an odd numbered card or a face card, $P(E)=\frac{n(E)}{n(S)}=\frac{28}{52}=\frac{7}{13}.$
Hence, the correct option is (b).

7. The number of even numbered cards $= 5\times4 = 20.$
The number of honours $= 4\times4 = 16.$
$\Rightarrow n(E) = 20 + 16 = 36.$
The probability of getting an odd numbered card or a face card, $P(E)=\frac{n(E)}{n(S)}=\frac{36}{52}=\frac{9}{13}.$
Hence, the correct option is (a).

8. The number of odd numbered black cards $= 4\times2 = 8.$
The number of honours card but not face cards $= 1\times4 = 4.$
$\Rightarrow n(E) = 8 + 4 = 12.$
The probability of getting black odd numbered card or an honours card but not face card, $P(E)=\frac{n(E)}{n(S)}$ $=\frac{12}{52}=\frac{3}{13}.$
Hence, the correct option is (e).

9. The number of black kings $= 1\times2 = 2.$
The number of red queens $= 1\times2 = 2$
$\Rightarrow n(E) = 2 + 2 = 4.$
The probability of getting black odd numbered card or an honours card but not face card, $P(E)=\frac{n(E)}{n(S)}$ $=\frac{4}{52}=\frac{1}{13}.$
Hence, the correct option is (f).

10. The number of even numbered red cards $= 5 \times 2 = 10$.

The number of composite numbered black cards $= 5 \times 2 = 10$

$\Rightarrow n(E) = 10 + 10 = 20$.

The probability of getting black odd numbered card or an honours card but not face card, $P(E) = \frac{n(E)}{n(S)}$

$= \frac{20}{52} = \frac{5}{13}$.

Hence, the correct option is (c).

Comprehension-Based Questions

Common Solutions for questions 11 to 15:

Given that the dice has 6 faces.

The numbers on the dice are 1, 2, 3, 4, 5, and 6.

The outcomes are:

(1, 1), (2, 1) … (6, 1)

(1, 2), (2, 2) … (6, 2)

.

.

.

(1, 6), (2, 6) … (6, 6).

$\Rightarrow n(S) = 36$.

11. The sum of the numbers is a prime number.

The favourable outcomes are:

(1, 1), (2, 1), (4, 1), (6, 1)

(1, 2), (3, 2), (5, 2)

(2, 3), (4, 3)

(1, 4), (3, 4)

(2, 5), (6, 5)

(1, 6), (5, 6)

$\Rightarrow n(E) = 15$.

$P(E) = \frac{n(E)}{n(S)} = \frac{15}{36} = \frac{5}{12}$.

Hence, the correct option is (c).

12. The sum of the numbers is a composite number.

The favourable outcomes are:

(3, 1), (5, 1)

(2, 2), (4, 2), (6, 2)

(1, 3), (3, 3), (5, 3), (6, 3)

(2, 4), (4, 4), (5, 4), (6, 4)

(1, 5), (3, 5), (4, 5), (5, 5)

(2, 6), (3, 6), (4, 6), (6, 6)

$\Rightarrow n(E) = 21$.

$P(E) = \frac{n(E)}{n(S)} = \frac{21}{36} = \frac{7}{12}$.

Hence, the correct option is (b).

13. A perfect square and a multiple of 3.

The favourable outcomes are:

(1, 3), (1, 6)

(4, 3), (4, 6)

(3, 1), (3, 4)

(6, 1), (6, 4)

$\Rightarrow n(E) = 8$.

$P(E) = \frac{n(E)}{n(S)} = \frac{8}{36} = \frac{2}{9}$.

Hence, the correct option is (d).

14. A prime number and a composite number.

The favourable outcomes are:

(2, 4), (2, 6)

(3, 4), (3, 6)

(5, 4), (5, 6)

(4, 2), (4, 3), (4, 5)

(6, 2), (6, 3), (6, 5)

$\Rightarrow n(E) = 12$.

$P(E) = \frac{n(E)}{n(S)} = \frac{12}{36} = \frac{1}{3}$.

Hence, the correct option is (a).

15. The difference of the numbers is a prime number.

The favourable outcomes are:

(1, 3), (1, 4), (1, 6)

(2, 4), (2, 5)

(3, 1), (3, 5), (3, 6)

(4, 1), (4, 2), (4, 6)

(5, 2), (5, 3)

(6, 1), (6, 3), (6, 4)

$\Rightarrow n(E) = 16$.

$P(E) = \frac{n(E)}{n(S)} = \frac{16}{36} = \frac{4}{9}$.

Hence, the correct option is (b).

Common Solutions for questions 16 to 20:

There are two straight lines l and m.

Ten points are marked on l, and the points are (2, 1), (4, 1), (6, 1), (8, 1) … (20, 1).

Thirteen points are marked on m and the points are (2, 6), (4, 6), (6, 6), (8, 6) … (26, 6).

From the above information we can deduce the following.

Both l and m are parallel to the x-axis.

The distance between any two consecutive points on each line is 1 unit.

The distance between the lines l and m is $6 - 1 = 5$ units.

By joining a point on l and a point on m, a straight line is formed.

The total number of straight lines formed = 10 × 13 = 130.

By joining two points on a line and a point on other line, a triangles is formed.

The number of triangles formed by joining a point on l and two points on $m = 10 \times {}^{13}C_2$

$$= 10 \times \frac{13 \times 12}{1 \times 2}$$
$$= 10 \times 13 \times 6 = 780.$$

The number of triangles formed by joining two points on l and a point on $m = {}^{10}C_2 \times 13$

$$= \frac{10 \times 9}{1 \times 2} \times 13$$
$$= 5 \times 9 \times 13 = 585.$$

The total number of triangles = 780 + 585 = 1365.

16. When we join (2, 1) and (2, 6), we will get a straight line parallel to the y-axis.
Likewise (4, 1) and (4, 6); (6, 1) and (6, 6) … (20, 1) and (20, 6).
Thus, the number of straight lines parallel to the y-axis = 10 = $n(E)$.
The total number of straight lines = 130 = $n(S)$.
The probability of getting a line parallel to the y-axis, $P(E) = \frac{n(E)}{n(S)} = \frac{10}{130} = \frac{1}{13}$.
Hence, the correct option is (a).

17. The total number of straight lines = 130 = $n(S)$.
The number of vertical lines = 10.
Thus, the number of slant lines = 130 – 10 = 120 = $n(E)$.
The probability of getting a slant line, $P(E) = \frac{n(E)}{n(S)} = \frac{120}{130} = \frac{12}{13}$.
Hence, the correct option is (d).

18. The number of triangles formed by joining a point on l and two points on m = 780 = $n(E)$.
The total number of triangles = 1365 = $n(S)$.
The probability of getting a triangle whose two vertices lie on the line m, $P(E) = \frac{n(E)}{n(S)} = \frac{780}{1365} = \frac{156}{273}$.
Hence, the correct option is (c).

19. The number of triangles formed by joining two points on l and a point on m = 585 = $n(E)$.
The total number of triangles = 1365 = $n(S)$.
The probability of getting a triangle whose two vertices lie on the line l, $P(E) = \frac{n(E)}{n(S)} = \frac{585}{1365} = \frac{117}{273}$.
Hence, the correct option is (a).

20. The total number of triangles = 1365 = $n(S)$.
The height of each triangle is 5 units since the distance between the lines l and m is 5 units.
As we need the triangles whose area is 5 sq units, the base of each triangle must be 2 units long.
If we consider a triangle whose one vertex on the line l and two vertices on the line m, we need to consider two consecutive points on the line m.
The number of triangles formed by joining a point on l and two points on m = 10 × (13 – 1) = 120.
If we consider a triangle whose one vertex on the line m and two vertices on the line l, we need to consider two consecutive points on the line l.
The number of triangles formed by joining a point on m and two points on l = 13 × (10 – 1) = 117.
The required number of triangles = 120 + 117 = 237 = $n(E)$.
The probability of getting a triangle whose area is 5 sq units, $P(E) = \frac{n(E)}{n(S)} = \frac{237}{1365} = \frac{79}{455}$.
Hence, the correct option is (c).

Common Solutions for questions 21 to 25:

In the given figure, $APQD$ is a rectangle and $ABCD$ is a square. A circle is inscribed in the square. MNR is an equilateral triangle inscribed in the circle. $BPQC$ is another rectangle.

$AB = BC = CD = AD = PQ = 14$ cm.

$AP = DQ = 21$ cm.

$PB = QC = 21$ cm – 14 cm = 7 cm.

The radius of the circle (R) = $\frac{14}{2}$ = 7 cm.

The circumradius of equilateral triangle MNR = The radius of the circle.

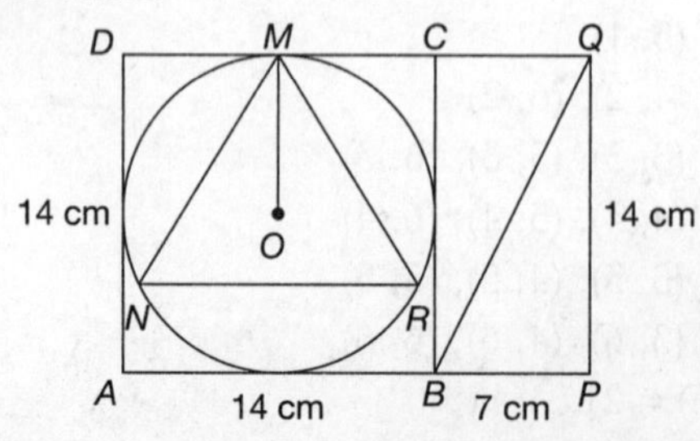

$\left(\frac{2}{3}\right)\left(\frac{\sqrt{3}}{2}\right)$NR = 7 cm.

$\left(\frac{1}{\sqrt{3}}\right)$NR = 7 cm.

NR = $7\sqrt{3}$ cm.

The area of rectangle $APQD = AP \times PQ$

$= 21 \times 14$ sq cm $= n(S)$.

21. The area of $\Delta PBQ = \frac{BP \times PQ}{2}$

$= \frac{7\times14}{2} = 7 \times 7$ sq cm = measure (E).

The probability that the point lies interior of ΔPBQ,

$P(E) = \frac{\text{measure}(E)}{\text{measure}(S)} = \frac{7\times7}{21\times14} = \frac{1}{6}$.

Hence, the correct option is (a).

22. The area of $\Delta MNR = \frac{\sqrt{3}(\text{NR})^2}{4}$.

$= \frac{\sqrt{3}(7\sqrt{3})^2}{4} = \frac{147\sqrt{3}}{4}$ sq cm = measure (E).

The probability that the point lies interior of ΔMNR,

$P(E) = \frac{\text{measure}(E)}{\text{measure}(S)}$

$= \frac{\frac{147\sqrt{3}}{4}}{21\times14}$

$= \frac{147\sqrt{3}}{4\times21\times14} = \frac{\sqrt{3}}{8}$.

Hence, the correct option is (d).

23. The area of circle but not the area of ΔMNR = Area of circle – Area of ΔMNR

$= \pi R^2 - \frac{147\sqrt{3}}{4}$

$= \frac{22}{7}(7^2) - \frac{147\sqrt{3}}{4}$

$= 7\left(22 - \frac{21\sqrt{3}}{4}\right)$

$= 7\left(\frac{88-21\sqrt{3}}{4}\right)$ sq cm = measure (E).

The probability that the point lies interior of the circle but not interior of ΔMNR,

$P(E) = \frac{\text{measure}(E)}{\text{measure}(S)}$

$= \frac{7\left(\frac{88-21\sqrt{3}}{4}\right)}{21\times14}$

$= \frac{7(88-21\sqrt{3})}{4\times21\times14} = \frac{88-21\sqrt{3}}{168}$.

Hence, the correct option is (a).

24. The area of square $ABCD$ but not the area of the circle = Area of square – Area of circle

$= (\text{AB})^2 - \pi R^2$

$= (14)^2 - \frac{22}{7}(7^2)$

$= 196 - 154 = 42$ sq cm = measure (E).

The probability that the point lies interior of square $ABCD$ but not interior of the circle, $P(E) = \frac{\text{measure}(E)}{\text{measure}(S)}$

$= \frac{42}{21\times14} = \frac{1}{7}$.

Hence, the correct option is (c).

25. The area of rectangle $BPQC = PB \times PQ$

$= 7 \times 14$ sq cm = measure (E).

The probability that the point lies interior of rectangle $BPQC$, $P(E) = \frac{\text{measure}(E)}{\text{measure}(S)} = \frac{7\times14}{21\times14} = \frac{1}{3}$.

Hence, the correct option is (b).

Assertion and Reason Type Questions

26. **Assertion:** We know that the probability of an event lies between 0 and 1. So, the probability of an event cannot be more than 1.

So, Assertion is false.

Reason: The probability of an event lies between 0 and 1, which is a true statement.

Hence, the correct option is (d).

27. **Assertion:** A coin is tossed:

The probability of getting head is $\frac{1}{2}$.

The probability of not getting head is same as the probability of getting tail which is $\frac{1}{2}$.

The sum of the probabilities $= \frac{1}{2} + \frac{1}{2} = 1$.

So, Assertion is true.

Reason: The sum of the probabilities of complementary events is 1, which is a true statement and is the correct explanation of Assertion.

Hence, the correct option is (a).

28. **Assertion:** A dice is rolled:

The probability of getting a natural number less than 7 is 1 since given event is a sure event.

The probability of getting a natural number more than 7 is 0 since given event is an impossible event.

So, Assertion is true.

Reason: The probability of an impossible event is 0. The probability of a sure event is 1.

So, Reason is false.

Hence, the correct option is (c).

29. **Assertion:** A coin is tossed 9 times; the number of possible outcomes = $2^n = 512$.

So, Assertion is true.

Reason: A coin is tossed n times; the number of possible outcomes is 2^n, which is a true statement and is the correct explanation of Assertion.

Hence, the correct option is (a).

30. **Assertion:** The probability that a day of the week selected at random will be Monday, is $\frac{1}{7}$.

Reason: The sum of the probabilities of all the elementary events of an experiment is 1.

Both the statements are true, but Reason is not the correct explanation of Assertion.

Hence, the correct option is (b).

Unit VI

Commercial Mathematics

In this Unit

- ✶ **Chapter 13** Banking
- ✶ **Chapter 14** Goods and Services Tax (GST)
- ✶ **Chapter 15** Shares and Dividends

CHAPTER

13

Banking

Remember

Before beginning this chapter, you should be able to:

- Recall remittance of funds, safe deposit lockers, public utility services

Key Ideas

After completing this chapter, you should be able to:

- Define terms such as HCF and LCM
- Understand deposit accounts—savings bank accounts, current accounts and term deposit accounts and processes related
- Study about types of cheques and parties dealing with cheques
- Do calculation of interest on loans
- Calculate interests on savings accounts in banks
- Study hire purchase and find the rate of interest on buying in installment scheme

Scientific Crypt

A Tribute to Banking

Banking is the foundation of our modern economy, influencing daily life, business operations, and the overall financial health of our nations. The term 'bank' is derived from the Old Italian word 'banco,' meaning 'table'. It plays a pivotal role in daily life, business operations, and the overall financial health of nations. Banks act as intermediaries, connecting savers and borrowers, thereby fostering economic growth. They provide secure payment systems, including accounts, cards, and online services, while also safeguarding funds through secure savings accounts. Banks are crucial in capital formation, channelling savings into investments, offering loans to businesses and individuals, and generating revenue through interest and fees. They operate under the regulatory authority of central banks to ensure economic stability.

The history of banking dates back thousands of years to ancient civilizations like Mesopotamia and Egypt. It evolved during the medieval and Renaissance periods in cities such as Florence, Venice, and Genoa, with influential families like the Medici and Rothschilds shaping early banking practices. The concept of banknotes, the precursor to modern paper money, emerged when London goldsmiths began issuing promissory notes for deposits. A significant milestone occurred in 1695 when the Bank of England introduced permanent banknotes, marking the central role of institutions like it in currency issuance and regulation.

FUN TIME

CROSSWORD

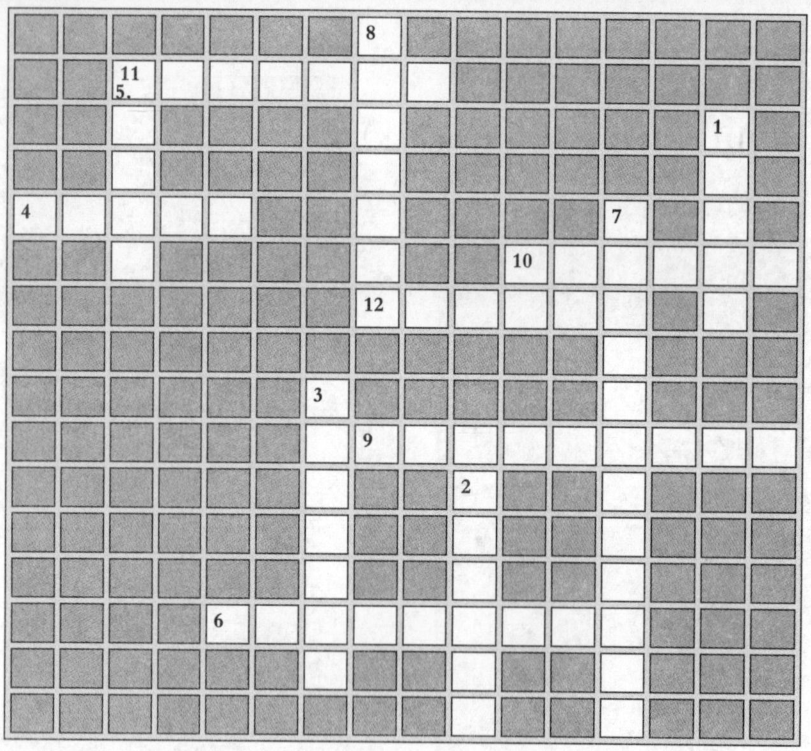

Across

4. The purpose of the banking system is to protect ___________.
6. An individual can buy a ________ to send money to someone else.
9. Customers can accumulate significant amounts through little deposits with the aid of ________ deposit accounts.
10. An individual to whom the cheque is drawn.
11. The banks are the one who provide them.
12. The account holder who signs and draws the cheques to withdraw funds __________.

Down

1. Who is entitled to receive the amount on the cheque.
2. A ________ cheque can be cashed by anybody who has the cheque.
3. The account name and type that companies make use of ________.
5. A banks primary source of income.
7. The method by which products were exchanged to complete transactions for purchases and sales.
8. A cheque is designated as a _______ cheque if two parallel lines are drawn at the left upper corner of the cheque.

INTRODUCTION

Before people began using money, purchase, and sale of goods used to be performed through exchange of goods. This system is called 'Barter system'. As there was no uniformity in the valuation of various goods under this system, the values of all goods were converted in terms of money, thus ensuring that a proper value is paid for the goods purchased.

Once the monetary system became a standard method of value exchange, the necessity to ensure the safety of money came into existence. With an intention to safeguard money and also to facilitate availability of money to everyone in the society, gradually the banking system developed.

Among the various services offered by the banks, taking deposits and providing loans are the basic ones. Apart from these, banks render the following ancillary services:

1. **Remittance of funds:** Banks help in transferring money from one place to another in a safe manner, through the issue of demand drafts, money transfer orders, and telegraphic transfers. Banks also issue travellers cheques to travellers in home currency as well as in foreign currency by which travellers can minimize the risk of theft or loss of money while travelling to a different place. These travellers' cheques can be easily converted into money. With the advent of technology, nowadays, money transfer has become simple through Internet and phone banking.
2. **Safe deposit lockers:** Banks provide safety lockers to customers to keep safely preserve their valuables. A customer can store their valuables, like gold ornaments, important documents in bank lockers by paying a small amount of rent charged by the bank.
3. **Public utility services:** Through bank accounts, the customers can pay their telephone bills, electricity bills, insurance premium, and other services.

Deposit Accounts

Deposit accounts offered by the banks are designed in such a way that they cater to various needs of the customers. These needs come according to their financial capabilities of the customers. At present, the following types of deposit accounts are offered by the banks:

Savings Bank Account

An Indian individual, either resident or non-resident, can open a savings bank account with a minimum balance of ₹500. The minimum balance may vary from bank to bank. A passbook is issued to the customer. It contains all the particulars of the transactions and the balance. Such an account can be opened in joint names also. It is known as a 'joint account'. If one of the joint account holders is a minor, the following guidelines are applicable: a minor who is at least ten-year old can open an account in a bank or a post office. However, the minimum age to open an account and to operate an account differs from bank to bank and post office. In a post office, the minimum age to open and operate a savings account is 10 years. If the minor's minimum age to operate an account is less than his/her minimum age to open an savings account, a guardian can operate the minor's account. The savings bank accounts carry a certain amount of interest compounded half-yearly. The rate of interest varies from bank to bank. It may also vary from time to time. Cheque books are issued to an account-holder against a requisition slip duly filled up and signed by the person. If a customer operates his/her account through cheques, then it is known as **'cheque-operated account'**.

Depositing Money in the Bank Accounts

Money can be deposited in a bank either by cash or through a duly filled pay-in-slip or challan. Pay-in-slips can be used for payment through cash or cheque.

Demand Draft

Money can be deposited through demand drafts (i.e., bank drafts). A person who wants to send money to another person can purchase a bank draft.

A bank draft is an order issued by a bank to its specified branch or to another bank (if there is a tie-up) to make payment of the amount to the party in whose name the draft is issued.

The purchaser of the draft specifies the name and address of the person to whom the money is being sent, which is written on the bank draft. The payee can encash the drafts by presenting it at the specified branch or bank.

Withdrawing Money From Saving Bank Account

Money deposited in these accounts can be withdrawn by using withdrawal slips or cheques.A specimen of a cheque is given below.

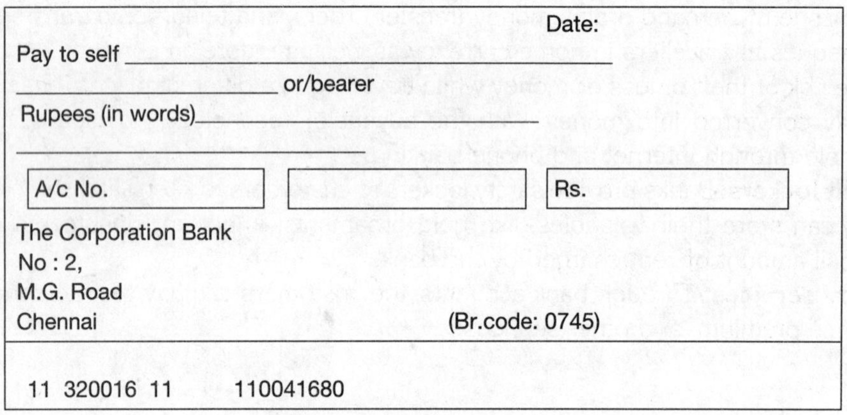

Figure 13.1

Cheque books are issued only to those account-holders who fulfill certain special requirements, such as maintenance of minimum balance, updated information related to the account.

Types of Cheques

A cheque can be classified into two types. These are as follows:

Bearer Cheque

A bearer cheque can be encashed by anyone who possesses the cheque, though the person's name is not written on the cheque. There is a risk of wrong, a person getting the payments.

If the word **'bearer'** is crossed-out in the cheque, then the person whose name appears on the cheque can alone encash the cheque. This type of cheque is known as an **'order cheque'**.

Crossed Cheque

If two parallel lines are drawn at the left-hand top corner of a cheque, it is called a **'crossed cheque'**. The words **'A/C payee'** may or may not be written between the two parallel lines. The payee has to deposit the crossed cheque in his/her account. The collecting bank collects the money from the drawer's bank, and it is credited to the payee's account.

Bouncing of Cheques

If an account-holder issues a cheque for an amount exceeding the balance in his account, the bank refuses to make payment. In such an instance, the cheque is said to be **dishonoured** one. This is known as **bouncing of cheque**. If a cheque bounces, the issuer of the cheque is liable for prosecution under the **Negotiable Instruments Act, 1887**.

Safeguards to be taken while Maintaining 'Cheque-Operated Accounts'

1. Immediately after receiving a cheque book, a customer verifies if all the leaves are serially arranged and printed with correct numbers.
2. Blank cheques should not be issued to anybody except the account holder.
3. Any changes, alterations, corrections made while filling a cheque, should be authenticated with full signature.
4. The amount on a cheque has to be written in words and figures legibly.
5. The amount of the cheque should be written immediately after the printed words **'Rupees'** or '₹.' Also, the word **'only'** should be mentioned after the amount in words.
6. A cheque becomes outdated or stale after six months from the date of issue. Hence, it should be presented within six months from the date of issue.

Parties Dealing with a Cheque

Drawer

The account-holder who writes the cheques and signs on it in order to withdraw money is called 'drawer' of the cheque.

Drawee

The Bank on whom the cheque is drawn is called the 'drawee bank' as they pay the money.

Payee

The party to whom the amount of cheque is payable is called the 'payee'. The payee has to affix his/her signature on the back of the cheque.

Any savings bank account-holder can withdraw money from his/her account using a withdrawal form, a specimen of which is given below:

State Bank of India
------------------------ Branch

Date:

Name of the account holder: ______________
Account No. | | | | | | |

Note: This form is not a cheque.
Payment will be rejected if this form is not submitted along with the pass book.

Please pay self/ourselves only.
Rupees ______________________________ only.
and debit the amount from my/our above savings bank account. Rs.

Token No.	PAY CASH	
Scroll No.	passing officer	Signature of the customer

Figure 13.2

Current Account

This account is very convenient for business people, companies, government offices, and various other institutes which need to make frequent and large amounts of monetary transactions. Banks do not give any interest on these accounts, but the operation of these accounts is flexible. There is no restriction on amounts deposited or withdrawn (i.e., on the number of transactions) as the savings bank accounts.

Term Deposit Accounts

These accounts are of two types:

1. Fixed deposit accounts
2. Recurring deposit accounts

Fixed Deposit Accounts

Customers can avail the facility of depositing a fixed amount for a definite period of time. As the time period is fixed, banks give a higher rate of interest on these accounts. If money is withdrawn from these accounts before the fixed time period, banks pay lesser interest than what was agreed upon. As this discourages premature withdrawal, banks rely more on these funds. The rate of interest payable varies with the period for which the money is deposited in these accounts, and it varies from bank to bank. The rates of interest offered by a bank on fixed deposits are as follows:

Time Period	Rate of Interest (%) per annum
15 days and upto 45 days	5.25
46 days and upto 179 days	6.50
180 days to, less than 1 year	6.75
1 year to less than 2 years	8.00
2 years to less than 3 years	8.25
3 years and above	8.50

Recurring Deposit Accounts

These accounts help customers to build up large amounts through small deposits. These accounts facilitate depositing a fixed amount per month for a time span of 6 months to 3 years, and above. This time period is called the **maturity period**.

The following table gives an idea about how the principal amounts are taken to calculate the interest in recurring deposit accounts.

Date	Deposit	Principal on which interest is to be paid
1-4-2006	₹3000	₹3000
1-5-2006	₹3000	₹6000
1-6-2006	₹3000	₹9000

Recurring deposit accounts are helpful to those who have low earnings. They can save large amounts through regular and fixed savings. A person who opens this account deposits an initially agreed amount each month. At the end of the maturity period, the cumulative amount with interest, which is called the 'maturity amount', is paid to the account-holder. The rates of interest payable on these accounts are same as those payable on fixed deposit accounts. The recurring deposit interest is calculated by applying the following formula.

We know that, $1+2+3+\cdots+n=\frac{n(n+1)}{2}$

If a man deposits ₹k per month, for n months at r% per annum, then simple interest $=₹\left[k\times\frac{n(n+1)}{2}\times\frac{1}{12}\times\frac{R}{100}\right]$.

EXAMPLE 13.1 Govind opened a bank account on 1-4-2006 by depositing ₹3000. He deposited ₹1000 on 11-4-2006 and withdrew ₹500 on 15-4-2006. Compute the interest paid by the bank for the month of April, if the rate of interest is 4% per annum.

SOLUTION

Balance as on 1-4-2006 = ₹3000

as on 11-4-2006 = ₹4000

as on 15-4-2006 = ₹3500

The minimum balance for the month of April = ₹3000

$\therefore$ The interest paid by the bank for the month of April $= \dfrac{3000 \times 1 \times 4}{1200} =$ ₹10.

EXAMPLE 13.2 Rajan makes fixed deposit of ₹8000 in a bank for a period of 2 years. If the rate of interest is 10% per annum compounded annually, find the amount payable to him by the bank after two years.

SOLUTION

The amount of fixed deposit = ₹8000.

$R = 10\%$ per annum and $n = 2$.

$$\therefore \text{ The amount returned by the bank } = P\left[1+\frac{r}{100}\right]^n$$

$$= 8000\left[1+\frac{10}{100}\right]^2$$

$$= 8000\,[1 + 0.1]^2 = 8000 \times 1.21 = ₹9680.$$

EXAMPLE 13.3 Mahesh deposits ₹600 per month in a recurring deposit account for 2 years at 5% per annum. Find the amount he receives at the time of maturity.

SOLUTION

Here, $P =$ ₹600,

$N = 2 \times 12$ months and $R = 5\%$ per annum

$$\text{SI} = P \times \frac{n(n+1)}{2} \times \frac{1}{12} \times \frac{R}{100} = 600 \times \frac{24(25)}{2} \times \frac{1}{12} \times \frac{5}{100} = 750$$

$\therefore$ The total amount = (24 × 600) + 750 = 14400 + 750 = ₹15,150.

Loans

The loans given by the banks can be classified into the following three types:

1. Demand loans
2. Term loans
3. Overdrafts (ODs)

Demand Loans

The borrower has to repay the loans on demand. The repayment of the loan has to be done within 36 months from the date of disbursement of the loan. The borrower has to execute a demand promissory note in favour of the bank, promising that he would repay the loan unconditionally as per the stipulations of the bank.

Term Loans

The borrower enters into an agreement with the bank regarding the period of loan and mode of repayment, number of instalments, etc. The repayment period is, generally, more than 36 months. These loans are availed by those who purchases machinery, build houses, etc.

Overdrafts (ODs)

A current account holder enters into an agreement with the bank which permits him to draw more than the amount available in his account, but upto a maximum limit fixed by the bank. These loans are availed by traders.

Calculation of Interest on Loans

Interest on loans is calculated on daily product basis. Once in every quarter the loan amount is increased by that amount.

$$\text{Daily product} = \text{Balance} \times \text{Number of days it has remained as balance.}$$

$$\text{Interest} = \frac{\text{Sum of daily products} \times \text{Rate}}{100 \times 365}$$

EXAMPLE 13.4 Ganesh takes a loan of ₹20,000 on 1-4-2005. He repays ₹2000 on the 10th of every month, starting from May 2005. If the rate of interest is 15% per annum, calculate the interest upto 30-6-2005.

SOLUTION

Loan Amount (in ₹)	Loan Period	No. of Days	Daily Product
₹20,000	1-4-2005 to 10-5-2005	40	40 × 20,000 = ₹800,000
Repays ₹2000 on 11-5-2005 Balance ₹18,000	11-5-2005 to 10-6-2005	31	31 × 18,000 = ₹558,000
Repay ₹2,000 on 11-6-2005 Balance ₹16,000	11-6-2005 to 30-6-2005	20	20 × 16,000 = ₹320,000

Total daily product (DP) = ₹1,678,000

$$\therefore \text{Interest} = \frac{\text{DP} \times \text{Rate}}{100 \times 365}$$

$$= \frac{1{,}678{,}000 \times 15}{100 \times 365} = ₹689.59.$$

Compound Interest

When interest is calculated on principal as well as on interest, it is known as compound interest. The interest is added to the principal at regular intervals, quarterly or half yearly or yearly, and further interest is calculated on the increased principal thus obtained.

The formula to find out the amount payable, when the interest is compounded annually is as follows:

$$A = P\left(1 + \frac{r}{100}\right)^n$$

where, P = Principal
r = Rate of interest, and
n = Number of years.

When interest is compounded k times a year, then $A = P\left(1 + \frac{r}{k \times 100}\right)^{n \times k}$

When interest is compounded quarterly $k = \frac{12}{3} = 4$.

When interest is compounded half-yearly $k = \frac{12}{6} = 2$, and so on.

Hire Purchase and Installment Scheme

When a buyer does not have purchasing capacity, the seller allows the buyer to make part payments in monthly, quarterly, half-yearly or yearly instalments. This scheme is of two types:

1. Hire purchase scheme
2. Instalment scheme

Hire Purchase Scheme

In this scheme, the buyer is called the 'hirer' and the seller is called the 'vendor' enters into an agreement which is known as 'hire purchase agreement'.

Important Features of Hire Purchase Scheme

1. The hirer pays an initial payment known as 'down payment'.
2. The vendor allows the hirer to take possession of the goods on the date of signing the agreement, but he does not transfer the ownership of the goods.
3. The hirer promises to pay the balances amount in instalments.
4. If the hirer fails to pay the instalments the vendor can repossess the goods.
5. Once goods are repossessed, the hirer cannot ask for repayment of the instalments of money already paid. This money paid will be treated as rent for the period.

Instalment Scheme

Under instalment scheme, the seller transfers the possession as well as the ownership of the goods to the buyer. The buyer has the right to resell or pledge the goods, but he has to repay the instalments due.

Finding the Rate of Interest on Buying in Installment Scheme

The formula that is used to calculate the rate of interest on instalment purchase is:

$$R = \frac{2400E}{n[(n+1)I - 2E]}$$

where, R = Rate of Interest

E = Excess amount paid

n = Number of instalments

I = Amount of each instalment

E = Down payment + Sum of instalment amounts − Cash price

Konnect

If the loan is repaid totally, the date on which it is repaid is not counted for calculation of interest. If the loan is repaid in part, the day of repayment of loan is also counted for calculating the interest.

EXAMPLE 13.5 A television set is sold for ₹9000 cash on ₹1000 cash down followed by six equal instalments of ₹1500 each. What is the rate of interest?

SOLUTION

$n = 6$

$I = ₹1500$

$E = [1000 + 6 \times 1500 - 9000] = ₹1000$

$$\therefore R = \frac{2400E}{n[(n+1)I - 2E]} = \frac{2400 \times 1000}{6[(6+1)1500 - 2000]} = 47.1\%.$$

POINTS TO REMEMBER

- ✔ Money can be deposited through demand drafts (i.e., bank drafts). A person who wants to send money to another person can purchase a bank draft.
- ✔ A bearer cheque can be encashed by anyone who possesses the cheque, though the person's name is not written on the cheque. There is a risk of wrong, a person getting the payments.
- ✔ If the word 'bearer' is crossed-out in the cheque, then the person whose name appears on the cheque can alone encash the cheque. This type of cheque is known as an 'order cheque.
- ✔ If two parallel lines are drawn at the left-hand top corner of a cheque, it is called a 'crossed cheque'.
- ✔ The account-holder who writes the cheques and signs on it in order to withdraw money is called 'drawer' of the cheque.
- ✔ The party to whom the amount of cheque is payable is called the 'payee'. The payee has to affix his/her signature on the back of the cheque.
- ✔ If a man deposits ₹k per month, for n months at r% per annum, then simple interest = ₹ $\left[k \times \frac{n(n+1)}{2} \times \frac{1}{12} \times \frac{R}{200}\right]$.
- ✔ Daily product = Balance number of days it has remained as balance.

  $$\text{Interest} = \frac{\text{Sum of daily products} \times \text{Rate}}{100 \times 365}$$
- ✔ When interest is compounded k times a year, then $A = P\left(1 + \frac{r}{k \times 100}\right)^{n \times k}$
- ✔ The hirer pays an initial payment known as 'down payment'.
- ✔ The formula that is used to calculate the rate of interest on instalment purchase is:

  $$R = \frac{2400E}{n[(n+1)I - 2E]}$$

DW

PRACTICE QUESTIONS CLASSROOM WING

Very Short Answer Type Questions

Directions of questions from 1 to 4:
Fill in the blanks.

1. Fixed deposit is also known as ________ deposit.
2. __________ is a utility service provided by the Banks.
3. Under a recurring deposit, a depositor is paid a lump sum payment after the period for which the deposit is made. This lump sum payment is called ________ value.
4. The rate of interest on current account is ________ % per annum.

Directions of questions from 5 to 6:
State whether the following statements are true or false.

5. Banks offer higher rate of interest on savings accounts than fixed deposit accounts. (True/false)
6. In the banks, safe deposit lockers are provided to the customers at free of cost. (True/False)

Essay Type Questions

7. (A) Javed makes a fixed deposit of ₹100,000 in a bank for one year. If the rate of interest is 6% per annum, compounded half-yearly, then find the maturity value.

   (B) Abhi and Kabhi deposit ₹15,000 per month each in recurring deposit schemes for 2 years at the rate of 6% pa and 7% respectively. Find the difference in the amounts received by them at the time of maturity.

8. **Directions for questions A and B:** Anu has opened a recurring deposit account in a bank that pays simple interest, with a monthly installment of ₹25,000 per month for 23 months. She received an amount of ₹6,26,750 at the end of the period.

   (A) What is the rate of interest per annum?

   (B) If the bank pays 1% pa more interest, what will be the extra amount earned by Anu?

9. Tilak opened a recurring deposit account with a bank and deposited ₹600 per month for one year. Find the interest that Tilak will receive, if the bank pays 6% per annum.

10. David makes a fixed deposit of ₹50,000 in a bank for $1\frac{1}{2}$ years. If the interest is compounded half-yearly and the maturity value is ₹66,550, then find the rate of interest per annum.

11. Tushar opens a recurring deposit account with a bank and deposits ₹500 per month for $1\frac{1}{2}$ years. If he receives ₹570 as interest, then find the rate of interest offered by the bank.

12. Ms Revathi deposits ₹10,000 per month in a recurring deposit account for 6 years at the rate of 8% per annum. Find the amount that she receives at the time of maturity.

13. Kesav deposits ₹12,600 per month in a recurring deposit account for 100 months. If he gets ₹16,31,175 at the time of maturity, find:

    (a) amount of interest paid by bank.

    (b) rate of interest.

PRACTICE QUESTIONS COMPETITION WING

Level 1: Apply Your Concepts

Directions of questions from 1 to 6:
Select the correct alternative from the given choices.

1. Madhu makes a fixed deposit of ₹15,000 in a bank, for two years. If the rate of interest is 10% per annum, compounded annually, then find the maturity value.
(a) ₹3150 (b) ₹17,500
(c) ₹16,750 (d) ₹18,150

2. Dinesh makes a fixed deposit of ₹50,000 in a bank, for one year. If the rate of interest is 12% per annum, compounded half-yearly, then find the maturity value.
(a) ₹66,125 (b) ₹56,180
(c) ₹57,500 (d) ₹63,250

3. Prabhu deposits ₹600 per month in a recurring deposit account for 1 year at 8% per annum. Find the interest received by Prabhu.
(a) ₹424 (b) ₹312
(c) ₹360 (d) ₹450

4. Kamal deposits ₹550 per month in a recurring deposit account for $1\frac{1}{2}$ year at 8% per annum. Find the interest that Kamal will receive at the time of maturity.
(a) ₹550 (b) ₹627
(c) ₹230 (d) ₹346

5. Vijay makes a fixed deposit of ₹10,000 in a bank for 2 years under compound interest. If the maturity value is ₹11,664, find the rate of interest per annum compounded annually.
(a) 4% (b) 5%
(c) 8% (d) 10%

6. Subhash makes a fixed deposit of ₹25,000 in a bank for 146 days. If the rate of interest is 7.5% annum, then what amount would he receive on the maturity of the fixed deposit?
(a) ₹27,500 (b) ₹25,750
(c) ₹26,500 (d) ₹28,450

Level 2: Review Your Concepts

7. Varsha opened a recurring deposit account with Oriental Bank of Commerce and deposited ₹800 per month at an interest rate of 4% per annum. If she receives ₹800 as interest, then find out the total time for which the account was held. (in years)
(a) $1\frac{1}{2}$ (b) 2
(c) $1\frac{3}{4}$ (d) $2\frac{1}{4}$

8. Susheel has a cumulative time deposit account of ₹800 per month at 6% per annum. If he receives ₹1,300 as interest, then find out the total time for which the account was held. (in months)
(a) 26 (b) 25
(c) 24 (d) 28

9. Vishal has a recurring deposit account in a finance company for 1 year at an interest rate of 8% per annum. If he receives ₹9390 at the time of maturity, then what amount, per month, was invested by Vishal?
(a) ₹650 (b) ₹700
(c) ₹750 (d) ₹800

10. Chetan deposited ₹1200 per month in a recurring deposit account for one year at 6% per annum Find the interest received by him. (in ₹)
(a) 384 (b) 426
(c) 468 (d) 492

11. Bala made a fixed deposit of ₹30,000 in a bank for two years at R% per annum under compound interest. The maturity value is ₹35,643. Find R.
(a) 7 (b) 9
(c) 11 (d) 13

12. Bhuvan made a fixed deposit of ₹15,000 in a bank on 1-1-2007 for 219 days under 12% per annum simple interest. Find out the maturity value. (in ₹)
(a) 15,840 (b) 15,960
(c) 16,080 (d) 16,140

13. Amar made a fixed deposit of ₹20,000 in a bank, for two, years at 8% per annum under compound interest. Find out the maturity value. (in ₹)
(a) 22,896 (b) 23,328
(c) 24,124 (d) 24,312

Level 3: Assess Your Concepts

14. Charan opened a cumulative time deposit account with a bank. For $1\frac{1}{2}$ years, he deposited ₹800 per month. He received an interest of ₹1140. Find the rate of interest. (in % per annum)

(a) 10 (b) 9
(c) 8 (d) 12

15. Kanna opened a recurring deposit account with an instalment of ₹12,000 per month at the rate of 5% pa. If he earned ₹3,63,000 as interest, find:

(a) the total time(in years) for this account
(b) the maturity value for this account.

(a) 12; 15,50,000 (b) 10; 18,03,000
(c) 120; 18,00,00 (d) None of these

16. Ashwin opened a savings account in a bank on 4-1-2006 with a deposit of ₹2000. On the 9th of every odd month of that year, he deposited ₹500 to his account. On the 9th of every even month of that year, he withdrew ₹500 from his account. He closed his account on 1-2-2007. Find the sum on which he would have received interest on closing the account. (in ₹)

(a) 22,500 (b) 24,000
(c) 25,500 (d) 27,000

17. Dinesh opened a recurring deposit account with State Bank of India. He deposited ₹900 per month at 7.5% per annum. He received ₹1687.5 as interest. Find the time period of his deposit. (in years)

(a) 3 (b) 3.5
(c) 2.5 (d) 2

18. Ganesh makes a fixed deposit of ₹40,000 in a bank for a year at 20% per annum simple interest. Harish makes a fixed deposit of an equal sum for the same period and at the same rate of interest, interest being compounded half-yearly. Find the difference between maturity values of investment of Harish and Ganesh. (in ₹)

(a) 400 (b) 360
(c) 440 (d) 300

19. Ramu deposited ₹400 per month in a recurring deposit account for 2 years at 9% per annum. Somu deposited ₹400 per month in a recurring deposit account for $2\frac{1}{2}$ years at 12% per annum. Which of the following can be concluded about the interests to be paid to them on maturities of their deposits?

(a) Ramu must be paid an interest of ₹860 less than that of Somu.
(b) Ramu must be paid an interest of ₹960 less than that of Somu.
(c) Ramu must be paid an interest of ₹916 less than that of Somu.
(d) Ramu must be paid an interest of ₹816 less than that of Somu.

20. Mr Karunya received ₹5,53,200 after 5 years from a recurring deposit scheme giving rate of 6% p.a. interest. What is the amount (in ₹) of monthly installment that he paid?

(a) ₹8000 (b) ₹7000
(c) ₹7500 (d) ₹4500

AT

PRACTICE QUESTIONS JEE SPECIAL WING

Multiple-Answer Type Questions

Directions for questions 1 to 5:

Each question has FOUR options (a), (b), (c), and (d). ONE OR MORE THAN ONE of these four option(s) is/are the correct answer(s).

1. Mythri deposits ₹50,000 per month in a recurring deposit scheme for 24 months, that pays 6 % p.a. simple interest. Which of the following is/are true about the given information?
   (a) She earns an interest of ₹75,000 at the time of maturity.
   (b) She gets ₹12,75,000 at the time of maturity.
   (c) She earns an interest of ₹90,000 at the time of maturity.
   (d) She gets ₹12,90,000 at the time of maturity.

2. Bhuvan deposits ₹40,000 per month in a recurring deposit scheme for 36 months, that pays x % p.a. simple interest. Which of the following is/are true about the given information?
   (a) If the scheme pays 1% extra p.a., he earns ₹22,200 more at the time of maturity.
   (b) If the scheme pays 1% less p.a., he earns ₹11,100 less at the time of maturity.
   (c) If the scheme pays 2% extra p.a., he earns ₹44,400 more at the time of maturity.
   (d) If the scheme pays 3% less p.a., he earns ₹33,300 more at the time of maturity.

3. Miyeon deposits ₹30,000 per month in a recurring deposit account for n months at r% per annum. She earns an interest of ₹6,300 at the time of maturity. Which of the following is/true about the given information?
   (a) n can be 7. (b) r can be 9.
   (c) n can be 8. (d) r can be 7.

4. Bhim deposits ₹10,000 per month in a recurring deposit scheme for n months, that pays 8% p.a. simple interest. He earns an interest of ₹8,000 at the time of maturity. Which of the following is/true about the given information?
   (a) The value of n is 12.
   (b) If she continues to deposit for 3 more months, she will get an interest of ₹11,400 at the time of maturity.
   (c) If she continues to deposit for 9 more months, she will get ₹2,60,000 at the time of maturity.
   (d) The value of n is 18.

5. Jora deposits ₹2,400 per month in a recurring deposit scheme for n months, that pays n % p.a. simple interest. She earns an interest of ₹14,400 at the time of maturity. Which of the following is/true about the given information?
   (a) The number of factors of n is 8.
   (b) The value of n is a factor of monthly deposit (in ₹) of Jora.
   (c) $(n-8)$ is a perfect square.
   (d) $(n+10)$ is a perfect cube.

Match The Column

Directions for questions 6 to 10:

Read the paragraph given below and answer the questions.

Naava deposits ₹1,00,000 per month in a recurring deposit account for n months at r% per annum. She earns an interest of ₹15,000 at the time of maturity.

Column A (n)	Column B (r)
6. 9	(a) 30
7. 8	(b) 24
8. 5	(c) 20
9. 4	(d) 18
10. 3	(e) 15
	(f) 12
	(g) 10
	(h) 6
	(i) 5
	(j) 4

Comprehension-Based Questions

Directions for questions 11 to 15:

Read the paragraph given below and answer the questions.

Zayn has opened a recurring deposit account in a bank that pays simple interest, with a monthly deposit of ₹20,000 per month for 2 years. He received an interest which is equal to one-sixteenth of his total deposits.

11. What is the rate of interest per annum?

(a) 8% (b) 6%
(c) 10% (d) 9%

12. If the bank pays 1% p.a. less interest, what will be the interest received by Zayn?

(a) ₹20,000 (b) ₹22,000
(c) ₹24,000 (d) ₹25,000

13. If he continues to deposit for 6 more months, what will be the maturity of his deposits?

(a) ₹6,46,500 (b) ₹6,45,000
(c) ₹6,40,250 (d) ₹6,36,000

14. If the bank pays 2% pa more interest, what will be the maturity of his deposits?

(a) ₹4,80,000 (b) ₹5,20,000
(c) ₹5,80,000 (d) ₹6,40,000

15. If he deposit for 5 months lesser than the actual period, what will be the interest received by Zayn?

(a) ₹21,000 (b) ₹20,000
(c) ₹19,000 (d) ₹18,000

Assertion and Reason Type Questions

Directions for questions 16 to 18:

In the light of the given statements, choose the most appropriate answer from the options given below.

(a) Both assertion (A) and reason (R) are true, and reason (R) is the correct explanation of the assertion.
(b) Both assertion (A) and reason (R) are true, and reason (R) is not the correct explanation of the assertion.
(c) Assertion (A) is true, but reason (R) is false.
(d) Assertion (A) is false, and reason (R) is true.

16. Assertion: Under recurring deposit scheme, the formula to calculate the maturity value is given by $P \times n + P \times \frac{n(n+1)r}{2400}$.

Reason: Under recurring deposit scheme, the formula to calculate interest is given by $P \times \frac{n(n+1)r}{2400}$.

17. Assertion: If the interest earned on depositing ₹10,000 per month in a recurring deposit scheme for 100 months at 6% p.a. simple interest is ₹2,52,500, the interest earned at 12% is ₹5,05,000.

Reason: Under recurring deposit scheme, if the interest earned at r% pa for m months is ₹ x, then the interest earned at $2r$% pa for m months is ₹ $2x$.

18. Assertion: If the interest earned on depositing ₹10,000 per month in a recurring deposit scheme for 12 months at 8% p.a. simple interest, is ₹5,200, the interest earned for 24 months at the same rate of interest is ₹20,000.

Reason: Under recurring deposit scheme, if the interest earned at r% pa for m months is ₹ x, then the interest earned at r% pa for $2m$ months is ₹ $2x$.

ANSWER KEYS

Crossword

Across

4. Money 6. Bank Draft 9. Recurring 10. Drawee 11. Lockers 12. Drawer

Down

1. Payee 2. Bearer 3. Current 5. Loans 7. Barter System 8. Crossed

Classroom Wing

Very Short Answer Type Questions

1. Term deposit 2. Receiving payment for telephone bills 3. Maturity 4. 0 5. False 6. False

Essay Type Questions

7. (A) ₹112,360 (B) ₹3,750 8. (A) 9% (B) ₹5,750 9. ₹234
10. $r = 20\%$ per annum 11. 8% per annum 12. ₹8,95,200
13. (a) ₹15,540 (b) 7% per annum

Competition Wing

Level 1: Apply Your Concepts

1. (d) 2. (b) 3. (b) 4. (b) 5. (c) 6. (b)

Level 2: Review Your Concepts

7. (b) 8. (b) 9. (c) 10. (c) 11. (b) 12. (c) 13. (b)

Level 3: Assess Your Concepts

14. (a) 15. (b) 16. (d) 17. (d) 18. (a) 19. (b) 20. (a)

JEE Special Wing

Multiple-Answer Type Questions

1. (a, b) 2. (a, c) 3. (a, b, c, d) 4. (b, c) 5. (a, b, c)

Match The Column

6. (j) 7. (i) 8. (f) 9. (d) 10. (a)

Comprehension-Based Questions

11. (b) 12. (d) 13. (a) 14. (b) 15. (c)

Assertion and Reason Type Questions

16. (b) 17. (a) 18. (c)

Hints and Explanations

Classroom Wing

Very Short Answer Type Questions

1. Term deposit
2. Receiving payment for telephone bills
3. Maturity
4. 0
5. False
6. False

Essay Type Questions

7. (A) Amount $= P\left[1+\frac{r}{100}\right]^n$

$P = 100,000 \quad r = 6\%$ p.a.

$n = 1$ year

Interest half yearly so $n = 2n$

$$\text{Amount} = 100,000\left[1+\frac{6}{100}\right]^2$$

$$= 100,000 \times \frac{106}{100} \times \frac{106}{100}$$

$$= 112360$$

(B) **Abhi:**

Given that $p =$ ₹15,000, $n = 2 \times 12 = 24$ and $r = 6$.

$$\text{Interest} = \frac{P \times n(n+1)}{2 \times 12} \times \frac{r}{100}$$

$$= \frac{15,000 \times 24(24+1)}{2 \times 12} \times \frac{6}{100} = ₹22,500.$$

Kabhi:

Given that $p =$ ₹15,000, $n = 2 \times 12 = 24$ and $r = 7$.

$$\text{Interest} = \frac{P \times n(n+1)}{2 \times 12} \times \frac{r}{100}$$

$$= \frac{15,000 \times 24(24+1)}{2 \times 12} \times \frac{7}{100} = ₹26,250.$$

The require difference = ₹26,250 − ₹22,500 = ₹3,750.

II Method:

Given that $p =$ ₹15,000, $n = 2 \times 12 = 24$ and difference in the rates = 1%.

The require difference

$$= \frac{P \times n(n+1)}{2 \times 12} \times \frac{\text{Difference in rates}}{100}$$

$$= \frac{15,000 \times 24(24+1)}{2 \times 12} \times \frac{1}{100} = ₹3,750.$$

8. Given that P = ₹ 25,000, n = 23 months, and the maturity value = ₹ 6,26,750.

Let the rate of interest be r %.

We know that the maturity value = Amount deposited + Interest

⇒ Interest = Maturity value − Amount deposited

⇒ Interest = ₹ 6,26,750 − 23 × 25,000

= ₹6,26,750 − ₹5,75,000

= ₹51,750

(A) We know that interest $= \frac{P \times n(n+1) \times r}{2400}$

$$\Rightarrow 51750 = \frac{25000 \times 23 \times 24 \times r}{2400}$$

$$\Rightarrow 51750 = \frac{25000 \times 23 \times r}{100}$$

$$\Rightarrow 51750 = 250 \times 23 \times r$$

$$\Rightarrow r = \frac{51750}{250 \times 23}$$

$$\Rightarrow r = \frac{1035}{5 \times 23}$$

$$\Rightarrow r = \frac{207}{23}$$

$$\Rightarrow r = 9$$

Hence, the rate of interest = 9 %.

(B) Given that P = ₹25,000, n = 23 months, and $r = 9 + 1 = 10$.

We know that interest $= \frac{P \times n(n+1) \times r}{2400}$

$$= \frac{25000 \times 23 \times 24 \times 10}{2400}$$

$$= \frac{25000 \times 23}{10}$$

$$= 2500 \times 23 = 57500.$$

The required difference $= ₹57{,}500 - ₹51{,}750$

$= ₹5{,}750.$

Hence, the extra amount earned by Anu = ₹5,750.

9. 600 per month for 1 years

$I = ?$

$r = 6\%$ p.a.

$N = 1 \times 12$ months

$$SI = p \times \frac{n(n+1)}{2} \times \frac{1}{12} \times \frac{r}{100}$$

$$= \overset{3}{\cancel{600}} \times \frac{\cancel{12} \times 13}{\cancel{2}} \times \frac{1}{\cancel{12}} \times \frac{6}{\cancel{100}}$$

$= ₹234$

10. $P = 50{,}000$

$T = 1\frac{1}{2}$ years

$A = 66550$

$₹ = ?$

$$\text{Amount} = P\left[1 + \frac{r}{100}\right]^n$$

$$\overset{1331}{\cancel{6655}\cancel{0}} = \cancel{5}0{,}00\cancel{0}\left[1 + \frac{r}{100}\right]^3$$

$$\frac{1331}{1000} = \left(1 + \frac{r}{100}\right)^3$$

$$\frac{11}{10} = 1 + \frac{r}{100} \Rightarrow \frac{11}{1\cancel{0}} = \frac{100 + r}{10\cancel{0}} r = 10$$

Rate of interest = 20% p.a.

11. 500 per month.

For $\frac{3}{2}$ years

Interest = 570

$r = ?$

$N = 1\frac{1}{2} = 18$ months

$$SI = P \times \frac{n(n+1)}{2} \times \frac{1}{2} \times \frac{R}{100}$$

$$570 = 5\cancel{00} \times \frac{\overset{\cancel{9}\,3}{\cancel{18}} \times 19}{\cancel{2}} \times \frac{1}{\cancel{12}\,4} \times \frac{R}{1\cancel{00}}$$

$$= \frac{\overset{2\,\cancel{38}}{\overset{\cancel{114}}{\cancel{570}}} \times 4}{\cancel{5} \times \cancel{3} \times \cancel{19}} = R$$

R = 8% per annum.

12. Given that $p = ₹10{,}000$, $n = 6 \times 12 = 72$ and $r = 8$.

$$\text{Interest} = \frac{P \times n(n+1)}{2 \times 12} \times \frac{r}{100}$$

$$= \frac{10{,}000 \times 72(72+1)}{2 \times 12} \times \frac{8}{100} = ₹1{,}75{,}200.$$

Maturity value = Total amount deposited + Interest received on it

$= (6 \times 12 \times ₹10{,}000) + ₹1{,}75{,}200.$

$= ₹7{,}20{,}000 + ₹1{,}75{,}200 = ₹8{,}95{,}200.$

13. Given that the maturity value = ₹16,31,175, $n = 100$ and $P = ₹12{,}600$.

We need to find interest and r.

Total amount deposited $= 100 \times ₹12{,}600 = ₹12{,}60{,}000.$

Interest paid by the bank = Maturity Value − Total amount deposited

$= ₹16{,}31{,}175 - ₹12{,}60{,}000 = ₹3{,}71{,}175.$

$$\text{We know that the interest} = \frac{P \times n(n+1)}{2 \times 12} \times \frac{r}{100}$$

$$\Rightarrow 3{,}71{,}175 = \frac{12{,}600 \times 100(100+1)}{2 \times 12} \times \frac{r}{100}$$

$$\Rightarrow 3{,}71{,}175 = 525 \times 101 \times r$$

$$\Rightarrow r = \frac{3{,}71{,}175}{525 \times 101}$$

$$\Rightarrow r = 7\%$$

Thus, the amount of interest paid by the bank is ₹15,540 at the rate of 7% p.a.

Competition Wing

Level 1: Apply Your Concepts

1. Use, $A = P\left(1+\frac{r}{100}\right)^n$

2. (i) $A = P\left(1+\frac{r}{100}\right)^n$

   (ii) Given, $P =$ ₹50,000, $n = 2$ half-years, $R = 6\%$ per half-year.

   (iii) Use, $A = \left(1+\frac{R}{100}\right)^n$ to find the maturity value (A).

3. Use, $\text{SI} = \frac{P \times n(n+1)}{2} \times \frac{R}{1200}$

4. (i) Use, $\text{SI} = \frac{P \times n(n+1)}{2} \times \frac{R}{1200}$

   (ii) Given $P =$ ₹550, $n = 18$ months, $R = 8\%$

   (iii) Use, $I = \frac{p \times n(n+1)}{2} \times \frac{R}{1200}$ to find interest revised.

5. Use, $A = P\left(1+\frac{r}{100}\right)^n$.

6. (i) $\text{SI} = \frac{P \times d \times R}{100 \times 365}$, where

   $d =$ Number of days.

   (ii) Total $= P + \text{SI}$.

Level 2: Review Your Concepts

7. Use, $\text{SI} = \frac{P \times n(n+1)}{2} \times \frac{R}{1200}$

8. (i) Use, $\text{SI} = \frac{P \times n(n+1)}{2} \times \frac{R}{1200}$

   (ii) Given $P =$ ₹800, $I = 1300$, $R = 6\%$

   (iii) Use, $I = \frac{p \times n(n+1)}{2} \times \frac{R}{1200}$ to find n.

9. (i) Use, $\text{SI} = \frac{P \times n(n+1)}{2} \times \frac{R}{1200}$.

   (ii) Let the amount deposited per month be ₹P.

   Amount $A =$ ₹9390, SI $= 9390 - P$.

   (iii) Use, $9390 = P + \frac{p \times n(n+1)}{2} \times \frac{R}{1200}$ to find P.

10. Time period = 1 year = 12 months

    Interest received by him (in ₹)

    $= 1200 \frac{(12)(13)}{2}\left(\frac{1}{12}\right)\left(\frac{6}{100}\right)$

    $= (12)\left(\frac{13}{2} \times 6\right) = 156 \times 3 = 468.$

11. $30,000\left(1+\frac{R}{100}\right)^2 = 35,643$

    $\left(1+\frac{R}{100}\right)^2 = \frac{35,643}{30,000} = \frac{11,881}{10,000}$

    $\left(1+\frac{R}{100}\right)^2 = \left(\frac{109}{100}\right)^2 \Rightarrow R = 9.$

12. Time period = 219 days $= \frac{219}{365}$ years

    $= \frac{3}{5}$ years

    Maturity value (in ₹)

    $= 15,000\left(1+\frac{\left(\frac{3}{5}\right).12}{100}\right)$

    $= 15,000 + (150)\left(\frac{3}{5}\right)(12)$

    $= 15,000 + 1080 = 16,080.$

13. Maturity value (in ₹) $= 20,000\left(1+\frac{8}{100}\right)^2$

    $= 20,000(1.08)^2 = 23,328.$

Level 3: Assess Your Concepts

14. Let the rate of interest be $R\%$ per annum time period

    $= 1\frac{1}{2}$ years = 18 months.

    Interest received by him (in ₹) = 800

    $\frac{(18)(19)}{2}\left(\frac{1}{12}\right)\left(\frac{R}{100}\right) = R\left[(8)\left(\frac{9 \times 19}{12}\right)\right]$

    $= R\left(\frac{72 \times 19}{12}\right) = 114R \Rightarrow 114R = 1140$

    (given) $R = 10.$

15. (a) Given that P = ₹12,000, r = 6 and interest = ₹3,63,000.

Let the time in months be 't'.

We know that the interest $= \frac{P \times n(n+1)}{2 \times 12} \times \frac{r}{100}$

$\Rightarrow 3,63,000 = \frac{12000 \times t(t+1)}{2 \times 12} \times \frac{5}{100}$

$\Rightarrow 3,63,000 = 25\ t(t + 1)$

$\Rightarrow t(t + 1) = 145200$

$\Rightarrow t^2 + t - 145200 = 0$

$\Rightarrow t^2 + 121t - 120t - 145200 = 0$

$\Rightarrow t(t + 121) - 120(t + 121) = 0$

$\Rightarrow (t + 121)\ (t - 120) = 0$

$\Rightarrow t = -121$ or $t = 120$.

Since 't' (number of months) cannot be negative, $t = 120$.

Time in years $= \frac{120}{10} = 10$.

(b) Maturity value = Total amount deposited + Interest received on it

= (120 × 12,000) + 3,63,000

= ₹14,44,000 + ₹3,63,000 = ₹18,03,000.

16. His minimum balances in the year 2006 (in ₹) are 2500, 2000, 2500, 2000, 2500, 2000, 2500 and 2000.

The sum on which Ashwin would have received interest (in ₹)

= 6(2500 + 2000) = 27,000.

17. Let the time period be T years.

T years = 12 T months.

Interest received by him

$= (900)\frac{(12T)(12T+1)}{2}\left(\frac{1}{12}\right)\left(\frac{7.5}{100}\right)$

= 1687.5

$\frac{9(T)(12T+1)(7.5)}{2} = 1,687.5$

$T(12T+1) = \frac{(1687.5)(2)}{(9)(7.5)} = 50 \qquad (1)$

$12T^2 + T - 50 = 0$

$12T^2 - 24T + 25T - 50 = 0$

$12T\ (T - 2) + 25(T - 2) = 0$

$(12T + 25)\ (T - 2) = 0$

$T = \frac{-25}{12}$ or 2

But $T > 0$

$\therefore T = 2$.

18. Maturity value of Ganesh's investment (in ₹)

$= 40,000\left(1 + \frac{20}{100}\right) = 40,000(1.2) = 48,000$

Maturity value of Harish's investment (in ₹)

$= 40,000\left(1 + \frac{20}{2(100)}\right)^2$

$= 40,000(1.1)^2$

= 40,000(1.21)

= 48,400

The required excess amount (in ₹)

= 48,400 – 48,000 = 400.

19. Time periods of Ramu's account and Somu's account are 2 years, i.e., 24 months and $2\frac{1}{2}$ years, i.e., 30 months, and respectively.

Interest to be paid to Ramu (in ₹)

$= \frac{400(24)(25)}{2}\left(\frac{1}{12}\right)\left(\frac{9}{100}\right)$

$= 4(300)\left(\frac{3}{4}\right) = 900$

Interest to be paid to Somu (in ₹)

$= \frac{400(30)(31)}{2}\left(\frac{1}{12}\right)\left(\frac{12}{100}\right) = 1,860$

Interest to be paid to Ramu is less than that to be paid to Somu by ₹960.

20. Given that the maturity value = ₹5,53,200, $n = 5 \times 12 = 60$ and $r = 6$.

We need to find the value of p.

Maturity value $= p \times n + \frac{P \times n(n+1)}{2 \times 12} \times \frac{r}{100}$

$= p\left[n + \frac{n(n+1)}{2 \times 12} \times \frac{r}{100}\right]$.

$\Rightarrow 5,53,200 = p\left[60 + \frac{60(60+1)}{2 \times 12} \times \frac{6}{100}\right]$

$\Rightarrow 5,53,200 = p\left[60 + \frac{60(61)}{2 \times 12} \times \frac{6}{100}\right]$

$$\Rightarrow 5,53,200 = p\left[60 + \frac{183}{20}\right]$$

$$\Rightarrow 5,53,200 = p\left[\frac{1200 + 183}{8}\right]$$

$$\Rightarrow 5,53,200 = p\left[\frac{1383}{20}\right]$$

$$\Rightarrow p = 5,53,200\left[\frac{20}{1383}\right]$$

$$\Rightarrow p = 400 \times 20$$

$$\Rightarrow p = ₹8,000.$$

Thus, the monthly instalment paid by Mr Karunya is ₹ 8,000.

JEE Special Wing

Multiple-Answer Type Questions

1. Monthly deposit (P) = ₹50,000.
   $n = 24$ and $r = 6$.
   $$\text{Interest} = P \times \frac{n(n+1)r}{2400}$$
   $$= ₹50000 \times \frac{24 \times 25 \times 6}{2400}$$
   $$= ₹500 \times 25 \times 6$$
   $$= ₹75,000.$$
   Maturity value = P × n + Interest
   $$= ₹50,000 \times 24 + ₹75,000$$
   $$= ₹12,00,000 + ₹75,000 = ₹12,75,000.$$
   Hence, choice (a and b) are correct.

2. Monthly deposit (P) = ₹40,000.
   $n = 36$ and $r = x$.
   If the rate of interest is 1% more or less:
   Interest more or less
   $$= P \times \frac{n(n+1) \times \text{Difference in the rate}}{2400}$$
   $$= ₹40000 \times \frac{36 \times 37 \times 1}{2400}$$
   $$= ₹200 \times 3 \times 37$$
   $$= ₹22,200.$$
   If the rate of interest is 2% more or less, interest more or less = 2(₹22,200) = ₹44,400.
   If the rate of interest is 3% more or less, interest more or less = 3(₹22,200) = ₹66,600.
   Hence, choice (a and c) are correct.

3. Monthly deposit (P) = ₹30,000.
   Interest = ₹6,300.
   $n = ?$ and $r = ?$
   $$\text{Interest} = P \times \frac{n(n+1)r}{2400}$$
   $$₹6300 = ₹30000 \times \frac{n(n+1)r}{2400}$$
   $$6300 = 300 \times \frac{n(n+1)r}{24}$$
   $$21 = \frac{n(n+1)r}{24}$$
   $$n(n+1)r = 21 \times 24$$
   $$n(n+1)r = 7 \times 8 \times 9$$
   If $n = 7$, $r = 9$.
   If $n = 8$, $r = 7$.
   Hence, choice (a, b, c, d) are correct.

4. Monthly deposit (P) = ₹10,000.
   Interest = ₹8,000.
   $n = ?$ and $r = 8$
   $$\text{Interest} = P \times \frac{n(n+1)r}{2400}$$
   $$₹8000 = ₹10000 \times \frac{n(n+1)8}{2400}$$
   $$8000 = 100 \times \frac{n(n+1)}{3}$$
   $$n(n+1) = 240$$
   $$n(n+1) = 15(15+1)$$
   $$n = 15.$$
   So, (a) and (d) are false statements.
   (b) Monthly deposit (P) = ₹10,000
   $r = 8$
   $n = 15 + 3 = 18.$
   $$\text{Interest} = P \times \frac{n(n+1)r}{2400}$$
   $$= ₹10000 \times \frac{18(18+1)8}{2400}$$
   $$= ₹100 \times \frac{18(19)}{3}$$
   $$= ₹100 \times 114 = ₹11,400.$$
   So, (b) is a true statement.
   (c) Monthly deposit (P) = ₹10,000
   $r = 8$
   $n = 15 + 9 = 24.$
   $$\text{Maturity value} = P \times n + \frac{n(n+1)r}{2400}$$
   $$= ₹10000 \times 24 + ₹10000 \times \frac{24(24+1)8}{2400}$$
   $$= ₹240000 + ₹100 \times 25 \times 8$$
   $$= ₹240000 + ₹20000$$
   $$= ₹2,60,000.$$
   So, (c) is a true statement.
   Hence, choice (b and c) are correct.

5. Monthly deposit (P) = ₹2,400
   Interest = ₹14,400
   $n = r.$
   $$\text{Interest} = P \times \frac{n(n+1)r}{2400}$$
   $$₹14400 = ₹2400 \times \frac{n(n+1)n}{2400}$$
   $$14400 = n(n+1)n$$

$n(n+1)n = 24 \times 25 \times 24$

$n = 24.$

(a) $n = 24 = 2^3 \times 3^1$

The number of factors of n is $(3 + 1)(1 + 1)$ i.e., 8.

(b) The value of $n(= 24)$ is a factor of monthly deposit (₹2400) of Jora.

(c) $(n-8) = 24-8 = 16$, which is a perfect square.

(d) $(n+10) = 24+10 = 34$, which is not a perfect cube.

Hence, choice (a, b, c) are correct.

Match The Column

Common Solutions for questions 6 to 10:

Monthly deposit (P) = ₹1,00,000.

Interest = ₹15,000.

$n = ?$ and $r = ?$

$$\text{Interest} = P \times \frac{n(n+1)r}{2400}$$

$$₹15000 = ₹100000 \times \frac{n(n+1)r}{2400}$$

$$15000 = 1000 \times \frac{n(n+1)r}{24}$$

$$15 = \frac{n(n+1)r}{24}$$

$$n(n+1)r = 15 \times 24$$

$$n(n+1)r = 360.$$

6. We know $n(n+1)r = 360$.

Given that $n = 9$.

$\Rightarrow 9(9+1)r = 360$

$\Rightarrow r = \dfrac{360}{90} = 4.$

Hence, the correct option is (j).

7. We know $n(n+1)r = 360$.

Given that $n = 8$.

$\Rightarrow 8(8+1)r = 360$

$\Rightarrow r = \dfrac{360}{72} = 5.$

Hence, the correct option is (i).

8. We know $n(n+1)r = 360$.

Given that $n = 5$.

$\Rightarrow 5(5+1)r = 360$

$\Rightarrow r = \dfrac{360}{30} = 12.$

Hence, the correct option is (f).

9. We know $n(n+1)r = 360$.

Given that $n = 4$.

$\Rightarrow 4(4+1)r = 360$

$\Rightarrow r = \dfrac{360}{20} = 18.$

Hence, the correct option is (d).

10. We know $n(n+1)r = 360$.

Given that $n = 3$.

$\Rightarrow 3(3+1)r = 360$

$\Rightarrow r = \dfrac{360}{12} = 30.$

Hence, the correct option is (a).

Comprehension-Based Questions

Common Solutions for questions 11 to 15:

Monthly deposit (P) = ₹20,000.

Monthly deposit (P) = ₹20,000.

$n = 24$ and $r = ?$

$$\text{Interest} = \frac{P \times 24}{16}$$

$$= \frac{₹20,000 \times 24}{16} = ₹30,000.$$

11. We know interest $= P \times \dfrac{n(n+1)r}{2400}$.

$$30000 = 20000 \times \frac{24(24+1)r}{2400}$$

$$3 = 2 \times \frac{24(25)r}{2400}$$

$$3 = \frac{(600)r}{1200}$$

$r = 6.$

Hence, the correct option is (b).

12. When $r\% = 6\%$, the interest is ₹30,000.

When $(r-1)\% = 5\%$, the interest is ₹30,000 $\times \dfrac{5}{6}$

= ₹25,000.

Hence, the correct option is (d).

13. Monthly deposit (P) = ₹20,000

$r = 6$

$n = 24 + 6 = 30.$

$$\text{Maturity value} = \text{P} \times n + \text{P} \times \frac{n(n+1)r}{2400}$$

$$= ₹20000 \times 30 + ₹20000 \times \frac{30(30+1)6}{2400}$$

$$= ₹600000 + ₹50 \times 30 \times 31$$

$= ₹600000 + ₹46500$

$= ₹6,46,500.$

Hence, the correct option is (a).

14. When $r\% = 6\%$, the interest is ₹30,000.
When $(r+2)\% = 8\%$, the interest is $₹30,000 \times \frac{8}{6}$
$= ₹40,000.$
Maturity value = P × n + Interest
$= ₹20000 \times 24 + ₹40000$
$= ₹480000 + ₹40000$
$= ₹5,20,000.$

Hence, the correct option is (b).

15. Monthly deposit (P) = ₹20,000
$r = 6$
$n = 24 - 5 = 19.$

$$\text{Interest} = \frac{n(n+1)r}{2400}$$

$$= ₹20000 \times \frac{19(19+1)6}{2400}$$

$$= ₹200 \times \frac{19(20)}{4}$$

$$= ₹200 \times 19 \times 5$$

$$= ₹19,000.$$

Hence, the correct option is (c).

Assertion and Reason Type Questions

16. If a person deposits ₹P per month in a recurring deposit account for n months at $r\%$ per annum, the interest is given by $\frac{n(n+1)r}{2400}$ and the maturity value is given by $P \times n + P \times \frac{n(n+1)r}{2400}$.
Both the statements are true, but Reason is not the correct explanation of Assertion.
Hence, the correct option is (b).

17. **Assertion:**
(i) Monthly deposit (P) = ₹10,000.
$n = 100$ and $r = 6\%$

$$\text{Interest} = P \times \frac{n(n+1)r}{2400}$$

$$= ₹10000 \times \frac{100(101)6}{2400}$$

$$= ₹2500 \times 101 = ₹2,52,500.$$

(ii) Monthly deposit (P) = ₹10,000.
$n = 100$ and $r = 12\%$

$$\text{Interest} = P \times \frac{n(n+1)r}{2400}$$

$$= ₹10000 \times \frac{100(101)12}{2400}$$

$$= ₹5000 \times 101 = ₹5,05,000.$$

So, Assertion is true.

Reason: Under recurring deposit scheme, if the interest earned at $r\%$ pa for m months is ₹ x, then the interest earned at $2r\%$ pa for m months is ₹ $2x$.
Reason is true and is the correct explanation of Assertion.
Hence, the correct option is (a).

18. **Assertion:**
(i) Monthly deposit (P) = ₹10,000.
$n = 12$ and $r = 8\%$

$$\text{Interest} = P \times \frac{n(n+1)r}{2400}$$

$$= ₹10000 \times \frac{12(13)8}{2400}$$

$$= ₹100 \times 52 = ₹5,200.$$

(ii) Monthly deposit (P) = ₹10,000.
$n = 24$ and $r = 8\%$

$$\text{Interest} = P \times \frac{n(n+1)r}{2400}$$

$$= ₹10000 \times \frac{24(25)8}{2400}$$

$$= ₹100 \times 200 = ₹20,000.$$

So, Assertion is true.

Reason: Under recurring deposit scheme, if the interest earned at $r\%$ pa for m months is ₹ x, then the interest earned at $r\%$ pa for $2m$ months is ₹ $2x$.
It is a false statement.
Hence, the correct option is (c).

CHAPTER 14

Goods and Services Tax (GST)

Remember

Before beginning this chapter, you should be able to:

- Understand concepts related to tax
- Learn about funds and solve numerical problems related to it

Key Ideas

After completing this chapter, you should be able to:

- Study direct and indirect Tax
- Understand the features of GST
- Learn about E-way Bill

Scientific Crypt

A Tribute to Goods and Services Tax (GST) in India

GST, an abbreviation for Goods and Services Tax, stands as a revolutionary tax reform within India. The journey to institute GST within the country unfolds over several decades. It commenced in 1986 with the introduction of MODVAT and involved extensive discussions regarding the implementation of a unified VAT system. In 1999, the concept of GST received approval. Several committees, including one headed by Asim Dasgupta, diligently worked on designing the GST model and the accompanying technology. Despite encountering obstacles and opposition boycotts, the GST Bill ultimately received approval in 2017, resulting in the unification of India's indirect taxation system on July 1, 2017. The endeavour necessitated an amendment to the Indian Constitution, empowering both central and state governments to levy GST, thereby establishing it as a comprehensive, multistage, and destination-based tax system. This transformative reform aimed at simplifying taxation processes and fostering uniformity across the nation.

GST in India effectively replaced various taxes, including central excise duty, services tax, additional customs duty, state-level value-added tax, and Octroi. It introduced a dual GST model, encompassing Central GST (CGST) for intra-state transactions and State GST (SGST), along with Integrated GST (IGST) for inter-state transactions and imported goods. GST operates as a consumption-based tax, with collection occurring in the state where goods or services are consumed.

GST encompasses five tax slabs (0%, 5%, 12%, 18%, and 28%) and excludes specific items like petroleum, alcohol, and electricity, which are subject to separate taxation by states. Particular goods are subject to special rates, while others incur a cess. The GST Council, responsible for governing rates and regulations, oversees the distribution of revenue between the central and state governments. Additionally, it has introduced initiatives such as the 'Invoice Incentive Scheme' to promote accurate billing practices. The tax reform streamlined transportation by eliminating check posts and introduced the e-Way Bill to enhance the efficiency of goods movement. The management of GST processes is overseen by GSTN, with Infosys Technologies playing a pivotal role.

FUN TIME

CROSSWORD

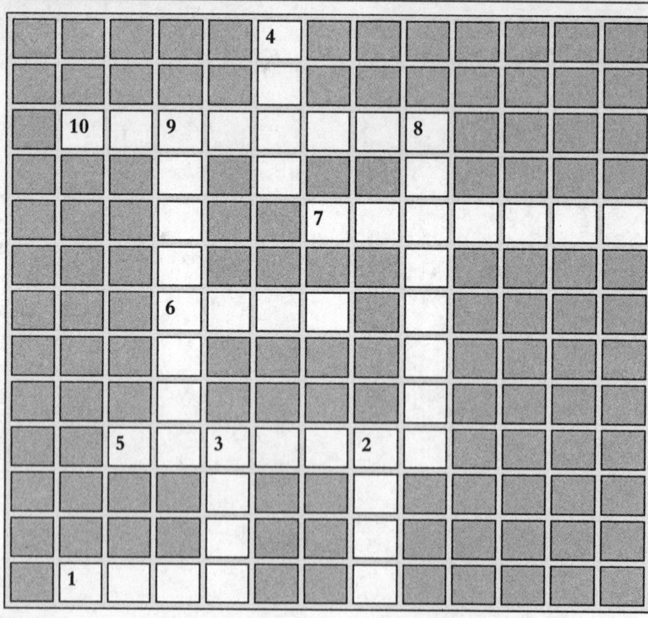

Across

1. GST that union government collects.
5. On which states SGST is not applicable ______.
6. GST that central government collects.
7. On which products and services, the GST rate is higher in India? ______
10. GST is a _______ tax.

Down

2. The goods and services tax (GST) collected for transaction involving the transfers of goods or services between states _________.
3. GST that state government collects. _______.
4. How much GST collected on vegetables. _______.
8. One who pays tax. _______.
9. Income tax is a _____ tax.

INTRODUCTION

The Indian government imposes a mandatory charge on the Indian citizens and various organisations and corporations, and this has been given the name '*tax*'.

Broadly, taxes can be categorized into:

- Direct taxes
- Indirect taxes

Direct Tax

A direct tax is one that an individual or an entity pays to the government directly, and not through someone else. This tax includes Income tax, Estate tax, Corporate tax, and Wealth tax.

Indirect Tax

An indirect tax is one that is levied by the Government on goods and services consumed and paid by an individual, and it is collected by another entity and remitted to the Government by this person or body.

Central excise duty, Additional customs duty, Service tax, and Sales tax, were some of the indirect taxes that the Government of India imposes.

However, with the introduction and subsequent implementation of the Goods and Services Tax or the GST, these indirect taxes have been subsumed into this reformed indirect tax, which is comprehensive and single.

Features of the Comprehensive Goods and Services Tax (GST)

Keeping in perspective the regressive nature of indirect taxation, the objective of which is to generate revenue for the government, and which has to be borne by every individual irrespective of income or affordability of tax, the Goods and Services Tax (GST) has been implemented as a destination tax.

It was launched on the midnight of the 1st of July, 2017 by the President of India and the GOI. It is the Government of India's tax reform initiative aimed at integrating major indirect taxes of the Centre and the states. This tax is levied on the manufacture, sale and consumption of goods and services, and collected on value-added goods and services.

Its noteworthy features are:

1. It creates a unified tax regime for indirect taxes and makes the country under a common market.
2. Taxes covered under the GST:
   (a) The three main indirect taxes for the centre-the Union Excise Duty, Service Tax, and Customs duty.
   (b) The two main indirect taxes for the states-sales tax and Sales Excise Duty.
   (c) Numerous low revenue generating taxes.
3. Taxes not covered under the GST: There are nine indirect taxes that are not subsumed by the GST:
   (a) Basic Customs Duty on imports is charged under the current law only.
   (b) Stamp Duty for registration of property.
   (c) Property tax.
   (d) Road Tax will be levied directly by states.
   (e) Entertainment Tax.
   (f) Toll Tax.
   (g) Excise on liquor.
   (h) Tax on petrol and petroleum products, diesel, ATF and Natural Gas.
   (i) Electricity Duty.

4. Only individuals and/or entities registered under the GST have the authority to charge and collect GST.

   It is mandatory for any entity with an annual turnover of more than ₹20 lakh toregister for the GST. However, the figure for special states such as Assam, Arunachal Pradesh, Mizoram, Nagaland, Meghalaya, Sikkim, Tripura, Manipur, Jammu and Kashmir, Himachal Pradesh and Uttarakhand is ₹10 lakh.

5. The GST that is charged and collected on sale of goods is called **Output GST,** the GST incurred on purchase and expenses is called **Input GST**. The input GST is set off against the output GST and the difference between the two is payable to the government. This mechanism ensures that only the value added is taxed at each stage of a supply tax, and the input tax can be claimed or is offset by the output tax.

6. The GST facilitates a **one country one tax system** in the entire nation, across all states and Union territories, on any specific good or service.

7. Assam was the foremost in the implementation of the GST while the twin states of Jammu and Kashmir was the last to do so.

8. The place of consumption of a good or service decides the state that will collect the GST. Therefore, the state(s) that produce or sell the good or service gets nothing, while the consuming state receives the complete portion of tax. This is why the GST is called a **destination** or **consumption-based tax**.

9. **Rate of slabs of the GST:** The GST proposes a four-tier rate structure. The tax slabs are fixed at 5%, 12%, 18% and 28% besides 0% tax on essentials. Gold is taxed at 3%, and semi-precious stones at 0.25% The GST tax structure takes into consideration the nature of good or service, and taxes a necessity at lower while a luxury at a higher rate.

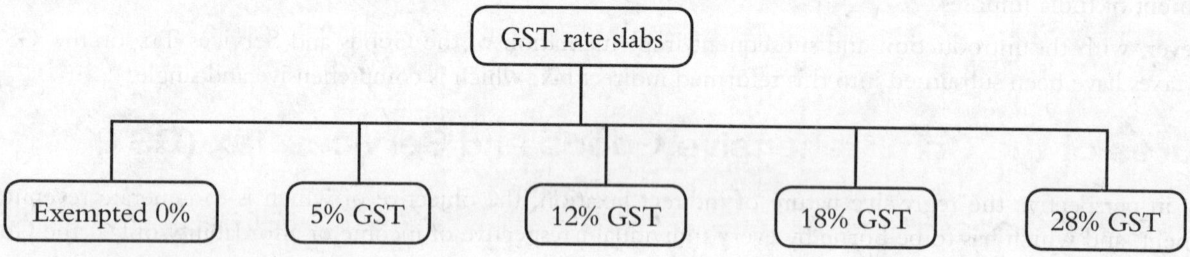

10. Advantages of the GST for:
    (a) **Traders**
    - (i) Creation of a common national market
    - (ii) Removal of cascading effect of taxes
    - (iii) Level playing field for the small trader
    - (iv) Simplified tax system

    (b) **Citizens of India**
    - (i) Reduction in the prices of goods and services due to elimination of cascading taxes
    - (ii) Uniform pricing throughout the country
    - (iii) Simple and transparent tax system

    (c) **Government**
    - (i) Single and simplified system of taxation is easy to administer
    - (ii) Revenue efficiency is high
    - (iii) Better control on leakages
    - (iv) Increased tax compliance

Components of GST

1. **CGST – The Central Goods and Services Tax** is collected by the government on sale within the state i.e., on an intra-state sale.
2. **SGST – The State (or Union Territory) Goods and Services Tax** is collected by the state government on an intrastate sale.
3. **IGST – The Integrated Goods and Services Tax** is collected by the central government on an interstate sale.

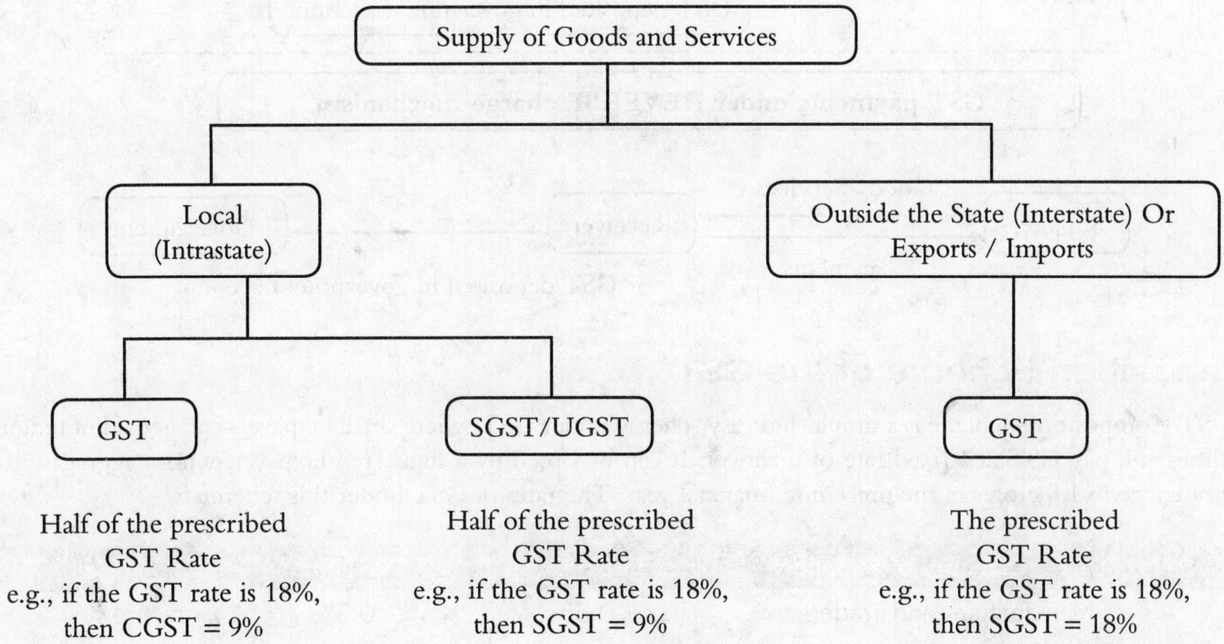

Reverse Charge mechanism under GST

Reverse charge is a mechanism where instead of the supplier, the recipient of the goods and/or services is liable to pay GST to the government.

Reverse charge is applicable under the following circumstances.

1. Supply from an unregistered dealer to a registered one.
2. Services through e-commerce operator.
3. Supply of certain goods and services specified by government.

Self-invoicing

When the purchase has been done from an unregistered supplier, such purchase of goods or services falls under reverse charge.

This is because the supplier cannot issue a GST-compliant invoice to the buyer, and thus the latter become liable to pay taxes on their behalf. Hence, self-invoicing, in this case, becomes necessary.

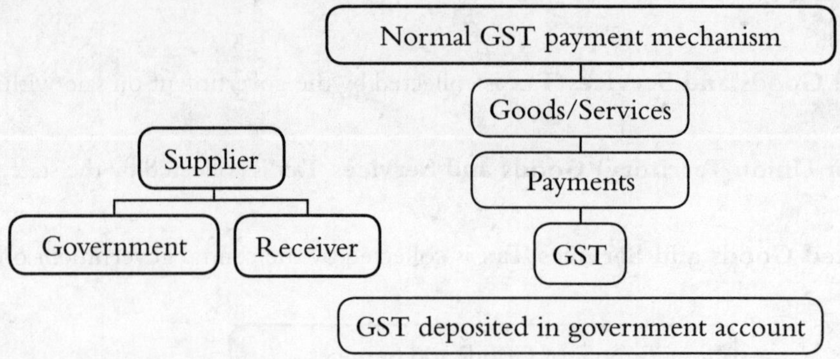

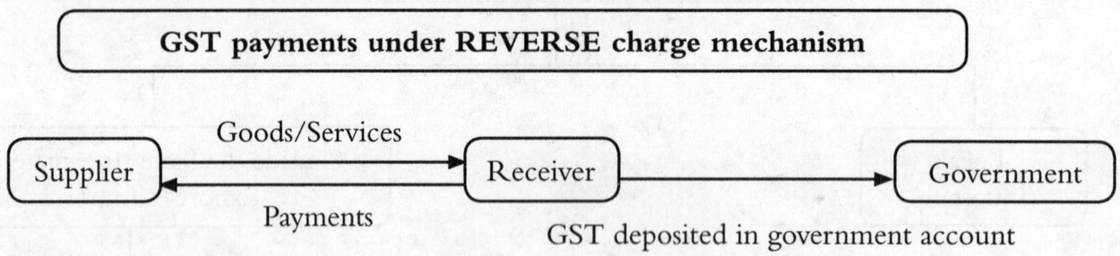

Composition Scheme of the GST

The GST Composition Scheme is a simple and easy scheme under GST where small taxpayers can get rid of tedious GST formalities and pay GST at a fixed rate of turnover. It can be opted by a registered taxpayer, whose aggregate turnover does not exceed ₹1.5 crores in the preceding financial year. The rates of GST under this scheme is

S.No	Category of Supplier	SGST Rate	CGST Rate	Total
1	Manufacturer and Traders	0.5%	0.5%	1%
2	Restaurants not serving alcohol	2.5%	2.5%	5%
3	Other service providers	3.0%	3.0%	6.0%

Additional Inputs of the Composite Scheme

Benefits

1. Limited Compliance
2. Limited Tax Liability
3. High Liquidity

Disadvantages

1. Limited Territory for Business.
2. No Credit for Input Tax.
3. Is not eligible for supplying goods through an e-commerce portal.

Input Tax Credit (ITC)

Input Tax Credit means claiming the credit of the GST paid on the purchase of Goods and Services that are used for the furtherance of businesses. The mechanism of **Input Tax Credit** is the backbone of the GST and is one of the most important reasons for the introduction of the tax.

E-way Bill

An e-way bill refers to an electronic way bill that is generated on the e-way portal, for the movement of goods. A person registered under GST cannot transport goods whose value exceeds ₹50,000 (Single invoice/bill/delivery challan) in a vehicle, without an e-way bill. An e-way bill is generated on ewaybillgst.gov.in. Alternatively, an e-way bill can also be generated or cancelled through SMS, Android App and by site-to-site integration through the API. When an eway bill is generated, a unique Eway Bill Number (EBN) is allocated and is available to the supplier, recipient, and the transporter.

EXAMPLE 14.1 Mr. Rohit took out a health insurance policy for his family and paid ₹855 as SGST. Find the total annual premium paid by him for this policy, rate of GST being 18%.

SOLUTION

Let the premium of health insurance be x.

SGST = 9% of x.

$$855 = \frac{9}{100} \times x$$

$$\Rightarrow x = \frac{855 \times 100}{9} \Rightarrow x = 9{,}500$$

The total premium paid by Rohit = Premium + CGST + SGST

= 9,500 + 855 + 855 = ₹11,210.

EXAMPLE 14.2 A dealer Vijay purchased a TV from a manufacturer for ₹48,000 and sold it to a retailer Ram at a profit of 20%. If the rate of GST is 18%, calculate

(i) the amounts of input CGST and input SGST for the dealer Vijay.

(ii) the amounts of GST that dealer Vijay should pay the Government.

(iii) the amount that the retailer Ram has to pay for TV

(Assume that all the transactions take place in the same state).

SOLUTION

(i) Given, the purchase price of the TV = ₹48,000.

Input CGST for dealer Vijay = 9% of 48,000 = ₹4,320.

Input SGST for dealer Vijay = 9% of 48,000 = ₹4,320

(ii) The total input GST for dealer Vijay = 4,320 + 4,320 = ₹8,640

The selling price for the dealer Mr. Vijay = ₹48,000 + 20% 48,000 = 48,000 + 9,600 = ₹57,600

Output GST for dealer Vijay = 18% of 57,600 = ₹10,368

The amount of GST to be deposited by dealer Mr. Vijay = output GST – Input GST.

= ₹10,368 – ₹8,640 = ₹1,728

(iii) The amount that retailer Ram has to pay dealer Vijay for the TV. = ₹57,600 + ₹10,368 = ₹67,968.

EXAMPLE 14.3 In a GST chain, dealer A purchases an article for ₹12,000 and supplies it to another dealer B at a profit of ₹3,000. Dealer B sells it to consumer C at a profit of ₹5,000. The rate of GST is 18% and all the transactions were intrastate. Calculate

(i) the ITC for dealer A.
(ii) the input tax payable by dealer B.
(iii) the total cost price of the article for consumer C.

SOLUTION

Details	CGST @ 9%	SGST @ 9%	Total GST @ 18%
Input tax (ITC) for dealer A at a purchase of ₹12,000	₹1,080	₹1,080	₹2,160
Input tax payable by dealer B at a purchase of ₹15,000; (12,000 + 3,000)	₹1,350	₹1,350	₹2,700
Tax payable by consumer C at a purchase of ₹20,000			₹3,600
Total cost price for consumer C = 20,000 + 3,600 = 23,600			

EXAMPLE 14.4 Mr. Akshay, a registered dealer, purchased goods worth ₹50,000 from another dealer (within the same state). If the rate of GST is18%

(i) calculate the input CGST and the input SGST.
(ii) If he sold these goods to Mr. Vijay (within the state) for ₹60,000, calculate Mr. Akshay's output CGST and output SGST.

SOLUTION

Input CGST = 9% of 50,000 = ₹4,500
Input SGST = 9% of 50,000 = ₹4,500

(i) Output CGST = 9% of 60,000 = ₹5,400
Output SGST = 9% of 60,000 = ₹5,400

(ii) CGST payable by Mr. Akshay = 9% of 10,000 = ₹900
SGST payable by Mr. Akshay = 9% of 10,000 = ₹900

EXAMPLE 14.5 A distributor of appliances in Meerut (UP) purchased a refrigerator for ₹32,000 from a company in Meerut and supplied it to a dealer in Lucknow (UP) for ₹38,000. This refrigerator was sold by the Lucknow dealer to an end-user in Jaipur (Rajasthan) for ₹43,000. If the rate of GST is 18% calculate,

(i) the net IGST, CGST and SGST payable by the dealer in Meerut.
(ii) the net IGST, CGST and SGST payable by the dealer in Lucknow.
(iii) the total cost of refrigerator for the end-user in Jaipur.

SOLUTION

(i) For the dealer in Meerut

Details	IGST @ 18%	CGST @ 9%	SGST @ 9%
Output tax payable at ₹38,000 intrastate transaction		₹3,420	₹3,420
Input Tax Credit (ITC) at @ ₹32,000		₹2,880	₹2,880
Net tax payable by dealer in Meerut		₹540	₹540

(ii) For the dealer in Lucknow

Details	IGST @ 18%	CGST @ 9%	SGST @ 9%
Output tax payable at ₹43,000 – Interstate transaction	₹7,740		
Input tax credit (ITC) at ₹38,000 Intrastate transaction		₹3,420	₹3,420
Utilization of ITC of ₹ (3,420 + 3,420)	₹6,840	₹0	₹0
Net tax payable by dealer in Lucknow	₹900	₹0	₹0

(iii) The total cost of the refrigerator for the end user in Jaipur

= the selling price of dealer in Lucknow + IGST @ 18% = ₹43,000 + (18% of ₹43,000)

= ₹43,000 + ₹7,740

= ₹50,740

POINTS TO REMEMBER

- ✔ Goods and Services Tax (GST) is an indirect tax levied on the supply of goods and services.
- ✔ GST has replaced many indirect taxes in India.
- ✔ GST is a comprehensive, multi-stage, destination-based tax.
- ✔ GST is levied at every point of sale.
- ✔ There are five rate slabs under GST: 0%, 5%, 12%, 18% and 28%.
- ✔ Central Goods and Services Tax (CGST) is equal to half of the GST, collected for any supply within the state.
- ✔ CGST is collected as the output GST and is deposited with the Central Government.
- ✔ State GST (SGST) is equal to half of the output GST, collected for any supply within the state and deposited with the state government as the beneficiary.
- ✔ Integrated GST (IGST) is levied on (a) the supply of goods and services between states within India and (b) in case of exports and imports.
- ✔ IGST collected is paid into the account of the Central Government.
- ✔ Input Tax Credit (ITC) is the GST paid by the registered dealer or the merchant for his purchases.
- ✔ Output tax is the tax collected by the dealer or the merchant from the retailer and the customer.
- ✔ ITC is a provision of reducing the tax already paid on purchases (inputs) in order to avoid the cascading of taxes (i.e., double taxation).
- ✔ ITC on account of IGST is utilized in the sequence of IGST, CGST and SGST.
- ✔ A dealer under composition scheme cannot collect GST and cannot claim ITC.
- ✔ GST payable = Output GST – Input Tax Credit (ITC).
- ✔ If the output GST is more than the Input Tax Credit, the balance is to be paid to the government.

PRACTICE QUESTIONS CLASSROOM WING

Essay Type Questions

Directions for questions 1 to 20:
Answer the following.

1. **Directions for questions 1(A) and 1(B):** Find the amount of the bill for the following a intra state transaction of goods/services.

Goods	Quantity	MRP of each unit (in ₹)	Discount %
A	20	2500	5
B	25	2000	10
C	30	1500	15
D	35	1000	20

The rate of GST is 5%.

(A) Find the total discount and the total GST.

(B) Find the total bill value of the goods.

2. M/s Hari Traders, Ahmedabad, Gujrat provided the following services to M/s Hara Traders, Cochin, Kerala. Find the CGST, SGST and IGST.

Service Type	P	Q	R	S
Number of services	500	600	700	800
Cost of each service (in ₹)	250	200	150	100
GST %	12	18	12	18

3. **Directions for questions *A, B, C* and *D*:** In a GST chain, a dealer Mr Robert purchases an article for ₹20,000 and supplies it to another dealer Mr Raheem at a profit of ₹2,000. Mr Raheem sells it to a consumer Ms Kinnera for a profit of ₹3,000. The rate of GST is 18% and all transactions were intrastate.

(A) Calculate the input tax credit for Raheem.

(B) Find the total cost price of the article for Ms Kinnera.

(C) What is the GST paid by Mr Raheem to the government?

(D) Find the amount of bill for the following intra state transaction of goods/services.

Goods	MRP(in ₹)	Discount %	GST %
T	2,50,000	10	12
R	2,00,000	12	18
S	1,50,000	15	28

4. Mr. Naresh went to Hyderabad. He took a room in a hotel for two days at the rate of ₹3,000 per day. On the same day, his friend Mr. Karan also joined him. The hotel provided an extra bed charging ₹750 per day for the bed. How much GST at the rate of 28% did the hotel charge Mr. Naresh in his bill for both the days?

5. A retailer purchases a bike for ₹45,000 from a company. He sold it to a consumer at a profit of ₹6,000. Calculate the tax liability of the retailer, if the GST rate on the bike is 18%.

6. A jewellery manufacturer in place A sold a necklace to a dealer in place B for ₹75,000. This necklace was then sold to a dealer in place C for ₹1,00,000. If the GST rate for gold jewellery is 3%, calculate

(i) the net GST payable at place B.

(ii) input Tax Credit for dealer in place C.

(**Note:** Only places A and B are in the same state)

7. Mr. Arun went to see a movie. He wanted to purchase a movie ticket for ₹110. As the ticket for ₹110 was not available, he purchased a ticket for ₹150 of upper class. How much extra GST did he pay for the ticket?
(GST for a ticket upto ₹110 is 18% and GST for a ticket above ₹110 is 28%).

8. Dealer A purchased goods for ₹3,000 and sold them for ₹3,500 within the state. If the GST rate is 12%, find the net CGST and SGST payable by the dealer.

9. Mr. Jain purchased goods worth ₹78,000. He sold 50% of the goods purchased for ₹30,000 in intrastate trade and the rest of the goods remain in his stock. If the GST rate is 18%, find the excess credit of CGST and SGST to be carried forward.

10. A manufacturing company in Hyderabad (Telangana) marks a machine at ₹65,000. It sells one machine to a dealer in Amaravathi (Andhra Pradesh) at a discount of

15% on the M.R.P. The dealer sells it to a consumer in Chennai (Tamil Nadu) at a discount of 8% on the M.R.P. If the rate of GST is 18%, calculate the amount of tax payable by the dealer to the Central Government.

11. The tax invoice of a telecom service in Hyderabad shows the cost of services provided by it as ₹1,050. If the GST rate is 18%, find the amount of the bill.

12. JK Cars Pvt. Ltd. (Hyderabad) sold 3 cars worth ₹8,50,000, ₹7,00,000, ₹15,00,000 to PK automobiles Pvt. Ltd. (Hyderabad). They incurred packing charges of ₹8,000 per car and provided a discount of 1% on account of seasonal sale. If the GST rate is 28%, calculate

(i) the IGST.

(ii) the CGST.

(iii) the SGST.

13. (A) A man took out an insurance policy and paid ₹1,728 as the SGST. Find the total amount of premium paid by him for his policy, the rate of GST being 18%?

(B) For the following transaction from Ahmedabad to Cochin, fill in the blanks to find the amount of bill: MRP = ₹50,000, Discount % = 30 %, and GST = 28 %.

Discount = ____.

Selling price (discounted value) = ____.

CGST = ______.

SGST = ______.

IGST = ______.

Amount of bill =______.

14. A dealer supplied goods worth ₹7,500 in inter-state transaction and worth ₹12,000 transactions within the state. The value of his receipt of goods and services within the state was ₹9,000. Find the net tax payable by him, if the rate of GST is 18%.

15. A distributor of appliances in Indore (MP) purchased a washing machine for ₹36,000 from the company in Indore and supplied it to a dealer in Bhopal (MP) for a profit of ₹4000. This washing machine was sold by the Bhopal dealer to an end-user in Orissa (Bhuvaneswar) for ₹45,000. If the rate of GST is 18%, calculate

(i) the net IGST, CGST and SGST payable by the dealer in Indore.

(ii) the net IGST, CGST and SGST payable by the dealer in Bhopal.

(iii) the total cost of washing machine for end-user in Orissa.

16. A dealer K in Hyderabad (Telangana) sold an article for ₹8,000 to a consumer in Secunderabad (Telangana). If the GST rate is 18%, calculate

(i) the IGST.

(ii) the CGST.

(iii) the SGST.

17. (A) A wholesaler M sells a machine to a retailer N for ₹13,000 and retailer N sells it to a consumer at a profit of ₹2,000. If the GST rate is 12%, calculate the tax liability of retailer N.

(B) Find the amount of bill for the intra state transaction of goods/services. The GST rate is 5 %.

Item	A	B	C
Quantity (no. of items)	50	40	30
MRP of each item (in ₹)	400	750	800
Discount %	20	18	15

18. A microwave oven having a marked price of ₹28,000 was sold by a dealer in Mysore (Karnataka) to a consumer in Bengaluru (Karnataka) at a discount of 25%. If the rate of GST is 18%, calculate the IGST, CGST and SGST chargeable to the consumer. Also, determine the total amount of the bill.

19. A dealer in Bengaluru (Karnataka) sold a mobile phone to an end-user in Chennai (Tamil Nadu). The marked price of the mobile phone was `18,000 and the dealer offered a discount of 15%. If the rate of GST is 28%, calculate the IGST, CGST and SGST chargeable to the end-user. Also determine the total amount of the bill.

20. A dealer purchased a music system from a manufacturing company for ₹30,000 and sold it to a consumer at a profit of 30%. If the rate of GST is 18%, calculate: (Assume that all transactions take place in the same state).

(i) the amounts of the input CGST and the input SGST for the dealer.

(ii) the amounts of GST payable by the dealer to the Government.

(iii) the amount that the consumer has to pay for the music system.

PRACTICE QUESTIONS COMPETITION WING

Level 1: Apply Your Concepts

Directions of questions from 1 to 6:
Select the correct alternative from the given choices.

1. A Suraj in Ahmedabad (Gujarat) supplies goods worth ₹28,000 to Manoj who stays in Gandhi Nagar (Gujarat). If the rate of GST is 18% find the

(i) Central GST.
(a) ₹0 (b) ₹2520
(c) ₹5040 (d) ₹3920

(ii) State GST.
(a) ₹5040 (b) ₹3920
(c) ₹0 (d) ₹2520

(iii) Integrated GST.
(a) ₹3920 (b) ₹5040
(c) ₹2520 (d) ₹0

2. A shopkeeper buys a machine at a discount of 20% from a wholesaler. The printed price of the machine is ₹25,000 and the rate of GST is 18%The shopkeeper sells it to the consumer at the printed price. Calculate

(i) The price at which the machine is bought by the consumer.
(a) ₹28600 (b) ₹25000
(c) ₹29500 (d) ₹23600

(ii) The CGST and the SGST payable by the shopkeeper to the Government assuming that all the transactions were intrastate.
(a) ₹450, ₹450 (b) ₹900, ₹900
(c) ₹2250, ₹2250 (d) ₹450, ₹900

3. A wholesaler buys a machine from a manufacturer for ₹18,000. He marks the price of the machine 25% above his cost price and sells it to a retailer at 15% discount on the marked price. If the rate of GST is 18% and assuming that all transactions are made within the same state, calculate

(i) The marked price of the machine.
(a) ₹18000 (b) ₹22500
(c) ₹20700 (d) ₹19125

(ii) The retailer cost price inclusive of GST.
(a) ₹19125 (b) ₹22567.50
(c) ₹3442.50 (d) ₹26550

(iii) The CGST and SGST payable by the wholesaler to the Government.
(a) ₹101.25, ₹303.75 (b) ₹405, ₹405
(c) ₹303.75, ₹303.75 (d) ₹101.25, ₹101.25

4. A manufacturer sells a dishwasher to a wholesaler for ₹10,000. The wholesaler sells it to a dealer at a profit of ₹2,000 and the dealer sells it to a consumer at a profit of ₹3,000. If the rate of GST is 12% and assuming that all transactions are made within the same state, calculate;

(i) The total amount of GST received by the central and the state governments on the sale of the dishwasher from the manufacturer to the consumer.
(a) 900 (b) ₹1800
(c) ₹1200 (d) ₹1440

(ii) The amount paid by the consumer for the dishwasher.
(a) ₹13440 (b) ₹15000
(c) ₹16800 (d) ₹11200

5. A shopkeeper bought an air-conditioner at a discount of 15% from a wholesaler, the printed price of the air-conditioner being ₹20,000. The shop keeper sells it to a consumer at a discount of 10% on the printed price. If the GST rate is 18%, find

(i) The CGST and SGST payable by the shopkeeper to the government.
(a) ₹90, ₹90 (b) ₹1800, ₹1800
(c) ₹180, ₹180 (d) ₹90, ₹180

(ii) The total amount paid by the consumer for the air-conditioner.
(a) ₹18000 (b) ₹19620
(c) ₹21240 (d) ₹23600

6. A dealer in Hyderabad supplied several items to another dealer in Hyderabad and these items fall into different GST slabs. Find the total amount of the bill if the details of the supplied items are as given below:

Item	Quantity (No. of pieces)	Rate per piece MRP (in ₹)	Discount allowed	GST Rate
A	60	80	20%	5%
B	80	100	12%	15%

(a) ₹12800 (b) ₹12128
(c) ₹10880 (d) ₹14240

Level 2: Review Your Concepts

7. A chair manufacturer in Ahmedabad (Gujarat) sold a chair to a dealer in Surat (Gujarat) for ₹8,000. This chair was then sold to a dealer in Lucknow (UP) for ₹10,000. If the GST rate for the chair is 12%, calculate:
   (i) The net GST payable at Surat.
   (a) ₹120 (b) ₹960
   (c) ₹1200 (d) ₹240
   (ii) The input tax credit for the dealer in Lucknow.
   (a) ₹1200 (b) ₹600
   (c) ₹960 (d) ₹480

8. In a GST chain, a dealer Mr. Hari purchases an article for ₹20,000 and supplies it to another dealer Mr. Ravi at a profit of ₹5,000. Mr Ravi sells it to a consumer Mrs. Varma at a profit of ₹3,000. If the rate of GST is 18% and all transactions were intrastate, calculate:
   (i) The ITC for Mr. Hari.
   (a) ₹3600 (b) ₹1800
   (c) ₹5400 (d) ₹7200
   (ii) The input tax payable by Mr. Ravi.
   (a) ₹2250 (b) ₹4500
   (c) ₹9000 (d) ₹6750
   (iii) The total cost price of the article for Mrs.Varma.
   (a) ₹33040 (b) ₹28000
   (c) ₹38080 (d) ₹30520
   (iv) The output GST for Mrs. Varma.
   (a) ₹0 (b) ₹540
   (c) ₹4140 (d) ₹5040

9. Mr. Anand, a registered dealer, purchased blankets worth ₹15,000. He sold 50% of these blankets to a dealer in intra – state trade for ₹9,000 and the rest of the goods remain in his stock. If the GST rate is 12%, find the excess credit of CGST and SGST to be carried forward.
   (a) ₹900, ₹900 (b) ₹360, ₹360
   (c) ₹540, ₹540 (d) ₹360, ₹720

10. A furniture dealer in Bengaluru supplied goods worth ₹3,20,000 to a dealer in Hyderabad and sold goods worth ₹4,00,000 in retail within Bengaluru. The total value of his receipts was ₹6,00,000. If he purchases his entire stock from a manufacturer in Delhi, then find the net IGST, CGST and SGST payable by him. The rate of GST is 12%.
    (a) ₹0, ₹0, ₹14400 (b) ₹0, ₹24000, ₹24000
    (c) ₹38400, ₹0, ₹0 (d) ₹0, ₹14400, ₹14400

11. A dealer in Bhopal (MP), say X, supplies goods services worth ₹ 8,000 to Y a person in Indore (MP). If the rate of GST is 28%, then find: central GST, state GST and integrated GST.
    (a) ₹1000, ₹1000, ₹0 (b) ₹1120, ₹1120, ₹0
    (c) ₹1200, ₹1200, ₹0 (d) ₹1150, ₹1150, ₹0

12. Let A, B and C be three traders belonging to different states. Trader A sells some goods/services to trader B for ₹500 and trader B sells the same goods/services to trader C at a profit of ₹200. Calculate the tax liability of B, if the rate of GST is 12%.
    (a) ₹20 (b) ₹15
    (c) ₹34 (d) ₹24

13. A dealer in Jaipur (Rajasthan) sold an article to a dealer in Indore (M.P) for ₹5000. The dealer in Indore (MP) sold the article to a dealer in Bhopal (M.P). If the rate of tax under GST system is 18% and the profit made by the dealer in Indore is ₹2000 find:
    (i) The net GST payable by the dealer in Indore.
    (ii) The C.P. for the company in Bhopal.
    (a) ₹300, ₹8100 (b) ₹400, ₹7500
    (c) ₹360, ₹8260 (d) ₹350, ₹8500

14. Find the amount of bill for the following intra-state transaction of goods. The rate of GST is 12%.

MRP	₹250	₹200	₹150	₹300
Discount	30%	40%	32%	20%

    (a) ₹750.44 (b) ₹713.44
    (c) ₹756.56 (d) ₹721.12

Level 3: Assess Your Concepts

15. (A) The market price of an article is ₹9000 and the rate of GST on it is 18%. A shopkeeper buys this article at a reduced price and sells it at its marked price. If the shopkeeper paid ₹162 as CGST to the government, Find the amount (inclusive of GST) paid by the shopkeeper.
    (a) ₹8450 (b) ₹8496
    (c) ₹8515 (d) ₹8430

(B) Find the amount of bill for the following interstate transaction of goods/ services.

Item	P	Q	R	S
MRP (in ₹)	15,000	13,000	12,000	11,000
Discount %	12	15	30	30
IGST %	5	5	28	28

(a) 46,480 (b) 35,870
(c) 40,600 (d) None

16. Let A, B, and C be three dealers in a GST chain. A buys some goods/services for ₹2000 and sells it to B at a profit of ₹500. B, in turn, sells the same goods/services to C at a profit of ₹1000. Taking the rate of GST as 18%, find:

(i) Input-tax payable by dealer A.
(ii) Input-tax payable by dealer A.
(iii) Total cost price for dealer C, if he is the end-user.
(iv) Output GST for dealer C (the end-user).

(a) ₹260, ₹410, ₹3100, ₹0
(b) ₹310, ₹480, ₹3200, ₹0
(c) ₹360, ₹450, ₹3500, ₹0
(d) ₹350, ₹300, ₹3000, ₹0

17. Find the amount for the following intra-state transaction.

MRP(₹) for each item	125	200	160	150	180
Number of items	20	27	35	32	25
GST%	12	12	18	28	18

(a) ₹26780 (b) ₹27100
(c) ₹26560 (d) ₹26910

18. A manufacturer in Delhi manufactures a machine and marks it at ₹60000. He sells the machine to a wholesaler (in Patna) at a discount of 20%. The wholesaler sells the machine to a dealer (in Agra) at a discount of 10% on the marked price. If the rate of GST is 28%, find the tax paid by the wholesaler to the central-government.

(a) ₹1600 (b) ₹1680
(c) ₹1675 (d) ₹1660

19. For a trader, the marked price of a refrigerator is ₹15680, inclusive of GST at 12% on the marked price. Gagan, a customer for this refrigerator, asks the trader to reduce the marked price of the refrigerator to such an extent that its reduced price plus GST on it is equal to the marked price of the refrigerator. Find the required reduction.

(a) ₹1350 (b) ₹1200
(c) ₹1440 (d) ₹1500

20. A dealer Varun purchased a washing machine from a manufacturer for ₹50,000 and sold it to a retailer Shyam at a profit of 15%. If the rate of GST is 18%, calculate

(i) The amounts of input SGST for the dealer Varun.
(ii) The amounts of GST that dealer Varun should pay the Government.
(iii) The amount that the retailer Shiyam has to pay for TV (Assume that all the transactions take place in the same state).

(a) ₹4500, ₹1350, ₹67850 (b) ₹4100, ₹1250, ₹65780
(c) ₹3900, ₹1300, ₹64850 (d) ₹4400, ₹1375, ₹67875

21. A distributor of appliances in Hyderabad (T.S) purchased a TV for ₹40,000 from a company in Hyderabad and supplied it to a dealer in Warangal (T.S) for ₹42,000. This refrigerator was sold by the Warangal dealer to an end-user in Amaravati (Andhra Pradesh) for ₹46,000. If the rate of GST is 18% calculate,

(i) The net IGST, CGST, and SGST payable by the dealer in Hyderabad.
(a) ₹0, ₹150, ₹150 (b) ₹0, ₹180, ₹180
(c) ₹0, ₹200, ₹200 (d) ₹0, ₹175, ₹175

(ii) The net IGST, CGST and SGST payable by the dealer in Warangal.
(a) ₹720, ₹0, ₹0 (b) ₹650, ₹0, ₹0
(c) ₹575, ₹0, ₹0 (d) ₹750, ₹0, ₹0

(iii) The total cost of refrigerator for the end-user in Amaravati.
(a) ₹55280 (b) ₹56750
(c) ₹53280 (d) ₹54280

22. A famous AC repairer in Mumbai charges repairing cost from five different persons *P*, *Q*, *R*, S, and *T* with certain discounts. The repairing costs and the discounts are as given below.

Name of Person	P	Q	R	S	T
Repairing cost (in ₹)	2,000	1,800	1,900	2,400	2,500
Discount %	15	5	10	25	30

If the rate of GST is 18 %, then find the total money (including GST) received by the repairer.

(a) 10231 (b) 1505.5
(c) 10,200 (d) 10,230.6

23. A distributor of appliances in Hyderabad (Telangana) purchased a *TV* for ₹60,000 (exclusive of GST) from a company in Hyderabad and supplied it to a dealer in Bangalore (Karnataka) at ₹70,000 (exclusive of GST). The *TV* was sold by the Bangalore dealer to an end user in Cochin (Kerala) for ₹80,000 (exclusive of GST). If the rate of *GST* is 18%, calculate

(i) the net IGST, CGST, *SGST* payable by the distributor in Hyderabad.

(a) 0, 900, 900 (b) 900, 0, 0
(c) 0, 900, 0 (d) None

(ii) the net IGST, CGST, *SGST* payable by the dealer in Bangalore.

(a) 0, 1800, 900 (b) 1800, 0, 0
(c) 0, 1800, 1800 (d) None

(iii) the total cost of the *TV* for the end user in Cochin.

(a) 94, 400 (b) 95, 000
(c) 80, 600 (d) None

AT

PRACTICE QUESTIONS JEE SPECIAL WING

Multiple-Answer Type Questions

Directions for questions 1 to 5:
Each question has FOUR options (a), (b), (c), and (d). ONE OR MORE THAN ONE of these four option(s) is/are the correct answer(s).

1. For the following transaction within Indore;
MRP = ₹10,000, Discount % = 20%, and
GST = 12%.
Which of the following is/are correct?
(a) Discount = ₹2,000 (b) Selling price = ₹8,000
(c) CGST = ₹960. (d) Total bill = ₹8960.

2. For the following transaction from Kochi to Hyderabad:
MRP = ₹50,000, Discount % = 12%, GST = 18%.
Which of the following is/are correct?
(a) Discount = ₹6,000 (b) CGST = ₹3,960
(c) IGST = ₹7,920 (d) Total bill = ₹51,920

3. Which of the following statements is/are correct?
(a) For intra state transactions CGST and SGST are applied.
(b) For interstate transactions, only IGST is applied.
(c) The GST on some goods like fruits and vegetables is 0%.
(d) Input Tax Credit on the supply of taxable goods is allowed under GST.

4. A retailer buys an electric two-wheeler for ₹1,10,000 from a company. He sold it to a consumer at a profit of ₹15,000. The rate of GST is 5%.
Which of the following is/are correct?
(a) The tax liability by the retailer is ₹5,500.
(b) The total GST received by the government is ₹5,500.
(c) The total GST received by the government is ₹6,250.
(d) The tax liability by the retailer is ₹750.

5. In a GST chain, a dealer P purchases an article for ₹26,000 and supplies it to another dealer Q for a profit of ₹4,000. Dealer Q sells it to a consumer R at a profit of ₹5,000. The rate of GST was 5% and all the transactions were intrastate. Which of the following is/are correct about the given information?
(a) The ITC for dealer P is ₹1300.
(b) The input tax payable by the dealer Q is ₹1,500.
(c) The total GST received by the government is ₹1,750.
(d) The total cost price of the article for the consumer R is ₹36,750.

Match The Column

Directions for questions 6 to 10:
Read the paragraph given below and answer the questions.

Column A (Cost of the Services)	Column B (Rate of GST)	Column C (Value of the Services Including GST)
6. ₹1,10,000	(a) 18%	(p) ₹1,44,100
7. ₹1,15,000	(b) 12%	(q) ₹1,44,900
8. ₹1,25,000	(c) 5%	(r) ₹1,45,600
9. ₹1,30,000	(d) 28%	(s) ₹1,47,200
10. ₹1,38,000	(e) 31%	(t) ₹1,47,500

Comprehension-Based Questions

Directions for questions 11 to 15:

Read the paragraph given below and answer the questions.

An intra state transaction of goods/services are given below.

Goods	Quantity	MRP of Each Unit (in ₹)	Discount %
M	100	2500	12
N	125	2000	11
O	150	1500	10
P	175	1000	9
R	200	800	8

The rate of GST is 12%.

11. What is the total *MRP* of all the goods?

(a) ₹10,60,000 (b) ₹10,80,000
(c) ₹11,30,000 (d) ₹11,90,000

12. What is the total discount availed by the customer?

(a) ₹1,12,500 (b) ₹1,10,250
(c) ₹1,08,550 (d) ₹1,05,250

13. What is the total selling price of the goods?

(a) ₹10,77,500 (b) ₹10,19,750
(c) ₹9,74,750 (d) ₹9,51,450

14. What is the total *CGST*?

(a) ₹64,650 (b) ₹61,185
(c) ₹58,485 (d) ₹57,087

15. What is the total amount of the bill?

(a) ₹10,91,720 (b) ₹10,65,624
(c) ₹12,06,800 (d) ₹11,42,120

Directions for questions 16 to 20:

Read the paragraph given below and answer the questions.

Chandra is a dealer in Karimnagar (Telangana). He supplies goods/services of worth ₹1,50,000 to another dealer Tarak in Vijaywada (Andhra Pradesh). Dealer Tarak, in turn, supplies the same goods/services to a dealer Jaggu in Visakhapatnam (Andhra Pradesh) at a profit of ₹12,000. The rate of GST for providing the goods/services is 28%.

16. For the transaction from dealer Chandra to dealer Tarak, which of the following is applicable?

(a) CGST = ₹21,000 (b) SGST = ₹21,000
(c) IGST = ₹42,000 (d) Both (a) and (b)

17. Input tax for dealer Tarak?

(a) ₹21,000 (b) ₹42,000
(c) ₹1,680 (d) ₹3360

18. Output tax for dealer Tarak?

(a) ₹21,000 (b) ₹42,000
(c) ₹22,680 (d) ₹45,360

19. The net GST payable by dealer Tarak?

(a) ₹1,680 (b) ₹3,360
(c) ₹21,000 (d) ₹42,000

20. The cost of the goods/services for dealer Jaggu?

(a) ₹2,07,360 (b) ₹2,04,000
(c) ₹1,92,000 (d) ₹1,84,680

Assertion and Reason Type Questions

Directions for questions 21 to 24:

Given below are two statements, one is labeled as Assertion (A) and the other is labeled as Reason (R). In the light of the given statements, choose the most appropriate answer from the options given below.

(a) Both assertion (A) and reason (R) are correct, and reason (R) is the correct explanation of the assertion.
(b) Both assertion (A) and reason (R) are correct, and reason (R) is not the correct explanation of the assertion.
(c) Assertion (A) is correct, but reason (R) is false.
(d) Assertion (A) is false, and reason (R) is correct.

21. Assertion: A dealer in Mumbai (Maharashtra) buys goods for ₹1,00,000 from another dealer from Ahmedabad (Gujarat). The rate of GST is 18%. In this transaction, IGST is applicable.

Reason: In interstate transaction, IGST is applicable.

22. Assertion: A dealer in Coimbatore (Tamil Nadu) buys goods for ₹20,000 from another dealer from Chennai (Tamil Nadu). The rate of GST is 12%. In this transaction, SGST and CGST are applicable.

Reason: In intra-state transaction, IGST is applicable.

23. **Assertion:** A dealer buys goods for ₹25,000 from another dealer from within the city. The rate of GST is 28%. In this transaction, each of SGST and CGST is 14% of ₹25,000.

Reason: In intra-state transaction, SGST and CGST are applicable. Each is equal to half of the total GST.

24. **Assertion:** A dealer in Jodhpur (Rajasthan) buys tomatoes of worth ₹5,00,000 from another dealer from Guntur (Andhra Pradesh). The GST on this transaction is ₹15,000.

Reason: If the GST on transaction of goods of worth ₹5,00,000 is 15,000, the rate of GST = $\frac{₹15,000}{₹5,00,000} \times 100\% = 3\%$.

ANSWER KEYS

Crossword

Across

1. UGST 5. Kashmir 6. CGST 7. Luxury 10. Indirect

Down

2. IGST 3. SGST 4. Zero 8. Tax Payer 9. Direct

Classroom Wing

Essay Type Questions

1. (A) ₹7,937.5 (B) ₹1,66,687.5
2. ₹63,600
3. (A) ₹3,960 (B) ₹29,500 (C) ₹540 (D) ₹6,22,880
4. ₹9600
5. ₹1080
6. (i) ₹750 (ii) ₹3000
7. ₹22.2
8. ₹60
9. ₹8640
10. ₹59,800
11. ₹1239
12. (i) ₹0 (ii) ₹4,26,090 (iii) ₹4,26,090
13. (A) ₹22656 (B) ₹15,000; ₹35,000; ₹0; ₹0; ₹9,800; ₹44,800
14. ₹1890
15. (i) ₹720 (ii) ₹900 (iii) ₹53100
16. (i) ₹0 (ii) ₹720 (iii) ₹720
17. (A) ₹240 (B) 64,050
18. 0, ₹1890, ₹1890, ₹24,780
19. ₹4284, 0, 0, ₹19,584
20. (i) ₹2700 (ii) ₹1600 (iii) ₹46,020

Competition Wing

Level 1: Apply Your Concepts

1. (i) (d) (ii) (b) (iii) (d)
2. (i) (c) (ii) (a)
3. (i) (b) (ii) (b) (iii) (d)
4. (i) (b) (ii) (c)
5. (i) (a) (ii) (c)
6. (b)

Level 2: Review Your Concepts

7. (i) (d) (ii) (a)
8. (i) (a) (ii) (b) (iii) (a) (iv) (a)
9. (b)
10. (a)
11. (b)
12. (d)
13. (c)
14. (b)

Level 3: Assess Your Concepts

15. (A) (b) (B) (a)
16. (c)
17. (d)
18. (b)
19. (d)
20. (a)
21. (i) (b) (ii) (a) (iii) (d)
22. (d)
23. (i) (a) (ii) (b) (iii) (a)

JEE Special Wing

Multiple-Answer Type Questions

1. (a, b, d) 2. (a, c, d) 3. (a, b, c, d) 4. (c, d) 5. (a, b, c, d)

Match The Column

6. (e ↔ p) 7. (d ↔ s) 8. (a ↔ t) 9. (b ↔ r) 10. (c ↔ q)

Comprehension-Based Questions

11. (a)	12. (c)	13. (d)	14. (d)	15. (b)
16. (c)	17. (b)	18. (d)	19. (b)	20. (a)

Assertion and Reason Type Questions

21. (a)	22. (c)	23. (a)	24. (d)

Hints and Explanations

Classroom Wing

Essay Type Questions

1. This is an intra state transaction, so CGST and SGST are applicable on this transaction.

Goods	Quantity	MRP (in ₹)	Total MRP (in ₹)	Discount %	Discount (in ₹)	Selling Price (in ₹)	CGST (2.5%) (in ₹)	SGST (2.5%) (in ₹)
A	20	2500	50000	5	2500	47500	1187.5	1187.5
B	25	2000	50000	10	5000	45000	1125	1125
C	30	1500	45000	15	6750	38250	956.25	956.25
D	35	1000	35000	20	7000	28000	700	700
		Total			**21250**	**158750**	**3968.75**	**3968.75**

(A) Total discount = ₹21,250
Total GST = Total CGST + Total SGST
= ₹3,968.75 + ₹3,968.75 = ₹7,937.5

(B) Total bill value = Total selling price + Total GST
= ₹1,58,750 + ₹7,937.5 = ₹1,66,687.5

2. This is an interstate transaction, so IGST is applicable on this transaction.

Service Type	Number of services	Cost of each service (in ₹)	Total Cost of each service (in ₹)	IGST %	IGST (in ₹)
P	500	250	125000	12	15000
Q	600	200	120000	18	21600
R	700	150	105000	12	12600
S	800	100	80000	18	14400
		Total			**63600**

Total IGST = ₹63600.

3.

Details	CGST @ 9%	SGST @9%	GST @18%
Input tax credit for Robert for a purchase of ₹20,000	₹1,800	₹1,800	₹3,600
Input tax for Raheem for a purchase of ₹22,000	₹1,980	₹1,980	₹3,960
Input tax payable by Ms Kinnera on a purchase of ₹25,000	₹2,250	₹2,250	₹4,500
Output GST for the consumer Ms Kinnera (Since she does not sell it further)	Nil	Nil	Nil

(A) Input tax credit for Raheem = ₹3,960.
(B) The total cost price of the article for Ms Kinnera = ₹(25,000 + 4,500) = ₹29,500.
(C) The GST paid by Mr Raheem to the government = ₹4,500 – ₹3,960 = ₹540.

(D)

Goods	MRP (in ₹)	Discount %	SP (in ₹)	GST %	GST (in ₹)
T	2,50,000	10	2,25,000	12	27,000
R	2,00,000	12	1,76,000	18	31,680
S	1,50,000	15	1,27,500	28	35,700
	Total		**5,28,500**		**94,380**

The amount of bill = Total SP + Total GST
= ₹5,28,500 + ₹94,380 = ₹6,22,880.

4. Room charge = ₹3,000 per day
Extra bed charge = ₹750 per day
Total daily charge = ₹3,750 per day
Hotel charges for 2 days = 2 × 3,750 = ₹7,500
GST charged = $7{,}500 \times \frac{28}{100}$ = ₹2,100
Total bill amount = ₹7,500 + ₹2,100
= ₹9,600

5. Tax liability of the retailer = 18% of ₹6,000
C = ₹1,080

6. The purchase price of necklace = ₹75,000
Input GST = 3% of 75,000
= ₹2,250
∴ Input tax credit = ₹2,250
Selling price = ₹1,00,000
Output GST = 3% of 1,00,000 = ₹3,000
(i) Net GST payable at place B = Output GST – ITC
= ₹3,000 – ₹2,250
= ₹750
(ii) ITC for dealer in place C = IGST for the dealer in place B = ₹3,000

7. GST for a ticket up to ₹110 = 18% of 110 = ₹19.8
GST for a ticket above ₹110 = 28%
∴ 28% of 150 = ₹42
Extra GST paid by Arun = ₹42 – ₹19.8 = ₹22.2

8.

Details	CGST @ 6%	SGST @ 6%
Output tax payable on supply of worth ₹3,500	₹210	₹210
Input tax paid on purchase of worth ₹3,000	₹180	₹180
Net tax payable by the dealer	₹30	₹30

9.

Details	CGST @ 9%	SGST @ 9%
Input tax credit on purchase worth ₹78,000	₹7,020	₹7,020
Output tax payable on sale worth ₹30,000	₹2,700	₹2,700
Excess credit	₹4,320	₹4,320

Excess credit carry forward ⇒ ₹4,320 + ₹4,320 = ₹8,640

10. The cost price of the machine for the dealer
= M.P – discount
= ₹65,000 – 15% of 65,000
= ₹65,000 – ₹9,750
= ₹55,250
The selling price of the machine for the dealer
= M.P – 8% of M.R.P
= ₹65,000 – 8% of 65,000
= ₹65,000 – 5,200 = ₹59,800

Details	IGST @ 18%	CGST @ 9%	SGST @ 9%
Output tax payable at ₹59,800 (Interstate transaction)	₹10,764	–	–
Input tax credit at ₹55,250 (Interstate transaction)	₹9,945	–	–
Net tax payable by the dealer	₹819	–	–

IGST paid to the Central Govt. = ₹819

11. The cost of service = ₹1,050
CGST @ 9% = 9% of 1,050
= 94.5
SGST @9% = 9% of 105
= 94.5

Total bill amount = 1,050 + 94.5 + 94.5
= ₹1,239

12. The cost of cars = ₹8,50,000 + ₹7,00,000 + ₹15,00,000
= ₹30,50,000

Packing charges = 8,000 ₹ 3 = ₹24,000

Discount = 1% of 30,50,000
= ₹30,500

The total cost of goods = ₹30,50,000 + ₹24,000 – ₹30,500
= ₹30,43,500

(i) IGST = Nil

(ii) CGST = 14% of ₹30,43,500
= ₹4,26,090

(iii) SGST = 14% of ₹3,04,350
= ₹4,26,090

13. (A) The premium of health insurance be x

SGST = 9% of x

1,728 = 9% of x

$\Rightarrow x = \dfrac{1,728 \times 100}{9}$

$\Rightarrow x = 19,200$

The total premium paid by him = premium + CGST + SGST

= 19,200 + 1,728 + 1,728

= ₹22,656

(B) MRP = ₹50,000, Discount % = 30 %, GST = 28 %.

The transaction is interstate, so IGST is applied.

Discount = 30 % of 50,000 = $\dfrac{30}{100} \times 50000$
= ₹15,000.

Selling Price (discounted value)
= ₹50,000 – ₹15,000 = ₹35,000.

CGST = ₹0

SGST = ₹0

IGST = 28 % of ₹35,000 = $\dfrac{28}{100} \times$ ₹35,000
= ₹9,800.

Amount of bill = Selling price + IGST
= ₹35,000 + ₹9,800 = ₹44,800.

14.

Details	IGST @ 18%	CGST @ 9%	SGST @ 9%
Output tax payable at ₹7,500 (Interstate transaction)	₹1,350		
Output tax payable at ₹12,000		₹1,080	₹1,080
ITC at ₹9,000 Intrastate transactions		₹810	₹810
Net tax payable by dealer	₹1,350	₹270	₹270

15. (i) For the dealer in Indore:

Details	IGST @ 18%	CGST @ 9%	SGST @ 9%
Output tax payable at ₹40,000		₹3,600	₹,3600
Input tax credit (ITC) at ₹36,000		₹3,240	₹3,240
Net tax payable by dealer in Indore		₹360	₹360

(ii) For the dealer in Bhopal:

Details	IGST @ 18%	CGST @ 9%	SGST @ 9%
Output tax payable at @ 45,000. Interstate transaction	₹8,100		
Input tax credit (ITC) at ₹40,000 Intrastate transaction		₹3,600	₹3,600
Utilization of ITC of ₹(3,600 + 3,600)	₹7,200	₹0	₹0
Net tax payable by dealer in Bhopal	₹900	₹0	₹0

(iii) The total cost of the washing machine for the end user in Orissa.

= The selling price of dealer in Bhopal + IGST @ 18%

= ₹45,000 + ₹8,100

= ₹53,100

16. (i) IGST = Nil (the trade in intrastate)
(ii) CGST = 9% of 8,000 = ₹720
(iii) SGST = 9% of 8,000 = ₹720

17. (A) Tax liability of the retailer
= Tax on profit
= 12% of 2,000
= ₹240

(B) This is an intra state transaction, so CGST and SGST are applicable on this transaction.

Item	Quantity	MRP (in ₹)	Total MRP (in ₹)	Discount %	Discount (in ₹)	Selling Price (in ₹)	CGST (2.5 %)	SGST (2.5%)
A	50	400	20,000	20	4,000	16,000	400	400
B	40	750	30,000	18	5,400	24,600	615	615
C	30	800	24,000	15	3,600	20,400	510	510
Total						61,000	1,525	1,525

Amount of bill = Selling price + *CGST* + SGST
= ₹61,000 + ₹1,525+ ₹1,525 = ₹64,050.

18. Selling price of microwave oven for the dealer
= M.P – Discount
= 28,000 – 25% of 28,000
= 28,000 – 7,000
= ₹21,000
CGST = SGST = 9% of 21,000
= ₹1,890
Total amount of bill = ₹21,000 + ₹1,890 + ₹1,890
= ₹24,780
Since the trading is intrastate, IGST I is nil.

19. Marked priced of the mobile phone = ₹18,000
The selling price of the mobile = 18,000 – 15% of 18,000
= 18,000 – 2,700
= ₹15,300
IGST = 28% of 15,300 = ₹4,284
Since the trading is interstate the CGST = Nil and the SGST = Nil
The total amount of bill = ₹15,300 + ₹4,284 = ₹19,584

20. The amount of purchase of music system = ₹30,000
The selling price of the music system for the dealer
= ₹30,000 + 30% of ₹30,000 = ₹30,000 + 9,000 = ₹39,000
(i) The amounts of input CGST for the dealer
= 9% of 30,000 = ₹2,700
The amount of input SGST for the dealer
= 9% of 30,000 = ₹2,700
(ii) The amount of GST payable by dealer to the Government = 18% of ₹9,000.
= ₹1,600
(iii) The amounts that the consumer has to pay for the music system = ₹39,000 + ₹351 + ₹3,510
= ₹46,020.

Competition Wing

Level 1: Apply Your Concepts

1. (i) Central GST = 14% of 28,000 = $\frac{14}{100} \times 28,000$ = ₹3,920

(ii) The state GST = 14% of 28,000 = $\frac{14}{100} \times 28,000$ = ₹3,920

(iii) Integrated GST = Nil

(Since the trading is intrastate)

2. (i) The price of the machine to the consumer
= 25,000 + 18% 25,000
= 25,000 + 4,500
= ₹29,500

(ii) The cost price to the shopkeeper
= 25,000 – 20% of 25,000
= 25,000 – 5,000 = 20,000

CGST = 9% (25,000 – 20,000)
= 9% of 5,000 = ₹450

SGST = 9% of 5,000 = ₹450

3. (i) The marked price of the machine = ₹18,000 + 25% of ₹18,000 = ₹18,000 + ₹4,500 = ₹22,500

(ii) The selling price of the machine for the wholesaler
= Marked price – 15% of marked price
= 22,500 – 15% of 22,500
= 22,500 – 3,375
= ₹19,125

GST on ₹19,125 = 18% of 19,125
= ₹3,442.5

∴ The retailers cost price inclusive of GST
= ₹19,125 + ₹3,442.5 = ₹22,567.5

(iii) CGST payable by the wholesaler = 9% of (4,500 – 3,375)
= 9% of 1,125
= ₹101.25

SGST payable by wholesaler = 9% of (4,500 – 3,375)
= 9% of 125
=₹101.25

4. The cost price for the wholesaler = ₹10,000
The cost price for the dealer = ₹10,000 + ₹2,000
= ₹12,000

The cost price for the consumer = ₹12,000 + ₹3,000
= ₹15,000

(i) SGST and CGST payable by the shopkeeper
= 6% of 15,000
= $\frac{6}{100} \times 15,000$.

SGST = ₹900 and CGST = ₹900

(ii) The amount paid by the consumer
= ₹15,000 + 12% of ₹15,000
= ₹15,000 + 1,800
= ₹16,800.

5. The printed price of the air-conditioner = ₹20,000
The cost price to the shop keeper = ₹20,000 – 15%(20,000)
= 20,000 – 3,000
= 17,000

The cost price for the consumer = ₹20,000 – 10% of ₹20,000.
= ₹ 20,000 – ₹2,000
= ₹18,000

(i) The value added by the shopkeeper = 1,80,000 – 17,000
= 1,000

CGST payable by the shopkeeper
= 9% of 1,000
= ₹90

SGST payable by the shopkeeper = 9% of 1,000
= ₹90

(ii) The total amount paid by the consumer
= ₹18,000 + 18% of 18,000
= ₹18,000 + ₹3,240
= ₹21,240

6. Price of item A = 60 × 80 = 4,800.
The discount amount of item A = 20% of 4,800
= $\frac{20}{100} \times 4,800 = 960$

Price of item A after discount = ₹3,840
GST on item A = 5% of 3,840
= ₹192

The total amount of bill for item A = ₹3,840 + ₹192
= ₹4,032 → (1)

The price of item B = 80 ₹ 100 = ₹8,000
Discount amount of item B = 12% of ₹8,000
= ₹960

The price of item B after discount = ₹8,000 – ₹960

= ₹7,040

GST on item B = 15% of ₹7,040

= ₹1,056

The total amount of bill for item B = ₹7,040 + ₹1,050

= ₹8,096 → (2)

Total amount of bill = ₹4,032 + ₹8,096

= ₹12,128

Level 2: Review Your Concepts

7. (i) The net GST payable at Surat

= 12% of (10,000 – 8,000)

= 12% of 2,000

= ₹240

(ii) The input tax credit for the dealer in Lucknow

= 12% of 10,000

$= \frac{12}{100} \times 10{,}000$

= ₹1,200

8.

S.no.	Details	SGST @ 9%	CGST @ 9%	GST @ 18%
(i)	ITC for Mr. Hari at a purchase of ₹20,000	₹1,800	₹1,800	₹3,600
(ii)	Input tax for Mr. Ravi on purchase of ₹25,000	₹2,250	₹2,250	₹4,500
(iii)	Input tax payable by consumer Mrs. Varma at a purchase of ₹28,000 Total cost price of the article for Mrs. Varma = (₹28,000 +₹5,040)= ₹33,040	₹2,520	₹2,520	₹5,040
(iv)	Output GST for consumer Mrs. Varma (Since she does not sell it further)	Nil	Nil	Nil

9.

Details	CGST @ 6%	SGST @ 6%
Input tax credit on purchase worth ₹15,000	₹900	₹900
Output tax payable on sale worth ₹9,000	₹540	₹540
Excess credit	₹360	₹360

10. For the dealer

Details	IGST @ 12%	CGST @ 6%	SGST @ 6%
Output tax payable at ₹3,20,000	₹38,400		
Output tax payable at ₹4,00,000		₹24,000	₹24,000
ITC at ₹6,00,000	₹7,2000		
Utilization of ITC	₹38,400	₹24,000	₹9,600

11. (i) Central GST (CGST) = 14% of ₹ 8,000 = $\frac{14}{100}$ × ₹8,000 = ₹1120

(ii) State GST (SGST) = 14% of ₹ 8,000 = $\frac{14}{100}$ × ₹8,000 = ₹1120

(iii) Integrated GST (IGST) = Nil

12. It is a case of inter-state-transaction.

For trader A: S.P. = ₹500

IGST = 12% of ₹ 500 = $\frac{12}{100}$ × ₹500 = ₹60

For trader B: C.P. = ₹500

S.P. = ₹500 + ₹200 = ₹700

C.P. = ₹500 and profit of ₹200

Input-tax credit (ITC) = Tax on purchase of goods/services (input-tax)

Tax liability on trader B = Output tax – Input-tax credit

= ₹84 – ₹60 = ₹24

13.

S.P. for the dealer in Jaipur = ₹5000	(i) Net GST payable by the dealer in Indore
IGST = 18% of ₹5000 = $\frac{18}{100}$ × ₹5000 = ₹900	= Output GST – Input GST
C.P. for the dealer in Indore = ₹5000 and profit = ₹2000	= (₹630 + ₹630) – ₹900 = ₹360
S.P. In Indore = ₹5000 + ₹2000 = ₹7000 CGST = 9% of ₹7000 = $\left(\frac{9}{100}\right)$ × ₹7000 = ₹630	(ii) C.P. for the dealer in Bhopal = S.P for the dealer in Indore + GST
SGST = $\left(\frac{9}{100}\right)$ × ₹7000 = ₹630	= ₹7000 + (₹630 + ₹630) = ₹8260

14.

MRP	Discount	Discount Value (Selling Price)
₹250	30%	70% of ₹250 = $\frac{70}{100}$ × ₹250 = ₹175
₹200	40%	60% of ₹200 = $\frac{60}{100}$ × ₹200 = ₹120
₹150	32%	68% of ₹150 = $\frac{70}{100}$ × ₹150 = ₹102
₹300	20%	80% of ₹300 = $\frac{680}{100}$ × ₹300 = ₹240
Total		₹ 637

CGST = 6% of ₹637 = $\frac{6}{100}$ × ₹ 637 = ₹38.22, SGST = ₹38.22

Amount of bill = ₹713.44

Level 3: Assess Your Concepts

15. (A) Let the shopkeeper buy the articles for ₹x. For him, C.P. = ₹x and S.P. = ₹9000

CGST paid to the government = ₹162 SGST paid to be government = ₹162

So, total GST paid to the government = ₹162 + ₹162 = ₹324

GST on S.P. - GST on C.P. = ₹324

18% of 9000 – 18% of ₹x = ₹324 x (₹9000 – ₹x) = ₹324

On solving, it gives x = 7200

The shopkeeper buys the article for ₹7200

Amount paid by the shopkeeper = C.P. Of the article + GST on it.

= ₹7200 + 18% of ₹7200 = ₹8496 choice (2)

(B) This is an interstate transaction, so IGST is applicable on this transaction.

Item	MRP (in ₹)	Discount %	Discount (in ₹)	Selling price (in ₹)	IGST %	IGST (in ₹)
P	15,000	12	1,800	13,200	5	660
Q	13,000	15	1,560	11,440	5	572
R	12,000	30	3,600	8,400	28	2352
S	11,000	30	3,300	7,700	28	2156
Total				40,740		5,740

Total bill = Selling price + IGST = ₹40,740 + ₹5,740 = ₹46,480.

16. (i) For dealer A : C.P. = ₹2000 i.e. Purchase price

= ₹2000 Input-tax payable by dealer A

= Tax on purchase = 18% of ₹2000

= ₹360

As a profit = ₹500, S.P. = ₹2000 + ₹500 = ₹2500

(ii) For dealer B : C.P. = ₹2500

Input-tax payable by dealer B = Tax on purchase

= 18% of ₹2500

= ₹450 Ans.

Profit of dealer B = ₹1000

S.P. for dealer B = ₹2500 + ₹1000

= ₹3500

(iii) Since, dealer C is the end-user,The total cost price for dealer C = S.P of B + GST on it

= ₹3500 + 18% of ₹3500

= ₹4130

(iv) Since, dealer C is the end-user of the product, dealer C does not sell the product. Output GST tax (tax on sale) = ₹00

17.

MRP of each zitem (₹)	No. of items	Total cost of while quantity in (₹)	GST%	CGST(in ₹)	SCGST (in ₹)	Amount (MRP + CGST + SGST) (in ₹)
125	20	2500	12	$\frac{6}{100} \times 2500 = 150$	150	2800
200	27	5400	12	$\frac{6}{100} \times 5400 = 324$	324	6048
160	35	5600	18	$\frac{9}{100} \times 5600 = 504$	504	6608
150	32	4800	28	$\frac{14}{100} \times 4800 = 672$	672	6144
180	25	4500	18	$\frac{9}{100} \times 4500 = 405$	405	5310

Amount of bill = ₹26910

18.

At each stage of the sale of the machine, there is an inter-state-transaction	= ₹60000 – 10% of ₹60000 = ₹60000 – ₹6000
The rate of GST on each transaction of the machine is 28%.	= ₹540000
For the manufacturer : Marked price = ₹60000, discount = 20% of ₹60000 = ₹1200	Tax paid by the wholesaler to the central government : = Output tax – Input tax
S.P. = M.P. - Discount	= Tax on S.P. - Tax on C.P
= ₹60000 – ₹12000 = ₹48000	= 28% of ₹54000 – 28% of 48000
For the wholesaler : C.P. = ₹48000 S.P. = M.P. – Discount	$= \frac{28}{100} \times$ ₹6000 = ₹1680

19.

Part 1	Part 2
$x + 12\%\ x = 15680$	y + 12% of y = 14,000
x = ₹14,000	y = ₹12,500
Marked price = ₹14,000	Marked price = 12,500
	Part 3
	Reduction = 14,000 – 12500 = ₹1,500

20. (i) Given, the purchased price of the TV = ₹50,000.

Input SGST for dealer Varun = 9% of 50,000
= ₹4,500

(ii) The total input GST for dealer Varun = 4,500 + 4,500
= ₹9,000

The selling price for the dealer Mr. Varun = ₹50,000 + 15% 50,000
= 50,000 + 7,500 = ₹57,500

Output GST for dealer Varun = 18% of 57,500
= ₹10,350

The amount of GST to be deposited to the government by dealer Varun = output GST – Input GST.
= ₹10,350 – ₹9,000 = ₹1,350

(iii) The amount that retailer Shyam has to pay the dealer Varun for the TV. = ₹57,500 + ₹10,350 = ₹67,850.

21. (i) For the dealer in Hyderabad

Details	IGST @ 18%	CGST @ 9%	SGST @ 9%
Output tax payable at ₹42,000 intrastate transaction		₹3,780	₹3,780
Input Tax Credit (ITC) at @ ₹40,000		₹3,600	₹3,600
Net tax payable by dealer in Hyderabad		₹180	₹180

(ii) For the dealer in Warangal:

Details	IGST @ 18%	CGST @ 9%	SGST @ 9%
Output tax payable at ₹46,000 – Interstate transaction	₹8,280		
Input tax credit (ITC) at ₹42,000 Intra state transaction		₹3,780	₹3,780
Utilization of ITC of ₹(3,780 + 3,780)	₹7,560	₹0	₹0
Net tax payable by dealer in Warangal	₹720	₹0	₹0

(iii) The total cost of the TV for the end user in Amaravati = the selling price of dealer in Warangal + IGST @ 18%
= ₹46000 + (18% of ₹46,000)
= ₹46,000 + ₹8,280
= ₹54,280

22. The transaction is intra state. Thus, CGST and SGST are applied to this transaction.

Name of the person	Repairing cost (in ₹)	Discount %	Discount (in ₹)	Selling price (in ₹)	CGST (@9 %)	SGST (@9 %)
P	2,000	15	300	1,700	153	153
Q	1,800	5	90	1,710	153.9	153.9
R	1,900	10	190	1,710	153.9	153.9
S	2,400	25	600	1,800	162	162
T	2,500	30	750	1,750	157.5	157.5
Total				8,670	780.3	780.3

The total money (including GST) received by the repairer = ₹8,670 + ₹780.3 + ₹780.3 = ₹10,230.6

23. **For dealer in Hyderabad:**

Details	IGST @ 18%	CGST @ 9%	SGST@ 9%
Output tax payable at ₹70,000	₹12,600	0	0
Input tax credit at ₹60,000	0	₹5,400	₹5,400
Net tax payable	0	₹900	₹900

For dealer in Bangalore:

Interstate transaction	IGST @ 18%	CGST @ 9%	SGST@ 9%
Input tax credit @ ₹70,000 intrastate transaction	₹12,600	0	0
Utilization of ITC	₹12,600	0	0
Output tax payable at ₹80,000	₹14,400	0	0
Net tax payable by dealer at Bangalore	₹1,800	0	0

The total cost of the TV for the end user in Cochin
= Selling price of dealer in Bangalore + IGST @ 18%
= ₹80,000 + ₹14,400 = ₹94,400.

JEE Special Wing

Multiple-Answer Type Questions

1. MRP = ₹10,000, Discount % = 20%, GST = 12%.
   The transaction is intra state, thus CGST and SGST are applied.
   Discount $= \frac{20}{100} \times$ ₹10,000 = ₹2,000.
   Selling price (discounted value) = ₹10,000 – ₹2,000 = ₹8,000.
   CGST = 6% of ₹8,000 $= \frac{6}{100} \times$ ₹8,000 = ₹480.
   SGST = 6% of ₹8,000 $= \frac{6}{100} \times$ ₹8,000 = ₹480.
   Amount of bill = Selling price + CGST + SGST = ₹8,000 + ₹480 + ₹480 = ₹8,960.
   Hence, choice (a, b, d) are correct.
2. MRP = ₹50,000, Discount % = 12%, GST = 18%.
   The transaction is interstate so, IGST is applied.
   Discount $= \frac{12}{100} \times$ ₹50,000 = ₹6,000.
   Selling price (discounted value) = ₹50,000 – ₹6,000 = ₹44,000.
   IGST = 18 % of ₹44,000 $= \frac{18}{100} \times$ ₹44,000 = ₹7,920.
   Amount of bill = Selling price + IGST = ₹44,000 + ₹7,920 = ₹51,920.
   Hence, choice (a, c, d) are correct.
3. All the given statements are correct.
   Hence, choice (a, b, c, d) are correct.
4. The tax liability by the retailer is the GST on the profit made by the retailer.
   = 5% of ₹15,000 $= \frac{5}{100} \times$ ₹15,000 = ₹750.
   The total GST received by the government is the GST on the selling price.
   = 5% of (₹1,10,000 + ₹15,000)
   $= \frac{5}{100} \times$ ₹1, 25, 000 = ₹6, 250.
   Hence, choice (c and d) are correct.
5. The cost price of the article for the dealer P = ₹26,000.
   Input tax credit (ITC) for dealer A = Total GST on ₹26,000.
   = 5% of ₹26,000 $= \frac{5}{100} \times$ ₹26, 000 = ₹1,300.
   The input tax payable by the dealer Q is the tax on the cost price of the article for Q.
   = 5% of (₹26,000 + ₹4,000) $= \frac{5}{100} \times$ ₹30,000 = ₹1,500.
   The total GST received by the government = 5% of (₹26,000 + ₹4,000 + ₹5,000)
   $= \frac{5}{100} \times$ ₹35, 000 = ₹1,750.
   The total cost price of the article for the consumer R = Selling Price + GST
   = (₹26,000 + ₹4,000 + ₹5,000) + ₹1,750
   = ₹36,750.
   Hence, choice (a, b, c, d) are correct.

Match The Column

Common Solutions for questions 6 to 10:

Cost\GST Rate	Value of the services including GST 5%	12%	18%	28%	31%
₹1,10,000	₹1,15,500	₹1,23,200	₹1,29,800	₹1,40,800	₹1,44,100
₹1,15,000	₹1,20,750	₹1,28,800	₹1,35,700	₹1,47,200	₹1,50,650
₹1,25,000	₹1,31,250	₹1,40,000	₹1,47,500	₹1,60,000	₹1,63,750
₹1,30,000	₹1,36,500	₹1,45,600	₹1,53,400	₹1,66,400	₹1,70,300
₹1,38,000	₹1,44,900	₹1,54,560	₹1,62,840	₹1,76,640	₹1,80,780

6. 6 ↔ e ↔ p
7. 7 ↔ d ↔ s
8. 8 ↔ a ↔ t
9. 9 ↔ b ↔ r
10. 10 ↔ c ↔ q

Comprehension-Based Questions

Common Solutions for questions 11 to 15:

This is an intra state transaction, so CGST and SGST are applicable on this transaction.

Goods	Quantity	M R P (in ₹)	Total M R P (in ₹)	Discount %	Discount (in ₹)	Selling Price (in ₹)	CGST (6%) (in ₹)	SGST (6%) (in ₹)
M	100	2500	250000	12	30000	220000	13200	13200
N	125	2000	250000	11	27500	222500	13350	13350
O	150	1500	225000	10	22500	202500	12150	12150
P	175	1000	175000	9	15750	159250	09555	09555
R	200	800	160000	8	12800	147200	08832	08832
Total			**1060000**		**108550**	**951450**	**57087**	**57087**

11. The total MRP of all the goods = ₹10,60,000.
    Hence, the correct option is (a).
12. Total discount availed by the customer = ₹1,08,550.
    Hence, the correct option is (c).
13. Total selling price of the goods = ₹9,51,450.
    Hence, the correct option is (d).
14. Total CGST = ₹57,087.
    Hence, the correct option is (d).
15. Total amount of the bill = Selling Price + CGST + SGST
    = ₹9,51,450 + ₹57,087 + ₹57,087 = ₹10,65,624.
    Hence, the correct option is (b).

Common Solutions for questions 16 to 20:

16. Selling price of the goods/services for Chandra = Cost price of the goods/services for Tarak = ₹1,50,000.
    For the transaction from dealer Chandra (Telangana) to Tarak (AP), IGST is applicable since it is an inter-state transaction.
    IGST = 28% of ₹1,50,000
    $= \frac{28}{100} \times ₹1,50,000 = ₹42,000.$
    Hence, the correct option is (c).
17. Input tax for dealer Tarak = IGST = ₹42,000.
    Hence, the correct option is (b).
18. The selling price of the goods/services for Tarak
    = Cost price of the goods/services for Tarak + Profit
    = ₹1,50,000 + ₹12,000 = ₹1,62,000.
    For the transaction from dealer Tarak (AP) to Jaggu (AP), SGST and CGST are applicable since it is an intra-state transaction.
    SGST = CGST = 14% of ₹1,62,000
    $= \frac{14}{100} \times ₹1,62,000 = ₹22,680.$
    Output tax for dealer Tarak = SGST + CGST
    = ₹22,680 + ₹22,680 = ₹45,360
    Hence, the correct option is (d).
19. The net GST payable by dealer Tarak = Output Tax – Input Tax
    = ₹45,360 – ₹42,000 = ₹3,360.
    Hence, the correct option is (b).
20. The cost of the goods/services for dealer Jaggu
    = Selling price of the goods/services for Tarak + Output Tax
    = ₹1,62,000 + ₹45,360 = ₹2,07,360.
    Hence, the correct option is (a).

Assertion and Reason Type Questions

Solutions for questions 21 to 24:

21. **Assertion:** A transaction from Ahmedabad (Gujarat) to Mumbai (Maharashtra) is an interstate transaction. So, IGST is applicable.
    So, Assertion is correct.
    Reason: In interstate transaction, IGST is applicable.
    Reason is correct and is the correct explanation of Assertion.
    Hence, the correct option is (a).
22. **Assertion:** A dealer in Coimbatore (Tamil Nadu) buys goods for ₹20,000 from another dealer from Chennai (Tamil Nadu). The rate of GST is 12%. In this transaction,

A transaction from Chennai (Tamil Nadu) to Coimbatore (Tamil Nadu) is an intra-state transaction. So, SGST and CGST are applicable.

So, Assertion is correct.

Reason: In intra-state transaction, SGST and CGST are applicable.

So, Reason is false.

Hence, the correct option is (c).

23. **Assertion:** A dealer buys goods for ₹25,000 from another dealer from within the city. The rate of GST is 28%. In this transaction, each of SGST and CGST is 14% of ₹25,000.

So, SGST and CGST are applicable.

$$\text{SGST} = \frac{28\%}{2} = 14\% \text{ of ₹}25{,}000 \text{ and CGST} = \frac{28\%}{2}$$

$= 14\%$ of ₹25,000.

So, Assertion is correct.

Reason: In intra-state transaction, SGST and CGST are applicable. Each is equal to half of the total GST.

Reason is correct and is the correct explanation of Assertion.

Hence, the correct option is (a).

24. **Assertion:** As the rate of GST on vegetables is 0%, the Assertion is false.

Reason: If the GST on transaction of goods of worth ₹5,00,000 is 15,000, the rate of GST = $\frac{\text{₹}15{,}000}{\text{₹}5{,}00{,}000} \times 100\% = 3\%$.

Reason is correct.

Hence, the correct option is (d).

CHAPTER

15

Shares and Dividends

Remember

Before beginning this chapter, you should be able to:

- Recall some basic concepts related to shares and dividends
- Understand the term dividend

Key Ideas

After completing this chapter, you should be able to:

- Study classification of share capital
- Learn about nominal value and market value
- Understand about dividend in detail
- Find return on investments

A Tribute to Warren Buffet (Oracle of Omaha)

In the expansive realm of finance and investment, few names shine as brightly as Warren Buffett's. Often hailed as the 'Oracle of Omaha,' his life journey stands as a testament to the enduring power of wisdom, discipline, and unwavering commitment to principles that transcend the ever-shifting tides of the financial world.

Born in Omaha, Nebraska, on August 30, 1930, Warren Buffett was nurtured by his father, Howard Buffett, a stockbroker and congressman. His fascination with numbers and finance was kindled at a young age. Displaying an entrepreneurial spirit, he peddled chewing gum and soda door-to-door. Remarkably, he embarked on his maiden stock investment at the tender age of 11 and filed his inaugural tax return by the age of 14. This enduring fascination would ultimately blossom into a lifelong passion for the world of finance, solidifying his status as a true luminary in the financial realm.

After high school, Buffett enrolled at the Wharton School of Business at the University of Pennsylvania, later transferring to the University of Nebraska. His educational journey culminated in the attainment of a master's degree in economics from Columbia Business School, where he was mentored by the influential Benjamin Graham. His investment philosophy is deeply rooted in the principles of value investing, prioritizing undervalued stocks with robust fundamentals that he holds for the long term. In 1965, he took control of Berkshire Hathaway, originally a textile firm, and skilfully transformed it into a global conglomerate boasting diverse holdings in insurance, energy, and consumer brands.

FUN TIME

CROSSWORD

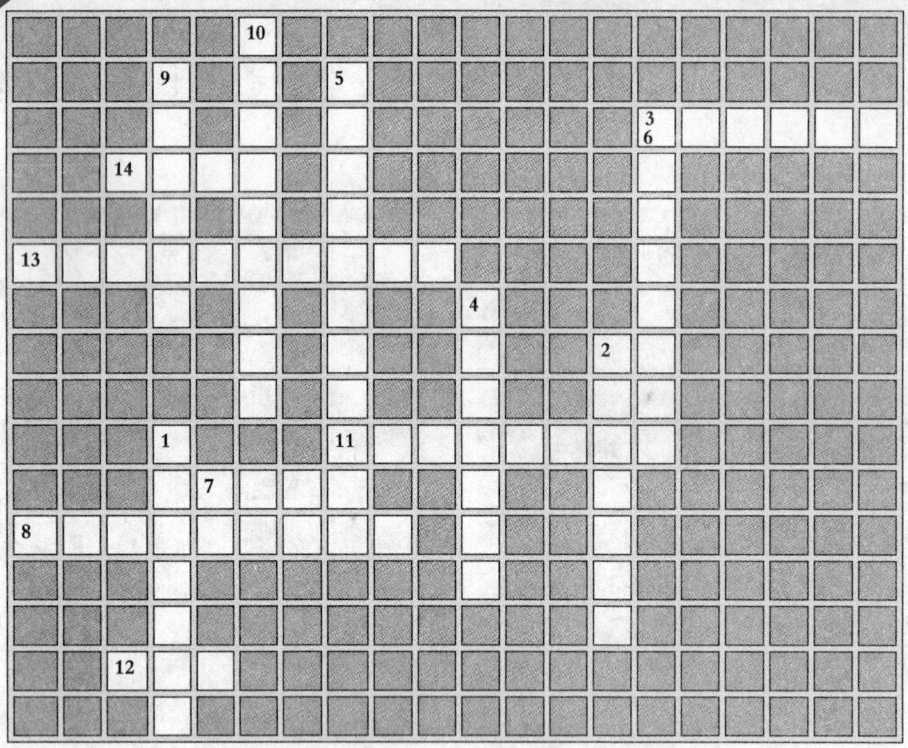

Across

14. A share's market value fluctuates constantly.
13. The funds collected and utilised to establish a business.
12. The value mentioned on the share certificate is the _______ value of a share.
11. A portion of the yearly profit which is distributed to each stakeholder is called _____.
8. A team of business owners.
7. Based on the share's _____ value, the dividend rate is calculated.
6. Calculate the return on one share: 10%, 120 shares at ₹140.

Down

1. A share's face value is also known as its _______ value.
2. ₹90 share is available at a premium of ₹10. The market value of the share is ________.
3. Dividend received (₹) at the end of the year from 160 shares: 5% or ₹125 shares at ₹110.
4. The total amount of money needed for the establishment of a firm.
5. An individual to whom shares are allocated.
9. The price at which a share is purchased or sold on the stock market is known as its _______ value.
10. A person who arrange the capital needed to establish a business.

INTRODUCTION

The total amount of money required to start a business enterprise or a company is called the 'capital'. A business enterprise may be a sole proprietary concern, a partnership firm, or a company.

The capital received to start a significantly big company runs into several crores of rupees. A group of entrepreneurs called 'promoters' start a company, but they cannot possibly invest huge amount capital. Hence, the whole capital is divided into many small and equal units. These units are called 'shares'. Later, the company invites the public to invest money in its business by buying these shares. All companies cannot raise capital from the public. Only public limited companies can exercise this right.

The money arranged and used for setting up a company or a business enterprise is called the 'investment'. Those who arrange this money are called 'investors'.

A public limited company is a company limited by shares with no restriction on the maximum number of shareholders, transfer of shares, and acceptance of public deposits. The minimum number of shareholders is seven.

Classification of Share Capital

Authorized capital is the capital limit authorized by the registrar of companies. It is the specified amount up to which shares can be issued to the members or public. The paid-up share capital is the paid portion of the capital subscribed by the shareholders. The minimum limit of authorized capital for a public limited company is ₹500,000.

In other words, authorized capital is the capital with which a company is registered. The company can issue shares up to the maximum level of its authorized capital. Paid-up capital means the amount of capital actually paid by the shareholders in respect of shares allotted to them.

The following example gives a clear idea of the division of capital into shares.

Example: Suppose the capital requirement of a company is ₹15 crores.

Then, the whole capital can be divided into:

1. 15 lakh shares of ₹100 each or
2. 30 lakh shares of ₹50 each or
3. 60 lakh shares of ₹25 each.

For every investment, the company issues a share certificate reflecting the value of each share and the number of shares held by the investors.

A person who is allotted shares or who buys shares is called a 'shareholder'. After the shares are allotted, the shareholder can sell those in the stock market.

Nominal Value of a Share (NV)

Nominal value of a share is the value printed on the share certificate. It is also known as the 'face value' (FV) or 'par value'.

Market Value of a Share (MV)

Market value is the value of a share at which it is bought or sold in the stock market.

Info Bytes!

A share is said to be:

1. At premium or above par, if MV > FV.
2. At discount or below par, if MV < FV.
3. At par, if MV = FV.

Dividend

Dividend is a part of the annual profit distributed among the shareholders.

Dividend is paid on per share or as a percentage. If it is paid as a percentage, it is reckoned on the face value of the share.

Return on Investment

$$\text{Rate of return} = \frac{\text{Annual income}}{\text{Total investment}} \times 100$$

Konnect

1. The face value of a share always remains the same.
2. The market value of a share changes from time to time.
3. Dividend is always paid on the face value of a share.
4. The number of shares held by a person

$$= \frac{\text{Total income}}{\text{Income from each share}} = \frac{\text{Total face value}}{\text{Face value of each share}}.$$

EXAMPLE 15.1

Find the market value of ₹200 share bought at a premium of ₹50.

SOLUTION

Face value of the share = ₹200

The share was bought at a premium of ₹50.

∴ Market value of the share = ₹(200 + 50) = ₹250.

EXAMPLE 15.2

If a ₹100 share is available at a discount of ₹10, then find the market value of 270 such shares.

SOLUTION

Face value of the share = ₹100

The share is available at a discount of ₹10

Market value of each share = 100 – 10 = ₹90

∴ Market value of 270 such shares = 90(270) = ₹24,300.

EXAMPLE 15.3

Satish invests a certain amount of money in 200, ₹60 shares of a company by paying a dividend of 8%. Find his annual income from the investment.

SOLUTION

Face value of the share = ₹60

Number of shares bought = 200

Rate of dividend paid = 8%

Annual income from each share $= \frac{8}{100}(60) = \frac{480}{100} =$ ₹4.80.

∴ Annual income Satish earned from 200 shares = 4.8 × 200 = ₹960.

EXAMPLE 15.4

Karan invests ₹18,000 by buying ₹100 shares of a company available at a discount of ₹10. If the company pays a dividend of 10%, then find the number of shares bought by Karan, and the rate of return on his investment.

SOLUTION

Total investment = ₹18,000

Face value of each share = ₹100

The shares are available at a discount of ₹10.

Market value of each share = 100 −10 = ₹90.

$$\text{Number of shares bought} = \frac{\text{Total investment}}{\text{Market value of each share}} = \frac{18,000}{90} = 200$$

⇒ Number of shares bought by Karan = 200

Rate of dividend = 10%

His annual income from each share = 10% (100) = ₹10

⇒ His annual income from 200 shares = 200 (10) = ₹2000

⇒ The rate of return on his investment $= \frac{\text{Annual income}}{\text{Total investment}}(100) = \frac{2000}{18{,}000}(100)$

$= \frac{100}{9}\% = 11\frac{1}{9}\%$

∴ Karan receives a return of $11\frac{1}{9}\%$ per annum on his investment.

Alternative solution:

We have, FV × Rate of dividend = MV × Rate of return.

100 × 10% = 90 × Rate of return

⇒ Rate of return $= 11\frac{1}{9}\%$.

EXAMPLE 15.5 Which is a better investment: ₹200 shares at ₹220 which pay a dividend of 10%, or ₹100 shares at ₹120 which pay a dividend of 12%?

SOLUTION

Case 1: ₹200 shares at ₹220 paying a dividend of 10%

$$\text{Rate of return} = \frac{\text{FV} \times \text{Rate of dividend}}{\text{MV}} = \frac{200 \times 10\%}{220} = 9\frac{1}{11}\%.$$

Case 2: ₹100 shares at ₹120 paying a dividend of 12%

$$\text{Rate of return} = \frac{\text{FV} \times \text{Rate of dividend}}{\text{MV}}$$

$$= \frac{100 \times 12\%}{120} = 10\%.$$

∴ 12%, ₹100 shares at ₹120 is a better investment.

POINTS TO REMEMBER

- ✔ Nominal value of a share is the value printed on the share certificate. It is also known as the 'face value' (FV) or 'par value'.
- ✔ Market value is the value of a share at which it is bought or sold in the stock market.
- ✔ Dividend is a part of the annual profit distributed among the shareholders.
- ✔ The number of shares held by a person $= \frac{\text{Total income}}{\text{Income from each share}} = \frac{\text{Total face value}}{\text{Face value of each share}}$
- ✔ Rate of return $= \frac{\text{Annual income}}{\text{Total investment}} \times 100$

PRACTICE QUESTIONS CLASSROOM WING

Very Short Answer Type Questions

Directions of questions from 1 to 3:
Fill in the blanks.

1. A person who is allotted shares or who buys shares is called a ______ of the company.

2. If a ₹180 share is quoted at a premium of ₹27, then the market value of each share is ______.

3. If a ₹100 share is available at par, then its market value is ______.

Directions of questions from 4 to 5:
State whether the following statements are true or false.

4. Does the face value of a share remain constant all the time?

5. Is the market value of a share always constant?

Short Answer Type Questions

Directions of questions from 6 to 15:
Answer the following questions.

6. If Anil bought a ₹150 share at a premium of ₹20 while Raju bought the same kind of share at a discount of ₹20 of the same company, then the dividend earned by Anil is ______ the dividend earned by Raju. [equal to/ less than/more than]

7. Find the market value of 300, ₹150 shares bought at a premium of ₹30.

8. Find the annual income derived from an investment of ₹18,000 in ₹150 shares available at ₹180 of a company paying 11% dividend.

9. ₹60,000 is invested in buying ₹120 shares of a company which are available at a premium of 25%. Find the number of shares bought and the annual rate of return on the investment, if dividend is paid at the rate of 10% per annum.

10. An investment of ₹36 on a share earns the investor a return of 10%. If dividend is 12% on each share, then what is its face value?

11. (A) A man invests ₹20,000 in ₹80 shares of a company available at a premium of ₹20. If the company pays a dividend of 8%, then find the rate of return on the investment.

    (B) Ms. Najwa purchased 10%, ₹110 shares available at ₹120. Ms. Nagina purchased 8%, ₹120 shares available at ₹110. If they invested same amount, who (between them) earns more on the investment.

12. If Satish bought 120, ₹200 shares of a particular company at a premium of ₹24, paying 9% dividend, then find Satish's annual income.

13. If an investment of ₹42,000 in ₹300 shares of a company, paying a dividend of 7%, results in an annual income of ₹2100, then find the market value of each share.

14. A person invested ₹18,000 in buying ₹150 shares of a company which are available at a premium of ₹50. If the company pays a 9% dividend, then find the number of shares bought by him and also the annual income he earned from the investment.

15. Which is a better investment, (A) ₹60 shares at ₹75 paying a dividend of 10% or (B) ₹100 share at ₹120 paying a dividend of 12%?

Essay Type Questions

16. Naresh invested a certain amount of money in ₹100 shares at a discount of ₹20 paying a dividend of 7%, while Sahil invested an equal amount in ₹90 shares at a discount of ₹10 paying a dividend of 8%. Who earns more?

17. **Directions for Questions 17 (A and B):** Kevin invested certain amounts in shares of two companies A and B. From A, he bought 25000 shares of ₹x at 15% discount paying 5% per annum. From B, he bought 30000 shares of ₹y at 10% premium paying 10% per

annum. The annual income from each of the investments is ₹375000.

(A) Find the market value of a share of the company A.

(B) Find the ratio of the market value of shares of A to that of B.

18. Directions for Questions 18 (A and B): Tina invested 60% of her amount in 12%, ₹800 shares of company X at ₹1000 and the rest in 15% ₹750 shares of company Y at ₹800. If her total annual income from both the investments is ₹45540.

(A) What is the ratio of the dividends received from the shares of X to that Y?

(B) Find the total amount invested in the shares of both the companies.

19. Rahul invested a certain amount in buying ₹25 shares of a company, which pays a dividend of 12%. If he earns 10% per annum on his investment, then find the market value of each share.

20. Kavya bought 300, ₹50 shares paying a dividend of 8%. If she sold them when the price rose to ₹90 and invested the proceeds in 10%, ₹50 shares at ₹30, then find the change in her annual income.

PRACTICE QUESTIONS COMPETITION WING

Level 1: Apply Your Concepts

Directions of questions from 1 to 5:
Fill in the blanks.

1. The whole capital divided into small and equal units are called ______.
2. The value of a share printed on the share certificate is called its ______.
3. Dividend is always calculated on the ______ of a share.
4. ______ is the annual profit distributed among the shareholders.
5. The value at which a share is bought or sold in the market is called its ______.

Directions of questions from 6 to 13:
Select the correct alternative from the given choices.

6. If a ₹200 share is bought at a discount of ₹50 and the dividend paid is 9%, then the rate of return is ______ per annum.
   (a) 18% (b) 9%
   (c) 10% (d) 12%
7. A person invests ₹20,000 at 20%, ₹150 shares at a premium of ₹50. The income from these shares in is ₹ ______.
   (a) 1,000 (b) 3,000
   (c) 1,500 (d) 2,000
8. A person invests ₹15,000 in ₹50 shares of a company paying 10% dividend. If the company pays a dividend of ₹6250, the market value of each share is ______.
   (a) ₹8 (b) ₹10
   (c) ₹12 (d) ₹7
9. A man buys 24 shares at ₹150 per share having the par value of ₹100. If the dividend is 7.5% per annum, then the ratio of total annual income to his total investment is______.
   (a) 1 : 10 (b) 10 : 1
   (c) 1 : 20 (d) 20 : 1
10. The total investment made in buying ₹X shares at a premium of 25% is ₹125X. The number of shares bought is ______.
    (a) 500 (b) 250
    (c) 125 (d) 100
11. Praveen invests ₹24,000 in ₹100 shares of a company paying 10% dividend. If his annual income from these shares is ₹1200, then the market value of each share is ₹______.
    (a) 100 (b) 200
    (c) 300 (d) 400
12. A man has 62 shares of ₹100 each, dividend is 7.5% per annum. If he wants to increase his annual income by ₹150, then he should buy ______ more shares.
    (a) 20 (b) 40
    (c) 10 (d) 30
13. The market value of x, ₹50 shares, at a discount of ₹10 is ₹4000, then x = ______.
    (a) 10 (b) 100
    (c) 50 (d) 75

Level 2: Review Your Concepts

14. A man buys 500, ₹10 shares at a premium of ₹3 on each share. If the rate of dividend is 12%, then the rate of interest received by him on his money is ______ (approximately).
    (a) 6.5% (b) 7.5%
    (c) 9.23% (d) 5%
15. Rishi bought ₹50 shares of a company for ₹75 each. The company pays a dividend of 12% per annum. The effective rate of return on his investments is ______.
    (a) 6% (b) 8%
    (c) 9% (d) 10%
16. If ₹56,000 is invested in buying ₹120 shares at a discount of ₹$16\frac{2}{3}$%, then find the number of shares bought is ______.
    (a) 2,800 (b) 560
    (c) 280 (d) 400
17. Ankit invests ₹18,000 in buying ₹270 shares in a company at a premium of ₹30. If the dividend paid is 10%

per annum, then Ankit's annual income from these shares is ________.

(a) ₹162 (b) ₹1620
(c) ₹16.20 (d) ₹16,200

18. Which is a better investment: '15%, ₹220 shares at ₹240 of Company A' or '18%, ₹200 shares at ₹240 of Company B'?

(a) Company A (b) Company B
(c) Both (a) and (b) (d) Cannot say

19. Mr Gellard invested ₹16,000 in 7%, ₹200 shares at ₹160. He sold the shares at ₹150 each. He incurred a ________.

(a) loss of ₹1300 (b) loss of ₹1000
(c) profit of ₹1000 (d) profit of ₹1200

20. Priya invested ₹27,000 in ₹180 shares at ₹150 at the beginning of a financial year. The company paid a dividend of 12%. Priya sold all her shares at the end of the year. Over this period, her net earnings were ₹1828. She sold the shares for ________ each.

(a) ₹160.15 (b) ₹181.75
(c) ₹185 (d) ₹138.56

21. Teja brought ₹80 shares of a company which pays 15% dividend. If the rate of return is 12%, then the market price is ________.

(a) ₹90 (b) ₹80
(c) ₹100 (d) ₹99

22. Randeep invests ₹25,200 in buying shares of face value of ₹40 each at 5% premium. The dividend on these shares is 10% per annum. Find the dividend he receives annually.

(a) ₹2520 (b) ₹2400
(c) ₹4200 (d) ₹3680

23. The dividend received from 10% ₹125 shares at ₹150, is ₹1875. Find the number of shares.

(a) 125 (b) 150
(c) 270 (d) 135

24. Find the market value of 200 shares worth ₹120, each bought at a discount of ₹20. (in ₹)

(a) 28,000 (b) 24,000
(c) 26,000 (d) 20,000

25. Ms Meenakshi invested ₹32,400 in buying certain shares of a company. If the amount of dividend received by her is ₹4860, then find the rate of return.

(a) 15% (b) 12%
(c) 14% (d) 13%

26. Ms Shriya bought 1000 shares worth ₹500 each at 12% premium. Find the market value of each share.

(a) ₹612 (b) ₹560
(c) ₹760 (d) ₹840

Level 3: Assess Your Concepts

27. Which of the following is a better investment?

(A) 10%, ₹100 shares at ₹120.

(B) 9%, ₹100 shares at ₹110.

(a) A
(b) B
(c) Both (A) and (B)
(d) Data insufficient

28. Vamsi invested some amount buying ₹150 shares of a company which pays dividend at the rate of 8% per annum. If he gets back 10% per annum on his investment, then the value at which he bought the shares is ________.

(a) ₹100 (b) ₹120
(c) ₹180 (d) ₹210

29. Mr Sirkar bought ₹80 shares of a company at a premium of ₹10. If the company pays a dividend at the rate of x % per annum, and Mr Sirkar earns at the rate of y % per annum on his investment, then $x : y$ is ________.

(a) 1 : 8 (b) 8 : 1
(c) 8 : 1 (d) 9 : 8

30. Sachin invests ₹15,000 on buying ₹100 shares of a company at a premium of ₹50 and gets $6\frac{2}{3}$% per annum on his investment. Then the rate at which the company pays the dividend is ________.

(a) 5% (b) 8%
(c) 9% (d) 10%

31. Praveen made an investment of ₹54,000 in 10%, ₹100 shares at ₹90, while Vijay made an investment of ₹60,000 in 8%, ₹150 shares at ₹120. If both of them sold their shares at the end of the year for ₹110 each, then their individual earnings are ________, respectively.

(a) ₹12,000 and ₹12,000 (b) ₹18,000 and ₹1000
(c) ₹12,000 and ₹1000 (d) ₹18,000 and ₹1200

32. Which of the following is/are true for the statement: '15%, ₹120 shares at ₹200'?
(a) Face value of each share is ₹120.
(b) Market value of each share is ₹200.
(c) Dividend from each share is ₹18.
(d) All of these

33. Mrs Pravallika has 100 shares worth ₹100 at a premium of ₹100. If the rate of dividend is 10%, then find the total dividend received by her at the end of a year. (in ₹)
(a) ₹4000 (b) ₹3000
(c) ₹2000 (d) ₹1000

34. Mr Anil bought ₹110 shares of a company at a discount of ₹10. If the company pays a dividend at the rate of x% per annum, and Mr Anil earns at the rate of y% per annum on his investment, then $x : y$ is ______.
(a) 10 : 9 (b) 9 : 10
(c) 11 : 10 (d) 10 : 11

35. Mr Balu invested ₹15,000 in 10%, ₹100 shares at ₹120, and also invested ₹24,000 in 12%, ₹120 shares at ₹100. The total earnings from the two investments is ______.
(a) ₹4500 (b) ₹4706
(c) ₹4700 (d) ₹4509

36. Mrs Apoorva invests ₹12,000 in buying ₹200 shares in a company at a premium of ₹50. If the dividend paid is 10% per annum, then Apoorva's annual income from these shares is ______.
(a) ₹1,020 (b) ₹960
(c) ₹840 (d) ₹780

37. Mr Krish made an investment of ₹27,000 in 10%, ₹100 shares at ₹90 while Mr Ram made an investment of ₹30,000 in 8%, ₹150 shares at ₹120. If both of them sold their shares at the end of a year for ₹110 each, then their individual earnings are ______, respectively.
(a) ₹2000 and ₹1200 (b) ₹1800 and ₹1000
(c) ₹9000 and ₹500 (d) ₹1800 and ₹1200

38. Mrs Karuna invested some amount in buying ₹120 shares of a company which pays a dividend at the rate of 10% per annum. If she gets back 8% per annum on her investment, then the value at which she bought the shares is ______.
(a) ₹100 (b) ₹150
(c) ₹180 (d) ₹210

AT

PRACTICE QUESTIONS JEE SPECIAL WING

Multiple-Answer Type Questions

Directions for questions 1 to 5:
Each question has FOUR options (a), (b), (c), and (d). ONE OR MORE THAN ONE of these four option(s) is/are the correct answer(s).

1. Which of the following is/are true for the given statement:
"20%, ₹1250 shares available at a discount of 20%"?
(a) Face value of each share is ₹1250.
(b) Market value of each share is ₹1000.
(c) Dividend from each share is ₹250.
(d) Rate of return is 25%.

2. Vurvi invests a certain amount of money in 500, ₹600 shares of a company available at a premium of 25% which pays a dividend of 5%.
Which of the following is/are true about the given data?
(a) The total investment is ₹3,00,000.
(b) Market value of each share is ₹750.
(c) Total dividend is ₹15,000.
(d) Rate of return is 4%.

3. Dhanush invests ₹1,80,000 by buying ₹200 shares of a company available at a discount of 10%. The company pays a dividend of 9%.
Which of the following is/are true about the given data?
(a) The number of shares purchased is 1000.
(b) The market value of 50 shares is ₹9000.
(c) The total annual return on his investment is ₹18,000.
(d) Rate of return is 12%.

4. **Investment A:** ₹450 shares at ₹500 which pays a dividend of 10%.
Investment B: ₹225 shares at ₹200 which pays a dividend of 8%.
Which of the following is/are false for the given statements?
(a) Investment A is better than that of B.
(b) Investment B is better than that of A.
(c) The investments give the same return.
(d) An investment of one lakh rupees on A is better than that on B.

5. Which of the following is/are true for the given statement:
"10%, ₹40 shares available at a premium of 10%"?
(a) The dividend from 85 such shares is ₹340.
(b) The dividend from 15 such shares is ₹66.
(c) The annual return from 193 such shares is ₹772.
(d) The annual return from 25 such shares is ₹150.

Match The Column

Directions for questions 6 to 10:
Read the paragraph given below and answer the questions.

Manvita invested ₹6,30,000 in each of the following stocks.

Name of the Share	Face Value	Market Value	Rate of Dividend
P	₹100	₹120	6%
Q	₹220	₹350	7%
R	₹1100	₹1800	9%
S	₹1150	₹2000	8%
T	₹1200	₹2500	10%

Match the values in column A with the values in column B.

Column A (Name of the Share)	Column B (Annual Dividend)
6. P	(a) ₹27,720
7. Q	(b) ₹28,980
8. R	(c) ₹30,240
9. S	(d) ₹31,500
10. T	(e) ₹34,650

Comprehension-Based Questions

Directions for questions 11 to 15:

Read the paragraph given below and answer the questions.

Name of the Share	Face Value	Discount	Premium
P	₹100		20%
Q	₹110		10%
R	₹120		5%
S	₹125	4%	
T	₹160	20%	

11. If Mahesh buys 135 shares of *P*, what is the amount required to purchase the shares?
    (a) ₹16,200 (b) ₹14,850
    (c) ₹12,150 (d) ₹10,800

12. What is the market value of 121 shares of *Q*?
    (a) ₹15,609 (b) ₹14,641
    (c) ₹12,221 (d) ₹10,769

13. Krishna wants to invest ₹15,624. How many shares of *R* is he eligible for?
    (a) 129 (b) 124
    (c) 119 (d) 114

14. What is the amount required to purchase 84 shares of *S* and 22 shares of *T*?
    (a) ₹14,210 (b) ₹13,392
    (c) ₹13,032 (d) ₹12,896

15. If Pavan wants to purchase 22 shares of each of *P*, *Q*, *R*, *S* and *T*, what is the total amount required to purchase the same?
    (a) ₹13,090 (b) ₹13,310
    (c) ₹13,530 (d) ₹13,750

Assertion and Reason Type Questions

Directions for questions 16 to 20:

In the light of the given statements, choose the most appropriate answer from the options given below.

(a) Both assertion (A) and reason (R) are true, and reason (R) is the correct explanation of the assertion.
(b) Both assertion (A) and reason (R) are true, and reason (R) is not the correct explanation of the assertion.
(c) Assertion (A) is true, but reason (R) is false.
(d) Assertion (A) is false, and reason (R) is true.

16. **Assertion:** A shareholder invested in the shares of a company. The number of shares of the company held by the person is the ratio of the annual income from the shares and the income from each share.

    Reason: Rate of return $= \dfrac{\text{Annual Income}}{\text{Total Investment}} \times 100\%$.

17. **Assertion:** We say that a share is available at premium when the market value is more than the face value of the share.

    Reason: We say that a share is available at par when the market value is less than the face value of the share.

18. **Assertion:** A shareholder invested ₹1,25,000 in the shares of a company and earned an annual dividend of ₹20,000. The rate of dividend is 16%.

    Reason: Rate of return $= \dfrac{\text{Annual Income}}{\text{Total Investment}} \times 100\%$.

19. **Assertion:** A shareholder invested ₹15,00,000 in 1000 shares of a company whose face value of each share is ₹1000 and earned an annual dividend of ₹3,00,000. The rate of dividend is 30%.

    Reason: Rate of dividend $= \dfrac{\text{Annual Income}}{\text{Total Face Value}} \times 100\%$.

20. **Assertion:** Alok invested ₹9,00,000 in ₹80 shares available at ₹120 which pays a dividend of 9.3%. Bhuvan invested ₹9,00,000 in ₹60 shares available at ₹120 which pays a dividend of 12.2%. The annual return of Alok is more than that of Bhuvan.

    Reason: The investment in shares which give more rate of return is a better investment.

ANSWER KEYS

Crossword

Across

6. Twelve 7. Face 8. Promoters 11. Dividend 12. Par
13. Investment 14. True

Down

1. Nominal 2. Hundred 3. Thousand 4. Capital 5. Shareholder
9. Market 10. Investors

Classroom Wing

Very Short Answer Type Questions

1. Shareholder 2. ₹207 3. ₹100 4. True 5. False

Short Answer Type Questions

6. Equal to 7. ₹54,000 8. ₹1650 9. 400; 8% 10. ₹30
11. (A) 6.4% (B) $8\frac{8}{11}\%$ 12. ₹2160 13. ₹140
14. 90; ₹1215 15. (*B*) is better investment

Essay Type Questions

16. Sahil 17. (A) ₹255 (B) 102 : 55 18. (A) 128 : 125 (B) ₹4,00,000
19. ₹30 20. ₹3300

Competition Wing

Level 1: Apply Your Concepts

1. Shares 2. Face value (or) nominal value (or) par value 3. Face value
4. Dividend 5. Market value 6. (d) 7. (b)
8. (c) 9. (c) 10. (d) 11. (b)
12. (a) 13. (b)

Level 2: Review Your Concepts

14. (c) 15. (b) 16. (b) 17. (b)
18. (b) 19. (b) 20. (d) 21. (c) 22. (b)
23. (b) 24. (d) 25. (a) 26. (b)

Level 3: Assess Your Concepts

27. (a) 28. (b) 29. (d) 30. (d) 31. (b)
32. (d) 33. (d)
34. (d) 35. (b) 36. (b) 37. (c) 38. (b)

JEE Special Wing

Multiple-Answer Type Questions

1. (a, b, c, d)	**2.** (b, c, d)	**3.** (a, b, c)	**4.** (a, b)	**5.** (a, c)

Match The Column

6. (d)	**7.** (a)	**8.** (e)	**9.** (b)	**10.** (c)

Comprehension-Based Questions

11. (a)	**12.** (b)	**13.** (b)	**14.** (d)	**15.** (c)

Assertion and Reason Type Questions

16. (b)	**17.** (c)	**18.** (d)	**19.** (a)	**20.** (a)

Hints and Explanations

Classroom Wing

Very Short Answer Type Questions

1. Share holder
2. 180 + 77 = ₹ 207
3. ₹ 100
4. Yes
5. No, changes every second

Short Answer Type Questions

6. Market value = 150 + 20 = 170 – Anil

   Raju M.V. = 150 – 20 = 130

   Equal to

   Since dividend is on face value not on market value

7. M.V. of 1 share = 150 + 30

   = 180

   ∴ 300 shares = 180 × 300

   = ₹ 54,000

8. $\text{No. of shares} = \frac{18{,}00\not{0}}{18\not{0}} = 100$

   $\text{Income on 1 share} = \frac{11}{10\not{0}} \times 15\not{0}$

   $\text{Income on 100 shares} = \frac{11 \times 15 \times 10\not{0}}{1\not{0}}$

   = ₹ 1650

9. Investment = 60,000

   $\text{Premium} = \frac{\overset{}{\not{25}}}{\underset{4}{\not{100}}} \times 1\overset{30}{\not{20}}$

   ∴ Market value = 120 + 30

   = 150

   $\text{No. of shares} = \frac{\overset{4}{\not{60},00\not{0}}}{\not{15}\,\not{0}} = 400$

   $\text{Dividend} = \frac{1\not{0}}{1\not{0}\,\not{0}} \times 12\not{0} = 12$

   Dividend on 400 shares = 12 × 400

   = 4800

   $\text{Rate of return} = \frac{48\not{0}\not{0}}{6\not{0},\not{0}\,\not{0}\not{0}} \times 1\not{0}\not{0} = 8\%$

10. $\text{Rate of return} = \frac{10}{100} = \frac{\text{dividend}}{36}$

    $\text{Dividend} = \frac{360}{100} = \frac{12}{100} \times \text{F.V.}$

    $\text{F.V.} = \frac{\overset{3}{\not{3}}\,60 \times 1\not{0}\not{0}}{\not{12} \times 1\not{0}\not{0}} = 30$

11. (A) Investment = 20,000

    $\text{M.V. of 80 shares} = \frac{20000}{100} = 200$

    $\text{Profit} = \frac{8}{100} \times 200 \times 8 = 1280$

    $\text{Rate of return} = \frac{1280}{20{,}0\not{0}\not{0}} \times 1\not{0}\not{0}$

    = 6.4%

    (B) Rate of return on Najwa's shares

    $= \frac{FV \times RD}{MV}$

    $= \frac{110 \times 10\%}{120} = 9\frac{1}{6}\%$

    $\text{Rate of return on Nagina's shares} = \frac{120 \times 8\%}{110}$

    $= 8\frac{8}{11}\%$

    Annual income of Najwa is more than that of Nagina.

12. Market value = (Investment) = 120 × 224

    $\text{Dividend} = \frac{9}{1\not{0}\not{0}} \times 2\not{0}\not{0} = 18$

    Income = 18 × 120 = ₹2160

13. $\text{Market value} = \frac{420\not{0}\not{0}}{3\not{0}\not{0}} = ₹140$

14. $\text{No. of shares} = \frac{18{,}0\not{0}\not{0}}{2\not{0}\not{0}} = 90$

    $\text{Dividend} = \frac{9}{1\,\not{0}\not{0}_{\not{2}}} \times \overset{3}{\not{15}}\,\not{0} \times \overset{45}{\not{90}} = ₹1215$

15.

(A)	(B)
Dividend $= \frac{10}{100} \times 60$	Dividend $= \frac{12}{100} \times 100$
$= 6$	$= 12$

∴ Since dividend is more ∴ (B) is better.

Essay Type Questions

16. M.V. = ₹ 80

$$\text{Profit} = \frac{7}{100} \times 100 = ₹7$$

Sahil M.V. = ₹ 80

$$\text{Profit} = \frac{8}{100} \times 90 = 7.2$$

∴ 7.2 > 7

∴ Sahil

17. Shares of company A:

Number of shares = 25000

Rate of dividend = 5%

FV of each share = x

Total dividend = ₹375000.

$$\Rightarrow 25000 \times \frac{5}{100} \times x = ₹375000$$

$$\Rightarrow x = \frac{₹375000 \times 100}{25000 \times 5}$$

$$\Rightarrow x = \frac{₹375 \times 100}{125}$$

$$\Rightarrow x = ₹300$$

Face value of each share = ₹300.

Discount = 15%.

The market value of each share = (100-15)% of ₹300

$$= \frac{85}{100} \times ₹300 = ₹255$$

Shares of company B:

Number of shares = 30000

Rate of dividend = 10%

FV of each share = y

Total dividend = ₹375000.

$$\Rightarrow 30000 \times \frac{12}{100} \times y = ₹375000$$

$$\Rightarrow y = \frac{₹375000 \times 100}{30000 \times 10}$$

$$\Rightarrow y = \frac{₹375}{3}$$

$$\Rightarrow y = ₹125$$

Premium = 10%.

The market value of each share = (100+10)% of ₹125

$$= \frac{110}{100} \times ₹125 = ₹137.5$$

The required ratio = 255 : 137.5

=2550 : 1375 = 102 : 55.

Hence, the ratio of the market value of shares of A to that of B = 102 : 55.

18. Solutions for 18 (A and B): Let the total investment be x.

$$\text{Investment in shares of company } X = ₹x \times \frac{60}{100} = ₹\frac{3x}{5}$$

$$\text{Investment in shares of company } Y = ₹\left(x - \frac{3x}{5}\right) = ₹\frac{2x}{5}$$

Number of shares of company X

$$= \frac{\text{Investment}}{\text{MP}} = \frac{3x}{5 \times 1000} = \frac{3x}{5000}$$

Number of shares of company Y

$$= \frac{\text{Investment}}{\text{MP}} = \frac{2x}{5 \times 800} = \frac{x}{2000}$$

(A) Dividend from shares of X = 12% of FV × Number of Shares

$$= \frac{12}{100} \times 800 \times \frac{3x}{5000} = 12 \times 8 \times \frac{3x}{5000} = \frac{36x}{625}$$

Dividend from shares of Y = 15% of FV × Number of Shares

$$= \frac{15}{100} \times 750 \times \frac{x}{2000} = \frac{9x}{160}$$

$$\text{The required ratio} = \frac{36x}{625} : \frac{9x}{160}$$

$$= \frac{4}{125} : \frac{1}{32} = 128 : 125$$

Hence, the ratio of the dividends received from the shares of X to that of Y = 128 : 125.

(B) Given that the total dividend = ₹45540.

$$\frac{36x}{625} + \frac{9x}{160} = ₹45540$$

$$\frac{1152x + 1125x}{20000} = ₹45540$$

$$\frac{2277x}{20000} = ₹45540$$

$$x = \frac{₹45540 \times 20000}{2277}$$

$$x = ₹20 \times 20000 = ₹400000$$

Hence, the amount invested in both the shares = ₹4,00,000

19. (A) Dividend $= \frac{\overset{3}{\cancel{12}}}{\underset{4}{\cancel{100}}} \times \cancel{25} = ₹3$

Let investment be x

Earning $= 3 = \frac{1\cancel{0}}{10\cancel{0}} x \Rightarrow x = 30$

$$\text{M.V.} = \frac{\text{Investment}}{\text{No. of shores}} = \frac{30}{1} = ₹30$$

20. Dividend $= \frac{8}{1\cancel{00}} \times 50 \times 3\cancel{00}$

$= ₹1200$

S.P. $= 90 \times 300 = 27000$

No. of shares $= \frac{2700\cancel{0}}{3\cancel{0}} = 900$

Dividend $= \frac{10}{1\cancel{00}} \times 50 \times 9\cancel{00} = 4500$

Change in income $= 4500 - 1200$

$= ₹3300$

Competition Wing

Level 1: Apply Your Concepts

1. Shares
2. Face value
3. Face value
4. Divided
5. Market value
6. Rate of dividend × FV = Rate of return × MV
7. (i) First of all, the annual income from one share is to be found.
   (ii) MV = FV + Premium.
   (iii) Find the number of shares.
   (iv) $\text{Income} = \dfrac{(\text{Number of shares} \times \text{FV}) \times (\text{Rate of dividend})}{100}$.
8. (i) $\text{Rate of return} = \dfrac{\text{Annual income}}{\text{Total investment}} \times 100$.
   (ii) By using the following formula find MV.
   Use, FV × Rate of dividend = MV × Rate of return.
9. (i) Require rates = Annual income = MV of 1 share.
   (ii) $\text{Income from 1 share} = \dfrac{(\text{FV} \times \text{Rate of dividend})}{100}$.
   (iii) Then find the total income from 24 shares.
   (iv) MV = (150 + 100)
   Total investment = MV × 24.
10. $\text{Number of share} = \dfrac{\text{Total investment}}{\text{MV}}$.
11. (i) $\text{MV} = \dfrac{\text{Total investment}}{\text{Number of shares}}$
    (ii) $\text{Rate of return} = \dfrac{\text{Annual income}}{\text{Total investment}} \times 100$.
    (iii) By using the following formula find MV.
    Use, FV × Rate of dividend = MV × Rate of return.
12. Find annual income from one share.

Level 2: Review Your Concepts

14. (i) Rate of dividend × FV = MV × Rate of return
    (ii) In the given data, rate of interest is same as the rate of return.
    (iii) FV × Rate of dividend = MV × Rate of return.
15. (i) Number of share =
    $\text{Number of shares} = \dfrac{\text{Total investment}}{\text{MV}}$.
    Use the following formula to find the rate of return.
    FV × Rate of dividend = MV × Rate of return.
16. $\text{Number of shares} = \dfrac{\text{Amount invested}}{\text{MV}}$.
17. First of all, the number of shares is to be found.
18. (i) Find the dividends of the two companies.
    (ii) Find the rate of return in two cases by using the following formula.
    FV × Rate of dividend = MV × Rate of return.
    (iii) The one with greater rate of return is better.
19. (i) $\text{Number of shares} = \dfrac{\text{Total investment}}{\text{MV}}$.
    (ii) $\text{Number of shares} = \dfrac{\text{Total investment}}{\text{MV of each share}}$.
    (iii) SP of total shares = ₹150 × Number of shares.
20. (i) $\text{Number of shares} = \dfrac{(\text{Total investment})}{(\text{MV of each share})}$.
    (ii) Find the dividend paid on all the shares.
    (iii) $\text{SP} = \dfrac{(27{,}000 + 1828 - \text{Dividend})}{\text{Number of shares}}$.
21. MV × Rate of return = Rate of dividend × FV.
23. FV = ₹125
    MV = ₹150
    Rate of dividend = 10%
    Dividend from each shares = 10% of ₹125
    = ₹12.5
    Given, total dividend = ₹1875.
    $\text{The number of shares} = \dfrac{1875}{12.5} = 150.$
24. The number of shares = 200
    Face value (FV) of each share = ₹120
    Discount on each share = ₹20
    Market value of each share = FV – Discount
    = ₹120 – ₹20
    = ₹100
    ∴ Market value of 200 shares (in ₹) = 200 × 100 = ₹20,000.

25. Total investment = ₹32,400

Dividend = ₹4860

Rate of return = $\frac{4860}{32400} \times 100\% = 15\%$.

26. The number of shares = 1000

FV = ₹500

Premium = 12% of ₹500 = ₹60

MV = FV + Premium = ₹560.

Level 3: Assess Your Concepts

28. (i) Number of share =

Number of shares = $\frac{\text{Total investment}}{\text{MV}}$.

Use the following formula to find the MV.

FV × Rate of dividend = MV × Rate of return.

29. MV × Rate of return = Rate of dividend × FV.

30. (i) MV = FV + Premium.

(ii) Use the following formula to find the rate of dividend.

FV × Rate of dividend = MV × Rate of return.

31. (i) Find the dividends received by two persons.

(ii) Number of shares = $\frac{\text{Total investment}}{\text{MV of each share}}$.

(iii) Find their dividends by using FV and rate of dividend.

(iv) Find their profit/loss obtained by selling each at ₹110.

32. FV = ₹120

MV = ₹200

Rate of dividend = 15%

Dividend from each share (in ₹) = 15% of 120 = 18

All the given options are true.

33. FV = ₹100

Rate of dividend = 10%

Number of shares = 100

Dividend from each share (in ₹) = 10% of 100 = 10

Total dividend from 100 shares (in ₹) = 100 × 10 = 1000.

34. Dividend × Face value = Market value × Rate of return

$\Rightarrow 110 \times x = 100 \times y \Rightarrow \frac{x}{y} = \frac{10}{11}$.

35. On the first Investment:

Number of shares $= \frac{15,000}{120} = 125$

Dividend earned $= \left(\frac{10}{100} \times 125\right) 125 = ₹1250$ ₹1250

On the second Investment:

Number of shares $= \frac{24,000}{100} = 240$

$\Rightarrow$ Dividend earned $= 240 \times \frac{12}{100} \times 120 = ₹3456$ ₹3456

Total earnings = ₹4706.

36. Market value = Face value + Premium = 200 + 50 = ₹250

Number of shares purchased

$= \frac{\text{Total investment}}{\text{Market value}} = \frac{12,000}{250} = 48$

Dividend is 10% of ₹200 ₹200 $= \frac{10}{100} \times 200 = ₹20$ ₹20

$\Rightarrow$ Total income from 48 shares = 48 × 20

= ₹960.

37. Number of shares bought by Krish $= \frac{27,000}{90} = 300$

$\Rightarrow$ Dividend earned on 300 shares

$= 300 \times \frac{10}{100} \times 100 = ₹3000$ ₹3000

Money received by selling these 30 shares = 300 × 110 = ₹33,000

$\Rightarrow$ Earnings received by Krish = 33,000 + 3000 − 27,000 = ₹9000

Number of shares bought by Ram

$= \frac{\text{Total investment}}{\text{Market value}} = \frac{30,000}{120} = 250$

$\Rightarrow$ Total dividend earned on 500 shares

$= 250 \times \frac{8}{10} \times 150 = ₹3000$

Money received by selling these 500 shares = 250 × 110 = ₹27,500

$\Rightarrow$ Earnings received by Ram = 27,500 + 3000 − 30,000 = ₹500.

38. Rate of dividend × FV = Rate of return × MV

10 × 120 = 8 × Market value

∴ Market value = ₹150.

JEE Special Wing

Multiple-Answer Type Questions

1. From the given statement we can deduce the following:

Rate of dividend = 20%.

The face value of each share is ₹1250. So, (a) is true.

Discount % = 20%

Discount on each share = 20% of ₹1250

$= \frac{20}{100} \times ₹1,250 = ₹250.$

The market value of each share = Face value – discount = ₹1250 – ₹250 = ₹1000. So, (b) is true.

Dividend from each share = 20% of face value of each share

$= \frac{20}{100} \times ₹1,250 = ₹250.$ So, (c) is true.

We know that:

Face value × Rate of dividend = Market value × Rate of return

₹1250 × 20% = ₹1000 × Rate of return

Rate of return $= \frac{₹1250 \times 20\%}{₹1000} = 25\%$. So, (d) is true.

Hence, choice (a, b, c, d) are correct.

2. From the given statement we can deduce the following:

The number of shares purchased = 500.

Rate of dividend = 5%.

The face value of each share is ₹600.

Premium% = 25%

The premium of each share = 25% of ₹600

$= \frac{25}{100} \times ₹600 = ₹150.$

The market value of each share = Face value + Premium = ₹600 + ₹150 = ₹750. So, (b) is true.

The total investment = No. of shares × Market value of each share

= 500 × ₹750 = ₹3,75,000. So, (a) is false.

Dividend from each share = 5% of face value of each share

$= \frac{5}{100} \times ₹600 = ₹30.$

Dividend from 500 shares = ₹30 × 500 = ₹15,000.

So, (c) is true.

We know that:

Face value × Rate of dividend = Market value × Rate of return

₹600 × 5% = ₹750 × Rate of return

Rate of return $= \frac{₹600 \times 5\%}{₹750} = 4\%$. So, (d) is true.

Hence, choice (b, c, d)are correct.

3. From the given statement we can deduce the following:

Total investment = ₹1,80,000

Rate of dividend = 9%.

The face value of each share is ₹200.

Discount % = 10%

Discount on each share = 10% of ₹200

$= \frac{10}{100} \times ₹200 = ₹20.$

The market value of each share = Face value – discount = ₹200 – ₹20 = ₹180.

The number of shares purchased

$= \frac{\text{Total investment}}{\text{The market value of each share}}$

$= \frac{₹1,80,000}{₹180} = 1,000.$ So, (a) is true.

The market value of 50 shares = 50 × ₹180 = ₹9,000. So, (b) is true.

The total annual return on his investment is the dividend earned from 1000 shares.

= 1000 × 9% of Face Value of each share

$= 1000 \times \frac{9}{100} \times ₹200 = ₹18,000.$ So, (c) is true.

We know that:

Face value × Rate of dividend = Market value × Rate of return

₹200 × 9% = ₹1800 × Rate of return

Rate of return $= \frac{₹200 \times 9\%}{₹180} = 10\%$. So, (d) is false.

Hence, choice (a, b, c) are correct.

4. **Investment A:** ₹450 shares at ₹500 which pay a dividend of 10%.

We know that:

Face value × Rate of dividend = Market value × Rate of return

₹450 × 10% = ₹500 × Rate of return

Rate of return $= \frac{₹450 \times 10\%}{₹500} = 9\%.$

Investment B: ₹225 shares at ₹200 which pay a dividend of 8%.

We know that:

Face value × Rate of dividend = Market value × Rate of return

₹225 × 8% = ₹200× Rate of return

$$\text{Rate of return} = \frac{₹225 \times 8\%}{₹200} = 9\%.$$

Both the investments provide equal returns.

Hence, choice (a and b) are false statements.

5. From the given statement we can deduce the following:

Rate of dividend = 10%.

The face value of each share is ₹40.

Premium % = 10%

Premium of each share = 10% of ₹40

$$= \frac{10}{100} \times ₹40 = ₹4$$

The market value of each share = Face value + premium

= ₹40 + ₹4 = ₹44.

Dividend from each share = 10% of face value of each share

$$= \frac{10}{100} \times ₹40 = ₹4.$$

(a) The dividend from 85 such shares

= 85 × ₹4 = ₹340.

(b) The dividend from 15 such shares = 15 × ₹4 = ₹60.

(c) The annual return from 193 such shares = The dividend from 193 shares

= 193 × ₹4 = ₹772.

(d) The annual return from 25 such shares = The dividend from 25 shares

= 25 × ₹4 = ₹100.

Hence, choice (a and c) are correct.

Match The Column

Common Solutions for questions 6 to 10:

Manvita invested ₹6,30,000 in each of the following stocks.

Name of the Share	Face Value	Rate of Dividend	Dividend from Each Share	Market Value	No. of Shares
h	₹100	6%	6% of ₹100 = ₹6	₹120	$\frac{₹6,30,000}{₹120} = 5250$
Q	₹220	7%	7% of ₹220 = ₹15.4	₹350	$\frac{₹6,30,000}{₹350} = 1800$
R	₹1100	9%	9% of ₹1100 = ₹99	₹1800	$\frac{₹6,30,000}{₹1800} = 350$
S	₹1150	8%	8% of ₹1150 = ₹92	₹2000	$\frac{₹6,30,000}{₹2000} = 315$
T	₹1200	10%	10% of ₹1200 = ₹120	₹2500	$\frac{₹6,30,000}{₹2500} = 252$

6. Annual dividend from shares P = No. of shares × Dividend from each share

= 5250 × ₹6 = ₹31,500.

Hence, the correct option is (d).

7. Annual dividend from shares Q = No. of shares × Dividend from each share

= 1800 × ₹15.4 = ₹27,720.

Hence, the correct option is (a).

8. Annual dividend from shares R = No. of shares × Dividend from each share

= 350 × ₹99 = ₹34,650.

Hence, the correct option is (e).

9. Annual dividend from shares S = No. of shares × Dividend from each share

= 315 × ₹92 = ₹28,980.

Hence, the correct option is (b).

10. Annual dividend from shares T = No. of shares × Dividend from each share

= 252 × ₹120 = ₹30,240.

Hence, the correct option is (c).

Comprehension-Based Questions

Common Solutions for questions 11 to 15:

Name of the Share	Face Value	Discount	Premium	Market Value
P	₹100		20%	120% of ₹100 = ₹120
Q	₹110		10%	110% of ₹110 = ₹121
R	₹120		5%	105% of ₹120 = ₹126
S	₹125	4%		96% of ₹125 = ₹120
T	₹160	20%		80% of ₹160 = ₹128

11. The amount required to purchase 135 shares of P = 135 × ₹120
    = ₹16,200.
    Hence, the correct option is (a).
12. The market value of 121 shares of Q = 121 × ₹121
    = ₹14641.
    Hence, the correct option is (b).
13. The available investment = ₹15,624.
    The number of shares of R that Krishna gets $= \frac{₹15,624}{₹126}$
    = 124.
    Hence, the correct option is (b).
14. The amount required to purchase 84 shares of S and 22 shares of T
    = 84 × ₹120 + 22 × ₹128
    = ₹12,896.
    Hence, the correct option is (d).
15. The total amount required to purchase 22 shares each of P, Q, R, S and T
    = 22 ×(₹120 + ₹121 + ₹126 + ₹120 + ₹128)
    = 22 ×(₹615) = ₹13,530.
    Hence, the correct option is (c).

Assertion and Reason Type Questions

Solutions for questions 16 to 20:

16. **Assertion:** A shareholder invested in the shares of a company. The number of shares of the company held by the person is the ratio of the annual income from the shares and the income from each share.
    Reason: Rate of return $= \frac{\text{Annual Income}}{\text{Total Investment}} \times 100\%$.
    Both the statement are true. But Reason is not the correct explanation of Assertion.
    Hence, the correct option is (b).
17. **Assertion:** We say that a share is available at premium when the market value is more than the face value of the share.
    It is a true statement.
    Reason: We say that a share is available at par when the market value is less than the face value of the share.
    It is a false statement.
    Hence, the correct option is (c).
18. **Assertion:**
    As there is no information about the total face value of the shares, we cannot find the rate dividend. So, given statement is false.
    Reason: Rate of return $= \frac{\text{Annual Income}}{\text{Total Investment}} \times 100\%$.
    It is a true statement.
    Hence, the correct option is (d).
19. **Assertion:** Annual income = Annual dividend = ₹3,00,000.
    Total face value = No. of shares × Face value of each share
    = 1000 × ₹1000 = ₹10,00,000.
    Rate of dividend $= \frac{\text{Annual Income}}{\text{Total Face Value}} \times 100\%$
    $= \frac{₹3,00,000}{₹10,00,000} \times 100\% = 30\%$.
    So, Assertion is true.
    Reason: Rate of dividend $= \frac{\text{Annual Income}}{\text{Total Face Value}} \times 100\%$.
    Reason is true and is the correct explanation of Assertion.
    Hence, the correct option is (a).
20. **Assertion:** Alok invested ₹9,00,000 in ₹80 shares available at ₹120 which pay a dividend of 9.3%. Bhuvan invested ₹9,00,000 in ₹60 shares available at ₹120 which pay a dividend of 12.2%. The annual return of Bhuvan is more than that of Alok.
    Alok:
    Investment = ₹9,00,000.
    Face value = ₹80
    Market value = ₹120.
    Rate of dividend = 9.3%.

We know that:

Face value × Rate of dividend = Market value × Rate of return

₹80 × 9.3% = ₹120× Rate of return

Rate of return = $\frac{₹80 \times 9.3\%}{₹120}$ = 6.2%.

Annual return on Alok's investment = 6.2% of ₹9,00,000 = ₹55,800.

Bhuvan:

Investment = ₹9,00,000.

Face value = ₹60

Market value = ₹120.

Rate of dividend = 12.2%.

We know that:

Face value × Rate of dividend = Market value × Rate of return

₹60 × 12.2% = ₹120× Rate of return

Rate of return = $\frac{₹60 \times 12.2\%}{₹120}$ = 6.1%.

Annual return on Bhuvan's investment = 6.1% of ₹9,00,000 = ₹54,900.

So, Assertion is true.

Reason: The investment in shares which give more rate of return is a better investment.

Reason is true and is the correct explanation of Assertion.

Hence, the correct option is (a).

Unit VII

Bridge to Grade XI

In this Unit

CHAPTER 16

Statements

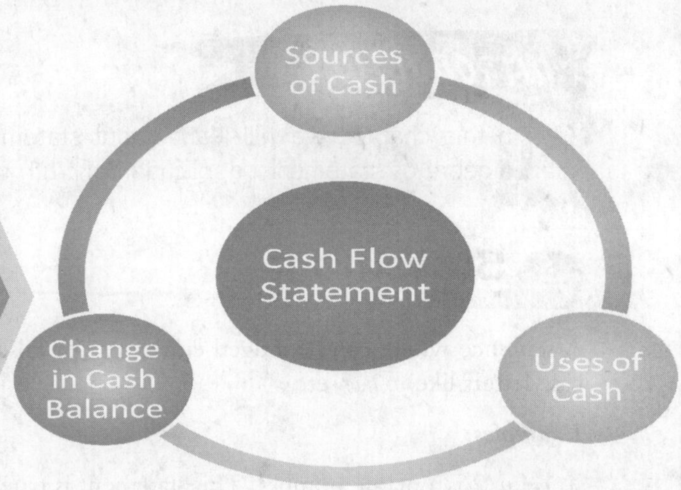

Remember

Before beginning this chapter, you should be able to:

- Have knowledge of different types of numbers
- Apply fundamental operations on numbers

Key Ideas

After completing this chapter, you should be able to:

- Understand statements and truth tables of different compound statements
- Study laws of algebra of statements
- Learn methods of proof and disproof to explain validity of a statement
- Understand application to switching networks, etc.

INTRODUCTION

In this chapter, we will learn about statements, truth tables of different compound statements, laws of algebra of statements, application of truth tables to switching networks, etc.

Statement

A sentence which can be judged either true or false but not both is called a statement. Statements are denoted by lower case letters like p, q, r, etc.

Examples:

1. p: 2 is a prime number. This statement is true.
2. q: $2 + 3 = 6$. This statement is false.

Truth Value

The truthness or falsity of a statement is called its truth value.

Truthness of a statement is denoted by T, while its falsity is denoted by F.

Examples:

1. The truth value of the statement, p: The sun rises in the east, is True.
2. The truth value of the statement q: All odd numbers are prime, is False.

Negation of a Statement

The denial of a statement is called its negation. Negation of a statement p is denoted by $\sim p$ and read as *not p* or *negation p*.

Table 16.1

p	$\sim p$
T	F
F	T

Examples:

1. p: $2 + 4 = 6$

   $\sim p$: $2 + 4 \neq 6$
2. p: 3 is a factor of 10

   $\sim p$: 3 is not a factor of 10
3. p: Charminar is in Delhi

   $\sim p$: Charminar is not in Delhi

Compound Statement

A statement obtained by combining two or more simple statements using connectives is called a compound statement.

Examples: Consider the two statements.

p: 2 is a prime number and

q: 2 is an even number.

Some compound statements that can be formed by using the statements p and q are:

1. 2 is a prime number and 2 is an even number.
2. 2 is a prime number or 2 is an even number.
3. 2 is neither a prime number nor an even number.

Let us look at some basic compound statements.

Conjunction

If p and q are two simple statements, the compound statement p and q is called the conjunction of p and q. It is denoted by $p \wedge q$.

Table 16.2

p	q	$p \wedge q$
T	T	T
T	F	F
F	T	F
F	F	F

We observe that $p \wedge q$ is true only when both p and q are true.

Examples:

1. Let p: 4 is a perfect square and q: 2 is an odd number.

   $p \wedge q$: 4 is a perfect square and 2 is an odd number.

   As p is T and q is F, the truth value of $p \wedge q$ is F.
2. Let p: $3 > 2$ and q: $\sqrt{2}$ is an irrational number.

   Then, $p \wedge q$: $3 > 2$ and $\sqrt{2}$ is an irrational number.

   The truth value of $p \wedge q$ is true as both p and q are true.

Disjunction

If p and q are two simple statements, then the compound statement p or q is called the disjunction of p and q. It is denoted by $p \vee q$.

Table 16.3

p	q	$p \vee q$
T	T	T
T	F	T
F	T	T
F	F	F

We observe that, $p \vee q$ is false only when both p and q are false.

Examples:

1. Let p: The set of even primes is an empty set.
   q: 1 is a factor of every natural number.
   $p \vee q$: The set of even primes is an empty set or 1 is a factor of every natural number.
   As p is false and q is true, truth value of $p \vee q$ is true.

2. Let p: 5 is a factor of 18.
   q: 12 divides 6.
   Then, $p \vee q$: 5 is factor of 18 or 12 divides 6.
   The truth value of $p \vee q$ is false as both p and q are false.

Implication or Conditional

If p and q are two statements, the compound statement ***if p then q***, is called a conditional statement. It is denoted by $p \Rightarrow q$.

The statement p is called the hypothesis (or given) and the statement q is called the conclusion (or result).

Table 16.4

p	q	$p \Rightarrow q$
T	T	T
T	F	F
F	T	T
F	F	T

We observe that, a true statement cannot imply a false statement.

Examples:

1. Let p: Every set is a subset of itself.
   q: $3 + 5 = 8$
   $p \Rightarrow q$: If every set is a subset of itself, then $3 + 5 = 8$.
   As p is true and q is true, the truth value of $p \Rightarrow q$ is true.
2. Let p: ABC is a right triangle if $\angle A = 100°$.
   q: $\angle A + \angle B + \angle C = 180°$
   $p \Rightarrow q$: ABC is a right triangle if $\angle A = 100°$, then $\angle A + \angle B + \angle C = 180°$.
   As p is false and q is true, the truth value of $p \Rightarrow q$ is true.

Bi-conditional or Bi-implication

If p and q are two statements, then the compound statement ***p if and only if q*** is called the bi-conditional of p and q. It is denoted by $p \Leftrightarrow q$.

Table 16.5

p	q	$p \Leftrightarrow q$
T	T	T
T	F	F
F	T	F
F	F	T

We observe that, $p \Leftrightarrow q$ is true if both p and q have the same truth values.

Examples:

1. Let p: $2 \times 3 = 6$
   q: $2 + 8 = 10$
   $p \Leftrightarrow q$: $2 \times 3 = 6$ if and only if $2 + 8 = 10$.
   Since both p and q are true, the truth value of $p \Leftrightarrow q$ is true.

2. Let p: Every triangle is equilateral.

   q: Charminar is in Hyderabad.

   $p \Leftrightarrow q$: Every triangle is equilateral if and only if Charminar is in Hyderabad.

   As p is false and q is true, the truth value of $p \Leftrightarrow q$ is false.

Converse, Inverse and Contrapositive of a Conditional

Let $p \Rightarrow q$ or *if p then q* be a conditional,

1. If q then p, i.e., $q \Rightarrow p$, is called the converse of $p \Rightarrow q$.
2. If not p then not q, i.e., $\sim p \Rightarrow \sim q$, is called the inverse of $p \Rightarrow q$.
3. If not q then not p, i.e., $\sim q \Rightarrow \sim p$ is called the contrapositive of $p \Rightarrow q$.

Table 16.6

p	q	$\sim p$	$\sim q$	Conditional $p \Rightarrow q$	Converse $q \Rightarrow p$	Inverse $\sim p \Rightarrow \sim q$	Contrapositive $\sim q \Rightarrow \sim p$
T	T	F	F	T	T	T	T
T	F	F	T	F	T	T	F
F	T	T	F	T	F	F	T
F	F	T	T	T	T	T	T

EXAMPLE 16.1 Write the converse, inverse, and contrapositive of the conditional 'If x is odd then x^2 is odd'.

SOLUTION

Conditional: If x is odd, then x^2 is odd.

Converse: If x^2 is odd, then x is odd.

Inverse: If x is not odd, then x^2 is not odd.

Contrapositive: If x^2 is not odd, then x is not odd.

EXAMPLE 16.2 Write the converse and the contrapositive of the conditional, 'If ABC is a triangle, then $\angle A + \angle B + \angle C = 180°$'.

SOLUTION

Conditional: If ABC is a triangle, then $\angle A + \angle B + \angle C = 180°$.

Converse: If $\angle A + \angle B + \angle C = 180°$, then ABC is a triangle.

Contrapositive: If $\angle A + \angle B + \angle C \neq 180°$, then ABC is not a triangle.

Let us now look at the truth tables of some compound statements:

EXAMPLE 16.3 Write the truth table of $p \vee \sim q$.

SOLUTION

Table 16.7

p	q	$\sim q$	$p \vee \sim q$
T	T	F	T
T	F	T	T
F	T	F	F
F	F	T	T

EXAMPLE 16.4 Write the truth table of $\sim p \vee (p \wedge q)$.

SOLUTION

Table 16.8

p	q	$\sim p$	$p \wedge q$	$\sim p \vee (p \wedge q)$
T	T	F	T	T
T	F	F	F	F
F	T	T	F	T
F	F	T	F	T

EXAMPLE 16.5 Write the truth table of $\sim p \Rightarrow p \vee q$.

SOLUTION

Table 16.9

p	q	$\sim p$	$p \vee q$	$\sim p \Rightarrow p \vee q$
T	T	F	T	T
T	F	F	T	T
F	T	T	T	T
F	F	T	F	F

Tautology

A compound statement which always takes **True** as its truth value is called a tautology.

Example: The truth table of $p \vee \sim p$ is

p	$\sim p$	$p \vee \sim p$
T	F	T
F	T	T

We observe that $p \vee \sim p$ always takes T as its truth value. So, $p \vee \sim p$ is a tautology.

EXAMPLE 16.6 Show that the compound statement $p \Rightarrow p \vee q$ is a tautology.

SOLUTION

Table 16.10

p	q	$p \vee q$	$p \Rightarrow (p \vee q)$
T	T	T	T
T	F	T	T
F	T	T	T
F	F	F	T

We observe that $p \Rightarrow p \vee q$ is always True.

Hence, $p \Rightarrow p \vee q$ is a tautology.

Contradiction

A compound statement which always takes **False** as its truth value is called a contradiction.

Example: The truth table of $p \wedge \sim p$ is

p	$\sim p$	$p \wedge \sim p$
T	F	F
F	T	F

We observe that $p \wedge \sim p$ always takes F as its truth value. So $p \wedge \sim p$ is a contradiction.

EXAMPLE 16.7 Show that the compound statement $(p \vee \sim p) \Rightarrow (q \wedge \sim q)$ is a contradiction.

SOLUTION

Table 16.11

p	q	$\sim p$	$\sim q$	$p \vee \sim p$	$q \wedge \sim q$	$p \vee \sim q \Rightarrow q \wedge \sim q$
T	T	F	F	T	F	F
T	F	F	T	T	F	F
F	T	T	F	T	F	F
F	F	T	T	T	F	F

We observe that $p \vee \sim p \Rightarrow q \wedge \sim q$ is always False.

Hence, $p \vee \sim p \Rightarrow q \wedge \sim q$ is a contradiction.

Contingency

A compound statement which is neither a tautology nor a contradiction is called a contingency.

Example: $p \vee q \Rightarrow \sim p$

Table 16.12

p	q	$\sim p$	$p \vee q$	$p \vee q \Rightarrow \sim p$
T	T	F	T	F
T	F	F	T	F
F	T	T	T	T
F	F	T	F	T

Info Bytes!

$r \Leftrightarrow s$ is always true only if both r and s have same truth values.

Logically Equivalent Statements

Two statements r and s are said to be logically equivalent, if the last columns of their truth tables are identical.

(OR)

Two statements r and s are said to be logically equivalent if $r \Leftrightarrow s$ is a tautology. Generally, r and s will be compound statements.

If the statements r and s are logically equivalent, then we denote this as $r \equiv s$.

EXAMPLE 16.8 Show that $p \wedge q \equiv q \wedge p$.

SOLUTION

Table 16.13

p	q	$p \wedge q$	$q \wedge p$
T	T	T	T
T	F	F	F
F	T	F	F
F	F	F	F

We observe that $p \wedge q$ and $q \wedge p$ have the same truth values. Hence, $p \wedge q \equiv q \wedge p$.

EXAMPLE 16.9 Show that $p \Rightarrow q \equiv \sim p \vee q$.

SOLUTION

Table 16.14

p	q	$\sim p$	$p \Rightarrow q$	$\sim p \vee q$
T	T	F	T	T
T	F	F	F	F
F	T	T	T	T
F	F	T	T	T

We observe that, $p \Rightarrow q$ and $\sim p \vee q$ have the same truth values.

Hence, $p \Rightarrow q \equiv \sim p \vee q$.

Laws of Algebra of Statements

Some logical equivalences are listed under the following laws:

1. **Commutative Laws:**
   (i) $p \vee q \equiv q \vee p$
   (ii) $p \wedge q \equiv q \wedge p$
2. **Associative Laws:**
   (i) $(p \vee q) \vee r \equiv p \vee (q \vee r)$
   (ii) $(p \wedge q) \wedge r \equiv p \wedge (q \wedge r)$
3. **Distributive Laws:**
   (i) $p \wedge (q \vee r) \equiv (p \wedge q) \vee (p \wedge r)$
   (ii) $p \vee (q \wedge r) \equiv (p \vee q) \wedge (p \vee r)$
4. **Idempotent Laws:**
   (i) $p \vee p \equiv p$
   (ii) $p \wedge p \equiv p$
5. **De Morgan's Laws:**
   (i) $\sim(p \vee q) \equiv (\sim p) \wedge (\sim q)$
   (ii) $\sim(p \wedge q) \equiv (\sim p) \vee (\sim q)$
6. **Identity Laws:**
   (i) $p \vee F \equiv p$, $p \vee T \equiv T$
   (ii) $p \wedge F \equiv F$, $p \wedge T \equiv p$
7. **Complement Laws:**
   (i) $p \vee (\sim p) \equiv T$
   (ii) $p \wedge (\sim p) \equiv F$
   (iii) $\sim(\sim p) \equiv p$
   (iv) $\sim T \equiv F$
   (v) $\sim F \equiv T$

List of Equivalences Based on Implications

1. $p \Rightarrow q \equiv \sim p \vee q$
2. $\sim(p \Rightarrow q) \equiv p \wedge \sim q$
3. $p \Rightarrow q \equiv \sim q \Rightarrow \sim p$
   (i.e., a conditionai and its contrapositive are logically equivalent)
4. $q \Rightarrow p \equiv \sim q \Rightarrow \sim p$
   (i.e., converse and inverse of a conditional are logically equivalent)
5. $p \Leftrightarrow q \equiv (p \Rightarrow q) \wedge (q \Rightarrow p)$
6. $\sim(p \Leftrightarrow q) \equiv (\sim p) \Leftrightarrow q$ or $p \Leftrightarrow (\sim q)$

Open Sentence

A sentence involving one or more variables is called an open sentence, it becomes TRUE or FALSE when the variables are replaced by some specific values from the given set. The set from which the values of a variable can be considered is called the replacement set or domain of the variable.

Examples:

1. $x + 2 = 9$ is an open sentence.
   For $x = 7$, it becomes True and for other real values of x it becomes False.
2. $x^2 + 1 > 0$ is an open sentence.
   For all real values of x it is True.

Quantifiers

A quantifier is a word or phrase which quantifies a variable in the given open sentence.

There are two types of quantifiers.

1. Universal quantifier
2. Existential quantifier

Universal Quantifier

The quantifiers like *for all*, *for every*, *for each* are called universal quantifiers. A universal quantifier is denoted by '∀'.

Examples:

1. Consider an open sentence, $|x| \geq 0$.
   This is true for all $x \in R$. So, we write $|x| \geq 0, \forall x \in R$.
2. Consider the sentence,
   $$1+2+3+\cdots+n=\frac{n(n+1)}{2}, \forall n \in N.$$

Existential Quantifier

The quantifiers like *for some, not all, there is/exists at least one* are called existential quantifiers.

An existential quantifier is denoted by '∃'.

Examples:

1. Not all prime numbers are odd.
2. $\exists\, x \in R$ such that $x + 4 = 11$.

Negation of Statements Involving Quantifiers

1. *p*: All odd numbers are prime.
   ~*p*: Not all odd numbers are prime
   (or)
   Some odd numbers are not prime.
   (or)
   There is an odd number which is not prime.
2. *p*: All questions are difficult.
   ~*p*: Not all questions are difficult.
   (or)
   Some questions are not difficult.
   (or)
   There is at least one question which is not difficult.
3. *p*: All birds can fly.
   ~*p*: Not all birds can fly.
   (or)
   There are some birds which cannot fly.
   (or)
   There is at least one bird which cannot fly.

Methods of Proof

Statements in mathematics are usually examined for their validity. The various steps involved in the process is referred as proof.

There are two important types of proofs.

Direct Proof

In this method, we begin with the hypothesis and end up with the desired result through a logical sequence of steps.

Example: If x is odd, then x^2 is odd.
Given, x is an odd number.
Conclusion: x^2 is an odd number.

Proof:
$\Rightarrow x = 2k + 1$ (for some $k \in Z$)
$\Rightarrow x^2 = (2k + 1)^2$
$= 4k^2 + 4k + 1$
$= 2(2k^2 + 2k) + 1$
$= 2m + 1$, where $m = 2k^2 + 2k \in Z$ $(\because k \in Z \Rightarrow 2k^2 + 2k \in Z)$.
$\therefore x^2 = 2m + 1, m \in Z$
$\Rightarrow x^2$ is an odd number.
Hence, if x is an odd number, then x^2 is an odd number.

Indirect Proof

In this method, we proceed by assuming that the conclusion is false. Then we arrive at a contradiction. This implies that the desired result must be true.

Example: If $a + b = 0$, then $(a + b)^2 = 0$. where $a, b \in Z - \{0\}$
Given: $a + b = 0$
Conclusion: $(a + b)^2 = 0$

Proof: Let us assume that $(a + b)^2 \neq 0$
$\Rightarrow (a + b)^2 > 0$ (As $(a + b)^2$ cannot be negative)
$\Rightarrow a + b > 0$ or $a + b < 0$
Which is a contradiction to the hypothesis, i.e., $a + b = 0$.
$\therefore$ Our assumption, i.e., $(a + b)^2 \neq 0$ is false.
Hence, if $a + b = 0$, then $(a + b)^2 = 0$.

Methods of Disproof

There are two methods to disprove a given statement.

Counter Example Method

In this method, we look for a counter example which disproves the given statement.

Examples:

1. Every odd number is a prime number.
   This statement is false, as 9 is an odd number but it is not a prime.
2. $x^2 - x - 6 = 0$, for all real values of x.
   This statement is false, as for $x = 2$, $x^2 - x - 6 = (2)^2 - 2 - 6 = -4 \neq 0$.
   $\therefore x = 2$ is a counter example here.

Method of Contradiction

In this method, we assume that the given statement is true. Then we arrive at a contradiction. This implies that the given statement is false.

EXAMPLE 16.10 Disprove the statement, 'There can be two right angles in a triangle'.

SOLUTION

Let ABC be a triangle.

If possible, let $\angle A = 90°$ and $\angle B = 90°$

We know that, the sum of the three internal angles of a triangle is 180°.

That is, $\angle A + \angle B + \angle C = 180°$

$\Rightarrow 90° + 90° + \angle C = 180°$

$\Rightarrow \angle C = 0°$ which is a contradiction.

Hence, there cannot be two right angles in a triangle.

Application To Switching Networks

Now we consider the statements p and p' as switches with the property that if one is on, then the other is off and vice versa.

Further, a switch allows only two possibilities.

1. It is either open (F), in which case there is no flow of current.

(Or)

2. It is closed (T), in which case there is a flow of current.

Hence, every switch has two truth values: T or F only.

Let p and q denote two switches. We can connect p and q by using a wire in a series or parallel combination as shown in Fig. 16.1.

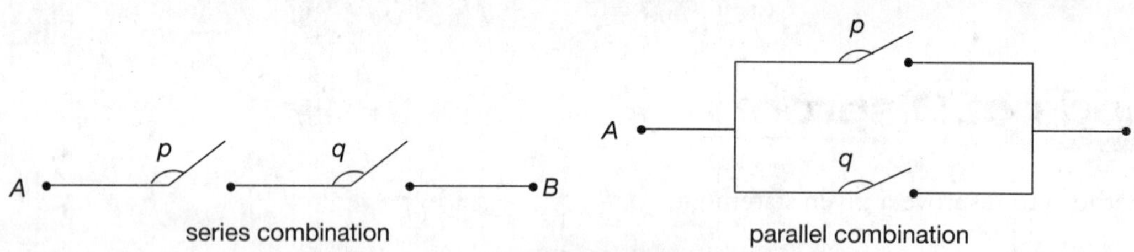

Figure 16.1

Switching Network

A switching network is a repeated arrangement of wires and switches in series and parallel combinations.

So, such a network can be described by using the connectives $\wedge$ and $\vee$.

> **Konnect**
> $p \wedge q$ denote the series combination and $p \vee q$ denote the parallel combination.

EXAMPLE 16.11

Describe the behaviour of flow of current from A to B in the following circuit network (see Fig. 16.2).

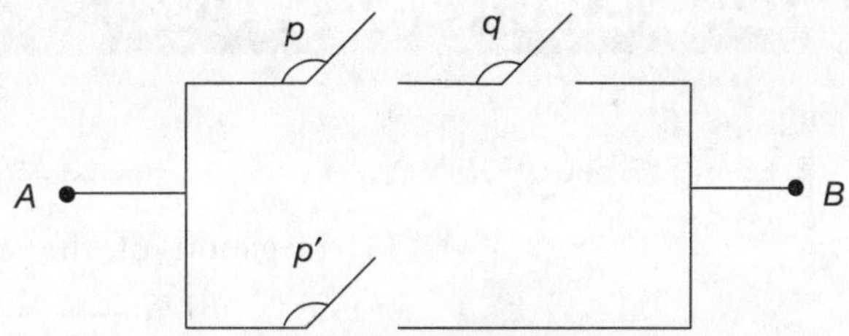

Figure 16.2

SOLUTION

The given network can be described by the compound statement $(p \wedge q) \vee p'$. Truth table of $(p \wedge q) \vee p'$ is:

Table 16.15

p	q	p'	$p \wedge q$	$(p \wedge q) \vee p'$
T	T	F	T	T
T	F	F	F	F
F	T	T	F	T
F	F	T	F	T

So, current flows from A to B if:

1. p is closed, q is closed
2. p is open, q is closed
3. p is open, q is open.

POINTS TO REMEMBER

- ✔ A sentence which can be judged either true or false but not both is called a **statement**.
- ✔ The denial of a statement is called its negation. Negation of a statement p is denoted by $\sim p$ and read as *not p* or *negation p*.
- ✔ A statement obtained by combining two or more simple statements using connectives is called a compound statement.
- ✔ If p and q are two simple statements, the compound statement p and q is called the conjunction of p and q.
- ✔ If p and q are two simple statements, then the compound statement p or q is called the disjunction of p and q. It is denoted by $p \vee q$.
- ✔ If p and q are two statements, the compound statement ***if p then q***, is called a conditional statement. It is denoted by $p \Rightarrow q$.
- ✔ If p and q are two statements, then the compound statement ***p if and only if q*** is called the bi-conditional of p and q. It is denoted by $p \Leftrightarrow q$.
- ✔ A compound statement which always takes **True** as its truth value is called a tautology.
- ✔ A compound statement which always takes **False** as its truth value is called a contradiction.
- ✔ A compound statement which is neither a tautology nor a contradiction is called a contingency.
- ✔ A sentence involving one or more variables is called an open sentence, it becomes TRUE or FALSE when the variables are replaced by some specific values from the given set.

PRACTICE QUESTIONS CLASSROOM WING

Very Short Answer Type Questions

Directions of questions from 1 to 14:
Fill in the blanks.

1. The truth value of 'Hyderabad is the capital city of AP' is _________.
2. If p is F and q is T, then $\sim q \Rightarrow p$ is _________.
3. Truth value of '$3 \times 7 = 28$, iff $3 + 7 = 12$' is _________.
4. 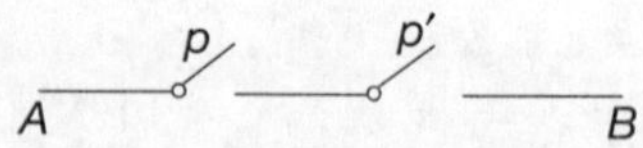

   The current _________ flow from A to B.
5. The quantifier to be used to describe the statement, 'not all isosceles triangles are equilateral is _________. ($\forall$ or $\exists$)'.
6. If $p \vee \sim q$ is F, then q is _________.
7. The connective used in the negation of 'if the grass is green, then sky is blue' is _________.
8. The symbolic form of the statement, 'If p, then neither q nor r' is _______.
9. The converse of converse of the statement $p \Rightarrow \sim q$ is _______.
10. $p \Rightarrow q$ is logically equivalent to ______.
11. The counter example of the statement, 'All odd numbers are primes', is ______.
12. The negation of the statement, 'I go to school everyday', is ______.
13. The contrapositive of the statement $p \Rightarrow \sim q$ is. ______.
14. Negation of the compound statement $[(p \wedge q) \vee (p \wedge \sim q)]$ is _______.

Directions of questions from 15 to 16:
State whether the following statements are true or false

15. $\sim(\sim p \Rightarrow q) = \sim(p \vee q)$ (True/False)
16. The negation of '$a > b$' is $a = b$. (True/False)

Directions of questions from 17 to 25:
Answer the following questions.

17. Write the conjunction and implication of the statement: He is smart; He is intelligent.
18. Write the suitable quantifier for the sentence: there exists a real number x such that $x + 2 = 3$.
19. Find the truth value of 'Are you attending the meeting tomorrow?'.
20. Find the inverse of the conditional, 'If I am tired, then I will take rest'.
21. Find the truth value of the statement, 'The sum of any two odd numbers is an odd number'.
22. Find the negation of the statement, 'Some odd numbers are not prime'.
23. What is the truth value of the statement, '$2 \times 3 = 6$ or $5 + 8 = 10$'?
24. Find the converse of the statement, 'If $ABCD$ is square, then it is a rectangle'.
25. Write the compound statement, 'If p, then q and if q, then p' in symbolic form.

Short Answer Type Questions

Directions of questions from 26 to 39:
Answer the following questions.

26. What is the converse of the statement $p \Rightarrow p \vee q$?
27. Write the converse, inverse and contrapositive of the conditional, 'If she is rich, then she is happy'.
28. Show that $p \Rightarrow p \vee q$ is a tautology.
29. Write the converse, inverse and contrapositive, of the statement 'In a ΔABC, if $AB \neq AC$, then $\angle B \neq \angle C$'.
30. (A) Show that $\sim(p \wedge q) \equiv \sim p \vee \sim q$.
    (B) Show that $p \Leftrightarrow q \equiv (p \Rightarrow q) \wedge (q \Rightarrow p)$.
31. Write the truth table of $(p \vee q) \vee \sim r$.
32. Show that $p \Rightarrow q \equiv \sim p \vee q$.
33. Write the truth table of $p \wedge \sim q$.
34. (A) Show that $(p \wedge q) \vee \sim q \equiv p \vee \sim q$.

(B) Show that $(p \wedge q) \Rightarrow q$ is a tautology.

35. Write the truth table of $p \Rightarrow (p \wedge q)$.

36. Write the suitable quantifier for the following sentences:

(a) $x + 1 > x$ for all real values of x.

(b) There is no real number x such that $x^2 + 2x + 2 = 0$.

37. Prove that $(\sim p \wedge q) \wedge q$ is neither a tautology nor a contradiction.

38. Write the truth table of $\sim p \vee (p \wedge q)$.

39. (A) Show that $(p \wedge \sim p) \wedge (p \vee q)$ is a contradiction.

(B) Show that $\sim(p \vee q) \equiv \sim p \wedge \sim q$.

Essay Type Questions

Directions of questions from 40 to 46: Answer the following questions.

40. Discuss when does the current flow from A to B in the given network.

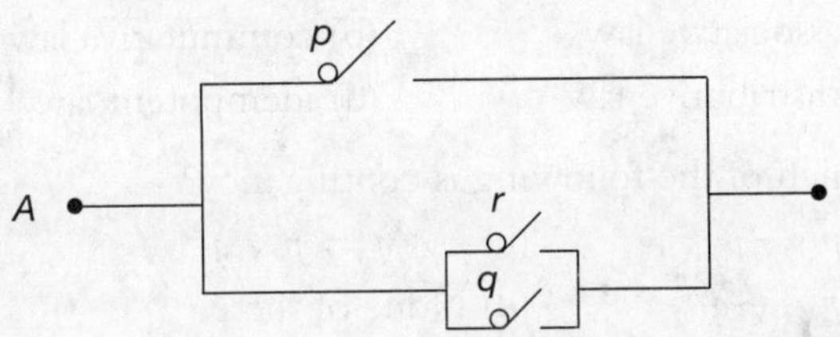

41. Discuss when does the current flow from A to B in the given network.

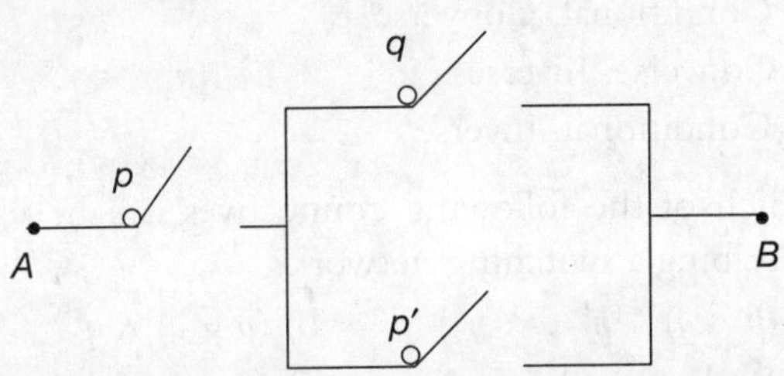

42. Discuss when does the current flow from A to B in the given network.

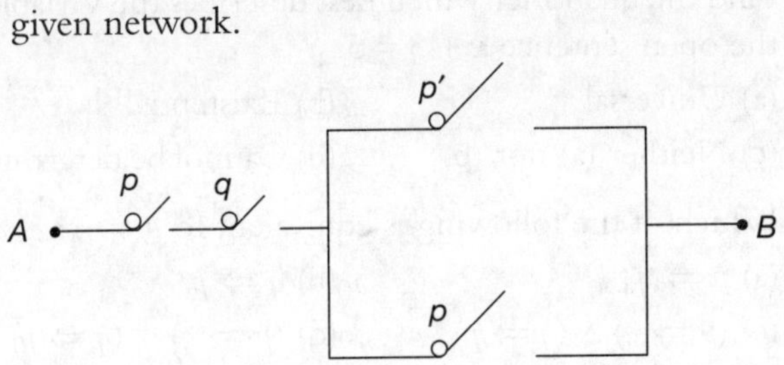

43. Discuss when does the current flow from A to B in the given network.

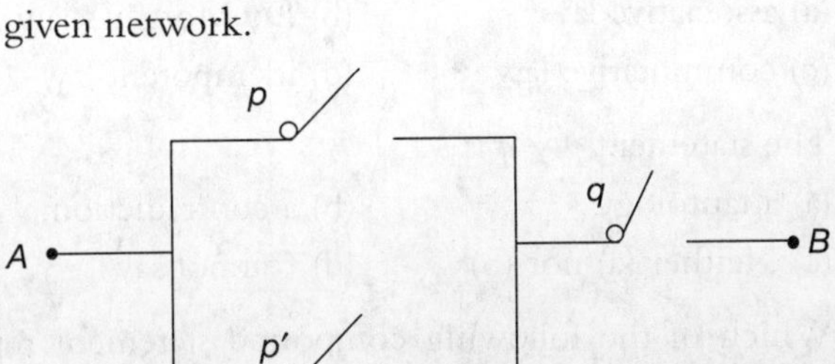

44. Discuss when does the current flow from the points A to B in the given network.

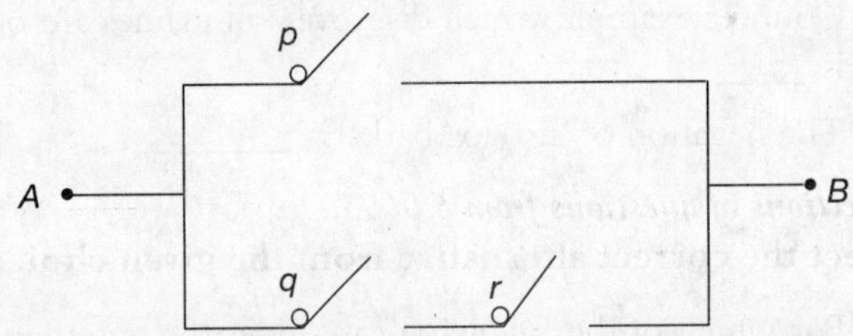

45. Discuss when does the current flow from A to B in the given network.

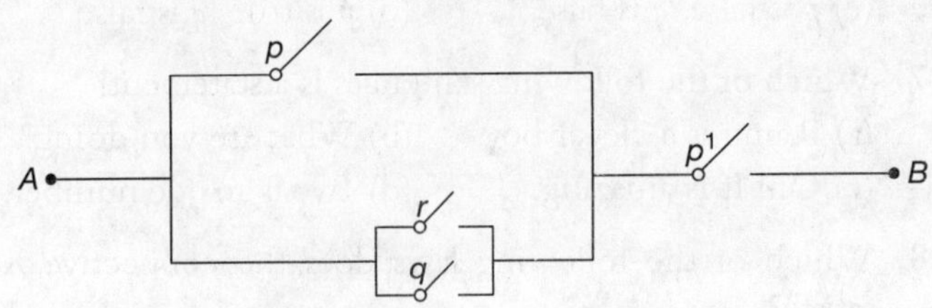

46. Discuss when does the current flow from A to B in the network given.

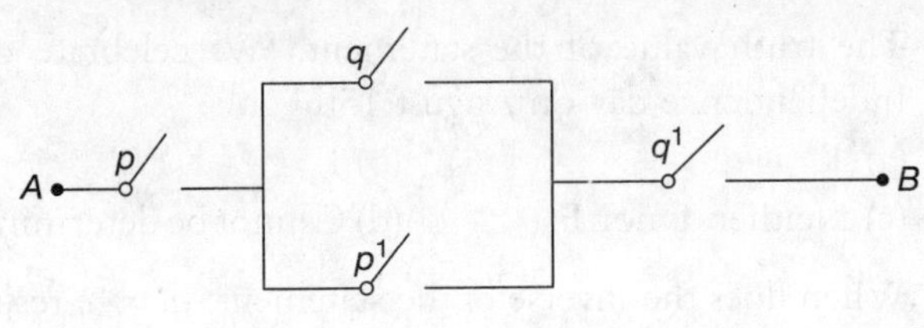

PRACTICE QUESTIONS COMPETITION WING

Level 1: Apply Your Concepts

Directions of questions from 1 to 5:
Fill in the blanks.

1. If truth value of $(\sim p)$ is T, then truth value $\sim(\sim p)$ is ________.
2. $\sim(p \vee \sim q) \equiv$ ________.
3. Truth value of 'If x is even, then x^2 is even' is ________.
4. Counter example which disproves 'all primes are odd' is ________.
5. The negation of 'no dog barks' is ________.

Directions of questions from 6 to 75:
Select the correct alternative from the given choices.

6. For which of the following cases does the statement $p \wedge \sim q$ take the truth value as true?
(a) p is true, q is true (b) p is false, q is true
(c) p is false, q is false (d) p is true, q is false

7. Which of the following sentences is a statement?
(a) Ramu is a clever boy. (b) What are you doing?
(c) Oh! It is amazing. (d) Two is an odd number.

8. Which of the following laws does the connective $\wedge$ satisfy?
(a) Commutative law (b) Idempotent law
(c) Associative law (d) All of these

9. The truth value of the statement, 'We celebrate our Independence day on August 15th', is
(a) T (b) F
(c) Neither T nor F (d) Cannot be determined

10. When does the inverse of the statement $\sim p \Rightarrow q$ results in T?
(a) $p = \text{T}, q = \text{T}$ (b) $p = \text{T}, q = \text{F}$
(c) $p = \text{F}, q = \text{F}$ (d) Both (b) and (c).

11. Which of the following is a contradiction?
(a) $p \vee q$ (b) $p \wedge q$
(c) $p \vee \sim p$ (d) $p \wedge \sim p$

12. In which of the following cases, $p \Leftrightarrow q$ is true?
(a) p is true, q is true (b) p is false, q is true
(c) p is true, q is false (d) p is false, q is false

13. Find the counter example of the statement 'Every natural number is either prime or composite'.
(a) 5 (b) 1
(c) 6 (d) None of these

14. Which of the following pairs are logically equivalent?
(a) Conditional, Contrapositive
(b) Conditional, Inverse
(c) Contrapositive, Converse
(d) Inverse, Contrapositive

15. The property $p \wedge (q \vee r) \equiv (p \wedge q) \vee (p \wedge r)$ is called
(a) associative law (b) commutative law
(c) distributive law (d) idempotent law

16. Which of the following is contingency?
(a) $p \vee \sim p$ (b) $p \wedge q \Rightarrow p \vee q$
(c) $p \wedge (\sim q)$ (d) None of these

17. Which of the following pairs are logically equivalent?
(a) Converse, Contrapositive
(b) Conditional, Converse
(c) Converse, Inverse
(d) Conditional, Inverse

18. Which of the following connectives can be used for describing a switching network?
(a) $(p \wedge q) \vee p'$ (b) $(p \vee q) \wedge q'$
(c) Both (a) and (b) (d) None of these

19. Find the quantifier which best describes the variable of the open sentence $x + 3 = 5$.
(a) Universal (b) Existential
(c) Neither (a) nor (b) (d) Cannot be determined

20. Which of the following is equivalent to $p \Leftrightarrow q$?
(a) $p \Rightarrow q$ (b) $q \Rightarrow p$
(c) $(p \Rightarrow q) \wedge (q \Rightarrow p)$ (d) $(p \Rightarrow q) \vee (q \Rightarrow p)$

21. The property $\sim(p \wedge q) \equiv \sim p \vee \sim q$ is called ________.
(a) associative law (b) De Morgan's law
(c) commutative law (d) idempotent law

22. The statement $p \vee q$ is
(a) a tautology. (b) a contradiction.
(c) Neither (a) nor (b) (d) Cannot say

23. Which of the following compound statement represents a series network?

(a) $p \vee q$ (b) $p \Rightarrow q$
(c) $p \wedge q$ (d) $p \Leftrightarrow q$

24. Which of the following is a tautology?
(a) $p \wedge q$ (b) $p \vee q$
(c) $p \vee \sim p$ (d) $p \wedge \sim p$

25. Find the truth value of the compound statement, 'If 2 is a prime number, then hockey is the national game of India'.
(a) T (b) F
(c) Neither (a) nor (b) (d) Cannot be determined

26. Find the truth value of the compound statement, '4 is the first composite number and 2 + 5 = 7'.
(a) T (b) F
(c) Neither (a) nor (b) (d) Cannot be determined

27. Find the inverse of the statement, 'If ΔABC is equilateral, then it is isosceles'.
(a) If ΔABC is isosceles, then it is equilateral.
(b) If ΔABC is not equilateral, then it is isosceles.
(c) If ΔABC is not equilateral, then it is not isosceles.
(d) If ΔABC is not isosceles, then it is not equilateral.

28. The statement $p \Rightarrow p \vee q$ is
(a) a tautology. (b) a contradiction.
(c) Both (a) and (b) (d) Neither (a) nor (b)

29. What is the truth value of the statement 'Two is an odd number, iff 2 is a root of $x^2 + 2 = 0$'?
(a) T (b) F
(c) Neither (a) nor (b) (d) Cannot be determined

30. Which of the following connectives satisfy commutative law?
(a) $\wedge$ (b) $\vee$
(c) $\Leftrightarrow$ (d) All of these

31. $\sim[\sim p \wedge (p \Leftrightarrow q)] \equiv$ ______.
(a) $p \vee q$ (b) $q \wedge p$
(c) T (d) F

32. Write the negation of the statement 'If the switch is on, then the fan rotates'.
(a) 'If the switch is not on, then the fan does not rotate'.
(b) 'If the fan does not rotate, then the switch is not on'.
(c) 'The switch is not on or the fan rotates'.
(d) 'The switch is on and the fan does not rotate'.

33. If p: The number of factors of 20 is 5 and q: 2 is an even prime number, then the truth values of inverse and contrapositive of $p \Rightarrow q$, respectively, are:
(a) T, T (b) F, F
(c) T, F (d) F, T

34. 'No square of a real number is less than zero' is equivalent to
(a) for every real number a, a^2 is non-negative.
(b) $\forall\ a \in R, a^2 \geq 0$.
(c) Either (a) or (b)
(d) None of these

35. If a compound statement r is contradiction, then find the truth value of $(p \Rightarrow q) \wedge (r) \wedge [p \Rightarrow (\sim r)]$.
(a) T (b) F
(c) T or F (d) None of these

Level 2: Review Your Concepts

36. Which of the following is/are counter example(s) of the statement $x^2 - 7x + 10 > 0$, for all real x?
(A) 2 (B) 3
(C) 4 (D) 5
(a) Only (A) and (D)
(b) Only (B) and (C)
(c) All (A), (B), (C), and (D)
(d) None of these

37. If p: 3 is an odd number and q: 15 is a prime number, then the truth value of $[\sim(p \Leftrightarrow q)]$ is equivalent to that of ______.
(A) $p \Leftrightarrow (\sim q)$ (B) $(\sim p) \Leftrightarrow q$
(C) $\sim(p \wedge q)$
(a) Only (A) (b) Only (C)
(c) Both (A) and (B) (d) All (A), (B), and (C)

38. The compound statement, 'If you want to top the school, then you do not study hard' is equivalent to
(a) 'If you want to top the school, then you need to study hard'.
(b) 'If you will not top the school, then you study hard'.
(c) 'If you study hard, then you will not top the school'.
(d) 'If you do not study hard, then you will top the school'.

39. If p: 25 is a factor of 625 and q: 169 is a perfect square, then $\sim(p \Rightarrow q)$ is equivalent to

(a) $p \wedge q$ (b) $(\sim p) \wedge q$
(c) $p \wedge (\sim q)$ (d) Both (b) and (c)

40. The compound statement, 'If you won the race, then you did not run faster than others' is equivalent to
(a) 'If you won the race, then you ran faster than others'.
(b) 'If you ran faster than others, then you won the race'.
(c) 'If you did not win the race, then you did not run faster than others'.
(d) 'If you ran faster than others, then you did not win the race'.

41. 'If x is a good actor, then y is bad actress' is:
(a) a tautology (b) a contradiction
(c) a contingency (d) None of these

42. Which of the following is negation of the statement 'All birds can fly'.
(a) 'Some birds cannot fly'.
(b) 'All the birds cannot fly'.
(c) 'There is at least one bird which can fly'.
(d) All of these

43. What are the truth values of $(\sim p \Rightarrow \sim q)$ and $\sim(\sim p \Rightarrow q)$, respectively, when p and q always speak true in any argument?
(a) T, T (b) F, F
(c) T, F (d) F, T

44. If p: 4 is an odd number and q: 4^3 is an even number, then which of the following is equivalent to $\sim(p \Rightarrow q)$?
(a) '4 is an odd number and 4^3 is an even number'.
(b) 'The negation of the statement '4 is not an odd number or 4^3 is not an even number'.
(c) Both (a) and (b)
(d) None of these

45.

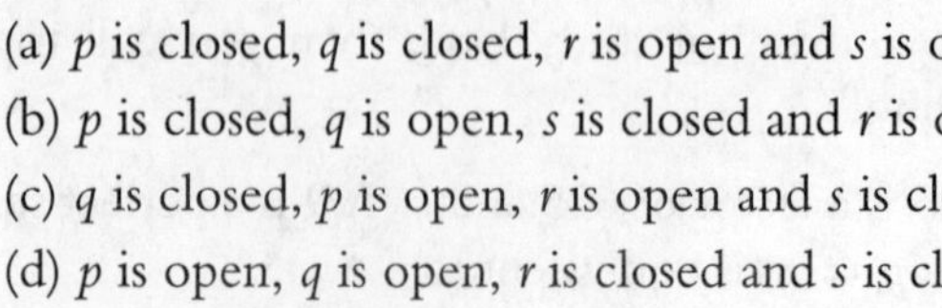

In the above network, current flows from N to T, when:
(a) p is closed, q is closed, r is open and s is open.
(b) p is closed, q is open, s is closed and r is open.
(c) q is closed, p is open, r is open and s is closed.
(d) p is open, q is open, r is closed and s is closed.

46. If p: In a triangle, the centroid divides each median in the ratio 1 : 2 from the vertex and q: In an equilateral triangle, each median is perpendicular bisector of one of its sides. The truth values of inverse and converse of $p \Rightarrow q$ are, respectively:
(a) T, T (b) F, F
(c) T, F (d) F, T

47. If p always speaks against q, then $p \Rightarrow p \vee \sim q$ is:
(a) a tautology (b) contradiction
(c) contingency (d) None of these

48. If p: Every equilateral triangle is isosceles and q: Every square is a rectangle, then which of the following is equivalent to $\sim(p \Rightarrow q)$?
(a) The negation of 'Every equilateral triangle is not isosceles or every square is rectangle'.
(b) 'Every equilateral triangle is not isosceles, then every square is not a rectangle'.
(c) 'Every equilateral triangle is isosceles, then every square is a rectangle'.
(d) None of these

49. When does the value of the statement $(p \wedge r) \Leftrightarrow (r \wedge q)$ become false?
(a) p is T, q is F
(b) p is F, r is F
(c) p is F, q is F and r is F
(d) None of these

50. If the truth value of $p \vee q$ is true, then truth value $\sim p \wedge q$ is
(a) false if p is true. (b) true if p is true.
(c) false if q is true. (d) true if q is true.

51. The compound statement, 'If you want to win the gold medal in Olympics, then you need to work hard' is equivalent to
(a) 'If you will not win the gold medal in Olympics, then you need not to work hard.'
(b) 'If you do not work hard, then you will not win the gold medal in Olympics.'
(c) Both (a) and (b)
(d) None of these

52. If p: sum of the angles in a triangle is 180° and q: every angle in a triangle is more than 0°, then $(p \Rightarrow q) \vee p$ is equivalent to
(a) $p \vee \sim q$ (b) $(p \wedge q) \Rightarrow p$
(c) $\sim p \wedge \sim q$ (d) Both (a) and (b)

53. Which of the following is the negation of the statement, 'All animals are carnivores'?

(a) Some animals are not carnivores.

(b) Not all animals are carnivores.

(c) There is atleast one animal which is not carnivores.

(d) All of these

54. $(p \Leftrightarrow q) \Leftrightarrow (\sim p \Leftrightarrow \sim q)$ is a

(a) tautology (b) contradiction

(c) contingency (d) None of these

55. Which of the following is a counter example of $x^2 - 6x + 8 \leq 0$?

(a) $x = 2$ (b) $x = 3$

(c) $x = 4$ (d) $x = 5$

Level 3: Assess Your Concepts

56. If p and q are two statements, then $p \vee \sim(p \Rightarrow \sim q)$ is equivalent to:

(a) $p \wedge \sim q$ (b) p

(c) q (d) $\sim p \wedge q$

57.

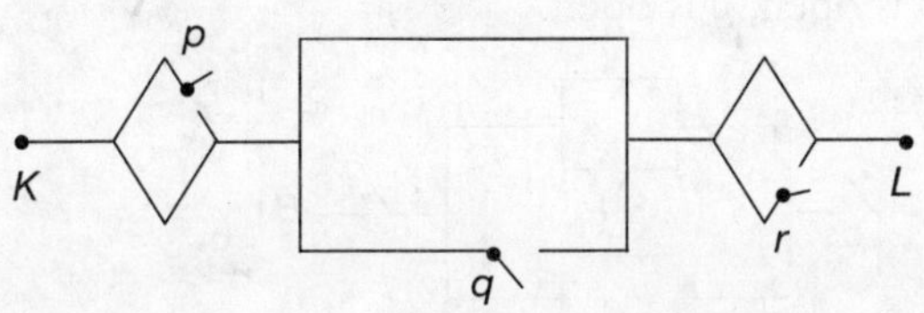

In the above network, current does not flow, when:

(a) p is open, q is open and r is open.

(b) p is closed, q is open and r is open.

(c) p is open, q is closed and r is closed.

(d) None of these

58. The contrapositive of the statement $\sim p \Rightarrow (p \wedge \sim q)$ is:

(a) $p \Rightarrow (\sim p \vee q)$ (b) $p \Rightarrow (p \wedge q)$

(c) $p \Rightarrow (\sim p \wedge q)$ (d) $(\sim p \vee q) \Rightarrow p$

59.

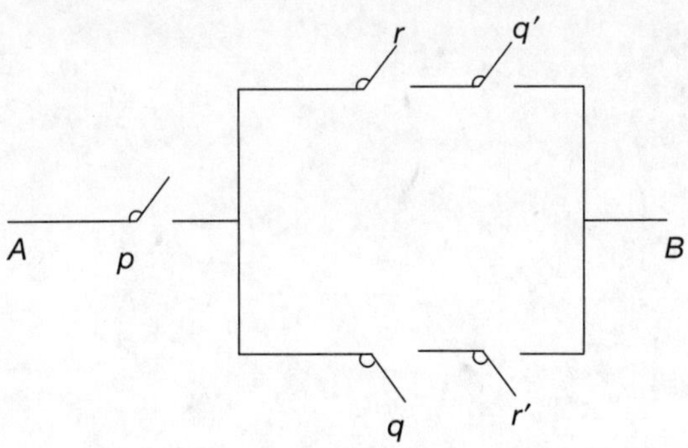

In the above circuit, the current flows from A to B when:

(a) p is closed, q is open and r is open.

(b) p is closed, q is closed and r is open.

(c) p is closed, q is closed and r is closed.

(d) All of these

60. If p: $5x + 6 = 8$ is an open sentence and q: 3, 4 are the roots of the equation $x^2 - 7x + 12 = 0$, then which of following is equivalent to $\sim[\sim p \vee q]$?

(a) The negation of 'If $5x + 6 = 8$ is an open sentence, then 3, 4 are the roots of the equation $x^2 - 7x + 12 = 0$'.

(b) $5x + 6 = 8$ is an open sentence or 3, 4 are not roots of the equation $x^2 - 7x + 12 = 0$.

(c) $5x + 6 = 8$ is not an open sentence and 3, 4 are the roots of the equation $x^2 - 7x + 12 = 0$.

(d) None of these

61. If the truth value of $p \vee q$ is T, then the truth value $p \wedge q$ is:

(a) T (b) F

(c) Neither (a) nor (b) (d) Cannot be determined

62. $(p \wedge \sim q) \wedge q$ is equivalent to:

(a) $p \vee q$ (b) $p \wedge q$

(c) $p \vee \sim q$ (d) $p \wedge \sim q$

63. Which of the following is a tautology?

(a) $p \Rightarrow (q \vee \sim q)$ (b) $p \Leftrightarrow (\sim q \wedge p)$

(c) $p \Leftrightarrow (p \wedge \sim p)$ (d) $(p \wedge \sim p) \wedge q$

64. $\sim[\sim p \vee (\sim p \Leftrightarrow q)]$ is equivalent to:

(a) $p \wedge (p \Leftrightarrow q)$. (b) $p \wedge q$.

(c) Both (a) and (b) (d) None of these

65. When does the truth value of the statement $(p \Rightarrow q) \vee (r \Leftrightarrow s)$ become true?

(a) p is true (b) q is true

(c) r is true (d) s is true

66. Given that p: x is a prime number and q: x^2 is a composite number. Then $\sim(\sim p \Rightarrow q)$ is equivalent to

(a) x is not a prime number and x^2 is not a composite number.

(b) x is not a prime number and x^2 is a composite number.

(c) Both (a) and (b)

(d) None of these

67. Which of the following is a contradiction?
(a) $(p \vee q) \Leftrightarrow (p \wedge q)$ (b) $(p \vee q) \Rightarrow (p \wedge q)$
(c) $(p \Rightarrow q) \vee (q \Rightarrow p)$ (d) $(\sim q) \wedge (p \wedge q)$

68. When does the truth value of the statement $[(p \Leftrightarrow q) \Rightarrow (q \Leftrightarrow r)] \Rightarrow (r \Leftrightarrow p)$ become false?
(a) p is true, q is false, r is true
(b) p is false, q is true, r is true
(c) p is false, q is false, r is false
(d) p is true, q is true, r is true

69. If p is negation of q, then $(p \Rightarrow q) \vee (q \Rightarrow p)$ is a:
(a) tautology (b) contradiction
(c) contingency (d) None of these

70. Which of the following is a contingency?
(a) $\sim p \wedge q$ (b) $p \vee \sim q$
(c) $\sim p \wedge \sim q$ (d) All of these

71. Which among the following is negation of $\sim(p \wedge q) \vee r$?
(a) $(p \wedge q) \vee r$ (b) $(p \vee q) \vee \sim r$
(c) $(p \vee q) \vee r$ (d) $(p \wedge q) \wedge \sim r$

72. The inverse of a conditional statement is, 'If ABC is a triangle, then $\angle A + \angle B + \angle C = 180°$'. Then the contrapositive of the conditional statement is:
(a) 'If $\angle A + \angle B + \angle C = 180°$, then ABC is a triangle'.
(b) 'If $\angle A + \angle B + \angle C \neq 0$, then ABC is not a triangle'.
(c) 'If ABC is not a triangle, then $\angle A + \angle B + \angle C \neq 180°$'.
(d) 'If ABC is a triangle, then $\angle A + \angle B + \angle C = 180°$'.

73. 'There is atleast one prime number which is not odd number'. The quantifier used in the above statement is ______.
(a) universal quantifier (b) existential quantifier
(c) Both (a) and (b) (d) No quantifier is used

74.

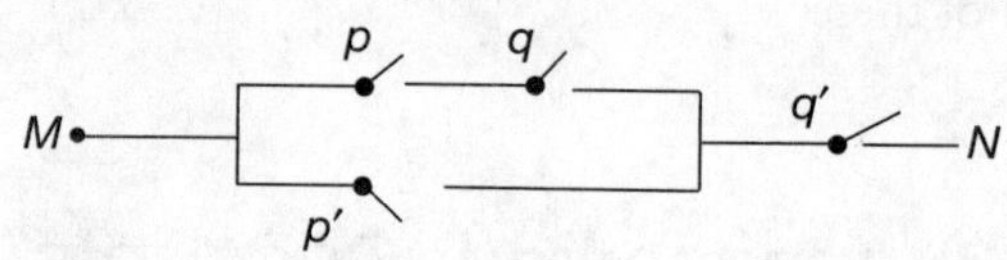

In the above network, current flows from M to N, when:
(a) p is closed, q is closed.
(b) p is closed, q is open.
(c) p is open, q is closed.
(d) p is open, q is open.

75.

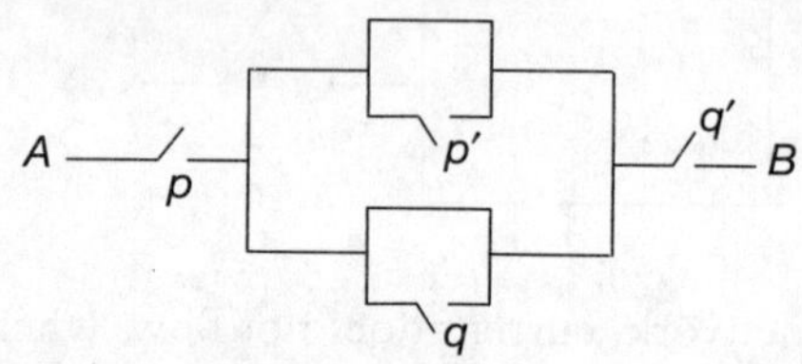

In the above network, current flows from A to B, when:
(a) p is open, q is open.
(b) p is closed, q is closed.
(c) p is closed, q is open.
(d) p is open, q is closed.

AT

ANSWER KEYS

Classroom Wing

Very Short Answer Type Questions

1. True
2. True
3. True
4. Does not
5. ∃
6. True
7. And
8. $p \Rightarrow \sim q \wedge \sim r$.
9. $p \Rightarrow \sim q$
10. $\sim p \vee q$
11. 9
12. Some days I do not go to school.
13. $q \Rightarrow \sim p$
14. $\sim p \vee [-q \vee q]$
15. True
16. False
17. He is smart and he is intelligent.
    If he is smart, then he is intelligent.
18. $\exists\, x \in R$ such that $x + 2 = 3$
19. Neither true nor false
20. 'If I am not tired, then I will not take rest'.
21. False
22. All odd numbers are primes.
23. True
24. If $ABCD$ is a rectangle, then it is square.
25. $(p \Rightarrow q) \wedge (q \Rightarrow p)$.

Short Answer Type Questions

26. $p \vee q \Rightarrow p$

27. Converse: If she is happy, then she is rich.
    Inverse: If she is not rich, then she is not happy.
    Contrapositive: If she is not happy, then she is not rich.

29. Converse: In a ΔABC, if $\angle B \neq \angle C$, then $AB \neq AC$.
    Inverse: In a ΔABC, if $AB = AC$, then $\angle B = \angle C$.
    Contrapositive: In a ΔABC, if $\angle B = \angle C$, then $AB = AC$.

36. (a) ∀
    (b) ∀

Essay Type Questions

40. (i) p is closed, q is closed, r is closed
    (ii) p is closed, q is closed, r is open
    (iii) p is closed, q is open, r is closed
    (iv) p is open, q is closed, r is closed
    (v) p is closed, q is open, r is open
    (vi) p is open, q is closed, r is open
    (vii) p is open, q is open, r is closed

41. p is closed, q is closed

42. p is closed, q is closed.

43. (i) p is closed, q is closed
    (ii) p is open, q is closed

44. (i) p is closed, q is closed, r is closed
    (ii) p is closed, q is closed, r is open
    (iii) p is closed, q is open, r is closed
    (iv) p is open, q is closed, r is closed
    (v) p is closed, q is open, r is open

Competition Wing

Level 1: Apply Your Concepts

1. False
2. $\sim p \wedge q$
3. True
4. 2 is even prime
5. Some dogs bark.
6. (d)
7. (d)
8. (d)
9. (a)
10. (d)
11. (d)
12. (a)
13. (b)
14. (a)

15. (c)	16. (c)	17. (c)	18. (c)	19. (c)
20. (c)	21. (b)	22. (c)	23. (c)	24. (c)
25. (a)	26. (a)	27. (c)	28. (a)	29. (a)
30. (d)	31. (a)	32. (d)	33. (d)	34. (c)
35. (b)				

Level 2: Review Your Concepts

36. (c)	37. (d)	38. (c)	39. (d)	40. (d)
41. (d)	42. (a)	43. (c)	44. (d)	45. (c)
46. (b)	47. (a)	48. (a)	49. (d)	50. (a)
51. (b)	52. (d)	53. (d)	54. (a)	55. (d)

Level 3: Assess Your Concepts

56. (b)	57. (d)	58. (d)	59. (b)	60. (a)
61. (d)	62. (b)	63. (a)	64. (c)	65. (b)
66. (a)	67. (d)	68. (b)	69. (a)	70. (d)
71. (d)	72. (a)	73. (b)	74. (d)	75. (c)

Hints and Explanations

Classroom Wing

Very Short Answer Type Questions

1. True
2. $\sim q \Rightarrow p \equiv \sim(\sim q) \vee p$

   $= q \vee p$

   $= T \vee F$

   $=$ True
3. True
4. 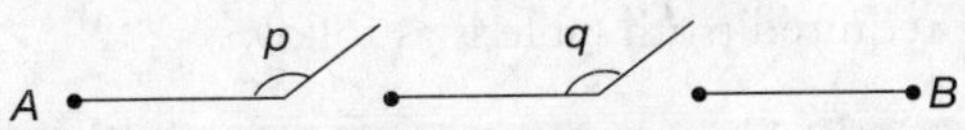

   Open so current will not follow.

   Does not.
5. $\exists$
6. $p \vee \sim q$

   $\Rightarrow$

p	q	$\sim q$	$p \vee \sim q$
T	T	F	T
T	F	T	T
F	F	T	T
F	T	F	F

   So q is True.

7. And
8. $p \Rightarrow -q \wedge \sim r$
9. Converse of $p \Rightarrow -q$ is $\sim q \Rightarrow p$

   Converse of $\sim q \Rightarrow p$ is $p \Rightarrow \sim q$
10. $\sim p \vee q$, direct property
11. 9
12. Some days, I do not go to school.
13. $q \Rightarrow \sim p$
14. $\sim[(p \wedge q) \vee (p \wedge \sim q)]$

    $\sim(p \wedge q) \wedge \sim(p \wedge \sim q)$

    $(\sim p \vee \sim q) \wedge (\sim p \vee q)$

    $\sim p \vee (-q \vee q)$
15. True
16. Negation of $a > b$ is $a < b$

    So False
17. He is smart and he is intelligent

    If he is smart, then he is intelligent
18. $\exists x \in R$ such that $x + 2 = 3$
19. Neither true nor false
20. If I am not tired, then I will not take rest
21. $3 + 3 = 6$

    i.e., False
22. All odd numbers are prime.
23. $2 \times 3 = 6$

$2 \times 3 = 6$	$5 + 8 = 10$	OR
T	F	T

    So True.

24. If converse of $p \Rightarrow q$ is $q \Rightarrow p$

    If ABCD is a rectangle, then it is square.
25. $(p \Rightarrow q) \wedge (q \Rightarrow p)$

Short Answer Type Questions

26. Converse of $p \Rightarrow p \vee q$ is $p \vee q \Rightarrow p$
27. Converse: If she is happy, then she is rich

    Inverse: If she is not rich, then she is not happy

    Contrapositive: If she is not happy, then she is not rich.
28. $p \Rightarrow p \vee q$

p	q	$p \vee q$	$p \Rightarrow p \vee q$
T	T	T	T
T	F	T	T
F	T	T	T
F	F	F	T

    Hence, it is a tautology.

29. Converse: In a ΔABC if $\angle B \neq \angle C$, then $AB \neq AC$
Inverse: In a ΔABC, if $AB = AC$, then $\angle B = \angle C$
Contrapositive: In a ΔABC, if $\angle B = \angle C$, then $AB = AC$

30. (A)

p	q	$p \wedge q$	$\sim(p \wedge q)$	$\sim(p \vee \sim q)$
T	T	T	F	F
T	F	F	T	T
F	T	F	T	T
F	F	F	T	T

Hence proved.

(B) The required truth table is as follows.

p	q	$p \Leftrightarrow q$	$p \Rightarrow q$	$q \Rightarrow p$	$(p \Rightarrow q) \wedge (q \Rightarrow p)$
T	T	T	T	T	T
T	F	F	F	T	F
F	T	F	T	F	F
F	F	T	T	T	T

The truth values of $p \Leftrightarrow q$ and $(p \Rightarrow q) \wedge (q \Rightarrow p)$ are the same.

Hence, $p \Leftrightarrow q \equiv (p \Rightarrow q) \wedge (q \Rightarrow p)$.

31.

p	q	r	$p \vee q$	$p \vee q \vee \sim r$
T	T	T	T	T
T	T	F	T	T
T	F	T	T	T
T	F	F	T	T
F	T	T	T	T
F	T	F	T	T
F	F	T	T	T
F	F	F	F	T

32.

p	q	$p \Rightarrow q$	$\sim p \vee q$
T	T	T	T
T	F	F	F
F	T	T	T
F	F	T	T

Hence proved.

33.

p	q	$\sim q$	$p \wedge \sim q$
T	T	F	F
T	F	T	T
F	T	F	F
F	F	T	F

34. (A)

p	q	$p \wedge q$	$(p \wedge q) \vee \sim q$	$p \vee \sim q$
T	F	F	T	T
T	T	T	T	T
F	F	F	T	T
F	T	F	F	F

Hence proved.

(B) The required truth table is as follows.

p	q	$p \wedge q$	$(p \wedge q) \Rightarrow q$
T	T	T	T
T	F	F	T
F	T	F	T
F	F	F	T

Since $q \Rightarrow p \wedge q$ is always true, $(p \wedge q) \Rightarrow q$ is a tautology.

35. $p \Rightarrow (p \wedge q)$

p	q	$p \wedge q$	$p \Rightarrow (p \wedge q)$
T	T	T	T
T	F	F	F
F	T	F	F
F	F	F	T

36. a. $\forall$ b. $\forall$

37.

p	q	$\sim p \wedge q$	$(\sim p \wedge q) \wedge q$
T	T	F	F
T	F	F	F
F	T	T	T
F	F	F	F

So neither tautology nor contradiction.

38.

p	q	$\sim p$	$p \wedge q$	$\sim p \vee (p \wedge q)$
T	T	F	T	T
T	F	F	F	F
F	T	T	F	T
F	F	T	F	T

39. (A)

p	q	$p \wedge \sim p$	$p \vee q$	$(p \wedge \sim p) \wedge (p \vee q)$
T	T	F	T	F
T	F	F	T	F
F	T	F	T	F
F	F	F	F	F

Hence, it is contradiction.

(B) The required truth table is as follows.

p	q	$\sim p$	$\sim q$	$p \vee q$	$\sim(p \vee q)$	$\sim p \wedge \sim q$
T	T	F	F	T	F	F
T	F	F	T	T	F	F
F	T	T	F	T	F	F
F	F	T	T	F	T	T

The truth values of $\sim(p \vee q)$ and $\sim p \wedge \sim q$ are the same.

Hence, $\sim(p \vee q) \equiv \sim p \wedge \sim q$.

Essay Type Questions

40. (i) p, q, r all are closed

(ii) p is closed, q closed, r open

(iii) p is closed, q is open, r is closed

(iv) p is open, q is closed, r is closed

(v) p is closed, q is open, r is open

(vi) p is open, q is closed, r is open

(vii) p is open, q is open, r is closed

41. Using truth table

p	q	p'	$(q \vee p')$	$p \wedge (q \vee p')$
T	T	T	T	T
T	F	T	T	T
F	T	T	T	F
F	F	T	T	F
T	T	F	T	T
T	F	F	F	F
F	T	F	T	F
F	F	F	F	F

So,

When p is closed q is closed, p' is open

When p is closed, p' is closed, q' is open

When p, p', q is closed.

42. Using truth table

p	q	p'	$(p \wedge q)$	$(p \wedge q) \wedge (p' \vee q)$
T	T	F	T	T
T	T	T	T	T
T	F	F	F	F
T	F	T	F	F
F	T	T	F	F
F	F	T	F	F
F	T	F	F	F
F	F	F	F	F

So,

p is closed, q is closed, p' is open

p is closed, q is closed, p' is closed

43.

p	q	p'	$p \vee p'$	$(p \vee p') \wedge q$
T	T	F	T	T
T	T	T	T	T
T	F	F	T	F
T	F	T	T	F
F	T	T	T	T
F	F	T	T	F
F	T	F	F	F
F	F	F	F	F

p is closed, q is closed, p' is open
p is closed, p' is closed, q is closed
p' is closed, q is closed, p is open

44.

p	q	r	$q \wedge r$	$p \vee (q \wedge r)$
T	T	F	F	T
T	T	T	T	T
T	F	F	F	T
T	F	T	F	T
F	T	T	T	T
F	F	T	F	F
F	T	F	F	F
F	F	F	F	F

So,
(i) p is closed, q is closed, r is open
(ii) p is closed, q is closed, r is closed
(iii) p is closed, q is open, r is open
(iv) p is closed, q is open, r is closed
(v) p is open, q is closed, r is closed

45. The network can be described by the statement of $[p \vee (q \vee r)] \wedge p^{I}$.

p	q	r	p^{I}	$q \vee r$	$p \vee (q \vee r)$	$[p \vee (q \vee r)] \wedge p^{I}$
T	T	T	F	T	T	F
T	T	F	F	T	T	F
T	F	T	F	T	T	F
F	**T**	**T**	**T**	**T**	**T**	**T**
T	F	F	F	F	T	F
F	**T**	**F**	**T**	**T**	**T**	**T**
F	**F**	**T**	**T**	**T**	**T**	**T**
F	F	F	T	F	F	F

So, the current flows from A to B in the following cases.
(i) p is open, q is closed, r is closed
(ii) p is open, q is closed, r is open
(iii) p is open, q is open, r is closed.

46. The network can be described by the compound statement $[p \wedge (q \vee p^{I})] \wedge q^{I}$.

p	q	p^{I}	q^{I}	$q \vee p^{I}$	$p \wedge (q \vee p^{I})$	$[p \wedge (q \vee p^{I})] \wedge q^{I}$
T	T	F	F	T	T	F
T	F	F	T	F	F	F
F	T	T	F	T	F	F
F	F	T	T	T	F	F

The current does not flow through the given network.

Competition Wing

Level 1: Apply Your Concepts

1. $\sim p = T$

   $\sim(\sim p)$

   $= \sim(T)$

   = False

2. $\sim(p \vee \sim q)$

   $\sim p \wedge q$

3. True

4. 2 is an even prime

5. Some dogs bark

7. Recall the definition of statement.

8. Recall the properties.

11. Verify through truth tables.

12. Check from truth tables.

15. Recall the properties.

16. Converse of $p \Rightarrow q$ is $q \Rightarrow p$.

18. Recall the concept of switching network.

19. For only one value of 'x' the equation is true.

20. Check from truth tables.

21. Recall the properties.

22. Verify through truth tables.

23. Recall the concept of switching networking.

24. Check from truth tables.

25. If $p \Rightarrow q$ is false only p is true, q is false.

26. Conjunction is true only when both the statements are true.

27. Inverse of $p \Rightarrow q$ is $\sim p \Rightarrow \sim q$.

28. Use truth table.

29. Recall bi-conditional truth table.

30. Recall the properties.

31. Inverse of $p \Rightarrow q$ is $\sim p \Rightarrow \sim q$.

32. $\sim(p \Rightarrow q) \equiv \sim(\sim p \vee q) \equiv (p \wedge \sim q)$.

33. (i) The inverse of $p \Rightarrow q$ is $\sim p \Rightarrow \sim q$.
   The contrapositive of $p \Rightarrow q$ is $\sim q \Rightarrow \sim p$.
   (ii) $p \Rightarrow q$ is false only when p is true and q is false.

34. Square of a real number is always non-negative.

35. Conjunction is false if atleast one of the statements is false.

Level 2: Review Your Concepts

36. (i) Check from the options.
   (ii) Go contrary to the given statement by substituting the value of x in it.

37. (i) Use truth table of double implication.
   (ii) Apply the identity, $\sim(p \Leftrightarrow q) \equiv (\sim p \Leftrightarrow q) \equiv (p \Leftrightarrow \sim q)$.

38. $p \Rightarrow q$ is equivalent to $\sim q \Rightarrow \sim p$.

39. (i) Both p and q are true.
   (ii) $\sim(p \Rightarrow q) \equiv p \wedge \sim q$.

40. A conditional is equivalent to its contrapositive. That is, $p \Rightarrow q \equiv \sim q \Rightarrow \sim p$.

41. Given sentence is not a statement.

42. Contradict the given statement by using different quantifiers.

43. $p \Rightarrow q$ is false only when p is true and q is false.

44. $\sim(p \Rightarrow q) \equiv p \wedge \sim q \equiv \sim(p \vee q)$.

45. Current flows only when p and r are closed or q and s are closed.

46. (i) p is false and q is true.
   (ii) The inverse of $p \Rightarrow q$ is $\sim p \Rightarrow \sim q$. The converse of $p \Rightarrow q$ is $q \Rightarrow p$.
   (iii) $p \Rightarrow q$ is false only when p is true and q is false.

47. Verify through truth table.

48. $\sim(p \Rightarrow q) \equiv p \wedge \sim q \equiv \sim(p \vee q)$.

49. (i) $x \wedge y$ is always false when y is false.
   (ii) Compare with truth table of double implication.

51. We know that, a conditional statement is equivalent to its contrapositive.
   Let the given statement be $p \Rightarrow q$.
   $\therefore$ Option (a) represents $\sim p \Rightarrow \sim q$
   Option (b) represents $\sim q \Rightarrow \sim p$.
   $\therefore$ Option (b) follows.

52. Given that p is true and q is true.
   $\therefore (p \Rightarrow q) \vee p \equiv t$.
   Option (a): $p \vee \sim q \equiv t$.
   Option (b): $(p \wedge q) \Rightarrow p \equiv t$.

Option (c): $\sim p \wedge \sim q \equiv f$.

Option (d) follows.

53. Negation of all is all not follows.

54. Let $(p \Leftrightarrow q) \Leftrightarrow (\sim p \Leftrightarrow \sim q) \equiv r$

p	q	$p \Leftrightarrow q$	$\sim p$	$\sim q$	$\sim p \Leftrightarrow \sim q$	r
T	T	T	F	F	T	T
T	F	F	F	T	F	T
F	T	F	T	F	F	T
F	F	T	T	T	T	T

∴ Given statement is tautology.

55. $x^2 - 6x + 8 \leq 0$

$(x - 2)(x - 4) \leq 0$

$x \in [2, 4]$

$\therefore x = 5 \notin [2, 4]$.

Level 3: Assess Your Concepts

56. (i) $\sim(p \Rightarrow q) = \sim p \vee q$.

(ii) $p \vee (q \vee r) = (p \vee q) \vee r$.

57. Current flows irrespective of p, q, and r whether closed or open.

58. The contrapositive of $p \Rightarrow q \Rightarrow \sim q \Rightarrow \sim p$.

59. (i) Parallel connection is represented by $x \wedge y$.

(ii) Series connection is represented by $x \vee y$.

60. $\sim(\sim p \vee q) = p \wedge \sim q$.

61. Given $p \vee q$ is true, i.e., any one of p or q is true, so we cannot say the truth value of $p \wedge q$.

62. $(p \vee \sim q) \wedge q$

$\equiv (p \wedge q) \vee (\sim q \wedge q)$ (distributive property)

$\equiv (p \wedge q) \vee F \equiv p \wedge q$.

63. Consider Option (a)

Since $q \vee \sim q$ is true

$p \Rightarrow (q \vee \sim q)$ is always true

$\therefore p \Rightarrow (q \vee \sim q)$ is tautology.

64. $\sim[\sim p \vee (\sim p \Leftrightarrow q)]$

$\equiv [p \wedge \sim(\sim p \Leftrightarrow q)]$

$\equiv p \wedge (p \Leftrightarrow q)$ or $p \wedge (\sim p \Leftrightarrow \sim q)$

From truth tables,

$p \wedge (p \Leftrightarrow q) \equiv p \wedge q$.

65. When q is true, $p \Rightarrow q$ is always true.

$\therefore (p \Rightarrow q) \vee (r \Leftrightarrow s)$ is true. When q is true.

66. $\sim(\sim p \Rightarrow q) \equiv \sim p \wedge \sim q$.

$\therefore \sim p \wedge \sim q = x$ is not a prime number and x^2 is not a composite number.

67. From the truth tables, first three options are not contradictions.

Option (d): $(\sim q) \wedge (p \wedge q)$

$\equiv p \wedge (\sim q \wedge q)$

$\equiv p \wedge (F) \equiv F$.

68. From the options,

$(p \Leftrightarrow q) \Rightarrow (q \Leftrightarrow r)$

$\Rightarrow (r \Leftrightarrow p)$ is false, when p is false, q is true and r is true.

69. Given, p is negation of $q \Rightarrow p \equiv \sim q$

$\therefore (p \Rightarrow q) \vee (q \Rightarrow p)$

$\Rightarrow (\sim q \Rightarrow q) \vee (q \Rightarrow \sim q)$

$\therefore$ If $(\sim q \Rightarrow q)$ is T, then $(q \Rightarrow \sim q)$ is F.

If $(\sim q \Rightarrow q)$ is F, then $(q \Rightarrow \sim q)$ is T.

$\therefore$ T or F $\equiv$ F or T $\equiv$ T.

70. From the truth table

All the options are contingencies.

71. $\sim[\sim(p \wedge q) \vee r] \equiv (p \wedge q) \wedge \sim r$.

72. Let inverse of a conditional statement be $p \Rightarrow q$.

$\therefore$ The conditional statement is $\sim p \Rightarrow \sim q$.

$\therefore$ The contrapositive of the conditional is $q \Rightarrow p$.

That is, if $\angle A + \angle B + \angle C = 180°$, then ABC is a triangle.

73. According to the statement, some prime numbers of are not odd numbers, the quantifier is existential quantifier.

74. For the given network, current flows from M to N when p is open and q is open.

75. For the given network, current flows from A to B when p is closed and q is open.

CHAPTER

17

Sets, Relations, and Functions

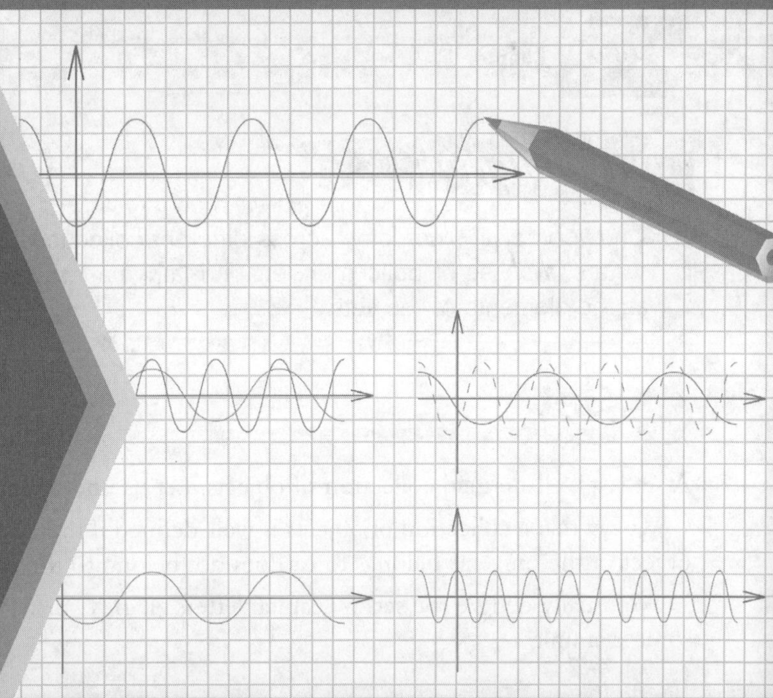

Remember

Before beginning this chapter, you should be able to:

- Know the use of sets and some definitions of sets
- Apply fundamental operations on sets
- Recall the term Venn diagram
- Define terms such as relations, functions, etc.

Key Ideas

After completing this chapter, you should be able to:

- Learn representation of sets using different methods
- Apply advanced operations on sets such as union, intersection, etc.
- Represent sets using Venn diagrams and apply operations on it
- Define advanced form of terms such as relations, functions, domain, range, etc.
- Present relations and functions by methods such as arrow diagram, tree diagram, graphs, etc.

INTRODUCTION

In everyday life we come across different collections of objects. For example: A herd of sheep, a cluster of stars, a posse of policemen, etc. In Mathematics, we call such collections as sets. The objects are referred as the elements of the sets.

Set

A set is a well-defined collection of objects. Let us understand the meaning of a well-defined collection of objects.

We say that a collection of objects is well-defined if there is some reasons or rules by which we can say, whether a given object of the universe belongs to or does not belong to the collection.

We usually denote the sets by capital letters A, B, C or X, Y, Z, etc. To understand the concept of a set, let us look at some examples.

Examples:

1. Let us consider the collection of odd natural numbers less than or equal to 15.

   In this example, we can definitely say what the collection is. The collection comprises the numbers 1, 3, 5, 7, 9, 11, 13, and 15.

2. Let us consider the collection of students in a class who are good at painting. In this example, we cannot say precisely which students of the class belong to our collection. So, this collection is not well-defined.

Hence, the first collection is a set whereas the second collection is not a set. In the first example given above, the set of the odd natural numbers less than or equal to 15 can be represented as set $A = \{1, 3, 5, 7, 9, 11, 13, 15\}$.

Elements of a Set

The objects in a set are called its elements or members.

If a is an element of a set A, then we say that a belongs to A and we write it as, $a \in A$.

If a is not an element of A, then we say that a does not belong to A and we write it as, $a \notin A$.

Some Sets of Numbers and Their Notations

N = Set of all natural numbers = $\{1, 2, 3, 4, 5, \ldots\}$

W = Set of all whole numbers = $\{0, 1, 2, 3, 4, 5, \ldots\}$

Z or I = Set of all integers = $\{0, \pm 1, \pm 2, \pm 3, \ldots\}$

Q = Set of all rational numbers $= \left\{\dfrac{p}{q} \text{ where } p, q \in Z \text{ and } q \neq 0\right\}$

Cardinal Number of a Set

The number of elements in a set A is called its cardinal number. It is denoted by $n(A)$. A set which has finite number of elements is a finite set and a set which has infinite number of elements is an infinite set.

Examples:

1. Set of English alphabets is a finite set.
2. Set of number of days in a month is a finite set.
3. The set of all even natural numbers is an infinite set.
4. Set of all the lines passing through a point is an infinite set.

5. The cardinal number of the set $X = \{a, c, c, a, b, a\}$ is $n(X) = 3$, as in sets only distinct elements are counted.
6. If $A = \{a, \{a, b\}, b, c, \{c, d\}\}$, then $n(A) = 5$.

Representation of Sets

We represent sets by the following methods:

Roster or List Method

In this method, a set is described by listing out all the elements in the set within curly brackets.

Examples:

1. Let W be the set of all letters in the word JANUARY.

   Then we represent W as, $W = \{A, J, N, R, U, Y\}$.
2. Let M be the set of all multiples of 3 less than 20.Then we represent the set M as, $M = \{3, 6, 9, 12, 15, 18\}$.

Set-builder Method

In this method, a set is described by using a representative and stating the property or properties which the elements of the set satisfy, through the representative.

Examples:

1. Let D be the set of all days in a week. Then we represent D as, $D = \{x \mid x \text{ is a day in a week}\}$.
2. $N = \{x \mid 10 < x < 20 \text{ and } x \in N\}$.

Types of Sets

Empty Set or Null Set or Void Set

A set with no elements in it is called an empty set (or) void set (or) null set. It is denoted by { } or ϕ. (read as 'phi').

Examples:

1. Set of all positive integers less than 1 is an empty set.
2. Set of all mango trees with apples.

Info Bytes!

$n(\phi) = 0$.

Singleton Set

A set consisting of only one element is called a singleton set.

Examples:

1. The set of all vowels in the word MARCH is a singleton, as A is the only vowel in the word.
2. The set of whole numbers which are not natural numbers is a singleton, as 0 is the only whole number which is not a natural number.
3. The set of all SEVEN WONDERS in India is a singleton, as Tajmahal is the only wonder in the set.

Equivalent Sets

Two sets A and B are said to be equivalent if their cardinal numbers are equal.

We write this symbolically as $A \sim B$ or $A \leftrightarrow B$.

Konnect

If the sets A and B are equivalent, we can establish a one-one correspondence between the two sets, i.e., we can pair up elements in A and B such that every element of A is paired with a distinct element of set B and every element of set B is paired with a distinct element of set A.

Examples:

1. Sets, $X = \{2, 4, 6, 8\}$ and $Y = \{a, b, c, d\}$ are equivalent as $n(X) = n(Y) = 4$.
2. Sets, X = {Dog, Cat, Rat} $Y = \{\triangle, \bigcirc, \square\}$ are equivalent.
3. Sets, $X = \{-1, -7, -5\}$ and B = {Delhi, Hyderabad} are not equivalent, as $n(X) \neq n(B)$.

Equal Sets

Two sets A and B are said to be equal if they have the same elements.

Examples:

1. Sets, $A = \{a, e, i, o, u\}$ and $B = \{x \mid x$ is a vowel in the English alphabet$\}$ are equal sets.
2. Sets, $A = \{1, 2, 3\}$ and $B = \{x, y, z\}$ are not equal sets.
3. Sets, $A = \{1, 2, 3, 4, \ldots\}$ and $B = \{x \mid x$ is a natural number$\}$ are equal sets.

Info Bytes!

If A and B are equal sets, then they are equivalent but the converse need not be true.

Disjoint Sets

Two sets A and B are said to be disjoint, if they have no elements in common.

Examples:

1. Sets $X = \{3, 6, 9, 12\}$ and $Y = \{5, 10, 15, 20\}$ are disjoint as they have no element in common.
2. Sets $A = \{a, e, i, o, u\}$ and $B = \{e, i, j\}$ are not disjoint as they have common elements e and i.

Subset and Superset

Let A and B be two sets. If every element of set A is also an element of set B, then A is said to be a subset of B or B is said to be a superset of A. If A is a subset of B, then we write $A \subseteq B$ or $B \supseteq A$.

Examples:

1. Set $A = \{2, 4, 6, 8\}$ is a subset of set $B = \{1, 2, 3, 4, 5, 6, 7, 8\}$.
2. Set of all primes except 2 is a subset of the set of all odd natural numbers.
3. Set $A = \{1, 2, 3, 4, 5, 6, 7, 8\}$ is a superset of set $B = \{1, 3, 5, 7\}$.

Proper Subset

If $A \subseteq B$ and $A \neq B$, then A is called a proper subset of B and is denoted by $A \subset B$. When $A \subset B$ then B is called a superset of A and is denoted as $B \supset A$, if $A \subset B$ then $n(A) < n(B)$ and if $B \supset A$ then $n(B) > n(A)$.

Power Set

The set of all subsets of a set A is called its power set. It is denoted by $P(A)$.

Example: Let $A = \{x, y, z\}$. Then the subsets of A are ϕ, $\{x\}$, $\{y\}$, $\{z\}$, $\{x, y\}$, $\{x, z\}$, $\{y, z\}$, $\{x, y, z\}$.

So, $P(A) = \{\phi, \{x\}, \{y\}, \{z\}, \{x, y\}, \{x, z\}, \{y, z\}, \{x, y, z\}\}$.

We observe that the cardinality of $P(A)$ is $8 = 2^3$.

Konnect

1. Empty set is a subset of every set.
2. Every set is a subset of itself.
3. If a set A has n elements, then the number of subsets of A is 2^n.
4. If a set A has n elements, then the number of non-empty subsets of A is $2^n - 1$.

Universal Set

A set which consists of all the sets under consideration or discussion is called the universal set. It is usually denoted by U or μ.

Example: Let $A = \{a, b, c\}$, $B = \{c, d, e\}$ and $C = \{a, e, f, g, h\}$. Then, the set $\{a, b, c, d, e, f, g, h\}$ can be taken as the universal set here.

$\therefore \mu = \{a, b, c, d, e, f, g, h\}$.

Konnect

1. If a set A has n elements, then the number of subsets of A is 2^n, i.e., the cardinality of the power set is 2^n.
2. If a set A has n elements, then the number of proper subsets of A is $2^n - 1$.

Complement of a Set

Let μ be the universal set and $A \subseteq \mu$. Then, the set of all those elements of μ which are not in set A is called the complement of the set A. It is denoted by A' or A^c. $A' = \{x \mid x \in \mu \text{ and } x \notin A\}$.

Examples:

1. Let $\mu = \{3, 6, 9, 12, 15, 18, 21, 24\}$ and $A = \{6, 12, 18, 24\}$. Then, $A' = \{3, 9, 15, 21\}$.
2. Let $\mu = \{x \mid x \text{ is a student and } x \in \text{Class } X\}$

   and $B = \{x \mid x \text{ is a boy and } x \in \text{Class } X\}$.

   Then, $B' = \{x \mid x \text{ is a girl and } x \in \text{Class } X\}$.

Info Bytes!

1. A and A' are disjoint sets.
2. $\mu' = \phi$ and $\phi' = \mu$.

EXAMPLE 17.1 If $X = \left\{ p : \text{where } p = \dfrac{(n+2)(2n^5 + 3n^4 + 4n^3 + 5n^2 + 6)}{n^2 + 2n} \text{ and } n, p \in Z^+ \right\}$, then find the number of elements in the set X.

SOLUTION

$$\frac{(n+2)(2n^5 + 3n^4 + 4n^3 + 5n^2 + 6)}{(n+2)(n)}$$

$$= 2n^4 + 3n^3 + 4n^2 + 5n + \frac{6}{n}$$

$= \dfrac{6}{n}$ should be an integer for $n = 1, 2, 3, 6$

$\Rightarrow X$ has 4 elements.

Operations on Sets

Union of Sets

Let A and B be two sets. Then, the union of A and B, denoted by $A \cup B$, is the set of all those elements which are either in A or in B or in both A and B. That is, $A \cup B = \{x \mid x \in A \text{ or } x \in B\}$.

Examples:

1. Let $A = \{-1, -3, -5, 0\}$ and $B = \{-1, 0, 3, 5\}$. Then, $A \cup B = \{-5, -3, -1, 0, 3, 5\}$.
2. Let $A = \{x \mid 5 \le 5x < 25 \text{ and } x \in N\}$ and $B = \{x \mid 5 \le (10x) \le 20 \text{ and } x \in N\}$, Then, $A \cup B = \{x \mid 5 \le 5x \le 20 \text{ and } x \in N\}$.

Konnect

1. If $A \subseteq B$, then $A \cup B = B$.
2. $A \cup \mu = \mu$ and $A \cup \phi = A$.
3. $A \cup A' = \mu$.

Intersection of Sets

Let A and B be two sets. Then the intersection of A and B, denoted by $A \cap B$, is the set of all those elements which are common to both A and B. That is, $A \cap B = \{x \mid x \in A \text{ and } x \in B\}$.

Examples:

1. Let $A = \{1, 2, 3, 5, 6, 7, 8\}$ and $B = \{1, 3, 5, 7\}$. Then, $A \cap B = \{1, 3, 5, 7\}$.
2. Let A be the set of all English alphabet and B be the set of all consonants, then, $A \cap B$ is the set of all consonants in the English alphabet.
3. Let E be the set of all even natural numbers and O be the set of all odd natural numbers. Then $E \cap O = \{\ \}$ or ϕ.

Konnect

1. If A and B are disjoint sets, then $A \cap B = \phi$.
2. If $A \subseteq B$, then $A \cap B = A$.
3. $A \cap \mu = A$ and $A \cap \phi = \phi$.
4. $A \cap A' = \phi$.

Difference of Sets

Let A and B be two sets. Then the difference $A - B$ is the set of all those elements which are in A but not in B.

That is, $A - B = \{x \mid x \in A \text{ and } x \notin B\}$.

Example: Let $A = \{3, 6, 9, 12, 15, 18\}$ and $B = \{2, 6, 8, 10, 14, 18\}$. $A - B = \{3, 9, 12, 15\}$ and $B - A = \{2, 8, 10, 14\}$.

Info Bytes!

1. $A - B \neq B - A$ unless $A = B$.
2. For any set A, $A' = \mu - A$.

Symmetric Difference of Sets

Let A and B be two sets. Then the symmetric difference of A and B, denoted by $A \Delta B$, is the set of all those elements which are either in A or in B but not in both. That is, $A \Delta B = \{x \mid x \in A \text{ and } x \notin B \text{ or } x \in B \text{ and } x \notin A\}$.

Example: Let $A = \{1, 2, 4, 6, 8, 10, 12\}$ and $B = \{3, 6, 12\}$. Then,

$$\begin{aligned} A \Delta B &= (A - B) \cup (B - A) \\ &= \{1, 2, 4, 8, 10\} \cup \{3\} \\ &= \{1, 2, 3, 4, 8, 10\}. \end{aligned}$$

Info Bytes!

$A \Delta B = (A - B) \cup (B - A)$ (or) $A \Delta B = (A \cup B) - (A \cap B)$.

Some Results

For any three sets A, B and C, we have the following results.

1. **Commutative Law:**
   (i) $A \cup B = B \cup A$
   (ii) $A \cap B = B \cap A$
   (iii) $A \Delta B = B \Delta A$
2. **Associative Law:**
   (i) $(A \cup B) \cup C = A \cup (B \cup C)$
   (ii) $(A \cap B) \cap C = A \cap (B \cap C)$
   (iii) $(A \Delta B) \Delta C = A \Delta (B \Delta C)$
3. **Distributive Law:**
   (i) $A \cup (B \cap C) = (A \cup B) \cap (A \cup C)$
   (ii) $A \cap (B \cup C) = (A \cap B) \cup (A \cap C)$
4. **De Morgan's Law:**
   (i) $(A \cup B)' = A' \cap B'$
   (ii) $(A \cap B)' = A' \cup B'$
   (iii) $A - (B \cup C) = (A - B) \cap (A - C)$
   (iv) $A - (B \cap C) = (A - B) \cup (A - C)$
5. **Identity Law:**
   (i) $A \cup \phi = \phi \cup A = A$
   (ii) $A \cap \mu = \mu \cap A = A$
6. **Idempotent Law:**
   (i) $A \cup A = A$
   (ii) $A \cap A = A$
7. **Complement Law:**
   (i) $(A')' = A$
   (ii) $A \cup A' = \mu$
   (iii) $A \cap A' = \phi$

Dual of an Identity

An identity obtained by interchanging $\cup$ and $\cap$, and ϕ and μ in the given identity is called the dual of the identity.

Examples:

1. Consider the identity, $A \cup B = B \cup A$.

   Dual of the identity is, $A \cap B = B \cap A$.

2. Consider the identity, $A \cup \mu = \mu$.

   Dual of the identity is, $A \cap \phi = \phi$.

Venn Diagrams

We also represent sets pictorially by means of diagrams called Venn diagrams. In Venn diagrams, the universal set is usually represented by a rectangular region and its subsets by closed regions inside the rectangular region. The elements of the set are written in the closed regions and the elements which belong to the universal set are written in the rectangular region.

Example: Let $\mu = \{1, 2, 3, 4, 5, 6, 7, 8, 9, 10\}$, $A = \{1, 2, 4, 6, 7, 8\}$ and $B = \{2, 3, 4, 5, 9\}$.

We represent these sets in the form of Venn diagram as follows (see Fig. 17.1):

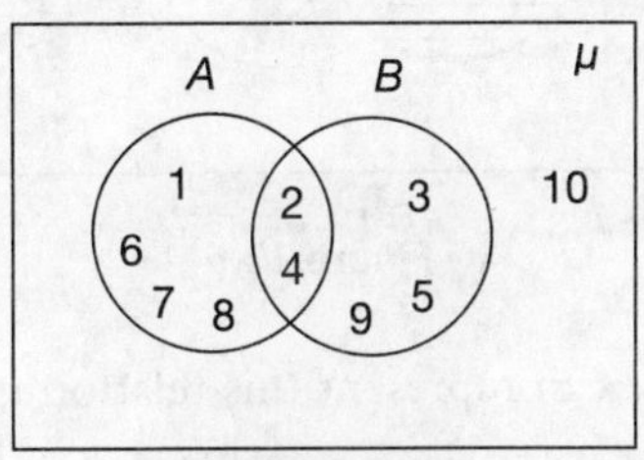

Figure 17.1

We can also represent the sets in Venn diagrams by shaded regions:

Examples:

1. Venn diagram of $A \cup B$, where A and B are two overlapping sets, is as shown in the Fig. 17.2.

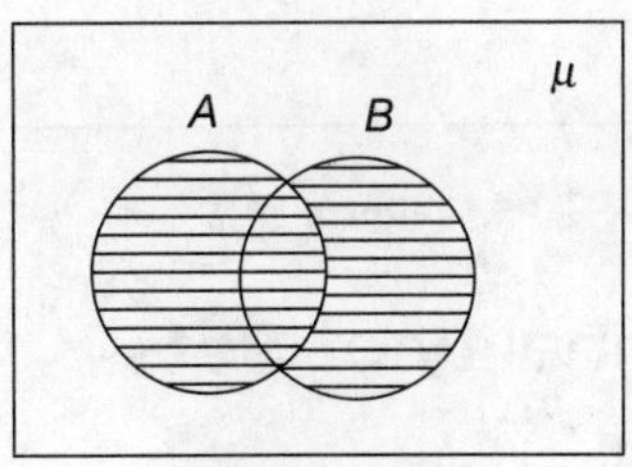

Figure 17.2

2. Let A and B be two overlapping sets. Then, the Venn diagram of $A \cap B$ is as shown in the Fig. 17.3.

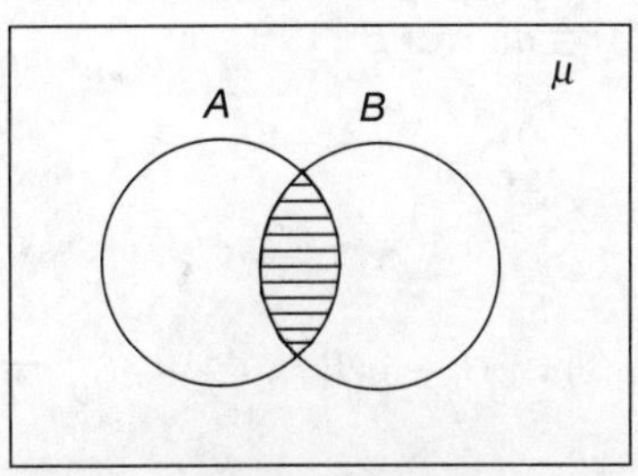

Figure 17.3

3. For a non-empty set A, Venn diagram of A' is as shown in the Fig. 17.4.

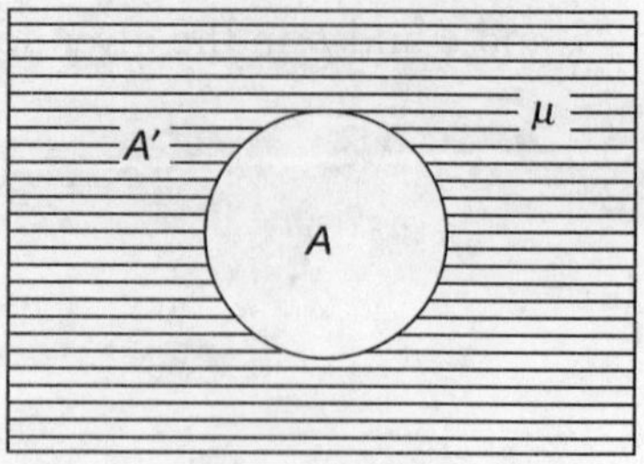

Figure 17.4

4. Let A and B be two overlapping sets. Then, the Venn diagram of $A - B$ is as shown in the Fig. 17.5.

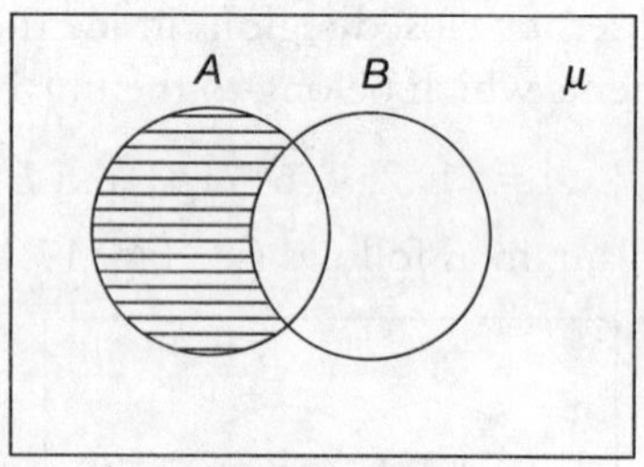

Figure 17.5

5. Let A and B be two sets such $A \subseteq B$. We can represent this relation using Venn diagram as follows (see Fig. 17.6).

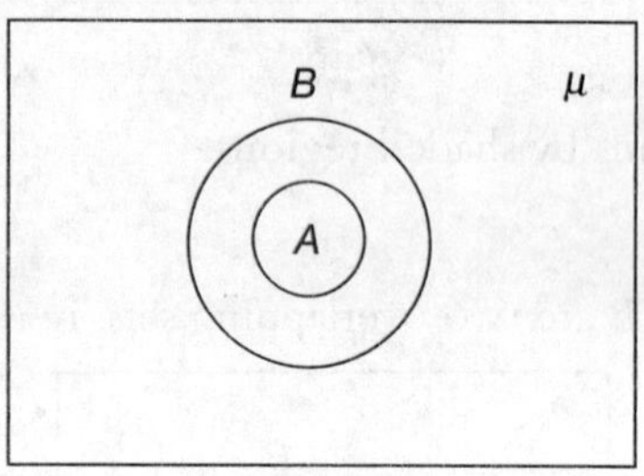

Figure 17.6

Some Formulae on the Cardinality of Sets

Let $A = \{1, 2, 3, 5, 6, 7\}$ and $B = \{3, 4, 5, 8, 10, 11\}$.

Then, $A \cup B = \{1, 2, 3, 4, 5, 6, 7, 8, 10, 11\}$ and $A \cap B = \{3, 5\}$.

In terms of the cardinal numbers, $n(A) = 6$, $n(B) = 6$, $n(A \cap B) = 2$ and $n(A \cup B) = 10$.

So, $n(A) + n(B) - n(A \cap B) = 6 + 6 - 2 = 10 = n(A \cup B)$.

We have the following formulae:

For any three sets A, B and C

1. $n(A \cup B) = n(A) + n(B) - n(A \cap B)$.
2. $n(A \cup B \cup C) = n(A) + n(B) + n(C) - n(A \cap B) - n(B \cap C) - n(C \cap A) + n(A \cap B \cap C)$.

EXAMPLE 17.2 If $n(A) = 7$, $n(B) = 5$ and $n(A \cup B) = 10$, then find $n(A \cap B)$.

SOLUTION

Given, $n(A) = 7$, $n(B) = 5$ and $n(A \cup B) = 10$.

We know that,

$n(A \cup B) = n(A) + n(B) - n(A \cap B)$

So, $\Rightarrow 10 = 7 + 5 - n(A \cap B)$

$\Rightarrow n(A \cap B) = 2.$

EXAMPLE 17.3 If $n(A) = 8$ and $n(B) = 6$ and the sets A and B are disjoint, then find $n(A \cup B)$.

SOLUTION

Given, $n(A) = 8$, $n(B) = 6$.

A and B are disjoint

$\Rightarrow A \cap B = \phi \Rightarrow n(A \cap B) = 0$

$\therefore n(A \cup B) = n(A) + n(B) - n(A \cap B)$

$= 8 + 6 - 0 = 14.$

3. If A and B are two disjoint sets then, $n(A \cup B) = n(A) + n(B)$. The Venn diagram and the summary of it when three overlapping sets are given, are as follows (see Fig. 17.7):

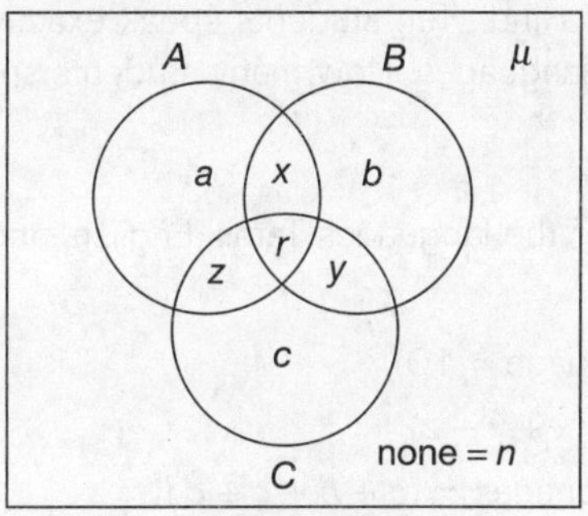

Figure 17.7

$A = a + x + r + z$

Only A (or) exactly $A = a$.

$B = b + x + r + y$

Only B (or) exactly $B = b$.

$C = c + y + r + z$

Only C (or) exactly $C = c$.

$A \cap B = x + r$

$A \cap B \cap C'$ (or) only $A \cap B = x$

$B \cap C = y + r$

$B \cap C \cap A'$ (or) only $B \cap C = y$; $C \cap A = z + r$; $C \cap A \cap B'$ (or) only $C \cap A = z$.

Only two sets (or) exactly two sets $= x + y + z$

$A \cap B \cap C$ (or) all the three $= r$

Atleast one set = Exactly one + Exactly two + Exactly three

$= a + b + c + x + y + z + r$

= Total - None

Atleast two sets = Exactly two + Exactly three

$= x + y + z + r$

Atleast three sets = Exactly three $= r$

Atmost two sets = Exactly two + Exactly one + Exactly zero

$= x + y + z + a + b + c + n$

$= n(\mu) - r$

Atmost three sets = Exactly three + Exactly two + Exactly one + Exactly zero

$= r + x + y + z + a + b + c + n$

$= n(\mu)$.

EXAMPLE 17.4 There are 40 students in a class. Each student speaks at least one of the languages Tamil, English, and Hindi. Ten students speak exactly one language. Twenty-five students speak atmost two languages. How many students speak atleast two languages?

SOLUTION

Number of students who speak at least one of the languages Tamil, English, and Hindi = 40

$= (x + y + z + a + b + c + d)$

Number of students who speak only one language = 10

$= (x + y + z)$

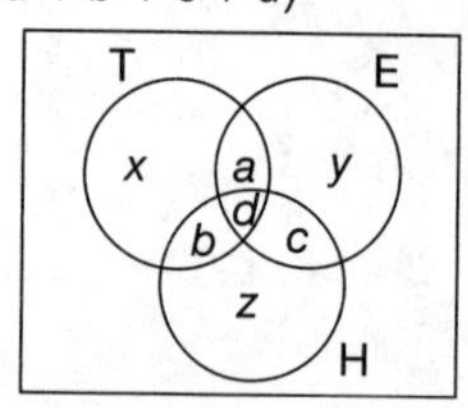

$\therefore$ No of students who speak at least two languages $= (a + b + c + d)$

$= 40 - 10 = 30.$

Ordered Pair

Let A be a non-empty set and $a, b \in A$. The elements a and b written in the form (a, b) is called an ordered pair. In the ordered pair (a, b), a is called the first coordinate and b is called the second coordinate.

So, $(1, 2) \neq (2, 1)$ and if $(a, 5) = (3, b) \Rightarrow a = 3$ and $b = 5$.

Cartesian Product of Sets

Let A and B be two non-empty sets. The Cartesian product of A and B, denoted by $A \times B$ is the set of all ordered pairs (a, b), such that $a \in A$ and $b \in B$. That is, $A \times B = \{(a, b)/a \in A, b \in B\}$.

Example: Let $A = \{1, 2, 3\}$ and $B = \{2, 4\}$.

$A \times B = \{(1, 2), (1, 4), (2, 2), (2, 4), (3, 2), (3, 4)\}$ and

$B \times A = \{(2, 1), (2, 2), (2, 3), (4, 1), (4, 2), (4, 3)\}$.

We observe that, $A \times B \neq B \times A$ and $n(A \times B) = 6 = n(B \times A)$.

Konnect

Two ordered pairs are said to be equal only when their first as well as the second coordinates are equal, i.e., $(a, b) = (c, d) \Leftrightarrow a = c$ and $b = d$.

Some Results on Cartesian Product

1. $A \times (B \cup C) = (A \times B) \cup (A \times C)$
2. $A \times (B \cap C) = (A \times B) \cap (A \times C)$
3. If $A \times B = \phi$, then either,
   (i) $A = \phi$ or
   (ii) $B = \phi$ or
   (iii) both $A = \phi$ and $B = \phi$.

Konnect

1. $A \times B \neq B \times A$, unless $A = B$.
2. For any two sets A and B, $n(A \times B) = n(B \times A)$.
3. If $n(A) = p$ and $n(B) = q$, then $n(A \times B) = pq$.

Cartesian product of sets can be represented in following ways:

1. Arrow diagram
2. Tree diagram
3. Graphical representation

Representation of $A \times B$ using Arrow Diagram

EXAMPLE 17.5 If $A = \{a, b, c\}$ and $B = \{1, 2, 3\}$, then find $A \times B$.

SOLUTION

In order to find $A \times B$, represent the elements of A and B as shown in the Fig. 17.8.

Now draw an arrow from each element of A to each element of B, as shown in the figure.

Now, represent all the elements related by arrows in ordered pairs in a set, which is the required $A \times B$.

That is, $A \times B = \{(a, 1), (a, 2), (a, 3), (b, 1), (b, 2), (b, 3), (c, 1), (c, 2), (c, 3)\}$.

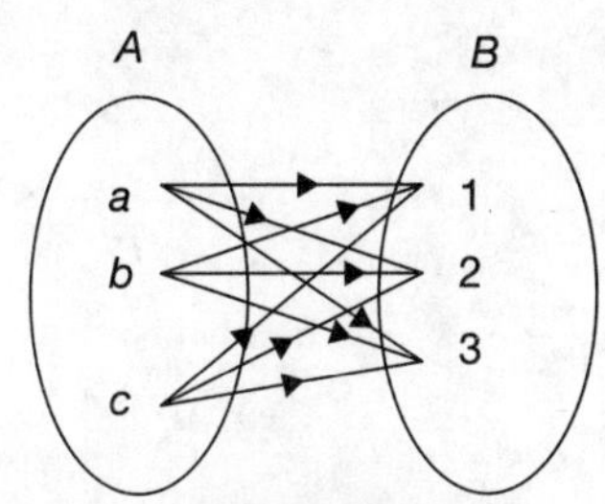

Figure 17.8

Representation of $A \times B$ Using a Tree Diagram

EXAMPLE 17.6 If $A = \{a, b, c\}$ and $B = \{1, 2, 3\}$, then find $A \times B$.

SOLUTION

To represent $A \times B$ using tree diagram, write all the elements of A vertically and then for each element of A, write all the elements of B and draw arrows as shown in the Fig. 17.9.

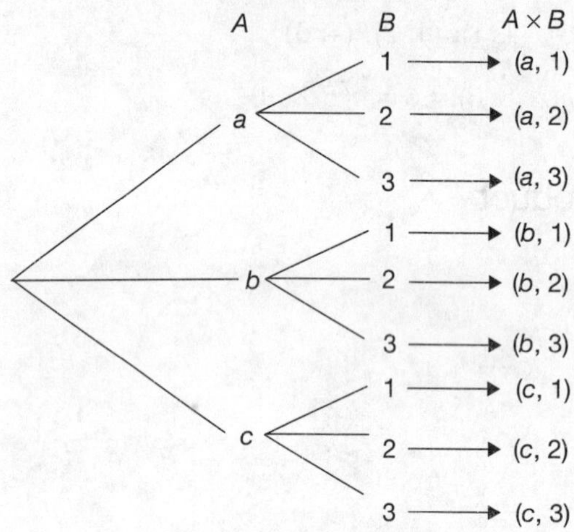

Figure 17.9

$\therefore A \times B = \{(a, 1), (a, 2), (a, 3), (b, 1), (b, 2), (b, 3), (c, 1), (c, 2), (c, 3)\}$.

Graphical Representation of $A \times B$

EXAMPLE 17.7 If $A = \{1, 2, 3\}$ and $B = \{3, 4, 5\}$, then find $A \times B$.

SOLUTION

Consider the elements of A on the X-axis and the elements of B on the Y-axis and mark the points (see Fig. 17.10).

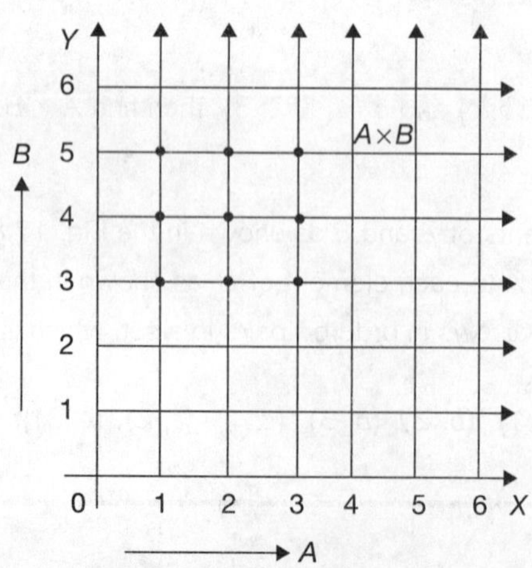

Figure 17.10

$\therefore A \times B = \{(1, 3), (1, 4), (1, 5), (2, 3), (2, 4), (2, 5), (3, 3), (3, 4), (3, 5)\}$.

Relation

We come across certain relations in real life and also in basic geometry, like *is father of, is a student of, is parallel to, is similar to*, etc. We now define the mathematical form of the sum.

Definition

Let A and B be two non-empty sets and $R \subseteq A \times B$. R is called a relation from the set A to B. (Any subset of $A \times B$ is called a relation from A to B).

$\therefore$ A relation contains ordered pairs as elements. Hence, 'A relation is a set of ordered pairs'.

Examples:

1. Let $A = \{1, 2, 4\}$ and $B = \{2, 3\}$

   Then, $A \times B = \{(1, 2), (1, 3), (2, 2), (2, 3), (4, 2), (4, 3)\}$

   Let $R_1 = \{(1, 2), (1, 3), (2, 3)\}$

   Clearly, $R_1 \subseteq A \times B$ and we also notice that, for every ordered pair $(a, b) \in R_1$, $a < b$.

   So, R_1 is the relation *is less than* from A to B.

2. In the previous example, let $R_2 = \{(4, 2), (4, 3)\}$

   Clearly, $R_2 \subseteq A \times B$ and we also notice that, for every ordered pair $(a, b) \in R_2$, $a > b$.

   So, R_2 is the relation *is greater than* from A to B.

Konnect

1. If $n(A) = p$ and $n(B) = q$, then the number of relations possible from A to B is 2^{pq}.
2. If $(x, y) \in R$, then we write $x\ R\ y$ and read as x is related to y.

Domain and Range of a Relation

Let A and B be two non-empty sets and R be a relation from A to B, we note that:

1. The set of first coordinates of all ordered pairs in R is called the domain of R.
2. The set of second coordinates of all ordered pairs in R is called the range of R.

Example: Let $A = \{1, 2, 4\}$, $B = \{1, 2, 3\}$ and $R = \{(1, 1), (1, 2), (2, 1), (2, 3), (4, 3)\}$ be a relation from A to B.

Then, domain of $R = \{1, 2, 4\}$ and range of $R = \{1, 2, 3\}$.

Representation of Relations

We represent the relations by the following methods:

Roster Method (or) List Method

In this method we list all the ordered pairs that satisfy the rule or property given in the relation.

Example: Let $A = \{1, 2, 3\}$. If R is a relation on the set A having the property *is less than*, then the roster form of R is,
$R = \{(1, 2), (1, 3), (2, 3)\}$.

Set-builder Method

In this method, a relation is described by using a representative and stating the property or properties, which the first and second coordinates of every ordered pair of the relation satisfy, through the representative.

Example: Let $A = \{1, 2, 3\}$. If R is a relation on the set A having the property *is greater than or equal to*, then the set-builder form of R is,
$R = \{(x, y) \mid x, y \in A \text{ and } x \geq y\}$.

Arrow Diagram

In this method, a relation is described by drawing arrows between the elements which satisfy the property or properties given in the relation.

Example: Let $A = \{1, 2, 4\}$ and $B = \{2, 3\}$. Let R be a relation from A to B with the property *is less than*. Then, the arrow diagram of R is as shown in the Fig. 17.11.

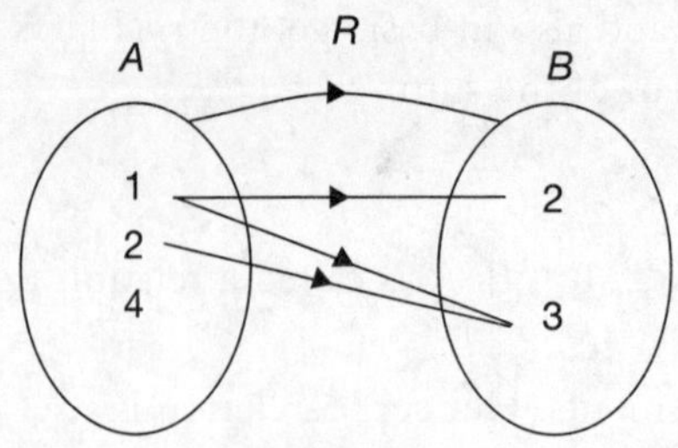

Figure 17.11

Inverse of a Relation

Let R be a relation from A to B. The inverse relation of R, denoted by R^{-1}, is defined as, $R^{-1} = \{(y, x) \mid (x, y) \in R\}$.

Example: Let $R = \{(1, 1), (1, 2), (2, 1), (2, 3), (4, 3)\}$ be a relation from A to B, where $A = \{1, 2, 4\}$ and $B = \{1, 2, 3\}$. Then, $R^{-1} = \{(1, 1), (1, 2), (2, 1), (3, 2), (3, 4)\}$.

Konnect

1. Domain of R^{-1} = Range of R.
2. Range of R^{-1} = Domain of R.
3. If R is a relation from A to B, then R^{-1} is a relation from B to A.
4. If $R \subseteq A \times A$, then R is called a binary relation or simply a relation on the set A.
5. For any relation R, $(R^{-1})^{-1} = R$.

Types of Relations

1. **One-One Relation:** A relation $R: A \to B$ is said to be one-one relation if different elements of A are paired with different elements of B. That is, $x \neq y$ in $A \Rightarrow f(x) \neq f(y)$ in B.

   Example: From the given Fig. 17.12, the relation $R = \{(1, 3), (2, 4), (3, 5)\}$.

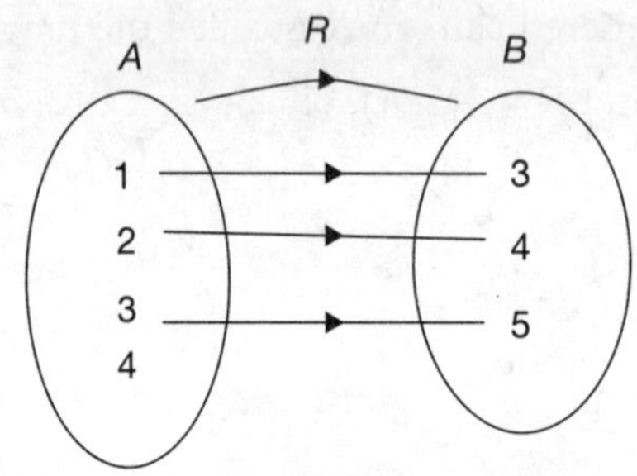

Figure 17.12

2. **One-Many Relation:** A relation $R: A \to B$ is said to be one-many relation if at least one element of A is paired with two or more elements of B.

   Example: From the given Fig. 17.13, the relation $R = \{(1, 3), (1, 4), (3, 5)\}$.

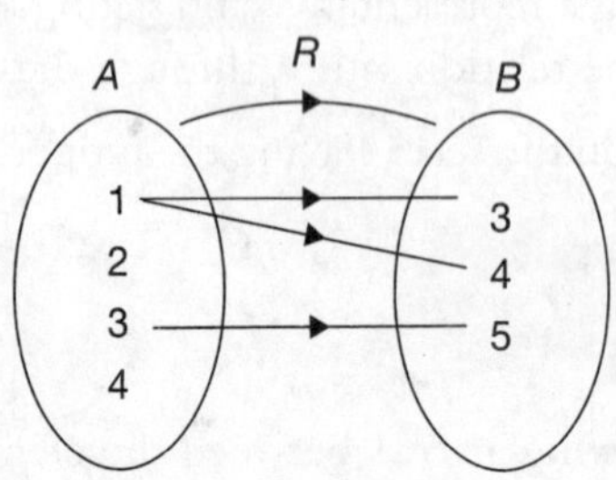

Figure 17.13

3. **Many-One Relation:** A relation $R: A \rightarrow B$ is said to be many-one relation if two or more elements of A are paired with an element of B.

Example: From the given Fig. 17.14, the relation $R = \{(1, 2), (2, 4), (3, 2), (5, 3)\}$.

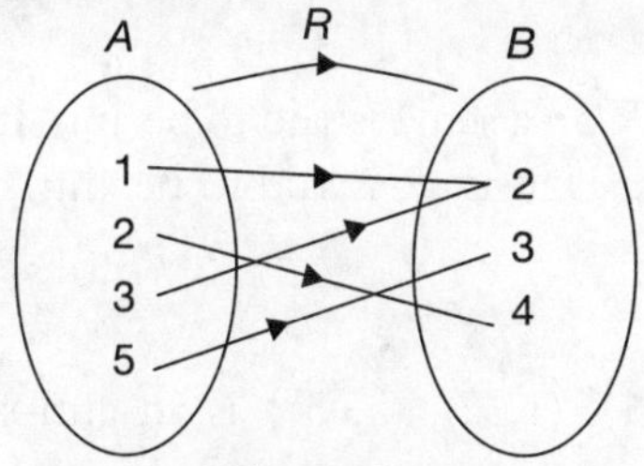

Figure 17.14

4. **Many-Many Relation:** A relation $R: A \rightarrow B$ is said to be many-many relation if two or more elements of A are paired with two or more elements of B.

Example: From the given Fig. 17.15, the relation $R = \{(1, 3), (1, 4), (2, 3), (2, 5), (3, 4), (3, 5)\}$.

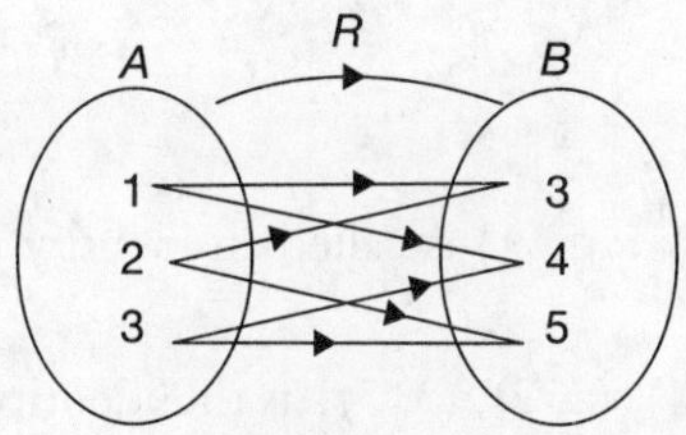

Figure 17.15

Properties of Relations

1. **Reflexive relation:** A relation R on a set A is said to be reflexive if for every $x \in A$, $(x, x) \in R$.

   Examples:

   1. Let $A = \{1, 2, 3\}$ then, $R = \{(1, 1), (1, 2), (2, 2), (3, 3), (2, 3)\}$ is a reflexive on A.
   2. Let $A = \{1, 2, 3\}$ then, $R = \{(1, 1), (2, 3), (1, 2), (1, 3), (2, 2)\}$ is not a reflexive relation as $(3, 3) \notin R$.

> **Info Bytes!**
> Number of reflexive relations defined on set having n elements is 2^{n^2-n}.

2. **Symmetric relation:** A relation R on a set A is said to be symmetric, if for every $(x, y) \in R$, $(y, x) \in R$.

   Examples:

   1. Let $A = \{1, 2, 3\}$. Then, $R = \{(1, 1), (1, 2), (2, 2), (2, 1), (3, 3)\}$ is a symmetric relation on A.
   2. Let $A = \{1, 2, 3\}$. Then, $R = \{(1, 1), (1, 2), (3, 1), (2, 2), (3, 3)\}$ is not a symmetric relation as $(1, 2) \in R$ but $(2, 1) \notin R$.

> **Info Bytes!**
> A relation R on a set A is symmetric, iff $R = R^{-1}$, i.e., R is symmetric, iff $R = R^{-1}$.

3. **Transitive relation:** A relation R on a set A is said to be transitive, if $(x, y) \in R$ and $(y, z) \in R$, then $(x, z) \in R$. That is, R is said to be transitive, whenever $(x, y) \in R$ and $(y, z) \in R \Rightarrow (x, z) \in R$.

Examples:

1. If $A = \{1, 2, 3\}$, then the relation on set A, $R = \{(1, 1), (1, 2), (1, 3), (2, 1), (3, 1), (2, 2), (2, 3), (3, 2), (3, 3)\}$ is a transitive relation.
2. Let $A = \{1, 2, 3\}$, then the relation on set A, $R = \{(1, 2), (2, 2), (2, 1), (3, 3), (1, 3)\}$ is not a transitive relation as $(1, 2) \in R$ and $(2, 1) \in R$ but $(1, 1) \notin R$.

4. **Anti-symmetric relation:** A relation R on a set A is said to be anti-symmetric, if $(x, y) \in R$ and $(y, x) \in R$, then $x = y$. That is, R is said to be anti-symmetric if for $x \neq y$, $(x, y) \in R \Rightarrow (y, x) \notin R$.

   Examples:

   1. Let $A = \{1, 2, 3\}$, then $R = \{(1, 1), (1, 2), (3, 3)\}$ is an anti-symmetric relation.
   2. Let $A = \{1, 2, 3\}$, then $R = \{(1, 1), (1, 2), (1, 3), (2, 1), (3, 3)\}$ is not an anti-symmetric relation as $(1, 2) \in R$ and $(2, 1) \in R$ but $1 \neq 2$.

5. **Equivalence relation:** A relation R on a set A is said to be an equivalence relation if it is,
   (i) reflexive
   (ii) symmetric and
   (iii) transitive.

Konnect

For any set A, $A \times A$ is an equivalence relation. In fact it is the largest equivalence relation.

Info Bytes!

Identity relation is the smallest equivalence relation on a set A.

Identity Relation

A relation R on a set A defined as, $R = \{(x, x) \mid x \in A\}$ is called an identity relation on A. It is denoted by I_A.

Example: Let $A = \{1, 2, 3\}$. Then, $R = \{(1, 1), (2, 2), (3, 3)\}$ is the identity relation on A.

EXAMPLE 17.8 If $A = \{a, b, c, x, y, z\}$, then the maximum number of elements in any relation on A is:

SOLUTION

Since, $A \times A$ has maximum number of elements, $n(A \times A) = 6 \times 6 = 36$.

Function

Let A and B be two non-empty sets. f is a relation from A to B. If f is such that

1. For every $a \in A$, there is $b \in B$ such that $(a, b) \in f$ and
2. No two ordered pairs in f have the same first element, then f is called a function from set A to set B and is denoted as $f: A \to B$.

Examples:

1.

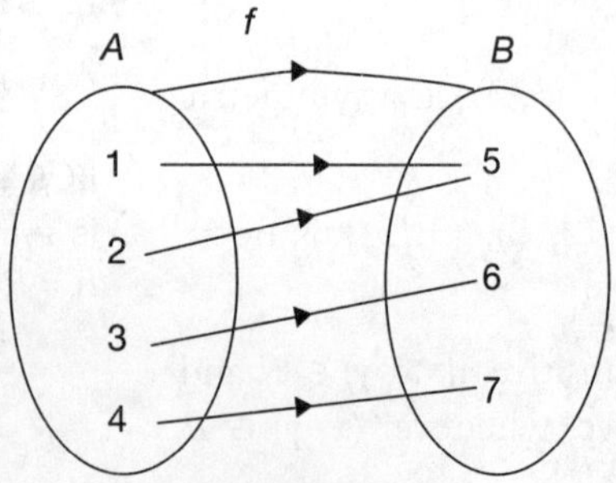

Figure 17.16

2.

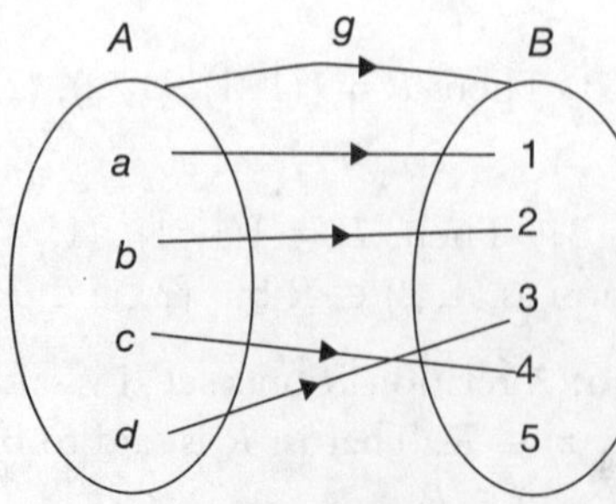

Figure 17.17

Let A and B be two non-empty sets. A relation f from A to B is said to be a function, if every element in A is associated with exactly one element in B. It is denoted by $f: A \to B$ (read as f is mapping from A to B). If $(a, b) \in f$, then b is called the f image of a and is written as $b = f(a)$. a is called the pre-image of b. Also in $f(a) = b$, a is called the independent variable and b is called the dependent variable.

Konnect

1. If $(a, b) \in f$, then $f(a) = b$ and b is called the f image of a. a is called the pre-image of b.
2. If $f: A \to B$ is a function, then A is called the domain of f and B is called the co-domain of f.
3. The set $f(A)$ which is all the images of elements of A under the mapping f is called the range of f.

Domain and Co-domain

If $f: A \to B$ is a function, then A is called domain and B is the co-domain of the function.

Range

If $f: A \to B$ is a function, then the set of all images of elements in its domain is called the range of f and is denoted by $f(A)$.

That is, $f(A) = \{f(a) \mid a \in A\}$.

If $f: A \to B$ is a function, and $n(A) = m$, $n(B) = p$, then the number of functions that can be defined from A to B is p^m.

Info Bytes!

Range of a function is always subset of its co-domain, i.e., $f(A) \subseteq B$.

Examples:

1. $A = \{1, 2, 3, 4\}$; $B = \{2, 3, 4, 5, 6\}$ are two sets. A relation f is defined as $f(x) = x + 2$. The relation $f: A \to B$ is a function and $f = \{(1, 3), (2, 4), (3, 5), (4, 6)\}$.
2. $A = \{-2, 2, 3, 4\}$, $B = \{4, 9, 16\}$ are two sets. The relation f, defined as $f(x) = x^2$, is a function from A to B, since every element in A is associated with exactly one element in B. The function $f = \{(-2, 4), (2, 4), (3, 9), (4, 16)\}$.
3. $A = \{-1, 1, 2, 5\}$, $B = \{1, 8, 125\}$ are two sets. The relation f defined as $f(x) = x^3$ is not a function from A to B. The relation $f = \{(1, 1), (2, 8), (5, 125)\}$. The number -1 is an element in A but it has no image in B.
4. $A = \{1, 2, 3, 4\}$, $B = \{x, y, z, t, u, v\}$ are two sets. A relation f is defined as follows:

   $f = \{(1, x), (2, y)\ (3, z), (4, t)\ (1, u)\}$. Here f is not a function, because the element 1 in A is associated with two elements x, u in B. Therefore, f is not a function.

Arrow Diagram

Functions can be represented by arrow diagrams.

Example: $A = \{1, 2, 3, 4, 5\}$, $B = \{1, 4, 9, 16, 25, 36\}$ are two sets. A relation f is defined as $f(n) = n^2$. The arrow diagram of this function is shown in the Fig. 17.18.

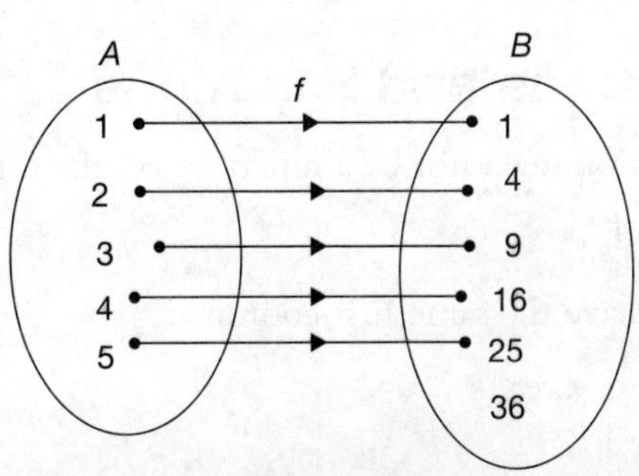

Figure 17.18

Every element in A is associated with exactly one element in B. So, $f: A \to B$ is a function.

Example:

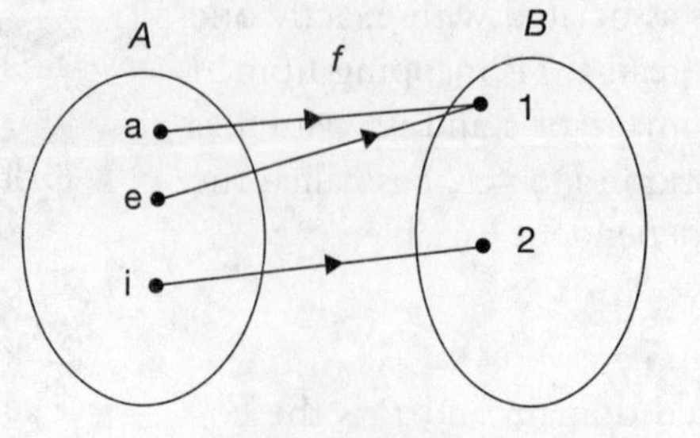

Figure 17.19

Every element in A is associated with exactly one element in B (see Fig. 17.19). So, $f: A \to B$ is a function.

Example:

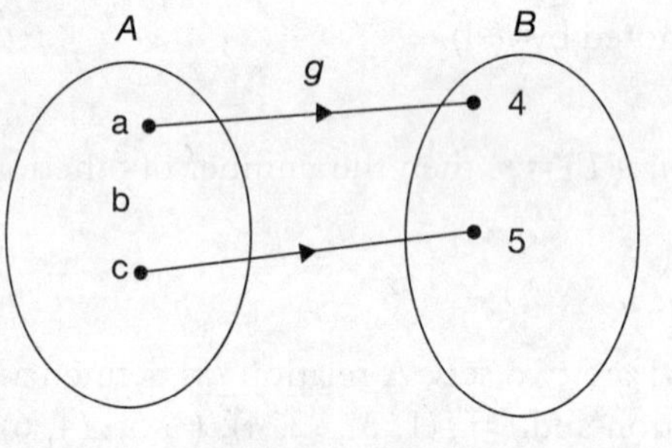

Figure 17.20

b is an element in A and it is not associated with any element in B (see Fig. 17.20). So, $g: A \to B$ is not a function.

Example:

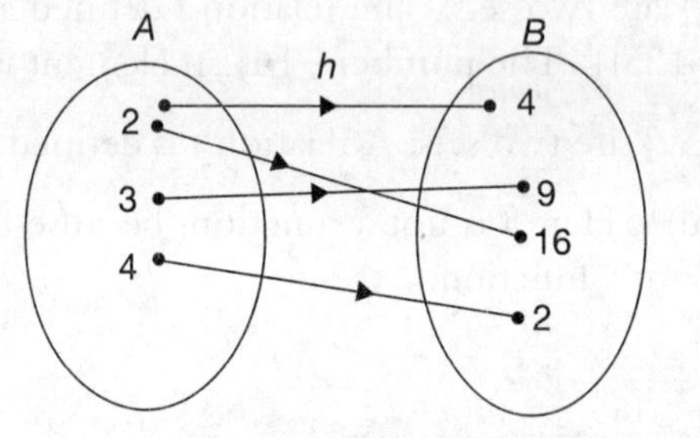

Figure 17.21

2 is an element in A. It is associated with two different elements in B (see Fig. 17.21). That is, 2 has two different images. So, $h: A \to B$ is not a function.

Difference Between Relations and Functions

Every function is a relation but every relation need not be a function. A relation f from A to B is called a function, if

1. Domain $(f) = A$,
2. No two different ordered pairs in f have the same first coordinate.

Example: Let $A = \{1, 2, 3, 4\}$, $B = \{a, b, c, d, e\}$.

Some relations f, g, h are defined as follows:

$f = \{(1, a), (2, b), (3, c), (4, d)\}$
$g = \{(1, a), (2, b), (3, c)\}$
$h = \{(1, a), (1, b), (2, c), (3, d), (4, e)\}$.

In the relation *f*, the domain of *f* is *A* and all first coordinates are different. So, *f* is a function. In the relation *g*, the domain of *g* is not *A*. So *g* is not a function. In the relation *h*, the domain of *h* is *A*, but two of the first coordinates are equal, i.e., 1 has two different images. So, *h* is not a function.

EXAMPLE 17.9 Find the domain of the function $f(x) = \frac{1}{x} + \frac{1}{\log(2-x)}$.

SOLUTION

$\frac{1}{x}$ is not defined for $x = 0$ and logarithmic function takes only positive values.

$\Rightarrow x < 2$

$\Rightarrow$ but $x \neq 0$, $x \neq 1$

Types of Functions

One-One Function or Injection

Let $f: A \rightarrow B$ be a function. If different elements in *A* are assigned to different elements in *B*, then the function $f: A \rightarrow B$ is called a one-one function or an injection.

That is, $a_1, a_2 \in A$ and $a_1 \neq a_2 \Rightarrow f(a_1) \neq f(a_2)$ then $f: A \rightarrow B$ is a one-one function (or) if $f(a_1) = f(a_2) \Rightarrow a_1 = a_2$, then $f: A \rightarrow B$ is a one-one function.

Example:

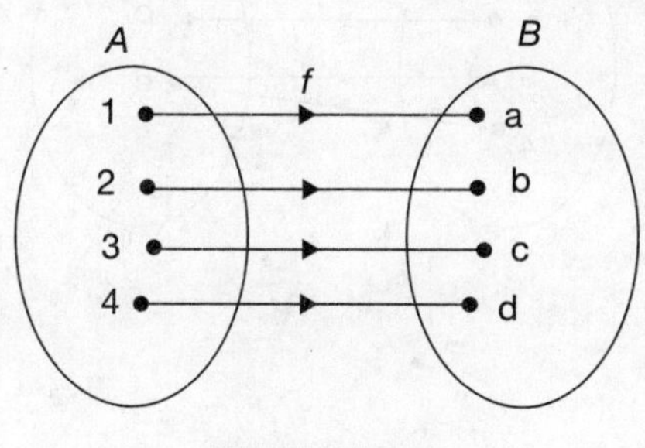

Figure 17.22

Different elements in *A* are assigned to different elements in *B*. $f: A \rightarrow B$ is a one-one function (see Fig. 17.22).

Example:

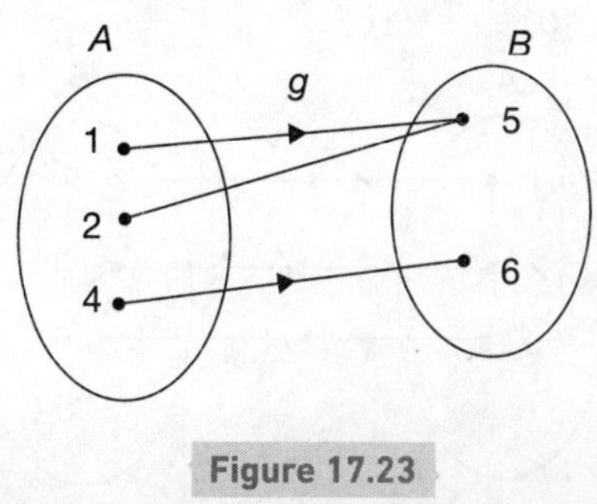

Figure 17.23

Info Bytes!

A and *B* are finite sets and $f: A \rightarrow B$ is one-one. Then $n(A) \leq n(B)$.

1 and 2 are two different elements in *A*, but they are assigned to the same element in *B*. So $g: A \rightarrow B$ is not a one-one function (see Fig. 17.23).

Many-One Function

If the function $f: A \to B$ is not one-one, then it is called a many-one function; i.e., two or more elements in A are assigned to the same element in B.

Example:

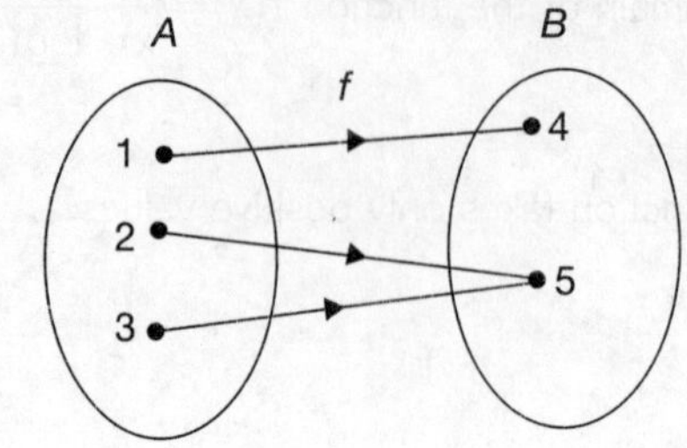

Figure 17.24

2, 3 are different elements in A, and they are assigned to the same element, i.e., 5 in B. So, $f: A \to B$ is a many to one function (see Fig. 17.24).

Onto Function or Surjection

$f: A \to B$ is said to be an onto function, if every element in B is the image of at least one element in A. That is, for every $b \in B$, there exists at least one element $a \in A$, such that $f(a) = b$.

Example:

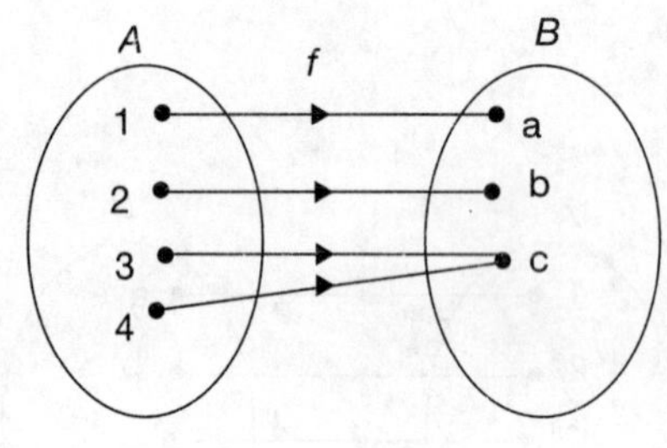

Figure 17.25

Konnect

If $f: A \to B$ is an onto function, then the co-domain of f must be equal to the range of f, i.e., $f(A) = B$.

Range = {a, b, c}

Co-domain = {a, b, c}

Range = Co-domain

In the Fig. 17.25, every element in B is the image of at least one element in A. Therefore, it is an onto function.

Example: In the Fig. 17.26, d is an element in B, but it is not the image of any element in A. Therefore, it is not an onto function.

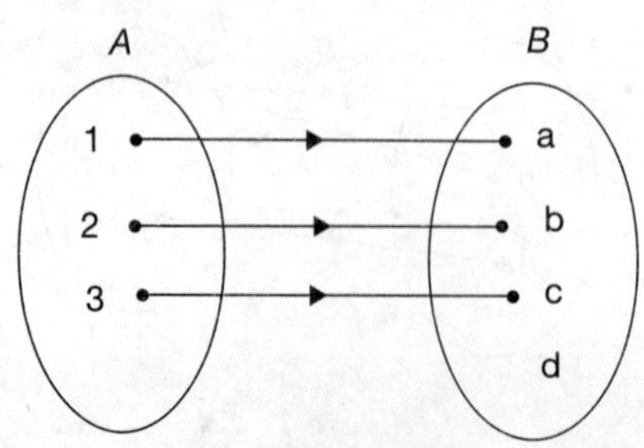

Figure 17.26

Info Bytes!

A and B are finite sets and $f: A \to B$ is onto. Then, $n(B) \leq n(A)$.

Into Function

If a function is not onto, then it is an into function, i.e., at least one element in B is not the image of any element in A, or the range is a subset of the co-domain.

Bijective Function

If the function $f: A \rightarrow B$ is both one-one and onto then it is called a bijective function.

Example:

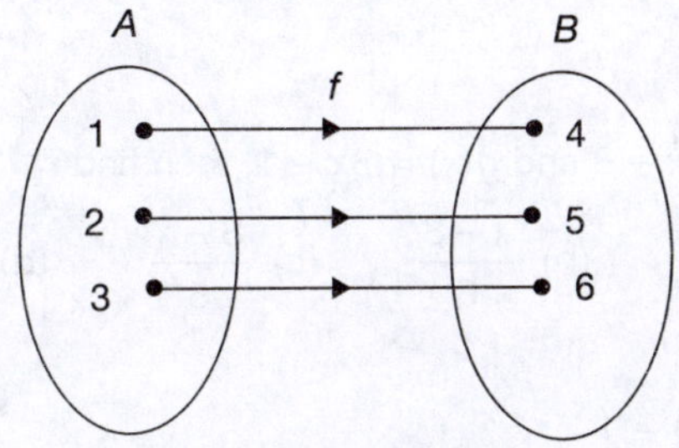

Figure 17.27

In the Fig. 17.27, $f: A \rightarrow B$ is both one-one and onto. So f is a bijective function.

Example:

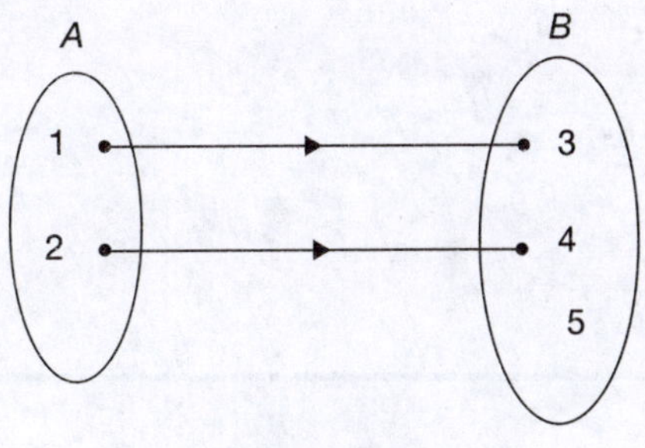

Figure 17.28

In the Fig. 17.28, it is only one-one but not onto, so it is not bijective.

Inverse of a Function

If $f: A \rightarrow B$ is a function, then the set of ordered pairs obtained by interchanging the first and second coordinates of each ordered pair in f is called the inverse of f and is denoted by f^{-1}. That is, $f: A \rightarrow B$ is a function then its inverse is $f^{-1}: B \rightarrow A$.

Konnect

A and B are finite sets and $f: A \rightarrow B$ is one-one and onto then $n(A) = n(B)$.

Examples:

1. $f = \{(1, 2), (2, 3), (3, 4)\}$
   $f^{-1} = \{(2, 1), (3, 2), (4, 3)\}$.
2. $g = \{(1, 4), (2, 4), (3, 5), (4, 6)\}$
   $g^{-1} = \{(4, 1), (4, 2), (5, 3), (6, 4)\}$.
3. $A = \{1, 2, 3, 4\}$, $B = \{x, y, z, a, b\}$ are two sets, the function $h: A \rightarrow B$ is defined as follows:
   $h = \{(1, a), (2, b), (3, x), (4, z)\}$
   $h^{-1} = \{(a, 1), (b, 2), (x, 3), (z, 4)\}$.

In the above examples only f^{-1} is a function, but g^{-1}, h^{-1} are not functions.

$\therefore$ $f: A \rightarrow B$ a function, then $f^{-1}: B \rightarrow A$ need not be a function.

Inverse Function

If $f: A \to B$ is a bijective function, then $f^{-1}: B \to A$ is also a function. That is, the inverse of a function is also a function, only when the given function is bijective.

Example: $A = \{1, 2, 3, 4, 5\}$; $B = \{a, e, i, p, u\}$. A function f is defined as follows:

$f = \{(1, a), (2, e), (3, i), (4, u), (5, p)\}$. Clearly, f is a bijective function.

Now $f^{-1} = \{(a, 1), (e, 2), (i, 3), (u, 4), (p, 5)\}$. Clearly, f^{-1} is also a function and it is also bijective.

EXAMPLE 17.10

If $f(x) = 2x + 3$ and $g(x) = 3x - 1$, then find $f^{-1} o\, g^{-1}$.

(a) $\frac{x+8}{6}$ (b) $\frac{x-8}{6}$ (c) $\frac{8-x}{6}$ (d) $\frac{x-8}{2}$

SOLUTION

$g\, o\, f(x) = g\,(f(x)) = g\,(2x + 3) = 3\,(2x + 3) - 1$

$= 6x + 9 - 1$

$= 6x + 8$

Let $(gof)\,(x) = 6x + 8 = y$

$\Rightarrow 6x = y - 8$

$x = \frac{y-8}{6}$

$\Rightarrow (gof)^{-1} = \frac{x-8}{6}$

$= f^{-1}og^{-1}$

Identity Function

$f: A \to A$ is said to be an identity function on A, if $f(a) = a$ for every $a \in A$, it is denoted by IA.

Example: $A = \{1, 2, 3, 4\}$. The identity function on A is $IA = \{(1, 1), (2, 2), (3, 3), (4, 4)\}$.

Konnect

1. Identity function is always bijective function.
2. The inverse of the identity function is the identify function itself.

Constant Function

A function $f: A \to B$ is a constant function if there is an element $b \in B$, such that $f(a) = b$, for all $a \in A$. That is, in a constant function the range has only one element.

Example: $A = \{1, 2, 3, 4\}$; $B = \{a, e, i, u\}$ are two sets and a function from A to B is defined as follows:

$f = \{(1, a), (2, a), (3, a), (4, a)\}$, therefore f is a constant function.

Info Bytes!

The range of a constant function is a singleton.

Equal Functions

Two functions f and g, defined on the same domain D are said to be equal, if $f(x) = g(x)$ for all $x \in D$.

Example: Let $f: R - \{2\} \to R$ be defined by $f(x) = x + 2$; and $g: R - \{2\} \to R$ be defined by $g(x) = \frac{x^2 - 4}{x - 2}$.

$\therefore f$: and g have the same domain $R - \{2\}$.

Given $f(x) = x + 2$;

$$g(x) = \frac{x^2 - 4}{x - 2} = \frac{(x-2)(x+2)}{x-2} = x + 2.$$

$\therefore f(x) = g(x)$ for all $x \in R - \{2\}$.

$\Rightarrow f$ and g are equal functions.

Composite Function (or) Product Function

Let f and g be two functions such that $f: A \to B$ and $g: B \to C$. Let a be an orbitary element in A.

Since f is a function from A to B, there exists an element $b \in B$, such that $f(a) = b$.

Since g is a function from B to C, there exists an element $c \in C$, such that $g(b) = c$.

$g(f(a)) = c \Rightarrow g \text{ o } f(a) = c$.

$g \text{ o } f$ is a function from A to C.

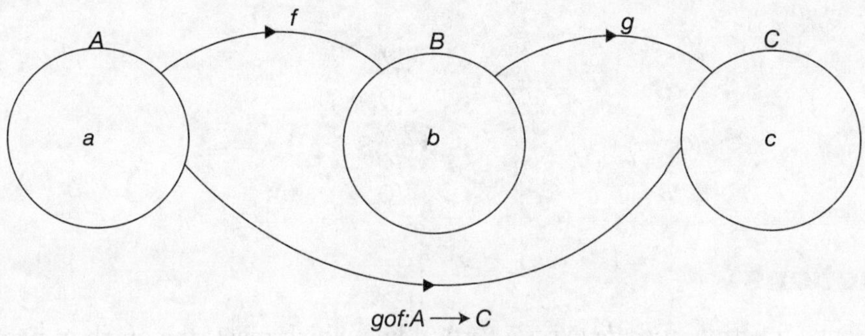

Figure 17.29

If $f: A \to B$ and $g : B \to C$ are two functions, then the function $g[f(x)] = g \text{ o } f$ from A to C, denoted by $g \text{ o } f$ is called the composite function of f and g.

In the composite function $g \text{ o } f$,

1. the co-domain of f is the domain of g.
2. the domain of $g \text{ o } f$ is the domain of f, the co-domain of $g \text{ o } f$ is the co-domain of g.
3. composite function does not satisfy commutative property, i.e., $g \text{ o } f \neq f \text{ o } g$.
4. if $f: A \to B$; $g: B \to C$; $h: C \to D$ are three functions, $h \text{ o } (g \text{ o } f) = (h \text{ o } g) \text{ o } f$, i.e., the composite function satisfies associative property.

Real Function

If $f: A \to B$ such that $A \subseteq R$, then f is said to be a real variable function.

If $f: A \to B$ such that $B \subseteq R$, then f is said to be a real valued function.

If $f: A \to B$, such that A and B are both subsets of the set of real numbers (R), then f is called a real function.

Even and Odd Functions

1. If $f(-x) = f(x)$, then the function $f(x)$ is called an even function.

   Example:

   $f(x) = x^2$

   $f(-x) = x^2$

   Here, $f(-x) = f(x)$

   $\Rightarrow f(x) = x^2$ is an even function.

Konnect

1. There are functions which are neither even nor odd.
2. If $f(x)$ is a real function, then $\frac{f(x)+f(-x)}{2}$ is always even and $\frac{f(x)-f(-x)}{2}$ is always odd.
3. Product of two even functions is even.
4. Product of two odd functions is even.
5. Product of an even function and an odd function is odd.
6. $f(x) = 0$ is both even and odd.

2. If $f(-x) = -f(x)$, then the function $f(x)$ is called an odd function.

Example:

$f(x) = x^3$

$f(-x) = -x^3$

Here, $f(x) = -f(x)$

$f(x) = x^3$ is an odd function.

Domain and Range of Some Functions are Listed below

Function	Domain	Range
$\frac{1}{x}$	$R - \{0\}$	R
$\sqrt{x}$	$[0, \infty)$	$[0, \infty)$
$\|x\|$	R	$[0, \infty)$
$\log x$	$(0, \infty)$	R
a^x $(a > 0)$	R	$(0, \infty)$

Graphs of Functions

A graph does not represent a function, if there exists a vertical line which meets the graph in two or more points, i.e., a vertical line meets the graph at only one point, then the graph represents a function.

Example:

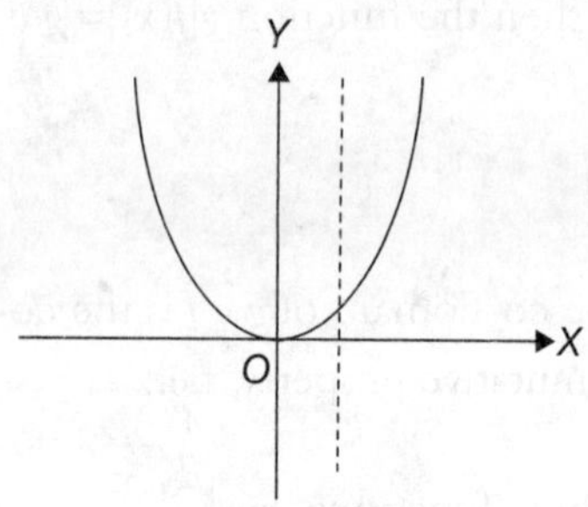

Figure 17.30

In the Fig. 17.30, the vertical dotted line meets the graph at only one point. So, the graph represents a function.

Example: In the Fig. 17.31, the vertical dotted line meets the graph at two points. So, it is not a function.

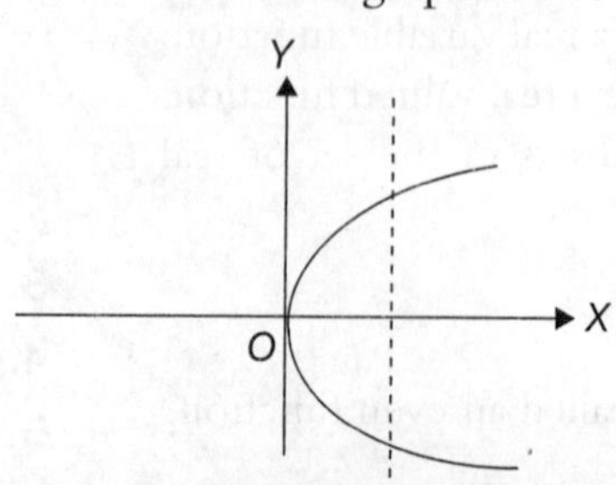

Figure 17.31

Info Bytes!

1. The Y-axis does not represent a function.
2. The X-axis represents a many-one function.

Zeroes of a Function

If $f: A \to R$ $(A \subset R)$, then the points $k \in A$, such that $f(k) = 0$ are called the zeroes of the function f.

If k is a zero of $f: A \to R$, then $(k, 0)$ is the corresponding point on the graph of f. k is called the x-intercept of the graph.

Example:

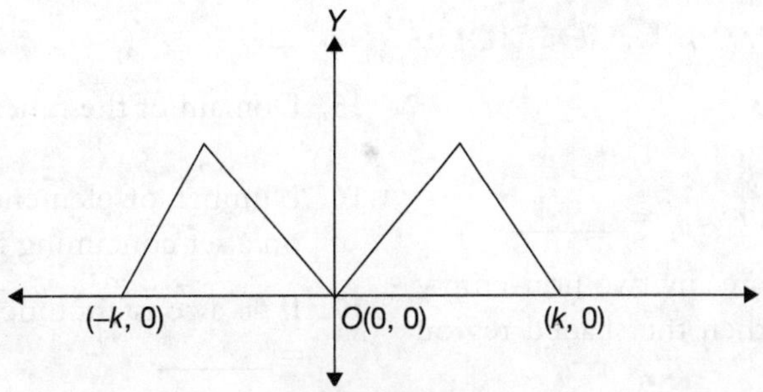

Figure 17.32

Graph of the Fig. 17.32, represents a function, zeroes of the graph are $-k$, 0, and k.

POINTS TO REMEMBER

- ✔ A set is a well-defined collection of objects. Let us understand the meaning of a well-defined collection of objects.
- ✔ The objects in a set are called its elements or members.
- ✔ The number of elements in a set A is called its cardinal number.
- ✔ A set with no elements in it is called an empty set (or) void set (or) null set. It is denoted by { } or φ. (read as 'phi').
- ✔ A set consisting of only one element is called a singleton set.
- ✔ Two sets A and B are said to be equivalent if their cardinal numbers are equal. We write this symbolically as $A \sim B$ or $A \leftrightarrow B$.
- ✔ Two sets A and B are said to be disjoint, if they have no elements in common
- ✔ If $A \subseteq B$ and $A \neq B$, then A is called a proper subset of B and is denoted by $A \subset B$. When $A \subset B$ then B is called a superset of A and is denoted as $B \supset A$, if $A \subset B$ then $n(A) < n(B)$ and if $B \supset A$ then $n(B) > n(A)$.
- ✔ A set which consists of all the sets under consideration or discussion is called the universal set. It is usually denoted by U or μ.
- ✔ Formulae

  Commutative Law

  (i) $A \cup B = B \cup A$

  (ii) $A \cap B = B \cap A$

  (iii) $A \Delta B = B \Delta A$

PRACTICE QUESTIONS CLASSROOM WING

Very Short Answer Type Questions

Directions of questions from 1 to 17:
Fill in the blanks.

1. If A and B are disjoint, then $(A \cap B)' =$ ______.
2. In the given figure, if A and B are any two non-empty sets and μ is an universal set, then the shaded region represents ______.

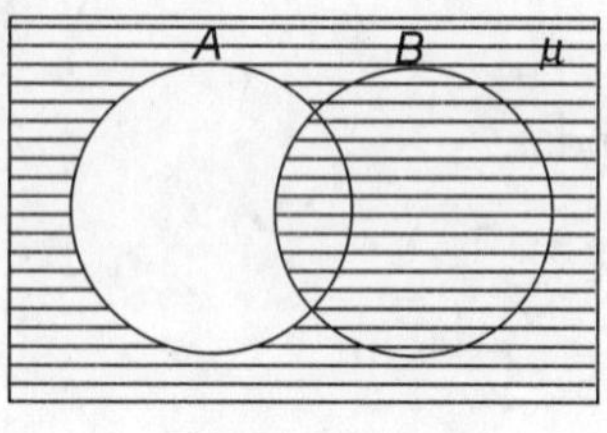

Figure 17.33

3. If any two of the sets $A_1, A_2, \ldots, A_n$ are disjoint, then $A_1 \cap A_2 \cap \ldots \cap A_n =$ ______.
4. If $n(A) = 25$, $n(B) = 10$ and also $B \subset A$, then $n(A - B)$ $=$ ______.
5. If $n(A) = 15$, $n(B) = 13$ and $n(A \cap B) = 10$, then the symmetric difference of A and B is ______.
6. $A = \{a, b, c\}$ and R is an identity relation on set A. Then the ordered pairs of R are ______.
7. $n(P \times Q) = 200$ and $n(P) = 100$, then $n(Q) =$ ______.
8. If $R = R^{-1}$, then the relation R is ______.
9. If $A = \{1, 2, 3, 4, 5, 6\}$ and $B = \{1, 3, 5, 7\}$, then $n(A \times B) =$ ______.
10. If A and B are two equivalent sets and $n(B) = 6$, then $n(A \times B) =$ ______.
11. The domain of the relation $R = \{(x, y): x, y \in N$ and $x + y \le 9\}$ is ______.
12. The range of the relation $R = \{(x, y): 3x + 2y = 15$ and $x, y \in N\}$ is ______.
13. Range of the function $|x - 5|$ is ______.
14. If the function $f: A \to \{a, b, c, d\}$ is an onto function, then the minimum number of elements in A must be equal to ______.
15. Domain of the function $\frac{1}{\sqrt{x}}$ is ______.
16. Number of elements of an identity function defined on a set containing four elements is ______.
17. If f is a constant function and $f(100) = 100$, then $f(2007)$ $=$ ______.

Directions of questions from 18 to 22:
State whether the following statements are true or false

18. The ordered pair (x, y) is a subset of $\{x, y\}$. (True/False)
19. If $A = \{a, b, c, d\}$ and $B = \{1, 2, 3\}$, then $R = \{(a, 2), (b, 1), (d, 3), (2, c)\}$ is a relation from A to B. (True/False)
20. (A) $A = \{x, y, z, p\}$; $B = \{7, 8, 9, 1\ 0\}$ and a rule f is given by $f(x) = 7, f(y) = 7, f(z) = 7, f(p) = 7$. The relation f is a function. [True/False]

    (B) A and B are any two sets. If the difference between the number of elements of the power sets of A and B is 4095, find the number of elements of the sets A and B.
21. In a bijection, the number of elements of the domain is equal to the number of elements of the co-domain. [True/False]
22. If $f: A \to B$ and $g: B \to C$ are such that $g\ o\ f$ is onto then g is necessarily onto. [True/false]

Directions of questions from 23 to 47:
Answer the following questions.

23. Relation $R = \{(x, y) : x > y$ and $x + y = 8$ where $x, y \in N\}$, then write R^{-1} in roster form.
24. If $f(x) = 2x + \frac{3}{2}$ then find $f(3)$ and $f\left(\frac{3}{2}\right)$.
25. $f: R \to R$ be defined by $f(x) = 7x + 6$. What is f^{-1}?

Short Answer Type Questions

26. (A) If $A = \{1, 2, 3, 6, 8, 9\}$, $B = \{3, 4, 5, 6\}$, and $\mu = \{1, 2, 3, \ldots, 10\}$, then find $(A \cup B)'$.

(B) If $A = \{1, 2, 3, 4, 5, 6, 7, 8, 9, 10\}$, find the number of subsets of A which consists of all the prime numbers less than 10.

27. Write the following sets in the roster form.
$X = \{a \mid 30 \le a \le 40 \text{ and } a \text{ is a prime}\}$

28. If $n(P - Q) = x + 37$, $n(Q - P) = 30 + 3x$, $n(P \cup Q) = 120 + 2x$ and $n(P \cap Q) = 35$, then find x.

29. In a club of 70 members 30 play Tennis but not cricket and 55 play Tennis. How many members play cricket but not Tennis? (Each member plays either Tennis or Cricket).

30. Find the value of $n(A \cap B \cap C)$, if $n(A) = 35$, $n(A \cap B \cap C') = 8$, $n(A \cap C \cap B') = 10$ and $n(A \cap B' \cap C') = 6$.

31. $R = \{(a, 2a - b)/a, b \in N \text{ and } 0 < a, b < 3\}$, then find the domain and range of the relation R.

32. If $n(X \cap Y') = 9$, $n(Y \cap X') = 10$ and $n(X \cup Y) = 24$, then find $n(X \times Y)$.

33. In a gathering, two persons are related 'if they have the same bike', then find the properties that are satisfied by the relation.

34. If $A = \{3, 5, 6, 9\}$ and R is a relation in A defined as $R = \{(x, y) \in R \text{ and } x + y < 18\}$, then write R in roster form.

35. Given R = {(a, a), (a, b), (b, c), (a, c), (b, b), (b, a), (c, a), (c, b)} on set A = {a, b, c}. What are the properties that R satisfies?

36. If $f(x) = \dfrac{2x+3}{4}$, then find $f^{-1}\left(\dfrac{3}{4}\right)$.

37. If $f(x)$ is a polynomial function of 4th degree, $f(x) \cdot f\left(\dfrac{1}{x}\right) = f(x) + f\left(\dfrac{1}{x}\right)$ and $f(2) = 17$, then find $f(3)$.

38. If $f(x) = (1 - x^3)^{1/3}$, then find $f \circ f(x)$.

39. If $f(x) = \dfrac{x^2 - 1}{3}$ for $x \in \{-2, -1, 0, 1, 2\}$, then find $f^{-1}(x)$.

40. Find the range of the function $f(x) = \dfrac{1}{2x^2 + 1}$.

Essay Type Questions

41. In a colony of 125 members, 70 members watch Telugu channel, 80 members watch Hindi channel and 95 watch English channel, 20 watch only Telugu and Hindi, 35 watch only English and Hindi and 15 watch only Telugu and English. How many members watch all the three channels, if each watches either of the channels?

42. If $f(a) = \log\left(\dfrac{1+a}{1-a}\right)$, then find $f\left(\dfrac{a_1 + a_2}{1 + a_1 a_2}\right)$ in terms of $f(a_1)$, $f(a_2)$.

43. (A) If $f(x) = 2x + 1$ and $g(x) = 3x - 5$, then find $(f \circ g)^{-1}(0)$.

(B) Given $R = \{(a, a), (a, b), (a, c), (a, d), (d, d), (b, c), (b, b), (b, a), (c, a), (c, b), (c, c), (d, a)\}$ on set $A = \{a, b, c, d\}$. Check whether R is an equivalence relation?

44. If $f(x) = x^3 - 1$, $x < 0 = x^2 - 1$, $x \ge 0$ and $g(x) = (x+1)^{1/3}$, $x < 1 = (x+1)^{1/2}$, $x \ge 1$, then find $g \circ f(x)$.

45. If $f = \{(1, 3), (2, 1), (3, 4), (4, 2)\}$ and $g = \{(1, 2), (2, 3), (3, 4), (4, 1)\}$, then find $f \circ g$.

46. Given that $f(x) = x^{15} - 1$, $x < 0$

$= x^3 - 1$, $x \ge 0$ and

$g(x) = (x+1)^{\frac{1}{15}}, x < 1$

$= (x+1)^{\frac{1}{3}}, x \ge 1.$

Find $gof(x)$.

47. If $f(x) = 3x + 2$ and $g(x) = 2x - 3$, then find the value of $(fog)^{-1}(0) + (fog)^{-1}(1)\ (fog)^{-1}(2) + (fog)^{-1}(3) \ldots + (fog)^{-1}(119)$.

PRACTICE QUESTIONS COMPETITION WING

Level 1: Apply Your Concepts

Directions of questions from 1 to 5:
Fill in the blanks.

1. If A is a non-empty set, then $(((A')')')'$ is ______.
2. The number of non-empty proper subsets of a set A is 0, then $n(A)$ = ______.
3. The number of non-empty proper subsets of a set containing 7 elements, is ______.
4. If A and B are disjoint sets, then $A \Delta B$ = ______.
5. $n(A \cup B \cup C)$ = ______.

Directions of questions from 6 to 70:
Select the correct alternative from the given choices.

6. A, B and C are three non-empty sets. If $A \subset B$ and $B \subset C$, then which of the following is true?
   (a) $B - A = C - B$ (b) $A \cap B \cap C = B$
   (c) $A \cup B = B \cap C$ (d) $A \cup B \cup C = A$
7. If S is the set of squares and R is the set of rectangles, then $(S \cup R) - (S \cap R)$ is:
   (a) S.
   (b) R.
   (c) set of squares but not rectangles.
   (d) set of rectangles but not squares.
8. If $A = \{1, 2, 3, 4, 5, 6\}$, then how many subsets of A contain the elements 2, 3, and 5?
   (a) 4 (b) 8
   (c) 16 (d) 32
9. If $A = \{a, b, c, d, e\}$, $B = \{a, c, e, g\}$ and $C = \{b, d, e, g\}$, then which of the following is true?
   (a) $C \subset (A \cup B)$ (b) $C \subset (A \cap B)$
   (c) $A \cup B = A \cup C$ (d) Both (a) and (c)
10. If $A_1 \subset A_2 \subset A_3 \subset \ldots \subset A_{50}$ and $n(A_x) = x - 1$, then find $n\left[\bigcap_{x=11}^{50} A_x\right]$.
   (a) 49 (b) 50
   (c) 11 (d) 10
11. A group of 30 people take either tea or coffee. If 12 people do not take tea and 15 people take coffee, then how many people take tea?
   (a) 18 (b) 16
   (c) 15 (d) 12
12. If P is the set of parallelograms, and T is the set of trapeziums, then $P \cap T$ is
   (a) P (b) T
   (c) ϕ (d) $P\ T$
13. If X, Y and Z are three sets such that $X \supset Y \supset Z$, then $(X \cup Y \cup Z) - (X \cap Y \cap Z)$ = ______.
   (a) $X - Y$ (b) $Y - Z$
   (c) $X - Z$ (d) $Z - X$
14. If $n(A_x) = x + 1$ and $A_1 \subset A_2 \subset A_3 \subset \ldots \subset A_{99}$, then $n\left[\bigcup_{x=1}^{99} A_x\right]$ = ______.
   (a) 99 (b) 98
   (c) 100 (d) 101
15. In a class every student can speak either English or Telugu. The number of students who can speak only English, the number of students who can speak only Telugu and the number of students who can speak both English and Telugu are equal. Then which of the following can represent the number of students of the class?
   (a) 20 (b) 25
   (c) 45 (d) 50
16. If $(2x - y, x + y) = (1, 11)$, then the values of x and y respectively are
   (a) 6, 5. (b) 7, 4.
   (c) 4, 7. (d) 7, 3.
17. A relation between two persons is defined as follows: $a\,R\,b$ 'if a and b born in different months', R is
   (a) reflexive. (b) symmetric.
   (c) transitive. (d) equivalence.
18. If A is a non-empty set, then which of the following is false?
   p: There is atleast one reflexive relation on A.
   q: There is atleast one symmetric relation on A.
   (a) p alone (b) q alone
   (c) Both p and q (d) Neither p nor q

19. In a set of teachers of a school, two teachers are said to be related if 'they teach the same subject', then the relation is:
(a) reflexive and symmetric
(b) symmetric and transitive
(c) reflexive and transitive
(d) equivalence

20. If $A = \{x, y, z\}$, then the relation $R = \{(x, x), (y, y), (z, z), (z, x), (z, y)\}$ is:
(a) symmetric (b) anti symmetric
(c) transitive (d) Both (b)and (c)

Direction for questions 21 and 22:
In the set of animals, a relation R is defined in each question.

21. $a\ R\ b$ if 'a and b are in different zoological parks', then R is:
(a) only reflexive (b) only symmetric
(c) only transitive (d) equivalence

22. On the set of human beings a relation R is defined as follows:
$a\ R\ b$ if 'a and b have the same brother', then R is:
(a) only reflexive (b) only symmetric
(c) only transitive (d) equivalence

23. Consider the following statements:
p: Every reflexive relation is a symmetric relation.
q: Every anti-symmetric relation is reflexive.
Which of the following is/are true?
(a) p alone (b) q alone
(c) Both p and q (d) Neither p nor q

24. In a set of ants in a locality, two ants are said to be related if they walk on a same straight line, then the relation is:
(a) reflexive and symmetric
(b) symmetric and transitive
(c) reflexive and transitive
(d) equivalence

25. If $n(A) = 4$ and $n(B) = 4$, then find the number of subsets of $A \times B$.
(a) 65636 (b) 65536
(c) 65532 (d) 65356

26. A function f is constant from set $A = \{1, 2, 3\}$ onto set $B = \{a, b, c\}$ such that $f(1) = a$, then the range of f is:
(a) {a, c} (b) {a}
(c) {a, b} (d) {a, b, c}

27. Which of the following is an odd function?
(a) $x + x^3$ (b) $x^3 - x^2 - 5$
(c) $x^2 + x^4$ (d) $\dfrac{3x^2}{x^2+1}$

28. Which of the following relations is a function?
(a)
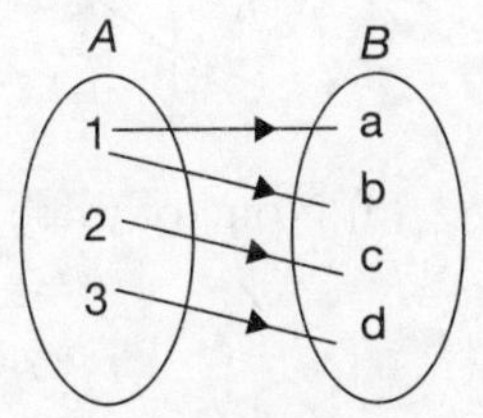

(b)
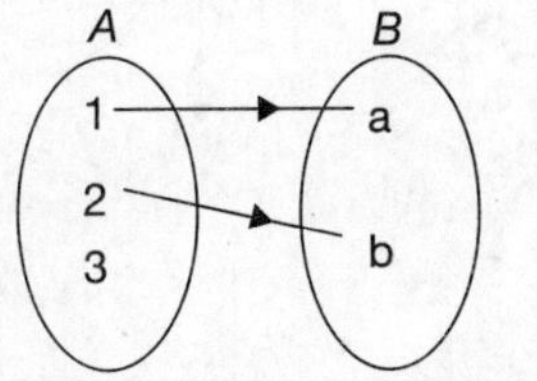

(c)
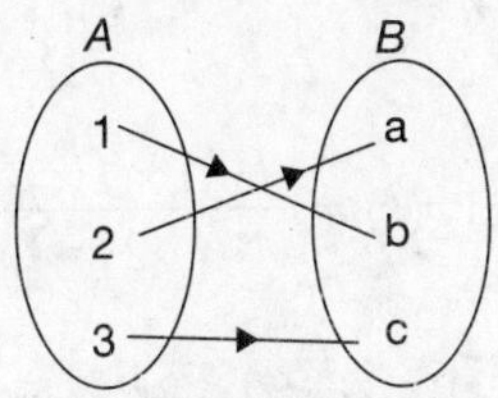

(d)
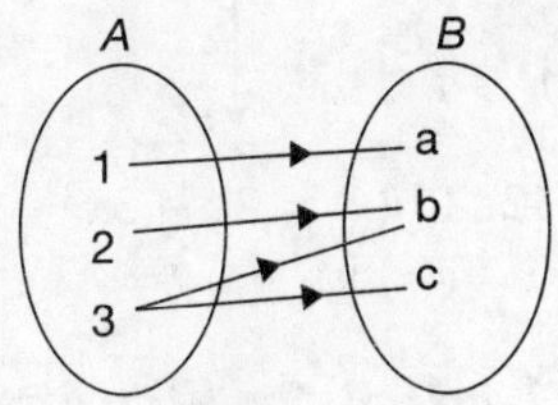

29. Which of the following relation is not a function?
(a)
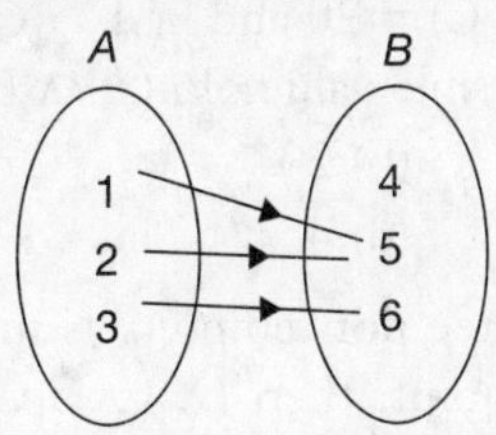

(b)
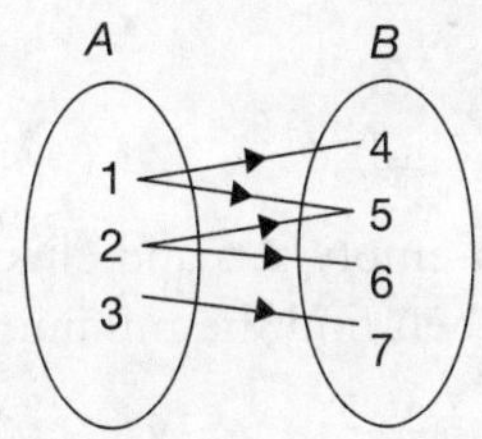

(c)
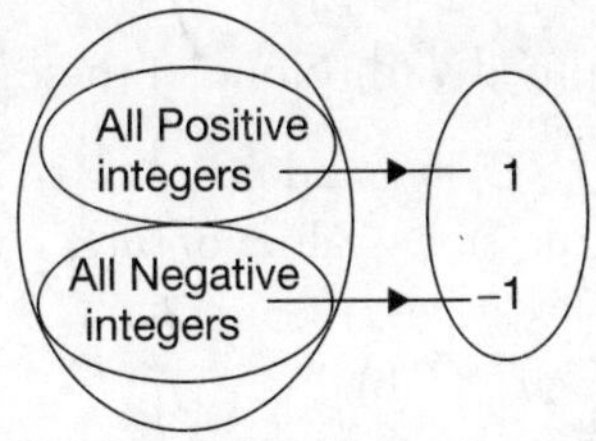

(d)
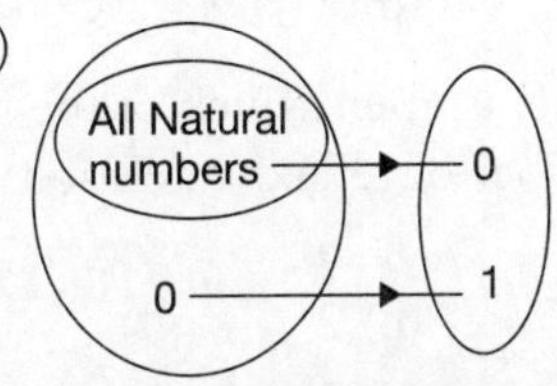

30. If $f: A \to B$ is an onto function defined by $f(x) = 3x - 4$ and $A = \{0, 1, 2, 3\}$, then the co-domain of f is:
(a) {−4, 0, 2, 5} (b) {−1, 2, 5, 6}
(c) {−4, −1, 2, 5} (d) {−4, 1, 2, 5}

31. Which of the following graphs represents a function?

(a)

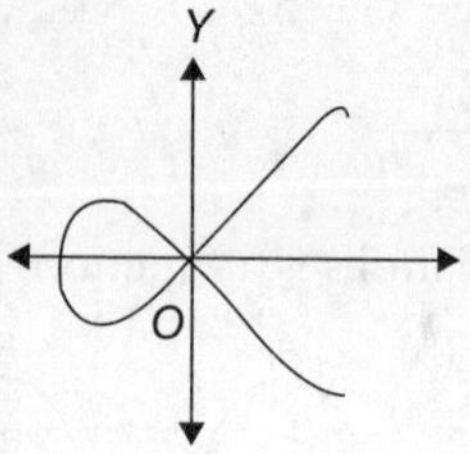

(b)

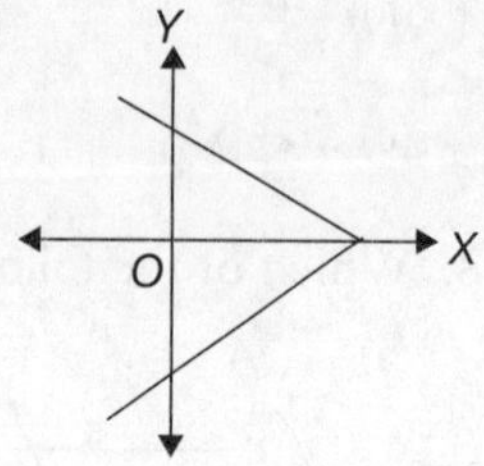

(c)

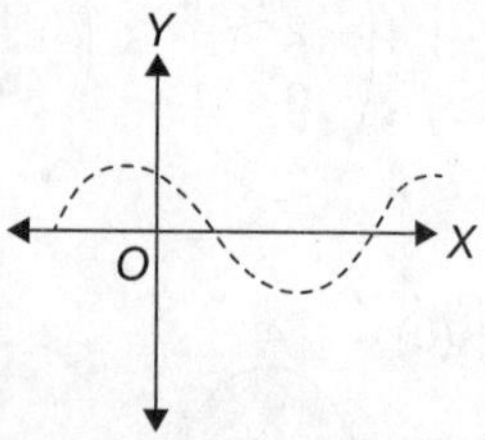

(d) None of these

32. If $f(x) = 2x - 3x^2 - 5$ and $g(x) = \frac{f(x)+f(-x)}{2}$, then $g(x)$ is:

(a) odd (b) even
(c) even as well as odd (d) Neither (a) nor (b)

33. Domain of the function $f(x) = \frac{5-x}{|3-x|}$ is

(a) $x \in R$ (b) $x \in Z$
(c) $R - \{3\}$ (d) $R - \{5\}$

34. $A = \{-1, 0, 1, 2\}$, $B = \{0, 1, 2\}$ and $f: A \to B$ defined by $f(x) = x^2$, then f is:

(a) only one-one function (b) only onto function
(c) bijective (d) not a function

35. If two sets A and B have p and q number of elements respectively and $f: A \to B$ is one-one, then the relation between p and q is:

(a) $p \geq q$ (b) $p > q$
(c) $p \leq q$ (d) $p = q$

Level 2: Review Your Concepts

36. If $n(A \cap B) = 10$, $n(B \cap C) = 20$ and $n(A \cap C) = 30$, then find the greatest possible value of $n(A \cap B \cap C)$.

(a) 15 (b) 20
(c) 10 (d) 4

37. If X, Y and Z are any three non-empty sets such that any two of them are disjoint, then $(X \cup Y \cup Z) \cap (X \cap Y \cap Z)$ is

(a) X (b) Y
(c) Z (d) ϕ

38. A and B are any two non-empty sets and A is proper subset of B. If $n(A) = 5$, then find the minimum possible value of $n\,(A \Delta B)$.

(a) 1 (b) 5
(c) Cannot be determined (d) None of these

39. If $n(A \cap B) = 5$, $n(A \cap C) = 7$ and $n(A \cap B \cap C) = 3$, then the minimum possible value of $n(B \cap C)$ is ______.

(a) 0 (b) 1
(c) 3 (d) 2

40. If a set contains n elements, then which of the following cannot be the number of reflexive relations in the set?

(a) 2^n (b) 2^{n-1}
(c) 2^{n^2-1} (d) 2^{n+1}

41. If $A = \{4, 6, 10, 12\}$ and R is a relation defined on A as 'two elements are related if they have exactly one common factor other than 1'. Then the relation R is:

(a) anti-symmetric (b) only transitive
(c) only symmetric (d) equivalence

42. X is the set of all members in a colony and R is a relation defined on X as 'two persons are related if they speak same language'. The relation R is:

(a) only symmetric
(b) only reflexive
(c) both symmetric and reflexive but not transitive
(d) equivalence

43. The relation 'is a factor of' on the set of natural numbers is not:

(a) reflexive (b) symmetric
(c) anti-symmetric (d) transitive

44. If $f(x) = \log x$, then $\frac{f(xy) + f\left(\frac{x}{y}\right)}{f(x)f(y)} =$ ______.

(a) $\frac{2}{\log x}$ (b) $2\log y$
(c) $2\log x$ (d) $\frac{2}{\log y}$

45. If $f(x) = \frac{x-1}{x+1}, x \neq -1$; then find $f\left(\frac{x-1}{x+1}\right)$.

(a) x (b) $-\frac{1}{x}$
(c) $f(x)$ (d) $f\left(\frac{1}{x}\right)$

46. If $f: R \to R$ defined by $f(x) = 3x - 5$, then $f^{-1}(\{-1, -2, 1, 2\}) =$ ______.

(a) $\left\{1, \frac{4}{3}, \frac{7}{3}\right\}$ (b) $\left\{-1, 2, \frac{-4}{3}\right\}$

(c) $\left\{1, 2, \frac{4}{3}, \frac{7}{3}\right\}$ (d) $\{1, 2, -1, -2\}$

47. If $f: R \to R$ is a function defined as $f(\alpha - f(\alpha)) = 5f(\alpha)$ and $f(1) = 7$, then find $f(-6)$.

(a) 37 (b) 35
(c) 7 (d) 21

Level 3: Assess Your Concepts

48. All the students of a class like Horlicks, Maltova or Viva. Number of students who like only Horlicks and Maltova, only Maltova and Viva and only Horlicks and Viva are all equal to twice the number of students who like all the three foods. Number of students who like only Horlicks, only Maltova and only Viva are all equal to thrice the number of students who like all the three foods. If four students like all the three, then find the number of students in the class.

(a) 64 (b) 48
(c) 68 (d) 52

49. The inverse of the function $f(x) = (x^3 - 1)^{1/4} - 12$ is

(a) $[1 + (x + 12)^3]^{1/4}$ (b) $[1 - (x + 12)^4]^{1/4}$
(c) $[(x + 12)^3 - 1]^{1/4}$ (d) $[1 + (x + 12)^4]^{1/4}$

50. The relation, $R = \{(1, 3), (3, 5)\}$ is defined on the set with minimum number of elements of natural numbers. The minimum number of elements to be included in R so that R is equivalence, is:

(a) 5 (b) 6
(c) 7 (d) 8

51. If $f(2x + 3) = 4x^2 + 12x + 15$, then the value of $f(3x + 2)$ is:

(a) $9x^2 - 12x + 36$ (b) $9x^2 + 12x + 10$
(c) $9x^2 - 12x + 24$ (d) $9x^2 - 12x - 5$

52. If a relation $f: A \to B$ is defined by $f(x) = x + 2$, where $A = \{-1, 0, 1\}$ and $B = \{1, 2, 3\}$, then f is:

(a) only one-one function (b) only onto function
(c) bijective (d) None of these

53. The domain of the function, $f(x) = \frac{|x| - 2}{|x| - 3}$ is ______.

(a) R (b) $R - \{2, 3\}$
(c) $R - \{2, -2\}$ (d) $R - \{-3, 3\}$

54. If $f(x + y) = f(xy)$ and $f(1) = 5$, then find the value of $\sum_{k=0}^{6} f(k)$.

(a) 25 (b) 35
(c) 36 (d) 24

55. If $f(x) = (x + 1)$ and $g(x) = (x - 1)$, then find $(f \circ g)((g \circ f)(2))$.

(a) 1 (b) 2
(c) 3 (d) 4

56. If $f(x) = x$, $g(x) = x^2$ and $h(x) = x^3$, then find $[(h \circ g) \circ f](x)$.

(a) x (b) x^2
(c) x^3 (d) x^6

57. If $f = \{(2, 4), (3, 6), (4, 8)\}$ and $g = \{(4, 3), (6, 4), (8, 2)\}$, then find $f \circ g$.

(a) $\{(2, 3), (3, 4), (4, 2)\}$ (b) $\{(4, 6), (6, 8), (8, 4)\}$
(c) $\{(3, 2), (4, 3), (2, 4)\}$ (d) $\{(6, 4), (8, 6), (4, 8)\}$

58. Find the domain of the function $f(x) = \frac{1}{\sqrt{2x^2 + 5x + 2}}$.

(a) R (b) $\left(-2, \frac{-1}{2}\right)$

(c) $(-\infty, -2] \cup \left[\frac{-1}{2}, \infty\right)$ (d) $(-\infty, -2) \cup \left(\frac{-2}{2}, \infty\right)$

59. Find the domain of function, $\sum_{p=1}^{10} \frac{1}{|2x - p|}$.

(a) R

(b) $R - \left\{\frac{1}{2}, 1, \frac{3}{2}, 2, \ldots, 10\right\}$

(c) $R - \left\{\frac{1}{2}, 1, \frac{3}{2}, 2, \ldots, 5\right\}$

(d) $R - \{1, 2, \ldots, 10\}$

60. Find the inverse function of $f(x) = 2x - 3$.

(a) $3x + 2$ (b) $3x - 2$
(c) $(x + 3)/2$ (d) $(x - 3)/2$

61. If $f(x) = x + 1$ and $g(x) = x - 2$, then find $(f^{-1} \circ g^{-1})(x)$.

(a) $x - 1$ (b) $x + 2$
(c) $g(x)$ (d) $f(x)$

62. If $f(x) + f(1 - x) = 10$, then the value of $f\left(\frac{1}{10}\right)+f\left(\frac{2}{10}\right)+\cdots+f\left(\frac{9}{10}\right)$

(a) is 45. (b) is 50.
(c) is 90. (d) is 40.

63. There are 60 students in a class. The number of students who passed in Mathematics is 45 and the number of students who passed in Physics is 40. The number of students who failed in both the subjects is 5. Find the number of students who passed in exactly one of the subjects.

(a) 35 (b) 25
(c) 15 (d) 40

64. If $X = \{2, 3, 5, 7, 11\}$ and $Y = \{4, 6, 8, 9, 10\}$, then find the number of one-one functions from X to Y.

(a) 720 (b) 120
(c) 24 (d) 12

Directions for questions 65 and 66:
These questions are based on the following data.

For any two sets A and B, $n(A) = 15$, $n(B) = 12$, $A \cap B \neq \phi$ and $B \not\subset A$.

65. Find the maximum possible value of $n(A \Delta B)$.

(a) 27 (b) 26
(c) 24 (d) 25

66. Find the minimum possible value of $n(A \Delta B)$.

(a) 3 (b) 4
(c) 5 (d) 6

Directions for questions 67 and 68:
These questions are based on the following data.

A and B are two finite sets. The difference of the number of elements of the power sets is 96. (Assume $n(A) > n(B)$)

67. Find $n(A) + n(B)$.

(a) 11 (b) 12
(c) 13 (d) 14

68. Find $n(A) - n(B)$.

(a) 2 (b) 3
(c) 4 (d) 5

Directions for questions 69 and 70:
These questions are based on the following data.

The relation R is defined on a set $P = \{a, b, c, d, e\}$ and R is a reflexive relation.

69. Which of the following is true about the number of elements of R?

(a) $1 \le n(R) \le 5$ (b) $1 \le n(R) \le 2^5$
(c) $5 \le n(R) < 2^5$ (d) $5 \le n(R) \le 2^5$

70. How many reflexive relations are possible on P?

(a) 2^5 (b) 2^{25}
(c) 2^{20} (d) 2^{18}

AT

ANSWER KEYS

Classroom Wing

Very Short Answer Type Questions

1. ϕ
2. A'
3. ϕ
4. 0
5. 5
6. $R = \{(a, a), (b, b), (c, c)\}$
7. 2
8. Symmetric
9. 24
10. $n(A \times B) = 36$
11. $\{1, 2, 3, 4, 5, 6, 7, 8\}$
12. $\{3, 6\}$
13. $(0, \infty)$
14. 4
15. R^+
16. 4
17. 100
18. False
19. False
20. (A) True (B) 12
21. True
22. True
23. $R^{-1} = \{(1, 7), (2, 6), (3, 5)\}$
24. $\frac{15}{2}, \frac{9}{2}$
25. $f^{-1}(y) = \frac{x-6}{7}$

Short Answer Type Questions

26. (A) $\{7, 10\}$ (B) 64
27. $X = \{31, 37\}$
28. 9
29. 15
30. 11
31. Domain = $\{1, 2\}$, Range = $\{0, 1, 2, 3\}$
32. 210.
33. It is reflexive, symmetric, and transitive.
34. $R = \{(3, 3), (3, 5), (3, 6), (3, 9), (5, 3), (5, 5), (5, 6), (5, 9), (6, 3), (6, 5), (6, 6), (6, 9), (9, 3), (9, 5), (9, 6)\}$
35. R is only symmetric.
36. 0
37. 82
38. x
39. Inverse does not exist
40. $(0, 1]$

Essay Type Questions

41. 25
42. $f(a_1) + f(a_2)$
43. (A) $\frac{3}{2}$
44. When $x < 0$ or $x \geq 1$, $g \, o \, f(x) = x$ and when $0 \leq x < 1$, $g \, o \, f(x) = x^{2/3}$
45. $\{(1, 1), (2, 4), (3, 2), (4, 3)\}$
46. $\sqrt[5]{x}$
47. 1330

Competition Wing

Level 1: Apply Your Concepts

1. A
2. 1
3. 128
4. $A \cup B$
5. $n(A) + n(B) + n(C) - n(A \cap B) - n(B \cap C) - n(C \cap A) + n(A \cap B \cap C)$
6. (c)
7. (d)
8. (b)
9. (d)
10. (d)
11. (a)
12. (a)
13. (c)
14. (c)
15. (c)
16. (c)
17. (b)
18. (d)
19. (d)
20. (d)
21. (b)
22. (d)
23. (d)
24. (d)
25. (b)
26. (b)
27. (a)
28. (c)
29. (b)
30. (c)
31. (c)
32. (b)
33. (c)
34. (d)
35. (c)

Level 2: Review Your Concepts

36. (c)
37. (d)
38. (a)
39. (c)
40. (d)
41. (c)
42. (d)
43. (b)
44. (d)
45. (b)
46. (c)
47. (b)

Level 3: Assess Your Concepts

48. (a)	49. (d)	50. (c)	51. (c)	52. (c)
53. (d)	54. (b)	55. (b)	56. (d)	57. (b)
58. (d)	59. (c)	60. (c)	61. (d)	62. (a)
63. (b)	64. (b)	65. (d)	66. (c)	67. (b)
68. (a)	69. (d)	70. (c)		

Hints and Explanations

Classroom Wing

Very Short Answer Type Questions

1. A and B are disjoint so $(A \cap B)' = \phi$
2. The shaded part does not have A, so shaded part represent what is not A i.e, A'
3. ϕ
4. $n(A) = 25, n(B) = 10, n(A - B) = ?$

   and $B \subset A$

   $n(A \cap B) = n(A)$

   $n(A) = n(A - B) + n(A \cap B)$

   $n(A - B) = 0$
5. $n(A) = 15$

   $n(B) = 13$

   $n(A \cap B) = 10$

   $n(A - B) = n(A \cup B) - n(B)$

   $n(A \cup B) = n(A) + n(B) - n(A \cap B)$

   $= 15 + 13 - 10$

   $= 28 - 10$

   $= 18$

   $n(A) = n(A - B) + n(A \cap B)$

   $15 - 10 = n(A - B)$

   $n(A - B) = 5$
6. $A = \{a, b, c\}$

   R is identity relation ordered pairs of $R = \{(a, a), (b, b), (c, c)\}$
7. $n(P \times Q) = 200$

   $n(P) = 100$

   $n(Q) = ?$

   $n(P \times Q) = n(P) \times n(Q)$

   $\frac{200}{100} = n(Q)$

   $n(Q) = 2$
8. Symmetric
9. $A = \{1, 2, 3, 4, 5, 6\}$

   $B = \{1, 3, 5, 7\}$

   $n(A \times B) = n(A) \times n(B)$

   $= 6 \times 4$

   $= 24$
10. Equivalent, so

    $n(B) = n(A) = 6$

    $n(A \times B) = n(A) \times n(B)$

    $= 36$
11. $x + y \leq 9$

    domain $= \{1, 2, 3, 4, 5, 6, 7, 8\}$
12. $3x + 2y = 15$

    $x = \frac{15 - 2y}{3}$

    As $x \in N$

    $1 = \frac{15 - 2y}{3}$

    $3 = 15 - 2y$

    $3 - 15 = -2y$

    $y = 6$

    Similarly, $y = 3$

    $y = \{3, 6\}$
13. Range of $|x - 5|$

    Range of an absolute function of the form $c|ax + b| + k$ is $f(x) \geq k$

    $k = 0$ here.

    $f(x) \geq 0$

    Range $= \{0, \infty\}$
14. For onto, every element y in the codomain y of f there is atleast one element x in the domain x of f such that $f(x) = y$

    So, minimum = 4
15. Domain $= \frac{1}{\sqrt{x}}$

    $x = 0$ is not defined

    $x < 0$ is not allowed

    Domain: $(0, \infty)$ or R^+
16. 4
17. $f(100) = 100$

    Constant function, so output will always be 100

    $f(2007) = 100$

18. False

19. $A = \{a, b, c, d\}$

$B = \{1, 2, 3\}$

R is incomplete so answer is False.

20. (A) True

(B) Let $n(A)$ and $n(B)$ be $\boldsymbol{a}$ and $\boldsymbol{b}$ respectively.

Given that $\left|n(P(A)) - n(P(B))\right| = 4095.$

$\Rightarrow \left|2^a - 2^b\right| = 4095.$

As the result is an odd number, one of 2^a and 2^b is an even number and the other is an odd number.

$\Rightarrow \left|2^a - 2^b\right| = 4095 = 2^{12} - 2^0.$

$\Rightarrow a = 12$ and $b = 0$ or $\Rightarrow a = 0$ and $b = 12$

$\Rightarrow \boldsymbol{n(A) = 12}$ and $\boldsymbol{n(B) = 0}$ **or** $\boldsymbol{n(A) = 0}$ and $\boldsymbol{n(B) = 12}$.

21. True

22. True

23. $x + y = 8$

Total pairs,

1 7
7 1
4 4
3 5
5 3
6 2
2 6

Sets that satisfy given relation:

$R = \{(7, 1), (5, 3), (6, 2)\}$

$R^{-1} = \{(1, 7), (3, 5), (2, 6)\}$

24. $f(x) = 2x + \frac{3}{2}$

$$f(3) = 3 \cdot 2 + \frac{3}{2}$$

$$= 6 + \frac{3}{2}$$

$$= \frac{15}{2}$$

$$f\left(\frac{3}{2}\right) = 2 \cdot \frac{3}{2} + \frac{3}{2}$$

$$= 3 + \frac{3}{2}$$

$$= \frac{9}{2}$$

25. $f(x) = 7x + 6$

$$y = 7x + 6$$

$$\frac{y-6}{7} = x$$

$$f^{-1}(y) = \frac{x-6}{7}$$

Short Answer Type Questions

26. (A) $n(A) = \{1, 2, 3, 6, 8, 9\}$

$n(B) = \{3, 4, 5, 6\}$

$n(A \cup B)' = \{1, 2, 3, 4, 5, 6, 8, 10\}$

$(A \cup B)' = m - A \cup B$

$= \{1, 2, 3, 4, 5, 6, 7, 8, 9, 10\}$

$- \{1, 2, 3, 4, 5, 6, 8, 10\}$

$= \{7, 10\}$

(B) Given that $A = \{1, 2, 3, 4, 5, 6, 7, 8, 9, 10\}$.

$\Rightarrow n(A) = 10.$

The number of subsets of $A = 2^n = 2^{10}$

The prime numbers which are less than 10 are 2, 3, 5, 7.

The number of subsets of A which consists of all the prime numbers less than 10 = the number of subsets of A which do not consists of the prime numbers $= 2^{10-4} = 2^6 = 64$.

27. $x = \left(\frac{a}{30} \leq a \leq 40 \text{ and } a \text{ is prime}\right)$

$30 \leq a \leq 40$

Prime number = 31, 37

$x = \{31, 37\}$

28. $n(P - Q) = x + 37$

$n(Q - P) = 30 + 3x$

$n(P \cup Q) = 120 + 2x$

$n(P \cap Q) = 35$

$n(P) = n(P - Q) + n(P \cap Q)$

$n(p) = x + 37 + 35$

$n(P) = x + 72$

$n(Q) = n(Q - P) + n(P \cap Q)$

$= 30 + 3x + 35$

$= 3x + 65$

$n(P \cup Q) = n(P) + n(Q) - n(P \cap Q)$

$120 + 2x = x + 72 + 3x + 65 - 35$

$120 + 2x = 4x + 102$

$2x = 18$

$x = 9$

29. $n(T \cup C) = 70$

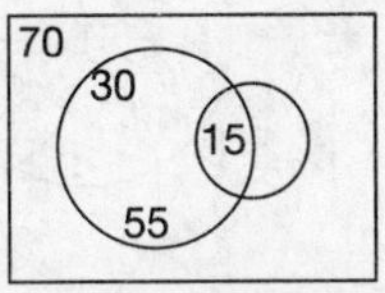

$n(T \cap C) = 25$

$n(T) = 30$

$n(C) = 70 - 30 - 25$

$= 15$

30. $n(A \cap B \cap C) = ?$

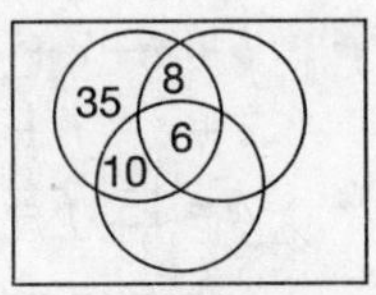

$n(A) = 35$

$n(A \cap B \cap C') = 8$

$n(A \cap C \cap B') = 10$

$n(A \cap B' \cap C') = 6$

$= 35 - 6 - 8 - 10$

$= 11$

$n(A) = 35$ Total.

But $n(A \cap B' \cap C') = 6$ only in A

In A and $B = 8$

In A and $C = 10$

In A, B, C = Total –only in A – only in B, A – only in A, C

$= 35 - 6 - 8 - 10$

$= 11$

31. $R = \{(a, 2a, -b) \mid a, b \in N \text{ and } 0 < a, b < 3\}$

Domain: 1, 2

Range:

At $a = 1, b = 1$

$2a - b = 1$

$a = 1, b = 2$

$2a - b = 0$

$a = 2, b = 1$

$2a - b = 3$

$a = 2, b = 2$

$2a - b = 2$

Range $= \{0, 1, 2, 3\}$

32. $n(X \cap Y') = 9$

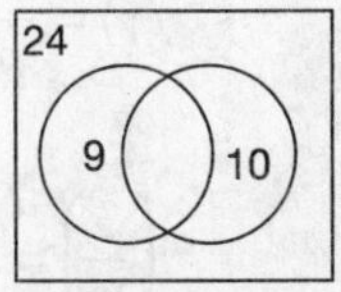

$n(Y \cap X') = 10$

$n(X \cup Y) = 24$

$n(X \times Y) = ?$

$n(X \cap Y) = 24 - 9 - 10$

$= 5$

$n(X) = 9 + 5$

$= 14$

$n(Y) = 10 + 5$

$= 15$

$n(X \times Y) = n(X) \times n(Y)$

$= 14 \times 15$

$= 210$

33. Reflective

Symmetric, if A is related to 8, B is also related A both have same bikes

Transitive: If A and B are related, they have same bike, if B and C are related they have same bike, therefore all three have same bike so A is also related to C.

34. $x + y < 18$

All pairs

$\{(3, 3), (3, 5), (3, 6), (3, 9), (5, 3), (5, 5), (5, 6),$
$(5, 9), (6, 3), (6, 6), (6, 9), (9, 3), (9, 5), (9, 6)\}$

35. $R = \{(a, a), (b, c), (a, c), (b, b), (b, a)$
$(c, a), (c, b), (a, b)\}$

Reflective = C does not satisfy

symmetric = $(a, b) \to (b, a)$

$(a, c) \to (c, a)$

$(b, c) \to (c, b)$

Symmetric satisfied

Transitive = $(a, b) \to (b, c)$

(a, c)

$(c, b), (b, c) \to (c, c)$

Not satisfied.

Not Transitive.

36. $f(x)=\dfrac{2x+3}{4}$

$$y=\frac{2x+3}{4}$$
$$4y=2x+3$$
$$\frac{4y-3}{2}=x$$
$$f^{-1}(y)=\frac{4y-3}{2}$$
$$f^{-1}\left(\frac{3}{4}\right)=\frac{4\left(\frac{3}{4}\right)-3}{2}$$
$$=0$$

37. $f(x)\times f\left(\dfrac{1}{x}\right)=f(x)+f\left(\dfrac{1}{x}\right)$

$$f(x)=\pm x^n+1$$
$$\because f(2)=17$$
$$\Rightarrow 2^n+1=17$$
$$\Rightarrow n=4$$

Now, $f(x)=\pm x^4+1$

$$f(3)=81+1=82$$

38. $f(x)=((1-x^3))^{1/3}$

$$f(x)=\left[(1-((1-x^3)^{1/3})^3\right]^{1/3}$$
$$=\left[(1-(1-x^3)\right]^{1/3}$$
$$=[x^3]^{1/3}$$
$$=x$$

39. $y-\dfrac{x^2-1}{3}$

$$3y+1=x$$
$$x=\sqrt{3y+1}$$

Does not satisfy -2, -1

So inverse does not exist.

40. $f(x)=\dfrac{1}{2x^2+1}$

$$\frac{1}{2x^2+1}=y$$
$$1=y(2x^2+1)$$
$$\frac{1}{y}=2x^2+1$$
$$\left(\frac{1}{y}-1\right)\frac{1}{2}=x^2$$
$$x=\sqrt{\frac{1}{2}}\sqrt{\frac{1}{y}-1}$$
$$\Rightarrow y\neq 0, y>0$$
$$\Rightarrow \frac{1}{y}\leq 1$$

On combining

Range = (0, 1]

Essay Type Questions

41.

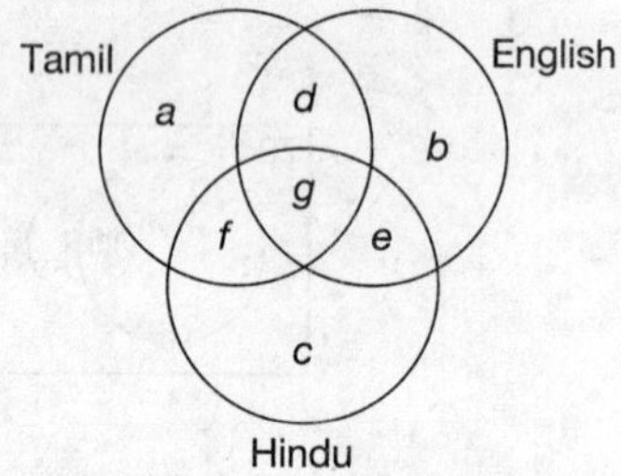

$$a+d+g+f=70 \quad (1)$$
$$b+d+e+g=95 \quad (2)$$
$$c+e+f+g=80 \quad (3)$$
$$d=15, f=20, e=35$$

Substituting these values in eq. 1, 2, 3:

$$a+g=70-15-20=35$$
$$b+g=95-15-35=45$$
$$c+g=80-20-35=25$$

Adding all three above:

$$a+b+c+3g=105$$
$$a+b+c=105-3g$$

Given $a+b+c+d+e+f+g=125$

Now,

$$105-3g+15+35+20+g=125$$
$$2g=50$$
$$g=25$$

25 people watch all 3 channels.

42. $f(a)=\log\left(\dfrac{1+a}{1-a}\right)$

$$f\left(\frac{a_1+a_2}{1+a_1a_2}\right)=\log\left(\frac{1+\dfrac{a_1+a_2}{1+a_1a_2}}{1-\dfrac{a_1+a_2}{1+a_1a_2}}\right)$$

$= \log\left(\frac{1+a_1a_2+a_1+a_2}{1+a_1a_2-a_1-a_2}\right)$

$= \log(1+a_1a_2+a_1+a_2)$
$\quad - \log(1+a_1a_2-a_1-a_2)$

$f(a_1) = \log\left(\frac{1+a_1}{1-a_1}\right)$

$f(a_2) = \log\left(\frac{1+a_2}{1-a_2}\right)$

$f(a_1)+f(a_2) = \log\left(\frac{1+a_1}{1-a_1}\right) + \log\left(\frac{1+a_2}{1-a_2}\right)$

$= \log\left(\left(\frac{1+a_1}{1-a_1}\right)\left(\frac{1+a_2}{1-a_2}\right)\right) = \log\left(\frac{(1+a_1)(1+a_2)}{(1-a_1)(1-a_2)}\right)$

$= \log\left(\frac{1+a_1+a_2+a_1a_2}{1+a_1a_2-a_1-a_2}\right)$

Hence, $f(a_1)+f(a_2)$

43. (A) $f(x) = 2x+1$

$g(x) = 3x-5$

$f(g(x)) = 2(3x-5)+1$

$= 6x-10+1$

$= 6x-9$

$y = 6x-9$

$\frac{y+9}{6} = x$

$f^{-1}(g(y)) = \frac{y+9}{6}$

$f^{-1}(0) = \frac{9}{6} = \frac{3}{2}$

(B) (i) Given that $A = \{a, b, c, d\}$.

(a, a), (b, b), (c, c) and $(d, d) \in R$.

$\therefore$ R is reflexive relation.

(ii) For every element $(x, x) \in R$, there exists $(y, x) \in R$.

$\therefore$ It is symmetric relation.

(iii) For all (x, y), $(y, z) \in R$ there exists $(x, z) \in R$.

$\therefore$ R is transitive relation.

Hence R is an equivalence relation.

44. $f(x) = x^3 - 1$

$g(x) = (x+1)^{\frac{1}{3}}$

$\Rightarrow g(f(u))$ when $x \geq 1$

$= ((x^2-1)+1)^{\frac{1}{2}}$

$= (x^2)^{\frac{1}{2}}$

$= x$

$\Rightarrow g(f(u))$ when $x < 0$

$\Rightarrow ((x^2-1)+1)^{\frac{1}{3}}$

$= (x^2)^{\frac{1}{3}} = x^{\frac{2}{3}}$

45. $f = \{(1, 3), (2, 1), (3, 4), (4, 2)\}$

$g = \{(1, 2), (2, 3), (3, 4), (4, 1)\}$

$f(g(x) = f(g(1)) = f(2) = 1\ (1, 1)$

$f(g(2) = f(3) = 4\ (2, 4)$

$f(g(3) = f(4) = 2\ (3, 2)$

$f(g(4) = f(1) = 3\ (4, 3)$

$f(g(x) = \{(1, 1), (2, 4), (3, 2), (4, 3)\}$

46. Given that $f(x) = x^{15} - 1, x < 0$

$= x^3 - 1, x \geq 0$ and

$g(x) = (x+1)^{\frac{1}{15}}, x < 1$

$= (x+1)^{\frac{1}{3}}, x \geq 1.$

Case (i): $x < 0$

$gof(x) = g(x^{15}-1)$

$= (x^{15}-1+1)^{\frac{1}{15}}$ $\quad \{\therefore g(x) = (x+1)^{\frac{1}{15}}\}$

$= (x^{15})^{\frac{1}{15}}$

$= x.$

Case (ii): $0 \leq x < 1$

$gof(x) = g(x^3 1)$

$= (x^3 1+1)^{\frac{1}{15}}$ $\quad \{\therefore g(x) = (x+1)^{\frac{1}{15}}\}$

$= (x^3)^{\frac{1}{15}}$

$= (x)^{\frac{1}{5}} = \sqrt[5]{x}.$

Case (iii): $x \geq 1$

$gof(x) = g(x^3 1)$

$= (x^3 1+1)^{\frac{1}{3}}$ $\quad \{\therefore g(x) = (x+1)^{\frac{1}{3}}\}$

$= \left(x^3\right)^{\frac{1}{3}}$

$= x$.

When $x < 0$ or $x \geq 1$, $gof(x) = x$ and when $0 \leq x < 1$, $gof(x) = \sqrt[5]{x}$.

47. Given that $f(x) = 3x + 2$ and $g(x) = 2x - 3$.

$fog(x) = f(2x - 3)$

$= 3(2x - 3) + 2 \quad \{\therefore f(x) = 3x + 2\}$

$= 6x - 9 + 2$

$= 6x - 7$.

$fog(x) = 6x - 7 = y$ (say)

$x = \dfrac{y+7}{6}$.

$(fog)^{-1}(y) = \dfrac{y+7}{6}$.

$(fog)^{-1}(0) = \dfrac{7}{6}$.

$(fog)^{-1}(1) = \dfrac{8}{6}$.

$(fog)^{-1}(2) = \dfrac{9}{6}$.

$(fog)^{-1}(3) = \dfrac{10}{6} \ldots (fog)^{-1}(119) = \dfrac{126}{6}$.

$\dfrac{7}{6}, \dfrac{8}{6}, \dfrac{9}{6}, \dfrac{10}{6}, \ldots$ are in AP with $a = \dfrac{7}{6}$, $d = \dfrac{1}{6}$ and $l = \dfrac{126}{6}$.

Also, $n = 120$.

We know that $S_n = \dfrac{n}{2}[a + l]$

$S_{120} = \dfrac{120}{2}\left[\dfrac{7}{6} + \dfrac{126}{6}\right]$

$S_{120} = \dfrac{120}{2}\left[\dfrac{133}{6}\right]$

$S_{120} = 1330$.

$(fog)^{-1}(0) + (fog)^{-1}(1)\ (fog)^{-1}(2) + (fog)^{-1}(3) \ldots + (fog)^{-1}(119) = 1330.$

Competition Wing

Level 1: Apply Your Concepts

1. $(A')' = A$

$(((A')')')' = (A')'$

$= A$

2. $n(A) = 1$

3. Total subsets $= 2^n$

$= 2^7$

$= 128$

One of them is the set itself, and one of them is 0.

So, total proper subsets $= 2^n - 2$

$= 128$

4. A and B are disjoint, then $A \Delta B = A \cup B$

5. $n(A \cup B \cup C) = n(A) + n(B) + n(C) - n(A \cap B)$
$-n(B \cap C) - n(C \cap A) + n(A \cap B \cap C)$

6. Using the concept of subset, verify the options.

7. Every square is a rectangle.

9. Find $A \cup B$, $A \cap B$ and $A \cup C$.

10. If $A_1 \subset A_2 \subset A_3$, ..., then $n(A_1 \cap A_2 \cap A_3 ...) = n(A_1)$.

11. Use Venn diagram concept.

12. Recall the properties of parallelogram and trapezium.

13. Recall the concept of superset, union of sets and intersection.

14. Recall the concepts of subset and union of sets.

15. $n(A \cup B) = n(\text{only } A) + n(\text{only } B) + n(A \cap B)$.

16. Equate the corresponding coordinates.

17. Use the definitions of reflexive, symmetric, anti-symmetric and transitive.

18. Recall the different types of relations.

19. Use the definitions of reflexive, symmetric, anti-symmetric and equivalence.

20. Recall the properties of relations.

21. Recall the properties of relations.

22. Use the definitions of reflexive, symmetric, anti-symmetric, transitive and equivalence.

23. Recall the definitions of reflexive, symmetric and anti-symmetric relations.

24. Recall the properties of relations.

25. Number of subsets of $A \times B$ is $2^{n(A) \cdot n(B)}$.

26. Constant function contains only one element in the range.

27. If $f(x)$ is an odd function, then $f(-x) = -f(x)$.

28. Recall the definition of function.

29. Recall the definition of function.

30. Substitute domain values in $f(x)$.

31. Use the definition of a function.

32. Find $\frac{f(x) + f(-x)}{2}$ and verify even or odd.

33. Function is defined when denominator is not equal to zero.

34. Substitute the domain values in $f(x)$ and find range.

35. Recall the definition of one-one function.

Level 2: Review Your Concepts

36. The greatest possible value of $n(A \cap B \cap C)$ is the least value amongst the values of $n(A \cap B)$, $(B \cap C)$ and $n(A \cap C)$.

37. A and B are disjoint $\Rightarrow A \cap B = \phi$ and $A \cap \phi = \phi$.

38. (i) A is proper subset of B, $A - B = \phi$, i.e., $n(A - B) = 0$.

(ii) Given $n(A) = 5$, the minimum number of elements in B is 6.

(iii) The minimum possible value of $n(A \Delta B)$ is $n(B) - n(A)$.

39. Number of elements in $(A \cap B \cap C)$ becomes the minimum number of elements in $B \cap C$.

40. Number of reflexive relations in a set containing 'n' elements is 2^{n^2-n}.

41. (i) Write the elements in R.

(ii) Apply definition of symmetric relation.

42. Recall the properties of relations.

43. Use the definitions of reflexive, symmetric, anti-symmetric and equivalence.

44. (i) Substitute $f(xy)$, $f(x/y)$ in the given equation.

(ii) $\log ab = \log a + \log b$.

(iii) $\log\left(\frac{a}{b}\right) = \log a - \log b$.

(iv) Replace x by xy and also by $\frac{x}{y}$ in $f(x)$ and simplify.

45. (i) Replace x by $\frac{x-1}{x+1}$ in $f(x)$.

(ii) Then simplify.

46. (i) Find $f^{-1}(x)$.

(ii) Put $x = -1, -2, 1, 2$ in $f^{-1}(x)$ and find their values.

47. Put $\alpha = 1$ in the given equation and simplify.

Level 3: Assess Your Concepts

48. (i) Let the number of students who like all the three be 'x.

(ii)

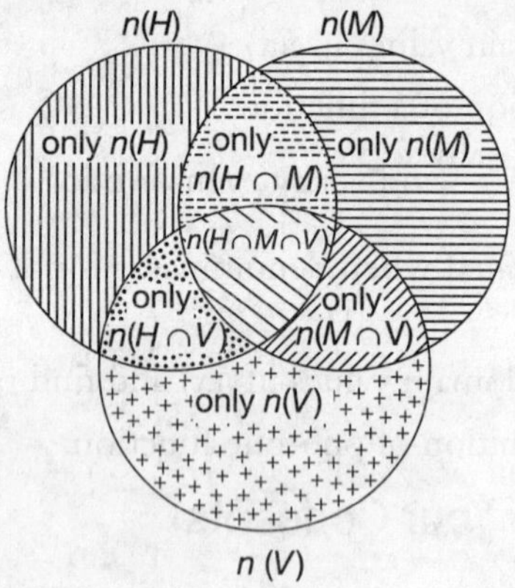

(iii) Substitute the given values in the above figure.

49. (i) Let $f(x) = y$.

(ii) Write the value of x in terms of y.

50. Recall the properties of equivalence relation.

51. (i) Put $2x + 3 = t$.

(ii) Replace x by t.

(iii) Again put $t = 3x + 2$.

52. Given, $f: A \to B$ $f(x) = x + 2$ $A = \{-1, 0, 2\}$ and $B = \{1, 2, 3\}$ $f(A) = B$ and $\forall x \in A$, $f(x_1) \neq f(x_2)$.

$\therefore f$ is bijective.

53. $F(x) = \dfrac{|x|-2}{|x|-3}$. Here, x cannot be ± 3.

(f is not defined when $x = \pm 3$)

$\therefore$ Domain $= R - \{-3, 3\}$

54. Given $f(x + y) = f(xy)$ (1)

and $f(1) = 5$

Put $x = 1$ and $y = 0$

$f(1 + 0) = f(0) \Rightarrow f(0) = 5$

Put $x = 1, y = 1$ in Eq. (1)

$f(1 + 1) = f(1)$

$\therefore f(2) = 5$

Put $x = 2, y = 1$ in Eq. (1)

$f(2 + 1) = f(2 \times 1)$

$\therefore f(3) = 5$

Similarly, $f(4) = f(5) = f(6) = 5$

$$\therefore \sum_{k=0}^{6} f(k) = f(0) + f(1) + \cdots + (6) = 7 \times 5 = 35.$$

55. Given $f(x) = x + 1$, $g(x) = x - 1$

$(g \circ f)(x) = g[f(x)] = g[x + 1] = (x + 1) - 1 = x$

$\therefore (g \circ f)(2) = 2$ (1)

$(g \circ f)(x) = f[g(x)]$

$= f(x - 1) = (x - 1) + 1$

$= x$ (2)

$\therefore (g \circ f)[(g \circ f)(2)]$

$= (g \circ f)(2)$ (from Eq. (1))

$= 2.$

56. Given $f(x) = x$, $g(x) = x^2$ and $h(x)$

$= x^3$ $[(h \circ g) \circ f](x) = (h \circ g)[f(x)]$

$= (h \circ g)(x) = h[g(x)] = h(x^2)$

$= (x^2)^3 = x^6.$

57. For $f \circ g$:

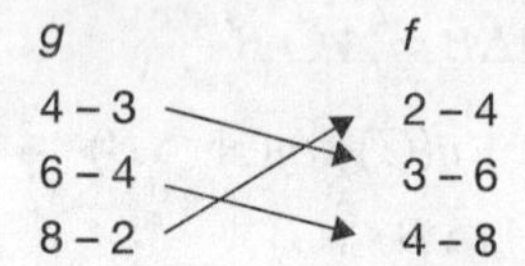

$\therefore f \circ g = \{(4, 6), (6, 8), (8, 4)\}$.

58. $f(x) = \dfrac{1}{\sqrt{2x^2 + 5x + 2}}$

$\therefore 2x^2 + 5x + 2 > 0$

$\Rightarrow (2x + 1)(x + 2) > 0$

$\Rightarrow 2x + 1 > 0$ and $x + 2 > 0$

(Or)

$\Rightarrow 2x + 1 < 0$ and $x + 2 < 0$

$\Rightarrow x < -2$ or $x > \dfrac{-1}{2}$

$\Rightarrow x \in (-\infty, -2) \cup \left(\dfrac{-2}{2}, \infty\right).$

59. $\displaystyle\sum_{p=1}^{10} \frac{1}{|2x - p|}$

$= \dfrac{1}{|2x-1|} + \dfrac{1}{|2x-2|} + \cdots + \dfrac{1}{|2x-10|}$

Here, for $x = \dfrac{1}{2}, 1, \dfrac{3}{2}, \ldots, 5$, it is not defined.

$\therefore$ Domain $= R - \left\{\dfrac{1}{2}, 1, \dfrac{3}{2}, 2 \ldots 5\right\}$.

60. Let $y = f(x) = 2x - 3$

$\Rightarrow y = 2x - 3 \Rightarrow x = \dfrac{y+3}{2}$

$y = f(x) \Rightarrow x = f^{-1}(y)$

$$f^{-1}(y) = \frac{y+3}{2}$$

Replace y by x.

$$f^{-1}(x) = \frac{x+3}{2}.$$

61. $f(x) = x + 1$ $\quad\quad$ $g(x) = x - 2$

$\Rightarrow x = yx - 1$ $\quad\quad$ $z = x - 2$

$x = z + 2$

$\therefore f^{-1}(y) = y - 1$ $\quad\quad$ $g^{-1}(z) = z + 2$

$\therefore f^{-1}(x) = x - 1$ $\quad\quad$ $g^{-1}(x) = x + 2$

Now, $(f^{-1o}\, g^{-1})\,(x) = f^{-1}\,(g^{-1}\,(x)\}$

$= f^{-1}\,(x + 2) = (x + 2) - 1$

$= x + 1 = f(x).$

62. Given $f(x) + f(1 - x) = 10$ $\quad$ (1)

$$f\left(\frac{1}{10}\right)+f\left(\frac{2}{10}\right)+\cdots+f\left(\frac{9}{10}\right)$$

$$=f\left(\frac{1}{10}\right)+f\left(\frac{9}{10}\right)+f\left(\frac{2}{10}\right)+f\left(\frac{8}{10}\right)+\cdots+f\left(\frac{5}{10}\right)$$

$$=\left[f\left(\frac{1}{10}\right)+f\left(1-\frac{1}{10}\right)\right]+\left[f\left(\frac{2}{10}\right)+f\left(1-\frac{2}{10}\right)\right]$$

$$+\cdots+f\left(\frac{5}{10}\right)$$

$$=4(10)+f\left(\frac{1}{2}\right)$$

Put $x = \frac{1}{2}$ in Eq. (1)

$$\therefore f\left(\frac{1}{2}\right)+f\left(1-\frac{1}{2}\right)=10$$

$$\Rightarrow 2\left[f\left(\frac{1}{2}\right)\right]=10 \Rightarrow f\left(\frac{1}{2}\right)=5$$

$$\therefore f\left(\frac{1}{10}\right)+f\left(\frac{1}{10}\right)+\cdots+f\left(\frac{9}{10}\right)40+5=45.$$

63. Number of students = 60

Number of students who passed in Mathematics = 45

Number of students who passed in Physics = 40

Number of students who failed in both the subjects = 5

$\therefore$ Number of students who passed in one of the subjects = 60 − 5 = 55

$\therefore$ Number of students who passed in both the subjects = 45 + 40 − 55 = 30

$\therefore$ Number of students who passed in one of the subjects exactly = (45 − 30) + (40 − 30) = 25.

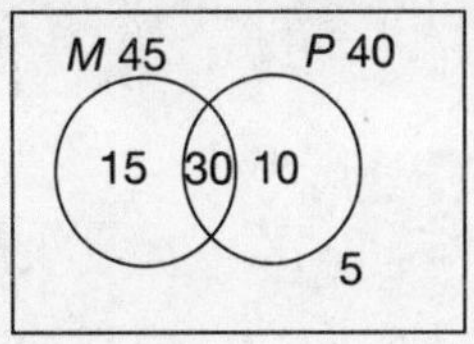

64. Given $X = \{2, 3, 5, 7, 11\}$ $Y = \{4, 6, 8, 9, 10\}$.

$\therefore n(X) = 5$ and $n(Y) = 5$.

Number of one to one functions from X to $Y = 5! = 120$.

Solutions 65 and 66:

$A \cap B \neq \phi$, $B \not\subset A$

$n\,(A) = 15$ and $n\,(B) = 12$

As $A \cap B \neq \phi$, $n\,(A \cap B) \neq 0$.

65. For the maximum value of $n(A\,\Delta\,B)$, $n(A \cap B)$ should be minimum.

The minimum value of $n(A \cap B) = 1$, ($\because n(A \cap B) \neq 0$).

Now, $n(A\,\Delta\,B) = n(A \cup B) - n(A \cap B)$

$= n(A) + n(B) - 2[\,n(A \cap B)]$

$= 15 + 12 - 2 = 25.$

66. For the minimum value of $n(A\,\Delta\,B)$, $n(A \cap B)$ should be maximum.

The maximum value of $n(A \cap B) = 11$,

($\therefore B \not\subset A$ and $n(B) = 12$).

Now $n(A\,\Delta\,B) = n(A \cup B) - n(A \cap B)$

$= n(A) + n(B) - 2\,[n(A \cap B)]$

$= 15 + 12 - 2(11) = 5.$

Solutions 67 and 68:

Let $n(A) = x$ and $n(B) = y$.

Given, $n[p(A)] - n[p(B)] = 96$.

$\therefore 2^x - 2^y = 96$

$\Rightarrow 2^x - 2^y = 2^5$ (3)

$\Rightarrow 2^{x-5} - 2^{y-5} = 3$

$\Rightarrow 2^{x-5} - 2^{y-5} = 2^2 - 2^0$

$\Rightarrow x - 5 = 2$ and $y - 5 = 0$

$\Rightarrow x = 7$ and $y = 5$.

67. $n(A) + n(B) = x + y = 7 + 5 = 12.$

68. $n(A) - n(B) = x - y = 7 - 5 = 2.$

Solutions 69 and 70:

69. R is reflexive relation defined on $P = \{a, b, c, d, e\}$.

And also $R \subseteq P \times P$.

$\therefore 5 \leq n\,(R) \leq 25.$

70. Number of possible reflexive relations

$= 2^{5^2-5} = 2^{20}.$

CHAPTER

18

Limits

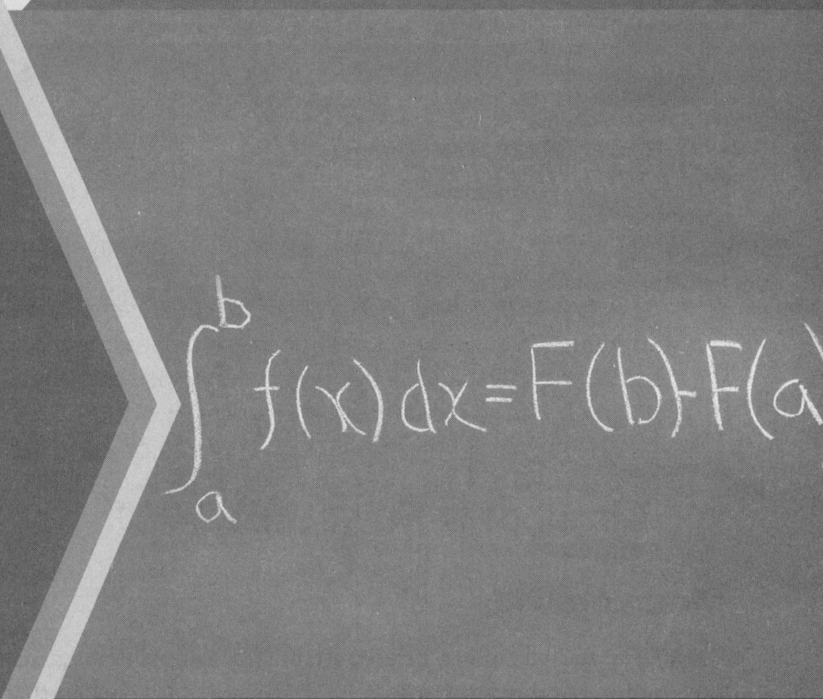

Remember

Before beginning this chapter, you should be able to:

- State the term function
- Apply basic operations on functions

Key Ideas

After completing this chapter, you should be able to:

- Identify limit of a function
- Understand meaning of symbols used in limits
- Study evaluation of limits by different methods
- Obtain limits of a function using a formula

INTRODUCTION

Let $y = f(x)$ be a function of x and let 'a' be any real number.

We first understand what a 'limit' is. A limit is the value, a function approaches, as the independent variable of the function (usually 'x') gets nearer and nearer to a particular value. In other words, when x is very close to a certain number, say a, what is $f(x)$ very close to? It may be equal to $f(a)$ but may be different. It may exist even when $f(a)$ is not defined.

Limit of a Function

Meaning of '$x \to a$'

Let x be a variable and 'a' be a constant. If x assumes values nearer and nearer to 'a', then we say that 'x tends to a' or 'x approaches a' and is written as '$x \to a$'. By $x \to a$, we mean that $x \neq a$ and x may approach 'a' from left or right, which is explained in the example given below.

What is the limit of the function $f(x) = x^2$ as x approaches 3? The expression 'the limit as x approaches to 3' is written as: $\lim\limits_{x\to 3}$. Let us check out some values of $\lim\limits_{x\to 3}$, as x increases and gets closer to 3, without ever exactly getting there.

When $x = 2.9, f(x) = 8.4100$

When $x = 2.99, f(x) = 8.9401$

When $x = 2.999, f(x) = 8.9940$

When $x = 2.9999, f(x) = 8.9994$

As x increases and approaches 3, $f(x)$ gets closer and closer to 9 and since x tends to 3 from the left this is called the 'left-hand limit' and is written as $\lim\limits_{x\to 3^-}$.

Now, let us see what happens when x is greater than 3.

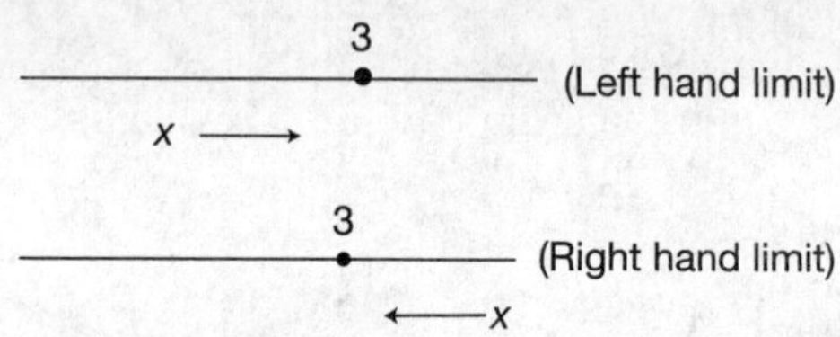

When $x = 3.1, f(x) = 9.6100$

When $x = 3.01, f(x) = 9.0601$

When $x = 3.001, f(x) = 9.0060$

When $x = 3.0001, f(x) = 9.0006$

As x decreases and approaches 3, $f(x)$ still approaches 9. This is called the 'right-hand limit' and is written as $\lim\limits_{x\to 3^+}$.

As $\lim\limits_{x\to 3^-} f(x) = \lim\limits_{x\to 3^+} f(x) = 9$, we write that $\lim\limits_{x\to 3} x^2 = 9$.

Meaning of the Symbol: $\lim\limits_{x\to a} f(x) = l$

Let $f(x)$ be a function of x where x takes values closer and closer to 'a' ($\neq a$), and let $f(x)$ assume values nearer and nearer to l.

We say, $f(x)$ tends to the limit 'l' as x tends to 'a'.

The following are some simple algebraic rules of limits.

1. $\lim\limits_{x\to a} k\, f(x) = k \lim\limits_{x\to a} f(x)$
2. $\lim\limits_{x\to a} [f(x) \pm g(x)] = \lim\limits_{x\to a} f(x) \pm \lim\limits_{x\to a} g(x)$
3. $\lim\limits_{x\to a} [f(x) \cdot g(x)] = \lim\limits_{x\to a} f(x) \cdot \lim\limits_{x\to a} g(x)$
4. $\lim\limits_{x\to a} \dfrac{f(x)}{g(x)} = \dfrac{\lim\limits_{x\to a} f(x)}{\lim\limits_{x\to a} g(x)}$ (where $\lim\limits_{x\to a} g(x) \neq 0$)

Example: The limit of a chord of a circle passing through a fixed point Q and a variable point P as P approaches Q is the tangent to the circle at P.

If PQ is chord of a circle, when P approaches Q along the circle, then the chord becomes the tangent to the circle at P.

Konnect

1. If the left-hand limit of a function is not equal to the right-hand limit of the function, then the limit does not exist.
2. A limit equal to infinity does not imply that the limit does not exist.

While evaluating the limits we use the following methods:

1. Method of substitution
2. Method of factorization
3. Method of rationalization
4. Using the formula $\lim_{x\to a}\left[\frac{x^n - a^n}{x-a}\right] = na^{n-1}$

Method of Substitution

In this method, we directly substitute the value of x in the given function to obtain the limit value.

Examples:

1. $\lim_{x\to 2}[x^2 + 5x + 6] = (2)^2 + 5(2) + 6 = 20.$
2. $\lim_{x\to 3}\left[\frac{x^2 + 4x + 1}{x+5}\right] = \frac{(3)^2 + 4(3) + 1}{3+5} = \frac{22}{8} = \frac{11}{4}.$

Indeterminate Form

If $f(x) = \frac{x^2 - 9}{x-3}$, then $f(3) = \frac{3^2 - 9}{3-3} = \frac{0}{0}$, which is not defined. By substituting $x = 3$, the function assumes a form whose value cannot be determined, this form is called an indeterminate form.

Method of Factorization

If $\frac{f(x)}{g(x)}$ assumes an indeterminate form when $x = a$, then there exists a common factor for $f(x)$ and $g(x)$.

We remove the common factors, and use the substitution method to find the limit.

EXAMPLE 18.1 Evaluate $\lim_{x\to 2}\left[\frac{x^2 - 5x + 6}{x^2 - 3x + 2}\right]$.

SOLUTION

When $x = 2$, $\frac{4 - 10 + 6}{4 - 6 + 2} = \frac{0}{0}$, which is an indeterminate form.

Now, $x^2 - 5x + 6 = (x - 3)(x - 2)$

$x^2 - 3x + 2 = (x - 1)(x - 2)$

$$\Rightarrow \lim_{x\to 2}\left[\frac{x^2 - 5x + 6}{x^2 - 3x + 2}\right] = \lim_{x\to 2}\left[\frac{(x-3)(x-2)}{(x-1)(x-2)}\right]$$

$$\Rightarrow \lim_{x\to 2}\left[\frac{x-3}{x-1}\right] = \left[\frac{2-3}{2-1}\right] = -1.$$

Method of Rationalization

If $\dfrac{f(x)}{g(x)}$ assumes an indeterminate form when $x = a$ and $f(x)$ or $g(x)$ are irrational functions, then we rationalize $f(x)$, $g(x)$ and cancel the common factor, then use the substitution method to find the limit.

EXAMPLE 18.2 Evaluate $\lim_{x\to 0}\left[\dfrac{x}{1-\sqrt{1-x}}\right]$.

SOLUTION

When $x = 0$, the given function assumes the form $\dfrac{0}{1-\sqrt{1-0}} = \dfrac{0}{0}$, which is an indeterminate form.

Since $g(x)$, the denominator is an irrational form, we multiply the numerator and denominator with the rationalizing factor of $g(x)$.

$$\lim_{x\to 0}\left[\frac{x}{1-\sqrt{1-x}}\right] = \lim_{x\to 0}\frac{x}{\left(1-\sqrt{1-x}\right)}\times\frac{\left(1+\sqrt{1-x}\right)}{\left(1+\sqrt{1-x}\right)}$$

$$= \lim_{x\to 0}\frac{x\left(1+\sqrt{1-x}\right)}{1-1+x}$$

$$= \lim_{x\to 0}\frac{x\left(1+\sqrt{1-x}\right)}{x}$$

$$= \lim_{x\to 0}\left(1+\sqrt{1-x}\right) = 1+\sqrt{1} = 2.$$

EXAMPLE 18.3 Evaluate $\lim_{x\to 3}\dfrac{\left(3-\sqrt{6+x}\right)}{x-3}$.

SOLUTION

When $x = 3$, $\dfrac{\left(3-\sqrt{6+3}\right)}{3-3} = \dfrac{0}{0}$, which is an indeterminate form. As $f(x)$ is irrational, we multiply the numerator and denominator with the rationalizing factor of $f(x)$.

$$\lim_{x\to 3}\frac{\left(3-\sqrt{6+x}\right)}{x-3} = \lim_{x\to 3}\frac{\left(3-\sqrt{6+x}\right)}{x-3}\times\frac{\left(3+\sqrt{6+x}\right)}{\left(3+\sqrt{6+x}\right)} = \lim_{x\to 3}\frac{9-(6+x)}{(x-3)\left(3+\sqrt{6+x}\right)}$$

$$= \lim_{x\to 3}\frac{3-x}{(x-3)\left(3+\sqrt{6+x}\right)} = \lim_{x\to 3}\frac{-1}{\left(3+\sqrt{6+x}\right)} = \frac{-1}{\left(3+\sqrt{6+3}\right)}$$

$$= \frac{-1}{(3+3)} = -\frac{1}{6}.$$

EXAMPLE 18.4 Evaluate $\lim_{x\to 0}\dfrac{\sqrt{4+x}-\sqrt{4-x}}{\sqrt{9+x}-\sqrt{9-x}}$.

SOLUTION

When $x = 0$, $\dfrac{\sqrt{4}-\sqrt{4}}{\sqrt{9}-\sqrt{9}} = \dfrac{0}{0}$, which an indeterminate form.

Here $f(x)$ and $g(x)$ both are irrational functions. We multiply both the numerator and the denominator with their rationalizing factors.

$$\lim_{x\to 0}\frac{\sqrt{4+x}-\sqrt{4-x}}{\sqrt{9+x}-\sqrt{9-x}}\times\frac{\sqrt{4+x}+\sqrt{4-x}}{\sqrt{9+x}+\sqrt{9-x}}\times\frac{\sqrt{9+x}+\sqrt{9-x}}{\sqrt{4+x}+\sqrt{4-x}}$$

$$\lim_{x\to 0}\frac{(4+x)-(4-x)}{(9+x)-(9-x)}\times\frac{\sqrt{9+x}+\sqrt{9-x}}{\sqrt{4+x}+\sqrt{4-x}}=\lim_{x\to 0}\frac{2x}{2x}\times\frac{\sqrt{9+x}+\sqrt{9-x}}{\sqrt{4+x}+\sqrt{4-x}}$$

$$=\lim_{x\to 0}\frac{\sqrt{9+x}+\sqrt{9-x}}{\sqrt{4+x}+\sqrt{4-x}}=\frac{\sqrt{9}+\sqrt{9}}{\sqrt{4}+\sqrt{4}}=\frac{2\sqrt{9}}{2\sqrt{4}}=\frac{3}{2}.$$

Using the Formula

1. $\lim_{x\to a}\left[\frac{x^n-a^n}{x-a}\right]=na^{n-1}$ (where 'n' is any rational number).

Proof:

Case 1: n is a positive integer.

$$\lim_{x\to a}\left[\frac{x^n-a^n}{x-a}\right]=\lim_{x\to a}\left[\frac{(x-a)(x^{n-1}+x^{n-2}a+x^{n-3}a^2+\cdots+a^{n-1})}{x-a}\right]$$

$$=\lim_{x\to a}[x^{n-1}+x^{n-2}a+x^{n-3}a^2+\cdots+a^{n-1}]$$

$$=a^{n-1}+a^{n-2}\,a+a^{n-3}\,a^2+\cdots+a^{n-1}(n\text{ terms})$$

$$=a^{n-1}+a^{n-1}+a^{n-1}+\cdots+a^{n-1}(n\text{ terms})=n\cdot a^{n-1}.$$

Case 2: n is negative integer.

Let $n=-m$ (m is positive integer)

$$\lim_{x\to a}\left[\frac{x^n-a^n}{x-a}\right]=\lim_{x\to a}\left[\frac{x^{-m}-a^{-m}}{x-a}\right]$$

$$=\lim_{x\to a}\frac{\frac{1}{x^m}-\frac{1}{a^m}}{x-a}=\lim_{x\to a}\frac{\frac{a^m-x^m}{x^ma^m}}{x-a}=\lim_{x\to a}\frac{-(x^m-a^m)}{(x-a)x^ma^m}=-\lim_{x\to a}\frac{x^m-a^m}{x-a}\times\lim_{x\to a}\frac{1}{x^ma^m}$$

$$=-ma^{m-1}\frac{1}{a^ma^m}$$ (∵ m is positive interget using case (1))

$$=-m\frac{a^{m-1}}{a^{2m}}=-ma^{m-1-2m}=(-m)a^{-m-1}$$

$$\Rightarrow\lim_{x\to a}\left[\frac{x^n-a^n}{x-a}\right]=na^{n-1}.$$ (∵ $n=-m$)

Case 3: n is a rational number.

Let $n=\frac{p}{q}$ where p, q are integers and $q\neq 0$.

$$\lim_{x\to a}\left[\frac{x^n-a^n}{x-a}\right]=\lim_{x\to a}\left[\frac{x^{p/q}-a^{p/q}}{x-a}\right]=\lim_{x\to a}\left[\frac{(x^{1/q})^p-(a^{1/q})^p}{x-a}\right]$$

Let $x^{1/q}=y$ then $x=y^q$ and $a^{1/q}=b$ then $a=b^q$.

$x \to a \Rightarrow y^q \to b^q \Rightarrow y \to b.$

$$\lim_{x\to a}\left[\frac{(x^{1/q})^p-(a^{1/q})^p}{x-a}\right]=\lim_{x\to a}\left[\frac{y^p-b^p}{y^q-b^q}\right]$$

$$=\lim_{y\to b}\frac{\frac{y^p-b^p}{y-b}}{\frac{y^q-b^q}{y-b}}=\frac{\lim_{y\to b}\frac{y^p-b^p}{y-b}}{\lim_{y\to b}\frac{y^q-b^q}{y-b}}=\frac{p\cdot b^{p-1}}{q\cdot b^{q-1}} \quad (\because\ p, q \text{ are integers}).$$

$$=\left(\frac{p}{q}\right)b^{p-1-(q-1)}=\left(\frac{p}{q}\right)b^{p-q}=\left(\frac{p}{q}\right)b^{q((p/q)-1)}=\left(\frac{p}{q}\right)(b^q)^{((p/q)-1)}$$

$$\lim_{x\to a}\left[\frac{x^n-a^n}{x-a}\right]=na^{n-1}. \qquad \left(\because\ n=\frac{p}{q};\ b^q=a\right)$$

Hence, when n is rational number,

$$\lim_{x\to a}\left[\frac{x^n-a^n}{x-a}\right]=na^{n-1}.$$

Info Bytes!

$$\lim_{x\to a}\left[\frac{x^m-a^m}{x^n-a^n}\right]=\frac{m}{n}a^{m-n}.$$

EXAMPLE 18.5 Evaluate $\lim_{x\to 4}\left[\frac{x^4-256}{x-4}\right]$.

SOLUTION

$$\lim_{x\to 4}\left[\frac{x^4-256}{x-4}\right]$$

$$=\lim_{x\to 4}\left[\frac{x^4-4^4}{x-4}\right]$$

$$=4\times 4^{4-1}=4\times 4^3=256.$$

EXAMPLE 18.6 Evaluate $\lim_{x\to 3}\left[\frac{x^5-243}{x^2-9}\right]$.

SOLUTION

$$\lim_{x\to 3}\left[\frac{x^5-243}{x^2-9}\right]=\lim_{x\to 3}\left[\frac{x^5-3^5}{x^2-3^2}\right]$$

$$=\frac{5}{2}3^{5-2} \qquad \left(\because\ \lim_{x\to a}\left[\frac{x^m-a^m}{x^n-a^n}\right]=\frac{m}{n}a^{m-n}\right)$$

$$=\frac{5}{2}\cdot 3^3=\frac{135}{2}.$$

EXAMPLE 18.7 If $\lim_{x\to 2}\left[\frac{x^n - 2^n}{x-2}\right] = 32$, then find the value of n.

SOLUTION

$$\lim_{x\to 2}\left[\frac{x^n - 2^n}{x-2}\right] = n\cdot 2^{n-1}$$

$32 = n\cdot 2^{n-1}$

$4\times 8 = n\cdot 2^{n-1}$

$4\times 2^3 = n\cdot 2^{n-1}$

$4\times 2^{4-1} = n\times 2^{n-1}$

$\therefore n = 4.$

Limits as x Tends to Infinity

We know that when x tends to infinity, $\frac{1}{x}$ tends to 0. While evaluating limits at infinity, put $x = \frac{1}{y}$.

EXAMPLE 18.8 Evaluate $\lim_{x\to\infty}\frac{2x+3}{x-5}$.

SOLUTION

Put $x = \frac{1}{y}$; if $x\to\infty$, $y\to 0$

$$\therefore \lim_{x\to\infty}\frac{2x+3}{x-5} \Rightarrow \lim_{y\to 0}\frac{\frac{2}{y}+3}{\frac{1}{y}-5} = \lim_{y\to 0}\frac{2+3y}{1-5y} = \frac{2+0}{1-0} = 2.$$

EXAMPLE 18.9 Evaluate $\lim_{x\to\infty}\frac{3x^2+4x+5}{4x^2+7}$.

SOLUTION

Put $x = \frac{1}{y}$, when $x\to\infty$, $y\to 0$

$$\lim_{x\to\infty}\frac{3x^2+4x+5}{4x^2+7} = \lim_{y\to 0}\frac{3\cdot\frac{1}{y^2}+4\cdot\frac{1}{y}+5}{4\cdot\frac{1}{y^2}+7}$$

$$= \lim_{y\to 0}\frac{3+4y+5y^2}{4+7y^2} = \frac{3+0+0}{4+7(0)} = \frac{3}{4}.$$

POINTS TO REMEMBER

- When $x = 2.9999$, $f(x) = 8.9994$
  As x increases and approaches 3, $f(x)$ gets closer and closer to 9 and since x tends to 3 from the left this is called the 'left-hand limit' and is written as $\lim_{x \to 3^-}$.
- When $x = 3.0001$, $f(x) = 9.0006$
  As x decreases and approaches 3, $f(x)$ still approaches 9. This is called the 'right-hand limit' and is written as $\lim_{x \to 3^-}$.
- As $\lim_{x \to 3^-} f(x) = \lim_{x \to 3^+} f(x) = 9$, we write that $\lim_{x \to 3} x^2 = 9$.
- If $\frac{f(x)}{g(x)}$ assumes an indeterminate form when $x = a$, then there exists a common factor for $f(x)$ and $g(x)$.
- We remove the common factors, and use the substitution method to find the limit.
- If $\frac{f(x)}{g(x)}$ assumes an indeterminate form when $x = a$ and $f(x)$ or $g(x)$ are irrational functions, then we rationalize $f(x)$, $g(x)$ and cancel the common factor, then use the substitution method to find the limit.
  $\lim_{x \to a}\left[\frac{x^n - a^n}{x - a}\right] = na^{n-1}$ (where 'n' is any rational number).

PRACTICE QUESTIONS CLASSROOM WING

Very Short Answer Type Questions

Directions of questions from 1 to 14:
Fill in the blanks.

1. $\lim_{x\to a} x^n + ax^{n-1} + a^2x^{n-2} + \cdots + a^n =$ _______.

2. $\lim_{x\to 3} \log(4x-11) =$ _______.

3. A circle is inscribed in a polygon. As the number of sides increases, the difference in areas of circle and polygon _______.

4. $\lim_{x\to 0} \frac{x^2+8x}{x} =$ _______.

5. $\lim_{x\to\infty} \frac{n(n+1)}{n^2} =$ _______.

6. $\lim_{x\to\infty} \frac{1}{n} =$ _______.

7. $\lim_{x\to 1} \frac{\sqrt[5]{x}-1}{\sqrt[4]{x}-1} =$ _______.

8. $\lim_{x\to -a} \frac{x^n+a^n}{x+a}$ (where n is an odd natural number) = _______.

9. $\lim_{x\to 0^-} \frac{|x|}{x} =$ _______.

10. $\lim_{x\to 3} \sqrt{9-x^2} =$ _______.

11. $\lim_{x\to 5} \frac{\sqrt{x}-\sqrt{5}}{x-5} =$ _______.

12. If $\lim_{x\to 0}\left[\frac{2x^2+3x+b}{x^2+4x+3}\right] = 2$, then the value of b is _______.

13. In finding $\lim_{x\to a} f(x)$, we replace x by $\frac{1}{n}$, then the limit becomes _______.

14. $\lim_{x\to\infty} \frac{7x-3}{8x-10} =$ _______.

Directions of questions from 15 to 46:
Answer the following questions.

15. Evaluate $\lim_{x\to 2}(2x-2)$.

16. Evaluate: $\lim_{x\to 3} \frac{|x-3|}{x-3}$.

17. Evaluate: $\lim_{x\to a}\left[\frac{x^n-a^n}{x^m-a^m}\right]$.

18. What is the value of $\lim_{x\to 1}(x^3+1)(x^2-2x+4)$?

19. Evaluate: $\lim_{x\to 3}\left[\frac{x^3-27}{x-3}\right]$.

20. Evaluate: $\lim_{x\to\infty}\left[\frac{x^2+x+6}{x+1}\right]$.

21. Evaluate: $\lim_{x\to\infty}\left[\frac{4x^n+1}{5x^{n+1}+5}\right]$.

22. Evaluate: $\lim_{x\to a} \frac{x^{1/4}-a^{1/4}}{x^4-a^4}$.

23. Evaluate: $\lim_{x\to -2} \frac{x^7+128}{x+2}$.

24. Evaluate: $\lim_{x\to 1}\left[\frac{x^2+3x+2}{x^2-5x+3}\right]$.

25. Evaluate: $\lim_{x\to 5} \sqrt{25-x^2}$.

Short Answer Type Questions

26. (A) Evaluate: $\lim_{x\to\infty} \frac{11|x|+7}{8|x|-9}$.

    (B) Evaluate: $\lim_{n\to\infty} \frac{n\left(1+8+27+64+\ldots+n^3\right)}{n^5+81n^4-2n^3}$

27. Evaluate: $\lim_{x\to 2}\left[\frac{2x^2-9x+10}{5x^2-5x-10}\right]$.

28. Evaluate: $\lim_{x\to 3} \frac{x^5-243}{x-3}$.

29. (A) Evaluate: $\lim_{x\to\infty} \frac{x^5+3x^4-4x^3-3x^2+2x+1}{2x^5+4x^2-9x+16}$.

(B) Evaluate: $\lim_{x\to 0} \frac{\sqrt{1+2x+3x^2+4x^3+5x^4}-1}{x}$

30. Evaluate: $\lim_{x\to a} \frac{x^{14}-a^{14}}{x^{-7}-a^{-7}}$.

31. Evaluate: $\lim_{x\to 2} \frac{x-2}{\sqrt{x+2}-2}$.

32. Evaluate: $\lim_{x\to 0} \frac{\sqrt{5+x}-\sqrt{5-x}}{\sqrt{10+x}-\sqrt{10-x}}$.

33. Evaluate: $\lim_{x\to 0} \frac{\sqrt{1+x+x^2+x^3}-1}{x}$.

34. Evaluate: $\lim_{x\to\infty} \frac{x^n+a^n}{x^n-a^n}$.

35. Evaluate: $\lim_{x\to 1} \left[\frac{x^4-2x^3-x^2+2x}{x-1}\right]$.

36. Evaluate: $\lim_{x\to a} \frac{\sqrt{x+a}-\sqrt{2a}}{x-a}$.

37. Evaluate: $\lim_{n\to\infty} \left(\sum_{r=0}^{n} \frac{1}{2^r}\right)$.

38. If $\lim_{x\to -3} \frac{x^k+3^k}{x+3} = 405$, where k is an odd natural number then, find the value of k.

39. (A) Evaluate: $\lim_{x\to 4^-} \frac{|x-4|}{x-4}$.

(B) Evaluate: $\lim_{n\to\infty} \left(\sum_{r=0}^{n} \frac{1}{3^r}\right)$

40. Evaluate: $\lim_{x\to 3} \frac{\log(2x-3)-\log(3x+2)}{\log(2x+1)}$.

Essay Type Questions

41. Evaluate: $\lim_{x\to\infty} \frac{n(1+4+9+16+\cdots+n^2)}{n^4+8n^3}$.

42. Evaluate: $\lim_{x\to\infty} \frac{n^2(1+2+3+4+\cdots+n)}{n^4+4n^2}$.

43. Simplify: $\lim_{x\to 1} \frac{\sqrt{x+1}-\sqrt{5x-3}}{\sqrt{2x+3}-\sqrt{4x+1}}$.

44. Evaluate: $\lim_{n\to\infty} \frac{1+3+5+7+\ldots n \text{ terms}}{2+4+6+8+\ldots n \text{ terms}}$.

45. Simplify: $\lim_{x\to 3} \left[\frac{2}{x-3}+\frac{2}{x^2-7x+12}\right]$.

46. Evaluate: $\lim_{x\to 5} \frac{x-5}{\sqrt{x+5}-\sqrt{10}}$

PRACTICE QUESTIONS COMPETITION WING

Level 1: Apply Your Concepts

Directions of questions from 1 to 5:
Fill in the blanks.

1. When the number of sides of a polygon tends to infinity, it approaches ______.

2. The scientists who put calculus in mathematical form are ______ and ______.

3. The radius of circle tends to zero then it approaches to ______.

4. ______ helps in finding the areas of the curves.

5. The limiting position of a secant is ______.

Directions of questions from 6 to 66:
Select the correct alternative from the given choices.

6. Evaluate: $\lim_{x\to3}(4x^2+3) =$ ______.

(a) 36 (b) 39
(c) 40 (d) None of these

7. $\lim_{x\to\infty}\frac{2x+4}{x-2} =$ ______.

(a) 1 (b) 0
(c) 2 (d) 6

8. $\lim_{x\to5^+}\frac{|x-5|}{x-5} =$ ______.

(a) 1 (b) −1
(c) 0 (d) Cannot be determined

9. Evaluate: $\lim_{x\to1}\frac{2x^2+4x+4}{2x-1}$.

(a) 1 (b) 10
(c) 20 (d) 5

10. Evaluate: $\lim_{x\to20}\frac{\sqrt{x+5}+5}{\sqrt{x+5}-5}$.

(a) 1 (b) 2
(c) 4 (d) ∞

11. $\lim_{x\to0}\frac{\sqrt{8-3x}+\sqrt{8+4x}}{\sqrt{2-3x}} =$ ______.

(a) 5 (b) 3
(c) 2 (d) 4

12. $\lim_{x\to\infty}\frac{(x-1)(2x-1)}{(x-4)(x-7)} =$ ______.

(a) 0 (b) 1
(c) 2 (d) −1

13. $\lim_{x\to2}\frac{x^{-8}-\frac{1}{256}}{x-2} =$ ______.

(a) $-\frac{1}{32}$ (b) $-\frac{1}{128}$
(c) $-\frac{1}{256}$ (d) $-\frac{1}{64}$

14. $\lim_{x\to2}\frac{x^2+2x-8}{2x^2-3x-2} =$ ______.

(a) $\frac{1}{5}$ (b) $\frac{6}{5}$
(c) $\frac{3}{2}$ (d) $-\frac{1}{6}$

15. $\lim_{x\to4^-}\sqrt{16-x^2}$ is a/an

(a) complex number. (b) real number.
(c) natural number. (d) integer.

16. $\lim_{x\to0}\log\left(\frac{2x+1}{5x+4}\right) =$ ______.

(a) −2log 2 (b) log 4
(c) $-\log\left(\frac{1}{2}\right)$ (d) −3log 2

17. $\lim_{x\to3}\frac{\sqrt{x+3}+\sqrt{x+6}}{\sqrt{x+1}-2} =$ ______.

(a) 1 (b) 7
(c) 14 (d) None of these

18. $\lim_{x\to5}\frac{\sqrt{x+20}-\sqrt{3x+10}}{5-x} =$ ______.

(a) $-\frac{2}{5}$ (b) $\frac{2}{5}$
(c) $\frac{1}{5}$ (d) $\frac{-1}{5}$

19. $\lim_{x\to-3}\frac{x^2-2x-15}{x^2+2x-3} =$ ______.

(a) 1 (b) 2
(c) −3 (d) −4

20. $\lim_{x\to\infty}\frac{(x-5)(x+7)}{(x+2)(5x+1)} =$ ______.

(a) $-\frac{1}{5}$ (b) 25

(c) 5 (d) $\frac{1}{5}$

21. Evaluate: $\lim_{x\to2}\frac{f(x)-f(2)}{x-2}$, where $f(x) = x^2 - 4x$.

(a) −1 (b) 2

(c) 0 (d) 4

22. Evaluate: $\lim_{x\to9}\frac{2x-7\sqrt{x}+3}{3x-11\sqrt{x}+6}$.

(a) $\frac{3}{4}$ (b) $\frac{5}{3}$

(c) $\frac{5}{7}$ (d) $\frac{3}{7}$

23. $\lim_{x\to b}\frac{\sqrt{x}-\sqrt{b}}{x-b} =$ ______.

(a) $\frac{1}{2b}$ (b) $\frac{\sqrt{2}}{b}$

(c) $\frac{1}{2\sqrt{b}}$ (d) $\frac{1}{\sqrt{2}\,b}$

24. $\lim_{x\to3}\frac{x-3}{\sqrt{x+6}-\sqrt{2x+3}} =$ ______.

(a) −5 (b) −6

(c) 9 (d) 6

25. $\lim_{x\to-2}\frac{x+2}{\sqrt{2x+8}-\sqrt{2-x}} =$ ______.

(a) $\frac{1}{3}$ (b) $\frac{2}{3}$

(c) 1 (d) $\frac{4}{3}$

26. Evaluate: $\lim_{x\to1}\left[\frac{\log x^3+\log\left(\frac{1}{x^2}\right)+\log 2}{\log(x^3+3)}\right]$.

(a) $\frac{3}{2}$ (b) 1

(c) $\frac{1}{2}$ (d) 2

27. $\lim_{x\to3}\frac{x^{-5}-\frac{1}{243}}{x-3} =$ ______.

(a) $-\frac{5}{729}$ (b) $-\frac{5}{243}$

(c) $\frac{5}{81}$ (d) $\frac{5}{729}$

28. $\lim_{x\to\infty}\frac{4x-3}{(2x+3)} =$ ______.

(a) 0 (b) 1

(c) $\frac{1}{2}$ (d) 2

29. Evaluate: $\lim_{d\to3}\frac{d^3-27}{d-3}$.

(a) 3 (b) 9

(c) 27 (d) 6

30. $\lim_{x\to3^-}\sqrt{9-x^2}$ is a/an

(a) natural number. (b) real number.

(c) imaginary number. (d) integer.

31. Evaluate: $\lim_{x\to4}\frac{3x-8\sqrt{x}+4}{5x-9\sqrt{x}-2}$.

(a) $\frac{1}{5}$ (b) $\frac{4}{11}$

(c) $\frac{3}{10}$ (d) 5

32. For some real number k, the value of $\lim_{x\to-k}\frac{x^5+k^5}{x+k}$ can be ______.

(a) 50 (b) 60

(c) 70 (d) 80

33. Evaluate: $\lim_{x\to1}\frac{f(x)-f(1)}{x-1}$, where $f(x) = x^2 - 2x$.

(a) −1 (b) 0

(c) 1 (d) 2

34. Evaluate: $\lim_{x\to a}\frac{x^{1/5}-a^{1/5}}{x^{-4/5}-a^{-4/5}}$.

(a) $\frac{-a}{4}$ (b) $\frac{-1}{4a}$

(c) $\frac{1}{4a}$ (d) $\frac{a}{4}$

35. $\lim_{x\to\infty}\frac{6x^4+7x^3+2x+1}{x^4+1} =$ ______.

(a) 1 (b) 2

(c) 3 (d) 6

Level 2: Review Your Concepts

36. Evaluate: $\lim_{x\to-2} \frac{2x^3 - x^2 - 13x - 6}{3x^2 + x - 10}$.

(a) $-\frac{5}{7}$ (b) $-\frac{17}{5}$
(c) $-\frac{15}{11}$ (d) $-\frac{10}{3}$

37. Evaluate: $\lim_{x\to-1} \frac{\log x^2 - \log\left(\frac{1}{x^4}\right) + \log 3}{\log\left(\frac{x^3}{-3}\right)}$.

(a) 1 (b) 0
(c) −1 (d) Does not exist

38. $\lim_{x\to\infty} \left\{\frac{3x}{\sqrt{x^2+5x-6}+2x}\right\} =$ ______.

(a) −1 (b) 1
(c) 0 (d) ∞

39. $\lim_{x\to\infty} \frac{(4x+5)(2x-1)}{(27x^2+1)} =$ ______.

(a) $\frac{4}{27}$ (b) $\frac{8}{27}$
(c) $\frac{2}{27}$ (d) $\frac{6}{27}$

40. $\lim_{x\to1} \frac{x^3 - 6x^2 + 11x - 6}{x^2 - 5x + 4} =$ ______.

(a) $\frac{2}{3}$ (b) $-\frac{5}{3}$
(c) $\frac{5}{3}$ (d) $\frac{-2}{3}$

41. If $\lim_{x\to a} \frac{x^5 - a^5}{x - a} = 5$, then find the sum of the possible real values of a.

(a) 0 (b) 2
(c) 3 (d) 5

42. $\lim_{x\to0} \frac{x}{\sqrt{3+x}-\sqrt{3-x}} =$ ______.

(a) $\sqrt{3}$ (b) $\sqrt{-3}$
(c) $2\sqrt{3}$ (d) $-2\sqrt{3}$

43. $\lim_{x\to1} \frac{4-\sqrt{15+x}}{1-x} =$ ______.

(a) $\frac{1}{6}$ (b) $\frac{1}{8}$
(c) $\frac{1}{10}$ (d) $\frac{1}{12}$

44. $\lim_{x\to0} \frac{\sqrt{1+x+x^2+x^3}-1}{x} =$ ______.

(a) 1 (b) 2
(c) $\frac{1}{2}$ (d) $\frac{1}{4}$

45. $\lim_{x\to0} \frac{\sqrt[4]{x+16}-2}{x} =$ ______.

(a) $\frac{1}{16}$ (b) $\frac{1}{8}$
(c) $\frac{1}{32}$ (d) $\frac{1}{20}$

46. $\lim_{x\to\infty} \frac{(x+2)^{10}+(x+4)^{10}+\cdots+(x+20)^{10}}{x^{10}+1} =$ ______.

(a) 12 (b) 20
(c) 40 (d) 10

47. $\lim_{x\to\infty} \frac{2+6+10+14+\ldots 2n \text{ terms}}{2+4+6+8+\ldots n \text{ terms}} =$ ______.

(a) 4 (b) 16
(c) 8 (d) 10

48. Evaluate: $\lim_{x\to-a} \frac{1}{x}\left[\frac{1}{x+a} + \frac{b+a}{x^2 - bx + ax - ab}\right]$.

(a) $\frac{1}{a}$ (b) $\frac{1}{a+b}$
(c) $\frac{1}{a(a+b)}$ (d) $\frac{1}{a(a-b)}$

49. $\lim_{x\to5} \frac{\sqrt{2x-3}-\sqrt{3x-8}}{\sqrt{2x-1}-\sqrt{3x-6}} =$ ______.

(a) $\frac{2\sqrt{7}}{3}$ (b) $\frac{3}{2\sqrt{7}}$
(c) $\frac{4}{3}\sqrt{7}$ (d) $\frac{3}{\sqrt{7}}$

50. If $\lim_{x\to a} \frac{x^7 - a^7}{x - a} = 7$, then find the number of possible real values of a.

(a) 0 (b) 1
(c) 2 (d) 7

Level 3: Assess Your Concepts

51. $\lim_{n\to\infty} \frac{1+4+9+16+\cdots+n^2}{4n^3+1} =$ ______.

(a) $\frac{1}{12}$ (b) $\frac{1}{24}$
(c) $\frac{1}{8}$ (d) $\frac{1}{16}$

52. $\lim_{x\to 0} \frac{\sqrt[5]{x+32}-2}{x} =$ ______.

(a) $\frac{1}{16}$ (b) $\frac{1}{45}$
(c) $\frac{1}{80}$ (d) $\frac{1}{100}$

53. $\lim_{x\to 2} \frac{\sqrt{x^3-2x^2+2x-3}-1}{x-2} =$ ______.

(a) 4 (b) 8
(c) 6 (d) 3

54. Evaluate: $\lim_{x\to\infty} \frac{(1^2+2^2+3^2+\cdots+n^2)}{n^2(1+3+5+7+\cdots+n \text{ terms})}$.

(a) 0 (b) 1
(c) ∞ (d) Does not exist

55. Evaluate: $\lim_{x\to 0} \frac{\sqrt{6+x}-\sqrt{6-x}}{\sqrt{8+x}-\sqrt{8-x}}$.

(a) $\sqrt{3}$ (b) $\frac{-5\sqrt{3}}{3}$
(c) $\frac{4\sqrt{3}}{3}$ (d) $\frac{2\sqrt{3}}{3}$

56. Evaluate: $\lim_{\theta\to 0} \cot\theta - \operatorname{cosec}\theta$.

(a) 0 (b) 2
(c) 4 (d) None of these

57. $\lim_{x\to\infty} \frac{(x+1)^{100}+(x+2)^{100}+\cdots+(x+50)^{100}}{x^{100}+x^{99}+\cdots+x+1} =$ ______.

(a) 100 (b) 1
(c) 21 (d) 50

58. $\lim_{x\to 3^-} \frac{|2x-6|}{2x-6}$ is ______.

(a) 1 (b) −1
(c) 0 (d) ∞

59. If $\lim_{x\to -2} \frac{x^p+2^p}{x+2} = 80$ (where p is an odd number), then p can be ____.

(a) 3 (b) 5
(c) 7 (d) 9

60. If $\lim_{x\to m} \frac{x^3-m^3}{x-m} = 3$, then find the number of possible values of m.

(a) 0 (b) 2
(c) 1 (d) 3

61. $\lim_{x\to 3} \frac{\sqrt{5x+1}-\sqrt{7x-5}}{\sqrt{7x+4}-\sqrt{5x+10}} =$ ______.

(a) 0 (b) $-\frac{5}{4}$
(c) $\frac{5}{4}$ (d) ∞

62. $\lim_{x\to a}(x-a)\left(\frac{1}{x-a}-\frac{1}{x^2-(a+b)x+ab}\right) =$ ______.

(a) $\frac{a-b-1}{a-b}$ (b) 0
(c) 1 (d) $\frac{a+b}{a-b}$

63. $\lim_{x\to \frac{2}{5}} \frac{1}{|5x-2|} =$ ______.

(a) 0 (b) ∞
(c) 1 (d) Does not exist

64. $\lim_{x\to\infty} \frac{5x^2}{\sqrt{25x^4+13x^3+14x^2+17x+6}}$ is ______.

(a) 1 (b) $\frac{1}{5}$
(c) $\frac{5}{14}$ (d) None of these

65. $\lim_{x\to -1} \frac{x^5+1}{x+1} =$ ______.

(a) 1 (b) −5
(c) 5 (d) None of these

66. Evaluate: $\lim_{x\to 0} \frac{\sqrt{125+x}-\sqrt{125-x}}{\sqrt{1000+x}-\sqrt{1000-x}}$

(a) $\sqrt{2}$ (b) 2
(c) $2\sqrt{2}$ (d) None

ANSWER KEYS

Classroom Wing

Very Short Answer Type Questions

1. na^n
2. 0
3. Decreases
4. 8
5. 1
6. 0
7. $\frac{4}{5}$
8. $n(-a)^{n-1}$
9. -1
10. 0
11. $\frac{1}{2\sqrt{5}}$
12. 6
13. $\lim\limits_{\frac{1}{n}\to a} f\left(\frac{1}{n}\right)$
14. $\frac{7}{8}$
15. 2
16. Limit does not exist
17. $\frac{n}{m}a^{n-m}$
18. 6
19. 27
20. ∞
21. 0
22. $\frac{1}{16}\cdot a^{-15/4}$
23. 448
24. -6
25. Limit does not exist

Short Answer Type Questions

26. (A) $\frac{11}{8}$ (B) $\frac{1}{4}$
27. $\frac{-1}{15}$
28. 405
29. (A) $\frac{1}{2}$
(B) 1
30. $-2a^{21}$
31. 4
32. $\sqrt{2}$
33. $\frac{1}{2}$
34. 1
35. -2
36. $\frac{1}{2\sqrt{2a}}$
37. 2
38. 5
39. (A) -1 (B) $\frac{3}{2}$
40. $\log_7\left(\frac{3}{11}\right)$

Essay Type Questions

41. $\frac{1}{3}$
42. $\frac{1}{2}$
43. $\sqrt{10}$
44. 1
45. -2
46. $2\sqrt{10}$

Competition Wing

Level 1: Apply Your Concepts

1. Circle
2. Newton and Leibnitz
3. Point
4. Integration
5. Tangent
6. (b)
7. (c)
8. (a)
9. (b)
10. (d)
11. (d)
12. (c)
13. (d)
14. (b)

15. (b)	16. (a)	17. (d)	18. (c)	19. (b)
20. (d)	21. (c)	22. (c)	23. (c)	24. (b)
25. (d)	26. (c)	27. (a)	28. (d)	29. (c)
30. (b)	31. (b)	32. (d)	33. (b)	34. (a)
35. (d)				

Level 2: Review Your Concepts

36. (c)	37. (c)	38. (b)	39. (b)	40. (d)
41. (a)	42. (a)	43. (b)	44. (c)	45. (c)
46. (d)	47. (c)	48. (c)	49. (d)	50. (c)

Level 3: Assess Your Concepts

51. (a)	52. (c)	53. (d)	54. (a)	55. (d)
56. (a)	57. (d)	58. (b)	59. (b)	60. (b)
61. (b)	62. (a)	63. (b)	64. (a)	65. (c)
66. (c)				

Hints and Explanations

Classroom Wing

Very Short Answer Type Questions

1. na_n

2. $\lim_{x\to 3} \log(4x-11) = \log(12-11) = 0$

3. Decreases

4. $\lim_{x\to 0} \frac{x^2+8x}{x}$

$\lim_{x\to 0} \frac{x(x+8)}{x}$

$\lim_{x\to 0}(x+8)$

$= 8$

5. $\lim_{x\to\infty} \frac{n(n+1)}{n^2}$

$\lim_{x\to\infty} \frac{n^2}{n^2} + \lim_{x\to\infty} \frac{1}{n^2}$

$1+0$

$= 1$

6. $\lim_{x\to\infty} \frac{1}{n} = 0$

7. $\lim_{x\to 1} \frac{(x)^{\frac{1}{5}}-1}{(x)^{\frac{1}{4}}-1}$

$= \frac{4}{5}$

8. Direct formula

$n(-a)^{n-1}$

9. $\lim_{x\to 0} \frac{|x|}{x}$

$\lim_{x\to 0} \frac{-x}{x}$

$= -1$

10. $\lim_{x\to 3} \sqrt{9-x^2}$

$= \sqrt{9-(3)^2}$

$= 0$

11. $\lim_{x\to 5} \frac{(x)^{\frac{1}{2}}-(5)^{\frac{1}{2}}}{x-5}$

$= \frac{1}{2}(5)^{\frac{1}{2}-1}$

$= \left(\frac{1}{2}\right)\cdot\frac{1}{\sqrt{5}}$

$= \frac{1}{2\sqrt{5}}$

12. $\lim_{x\to 0}\left(\frac{2x^2+3x+b}{x^2+4x+3}\right) = 2$

$\frac{2(0)+3(0)+b}{0+0+3} = 2$

$b = 6.$

13. $\lim_{x\to a} f(a)$

a replaced by $\frac{1}{n}$ $\lim_{\frac{1}{n}\to a} f\left(\frac{1}{n}\right)$

14. $\lim_{x\to 0} \frac{7x-3}{8x-10}$

Dividing numerator and denominator by x

$\lim_{x\to\infty} \frac{7-\frac{3}{x}}{8-\frac{10}{x}}$

Putting value

$= \frac{7}{8}$

15. $\lim_{x\to 2}(2x-2)$

$= (2)2-2$

$= 2$

16. Limit does not exist as mod will open ones with negative sign and once with positive sign.

17. $\lim_{x\to a}\left(\frac{x^n-a^n}{x^m-a^m}\right)$

$\lim_{x\to a}\left(\frac{nx^{n-1}}{nx^{m-1}}\right)$

Putting value $x = a$

$\frac{na^{n-1}}{ma^{m-1}}$

18. $\lim_{x\to 1}(x^3+1)(x^2-2x+4)$

Putting value $x = 1$

$= (1+1)(1-2+4)$

$= 2\times 3$

$= 6$

19. $\lim_{x\to 3}\left(\frac{x^3-3^3}{x-3}\right)$

Using formula

$= 3(3)^{3-1}$

$= 3\cdot 3^2$

$= 27$

20. $\lim_{x\to\infty}\left[\frac{x^2+x+6}{x+1}\right]$

Dividing numerator and denominator by x^2

$$\lim_{x\to\infty}\left[\frac{1+\frac{1}{x}+\frac{6}{x^2}}{\frac{1}{x}+\frac{1}{x^2}}\right]$$

$= \frac{1}{0}$

$= \infty$

21. $\lim_{x\to\infty}\left(\frac{4x^n+1}{4x^{n+1}+5}\right)$

Dividing both numerator and denominator by x^{n+1}

$$\lim_{x\to\infty}\left(\frac{\frac{4}{x}+\frac{1}{x^{n+1}}}{5+\frac{5}{x^n+1}}\right)$$

$= 0$

22. $\lim_{x\to a}\frac{(x)^{\frac{1}{4}}-(a)^{\frac{1}{4}}}{x^4-a^4}$

Using direct formula

$= \frac{\frac{1}{4}}{4}\cdot(4)^{\frac{1}{4}-4}$

$= \frac{1}{16}a^{-\frac{15}{4}}$

23. $\lim_{x\to -2}\frac{x^7+2^7}{x+2}$

$\lim_{x\to -2}\frac{x^7-(-2)^7}{x-(-2)}$

$= 7(-2)^6$

$= 448$

24. $\lim_{x\to 1}\left(\frac{x^2+3x+2}{x^2-5x+3}\right)$

Putting value $x = 1$

$= \left[\frac{1+3+2}{1-5+3}\right]$

$= \frac{6}{-1}$

$= -6$

25. $\lim_{x\to 5}\sqrt{25-x^2}$

Putting value $x = 5$

$\lim_{x\to 5}\sqrt{25-(5)^2}$

$= 0$

Limit does not exist.

Short Answer Type Questions

26. (A) Dividing numerator and denominator by $|x|$

$$\lim_{x\to\infty}\frac{11+\frac{7}{|x|}}{8-\frac{9}{|x|}}$$

$= \frac{11}{8}$

(B) $\lim_{n\to\infty}\frac{n\left(1+8+27+64+\ldots+n^3\right)}{n^5+81n^4-2n^3}$

$= \lim_{n\to\infty}\frac{n\times n^2\left(n+1\right)^2}{4(n^5+81n^4-2n^3)}$

$= \lim_{n\to\infty}\frac{n^5+2n^4+n^3}{4(n^5+81n^4-2n^3)}$

$$= \lim_{n\to\infty} \frac{1+\frac{2}{n}+\frac{1}{n^2}}{4\left(1+\frac{81}{n}-\frac{2}{n^2}\right)}$$

$$= \frac{1+0+0}{4(1+0-0)}$$

$$= \frac{1}{4}$$

27. $\lim_{x\to\infty}\left[\frac{2x^2-9x+10}{5x^2-5x-10}\right]$

$$2x^2-9x+10 = 2x^2-5x-4x+10$$
$$= x(2x-5)-2(2x-5)$$
$$= (x-2)(2x-5)$$

$$5x^2-5x-10 = 5x^2-10x+5x-10$$
$$= 5x(x-2)+5(x-2)$$
$$= (5x+5)(x-2)$$

$$\lim_{x\to 2}\left[\frac{(x-2)(2x-5)}{(5x+5)(x-2)}\right]$$

$$\lim_{x\to 2}\frac{2x-5}{5x+5}$$

Putting value $x = 2$

$$= \frac{2(2)-5}{5(2)+5}$$

$$= \frac{-1}{15}$$

28. $\lim_{x\to 3}\frac{x^5-243}{x-3}$

$$\lim_{x\to 3}\frac{x^5-3^5}{x-3}$$

Using formula

$$= 5(3)^{5-1}$$

$$= 405$$

29. (A) Dividing numerator and denominator by x^5

$$\lim_{x\to\infty}\left[\frac{1+\frac{3}{x}-\frac{4}{x^2}-\frac{3}{x^3}+\frac{2}{x^4}+\frac{1}{x^5}}{2+\frac{4}{x^3}-\frac{9}{x^4}+\frac{16}{x^5}}\right]$$

$$= \frac{1}{2}$$

(B) $\lim_{x\to 0}\frac{\sqrt{1+2x+3x^2+4x^3+5x^4}-1}{x}$

$$= \lim_{x\to 0}\frac{\left(\sqrt{1+2x+3x^2+4x^3+5x^4}-1\right)\left(\sqrt{1+2x+3x^2+4x^3+5x^4}+1\right)}{x\left(\sqrt{1+2x+3x^2+4x^3+5x^4}+1\right)}$$

$$= \lim_{x\to 0}\frac{1+2x+3x^2+4x^3+5x^4-1}{x\left(\sqrt{1+2x+3x^2+4x^3+5x^4}+1\right)}$$

$$= \lim_{x\to 0}\frac{2x+3x^2+4x^3+5x^4}{x\left(\sqrt{1+2x+3x^2+4x^3+5x^4}+1\right)}$$

$$= \lim_{x\to 0}\frac{2+3x+4x^2+5x^3}{\sqrt{1+2x+3x^2+4x^3+5x^4}+1}$$

$$= \frac{2}{1+1} = 1$$

30. $\lim_{x\to a}\frac{x^{14}-a^{14}}{x^{-1}-a^{-7}}$

$$= \frac{14}{-7}\cdot(a)^{14-(-7)}$$

$$= -2(a)^{21}$$

$$= -2a^{21}$$

31. Rationalize

$$\lim_{x\to 2}\frac{(x-2)(\sqrt{x+2}+2)}{(\sqrt{x+2}-2)(\sqrt{x+2}+2)}$$

$$\lim_{x\to 2}\frac{(x-2)(\sqrt{x+2}+2)}{(x+2)-(2)^2}$$

$$\lim_{x\to 2}\frac{(x-2)(\sqrt{x+2}+2)}{x+2-4}$$

$$\lim_{x\to 2}\frac{(x-2)(\sqrt{x+2}+2)}{x-2}$$

$$\lim_{x\to 2}(\sqrt{x+2}+2)$$

Putting value $x = 2$

$$= \sqrt{2+2}+2$$

$$= 2+2$$

$$= 4$$

32. $\lim_{x\to 0}\frac{\sqrt{5+x}-\sqrt{5-x}}{\sqrt{10+x}-\sqrt{10-x}}$

$=\frac{\sqrt{5+x}-\sqrt{5-x}}{\sqrt{10+x}-\sqrt{10-x}}\times\frac{\sqrt{10+x}+\sqrt{10-x}}{\sqrt{10+x}+\sqrt{10-x}}$

$\times\frac{\sqrt{5+x}+\sqrt{5-x}}{\sqrt{5+x}+\sqrt{5-x}}$

$\frac{(5+x)-(5-x)}{(10+x)-(10-x)}\times\frac{\sqrt{10+x}+\sqrt{10-x}}{\sqrt{5+x}+\sqrt{5-x}}$

putting $x = 0 = \sqrt{2}$

33. $\lim_{x\to 0}\left(\frac{\sqrt{1+x+x^2+x^3}-1}{x}\right)$

Multiply by conjugate,

$\lim_{x\to 0}\left(\frac{\frac{x^3+x^2+x}{\sqrt{1+x+x^2+x^3}+1}}{x}\right)$

$\lim_{x\to 0}\left(\frac{x^2+x+1}{\sqrt{x^3+x^2+x+1}+1}\right)$

Putting value $x=0$

$=\frac{0+0+1}{0+1+1}$

$=\frac{1}{2}=0.5$

34. $\lim_{x\to\infty}\frac{x^n+a^n}{x^n-a^n}$ Divide by x^n

$\lim_{x\to\infty}\frac{1+\frac{a^n}{x^n}}{1-\frac{a^n}{x^n}}$

$=1$

35. $\lim_{x\to 1}\left(\frac{x^4-2x^3+x^2+2x}{x-1}\right)$

$x^4-2x^3-x^2+2x = x(x^3-2x^2-x+2)$

$= x(x-1)(x^2-x-2)$

$\lim_{x\to 1}\left[\frac{x(x-1)(x^2-x-2)}{x-1}\right]$

$\lim_{x\to 1}[(x(x^2-x-2)]$

Putting value

$=1(1-1-2)$

$=-2$

36. Multiply by the conjugate of

$\sqrt{x+a}-2a$

$\lim_{x\to a}\left(\frac{\frac{x-a}{\sqrt{x+a}+\sqrt{2a}}}{x-a}\right)$

$\lim_{x\to a}\left(\frac{1}{\sqrt{x+a}+\sqrt{2a}}\right)$

Putting value $x=a$

$\frac{1}{\sqrt{2a}+\sqrt{2a}}=\frac{1}{2\sqrt{2a}}$

37. $\sum_{r=0}^{n}\frac{1}{2^r}$

$=\frac{2}{2\left(\frac{1}{2}n(n+1)\right)}$

$\lim_{n\to\infty}\left(\frac{1}{(2)\frac{n(n+1)}{2}}\right)$

$\lim_{n\to\infty}\left(\frac{1}{2\frac{n^2+n}{2}}\right)$

$\lim_{n\to\infty}\left(\frac{1}{2\frac{1+\frac{1}{n}}{\frac{2}{n^2}}}\right)$

Putting value

$\left(\frac{1}{2}\right)^{-1}=2$

38. $\lim_{x\to -3}\frac{x^k+3^k}{x+3}=405$

$\lim_{x\to -3}\frac{x^k-(-3)^k}{x-(-3)}=405$

$\Rightarrow k(-3)^{k-1} = 405$

$\Rightarrow k(-3)^{k-1} = 5(-3)^4$

$k = 5$

39. (A) $\lim_{x\to4}\frac{|x-4|}{x-4}$

Mod will open with negative sign,

$\lim_{x\to4}\frac{-(x-4)}{x-4}$

$= -1$

(B) $\lim_{n\to\infty}\left(\sum_{r=0}^{n}\frac{1}{3^r}\right)$

$= \lim_{n\to\infty}\left(\frac{1}{3^0}+\frac{1}{3^1}+\frac{1}{3^2}+\frac{1}{3^3}+\frac{1}{3^4}+\ldots+\frac{1}{3^n}\right)$

$= \lim_{n\to\infty}\left(1+\frac{1}{3^1}+\frac{1}{3^2}+\frac{1}{3^3}+\frac{1}{3^4}+\ldots+\frac{1}{3^n}\right)$

$= \frac{1}{1-\frac{1}{3}}$ $(\because S_\infty = \frac{a}{1-r})$

$= \frac{1}{\frac{2}{3}} = \frac{3}{2}$

40. $\lim_{x\to3}\frac{\log(2x-3)-\log(3x+2)}{\log(2x+1)}$

Putting value $x = 3$

$= \frac{\log(3)-\log(11)}{\log(7)}$

$= \frac{\log 3}{\log 7} - \frac{\log 11}{\log 7}$

$= \log_7 3 - \log_7 11$

$= \log_7\left(\frac{3}{11}\right)$

Essay Type Questions

41. $1+2^2+3^3+4^4+\cdots = \frac{n(n+1)(2n+1)}{6}$

$\lim_{n\to\infty}\frac{\frac{n(n+1)(2n+1)}{6}\cdot n}{n(n^3+8n^2)}$

$\lim_{n\to\infty}\frac{\frac{(n+1)(2n+1)}{6}\cdot n}{(n^3+8n^2)}$

$\frac{1}{6}\lim_{n\to\infty}\frac{(2n^2+2n+n+1)n}{n^3+8n^2}$

$\frac{1}{6}\lim_{n\to\infty}\frac{(2n^2+3n+1)}{n^2+8n}$

Divide by n^2

$\frac{1}{6}\lim_{n\to\infty}\frac{\left(2+\frac{3}{n}+\frac{1}{n^2}\right)}{\left(1+\frac{8}{n}\right)}$

$= \frac{2}{6}$

$= \frac{1}{3}$

42. $\lim_{n\to\infty}\frac{n^2(1+2+3+\cdots n)}{n^4+4n^2}$

$1+2+3+\cdots n = \frac{n(n+1)}{2}$

$= \frac{n^2+n}{2}$

$\frac{1}{2}\lim_{n\to\infty}\frac{n^2\cdot n(n+1)}{n^2(4+n^2)}$

$\frac{1}{2}\lim_{n\to\infty}\frac{n^2+n}{4+n^2}$

Dividing numerator and denominator by n^2

$\frac{1}{2}\lim_{n\to\infty}\frac{\left(1+\frac{1}{n}\right)}{\left(\frac{4}{n^2}+1\right)}$

$= \frac{1}{2}$

43. $\lim_{x\to1}\frac{\sqrt{x+1}-\sqrt{5x+3}}{\sqrt{2x+3}-\sqrt{4x+1}}$

Multiply both with their rationalizing factors.

$$\Rightarrow \lim_{x\to1}\frac{\sqrt{x+1}-\sqrt{5x+3}}{\sqrt{2x+3}-\sqrt{4x+1}}\times\frac{\sqrt{2x+3}+\sqrt{4x+1}}{\sqrt{2x+3}+\sqrt{4x+1}}$$

$$\times\frac{\sqrt{x+1}+\sqrt{5x+3}}{\sqrt{x+1}+\sqrt{5x+3}}$$

$$\Rightarrow \lim_{x\to1}\frac{4-4x}{2-2x}\cdot\frac{\sqrt{2x+3}+\sqrt{4x+1}}{\sqrt{x+1}+\sqrt{5x-3}}$$

$$\Rightarrow 2\lim_{x\to1}\frac{\sqrt{2x+3}+\sqrt{4x+1}}{\sqrt{x+1}+\sqrt{5x-3}}$$

$$\Rightarrow 2\times\left(\frac{\sqrt{5}+\sqrt{5}}{\sqrt{2}+\sqrt{2}}\right)$$

$$=2\times\frac{\sqrt{5}}{\sqrt{2}}\times\frac{\sqrt{2}}{\sqrt{2}}$$

$$=\frac{2\sqrt{10}}{2}$$

$$=\sqrt{10}$$

44. $1+3+5+7+\cdots n \text{ terms} = 2n-1$

$2+4+6+8+\cdots n \text{ terms} = 2n$

$$=\lim_{n\to\infty}\frac{2n-1}{2n}$$

$$=\lim_{n\to\infty}1-\lim_{n\to\infty}\frac{1}{2n}$$

$$=1$$

45. $$2\lim_{x\to3}\left(\frac{1}{x-3}+\frac{1}{x^2-7x+12}\right)$$

$$2\lim_{x\to3}\left(\frac{1}{x-3}+\frac{1}{x^2-4x-3x+12}\right)$$

$$2\lim_{x\to3}\left(\frac{1}{x-3}+\frac{1}{(x-4)(x-3)}\right)$$

$$2\lim_{x\to3}\left(\frac{1}{x-3}\left(1+\frac{1}{x-4}\right)\right)$$

$$2\lim_{x\to3}\left(\frac{x-4+1}{(x-4)(x-3)}\right)$$

$$2\lim_{x\to3}\left(\frac{x-3}{(x-4)(x-3)}\right)$$

$$2\lim_{x\to3}\left(\frac{1}{x-4}\right)$$

$$=-2$$

46. $$\lim_{x\to5}\frac{x-5}{\sqrt{x+5}-\sqrt{10})}=\lim_{x\to5}\frac{(x-5)\left(\sqrt{x+5}+\sqrt{10}\right)}{\left(\sqrt{x+5}-\sqrt{10}\right)\left(\sqrt{x+5}+\sqrt{10}\right)}$$

$$=\lim_{x\to5}\frac{(x-5)\left(\sqrt{x+5}+\sqrt{10}\right)}{x+5-10}$$

$$=\lim_{x\to5}\frac{(x-5)\left(\sqrt{x+5}+\sqrt{10}\right)}{x-5}$$

$$=\lim_{x\to5}\sqrt{x+5}+\sqrt{10}$$

$$=\sqrt{10}+\sqrt{10}$$

$$=2\sqrt{10}$$

Competition Wing

Level 1: Apply Your Concepts

1. Circle
2. Newton and Leibnitz
3. Point
4. Integration
5. Tangent
6. Substitute $x = 3$ in the given function.
7. Divide both numerator and denominator by x, then use if $x \to \infty$ then $\frac{1}{x} \to 0$.
8. When $x > 5, |x-5| = x-5$.
9. Substitute $x = 1$ in the given expression.
10. Substitute $x = 20$.
11. Substitute $x = 0$.
12. Divide both numerator and denominator by x^2. Now substitute, $\frac{1}{x} = 0$.
13. Use the formula, $\lim_{x\to a} \frac{x^n - a^n}{x - a} = na^{n-1}$.
14. Factorize the numerator and denominator and remove common factor. Now substitute $x = 2$.
15. Apply the concept of left-hand limit.
16. Substitute $x = 0$.
17. Rationalize the denominator.
18. Rationalize the numerator and cancel common factor. Then substitute, $x = 5$.
19. Factorize the numerator and denominator and cancel the common factor and then substitute $x = -3$.
20. Divide both the numerator and the denominator by x^2. Then substitute, $\frac{1}{x} = 0$.
21. Substitute then factorize numerator $f(x)$, then cancel the common factor in both the numerator and the denominator, then substitute $x = 2$.
22. Factorize numerator and denominator, eliminate the common factor then substitute $x = 9$.
23. Use the formula, $\lim_{x\to a} \frac{x^n - a^n}{x - a} = na^{n-1}$.
24. Rationalize the denominator and remove the common factor. Now substitute $x = 3$.
25. Rationalize the denominator and cancel the common factor and then substitute $x = -2$.
26. Put $x = 1$ in the given limit.
27. Use the formula, $\lim_{x\to a} \frac{x^n - a^n}{x - a} = na^{n-1}$, by converting the given limit into the form.
28. Divide both the numerator and the denominator by x and apply the concept hat, as $x \to \infty$, $\frac{1}{x} \to 0$.
29. Use the formula, $\lim_{x\to a} \frac{x^n - a^n}{x - a} = na^{n-1}$.
30. Apply the concept of left-hand limit.
31. Factorize the numerator and denominator and cancel the common factor which is in both numerator and denominator then substitute $x = 4$.
32. Use the formula, $\lim_{x\to a} \frac{x^n - a^n}{x - a} = na^{n-1}$.
33. Calculate $f(1)$ substitute $f(x)$ and $f(1)$, factorise numerator, then cancel the common factor and substitute $x = 1$.
34. Use the formula, $\lim_{x\to a} \frac{x^m - a^m}{x^n - a^n} = \frac{m}{n} a^{m-n}$.
35. (i) The highest power of x is to be taken common from numerator and denominator.

    (ii) Put $\frac{1}{x}, \frac{1}{x^2}, \ldots = 0$ as $x \to \infty \frac{1}{x}, \frac{1}{x^2} \to 0$.

Level 2: Review Your Concepts

36. Factorize the numerator and the denominator and cancel the common factor then substitute $x = -2$.
37. Put $x = -1$ in the given limit.
38. Numerator and denominator are of the same degree.

    $\therefore$ Limiting value of the given function

    $$= \frac{\text{Coefficient of } x \text{ in numerator}}{\text{Coefficient of } x \text{ in denominator}}.$$
39. Divide both the numerator and the denominator by x^2 and then use when

    $x \to \infty \Rightarrow \frac{1}{x} \to 0$.

40. Factorize the numerator and the denominator, and cancel the common factor, then substitute $x = 1$.

41. (i) $\lim_{x \to a} \frac{x^n - a^n}{x - a} = na^{n-1}$.

(ii) Equating na^{n-1} with 5 obtain the value of a.

(iii) Add all the possible real values of a.

42. Rationalize the denominator and cancel common factor and then substitute $x = 0$.

43. Rationalize the numerator and cancel the common factor and then substitute $x = 1$.

44. Rationalize the numerator and cancel the common factor x, then substitute $x = 0$.

45. Use the formula, $\lim_{x \to a} \frac{x^n - a^n}{x - a} = na^{n-1}$.

46. Take as the highest power of x common and cancel it, then substitute $\frac{1}{x} = 0$ as $x \to \infty$, $\frac{1}{x} \to 0$.

47. Find the sum of $2n$ terms in numerator and sum of n terms in denominator and take the highest power of n as common in both the numerator and the denominator and then substitute $\frac{1}{n} = 0$ as $n \to \infty$, $\frac{1}{n} \to 0$.

48. Simplify and then factorize the numerator. Cancel the common factor and then substitute $x = -a$.

49. Rationalize the numerator and denominator and cancel the common factor and then substitute $x = 5$.

50. (i) Use the formula, $\lim_{x \to a} \frac{x^m - a^m}{n^n - a^n} = \frac{m}{n} a^{m-n}$.

(ii) $7a^6 = 7$.

(iii) Now, find the number of possible real values of a.

Level 3: Assess Your Concepts

51. Write formula for sum of the squares of first n natural numbers, i.e., $\frac{n(n+1)(2n+1)}{6}$.

Divide the numerator and the denominator by n^3.

Then substitute $\frac{1}{n} = 0$, as $n \to \infty$, $\frac{1}{n} = 0$.

52. Use the formula, $\lim_{x \to a} \frac{x^n - a^n}{x - a} = na^{n-1}$.

53. (i) Rationalize the numerator and find its factors.

(ii) Cancel the common factor of numerator and denominator and substitute the value of limit.

54. Substitute the formulae for sum of the squares of n natural numbers and sum of n natural number and sum of n odd natural numbers and simplify.

55. Rationalize both numerator and denominator.

56. $\lim_{\theta \to 0} \cot\theta - \operatorname{cosec}\theta$

$= \infty - \infty$, i.e., indeterminate form.

$\cot\theta - \operatorname{cosec}\theta$

$= \frac{\cos\theta}{\sin\theta} - \frac{1}{\sin\theta} = \frac{\cos\theta - 1}{\sin\theta}$

$= \frac{\cos^2\theta - 1}{\sin\theta(\cos\theta + 1)}$

$= \frac{-\sin\theta}{\sin\theta(\cos\theta + 1)} = \frac{-\sin\theta}{\cos\theta + 1}$

$\therefore \lim_{\theta \to 0} \cot\theta - \operatorname{cosec}\theta$

$= \lim_{\theta \to 0} \frac{-\sin\theta}{\cos\theta + 1} = \frac{-\sin 0}{\cos 0 + 1} = \frac{-0}{1+1} = 0.$

57. $\lim_{x \to \infty} \frac{(x+1)^{100} + (x+2)^{100} + \cdots + (x+50)^{100}}{x^{100} + x^{99} + \cdots + x + 1}$

$\lim_{\frac{1}{x} \to \infty} \frac{x^{100}\left(\left(1+\frac{1}{x}\right)^{100} + \left(1+\frac{2}{x}\right)^{100} + \cdots + \left(1+\frac{50}{x}\right)^{100}\right)}{x^{100}\left(1+\frac{1}{x} + \cdots + \frac{1}{x^{99}} + \frac{1}{x^{100}}\right)}$

$= \frac{1+1+\cdots+1 \text{ (upto 50 terms)}}{1} = 50.$

58. $\lim_{x \to 3^-} \frac{|2x-6|}{2x-6}$

$= \lim_{x \to 3^-} \frac{-(2x-6)}{(2x-6)}$ (for $x < 3$, $2x - 6 < 0$) $= -1$.

59. $\lim_{x \to -2} \frac{x^p + 2^p}{x + 2} = 80$

$\Rightarrow \lim_{x \to -2} \frac{x^p - (-2)^p}{x - (-2)} = 80$

$\Rightarrow p(-2)^{p-1} = 5(-2)^{5-1} \therefore p = 5.$

60. $\lim_{x \to m} \frac{x^3 - m^3}{x - m} = 3$

$\Rightarrow 3m^2 = 3 \Rightarrow m^2 = 1 \Rightarrow m = \pm 1$

$\therefore$ There are two values for m.

61. $\lim_{x\to 3}\frac{\sqrt{5x+1}-\sqrt{7x-5}}{\sqrt{7x+4}-\sqrt{5x+10}}=\frac{0}{0}$

That is, indeterminate form.

Multiply both the numerator and the denominator with $\left(\sqrt{5x+1}+\sqrt{7x-5}\right)\left(\sqrt{7x+4}+\sqrt{5x+10}\right)$

$$\Rightarrow \lim_{x\to 3}\frac{[5x+1-(7x-5)]\left(\sqrt{7x+4}+\sqrt{5x+10}\right)}{(7x+4-5x-10)\left(\sqrt{5x+1}+\sqrt{7x-5}\right)}$$

$$\Rightarrow \lim_{x\to 3}\frac{(-2x+6)\left(\sqrt{7x+4}+\sqrt{5x+10}\right)}{(2x-6)\left(\sqrt{5x+1}+\sqrt{7x-5}\right)}$$

$$=\lim_{x\to 3}\frac{-\left(\sqrt{7x+4}+\sqrt{5x+10}\right)}{\left(\sqrt{5x+1}+\sqrt{7x-5}\right)}$$

$$=\frac{-\left(\sqrt{25}+\sqrt{25}\right)}{\left(\sqrt{16}+\sqrt{16}\right)}=\frac{-10}{8}=\frac{-5}{4}.$$

62. $\lim_{x\to a}(x-a)\left(\frac{1}{x-a}-\frac{1}{x^2-(a+b)x+ab}\right)$

$$=\lim_{x\to a}(x-a)\left(\frac{1}{x-a}-\frac{1}{(x-a)(x-b)}\right)$$

$$=\lim_{x\to a}(x-a)\left(\frac{x-b-1}{(x-a)(x-b)}\right)$$

$$\lim_{x\to a}(x-a)\left(\frac{x-b-1}{x-b}\right)=\frac{a-b-1}{a-b}.$$

63. $\lim_{x\to \frac{2}{5}}\frac{1}{|5x-2|}$

As $|5x-2|\geq 0$

$\lim_{x\to \frac{2}{5}}\frac{1}{|5x-2|}$ exists

$$\therefore \lim_{x\to \frac{2}{5}}\frac{1}{|5x-2|}=\frac{1}{0}=\infty.$$

64. $\lim_{x\to\infty}\frac{5x^2}{\sqrt{25x^4+13x^3+14x^2+17x+6}}$

$$=\lim_{x\to\infty}\frac{5x^2}{x^2\sqrt{25+13\left(\frac{1}{x}\right)+14\left(\frac{1}{x^2}\right)+17\left(\frac{1}{x^3}\right)+6\left(\frac{1}{x^4}\right)}}$$

As $x\to\infty, \frac{1}{x}\to 0$

$$=\lim_{\frac{1}{x}\to 0}\frac{5}{\sqrt{25+13\left(\frac{1}{x}\right)+14\left(\frac{1}{x}\right)^2+17\left(\frac{1}{x}\right)^3+6\left(\frac{1}{x}\right)^4}}$$

$$=\frac{5}{\sqrt{25+10}}=\frac{5}{5}=1.$$

65. $\lim_{x\to -1}\frac{x^5+1}{x+1}$

$$\lim_{x\to -1}\frac{x^5-(-1)^5}{x-(-1)}=5(-1)^{5-1}=5(-1)^4=5.$$

66. $\lim_{x\to 0}\frac{\sqrt{125+x}-\sqrt{125-x}}{\sqrt{1000+x}-\sqrt{1000-x}}$

$$=\lim_{x\to 0}\frac{\sqrt{125+x}-\sqrt{125-x}}{\sqrt{1000+x}-\sqrt{1000-x}}\times\frac{\sqrt{1000+x}+\sqrt{1000-x}}{\sqrt{1000+x}+\sqrt{1000-x}}$$

$$=\lim_{x\to 0}\frac{\sqrt{125+x}-\sqrt{125-x}}{1000+x-1000+x}\times\sqrt{1000+x}+\sqrt{1000-x}$$

$$=\lim_{x\to 0}\frac{\sqrt{125+x}-\sqrt{125-x}}{2x}\times\sqrt{1000+x}+\sqrt{1000-x}$$

$$=\lim_{x\to 0}\frac{\left(\sqrt{125+x}-\sqrt{125-x}\right)\left(\sqrt{125+x}+\sqrt{125-x}\right)}{2x\left(\sqrt{125+x}+\sqrt{125-x}\right)}\times\sqrt{1000+x}+\sqrt{1000-x}$$

$$=\lim_{x\to 0}\frac{125+x-125+x}{2x\left(\sqrt{125+x}+\sqrt{125-x}\right)}\times\sqrt{1000+x}+\sqrt{1000-x}$$

$$=\lim_{x\to 0}\frac{2x\left(\sqrt{1000+x}+\sqrt{1000-x}\right)}{2x\left(\sqrt{125+x}+\sqrt{125-x}\right)}$$

$$=\lim_{x\to 0}\frac{\sqrt{1000+x}+\sqrt{1000-x}}{\sqrt{125+x}+\sqrt{125-x}}$$

$$=\frac{\sqrt{1000}+\sqrt{1000}}{\sqrt{125}+\sqrt{125}}$$

$$=\frac{10\sqrt{10}+10\sqrt{10}}{5\sqrt{5}+5\sqrt{5}}$$

$$=\frac{20\sqrt{10}}{10\sqrt{5}}$$

$$=2\sqrt{2}$$

CHAPTER

19

Partial Fractions

Remember

Before beginning this chapter, you should be able to:

- State expressions and equations
- Have knowledge of polynomials

Key Ideas

After completing this chapter, you should be able to:

- Learn about rational fractions and partial fractions
- Study various methods to resolve polynomial equations to partial fractions

INTRODUCTION

An expression of the form $a_0x^n + a_1x^{n-1} + a_2x^{n-2} + \cdots + a_n$, where $a_0, a_1, \ldots, a_n$ are real numbers and $a_0 \neq 0$ is called a polynomial of degree n.

Rational Fraction

The quotient of any two polynomials $f(x)$ and $g(x)$ where $g(x) \neq 0$ is called a rational fraction.

In a rational fraction $\frac{f(x)}{g(x)}$, if the degree of $f(x)$ is less than the degree of $g(x)$, then the rational fraction $\frac{f(x)}{g(x)}$ is called a proper rational fraction or simply a proper fraction.

Example: $\frac{2x+3}{3x^2-5x+2}, \frac{3}{x-4}$ are some examples of proper fractions.

If the degree of $f(x)$ is greater than or equal to the degree of $g(x)$, then the rational fraction $\frac{f(x)}{g(x)}$ is called an improper fraction.

Example: $\frac{x^2+2x-1}{2x^2-5x+1}, \frac{3x^3+5x+7}{x^2+6x+5}, \frac{x^2+x+1}{2x+1}$ are some examples of improper fractions.

Info Bytes!
The sum of two proper rational fractions is a proper fraction.

Example: $\frac{2}{x+3}$ and $\frac{5}{2x+1}$ are two proper fractions.

Consider, $\frac{2}{x+3} + \frac{5}{2x+1} = \frac{2(2x+1)+5(x+3)}{(x+3)(2x+1)} = \frac{9x+17}{2x^2+7x+3}$, which is a proper fraction.

That is, a proper fraction may be split into sum of two or more proper fractions, which are also called partial fractions.

The process of expressing a proper fraction as the sum of two or more proper fractions is called resolving it into partial fractions.

Now let us discuss about the different methods of resolving a given proper fraction $\frac{f(x)}{g(x)}$ into partial fractions.

Konnect

If an improper fraction $\frac{f(x)}{g(x)}$ is to split into partial fractions, first we divide $f(x)$ by $g(x)$ till we obtain a remainder $r(x)$, which is of lower degree than $g(x)$ and then we express the given fraction as $\frac{f(x)}{g(x)} = \text{Quotient} + \frac{r(x)}{g(x)}$. Then we resolve the proper fraction $\frac{r(x)}{g(x)}$ into partial fractions.

Method 1

When $g(x)$ contains non-repeated linear factors only: For every non-repeated linear factor of the form $ax + b$ of $g(x)$, there exists a corresponding partial fraction of the form $\frac{A}{ax+b}$.

EXAMPLE 19.1 Resolve $\dfrac{3x+5}{(x+2)(3x-1)}$ into partial fractions.

SOLUTION

In the given fraction, the denominator has two linear, non-repeated factors.

$\therefore$ The given fraction can be written as the sum of two partial fractions.

Let $\dfrac{3x+5}{(x+2)(3x-1)} = \dfrac{A}{x+2} + \dfrac{B}{3x-1}$

$\Rightarrow 3x+5 = A(3x-1) + B(x+2)$ (1)

Put $x = -2$ in Eq. (1),

$\Rightarrow 3(-2) + 5 = A[3(-2) - 1] + B(-2+2) - 1 = -7A \Rightarrow A = \dfrac{1}{7}.$

Comparing the constant terms on both sides of Eq. (1), we have:

$5 = -A + 2B$

$5 = -\dfrac{1}{7} + 2B$ or $B = \dfrac{18}{7}.$

$$\therefore \frac{3x+5}{(x+2)(3x-1)} = \frac{\frac{1}{7}}{x+2} + \frac{\frac{18}{7}}{3x-1} = \frac{1}{7}\left[\frac{1}{x+2} + \frac{18}{3x-1}\right].$$

EXAMPLE 19.2 Resolve $\dfrac{2x^2+5x-1}{x^2-3x-10}$ into partial fractions.

SOLUTION

Given, $\dfrac{2x^2+5x-1}{x^2-3x-10}$

We can clearly notice that the given fraction is an improper fraction. So dividing the numerator by the denominator, we can express $\dfrac{2x^2+5x-1}{x^2-3x-10}$ as $2 + \dfrac{11x+19}{x^2-3x-10}$.

Let $\dfrac{11x+19}{(x+2)(x-5)} = \dfrac{A}{x+2} + \dfrac{B}{x-5}$

$\Rightarrow 11x + 19 = A(x-5) + B(x+2)$ (1)

Put $x = 5$ in Eq. (1) $\Rightarrow 55 + 19 = A(0) + B(7)$

$\therefore B = \dfrac{74}{7}.$

Again put $x = -2$ in Eq. (1) $\Rightarrow -22 + 19 = A(-7) + B(0) \Rightarrow A = \dfrac{3}{7}.$

$$\therefore \frac{2x^2+5x-1}{x^2-3x-10} = 2 + \frac{3}{7(x+2)} + \frac{74}{7(x-5)}.$$

Method 2

When $g(x)$ contains some repeated linear factors and the remaining are non-repeated linear factors: Let $g(x) = (px + q)^n (a_1x + \alpha_1)(a_2x + \alpha_2) \ldots (a_nx + \alpha_n)$, then there exist fractions of the form $\frac{A_1}{Px+q}, \frac{A_2}{(Px+q)^2}, \ldots, \frac{A_n}{(Px+q)^n}$ corresponding to every repeated linear factor and fractions of the form $\frac{B_1}{a_1x+\alpha_1}, \frac{B_2}{a_2x+\alpha_2}, \ldots, \frac{B_n}{a_nx+\alpha_n}$ corresponding to every non-repeated linear factors where $A_1, A_2, \ldots, A_n$, and $B_1, B_2, \ldots, B_n$ are real numbers.

EXAMPLE 19.3

Resolve $\frac{2x^2-5x+7}{(x+1)^2(x+3)(2x+1)}$ into partial fractions.

SOLUTION

Let $\frac{2x^2-5x+7}{(x+1)^2(x+3)(2x+1)} = \frac{A}{x+1} + \frac{B}{(x+1)^2} + \frac{C}{x+3} + \frac{D}{2x+1}$

$\Rightarrow 2x^2 - 5x + 7 = A(x+1)(x+3)(2x+1) + B(x+3)(2x+1) + C(x+1)^2(2x+1) + D(x+1)^2(x+3)$ (1)

Substituting $x = -1$ in Eq. (1), we have

$2(-1)^2 - 5(-1) + 7 = A(0) + B(-1+3)(-2+1) + C(0) + D(0) \Rightarrow 14 = -2B$

$B = -7$.

Substituting $x = -3$ in Eq. (1), we get

$40 = A(0) + B(0) + C(-20) + D(0) \Rightarrow -20C = 40$

$C = -2$.

Substituting $x = -\frac{1}{2}$ in Eq. (1), we have

$10 = \frac{5}{8}D \Rightarrow D = 16.$

Substituting $x = 0$, we have

$7 = 3A + 3B + C + 3D$

Substituting the values of B, C, D in the above equation, we get $A = -6$.

$\therefore \frac{2x^2-5x+7}{(x+1)^2(x+3)(2x+1)} = \frac{-6}{x+1} + \frac{-7}{(x+1)^2} + \frac{-2}{x+3} + \frac{16}{2x+1}.$

Method 3

When $g(x)$ contains non-repeated irreducible factors of the form $px^2 + qx + r$: Corresponding to every non-reducible non-repeated quadratic factors of $g(x)$, there exists a partial fraction of the form $\frac{Ax+B}{px^2+qx+r}$, where p, q, A, and B are real numbers.

EXAMPLE 19.4

Resolve $\frac{2x-5}{(x+2)(x^2-x+5)}$ into partial fractions.

SOLUTION

Let $\frac{2x-5}{(x+2)(x^2-x+5)} = \frac{A}{x+2} + \frac{Bx+C}{x^2-x+5}$

$\Rightarrow 2x - 5 = A(x^2 - x + 5) + (Bx + C)(x + 2)$ (1)

Put $x = -2$ in Eq. (1),

$\Rightarrow -9 = A(11) + 0$

$A = \frac{-9}{11}.$

Again put $x = 0$ in Eq. (1), we have,

$-5 = 5A + 2C$

$-5 = 5 \times \frac{-9}{11} + 2C$

$\Rightarrow C = \frac{-5}{11}.$

Comparing the coefficients of x^2 on both sides of Eq. (1), we have $A + B = 0$

$\Rightarrow B = -A = \frac{9}{11}.$

$$\therefore \frac{2x-5}{(x+2)(x^2-x+5)} = \frac{-9}{11(x+2)} + \frac{\frac{9}{11}x - \frac{5}{11}}{x^2-x+5} = \frac{1}{11}\left[\frac{9x-5}{x^2-x+5} - \frac{9}{x+2}\right].$$

Method 4

When $g(x)$ contains repeated and non-repeated irreducible quadratic factors of the form $(px^2 + qx + r)^n$: Corresponding to every repeated irreducible quadratic factor of $g(x)$ there exist partial fractions of the form $\frac{p_1x+q_1}{(px^2+qx+r)}, \frac{p_2x+q^2}{(px^2+qx+r)}, \ldots, \frac{p_nx+q_n}{(px^2+qx+r)^n}$, where $p_1, p_2, \ldots, p_n$ and $q_1, q_2, \ldots, q_n$ are real numbers.

EXAMPLE 19.5 Resolve $\frac{2x+1}{(x+3)(x^2+1)^2}$ into partial fractions.

SOLUTION

Let, $\frac{2x+1}{(x+3)(x^2+1)^2} = \frac{A}{x+3} + \frac{Bx+C}{x^2+1} + \frac{Dx+E}{(x^2+1)^2}.$

$\Rightarrow 2x + 1 = A(x^2 + 1)^2 + (Bx + C)(x + 3)(x^2 + 1) + (Dx + E)(x + 3)$ (1)

Put $x = -3$ in Eq. (1), we have

$-5 = 100A \Rightarrow A = \frac{-1}{20}$

Comparing the coefficients of x^4 on either sides of Eq. (1), we have

$0 = A + B \Rightarrow B = \frac{1}{20}$

Comparing the coefficients of x^3 on either sides of Eq. (1), we have

$0 = 3B + C \Rightarrow C = \frac{-3}{20}$

Put $x = 0$ in Eq. (1), we have,

$\Rightarrow 1 = A + 3C + 3E \Rightarrow 3E = 1 + \frac{1}{20} + \frac{9}{20}$

$\Rightarrow E = \frac{1}{2}$

By putting $x = 1$ in Eq. (1), we have,

$3 = 4A + 8B + 8C + 4D + 4E$

$$3=\frac{-4}{20}+\frac{8}{20}+8\left(\frac{-3}{20}\right)+4D+4\left(\frac{1}{2}\right)$$

$$3+\frac{4}{20}-\frac{8}{20}+\frac{24}{20}-2=4D$$

$$D=\frac{2}{4}=\frac{1}{2}$$

$$\therefore\ \frac{2x+1}{(x+3)(x^2+1)^2}=\frac{\frac{-1}{20}}{x+3}+\frac{\frac{x}{20}-\frac{3}{20}}{x^2+1}+\frac{\frac{1}{2}x+\frac{1}{2}}{(x^2+1)^2}$$

$$=\frac{-1}{20(x+3)}+\frac{(x-3)}{20(x^2+1)}+\frac{(x+1)}{2(x^2+1)^2}.$$

EXAMPLE 19.6

Resolve $\frac{3x^2-3x-11}{(x+3)(3x+4)^2}$ into partial fractions.

(a) $\frac{1}{x+3}+\frac{2}{3x+4}-\frac{1}{(3x+4)^2}$ (b) $\frac{1}{x+3}-\frac{2}{3x+4}-\frac{1}{(3x+4)^2}$

(c) $\frac{1}{x+3}+\frac{2}{3x+4}-\frac{1}{2(3x+4)^2}$ (d) None of these

SOLUTION

Let, $\frac{3x^2-3x-11}{(x+3)(3x+4)^2}=\frac{A}{x+3}+\frac{B}{3x+4}+\frac{C}{(3x+4)^2}.$

Consider

$$3x^2-3x-11=A(3x+4)^2+B(x+3)(3x+4)+C(x+3)$$
$$=A(9x^2+16+24x)+B(3x^2+13x+12)+C(x+3)$$

Comparing coefficient of x^2, coefficient of x and constant terms, we get,

$$9A+3B=3 \quad (1)$$
$$24A+13B+C=-3 \quad (2)$$
$$16A+12B+3C=-11 \quad (3)$$

Solving Eqs. (1), (2) and (3), we get,

$A=1, B=-2, C=-1$

$$\therefore\ \frac{3x^2-3x-11}{(x+3)(3x+4)^2}=\frac{1}{x+3}-\frac{2}{3x+4}-\frac{1}{(3x+4)^2}.$$

EXAMPLE 19.7

If $\frac{x}{(x-1)(x^2+1)^2}=\frac{P}{x-1}+\frac{Qx+R}{x^2+1}+\frac{Sx+T}{(x^2+1)^2}$, then $P+Q-R-S+T=$ ______.

(a) $\frac{5}{4}$ (b) $\frac{3}{2}$ (c) $\frac{9}{7}$ (d) $\frac{8}{9}$

SOLUTION

$$\frac{x}{(x-1)(x^2+1)^2}=\frac{P}{x-1}+\frac{Qx+R}{(x^2+1)}+\frac{Sx+T}{(x^2+1)^2}$$

Consider,

$$x=P(x^2+1)^2+(Qx+R)(x^2+1)(x-1)+(Sx+T)(x-1)$$

Put $x = 1$,

$\Rightarrow 4P = 1 \Rightarrow P = \frac{1}{4}$

Equating the coefficient of x^4, the coefficient of x^3, constant term and the coefficient of x^2 from both sides.

$P + Q = 0$, i.e., $P = -Q \;\therefore Q = -\frac{1}{4}$

$-Q + R = 0$, i.e., $Q = R$, $\therefore R = \frac{-1}{4}$

$P - R - T = 0$, i.e., $T = P - R$

$\therefore T = \frac{1}{2}$

$2P + Q - R + S = 0$

That is, $S = -2P = \frac{-1}{2}$

$P + Q - R - S + T = \frac{1}{4} - \frac{1}{4} + \frac{1}{4} + \frac{1}{2} + \frac{1}{2} = \frac{5}{4}.$

EXAMPLE 19.8 If $\frac{9x-13}{x^2-2x-15} = \frac{A}{x+3} + \frac{B}{x-5}$, then $A + B$ is ______.

(a) 9 (b) 13 (c) 12 (d) 8

SOLUTION

Given, $\frac{9x-13}{x^2-2x-15} = \frac{A}{x+3} + \frac{B}{x-5}$.

Consider, $9x - 13 = A(x - 5) + B(x + 3)$

$9x - 13 = Ax - 5A + Bx + 3B$

Comparing the coefficients of x, we get,

$A + B = 9$.

EXAMPLE 19.9 Resolve $\frac{x}{(x-2)(x^2+3)^2}$ into partial fractions.

(a) $\frac{1}{49}\left[\frac{2}{x-2} - \frac{2x+4}{x^2+3} + \frac{12-2x}{(x^2+3)^2}\right]$ (b) $\frac{1}{49}\left[\frac{2}{x-2} - \frac{2x+4}{x^2+3} - \frac{12-2x}{(x^2+3)^2}\right]$

(c) $\frac{1}{49}\left[\frac{2}{x-2} + \frac{2x+4}{x^2+3} - \frac{12-2x}{(x^2+3)^2}\right]$ (d) $\frac{1}{49}\left[\frac{2}{x-2} - \frac{2x+4}{x^2+3} + \frac{21-14x}{(x^2+3)^2}\right]$

SOLUTION

Let $\frac{x}{(x-2)(x^2+3)^2} = \frac{A}{x-2} + \frac{Bx+C}{x^2+3} + \frac{Dx+E}{(x^2+3)^2}$

Consider,

$x = A\,(x^2 + 3)^2 + (Bx + C)\,(x - 2)\,(x^2 + 3) + (Dx + E)\,(x - 2)$

Put $x = 2$, we get

$A = \frac{2}{49}$

Comparing the coefficients of x^4, x^3, x^2 and constant terms, we get,

$A + B = 0 \Rightarrow \therefore B = -\frac{2}{49}$.

$-2B + C = 0 \Rightarrow C = -\frac{4}{49}$.

$6A + 3B - 2C + D = 0$

$\Rightarrow \therefore D = \frac{-14}{49}$

and $-6C - 2E + 9A = 0$

$\Rightarrow E = \frac{21}{49}$

$$\frac{x}{(x-2)(x^2+3)^2} = \frac{\frac{2}{49}}{x-2} + \frac{\frac{-2}{49}x - \frac{4}{49}}{x^2+3} + \frac{-\frac{14}{49}x + \frac{21}{49}}{(x^2+3)^2}$$

$$= \frac{2}{49(x-2)} - \frac{2x+4}{49(x^2+3)} + \frac{21-14x}{49(x^2+3)^2}.$$

EXAMPLE 19.10 If $\frac{1}{(1-x)(1-2x)(1-3x)} = \frac{A}{(1-x)} + \frac{B}{(1-2x)} + \frac{C}{(1-3x)}$, then $A + B + C =$ ________.

(a) 0 (b) 1 (c) −1 (d) 2

SOLUTION

$$\frac{1}{(1-x)(1-2x)(1-3x)} = \frac{A}{1-x} + \frac{B}{1-2x} + \frac{C}{1-3x}$$

$$= \frac{A(1-2x)(1-3x) + B(1-3x)(1-x) + C(1-x)(1-2x)}{(1-x)(1-2x)(1-3x)}$$

Consider,

$A(1 - 2x)(1 - 3x) + B(1 - 3x)(1 - x) + C(1 - x)(1 - 2x) = 1$

Comparing constant terms, we get $A + B + C = 1$.

POINTS TO REMEMBER

- ✔ The quotient of any two polynomials $f(x)$ and $g(x)$ where $g(x) \neq 0$ is called a rational fraction.
- ✔ In a rational function $\frac{f(x)}{g(x)}$, if the degree of $f(x)$ is less than the degree of $g(x)$, then the rational function $\frac{f(x)}{g(x)}$ is called a proper rational fraction or simply a proper fraction.
- ✔ When $g(x)$ contains non-repeated linear factors only.
- ✔ When $g(x)$ contains some repeated linear factors and the remaining are non-repeated linear factors.
- ✔ When $g(x)$ contains non-repeated irreducible factors of the form $px^2 + qx + r$
- ✔ When $g(x)$ contains repeated and non-repeated irreducible quadratic factors of the form $(px^2 + qx + r)^n$

PRACTICE QUESTIONS CLASSROOM WING

Very Short Answer Type Questions

Directions of questions from 1 to 10:
Fill in the blanks.

1. The number of terms of the partial fraction of $\dfrac{x^3}{(x-1)(2x-3)(x-4)}$ is ________.

2. The partial fraction of $\dfrac{2(x^2+1)}{x^3-1}$ is $\dfrac{1}{x-1}-\dfrac{f(x)}{g(x)}$. Then the degree of $f(x)$ is ________.

3. There are three terms of partial fractions of the proper fraction $\dfrac{f(x)}{x^3}$. Then the degree of the polynomial $f(x)$ would be ________.

4. If $\dfrac{x^2-2x-9}{(x^2+x+6)(x+1)}=\dfrac{2x-3}{x^2+x+6}+\dfrac{A}{x+1}$, then A is ________.

5. If the partial fractions of $\dfrac{3x^2+4}{(x-1)^3}$ is $\dfrac{3}{x-1}+\dfrac{A}{(x-1)^2}+\dfrac{7}{(x-1)^3}$, then $A=$ ________.

6. If $\dfrac{f(x)}{x^2-x+1}-\dfrac{1}{f(x)}$ is the partial fraction of $\dfrac{3x}{x^3+1}$, then $f(x)$ is ________.

7. If $\dfrac{ax^2+bx+c}{(x+1)(x^2+3x-4)}=\dfrac{f(x)}{x+1}+\dfrac{g(x)}{x+4}+\dfrac{h(x)}{x-1}$, then the degree of $f(x)$, $g(x)$ and $h(x)$ is ________.

8. If $\dfrac{2x^2+3x+4}{(x+2)^4}=\dfrac{A}{(x+2)}+\dfrac{2}{(x+2)^2}-\dfrac{5}{(x+2)^3}+\dfrac{6}{(x+2)^4}$, then $A=$ ________.

9. If $\dfrac{x^2}{(x-a)(x-b)}=1+\dfrac{a^2}{(a-b)(x-a)}+\dfrac{B}{(x-b)}$, then B is ________.

10. If $\dfrac{x^4}{(x+1)(x+2)}=f(x)+\dfrac{A}{x+1}+\dfrac{B}{x+2}$, then the degree of the polynomial $f(x)$ is ________.

Short Answer Type Questions

Directions of questions from 11 to 32:
Answer the following questions.

11. Resolve into partial fractions: $\dfrac{1}{x^2-a^2}$.

12. Resolve into partial fractions: $\dfrac{2x+5}{x^2+3x+2}$.

13. Resolve into partial fractions: $\dfrac{3x+4}{x^2+x-12}$.

14. Resolve into partial fractions: $\dfrac{2x^2+5x+18}{(x-2)^3}$.

15. Resolve into partial fractions: $\dfrac{x+1}{(x+2)(x^2+4)}$.

16. Find the value of A, B and C if $\dfrac{2x^2-x-10}{(x-2)^3}=\dfrac{A}{(x-2)}+\dfrac{B}{(x-2)^2}+\dfrac{C}{(x-2)^3}$.

17. (A) If $\dfrac{x+5}{(x-1)^2}=\dfrac{A}{(x-1)}+\dfrac{B}{(x-1)^2}$, then find the values of A and B.

(B) Resolve $\dfrac{px-qx+2p}{(x+1)^2}$ into partial fractions.

18. Find the partial fractions of $\dfrac{ax+b}{(x-1)^2}$, where a and b are constants.

19. Resolve into partial fractions: $\dfrac{2x^2-3x+3}{x^3-2x^2+x}$.

20. Resolve into partial fractions: $\dfrac{x^2+5x+6}{x^3-7x-6}$.

21. Resolve into partial fractions: $\dfrac{x^3}{(x+1)(x+2)}$.

22. Resolve into partial fractions: $\dfrac{x+1}{x^3-1}$.

23. Resolve into partial fractions: $\dfrac{2x^2+4}{x^4+5x^2+4}$.

24. Find the partial fractions of $\dfrac{2x+3}{x^4+x^2+1}$.

25. (A) Resolve into partial fractions: $\dfrac{1}{x^4+x}$.

(B) Resolve $\dfrac{9x^2-3x+2}{3x^2-2x-1}$ into partial fractions.

Essay Type Questions

26. Resolve into partial fractions: $\dfrac{3x^2+4x+5}{x^3+9x^2+26x+24}$.

27. Resolve into partial fractions: $\dfrac{x+1}{(x+2)(x^2+4)}$.

28. Resolve into partial fractions: $\dfrac{3x+4}{x^3-2x-4}$.

29. (A) Resolve into partial fractions: $\dfrac{x^2-3}{x^3-2x^2-x+2}$.

(B) Resolve $\dfrac{13x+22}{(2x+3)(x+2)}$ into partial fractions.

30. Resolve into partial fractions: $\dfrac{x^4+1}{(x-2)(x+2)}$.

31. Resolve $\dfrac{3x^2-4x+2}{(x-1)^3}$ into partial fractions.

32. Resolve $\dfrac{2x^2+9x+11}{(x+2)^2(x+3)}$ into partial fractions.

PRACTICE QUESTIONS COMPETITION WING

Level 1: Apply Your Concepts

Directions of questions from 1 to 5:
Fill in the blanks.

1. Improper fraction is a fraction in which the degree of the numerator is _______ than or equal to the degree of denominator.

2. Improper fraction can always be written as the _______ of a polynomial and a proper fraction.

3. The partial fractions of $\frac{Ax+B}{x^4}$ has _______ terms.

4. A proper fraction is one in which the degree of numerator is _______ than the degree of denominator.

5. A proper fraction may be written as the sum of _______.

Directions of questions from 6 to 50:
Select the correct alternative from the given choices.

6. Resolve $\frac{1}{x^2-9}$ into partial fractions.

(a) $\frac{1}{3(x-3)}-\frac{1}{3(x+3)}$ (b) $\frac{1}{2(x-3)}-\frac{3}{2(x+3)}$

(c) $\frac{1}{6(x-3)}-\frac{1}{6(x+3)}$ (d) $\frac{1}{6(x-3)}+\frac{1}{6(x+3)}$

7. Resolve $\frac{2x+3}{x^2-6x+5}$ into partial fractions.

(a) $\frac{1}{4}\left(\frac{13}{x-5}-\frac{5}{x-1}\right)$ (b) $\frac{5}{x-5}-\frac{13}{4(x-1)}$

(c) $\frac{13}{5(x-1)}-\frac{4}{5(x-5)}$ (d) $\frac{5}{(x-5)}-\frac{4}{(x-1)}$

8. Resolve $\frac{x^2+x+1}{(x-1)^3}$ into partial fractions.

(a) $\frac{1}{x-1}+\frac{1}{(x-1)^2}+\frac{1}{(x-1)^3}$

(b) $\frac{1}{(x-1)}+\frac{2}{(x-1)^2}+\frac{1}{(x-1)^3}$

(c) $\frac{1}{x-1}+\frac{3}{(x-1)^2}+\frac{3}{(x-1)^3}$

(d) $\frac{2}{x-1}+\frac{3}{(x-1)^2}+\frac{3}{(x-1)^3}$

9. Resolve $\frac{3x+2}{x^2+5x+6}$ into partial fractions.

(a) $\frac{7}{(x+2)}+\frac{4}{(x+3)}$ (b) $\frac{4}{(x+3)}+\frac{8}{(x+2)}$

(c) $\frac{4}{(x+3)}-\frac{7}{(x+2)}$ (d) $\frac{7}{(x+3)}-\frac{4}{(x+2)}$

10. Resolve $\frac{1}{x^2+x+42}$ into partial fractions.

(a) $\frac{1}{13(x-6)}+\frac{1}{13(x+7)}$ (b) $\frac{1}{(x-7)}+\frac{1}{(x-6)}$

(c) $\frac{1}{(x-7)}-\frac{1}{(x-6)}$ (d) $\frac{1}{13(x-6)}-\frac{1}{13(x+7)}$

11. Resolve $\frac{x^2+4x+6}{(x^2-1)(x+3)}$ into partial fractions

(a) $\frac{11}{8(x-1)}-\frac{3}{21(x+1)}+\frac{3}{8(x+3)}$

(b) $\frac{11}{8(x-1)}-\frac{3}{4(x+1)}+\frac{3}{8(x+3)}$

(c) $\frac{11}{4(x+1)}-\frac{3}{8(x+1)}+\frac{3}{8(x+3)}$

(d) $\frac{11}{8(x-1)}-\frac{3}{4(x+1)}+\frac{3}{8(x+3)}$

12. Resolve $\frac{x+1}{x(x-1)(x+3)}$ into partial fractions.

(a) $\frac{-1}{3x}+\frac{1}{2(x-1)}-\frac{1}{6(x+3)}$

(b) $\frac{1}{3x}+\frac{1}{2(x-1)}-\frac{1}{6(x+3)}$

(c) $\frac{1}{3x}-\frac{1}{2(x-1)}+\frac{1}{6(x+3)}$

(d) $\frac{1}{2x}-\frac{1}{3(x-1)}+\frac{1}{6(x+3)}$

13. Resolve $\frac{1}{x^2-(a+b)x+ab}$ into partial fractions.

(a) $\frac{1}{a+b}\left[\frac{1}{x-a}+\frac{1}{x-b}\right]$ (b) $\frac{1}{a+b}\left[\frac{1}{x-a}-\frac{1}{x-b}\right]$

(c) $\frac{1}{a-b}\left[\frac{1}{x-a}+\frac{1}{x-b}\right]$ (d) $\frac{1}{a-b}\left[\frac{1}{x-a}-\frac{1}{x-b}\right]$

14. Resolve $\dfrac{1}{x^2 - 5x + 6}$ into partial fractions.

(a) $\dfrac{1}{x-3} - \dfrac{1}{x-2}$ (b) $\dfrac{1}{x-2} + \dfrac{1}{x-3}$

(c) $\dfrac{1}{x-3} + \dfrac{1}{x-2}$ (d) $\dfrac{2}{x-3} + \dfrac{2}{x-2}$

15. Resolve $\dfrac{x+2}{x^2 - 2x - 15}$ into partial fractions.

(a) $\dfrac{7}{8(x-5)} + \dfrac{1}{8(x+3)}$ (b) $\dfrac{8}{7(x-5)} + \dfrac{1}{7(x+3)}$

(c) $\dfrac{5}{8(x-5)} + \dfrac{1}{8(x+3)}$ (d) None of these

16. Resolve $\dfrac{3x^2 + 2x + 4}{(x-1)(x^2-4)}$ into partial fractions.

(a) $\dfrac{5}{x-2} + \dfrac{1}{x-1} + \dfrac{1}{x+2}$

(b) $\dfrac{5}{x-2} + \dfrac{2}{x-1} + \dfrac{1}{x+2}$

(c) $\dfrac{5}{x-2} + \dfrac{2}{x-1} - \dfrac{1}{x+2}$

(d) $\dfrac{5}{x-2} - \dfrac{3}{(x-1)} + \dfrac{1}{(x+2)}$

17. Resolve $\dfrac{2x+1}{x^2 - 2x - 8}$ into partial fractions.

(a) $\dfrac{3}{2(x-4)} - \dfrac{1}{2(x+2)}$ (b) $\dfrac{3}{2(x-4)} + \dfrac{1}{2(x+2)}$

(c) $\dfrac{1}{2(x-4)} - \dfrac{3}{2(x+2)}$ (d) None of these

18. Resolve $\dfrac{2x^2 + 3x + 18}{(x-2)(x+2)^2}$ into partial fractions.

(a) $\dfrac{2}{(x+2)} - \dfrac{5}{(x-1)^2}$

(b) $\dfrac{2}{x-2} + \dfrac{1}{(x+2)} + \dfrac{3}{(x+2)^2}$

(c) $\dfrac{2}{x-2} - \dfrac{5}{(x+2)^2}$

(d) $\dfrac{2}{x-2} - \dfrac{1}{(x+2)} + \dfrac{3}{(x+2)^2}$

19. Resolve $\dfrac{x^2 - x + 1}{x^3 - 1}$ into partial fractions.

(a) $\dfrac{1}{3(x-1)} + \dfrac{2x-2}{3(x^2+x+1)}$

(b) $\dfrac{1}{3(x-1)} - \dfrac{2x+2}{3(x^2+x+1)}$

(c) $\dfrac{1}{2(x-1)} + \dfrac{x+2}{2(x^2+x+1)}$

(d) $\dfrac{1}{3(x-1)} - \dfrac{x-2}{3(x^2+x+1)}$

20. Resolve $\dfrac{x-1}{x^3 - 3x^2 + 2x}$ into partial fractions.

(a) $\dfrac{1}{(x-2)} - \dfrac{1}{2x}$ (b) $\dfrac{1}{2(x-2)} - \dfrac{1}{2x}$

(c) $\dfrac{1}{(x-2)} + \dfrac{1}{x-1} + \dfrac{1}{2x}$ (d) $\dfrac{1}{x-2} - \dfrac{1}{x-1} + \dfrac{1}{2x}$

Level 2: Review Your Concepts

21. Resolve $\dfrac{x-b}{x^2 + (a+b)x + ab}$ into partial fractions.

(a) $\dfrac{2a}{(a+b)(x+a)} - \dfrac{2b}{(a+b)(x+b)}$

(b) $\dfrac{a+b}{(a-b)(x+a)} + \dfrac{2b}{(a-b)(x+b)}$

(c) $\dfrac{a+b}{(a-b)(x+a)} - \dfrac{2b}{(a-b)(x+b)}$

(d) None of these

22. Resolve $\dfrac{x+1}{x^2 - 4}$ into partial fractions.

(a) $\dfrac{3}{2(x-2)} + \dfrac{1}{2(x+2)}$

(b) $\dfrac{3}{2(x-2)} - \dfrac{1}{2(x+2)}$

(c) $\dfrac{3}{4(x-2)} + \dfrac{1}{4(x+2)}$

(d) $\dfrac{3}{4(x-2)} - \dfrac{1}{4(x+2)}$

23. Resolve $\frac{x}{(x+1)(x-1)^2}$ into partial fractions.

(a) $\frac{1}{2(x-1)^2}+\frac{1}{4(x-1)}+\frac{1}{4(x+1)}$

(b) $\frac{-1}{4(x+1)}+\frac{1}{4(x-1)}+\frac{1}{2(x-1)^2}$

(c) $\frac{-1}{4(x-1)}+\frac{1}{4(x+1)}+\frac{1}{2(x-1)^2}$

(d) None of these

24. Resolve $\frac{3x-5}{x^2+3x+2}$ into partial fractions.

(a) $\frac{7}{x+2}-\frac{5}{x+1}$ (b) $\frac{-8}{x+2}-\frac{11}{(x+1)}$

(c) $\frac{11}{x+2}-\frac{8}{x+1}$ (d) $\frac{7}{x+2}+\frac{5}{x+1}$

25. Resolve $\frac{3x+5}{x^2+8x-20}$ into partial fractions.

(a) $\frac{11}{24(x-2)}+\frac{25}{24(x+10)}$ (b) $\frac{11}{6(x-2)}+\frac{25}{6(x+10)}$

(c) $\frac{11}{12(x+2)}+\frac{25}{12(x-10)}$ (d) $\frac{11}{12(x-2)}+\frac{25}{12(x+10)}$

26. Resolve $\frac{ax+b^2}{x^2-(a+b)^2}$ into partial fractions.

(a) $\frac{a^2+ab+b^2}{2(a+b)(x-(a+b))}+\frac{a^2+ab-b^2}{2(a+b)(x+(a+b))}$

(b) $\frac{a^2+b^2}{2(a+b)(x-(a+b))}+\frac{a^2-b^2}{2(a+b)(x+(a+b))}$

(c) $\frac{a^2-b^2}{2(a+b)(x-(a-b))}+\frac{a^2+b^2}{2(a+b)(x+(a+b))}$

(d) $\frac{a^2+ab+b^2}{2(a+b)(x-(a+b))}-\frac{a^2+ab-b^2}{2(a+b)(x+(a+b))}$

27. Find the constants a, b, c and d, respectively, if $\frac{1}{x^4-x}=\frac{a}{x}+\frac{b}{x-1}+\frac{cx+d}{x^2+x+1}$.

(a) $-1, \frac{1}{3}, \frac{-1}{2}, \frac{-5}{6}$ (b) $-1, \frac{1}{3}, \frac{-1}{2}, \frac{5}{6}$

(c) $1, \frac{-1}{3}, \frac{1}{2}, \frac{5}{6}$ (d) None of these

28. If $\frac{x^3}{(x-1)(x-2)}=Ax+B+\frac{C}{x-1}+\frac{D}{x-2}$, then A, B, C, and D, respectively, are ______.

(a) 1, 3, 1, 8 (b) 1, −1, 3, 8

(c) 1, 3, −1, 8 (d) −1, −3, 1, 8

29. Resolve $\frac{2x^2+3}{x^4+8x^2+15}$ into partial fractions.

(a) $\frac{3}{2(x^2+3)}+\frac{5}{2(x^2+5)}$ (b) $\frac{3}{2(x^2-3)}+\frac{5}{2(x^2+5)}$

(c) $\frac{-3}{2(x^2+3)}+\frac{7}{2(x^2+5)}$ (d) $\frac{7}{2(x^2+3)}-\frac{3}{2(x^2+5)}$

30. Resolve $\frac{3x+1}{(x-1)^2}$ into partial fractions.

(a) $\frac{4}{(x-1)}-\frac{3}{(x-1)^2}$ (b) $\frac{3}{(x-1)}-\frac{4}{(x-1)^2}$

(c) $\frac{3}{(x-1)^2}-\frac{3}{(x-1)^2}$ (d) $\frac{3}{(x-1)}+\frac{4}{(x-1)^2}$

31. If $\frac{3x^2+14x+10}{x^2(x+2)}=\frac{A}{x}+\frac{B}{x^2}+\frac{C}{x+2}$, then A, B and C, respectively, are ______.

(a) $\frac{9}{2}, -5, \frac{3}{2}$ (b) $\frac{9}{2}, 5, \frac{-3}{2}$

(c) $\frac{9}{2}, \frac{3}{2}, -5$ (d) $\frac{-9}{2}, \frac{-3}{2}, 5$

32. If $\frac{2x-1}{(x+1)(x^2-1)}=\frac{A}{x-1}+\frac{B}{x+1}+\frac{C}{(x+1)^2}$, then A, B, C, respectively, are ______.

(a) $\frac{1}{4}, \frac{-1}{4}, \frac{3}{2}$ (b) $\frac{1}{4}, \frac{1}{4}, \frac{3}{2}$

(c) $\frac{1}{4}, \frac{-5}{2}, \frac{5}{4}$ (d) $\frac{1}{4}, \frac{5}{2}, \frac{5}{4}$

33. Resolve $\frac{ax-b}{(x+1)^2}$ into partial fractions.

(a) $\frac{a}{x+1}+\frac{a+b}{(x+1)^2}$ (b) $\frac{a}{x+1}+\frac{a-b}{(x+1)^2}$

(c) $\frac{a}{x+1}-\frac{a-b}{(x+1)^2}$ (d) $\frac{a}{x+1}-\frac{a+b}{(x+1)^2}$

34. Resolve $\frac{4x^2+3x+2}{(x-4)^3}$ into partial fractions.

(a) $\frac{25}{4(x-4)}+\frac{59}{2(x-4)}+\frac{78}{(x-4)^3}$

(b) $\frac{25}{4(x-4)}-\frac{69}{2(x-4)^2}+\frac{78}{(x-4)^3}$

(c) $\frac{35}{4(x-4)}+\frac{69}{2(x-4)^2}+\frac{78}{(x-4)^3}$

(d) $\frac{4}{x-4}+\frac{35}{(x-4)^2}+\frac{78}{(x-4)^3}$

35. Resolve $\dfrac{1}{x^2-7x-18}$ into partial fractions.

(a) $\dfrac{1}{11}\left(\dfrac{1}{x-9}-\dfrac{1}{x+2}\right)$ (b) $\dfrac{1}{11}\left(\dfrac{1}{x-9}+\dfrac{1}{x+2}\right)$

(c) $\dfrac{1}{11}\left(\dfrac{1}{x+9}-\dfrac{1}{x-2}\right)$ (d) $\dfrac{1}{11}\left(\dfrac{1}{x+9}+\dfrac{1}{x+2}\right)$

36. Resolve $\dfrac{10}{x^2-25}$ into partial fractions.

(a) $\dfrac{1}{x-5}-\dfrac{1}{x+5}$ (b) $\dfrac{1}{x-5}+\dfrac{2}{x+5}$

(c) $\dfrac{1}{x+5}+\dfrac{1}{x-5}$ (d) $\dfrac{1}{x-5}-\dfrac{2}{x+5}$

37. Resolve $\dfrac{2x}{3(x-1)(x-3)}$ into partial fractions.

(a) $\dfrac{1}{x+3}-\dfrac{1}{3(x+1)}$ (b) $\dfrac{1}{x-3}-\dfrac{1}{x+1}$

(c) $\dfrac{1}{x-3}-\dfrac{1}{3(x-1)}$ (d) $\dfrac{1}{x-3}-\dfrac{2}{3(x-1)}$

38. If $\dfrac{x}{(x+2)(x+3)}=\dfrac{A}{x+3}+\dfrac{B}{x+2}$, then $A-B$ is = ______.

(a) 4 (b) 5

(c) −6 (d) 2

39. Resolve $\dfrac{5}{(x+2)(x+3)}$ into partial fractions.

(a) $5\left(\dfrac{1}{x+2}+\dfrac{1}{x+3}\right)$ (b) $5\left(\dfrac{1}{x+2}-\dfrac{1}{x+3}\right)$

(c) $10\left(\dfrac{1}{x+2}-\dfrac{1}{x+3}\right)$ (d) $10\left(\dfrac{1}{x+2}+\dfrac{1}{x+3}\right)$

40. Resolve $\dfrac{1}{x^2-7x+12}$ into partial fractions.

(a) $\dfrac{1}{x-4}-\dfrac{1}{x-3}$ (b) $\dfrac{1}{x-3}+\dfrac{1}{x-4}$

(c) $\dfrac{2}{x-4}-\dfrac{1}{x-3}$ (d) $\dfrac{1}{x+3}-\dfrac{1}{x+4}$

Level 3: Assess Your Concepts

41. Resolve $\dfrac{1}{x^4-3x^2-4}$ into partial fractions.

(a) $\dfrac{1}{5(x^2-4)}+\dfrac{1}{5(x^2+1)}$ (b) $\dfrac{1}{5(x^2-4)}-\dfrac{1}{5(x^2+1)}$

(c) $\dfrac{1}{4(x^2+4)}-\dfrac{1}{4(x^2+1)}$ (d) $\dfrac{1}{4(x^2+4)}+\dfrac{1}{4(x^2+1)}$

42. Resolve $\dfrac{4x+3}{x^3-7x-6}$ into partial fractions.

(a) $\dfrac{1}{4(x+1)}+\dfrac{3}{4(x-3)}-\dfrac{1}{(x+2)}$

(b) $\dfrac{-1}{4(x+1)}+\dfrac{3}{4(x-3)}+\dfrac{1}{(x+2)}$

(c) $\dfrac{1}{4(x+1)}-\dfrac{3}{4(x-3)}+\dfrac{1}{(x+2)}$

(d) $\dfrac{1}{4(x+1)}-\dfrac{3}{4(x-3)}-\dfrac{1}{x+2}$

43. If $\dfrac{1}{(a^2-bx)(b^2-ax)}=\dfrac{A}{a^2-bx}+\dfrac{B}{b^2-ax}$, then the value of A and B respectively would be ______.

(a) $\dfrac{b}{b^3-a^3},\dfrac{a}{b^3-a^3}$ (b) $\dfrac{b}{b^3-a^3},\dfrac{a}{a^3-b^3}$

(c) $\dfrac{b}{a^3-b^3},\dfrac{a}{a^3-b^3}$ (d) $\dfrac{-b}{b^3-a^3},\dfrac{-a}{a^3-b^3}$

44. Resolve $\dfrac{3x-5}{(x-1)^4}$ into partial fractions.

(a) $\dfrac{1}{(x-1)}+\dfrac{2}{(x-1)^2}-\dfrac{3}{(x-1)^3}+\dfrac{4}{(x-1)^4}$

(b) $\dfrac{3}{(x-1)^2}+\dfrac{2}{(x-1)^3}-\dfrac{1}{(x-1)^4}$

(c) $\dfrac{3}{(x-1)^3}+\dfrac{2}{(x-1)^4}$

(d) $\dfrac{3}{(x-1)^3}-\dfrac{2}{(x-1)^4}$

45. Resolve $\dfrac{x^2+x+1}{x^3+1}$ into partial fractions.

(a) $\dfrac{1}{3(x+1)}+\dfrac{x+1}{3(x^2-x+1)}$

(b) $\dfrac{-1}{3(x+1)}+\dfrac{2x+2}{3(x^2-x+1)}$

(c) $\dfrac{1}{3(x+1)}+\dfrac{2x+2}{3(x^2-x+1)}$

(d) None of these

46. Resolve $\frac{2x^2+8x+13}{(x+1)^4}$ into partial fractions.

(a) $\frac{2}{(x+1)^2}+\frac{5}{(x+1)^3}+\frac{7}{(x+1)^4}$

(b) $\frac{1}{(x+1)^2}+\frac{5}{(x+1)^3}+\frac{7}{(x+1)^4}$

(c) $\frac{2}{(x+1)^2}+\frac{4}{(x+1)^3}+\frac{7}{(x+1)^4}$

(d) $\frac{4}{(x+1)^2}+\frac{5}{(x+1)^3}+\frac{7}{(x+1)^4}$

47. Resolve $\frac{6x^2-14x+6}{x(x-1)(x-2)}$ into partial fractions.

(a) $\frac{2}{x}+\frac{3}{x-1}+\frac{1}{x-2}$ (b) $\frac{3}{x}+\frac{2}{x-1}+\frac{1}{x-2}$

(c) $\frac{1}{x}+\frac{2}{x-1}+\frac{3}{x-2}$ (d) $\frac{1}{x}+\frac{3}{x-1}+\frac{2}{x-2}$

48. Resolve $\frac{1}{(x-4)(x^2+3)}$ into partial fractions.

(a) $\frac{1}{19}\left[\frac{1}{x-4}+\frac{x+4}{x^2+3}\right]$ (b) $\frac{1}{19}\left[\frac{1}{x-4}+\frac{x+3}{x^2+3}\right]$

(c) $\frac{1}{19}\left[\frac{1}{x-4}+\frac{x+3}{x^2+3}\right]$ (d) $\frac{1}{19}\left[\frac{1}{x-4}-\frac{x+4}{x^2+3}\right]$

49. Resolve $\frac{3x^2+7}{x^4-3x^2+2}$ into partial fractions.

(a) $\frac{10}{x^2-2}+\frac{5}{x-1}-\frac{5}{x+1}$ (b) $\frac{13}{x^2-2}+\frac{5}{x+1}-\frac{5}{x-1}$

(c) $\frac{5}{x^2-2}-\frac{10}{x-1}+\frac{10}{x+1}$ (d) $\frac{5}{x-1}-\frac{5}{x+1}-\frac{13}{x^2-2}$

50. If $\frac{4x^2+5x+6}{x^2(x+3)}=\frac{A}{x}+\frac{B}{x^2}+\frac{C}{x+3}$, then $2A+3B+4C=$ ______.

(a) 10 (b) 20

(c) 30 (d) 40

AT

ANSWER KEYS

Classroom Wing

Very Short Answer Type Questions

1. Four
2. Zero or 1
3. 2
4. -1
5. 6
6. $x+1$
7. Zero
8. Zero
9. $\dfrac{b^2}{b-a}$
10. 2

Short Answer Type Questions

11. $\dfrac{1}{2a(x-a)}-\dfrac{1}{2a(x+a)}$
12. $\dfrac{3}{x+1}-\dfrac{1}{x+2}$
13. $\dfrac{8}{7(x+4)}+\dfrac{13}{7(x-3)}$
14. $\dfrac{2}{x-2}+\dfrac{13}{(x-2)^2}+\dfrac{36}{(x-2)^3}$
15. $\dfrac{-1}{8(x+2)}+\dfrac{\frac{1}{8}x+\frac{3}{4}}{x^2+4}$
16. $A=2$, $B=7$ and $C=-4$
17. (A) $A=1$ and $B=6$ (B) $\dfrac{p-q}{x+1}+\dfrac{p+q}{(x+1)^2}$
18. $\dfrac{a}{(x-1)}+\dfrac{a+b}{(x-1)^2}$
19. $\dfrac{3}{x}-\dfrac{1}{(x-1)}+\dfrac{2}{(x-2)^2}$
20. $\dfrac{3}{2(x-3)}-\dfrac{1}{2(x+1)}$
21. $\dfrac{-1}{(x+1)}+\dfrac{1}{(x+2)}$
22. $\dfrac{2}{(x-1)}+\dfrac{(-2x+1)}{(x^2-x+1)}$
23. $\dfrac{2}{3(x^2+1)}+\dfrac{4}{3(x^2+4)}$
24. $\dfrac{\frac{-3x}{2}+\frac{5}{2}}{x^2-x+1}+\dfrac{\frac{3}{2}x+\frac{1}{2}}{x^2+x+1}$
25. (A) $\dfrac{1}{x}-\dfrac{1}{3(x+1)}+\dfrac{\frac{-2}{3}x+\frac{1}{3}}{x^2-x+1}$ (B) $3-\dfrac{3}{3x+1}+\dfrac{2}{x-1}$

Essay Type Questions

26. $\dfrac{9}{2}(x+2)-\dfrac{20}{(x+3)}+\dfrac{37}{2(x+4)}$
27. $\dfrac{-1}{8(x+2)}+\dfrac{\left(\frac{x}{8}+\frac{3}{4}\right)}{x^2+4}$
28. $\dfrac{1}{(x-2)}-\dfrac{x+1}{(x^2+2x+2)}$
29. (A) $\dfrac{1}{3(x-2)}+\dfrac{1}{(x-1)}-\dfrac{1}{3(x+1)}$ (B) $\dfrac{5}{2x+3}+\dfrac{4}{x+2}$
30. $x^2+4+\dfrac{17}{4(x-2)}-\dfrac{17}{4(x+2)}$
31. $\dfrac{3}{x-1}+\dfrac{2}{(x-1)^2}+\dfrac{1}{(x-1)^3}$
32. $\dfrac{1}{(x+2)^2}+\dfrac{2}{x+3}$

Competition Wing

Level 1: Apply Your Concepts

1. Greater
2. Sum
3. Two terms
4. Smaller
5. Partial fractions
6. (c)
7. (a)
8. (c)
9. (d)
10. (d)
11. (d)
12. (a)
13. (d)
14. (a)

15. (a)	16. (d)	17. (b)	18. (c)	19. (a)
20. (b)				

Level 2: Review Your Concepts

21. (c)	22. (c)	23. (b)	24. (c)	25. (d)
26. (a)	27. (d)	28. (c)	29. (c)	30. (d)
31. (b)	32. (a)	33. (d)	34. (d)	35. (a)
36. (a)	37. (c)	38. (b)	39. (b)	40. (a)

Level 3: Assess Your Concepts

41. (b)	42. (a)	43. (b)	44. (d)	45. (c)
46. (c)	47. (b)	48. (d)	49. (b)	50. (b)

Hints and Explanations

Classroom Wing

Very Short Answer Type Questions

1. Four
2. Zero or 1
3. 2 as it's a proper fraction and denominator is 3.
4. $(2x-3)(x+1)(x^2+x+6)A = x^2-2x-9$

$2x^2+2x-3x-3+(x^2+x+6)A = x^2-2x-9$

$x^2+x+6+(x^2+x+6)A = 1$

$(x^2+x+6)+(x^2+x+6)A = 1$

$(x^2+x+6)[A+1] = 1$

$\Rightarrow A = -1$

5. $\dfrac{3x^2+4}{(x-1)^3} = \dfrac{3}{x-1} + \dfrac{A}{(x-1)^2} + \dfrac{7}{(x-1)^3}$

$\dfrac{3x^2+4}{\cancel{(x-1)^3}} = \dfrac{3(x-1)^2 + A(x-1) + 7}{\cancel{(x-1)^3}}$

$3x^2+4 = 3[x^2+1-2x] + Ax - A + 7$

$\cancel{3x^2}+4 = \cancel{3x^2}+3-6x+Ax-A+7$

$1 = Ax-6x-A+6+1$

$(A-6)(x-1) = 0$

$A-6 = 0$

$A = 6$

6. $\dfrac{f(x)}{x^2-x+1} - \dfrac{1}{f(x)} = \dfrac{3x}{x^3+1}$

$\dfrac{[f(x)]^2 - (x^2-x+1)}{f(x)[x^2-x+1]} = \dfrac{3x}{x^3+1}$

$\therefore f(x) = \dfrac{x^3+1}{(x^2-x+1)} = \dfrac{(x+1)\cancel{(x^2+1-x)}}{\cancel{x^2+1-x}}$

$$\begin{array}{r|l} & x+1 \\ \hline x^2-x+1 & x^3+1 \\ & x^3 - x^2 + x \\ & \;\;\; + \;\;\;\; - \\ \hline & x^2+1-x \\ & x^2+1-x \\ \hline & 0 \end{array}$$

Then, $A = (x+1)$

7. $\dfrac{ax^2+bx+c}{(x+1)(x^2+3x-4)} = \dfrac{f(x)}{x+1} + \dfrac{g(x)}{x+4} + \dfrac{h(x)}{x-1}$

$= \dfrac{f(x)[x^2-x+4x-4] + g(x)(x^2-1) + h(x)[x^2+4x+x+4]}{(x+1)[x^2-x+4x-4]}$

$= \dfrac{f(x)[x^2+3x-4] + g(x)[x^2-1] + h(x)[x^2+5x+4]}{(x+1)[x^2+3x-4]}$

Now, degree of $f(x)$, $g(x)$ and $h(x)$ have to be zero since degree requirements are already satisfied.

8. $\dfrac{2x^2+3x+4}{(x+2)^4} = \dfrac{A}{(x+2)} + \dfrac{2}{(x+2)^2} - \dfrac{5}{(x+2)^3} + \dfrac{6}{(x+2)^4}$

$\dfrac{2x^2+3x+4}{(x+2)^4} = \dfrac{A(x+2)^3 + 2(x+2)^2 - 5(x+2) + 6}{(x+2)^4}$

$2x^2+3x+4 = A(x+2)^3 + 2(x+2)^2 - 5(x+2) + 6$

$A = 0$

9. $\dfrac{x^2}{(x-a)(x-b)} = 1 + \dfrac{a^2}{(a-b)(x-a)} + \dfrac{B}{(x-b)}$

$= \dfrac{(a-b)(x-a)(x-b) + a^2(x-b) + B(a-b)(x-a)}{(a-b)(x-a)(x-b)}$

$\Rightarrow \dfrac{x^2}{\cancel{(x-a)}\cancel{(x-b)}}$

$= \dfrac{(a-b)(x-a)(x-b) + a^2(x-b) + B(a-b)(x-a)}{(a-b)\cancel{(x-a)}\cancel{(x-b)}}$

$\Rightarrow x^2(a-b) = (a-b)(x-a)(x-b) + a^2(x-b)$
$\quad + B(a-b)(x-a)$

$x^2(a-b) = (a-b)\left[(x-a)(x-b) + \dfrac{a^2(x-b)}{(a-b)} + B(x-a)\right]$

$\cancel{x^2} = \cancel{x^2} - xb - ax + ab + \dfrac{a^2(x-b)}{a-b} + Bx - Ba$

$0 = -xb(a-b) - ax(a-b) + ab(a-b) + a^2(x-b)$
$\quad + Bx(a-b) - Ba(a-b)$

$$0 = -axb + xb^2 - a^2x + axb + \cancel{a^2b} - ab^2 + a^2x$$
$$- \cancel{a^2b} + Bxa - Bxb - Ba^2 + Bab$$

$$0 = x\begin{bmatrix} -\cancel{ab} + b^2 - \cancel{a^2} + \cancel{ab} + \cancel{a^2} \\ + aB - Bb - ab^2 - Ba^2 + Bab \end{bmatrix}$$

$$aB - Bb + b^2 = 0$$

$$B(a-b) = -b^2$$

10. $B = \frac{-b^2}{(x+a)(b x+b2)\,a} = \frac{b^2}{} = f(x) + \frac{A}{x+1} + \frac{B}{x+2}$

$$\Rightarrow \frac{x^4}{\cancel{(x+1)}\ \cancel{(x+2)}}$$

$$= \frac{f(x)(x+1)(x+2) + A(x+2) + B(x+1)}{\cancel{(x+1)}\ \cancel{(x+2)}}$$

$$\Rightarrow x^4 = f(x)\left(x^2 + 2x + x + 2\right) + A(x+2) + B(x+1)$$

$\therefore$ The degree of the polynomial $f(x)$ is Two

Short Answer Type Questions

11. $\frac{1}{x^2 - a^2}$

Denominator has 2 linear, non -repeated factors

$$\therefore \frac{1}{x^2 - a^2} = \frac{1}{(x-a)(x+a)}$$

let $\frac{1}{(x-a)(x+a)} = \frac{A}{(x-a)} + \frac{B}{(x+a)}$

$$1 = A(x+a) + B(x-a) \qquad (1)$$

put $x = +a$

$$1 = A(a+a) + B(a-a)$$

$$1 = A(2a)$$

$$A = \frac{1}{2a}$$

Comparing the constant terms,

$$1 = Aa - Ba$$

$$1 = a(A - B) \Rightarrow \frac{1}{a} = \frac{1}{2a} - B$$

$$B = \frac{1}{2a} - \frac{1}{a} = \frac{1-2}{2a} = \frac{-1}{2a}$$

$$\frac{1}{(x-a)(x+a)} = \frac{1}{2a(x-a)} + \frac{(-1/2a)}{(x+a)}$$

$$= \frac{1}{2a(x-a)} - \frac{1}{2a(x+a)}$$

12. $\frac{2x+5}{x^2+3x+2} = \frac{2x+5}{x^2+2x+x+2}$

$$= \frac{2x+5}{x(x+2)+1(x+2)}$$

$$= \frac{2x+5}{(x+1)(x+2)}$$

let $\frac{2x+5}{(x+1)(x+2)} = \frac{A}{x+1} + \frac{B}{x+2}$

$$2x + 5 = A(x+2) + B(x+1)$$

put $x = -1$

$$2(-1) + 5 = A(-1+2)$$

$$3 = A$$

Comparing constant terms,

$$5 = 2A + B$$

$$5 = 6 + B \Rightarrow B = -1$$

$$\therefore \frac{3}{(x+1)} - \frac{1}{(x+2)}$$

13. $\frac{3x+4}{x^2+x-12} = \frac{3x+4}{x^2+4x-3x-12}$

$$= \frac{3x+4}{x(x+4)-3(x+4)}$$

$$= \frac{3x+4}{(x-3)(x+4)}$$

Let $\frac{3x+4}{(x-3)(x+4)} = \frac{A}{(x-3)} + \frac{B}{(x+4)}$

$$3x + 4 = A(x+4) + B(x-3)$$

put $x = 3$

$$9 + 4 = 7A \Rightarrow A = \frac{13}{7}$$

Comparing constant terms

$$4 = 4A - 3B$$

$$4 = \frac{52}{7} - 3B \Rightarrow 3B = \frac{52}{7} - 4$$

$$= \frac{52 - 28}{7}$$

$$B = \frac{24}{7 \times 3} = \frac{8}{7}$$

$$\frac{3x+4}{(x-3)(x+4)} = \frac{13}{7(x-3)} + \frac{8}{7(x+4)}$$

14. Let $\dfrac{2x^2+5x+18}{(x-2)^3} = \dfrac{A}{(x-2)} + \dfrac{B}{(x-2)^2} + \dfrac{C}{(x-2)^3}$

$2x^2+5x+18 = A(x-2)^2 + B(x-2) + C$ (1)

$2x^2+5x+18 = A(x^2+4-4x) + B(x-2)$

$= Ax^2 + 4A - 4Ax + Bx - 2B$

$= Ax^2 + (B-4A)x + 4A - 2B + C$

$A = 2$

$B - 4A = 5 \Rightarrow B = 13$

$C + 4A - 2B = 18 \Rightarrow C = 36$

$\therefore = \dfrac{2}{x-2} + \dfrac{13}{(x-2)^2} + \dfrac{36}{(x-2)^3}$

15. $\dfrac{x+1}{(x+2)(x^2+4)}$

Let $\dfrac{(x+1)}{(x+2)(x^2+4)} = \dfrac{A}{(x+2)} + \dfrac{Bx+C}{(x^2+4)}$

$\Rightarrow (x+1) = A(x^2+4) + (Bx+C)(x+2)$ (1)

put $x = -2$

$(-2+1) = A(4+4) + (Bx+C)(-2+2)$

$-1 = 8A$

$\therefore A = \dfrac{-1}{8}$

Put $x = 0$

$1 = A(4) + (C)(2)$

$1 = 4A + 2C$

$2C = 1 - 4\left(\dfrac{-1}{8}\right) \Rightarrow 1 + \dfrac{1}{2} = \dfrac{2+1}{2} = \dfrac{3}{2}$

$C = \dfrac{3}{4}$

Comparing coefficient of x^2 both side,

$0 = A + B \Rightarrow A = -B$

$B = \dfrac{1}{8}$

$\therefore \dfrac{-1}{8(x+2)} + \dfrac{\frac{1}{8}x + \frac{3}{4}}{(x^2+4)}$

16. $\dfrac{2x^2-x-10}{(x-2)^3} = \dfrac{A}{(x-2)} + \dfrac{B}{(x-2)^2} + \dfrac{C}{(x-2)^3}$

$2x^2 - x - 10 = A(x-2)^2 + B(x-2) + C$

Put $x = 2$

$8 - 2 - 10 = C$

$C = -4$

$2x^2 - x - 10 = A(x^2+4-4x) + B(x-2) + C$

$= Ax^2 + 4A - 4Ax + Bx - 2B + C$

$= Ax^2 + x(B-4A) + 4A - 2B + C$

Comparing coefficient of x^2,

$2 = A$

Comparing coefficient of x $-1 = B - 4A$,

$\therefore -1 = B - 4(2)$

$-1 = B - 8$

$B = 8 - 1 = 7$

$\therefore \dfrac{2}{x-2} + \dfrac{7}{(x-2)^2} - \dfrac{4}{(x-2)^3}$

17. (A) $\dfrac{x+5}{(x-1)^2} = \dfrac{A}{(x-1)} + \dfrac{B}{(x-1)^2}$

$x + 5 = A(x-1) + B$ (1)

Put $n = 1$

$6 = B$

$A(x-1) = (x-1)$

$A = 1$

(B) The denominator of given fraction contains repeated linear factors.

Let $\dfrac{px - qx + 2p}{(x+1)^2} = \dfrac{A}{x+1} + \dfrac{B}{(x+1)^2}$.

$\Rightarrow px - qx + 2p = A(x+1) + B$ (1)

Put $x = -1$ in the equation (1).

$\Rightarrow -p + q + 2p = B$.

$\Rightarrow B = p + q$

Comparing the constant terms on both sides of the equation (1), we get

$\Rightarrow 2p = A + B$.

$\Rightarrow 2p = A + p + q$.

$\Rightarrow A = p - q.$

$$\Rightarrow \frac{px - qx + 2p}{(x+1)^2} = \frac{p-q}{x+1} + \frac{p+q}{(x+1)^2}.$$

18. $\dfrac{ax+b}{(x-1)^2} = \dfrac{A}{(x-1)} + \dfrac{B}{(x-1)^2}$

$ax + b = A(x-1) + B$ (1)

Put $x = 1$

$B = a + b$

and $a = A$

Comparing coefficient of x,

$$\therefore = \frac{a}{x-1} + \frac{a+b}{(x-1)^2}$$

19. $\dfrac{2x^2 - 3x + 3}{x^3 - 2x^2 + x} = \dfrac{2x^2 - 3x + 3}{x(x^2 - 2x + 1)}$

$$= \frac{2x^2 - 3x + 3}{x[x^2 - x - x + 1]}$$

$$= \frac{2x^2 - 3x + 3}{x[x(x-1) - 1(x-1)]}$$

$$= \frac{2x^2 - 3x + 3}{x(x-1)(x-1)} = \frac{2x^2 - 3x + 2}{x(x-1)^2}$$

Let $\dfrac{2x^2 - 3x + 3}{x(x-1)^2} = \dfrac{A}{x} + \dfrac{B}{(x-1)} + \dfrac{C}{(x-1)^2}$

$2x^2 - 3x + 3 = A(x-1)^2 + Bx(x-1) + Cx$ (1)

Put $x = 1$

$2 - \not{3} + \not{3} = C$

$\therefore C = 2$

Comparing coefficient of x^2,

$2 = A + B$ (2)

Put $x = 0$

$3 = A$

$\therefore B = 2 - A = -1$

$$\therefore \frac{3}{x} - \frac{1}{(x-1)} + \frac{2}{(x-2)^2}$$

20. $\dfrac{x^2 + 5x + 6}{x^3 - 7x - 6}$

$x^3 - 7x - 6 \Rightarrow x^2(x+1) - x(x+1) - 6(x+1)$

$\therefore (x^2 - x - 6)(x+1)$

$x^2 - x - 6 \Rightarrow x^2 - 3x + 2x - 6$

$= x(x-3) + 2(x-3)$

$\Rightarrow (x+2)(x+3)$

$\therefore (x+2)(x-3)(x+1)$

$x^2 + 5x + 6 \Rightarrow x^2 + 3x + 2x + 6$

$\Rightarrow x(x+3) + 2(x+3)$

$(x+2)(x+3)$

$$\therefore \frac{\cancel{(x+2)}(x+3)}{\cancel{(x+2)}(x-3)(x+1)} = \frac{x+3}{(x-3)(x+1)}$$

$$\therefore \frac{x+3}{(x-3)(x+1)} = \frac{A}{(x-3)} + \frac{B}{(x+1)}$$

$(x+3) = A(x+1) + B(x-3)$

but $x = 3$

$\therefore 6 = 4A$

$$\therefore A = \frac{\overset{3}{\cancel{6}}}{\underset{2}{\cancel{4}}}$$

$$A = \frac{3}{2}$$

Put $x = -1$

$(3-1) = 0(A) + B(-4)$

$$\frac{\cancel{2}}{-\underset{2}{\cancel{4}}} = B$$

$$\therefore B = \frac{1}{-2}$$

$\therefore$ Equation is $\dfrac{3}{2(x-3)} - \dfrac{1}{2(x+1)}$

21. $\dfrac{x^3}{(x+1)(x+2)} = \dfrac{A}{(x+1)} + \dfrac{B}{(x+2)}$

$x^3 = A(x+2) + B(x+1)$

Put $x = -1$

$-1 = A(1) \Rightarrow A = -1$

Comparing coefficient of x,

$0 = A + B \Rightarrow B = 1$

$$\therefore = -\frac{1}{(x+1)} + \frac{1}{(x+2)}$$

22. $\dfrac{x+1}{x^3-1} = \dfrac{x+1}{(x-1)(x^2+1-x)}$

Let $\dfrac{x+1}{(x-1)(x^2+1-x)} = \dfrac{A}{(x-1)} + \dfrac{Bx+C}{x^2+1-x}$

$x+1 = A(x^2+1-x)+(Bx+C)(x-1)$

$x+1 = A(x^2-x+1)+(Bx+C)(x-1)$ (1)

Put $x=1$

$2 = A(1-\not{1}+\not{1}) \Rightarrow A = 2$

Put $x=0$

$1 = A(1)+C(-1)$

$1 = A - C$

$C = A-1 = 2-1 = 1$

Comparing coefficient of x^2,

$0 = A+B$

$B = -2$

$\therefore = \dfrac{2}{(x-1)} + \dfrac{-2x+1}{x^2-x+1}$

23. $\dfrac{2x^2+4}{x^4+5x^2+4} = \dfrac{2x^2+4}{x^4+4x^2+x^2+4}$

$= \dfrac{2x^2+4}{x^2(x^2+4)+1(x^2+4)}$

$= \dfrac{2x^2+4}{(x^2+1)(x^2+4)}$

Let $\dfrac{2x^2+4}{(x^2+1)(x^2+4)} = \dfrac{A}{x^2+1} + \dfrac{B}{x^2+4}$

$\therefore 2x^2+4 = A(x^2+4)+B(x^2+1)$ (1)

Compare $A+B=2,$ (2)

$4 = 4A+B$ (3)

$\therefore\ 4A+B = 4$

$A+B = 2$

$(-)\ (-)\ (-)$

$3A = 2$

$A = \dfrac{2}{3}$

$B = 2-\dfrac{2}{3} = \dfrac{4}{3}$

$\therefore = \dfrac{2}{3(x^2+1)} + \dfrac{4}{3(x^2+4)}$

24. $\dfrac{2x+3}{x^4+x^2+1}$

Take $x^2 = t \Rightarrow x = \sqrt{t}$

$\dfrac{2\sqrt{t}+3}{t^2+t+1}$

Roots $\Rightarrow \dfrac{-1\pm\sqrt{1-4(1)(1)}}{2}$

$= \dfrac{-1\pm\sqrt{-3}}{2}$

$\therefore \dfrac{2\sqrt{t}+3}{t^2+t+1} = \dfrac{A}{(t+2)} + \dfrac{Bx+C}{(t^2+t+1)}$

$2\sqrt{t}+3 = A(t^2+t+1)+(Bx+C)(t+2)$

Put $t=-2$

$2\sqrt{-2}+3 = A(4-2+1)+0$

$2\sqrt{-2}+3 = 3A$

$\therefore A = \dfrac{2\sqrt{-2}+3}{3} = 1+\dfrac{2}{3}\sqrt{-2}$

Put $t=+1$

$2+3 = A(1+1+1)+(Bx+C)(3)$

$5 = 3A+(Bx+C)3$

$\dfrac{5}{3} = A+Bx+C$

$\dfrac{5}{3} = \dfrac{2\sqrt{-2}+3}{3} + Bx+C$

$\therefore B = \dfrac{3}{2} \therefore C = \dfrac{1}{2}$

$\therefore$ Equation $\dfrac{\frac{-3x}{2}+\frac{5}{2}}{x^2-x+1} + \dfrac{\frac{3}{2}x+\frac{1}{2}}{x^2+x+1}$

25. (A) $\dfrac{1}{x^4+x} = \dfrac{1}{x(x^3+1)} = \dfrac{1}{x(x+1)(x^2+1-x)}$

$= \dfrac{1}{x(x+1)(x^2-x+1)}$

$\therefore \dfrac{1}{x(x+1)(x^2-x+1)} = \dfrac{A}{x} + \dfrac{B}{(x+1)} + \dfrac{Cx+D}{(x^2-x+1)}$

$1 = A(x+1)(x^2-x+1)+Bx(x^2-x+1)$
$+(Cx+D)x(x+1)$

(1)

Put $x = -1$

$1 = -B(1+1+1)$

$\therefore 1 = -3B \Rightarrow B = \frac{-1}{3}$

Compare for x^3.

$0 = A + B + C$

Put $x = 0$

$1 = A(0 - 0 + 1) + 0$

$\therefore A = 1$

$\therefore C = -A - B = -1 + \frac{1}{3} = \frac{-3+1}{3} = \frac{-2}{3}$

Compare for constant

$$\therefore \frac{1}{x} - \frac{1}{3(x+1)} + \frac{\frac{-2}{3}x + \frac{1}{3}}{x^2 - x + 1}$$

(B) We can clearly notice that the given fraction is an improper fraction. So, dividing the numerator by the denominator we can express $\frac{9x^2 - 3x + 2}{3x^2 - 2x - 1}$ as $3 + \frac{3x+5}{3x^2 - 2x - 1}$.

$$\frac{3x+5}{3x^2 - 2x - 1} = \frac{3x+5}{(3x+1)(x-1)}.$$

Let $\frac{3x+5}{(3x+1)(x-1)} = \frac{A}{3x+1} + \frac{B}{x-1}$.

$\Rightarrow 3x + 5 = A(x-1) + B(3x+1)$ (1)

Put $x = 1$ in the equation (1).

$\Rightarrow 3 + 5 = A(1-1) + B(3+1)$

$\Rightarrow 8 = 4B$.

$\Rightarrow B = 2$.

Comparing the constant terms on both sides of the equation (1), we get

$5 = -A + B$.

$\Rightarrow A = -3$.

$$\therefore \frac{9x^2 - 3x + 2}{3x^2 - 2x - 1} = 3 + \frac{-3}{3x+1} + \frac{2}{x-1}$$

$$= 3 - \frac{3}{3x+1} + \frac{2}{x-1}.$$

Essay Type Questions

26. $\frac{3x^2 + 4x + 5}{x^3 + 9x^2 + 26x + 24}$

$$= \frac{3x^2 + 4x + 5}{x^2(x+2) + 7x(x+2) + 12(x+2)}$$

$$= \frac{3x^2 + 4x + 5}{(x+2)(x^2 + 7x + 12)}$$

$$= \frac{3x^2 + 4x + 5}{(x+2)(x^2 + 4x + 3x + 12)}$$

$$= \frac{3x^2 + 4x + 5}{(x+2)[x(x+4) + 3(x+4)]}$$

$$= \frac{3x^2 + 4x + 5}{(x+2)(x+3)(x+4)}$$

Let $\frac{3x^2 + 4x + 5}{(x+2)(x+3)(x+4)}$

$$= \frac{A}{(x+2)} + \frac{B}{(x+3)} + \frac{C}{x+4}$$

$$3x^2 + 4x + 5 = A(x+3)(x+4) + B(x+2)(x+4) + C(x+2)(x+3)$$

Put $x = -2$

$12 - 8 + 5 = A(1)(2)$

$2A = 9 \Rightarrow A = \frac{9}{2}$

Put $x = -3$

$27 - 12 + 5 = -B$

$B = -20$

Put $x = -4$

$48 - 16 + 5 = C(-2)(-1)$

$\frac{37}{2} = C$

$$\therefore = \frac{9}{2(x+2)} - \frac{20}{(x+3)} + \frac{37}{2(x+4)}$$

27. $\frac{x+1}{(x+2)(x^2+4)}$

Let $\frac{(x+1)}{(x+2)(x^2+4)} = \frac{A}{(x+2)} + \frac{Bx + C}{(x^2+4)}$

$\Rightarrow (x+1) = A(x^2+4) + (Bx+C)(x+2)$ (1)

Put $x = -2$

$\Rightarrow (-2+1) = A(4+4) + (Bx+C)(-2+2)$

$-1 = 8A$

$\therefore A = \frac{-1}{8}$

Put $x = 0$

$1 = A(4) + (C)(2)$

$1 = 4A + 2C$

$2C = 1 - \not{4}\left(\frac{-1}{\not{8}_2}\right) \Rightarrow 1 + \frac{1}{2} = \frac{2+1}{2} = \frac{3}{2}$

$C = \frac{3}{4}$

Comparing coefficient of x^2 both ends,

$0 = A + B \Rightarrow A = -B$

$B = \frac{1}{8}$

$= \frac{-1}{8(x+2)} + \frac{\frac{1}{8}x + \frac{3}{4}}{(x^2+4)}$

28. $\frac{3x+4}{x^3-2x-4} = \frac{3x+4}{x^2(x-2)+2x(x-2)+2(x-2)}$

$= \frac{3x+4}{(x-2)(x^2+2x+2)}$

Let $\frac{3x+4}{(x-2)(x^2+2x+2)} = \frac{A}{(x-2)} + \frac{Bx+C}{x^2+2x+2}$

$3x+4 = A(x^2+2x+2) + (Bx+C)(x-2)$

Put $x = 2$

$10 = (4+4+2)A$

$A = 1$

$4 = 2A - 2C$

$\therefore A - C = 2 \Rightarrow C = 1 - 2 = -1$

$3 = 2A - 2B + C \Rightarrow 3 = 2 - 2B - 1$

$-2B = 2$

$\therefore B = -1$

$= \frac{1}{x-2} + \frac{-x-1}{x^2+2x+2}$

29. (A)

$\frac{x^2-3}{x^3-2x^2-x+2} = \frac{x^2-3}{x^2(x-1)-x(x-1)-2(x-1)}$

$= \frac{x^3-3}{(x^2-x-2)(x-1)}$

$= \frac{x^2-3}{(x^2-2x+x-2)(x-1)}$

$= \frac{x^2-3}{[x(x-2)+1(x-2)](x-1)}$

$= \frac{x^2-3}{(x-2)(x+1)(x-1)}$

Let $\frac{x^2-3}{(x+1)(x-1)(x-2)} = \frac{A}{(x+1)} + \frac{B}{(x-1)} + \frac{C}{x-2}$

$x^2 - 3 = A(x-1)(x-2)$
$\quad + B(x+1)(x-2) + C(x+1)(x-1)$

Put $x = 1$

$1 - 3 = B(2)(-1) \Rightarrow -\not{2} = -\not{2}B$

$B = 1$

Put $x = 2$

$4 - 3 = C(3)(1) \Rightarrow C = \frac{1}{3}$

Put $x = -1$

$1 - 3 = A(-2)(+3) \Rightarrow A = \frac{-2}{3} = -\frac{1}{3}$

$\therefore -\frac{1}{3(x+1)} + \frac{1}{(x-1)} + \frac{1}{3(x-2)}$

(B) In the given fraction, the denominator has two linear, non-repeated factors.

$\therefore$ The given fraction can be written as the sum of two partial fractions.

Let $\frac{13x+22}{(2x+3)(x+2)} = \frac{A}{2x+3} + \frac{B}{x+2}$

$\Rightarrow 13x + 22 = A(x+2) + B(2x+3)$ (1)

Put $x = -2$ in the equation (1).

$\Rightarrow 13(-2) + 22 = A(-2+2) + B(2(-2)+3)$

$\Rightarrow -4 = -B$

$\Rightarrow B = 4$

Comparing the constant terms on both sides of the equation (1), we get

$22 = 2A + 3B.$

$\Rightarrow 22 = 2A + 3(4).$

$\Rightarrow A = 5.$

$$\therefore \frac{13x+22}{(2x+3)(x+2)} = \frac{5}{2x+3} + \frac{4}{x+2}.$$

30. $\dfrac{x^4+1}{(x-2)(x+2)} = \dfrac{x^4+1}{x^2-4}$

$$\begin{array}{r|l} & x^2+4 \\ \hline x^2-4 & x^4+1 \\ & x^4-4x^2 \\ & -\quad + \\ \hline & 4x^2+1 \\ & 4x^2-16 \\ & -\quad + \\ \hline & 17 \end{array}$$

$$(x^2+4)\frac{17}{x^2-4}$$

$$\therefore (x^2+4) + \frac{17}{(x^2-4)}$$

Now solve for $\dfrac{17}{x^2-4}$

$$= \frac{17}{(x-2)(x+2)}$$

$$\therefore \frac{17}{(x-2)(x+2)} = \frac{A}{(x-2)} + \frac{B}{(x+2)}$$

$17 = A(x+2) + B(x-2)$

Put $x = -2$

$17 = B(-4)$

$\therefore B = \dfrac{-17}{4}$

Put $x = 2$

$17 = A(4) + 0$

$A = \dfrac{17}{4}$

$$\therefore (x^2+4) + \frac{17}{4(x-2)} - \frac{17}{4(x+2)}$$

31. The denominator of given fraction contains repeated linear factors.

Let $\dfrac{3x^2-4x+2}{(x-1)^3} = \dfrac{A}{x-1} + \dfrac{B}{(x-1)^2} + \dfrac{C}{(x-1)^3}.$

$\Rightarrow 3x^2-4x+2 = A(x-1)^2 + B(x-1) + C \quad (1)$

Put $x = 1$ in the equation (1).

$\Rightarrow 3-4+2 = C.$

$\Rightarrow C = 1.$

Put $x = 2$ in the equation (1).

$\Rightarrow 6 = A+B+C.$

$\Rightarrow A+B = 5 \quad (2)$

Comparing the constant terms on both sides of the equation (1), we get

$\Rightarrow 2 = A-B+C.$

$\Rightarrow A-B = 1 \quad (3)$

Solving the equations (2) and (3) we get $A = 3$ and $B = 2$.

Let $\dfrac{3x^2-4x+2}{(x-1)^3} = \dfrac{3}{x-1} + \dfrac{2}{(x-1)^2} + \dfrac{1}{(x-1)^3}.$

32. The denominator of given fraction contains some repeated linear factors, and the remaining are non-repeated linear factors.

Let $\dfrac{2x^2+9x+11}{(x+2)^2(x+3)} = \dfrac{A}{x+2} + \dfrac{B}{(x+2)^2} + \dfrac{C}{x+3}.$

$\Rightarrow 2x^2+9x+11 = A(x+2)(x+3)$
$\quad + B(x+3) + C(x+2)^2 \quad (1)$

Put $x = -2$ in the equation (1).

$\Rightarrow 2(-2)^2 + 9(-2) + 11$
$\quad = A(-2+2)(-2+3) + B(-2+3) + C(-2+2)^2$

$\Rightarrow 8 - 18 + 11 = B$

$\Rightarrow B = 1.$

Put $x = -3$ in the equation (1).

$\Rightarrow 2(-3)^2 + 9(-3) + 11$
$\quad = A(-3+2)(-3+3) + B(-3+3) + C(-3+2)^2$

$\Rightarrow 18 - 27 + 11 = C$

$\Rightarrow C = 2.$

Comparing the constant terms on both sides of the equation (1), we get

$11 = 6A + 3B + 4C.$

$\Rightarrow 11 = 6A + 3(1) + 4(2).$

$\Rightarrow A = 0.$

$$\frac{2x^2+9x+11}{(x+2)^2(x+3)} = \frac{1}{(x+2)^2} + \frac{2}{x+3}.$$

Competition Wing

Level 1: Apply Your Concepts

1. Greater
2. Sum
3. Two terms
4. Smaller
5. Partial fraction
6. $\frac{1}{x^2-9} = \frac{A}{x-3} + \frac{B}{x+3}$.
7. $\frac{2x+3}{x^2-6x+5} = \frac{A}{(x-5)} + \frac{B}{(x-1)}$.
8. $\frac{x^2+x+1}{(x-1)^3} = \frac{A}{x-1} + \frac{B}{(x-1)^2} + \frac{C}{(x-1)^3}$.
9. $\frac{3x+2}{x^2+5x+6} = \frac{A}{x+2} + \frac{B}{x+3}$.
10. $\frac{1}{x^2+x-42} = \frac{A}{x+7} + \frac{B}{x-6}$.
11. $\frac{x^2+4x+6}{(x^2-1)(x+3)} = \frac{A}{x-1} + \frac{B}{x+1} + \frac{C}{x+3}$.
12. $\frac{x+1}{x(x-1)(x+3)} = \frac{A}{x} + \frac{B}{x-1} + \frac{C}{x+3}$.
13. $\frac{1}{x^2-(a+b)x+ab} = \frac{A}{x-a} + \frac{B}{x-b}$.
14. $\frac{1}{x^2-5x+6} = \frac{A}{x-3} + \frac{B}{x-2}$.
15. $\frac{x+2}{x^2-2x-15} = \frac{A}{x-5} + \frac{B}{x+3}$.
16. $\frac{3x^2+2x+4}{(x-1)(x^2-4)} = \frac{A}{x-1} + \frac{B}{x-2} + \frac{C}{x+2}$.
17. $\frac{2x+1}{x^2-2x-8} = \frac{A}{x-4} + \frac{B}{x+2}$.
18. $\frac{2x^2+3x+18}{(x-2)(x+2)^2} = \frac{A}{x-2} + \frac{B}{x+2} + \frac{C}{(x+2)^2}$.
19. Split the denominator into factors and use the relevant method to find its partial fractions.
20. (i) $x^3 - 3x^2 + 2x = x(x-1)(x-2)$.

    (ii) $\frac{x-1}{(x^3-3x^2+2x)} = \frac{A}{x} + \frac{B}{x-1} + \frac{C}{x-2}$.

Level 2: Review Your Concepts

21. $\frac{x-b}{x^2+(a+b)x+ab} = \frac{A}{x+a} + \frac{B}{x+b}$.
22. $\frac{x+1}{x^2-4} = \frac{A}{x+2} + \frac{B}{x-2}$.
23. $\frac{x}{(x+1)(x-1)^2} = \frac{A}{x+1} + \frac{B}{x-1} + \frac{C}{(x-1)^2}$.
24. $\frac{3x-5}{x^2+3x+2} = \frac{A}{x+1} + \frac{B}{x+2}$.
25. $\frac{3x+5}{x^2+8x-20} = \frac{A}{x+10} + \frac{B}{x-2}$.
26. $\frac{ax+b^2}{x^2-(a+b)^2} = \frac{A}{x-(a+b)} + \frac{B}{x+(a+b)}$.
27. (i) Simplify LHS and RHS.
    (ii) Put $x = 0$ and 1 and obtain the values of a and b.
    (iii) Compare the like terms and obtain the values of c and d.
28. (i) Simplify LHS and RHS by taking LCM.
    (ii) Compare the like terms and obtain the required values.
29. $\frac{2x^2+3}{x^4+8x^2+15} = \frac{Ax+B}{x^2+5} + \frac{Cx+D}{x^2+3}$.
30. $\frac{3x+1}{(x-1)^2} = \frac{A}{x-1} + \frac{B}{(x-1)^2}$.
31. (i) Simplify LHS and RHS by taking LCM.
    (ii) Put $x = 0$ and -2 and obtain the values of A and B.
    (iii) Compare the like terms and obtain the value of C.
32. (i) Simplify LHS and RHS by taking LCM.
    (ii) Compare the like terms and obtain the required values.
33. $\frac{ax-b}{(x+1)^2} = \frac{A}{x+1} + \frac{B}{(x+1)^2}$.
34. $\frac{4x^2+3x+2}{(x-4)^3} = \frac{A}{x-4} + \frac{B}{(x-4)^2} + \frac{C}{(x-4)^3}$.
35. $\frac{1}{x^2-7x-18} = \frac{A}{x-9} + \frac{B}{x+2}$.
36. Let $\frac{10}{x^2-25} = \frac{A}{x-5} + \frac{B}{x+5}$

    $\frac{10}{x^2-25} = \frac{A(x+5)+B(x-5)}{(x-5)(x+5)}$.

Consider, $A(x+5)+B(x-5)=10$

Put $x=5$, $10A=10 \Rightarrow A=1$

Put $x=-5$, $-10B=10 \Rightarrow B=-1$

$$\therefore \frac{10}{x^2-5}=\frac{1}{x-5}-\frac{1}{x+5}.$$

37. Let $\dfrac{\frac{2x}{3}}{(x-1)(x-3)}=\dfrac{A}{(x-1)}+\dfrac{B}{(x-3)}$

$$\frac{\frac{2x}{3}}{(x-1)(x-3)}=\frac{A(x-3)+B(x-1)}{(x-1)(x-3)}.$$

Consider, $A(x-3)+B(x-1)=\dfrac{2x}{3}$

Put $x=3$, $2B=2 \Rightarrow B=1$.

Put $x=1$, $-2A=\dfrac{2}{3} \Rightarrow A=-\dfrac{1}{3}$.

$$\therefore \frac{2x}{3(x-1)(x-3)}=\frac{1}{x-3}-\frac{1}{3(x-1)}.$$

38. Let $\dfrac{x}{(x+2)(x+3)}=\dfrac{A}{x+3}+\dfrac{B}{x+2}$

$$\frac{x}{(x+2)(x+3)}=\frac{A(x+2)+B(x+3)}{(x+2)(x+3)}.$$

Consider $A(x+2)+B(x+3)=x$

Put $x=-3$, $-A=-3 \Rightarrow A=3$

Put $x=-2$, $B=-2$.

$\therefore A-B=3-(-2)=3+2=5.$

39. Let $\dfrac{5}{(x+2)(x+3)}=\dfrac{A}{(x+2)}+\dfrac{B}{(x+3)}$

$$\frac{5}{(x+2)(x+3)}=\frac{A(x+3)+B(x+2)}{(x+2)(x+3)}.$$

Consider $A(x+3)+B(x+2)=5$

If $x=-3$, $-B=5 \Rightarrow B=-5$

If $x=-2$, $A=5$.

$$\therefore \frac{5}{(x+2)(x+3)}=\frac{5}{x+2}-\frac{5}{x+3}.$$

40. $\dfrac{1}{x^2-7x+12}=\dfrac{1}{(x-3)(x-4)}$

Let $\dfrac{1}{(x-3)(x-4)}=\dfrac{A}{x-3}+\dfrac{B}{x-4}$ (1)

$$\frac{1}{(x-3)(x-4)}=\frac{A(x-4)+B(x-3)}{(x-3)(x-4)}.$$

Consider, $A(x-4)+B(x-3)=1$

Put $x=4$, we get $B=1$

Put $x=3$, we get $-A=1$

$\Rightarrow A=-1.$

Substitute these values in Eq. (1), we get,

$$\frac{1}{(x-3)(x-4)}=\frac{1}{x-4}-\frac{1}{x-3}.$$

Level 3: Assess Your Concepts

41. $\dfrac{1}{x^4-3x^2-4}=\dfrac{Ax+B}{x^2-4}+\dfrac{Cx+D}{x^2+1}.$

42. (i) Use $x^3-7x-6=(x+1)(x+2)(x-3)$.

(ii) $\dfrac{4x+3}{x^3-7x-6}=\dfrac{A}{x+1}+\dfrac{B}{x+2}+\dfrac{C}{x-3}.$

43. (i) Simplify LHS and RHS by taking LCM.

(ii) Compare the like terms and obtain the required values.

44. $\dfrac{3x-5}{(x-1)^4}=\dfrac{A}{x-1}+\dfrac{B}{(x-1)^2}+\dfrac{C}{(x-1)^3}+\dfrac{D}{(x-1)^4}.$

45. $\dfrac{x^2+x+1}{x^3+1}=\dfrac{A}{x+1}+\dfrac{Bx+C}{x^2-x+1}.$

46. Given, $\dfrac{2x^2+8x+13}{(x+1)^4}$.

Let $y=x+1 \Rightarrow x=y-1$

$$=\frac{2(y-1)^2+8(y-1)+13}{y^4}$$

$$=\frac{2y^2+2-4y+8y-8+13}{y^4}$$

$$=\frac{2y^2+4y+7}{y^4}=\frac{2}{y^2}+\frac{4}{y^3}+\frac{7}{y^4}$$

$$=\frac{2}{(x+1)^2}+\frac{4}{(x+1)^3}+\frac{7}{(x+1)^4}.$$

47. Let $\dfrac{6x^2-14x+6}{x(x-1)(x-2)}=\dfrac{A}{x}+\dfrac{B}{x-1}+\dfrac{C}{x-2}$

$$\frac{6x^2-14x+6}{x(x-1)(x-2)}$$

$$=\frac{A(x-1)(x-2)+Bx(x-2)+Cx(x-1)}{x(x-1)(x-2)}$$

$6x^2 - 14x + 6$

$= A(x-1)(x-2) + Bx(x-2) + C(x-1)x$

Put $x = 1$,

$6 - 14 + 6 = B1(1-2) \Rightarrow -2 = -B$

$\Rightarrow B = 2.$

Put $x = 2$, $6(2)^2 - 14(2) + 6 = C(2-1)(2)$

$2 = 2C$

$1 = C$

Put $x = 0$, $6 = A(-1)(-2) \Rightarrow A = 3$

$$\therefore \frac{6x^2 - 14x + 6}{x(x-1)(x-2)} = \frac{3}{x} + \frac{2}{x-1} + \frac{1}{x-2}.$$

48. $$\frac{1}{(x-4)(x^2+3)} = \frac{A}{x-4} + \frac{Bx+C}{x^2+3}$$

$$\frac{1}{(x-4)(x^2+3)} = \frac{A(x^2+3) + (x-4)(Bx+C)}{(x-4)(x^2+3)}$$

Consider, $Ax^2 + 3A + Bx^2 + Cx - 4Bx - 4C = 1$

$(A + B)x^2 + (C - 4B)x + 3A - 4C = 1$

Comparing the like terms, we get

$A + B = 0$, $C - 4B = 0$ and $(3A - 4C) = 1$

Solving the above equations, we get

$$A = \frac{1}{19}, B = \frac{-1}{19} C = \frac{-4}{19}.$$

$$\therefore \frac{1}{(x-4)(x^2+3)} = \frac{1}{19}\left[\frac{1}{x-4} - \frac{x+4}{x^2+3}\right].$$

49. Let $x^2 = p$, then $\dfrac{3x^2+7}{x^4 - 3x^2 + 2} = \dfrac{3p+7}{p^2 - 3p + 2}$

Let $\dfrac{3p+7}{p^2 - 3p + 2} = \dfrac{A}{p-1} + \dfrac{B}{p-2}$

$$\Rightarrow \frac{3p+7}{(p-1)(p-2)} = \frac{A(p-2) + B(p-1)}{(p-1)(p-2)}$$

Consider,

$3p + 7 = A(p-2) + B(p-1)$

Put $p = 1$, $-A = 10 \Rightarrow A = -10$

$p = 2$, $B = 13$

$$\frac{3p+7}{p^2 - 3p + 2} = \frac{13}{p-2} - \frac{10}{p-1}.$$

But $p = x^2$,

$$\therefore \frac{3x^2+7}{x^4 - 3p^2 + 2} = \frac{13}{x^2-2} - \frac{10}{x^2-1}.$$

$$= \frac{13}{x^2-2} - 5\left[\frac{1}{x-1} - \frac{1}{x+1}\right]$$

$$= \frac{13}{x^2-2} + \frac{5}{x+1} - \frac{5}{x-1}.$$

50. $$\frac{4x^2 + 5x + 6}{x^2(x+3)} = \frac{A}{x} + \frac{B}{x^2} + \frac{C}{x+3}$$

$$\frac{4x^2 + 5x + 6}{x^2(x+3)} = \frac{Ax(x+3) + B(x+3) + Cx^2}{x^2(x+3)}$$

Consider,

$4x^2 + 5x + 6 = A\,x(x+3) + B(x+3) + cx^2$

Put $x = 0$, $6 = 3B \Rightarrow B = 2$

Put $x = -3$, $27 = 9C \Rightarrow C = 3$

Comparing the coefficient of x^2, we have

$A + C = 4 \Rightarrow A = 1.$

$2A + 3B + 4C = 2 + 6 + 12 = 20.$

CHAPTER 20

Logarithm

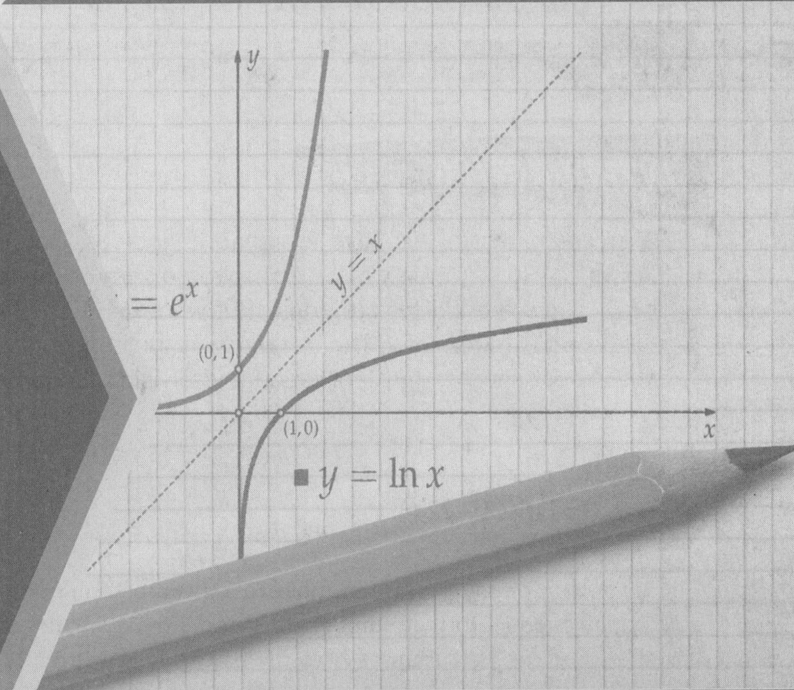

Remember

Before beginning this chapter, you should be able to:

- Define logarithms
- Recall properties of logarithms

Key Ideas

After completing this chapter, you should be able to:

- Study system of logarithms
- Study use of signs for log values
- Find the log of a number to base 10
- Use log tables
- Find the antilog

INTRODUCTION

In earlier classes, we have learnt about indices. One of the results we have learnt, if $2^x = 2^3$, then $x = 3$ and if $4^x = 4^y$, then $x = y$, i.e., if two powers of the same base are equal and the base is not equal to –1, 0 or 1, then the indices are equal. But when $3^x = 5^2$, just by using the knowledge of indices, we cannot find the numerical value of x. The necessity of the concept of logarithms arises here. Logarithms are useful in long calculations involving multiplication and division. Logarithms also useful in the study of Probability, Statistics, Psychology, etc.

Definition

The logarithm of any positive number to a given base (a positive number not equal to 1) is the index of the power of the base which is equal to that number. If N and a ($\neq 1$) are any two positive real numbers and for some real x, $a^x = N$, then x is said to be the logarithm of N to the base a. It is written as $\log_a N = x$, i.e., if $a^x = N$, then $x = \log_a N$.

Examples:

1. $3^4 = 81 \Rightarrow 4 = \log_3 81$
2. $7^3 = 343 \Rightarrow 3 = \log_7 343$
3. $2^5 = 32 \Rightarrow 5 = \log_2 32$
4. $5^4 = 625 \Rightarrow 4 = \log_5 625$
5. $10^2 = 100 \Rightarrow 2 = \log_{10} 100$

In a particular relation, if all the log expressions are to the same base, we normally do not specify the base.

From the definition of log, we get the following results:

When $a > 0$, $b > 0$ and $a \neq 1$,

1. $\log_a a^n = n$, e.g., $\log_6 6^3 = 3$
2. $a^{\log_a b} = b$, e.g., $9^{\log_9 5} = 5$

System of Logarithm

Though we can talk of the logarithm of a number to any positive base as not equal to 1, there are two systems of logarithms, viz., natural logarithms and common logarithms, which are used most often.

1. **Natural logarithm:** These were discovered by Napier. They are calculated to the base 'e', which is approximately equal to 2.7828. These are used in higher mathematics.
2. **Common logarithm:** Logarithms to the base 10 are known as common logarithms. This system was introduced by Briggs, a contemporary of Napier. In the rest of this chapter, we shall use the short form 'log' instead of 'logarithm'.

Properties

1. Logarithms are defined only for positive real numbers.
2. Logarithms are defined only for positive bases (other then 1).
3. In $\log_b a$ neither a is negative nor b is negative but the value of $\log_b a$ can be negative.
   Example: As $10^{-2} = 0.01$, $\log_{10} 0.01 = -2$.

4. Log of different numbers to the same base are different, i.e., if $a \neq b$, then $\log_m a \neq \log_m b$. In other words, if $\log_m a = \log_m b$, then $a = b$.

   Example:
   $\log_{10} 2 \neq \log_{10} 3$
   $\log_{10} 2 = \log_{10} y \Rightarrow y = 2.$

5. Log of the same number to different bases have different values, i.e., if $m \neq n$, then $\log_m a \neq \log_n a$. In other words, if $\log_m a = \log_n a$, then $m = n$.

   Example:
   $\log_2 16 \neq \log_4 16$
   $\log_2 16 = \log_n 16 \Rightarrow n = 2.$

6. Log of 1 to any base is 0.
   Example: $\log_2 1 = 0\ (\because 2^0 = 1)$

7. Log of a number to the same base is 1.
   Example: $\log_4 4 = 1.$

8. Log of 0 is not defined.

Laws

1. $\log_m (ab) = \log_m a + \log_m b$
   Example: $\log 56 = \log(7 \times 8) = \log 7 + \log 8$

2. $\log_m \left(\frac{a}{b}\right) = \log_m a - \log_m b$

   Example: $\log\left(\frac{81}{23}\right) = \log 81 - \log 23$

3. $\log a^m = m \log a$
   Example: $\log 216 = \log 6^3 = 3\log 6$

4. $\log_b a \log_c b = \log_c a$ **[Chain Rule]**
   Example: $\log_2 3 \times \log_8 2 \times \log_5 8 = \log_8 3 \times \log_5 8 = \log_5 3$

5. $\log_b a = \frac{\log_4 a}{\log_4 b}$ *or* $\log_b^a = \frac{\log_c{}^a}{\log_c{}^b}$ **[Change of Base Rule]**

   Example: $\log_9 25 = \frac{\log_4 25}{\log_4 9}$

   In this relation, if we replace b by a, then we get the following result:

   $\log_b a = \frac{1}{\log_a b}$

Variation of $\log_a x$ with x

For $1 < a$ and $0 < p < q$, $\log_a p < \log_a q$.

For $0 < a < 1$ and $0 < p < q$, $\log_a p > \log_a q$.

Example: $\log_{10} 2 < \log_{10} 3$ and $\log_{0.1} 2 > \log_{0.1} 3$

Bases which are greater than 1 are called **strong bases** and bases which are less than 1 are called **weak bases**. Therefore, for strong bases, the log increases with the number and for weak bases, the log decreases with the number.

Sign of $\log_a x$ for Different Values of x and a

Strong Bases ($a > 1$)

1. If $x > 1$, $\log_a x$ is positive.

   For example, $\log_2 8$, $\log_4 81$ are positive.

2. If $0 < x < 1$, then $\log_a x$ is negative.

   For example, $\log_4 0.02 = \dfrac{\log 0.02}{\log 4} = \dfrac{\log 2 - \log 100}{\log 4}$

   $\log 2 < \log 100$ and $0 < \log 4$ for strong bases

   $\therefore \dfrac{\log 2 - \log 100}{\log 4} < 0$

   $\Rightarrow \log_4 0.02$ is negative.

Weak Bases ($0 < a < 1$)

1. If $x > 1$, then $\log_a x$ is negative.

   For example, $\log_{0.3} 15$ and $\log_{0.4} 16$ are negative.

   Consider $\log_{0.3} 15 = \dfrac{\log 15}{\log 0.3} = \dfrac{\log 15}{\log 3 - \log 10}$

   $\log 3 < \log 10$ (for any strong base)

   $\Rightarrow \dfrac{\log 15}{\log 3 - \log 10} < 0.$

2. If $0 < x < 1$, then $\log_a x$ is positive.

   For example, $\log_{0.1} 0.2$, $\log_{0.4} 0.3$ are positive.

Info Bytes!

Log of numbers (>1) to strong bases and numbers (<1) to weak bases are positive.

EXAMPLE 20.1 If $p = \log_{2a} a$, $q = \log_{3a} 2a$ and $r = \log_{4a} 3a$, then find the value of $qr(2 - p)$.

(a) 1 (b) 0 (c) 2 (d) 3

SOLUTION

$qr = \log_{3a} 2a \log_{4a} 3a = \log_{4a} 2a$

$pqr = \log_{2a} a \log_{4a} 2a = \log_{4a} a$

Now $qr(2 - p) = 2qr - pqr$

$= 2\log_{4a} 2a - \log_{4a} a$

$= \log_{4a} 4a^2 - \log_{4a} a$

$= \log_{4a} \dfrac{4a^2}{a} = \log_{4a} 4a = 1.$

EXAMPLE 20.2 If $3x = (0.3)y = 10000$, then find the value of $\dfrac{1}{x} - \dfrac{1}{y}$.

(a) 1 (b) $\dfrac{1}{2}$ (c) $\dfrac{1}{4}$ (d) $\dfrac{1}{3}$

SOLUTION

Given,, $3^x = (0.3)^y = 10000$

$3^x = (0.3)^y = 10^4$

$x = 4 \log_3 10$ and $y = 4 \log_{0.3} 10$

$\frac{1}{x} = \frac{1}{4\log_3 10}$ and $\frac{1}{y} = \frac{1}{4\log_{0.3} 10}$

$\frac{1}{x} = \left(\frac{1}{4}\right)\log_{10} 3$ and $\frac{1}{y} = \left(\frac{1}{4}\right)\log_{10} 0.3$

$$\frac{1}{x} - \frac{1}{y} = \frac{1}{4}[\log_{10} 3 - \log_{10} 0.3]$$

$$= \frac{1}{4}\left[\log_{10}\frac{3}{0.3}\right]$$

$$= \frac{1}{4}[\log_{10} 10]$$

$$\Rightarrow \frac{1}{x} - \frac{1}{y} = \frac{1}{4}.$$

EXAMPLE 20.3 If $(2x)^{\log_{\sqrt{x}} x} = 16$, then find the value of x.

(a) 2 (b) −2 (c) Both (a) and (b) (d) None of these

SOLUTION

$(2x)^{\log_{\sqrt{x}} x} = 16$

$(2x)^{2\log_x x} = 16$

$(2x)^2 = 16$

$4x^2 = 16$

$x^2 = 4$

$x = \pm 2.$

When $x = -2, \log_{\sqrt{x}} x$ is not defined.

$\therefore x = 2.$

EXAMPLE 20.4 Find the value of $3^{\frac{4}{\log_2 9}} + 27^{\frac{1}{\log_{49} 9}} + 81^{\frac{1}{\log_4 3}}$.

(a) 603 (b) 585 (c) 676 (d) 524

SOLUTION

$3^{\frac{4}{\log_2 9}} + 27^{\frac{1}{\log_{49} 9}} + 81^{\frac{1}{\log_4 3}}$

$= 3^{4\log_9 2} + 27^{\log_9 49} + 81^{\log_3 4}$

$= 3^{2\log_3 2} + 3^{3\log_3 7} + 3^{4\log_3 4}$

$= 3^{\log_3 4} + 3^{\log_3 343} + 3^{\log_3 256}$

$= 4 + 343 + 256 = 603.$

EXAMPLE 20.5 If $p \in R$ and $q = \log_x\left(p+\sqrt{p^2+1}\right)$, then find the value of p in terms of x and q.

(a) $\frac{x^q + x^{-q}}{2}$ (b) $\frac{x^q - x^{-q}}{2}$ (c) $x^q + x^{-q}$ (d) $x^q - x^{-q}$

SOLUTION

Given, $q = \log_x\left(p+\sqrt{p^2+1}\right)$

$x^2 = p+\sqrt{p^2+1}$

$\Rightarrow x^{-q} = \frac{1}{x^q} = \frac{1}{p+\sqrt{p^2+1}}$

$= \frac{p-\sqrt{p^2+1}}{\left(p+\sqrt{p^2+1}\right)\left(p-\sqrt{p^2+1}\right)}$

$= \frac{p-\sqrt{p^2+1}}{p^2-(p^2+1)} = -p+\sqrt{p^2+1}$

$\therefore x^q - x^{-q} = p+\sqrt{p^2+1}-\left(\sqrt{p^2+1}-p\right)$

$x^q - x^{-q} = 2p$

$\frac{x^q - x^{-q}}{2} = p.$

To Find the log of a Number to the Base 10

Consider the following numbers:

2, 20, 200, 0.2 and 0.02.

We see that 20 = 10(2) and 200 = 100(2)

$\therefore$ log 20 = 1 + log 2 and log 200 = 2 + log 2.

Similarly, log 0.2 = –1 + log 2 and log 0.02 = –2 + log 2.

From the tables, we see that log 2 = 0.3010. ('Using the tables' is explained in greater detail in later examples).

$\therefore$ log 20 = 1.3010, log 200 = 2.3010, log 0.2 = –1 + 0.3010 and log 0.02 = –2 + 0.3010.

For numbers less than 1, it is convenient to express the log in the standard form. As the negative sign refers only to the integral part, it is written above the integral part, rather than in front, i.e., $\log 0.2 = \bar{1}.3010$ and not –1.3010.

The convenience of the standard form will be clear when we learn how to take the antilog, which will later be explained in detail.

antilog (–0.6090) = antilog (–1 + 0.3010) = antilog $\bar{1}.3010 = 0.2$.

When the logs of numbers are expressed in the standard form (for numbers greater than 1, the standard form of the log is the same as the normal form), the integral part is called the characteristic and the fractional part (which is always positive) is called the mantissa.

Konnect

1. Multiplying or dividing by a power of 10 changes only the integral part of the log, not the fractional part.
2. For numbers less than 1, (for example log 0.2) it is more convenient to leave the log value as –1 + 0.3010 instead of changing it to –0.6090. We refer to the first form (in which the fraction is positive) as the standard form and the second form as the normal form. Both the forms represent the same number.

EXAMPLE 20.6

Express –0.3448 in the standard form and locate it on the number line.

SOLUTION

$-0.3448 = -1 + 1 - 0.3448 = \bar{1}.6552.$

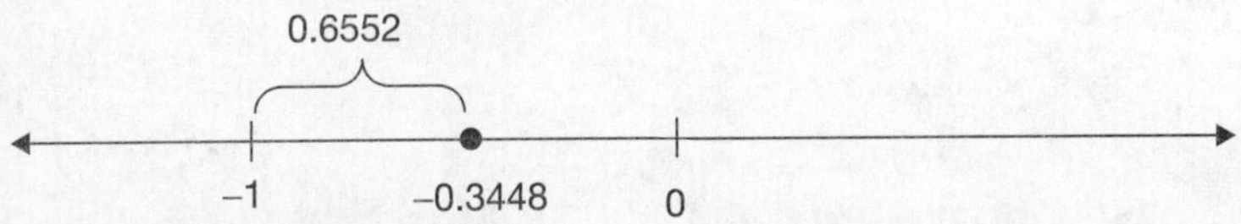

The Rule to Obtain the Characteristic of log *x*

1. If $x > 1$ and there are n digits in x, then the characteristic is $n - 1$.
2. If $x < 1$ and there are m zeroes between the decimal point and the first non-zero digit of x, then the characteristic is $(-m + 1)$ more commonly written as $\overline{(m+1)}$.

Info Bytes!

$-4 = \bar{4}$, but $-4.01 \neq \bar{4}.01$

To Find the log of a Number from the Log Tables

EXAMPLE 20.7

Find the values of log 36, log 3600, and log 0.0036.

SOLUTION

In log tables, we find the number 36 in the first column. In this row in the next column (under zero), we find .5563 (the decimal point is dropped in other columns). This gives 5563 as the mantissa for the log of all numbers whose significant digits are 3 and 6.

∴ Prefixing characteristic, we have log36 = 1.5563

Similarly log3600 = 3.5563 and log0.0036 = $\bar{3}.5563$.

EXAMPLE 20.8

Find the values of log 3.74, log 374000, and log 0.3740.

SOLUTION

In the log table, we locate 37 in the first column. In this row, in the column under 4, we find 5729. As in the earlier example, the same line as before gives the mantissa of logarithms of all numbers which begin with 37. From this line, we select the mantissa which is located in the column number 4. This gives 5729 as the mantissa for all numbers whose significant digits are 3, 7, and 4.

∴ log 3.74 = 0.5729

log 374000 = 5.5729 and

log 0.3740 = $\bar{1}.5729$.

EXAMPLE 20.9

Find the values of log 5.342 and log 0.05342.

SOLUTION

As found in the above example, we can find the mantissa for the sequence of digits 534 as 7275. Since there are four significant digits in 5342, in the same row where we found 7275 under the column 2 in the mean difference column, we can find the number 2.

∴ The mantissa of the logarithm of 5342 is 7275 + 2 = 7277.

Thus, log 5.342 = 0.7277

Similarly, log 0.05342 = $\bar{2}.7277$.

Antilog

As $\log_2 8 = 3$, 8 is the antilogarithm of 3 to the base 2, i.e., antilog of b to base m is m^b.

In the above example, we have seen that log5.342 = 0.7277.

∴ Antilog 0.7277 = 5.342.

To Find the Antilog

EXAMPLE 20.10 Find the antilog of 2.421.

SOLUTION

Step 1: In the antilog table, we find the number. 42 in the first column. In that row in the column under 1, we find 2636.

Step 2: As the characteristic is 2, we place the decimal after three digits from the left, i.e., antilog 2.421 = 263.6.

Konnect

If the characteristic is n (a non-negative integer), then we would place the decimal after $(n + 1)$ digits from the left.

EXAMPLE 20.11 Find the antilog of 1.4215.

SOLUTION

We have to locate 0.42 in the first column and scan along the horizontal line and pick out the number in the column headed by 1. We see that the number is 2636. The mean difference for 5 in the same line is 3.

∴ The sum of these numbers is 2636 + 3 = 2639.

As the characteristic is 1, the required antilog is 26.39.

EXAMPLE 20.12 Find the value of $\frac{7.211\times 0.084}{16.52\times 0.016}$.

SOLUTION

log of a fraction = (log of numerator) – (log of denominator)

log of numerator = $\log 7.211 + \log 0.084 = 0.8580 + \bar{2}.9243 = \bar{1}.7823$

log of denominator = $\log 16.52 + \log 0.016 = 1.2180 + \bar{2}.2041 = \bar{1}.4221$

log of the given fraction $= \bar{1}.7823 - \bar{1}.4221 = 0.3602$

Value of the fraction = antilog (0.3602) = 2.292. (As the characteristic is 0, the decimal is kept after one digit from the left)

EXAMPLE 20.13 If $\log_{10} 4 = 0.6021$ and $\log_{10} 5 = 0.6990$, then find the value of $\log_{10} 1600$.

SOLUTION

$$\begin{aligned}\log_{10} 1600 &= \log_{10}(64\times 25) = \log_{10}(4^3\times 5^2)\\ &= \log_{10} 4^3 + \log_{10} 5^2\\ &= 3\log_{10} 4 + 2\log_{10} 5\\ &= 3(0.6021) + 2(0.6990)\\ &= 1.8063 + 1.3980\end{aligned}$$

$\log_{10} 1600 = 3.2043.$

EXAMPLE 20.14 Find the value of $\sqrt[3]{16.51}$ approximately.

SOLUTION

Let $P = \sqrt[3]{16.51}$

$\log P = \log (16.51)^{1/3}$

$= \frac{1}{3}\log 16.51$

$= \frac{1}{3}(1.2178) = 0.4059$

$\log P = 0.4059$

$P = \text{antilog}\,(0.4059)$

$\therefore P = 2.546.$

POINTS TO REMEMBER

- ✔ The logarithm of any positive number to a given base (a positive number not equal to 1) is the index of the power of the base which is equal to that number.
- ✔ These were discovered by Napier. They are calculated to the base '*e*', which is approximately equal to 2.7828. These are used in higher mathematics.
- ✔ Logarithms to the base 10 are known as common logarithms. This system was introduced by Briggs, a contemporary of Napier. In the rest of this chapter, we shall use the short form 'log' instead of 'logarithm'.
- ✔ Log of different numbers to the same base are different.
- ✔ Log of the same number to different bases have different values.
- ✔ As $\log_2 8 = 3$, 8 is the antilogarithm of 3 to the base 2, i.e., antilog of b to base m is m^b.

DW

PRACTICE QUESTIONS CLASSROOM WING

Very Short Answer Type Questions

Directions of questions from 1 to 19:
Fill in the blanks.

1. The number of digits in the integral part of the number whose logarithm is 4.8345 is _______.
2. If $\log x = 32.756$, then $\log 10x =$ _______.
3. The characteristic of the logarithm of 0.0062 is _______.
4. If $\log_a x$ (where $a > 1$) is positive, then the range of x is _______.
5. If $\log 27.91 = 1.4458$, then $\log 2.791 =$ _______.
6. $\dfrac{\log 15 - \log 6}{\log 20 - \log 8} =$ _______.
7. If $\log 2 = 0.3010$, then $\log 5 =$ _______.
8. The value of $\log_{16} \sqrt[5]{64} =$ _______.
9. $\dfrac{\log 216}{\log 6} =$ _______.
10. If $\log_4 3 = x$, then $\log_{\sqrt[4]{3}} \sqrt[4]{64} =$ _______.
11. If $\log_x \left(\dfrac{1}{243}\right) = -5$, then find the value of x.
12. $7^{\log_{343} 27} =$ _______.
13. If $3^{\log_9 x} = 2$, then $x =$ _______.
14. If $\log_{xyz} x + \log_{xyz} y + \log_{xyz} z = \log_{10} p$, then $p =$ _______.
15. If $\log_{10} 4 + \log_{10} m = 2$, then $m =$ _______.
16. If $\log(a + 1) + \log(a - 1) = \log 15$, then $a =$ _______.
17. The value of $\log 10 + \log 100 + \log 1000 + \cdots + \log 10000000000 =$ _______.
18. If the number of zeroes between the decimal point and the first non-zero digit of a number is 2, then the characteristic of logarithm of that number is _______.
19. The value of $\log(\tan 10°) + \log(\tan 20°) + \log(\tan 45°) + \log(\tan 70°) + \log(\tan 80°) =$ _______.

Short Answer Type Questions

Directions of questions from 20 to 36:
Answer the following questions.

20. Simplify: $\log\left(\dfrac{3}{18}\right) + \log\left(\dfrac{45}{8}\right) - \log\left(\dfrac{15}{16}\right)$.
21. Show that $\dfrac{1}{\log_a abc} + \dfrac{1}{\log_b abc} + \dfrac{1}{\log_c abc} = 1$.
22. Solve for real value of x: $\log(x - 1) + \log(x^2 + x + 1) = \log 999$.
23. If $\dfrac{1}{1 + \log_a 10} = \dfrac{3}{2}$, then find the value of a.
24. (A) If $x^2 + y^2 = 23xy$, then show that $2\log(x + y) = 2\log 5 + \log x + \log y$.

    (B) Find the number of digits in the expansion of 256^{125}. Given that $\log_{10} x = 0.3010$.
25. If $\log_{10} 2 = 0.3010$ and $\log_{10} 3 = 0.4771$, then find the value $\log_{10} 135$.
26. If $\log_{10} 2 = x$ and $\log_{10} 3 = y$, then find $\log_{10} 21.6$.
27. If $\log_{10} 2 = 0.3010$, then find the number of digits in $(64)^{10}$.
28. Simplify $\dfrac{1}{\log_2 \log_2 \log_2 256}$.
29. Prove that $\log_3 810 = 4 + \log_3 10$.
30. Simplify: $3\log_3 5 + \log_3 10 - \log_3 625$.

Essay Type Questions

31. Solve: $x^{\log_4 3} + 3^{\log_4 x} = 18$.
32. (A) If $p^2 + q^2 = 14pq$, then prove that $\log\left(\dfrac{p+q}{4}\right) = \dfrac{1}{2}[\log p + \log q]$.

    (B) Arrange the following numbers in the ascending order of their magnitude.
    $\log_3 15$, $\log_5 4$, $\log_2 13$, and $\log_8 63$.

33. (A) Without using tables, find the value of

$$4\log_{10}5+5\log_{10}2-\frac{1}{2}\log_{10}4.$$

(B) Find the solution of $\log_{0.1}(x-3)\le\log_{0.01}(x-3)$.

34. (A) If $\frac{\log a}{b-c}=\frac{\log b}{c-a}=\frac{\log c}{a-b}$, then prove that $a^a b^b c^c=1$.

(B) If $\log_{\sqrt{2}}\left[\frac{3^{2x}+1}{3^x+2}\right]=2$, find the value of x.

35. Arrange the following numbers in the increasing order of their magnitude. $\log_7 9$, $\log_{18}16$, $\log_6 41$, $\log_2 10$.

36. If $\frac{\log(p+q)}{p-q}=\frac{\log(q+r)}{q-r}=\frac{\log(r+p)}{r-p}$, then prove that

$$(p+q)^{(p+q)}\times(q+r)^{(q+r)}\times(r+s)^{(r+p)}=1.$$

PRACTICE QUESTIONS COMPETITION WING

Level 1: Apply Your Concepts

Directions of questions from 1 to 5:
Fill in the blanks.

1. $\frac{1}{5}\log_2 32 + 3\log_{64} 4 =$ ________.

2. The characteristic of the logarithm of 3.6275 is ________.

3. If $4\log_x 8 = 3$, then $x =$ ________.

4. If $\log x - \frac{2}{3}\log x = 1$, then $x =$ ________.

5. If $a = \log\frac{3}{2}, b = \log\frac{4}{25}$ and $c = \log\frac{5}{9}$, then $a + b + c =$ ________.

Directions of questions from 6 to 60:
Select the correct alternative from the given choices.

6. If $\log_{16} x = 2.5$, then $x =$ ________.
(a) 40 (b) 256
(c) 1024 (d) 1025

7. If $\log 5 = 0.699$ and $(1000)^x = 5$, then find the value of x.
(a) 0.0699 (b) 0.0233
(c) 0.233 (d) 10

8. The value of $\log\left(\frac{18}{14}\right) + \log\left(\frac{35}{48}\right) - \log\left(\frac{15}{16}\right) =$
(a) 0 (b) 1
(c) 2 (d) $\log_{16} 15$

9. If $\log_3 a + \log_9 a + \log_{81} a = \frac{35}{4}$, then $a =$ ______.
(a) 27 (b) 243
(c) 81 (d) 240

10. If $\log_9[(\log_8 x)] < 0$, then x belongs to ______.
(a) (1, 8) (b) $(-\infty, 8)$
(c) $(8, \infty)$ (d) (8, 1)

11. If $\log_3 \frac{x^3}{3} - 2\log_3 3x^3 = a - b\log_3 x$, then find the value of $a + b$.
(a) 6 (b) −6
(c) 0 (d) −3

12. The value of $\log_{40} 5$ lies between ______.
(a) $\frac{1}{3}$ and $\frac{1}{2}$ (b) $\frac{1}{4}$ and $\frac{1}{3}$
(c) $\frac{1}{2}$ and 1 (d) 2 and 3

13. If $x = \log_{\frac{1}{2}} \frac{4}{3} \cdot \log_2 \frac{1}{3} \cdot \log_{\frac{2}{3}} 0.8$, then ________.
(a) $x > 0$ (b) $x < 0$
(c) $x = 0$ (d) $x \geq 0$

14. If $\log_{144} 729 = x$, then the value of $\log_{36} 256$ is ________.
(a) $\frac{4(3-x)}{(3+x)}$ (b) $\frac{4(3+x)}{(3-x)}$
(c) $\frac{(3+x)}{4(3-x)}$ (d) $\frac{(3-x)}{4(3+x)}$

15. The solution set of the equation $\log(2x - 5) - \log 3 = \log 4 - \log(x + 9)$ is ________.
(a) $\left\{\frac{-19}{2}, 3\right\}$ (b) $\left\{-3, \frac{19}{2}\right\}$
(c) $\left\{3, \frac{19}{2}\right\}$ (d) {3}

16. If $\log_{10}\tan 19° + \log_{10}\tan 21° + \log_{10}\tan 37° + \log_{10}\tan 45° + \text{long}_{10}\tan 69° + \log_{10}\tan 71° + \log_{10}\tan 53° = \log_{10}\frac{x}{2}$, then $x =$ ________.
(a) 0 (b) 1
(c) 2 (d) 4

17. The solution set of the equation $\log(x + 6) - \log 8 = \log 9 - \log(x + 7)$ is ________.
(a) {−15, 2} (b) {2}
(c) {−15, 0, 2} (d) {0, 2}

18. If $\log 40\ 4 = x$ and $\log_{40} 5 = y$, then express $\log_{40} 32$ in terms of x and y.
(a) $5(1 + x + y)$
(b) $5(1 - x + y)$
(c) $5(1 - x - y)$
(d) $5(1 + x - y)$

19. If $\log_{10} 11 = p$, then $\log_{10}\left(\frac{1}{110}\right) =$ ________.

(a) $(1+p)^{-1}$ (b) $-(1+p)$
(c) $1-p$ (d) $\frac{1}{10p}$

20. If $\log_4 \frac{x^4}{4} + 3\log_4 4x^4 = p + q\log_4 x$, then the value of $\log_p (q)$ is ________.

(a) 4 (b) −4
(c) 3 (d) 2

21. If $\log_4 x + \log_8 x^2 + \log_{16} x^3 = \frac{23}{2}$, then $\log_x 8 =$

(a) 2 (b) $\frac{1}{2}$
(c) 3 (d) $\frac{3}{4}$

22. If $\log_{(x+y)}(x-y) = 7$, then the value of $\log_{(x^2-y^2)}(x^2+2xy+y^2)$ is ________.

(a) 14 (b) $\frac{2}{7}$
(c) $\frac{7}{2}$ (d) $\frac{1}{4}$

23. The value of $\log_{35} 3$ lies between ________.

(a) $\frac{1}{4}$ and $\frac{1}{3}$ (b) $\frac{1}{3}$ and $\frac{1}{2}$
(c) $\frac{1}{2}$ and 1 (d) 3 and 4

24. If $\log\left(\frac{a+b}{6}\right) = \frac{1}{2}(\log a + \log b)$, then $\frac{a}{b} + \frac{b}{a} =$ ________.

(a) 30 (b) 31
(c) 32 (d) 34

25. If $\log_p q = x$, then $\log_{1/p}\left(\frac{1}{q}\right) =$ ________.

(a) $\frac{1}{x}$ (b) $-x$
(c) x (d) x^2

26. If $\log_{(x-y)}(x+y) = 5$, then what is the value of $\log_{x^2-y^2}(x^2-2xy+y^2)$?

(a) 1 (b) $\frac{\sqrt{5}}{3}$
(c) $\frac{1}{3}$ (d) 0

27. The value of $\log_a 1 + \log_2 2^2 + \log_3 3^3 \log_a 1 + \log_2 2^2 + \log_3 3^3$ (where a is a positive number and $a \neq 1$) is ________.

(a) 210 (b) 209
(c) 145 (d) 89

28. $\log_{\frac{1}{2}} \frac{2}{3}$ ______ $\log_{\frac{2}{3}} \frac{1}{2}$. The appropriate symbol in the blank is

(a) > (b) <
(c) = (d) Cannot be determined

29. The value of $\log_3[\log_2\{\log_4(\log_5 625^4)\}]$ is ________.

(a) 0 (b) 1
(c) 2 (d) 3 log 4

30. If $\log(x-3) + \log(x+2) = \log(x^2+x-6)$, then the real value of x, which satisfies the above equation is:

(a) is any value of x
(b) is any value of x except $x = 0$
(c) is any values of x except $x = 3$
(d) Does not exist

Level 2: Review Your Concepts

31. If $\log_{\left(\sqrt{b\sqrt{b\sqrt{b\sqrt{b}}}}\right)}\left(\sqrt{a\sqrt{a\sqrt{a\sqrt{a\sqrt{a}}}}}\right) = x\log_b a$, then $x =$

(a) $\frac{32}{16}$ (b) $\frac{31}{15}$
(c) $\frac{31}{30}$ (d) $\frac{1}{2}$

32. If $7^{\log x} + x^{\log 7} = 98$, then $\log_{10}\sqrt{x} =$ ________

(a) 2 (b) 1
(c) $\frac{1}{2}$ (d) −1

33. If $7^{\log x} + x^{\log 7} = 98$, then $\log_{10}\sqrt{x} =$

(a) 1 (b) $\frac{1}{2}$
(c) 2 (d) 0

34. The value of $\log_b a + \log_{b^2} a^2 + \log_{b^3} a^3 + \cdots + \log_{b^n} a^n$ is ________.

(a) n (b) $\log_b a$
(c) $\frac{n(n+1)}{2}\log_b a$ (d) $\log_b a^n$

35. If $(\log_2 x) + \log_2 (\log_4 x) = 2$, then find $\log_x 4$.

(a) 2 (b) $\frac{1}{2}$

(c) 1 (d) 0

36. If $pqr = 1$ then find the value of $\log_{rq} p + \log_{rp} q + \log_{pq} r$.

(a) 0 (b) −1

(c) −3 (d) 1

37. If $\log_3[\log_2\{\log_x(\log_6 216^3)\}] = 0$, then $\log_3(3x) =$ ______.

(a) $\log_3 12$ (b) 1

(c) 2 (d) $\log_3 6$

38. If a^x, b^x and c^x are in GP, then which of the following is/are true?

(A) a, b, c are in GP

(B) $\log a, \log b, \log c$ are in GP

(C) $\log a, \log b, \log c$ are in AP

(D) a, b, c are in AP

(a) A and B (b) A and C

(c) B and D (d) Only A

39. The value of

$$\frac{1}{\log_3 n} + \frac{1}{\log_4 n} + \frac{1}{\log_5 n} + \cdots + \frac{1}{\log_8 n} \text{ is } \_\_\_\_\_\_.$$

(a) $\log_n 8!$ (b) $\log_{n!} 8$

(c) $\log_n \left(\frac{8!}{2}\right)$ (d) $\log_{n!} 8!$

40. If $\frac{\log a}{y-z} = \frac{\log b}{z-x} = \frac{\log c}{x-y}$, then $abc =$ ______.

(a) $a^x b^y c^z$ (b) $a^{y+z} b^{z+x} c^{x+y}$

(c) 1 (d) All of these

41. If $\frac{1}{\log_x 10} = \frac{3}{\log_p 10} - 3$, then $x =$ ______.

(a) $100p^2$ (b) $\frac{p^2}{100}$

(c) $1000p^3$ (d) $\frac{p^3}{1000}$

42. If $\log_8 m = 3.5$ and $\log_2 n = 7$, then the value of m in terms of n is ______.

(a) $n\sqrt{n}$ (b) $2n$

(c) n^2 (d) $\sqrt[3]{n}$

43. If $\log_{12}(\log_7 x) < 0$, then x belongs to ______.

(a) $(1, \infty)$ (b) (1, 7)

(c) $(1, \infty)$ (d) (1, 7)

44. The value of $\log_{381} 7$ lies between ______.

(a) $\frac{1}{3}$ and $\frac{1}{2}$ (b) $\frac{1}{4}$ and $\frac{1}{3}$

(c) $\frac{1}{5}$ and $\frac{1}{4}$ (d) $\frac{1}{6}$ and $\frac{1}{5}$

45. If $\log_{10}\tan 31° \cdot \log_{10}\tan 32° \cdots \log_{10}\tan 60° = \log_{10} a$, then $a =$ ______.

(a) 10 (b) 1

(c) 4 (d) 2

Level 3: Assess Your Concepts

46. The solution set for $|1 - x|^{\log_{10}(x^2-5x+5)} = 1$, is ______.

(a) {0, 1, 4} (b) {1, 4}

(c) {0, 4} (d) {0, 2, 4}

47. The value of $\log\sqrt{2\sqrt{2\sqrt{2\ldots\infty \text{ times}}}} + \log\sqrt{3\sqrt{3\sqrt{3\ldots\infty \text{ times}}}}$ is

(a) 1 (b) 2

(c) log 5 (d) log 6

48. The least positive integral value of the expression $\frac{1}{2}\log_{10} m - \log_{m^{-2}} 10$ is ______.

(a) 0 (b) 1

(c) 2 (d) −1

49. The domain of log (3 − 5x) is ______.

(a) $\left(\frac{3}{5}, \infty\right)$ (b) $\left(0, \frac{3}{5}\right)$

(c) $\left(-\infty, \frac{3}{5}\right)$ (d) $\left(-\frac{3}{5}, 0\right)$

50. If $\log_7 x + \log_7 y \geq 2$, then the smallest possible integral value of $x + y$ (given $x \neq y$) is ______.

(a) 7 (b) 14

(c) 15 (d) 20

51. If p, q, r are in GP and $a^p = b^q = c^r$, then which of the following is true?

(a) $\log_c b = \log_a c$ (b) $\log_c b = \log_b a$

(c) $\log_c a = \log_b c$ (d) None of these

52. The value of $\log_5 \sqrt{5\sqrt{5\sqrt{5\ldots\infty}}}$ $+\log\left(\frac{1}{2}+\left(\frac{1}{2}\right)^2+\left(\frac{1}{2}\right)^3+\cdots\infty\right)$ is ________.

(a) 1 (b) 25
(c) 10 (d) 20

53. The solution set of $|x+2|^{\log_{10}(x^2+6x+9)}=1$ is ________.

(a) $\{-3, -4\}$ (b) $\{0, -3\}$
(c) $\{-4, -1\}$ (d) $\{-3, -1\}$

54. If $\log_p pq = x$, then $\log_q pq =$ ______.

(a) $\frac{x}{x-1}$ (b) $\frac{x-1}{x}$
(c) $\frac{x}{x+1}$ (d) $\frac{x+1}{x}$

55. If $\log_{1/8}(\log_4(x^2-5)) > 0$, then ________.

(a) $x \in (-\infty,-3)\cup(3,\infty)$
(b) $x \in \left(-\infty,-\sqrt{6}\right)\cup\left(\sqrt{6},\infty\right)$
(c) $x \in \left(-3,\sqrt{6}\right)\cup\left(\sqrt{6},\infty\right)$
(d) $x \in \left(-3,-\sqrt{6}\right)\cup\left(\sqrt{6},3\right)$

56. If $p = \log_a bc$, $q = \log_b ca$ and $r = \log_c ab$, then which of the following is true?

(a) $p+q+r+2 = pqr$ (b) $pqr = 2$
(c) $p+q+r = pqr$ (d) $pqr = 1$

57. If $\log_2 p + \log_8 p + \log_{32} p = \frac{46}{5}$, then $p =$ ________.

(a) 128 (b) 64
(c) 32 (d) 256

58. If p and q are positive numbers other than 1, then the least value of $|\log_q p + \log_p q|$ is ______.

(a) 3 (b) 1
(c) 2 (d) 4

59. If $\log_{48} 81 = x$, then $\log_{12} 3 =$ ________.

(a) $\frac{x+4}{2x}$ (b) $\frac{x+4}{x}$
(c) $\frac{x}{x+4}$ (d) $\frac{2x}{x+4}$

60. If $\log_l p$, $\log_m p$ and $\log_n p$ are in AP, then $(ln)^{\log_l m} =$ ________.

(a) n^2 (b) m^2
(c) l^2 (d) p^2

AT

ANSWER KEYS

Classroom Wing

Very Short Answer Type Questions

1. 5	**2.** 33.756	**3.** $\overline{3}$	**4.** $(1, \infty)$	**5.** 0.4458
6. 1	**7.** 0.6990	**8.** $\frac{3}{10}$	**9.** 3	**10.** $\frac{3}{x}$
11. 3	**12.** 3	**13.** 4	**14.** 10	**15.** 25
16. 4	**17.** 55	**18.** $\overline{3}$	**19.** 0	

Short Answer Type Questions

20. 0	**22.** $x = 10$	**23.** 10^{-3}	**24.** (B) 302	**25.** 2.1303
26. $3(x + y) - 1$	**27.** 19	**28.** $\log_3 2$	**30.** $\log_3 2$	

Essay Type Questions

31. 16 **32.** (B) $\log_5 4$, $\log_8 63$, $\log_3 15$ and $\log_2 13$

33. (A) 4 (B) $x \le 3$; $x \ge 4$ **34.** (B) 1 **35.** $\log_{18} 16, \log_7 9, \log_2 10, \log_6 41$

Competition Wing

Level 1: Apply Your Concepts

1. 2	**2.** 0	**3.** 16	**4.** 10^3	**5.** $\log \frac{2}{15}$
6. (c)	**7.** (c)	**8.** (a)	**9.** (b)	**10.** (a)
11. (c)	**12.** (a)	**13.** (a)	**14.** (a)	**15.** (d)
16. (c)	**17.** (b)	**18.** (c)	**19.** (b)	**20.** (a)
21. (b)	**22.** (d)	**23.** (a)	**24.** (d)	**25.** (c)
26. (c)	**27.** (b)	**28.** (b)	**29.** (a)	**30.** (d)

Level 2: Review Your Concepts

31. (c)	**32.** (b)	**33.** (a)	**34.** (d)	**35.** (b)
36. (c)	**37.** (c)	**38.** (b)	**39.** (c)	**40.** (d)
41. (d)	**42.** (a)	**43.** (b)	**44.** (b)	**45.** (b)

Level 3: Assess Your Concepts

46. (c)	**47.** (d)	**48.** (b)	**49.** (c)	**50.** (c)
51. (b)	**52.** (a)	**53.** (c)	**54.** (a)	**55.** (d)
56. (a)	**57.** (b)	**58.** (c)	**59.** (d)	**60.** (a)

Hints and Explanations

Classroom Wing

Very Short Answer Type Questions

1. 5

2. $\log x = 32.756$

   Then $\log 10x = 33.756$
   Since $\log 10 = 1$ so add 1

3. $\bar{3}$ (from table)

4. $(1, \infty)$

5. 0.4458

6. $\dfrac{\log \frac{15}{6}}{\log \frac{20}{8}} = \dfrac{\log \frac{5}{2}}{\log \frac{5}{2}} = 1$

7. $\log 2 = 0.3010$

   $\log_{10} 2 = \dfrac{1}{\log_2 10} - \dfrac{1}{0.3010} = 0.6990$

8. $\log_{16} \sqrt[5]{64} = \dfrac{3}{10}$

9. $\dfrac{\log 6^3}{\log 6} = 3$

10. $\log_4 3 = x, \log_3 64$

    $= 3\log_3 4 = \dfrac{3}{x}$

11. $\log_x \left(\dfrac{1}{3^5}\right) = -5$

    $-5\log_x 3 = -5$

    $\therefore x = 3$

12. $7^{\log_{343} 27} \Rightarrow 7^{\frac{1}{3}\log_7 3^3}$

    $= 7^{\log_7 3} = 3$

13. $3^{\log_9 x} = 2$

    $3^{\frac{1}{2}\log_3 x} = 2$

    $\therefore 3^{\log_3 x^{1/2}} = 2$

    $x = 4$

14. $\log_{xyz} x + \log_{xyz} y + \log_{xyz} z = \log_{10} p$

    $\log_{xyz} xyz = \log_{10} p$

    $1 = \log_{10} p$

    $\therefore p = 10$

15. $\log_{10} 4 + \log_{10} m = 2$

    $\log_{10} 4m = 2\log_{10} 10$

    $\therefore 4m = 100$

    $m = 25$

16. $\log(a+1) + \log(a-1) = \log 15$

    $\log(a+1)(a-1) = \log 15$

    $a^2 - 1 = 15 \Rightarrow a^2 = 16$

    $a = 4$

17. $\log 10 + \log 10^2 + \log 10^3 + \cdots + \log 10^{10}$

    $1 + 2 + 3 + \cdots + 10 = 55$

18. $\bar{3}$ from table

19. $\log(\tan 10°) + \log(\tan 20°) + \log(\tan 45°) + \log(\tan 70°)$

    $+ \log(\tan 80°)$

    $= \log 1 = 0$

Short Answer Type Questions

20. $\log\left(\dfrac{3}{18}\right) + \log\left(\dfrac{45}{8}\right) - \log\left(\dfrac{15}{16}\right)$

    $\log \dfrac{3}{18} \times \dfrac{45}{8} \times \dfrac{16}{15} = \log 1 = 0$

21. $\dfrac{1}{\log_a abc} + \dfrac{1}{\log_a abc} + \dfrac{1}{\log_c abc} = 1$

    $\log_{abc} a + \log_{abc} b + \log_{abc} c = 1$

    $\log_{abc} abc = 1$

    $\therefore 1 = 1$

22. $\log(x-1)+\log(x^2+x+1)=\log 999$

$\log(x-1)(x^2+x+1)=\log 999$

$\log x^3-1=\log 10^3-1$

$x^3=10^3$

$x=10$

23. $\dfrac{1}{1+\log_a 10}=\dfrac{3}{2}$

$2=3+3\log_a 10$

$-1=3\dfrac{\log 10}{\log a}$

$\log a=\log 10^{(-3)}$

$a=10^{(-3)}$

24. (A) $x^2+y^2=23xy$

$2\log(x+y)=2\log 5+\log x+\log y$

Adding $2xy$ on both sides,

$x^2+y^2+2xy=23xy+2xy$

$x^2+y^2+2xy=25xy$

Taking log both sides,

$\log[x^2+y^2+2xy]=\log 25+\log x+\log y$

$\log(x+y)^2=\log 5^2+\log x+\log y$

$2\log(x+y)=2\log 5+\log x+\log y$

(B) Let $x=256^{125}$.

$\Rightarrow \log_{10} x=\log_{10} 256^{125}$

$\Rightarrow \log_{10} x=\log_{10} 2^{1000}$

$\Rightarrow \log_{10} x=1000(\log_{10} 2)$

$\Rightarrow \log_{10} x=1000(0.3010)$

$\Rightarrow \log_{10} x=301.0$

$\Rightarrow \log_{10} 256^{125}=301.0$.

As the characteristic of $\log_{10} 256^{125}$ is 301, the number of digits in the expansion of 256^{125} number is 301 + 1 = 302.

25. $\log_{10} 2=0.3010$

$\log_{10} 3=0.4771$

$\log_{10} 135$

$\log_{10} 15\times 9$

$\log_{10} 15+\log_{10}$

$\log_{10}(16-1)+\log_{10} 3^2$

$\log_{10}(5\times 3)+2\log_{10} 3$

$\log_{10} 5+\log_{10} 3+2\log_{10} 3$

$\dfrac{1}{\log_5 10}+0.4771+2(0.4771)$

$=2.1303$

26. $\log_{10} 2=x$

$\log_{10} 3=y$

$\log_{10} 21$

$\log_{10} 2+2\log_{10} 3+\log_{10} 7$

$x+2y+\log_{10}(2^2+3)$

$=x+2y+\log_{10} 2^2+\log 3$

$=2x+x+2y+y-1=3(x+y)-1$

27. $\log_{10} 2=0.3010$

Multiply by 6,

$6\log_{10} 2=1.8060$

$\log_{10} 64=1.8060$

Multiply by 10 on both sides,

$10\log_{10} 64=1.8060$

Antilog(18.060)

$\therefore$ We have 19 digits (from antilog table).

28. $\dfrac{1}{\log_2\log_2\log_2 256}=\dfrac{1}{\log_2\log_2\log_2 2^8}$

$=\dfrac{1}{\log_2\log_2 2^3\log_2 2}$

$=\dfrac{1}{\log_2 3}$

$=\log_3 2$

29. $\log_3 810=\log_3(81\times 10)$

$=\log_3 81+\log_3 10$

$=\log_3 3^4+\log_3 10$

$=4+\log_3 10$

Hence proved.

30. $3\log_3 5+\log_3 10-\log_3 625$

$\log_3\dfrac{125\times 10}{625}=\log_3 2$

Essay Type Questions

31. $x^{\log_4 3} + 3^{\log_4 x} = 18$

if $x = 3$

$3^{\log_4 3} + 3^{\log_4 3} = 4 + 4 = 8$

if $x = 4$.

$4^{\log_4 3} + 3^{\log_4 4} = 3 + 3 = 6$

if $x = 16$

$4^{2\log_4 3} + 3^{\log_4 2} = 9 + 9 = 18$

$\therefore x = 16$

32. (A) $p^2 + q^2 = 14pq$

$$\log\left(\frac{p+q}{4}\right) = \frac{1}{2}[\log p + \log q]$$

Adding $2pq$ both sides,

$p^2 + q^2 + 2pq = 14pq + 2pq$

$(p+q)^2 = 16pq$

Taking log on both sides,

$2\log(p+q) = \log 16pq$

$2\log(p+q) = \log 16pq$

$2\log(p+q) = \log 16 + \log p + \log q$

$2\log(p+q) - \log 16 = \log p + \log q$

$2\log(p+q) - \log 4^2 = \log p + \log q$

$$\log\left(\frac{p+q}{4}\right) = \frac{1}{2}[\log p + \log q]$$

Hence proved.

(B) Since $3^2 < 15 < 3^3 2 < \log_3 15 < 3$.

Since $5^0 < 4 < 5^1 0 < \log_5 4 < 1$.

Since $2^3 < 13 < 2^4 3 < \log_2 13 < 4$.

Since $8^1 < 63 < 8^2 1 < \log_8 63 < 2$.

$\therefore$ Numbers in the ascending order of magnitude are: $\log_5 4$, $\log_8 63$, $\log_3 15$ and $\log_2 13$.

33. (A) $4\log_{10} 5 + 5\log_{10} 2 - \frac{1}{2}\log_{10} 4$

$\log_{10} 5^4 + \log_{10} 2^5 - \log_{10} 4^{1/2}$

$$\log\frac{5^4 \times 2^5}{2} = \log_{10} 10^4$$

$$= 4$$

(B) Given that $\log_{0.1}(x-3) \le \log_{0.01}(x-3)$.

$\Rightarrow \log_{0.1}(x-3) \le \log_{(0.1)^2}(x-3)$.

$\Rightarrow \log_{0.1}(x-3) \le \frac{1}{2}[\log_{0.1}(x-3)]$.

$\Rightarrow 2\log_{0.1}(x-3) \le \log_{0.1}(x-3)$.

$\Rightarrow \log_{0.1}(x-3)^2 \le \log_{0.1}(x-3)$.

$\Rightarrow (x-3)^2 \ge x-3$ (Since weak bases).

$\Rightarrow x^2 - 6x + 9 - x + 3 \ge 0$.

$\Rightarrow x^2 - 7x + 12 \ge 0$.

$\Rightarrow (x-3)(x-4) \ge 0$.

$\Rightarrow x \le 3$ or $x \ge 4$.

34. (A) $\dfrac{\log a}{b-c} = \dfrac{\log b}{c-a} = \dfrac{\log c}{a-b} = k$

Prove $a^a b^b c^c = 1$

Taking log on both sides,

$\log(a^a b^b c^c) = \log 1$

$\log a^a + \log b^b + \log c^c = \log 1$

$ak(b-c) + bk(c-a) + ck(a-b) = 0$

$akb - akc + bkc - bka + cka - ckb = 0$

$0 = 0$

Hence proved.

(B) Given that $\log_{\sqrt{2}}\left[\dfrac{3^{2x}+1}{3^x+2}\right] = 2$

$\Rightarrow \left[\dfrac{3^{2x}+1}{3^x+2}\right] = \sqrt{2}^2$

$\Rightarrow \left[\dfrac{3^{2x}+1}{3^x+2}\right] = 2$

Let 3^x be y

$\Rightarrow \left[\dfrac{y^2+1}{y+2}\right] = 2$

$\Rightarrow y^2 + 1 = 2(y+2)$

$\Rightarrow y^2 - 2y - 3 = 0$

$\Rightarrow (y-3)(y+1) = 0$

$\Rightarrow y = 3$ or $y = -1$

$\Rightarrow y = 3 \Rightarrow 3^x = 3 \Rightarrow x = 1$

Also, $y = -13^x = -1$ which is not possible

$\therefore x = 1$

35. $\log_7 9, \log_{18} 16, \log_6 41, \log_2 10$

$\frac{\log_{10} 9}{\log_{10} 7}, \frac{\log_{10} 16}{\log_{10} 18}, \frac{\log_{10} 41}{\log_{10} 6}, \frac{\log_{10} 10}{\log_{10} 2}$

$\log_{10}(9-7), \log_{10}(16-18), \log_{10}(41-6),$

$\log_{10}(10-2)$

$\log_{10} 2, -\log_{10} 2, \log_{10} 35, \log_{10} 8$

$\therefore -\log_{10} 2, \log_{10} 2, \log_{10} 8, \log_{10} 35$

$\therefore \log_{18} 16, \log_7 9, \log_2 10, \log_6 41$

36. Given that $\frac{\log(p+q)}{p-q} = \frac{\log(q+r)}{q-r} = \frac{\log(r+p)}{r-p} = k$ (say).

$\log(p+q) = k(p-q)$

$\Rightarrow (p+q)\log(p+q) = k(p-q)(p+q)$

$\Rightarrow \log(p+q)^{(p+q)} = k(p^2 - q^2).$

Similarly, $\log(q+r)^{(q+r)} = k(q^2 - r^2)$ and

$\log(r+p)^{(r+p)} = k(r^2 - p^2).$

Now, $= k(p^2 - q^2) + k(q^2 - r^2) + k(r^2 - p^2).$

$\Rightarrow \log(p+q)^{(p+q)} + \log(q+r)^{(q+r)} + \log(r+p)^{(r+p)} = 0$

$\Rightarrow \log\left[(p+q)^{(p+q)} \times (q+r)^{(q+r)} \times (r+p)^{(r+p)}\right] = 0$

$\Rightarrow (p+q)^{(p+q)} \times (q+r)^{(q+r)} \times (r+p)^{(r+p)} = 1$

Competition Wing

Level 1: Apply Your Concepts

1. $\frac{1}{5}\log_2 2^5 + 3\log_{64} 2^2$

$1+\frac{3}{\log_4 64}=1+\frac{3}{\log_4 4^3}=1+1=2$

2. 0 (From log table)

3. $4\log_x 8 = 3$

$\frac{4}{\log_8 x}=3$

$\therefore x = 16$

4. $\log x - \frac{2}{3}\log x = 1$

$\log\frac{x}{x^{2/3}} = 1 \Rightarrow \log x^{1-\frac{2}{3}} = 1$

$\log x^{\frac{1}{3}} = 1$

$\therefore x = 10^3$

5. $a = \log\frac{3}{2}$

$b = \frac{4}{25}$

$c = \log\frac{5}{9}$

$a+b+c \Rightarrow \log\frac{3}{2} + \log\frac{4}{25} + \log\frac{5}{9}$

$= \log\frac{3}{2}\times\frac{4}{25}\times\frac{5}{9} = \log\frac{2}{15}$

6. $\log_b a = n \Rightarrow a = b^n$.

7. Taking logarithms for $10^{3x} = 5$ and substituting in the given equation we get the value of x.

8. $\log a + \log b - \log c = \log\left(\frac{ab}{c}\right)$ and $\log 1 = 0$.

9. $\log_{b^n} a = \frac{1}{n}\log_b a$.

10. Given, $\log_9(\log_8 x) < 0$

$\log_8 x < 9^0$

$\log_8 x < 1$

$x < 8^1$

There fore $x \in (1, 8)$.

11. Use $\log a - \log b = \log\frac{a}{b}$ and $\log a + \log b = \log ab$.

12. Consider $5^2 < 40 < 5^3$ take logarithm with base 5.

13. $\log_b a > 0$; when $a > 1$ and $b < 1$

$\log_b a < 0$ when $a < 1$ and $b > 1$

$\log_b a > 0$ when $a < 1$ and $b < 1$.

14. Find the values of $\log_{12}4$, $\log_{12}36$, and using $\log_{12} 27 = x$.

15. $\log a - \log b = \log\left(\frac{a}{b}\right)$.

16. $\tan\theta \cdot \tan(90 - \theta) = 1$.

17. $\log a - \log b = \log\frac{a}{b}$.

18. Express $\log_{40}32$ in terms of x and y.

19. $\log\frac{1}{a} = \log a^{-1}$; $\log mn = \log m + \log n$ and $\log_a a = 1$.

20. $\log a + \log b = \log ab$

$\log a - \log b = \log\frac{a}{b}$.

21. $\log_{b^n} a^m = \frac{m}{n}\log_b a$.

22. Adding '1' on both sides and the '1' on the left side is expressed as $\log_{x+y}(x + y)$.

23. Consider the inequality and $3^3 < 35 < 3^4$ taking logarithm with base 3.

24. (i) Use, $\log a + \log b = \log ab$. remove the logarithms on both sides and evaluate $(a + b)^2$.

(ii) Use $m(\log a + \log b) = \log(ab)^m$.

(iii) Eliminate logarithms on both sides and obtain equations in terms of a and b.

(iv) Divide both sides of the equation with ab and obtain the required answer.

25. $\log_{b^n} a^m = \frac{m}{n}\log_b a$.

26. Adding '1' on both sides, the '1' on the left side is expressed as $\log_{x-y}(x - y)$.

27. (i) $\log_b a^m = m\log_b a$ and $\sum n = \frac{n(n+1)}{2}$.

(ii) $\log_a 1 = 0$, $\log_2 2^2 = 2$, $\log_3 3^3 = 3$, and so on.

(iii) The required answer is the sum of first 20 natural numbers except 1.

28. Use $a > b \Rightarrow \log_b a > 1$ and $a < b \Rightarrow \log_b a < 1$.

29. (i) $\log a^m = m\log a$.
(ii) Express 625 in terms of base 5 and simplify from the extreme right logarithm.

30. $\log a + \log b = \log ab$.

Level 2: Review Your Concepts

31. (i) Use, $\sqrt{a\sqrt{a\sqrt{a\cdots n \text{ terms}}}} = a^{(2^n-1/2^n)}$ and then $\log_{b^n} a^m = \frac{m}{n}\log_b a$ and simplify LHS.
(ii) Compare LHS and RHS and find the value of x.

32. (i) Use $\log a + \log b = \log ab$ and remove logarithms on both the sides and evaluate $(a-b)^2$.
(ii) Express RHS into single logarithm with coefficient 1.
(iii) Apply antilog and cancel the logarithms on both sides.
(iv) Divide LHS and RHS by ab and obtain the required value.

33. (i) $x^{\log y} = y^{\log x}$.
(ii) $7^{\log x} = x^{\log 7}$.
(iii) Convert LHS into $7^{\log x}$ (or) $x^{\log 7}$ and solve for x.

34. (i) $\log_{b^n} a^m = \frac{m}{n}\log_b a$.

$\log a + \log b = \log ab$.
(ii) Each term of the given expression is equal to $\log_b a$.
(iii) There are n terms in the expression.
(iv) Use the above information and find the required sum.

35. (i) Assume $\log_2 x = a$ then $\log_4 x = \frac{a}{2}$.
(ii) Take $\log_2(\log_4 x)$ as $2\log_4(\log_4 x)$ and convert LHS into single logarithm.
(iii) Express the result in terms of $\log_2 x$ and solve for $\log_2 x$.
(iv) Find $\log_x 2$ and then $\log_x 4$.

36. (i) Use $\log_a a = 1$.
(ii) Replace $rq = p^{-1}$, $rp = q^{-1}$ and $pq = r^{-1}$ in the given expression.
(iii) Simplify and eliminate logarithms.

37. (i) Remove logarithm one by one by using $\log_a x = b \Rightarrow x = a^b$.
(ii) Now substitute the value of x in $\log_3 3x$ and simplify.

38. (i) Verify from options.
(ii) Use if a, b and c are in GP, then $b^2 = ac$.
(iii) Substitute a^x, b^x and c^x in the above equation and simplify.
(iv) Apply logarithm for the above result and proceed.

39. (i) $\text{Log} \log_b a = \frac{1}{\log_a b}$.
(ii) Take all the logarithms to the numerators by using the formula $\frac{1}{\log_b a} = \log_a b$.
(iii) Use, $\log a + \log b + \cdots + \log n = \log(abc\ldots n)$ and simplify.

40. (i) Equate the given ratios to k and get the values of $\log a$, $\log b$, and $\log c$.
(ii) Add $\log a$, $\log b$, and $\log c$ and solve for abc.

41. Given, $\frac{1}{\log_x 10} = \frac{3}{\log_p 10} - 3$

$$\log_{10} x = 3\log_{10} p - 3\left(\because \log_b a = \frac{1}{\log_a b}\right)$$

$$\log_{10} x = 3(\log_{10} p - 1)$$
$$= 3(\log_{10} p - \log_{10} 10)$$
$$\log_{10} x = \log_{10}\left(\frac{p}{10}\right)^3$$
$$x = \left(\frac{p}{10}\right)^3 = \frac{p^3}{1000}.$$

42. Given, $\log_8 m = 3.5 \log_2 n = 7$

$\Rightarrow m = 8^{3.5}$ (1)

and $n = 2^7$ (2)

$$m = 8^{35/10}$$
$$m = (2^3)^{7/2}$$
$$= (2^7)^{3/2}$$
$$= n^{3/2} \quad (\because \text{from Eq. (1)})$$
$$\Rightarrow m = n\sqrt{n}.$$

43. Given, $\log_{12}(\log_7 x) < 0$ is defined when $\log_7 x > 0$

$x > 7^0 \Rightarrow x > 1$ (1)

$\log_{12}(\log_7 x) < 0 \Rightarrow \log_7 x < 12°$

$\Rightarrow \log_7 x < 1 = x < 7^1 \Rightarrow x < 7$ (2)

From Eqs. (1) and (2), we get $x \in (1, 7)$.

44. We know that $7^3 < 381 < 7^4$

$\Rightarrow \log_7 7^3 < \log_7 381 < \log_7 7^4$

$\Rightarrow 3 < \log_7 381 < 4$

$\Rightarrow \frac{1}{4} < \frac{1}{\log_7 381} < \frac{1}{3}$

$\frac{1}{4} < \log_{381} 7 < \frac{1}{3}\left(\because \log_b a = \frac{1}{\log_a b}\right).$

45. Given, $\log_{10} a = \log_{10}\tan 31° \log_{10} \tan 32° \ldots \log_{10} \tan 45° \ldots \log_{10} \tan 60°$

$= \log_{10} \tan 31° \ldots \log_{10} 1 \ldots \log_{10} \tan 60°$

$= 0$ ($\because \log_{10} 1 = 0$)

$\log_{10} a = 0 \Rightarrow a = 1.$

Level 3: Assess Your Concepts

46. (i) Use $a^0 = 1$ and $1^m = 1$.

(ii) Consider RHS, i.e., 1 as $|1 - x|^0$ and equate the exponents.

(iii) Convert the logarithm in the exponential form by using $\log_b a = N \Rightarrow a = b^N$.

(iv) Solve the quadratic equation for x.

47. (i) $\log a + \log b = \log ab$ and $\log\sqrt{x\sqrt{x\ldots\infty}} = x$.

(ii) Use, $\sqrt{a\sqrt{a\sqrt{a\sqrt{a\ldots\infty}}}} = a$ and then use $\log a + \log b = \log ab$.

48. (i) The least positive integral value of $x + \frac{1}{x} = 2$.

(ii) Let $\log_m 10 = x$ then $\log_m 10 = \frac{1}{x}$.

(iii) The given expression becomes $\frac{1}{2}\left(x + \frac{1}{x}\right)$.

(iv) Now the least positive value is obtained if $x + \frac{1}{x}$ is minimum.

49. (i) $\log f(x)$ is defined only when $f(x) > 0$.

(ii) logarithms take only positive values. That is, $(3 - 5x) > 0$.

(iii) Solve the above inequation for x.

50. $\log_7 x + \log_7 y \geq 2$

$\log_7 xy \geq 2$

$xy \geq 7^2$

$xy \geq 49$

$\therefore$ The possible values of (x, y) are (1, 49), (2, 25), (3, 17), (4, 14), (5, 10), (6, 9), (7, 8), …

$\therefore$ Smallest possible value of $5 + 10 = 6 + 9 = 7 + 8 = 15$

$\therefore$ Hence, option (c) is the correct answer.

51. Let $ap = bq = cr = k$

Then $p = \log_a k$, $q = \log_b k$ and $r = \log_c k$

Also given $q^2 = pr$

$(\log_b k)^2 = (\log_a k)(\log_c k)$

$(\log_b k)(\log_b k) = (\log_a k)(\log_c k)$

$\frac{\log_b k}{\log_a k} = \frac{\log_c k}{\log_b k}$

$\log_b a = \log_c b.$

52. Let $x = \sqrt{5\sqrt{5\sqrt{5\ldots\infty}}}$

$x = \sqrt{5x}$

$x^2 = 5x$

$\Rightarrow x = 5$ ($\because x \neq 0$)

$\therefore \log_5 \sqrt{5\sqrt{5\ldots\infty}} = \log_5 5 = 1.$

Consider $\frac{1}{2} + \left(\frac{1}{2}\right)^2 + \left(\frac{1}{2}\right)^3 + \cdots + \infty$

Clearly it is a GP, $s_\infty = \frac{a}{1 - S}$

Here $a = \frac{1}{2}$ and $r = \frac{1}{2}$

$= \frac{\frac{1}{2}}{1 - \frac{1}{2}} = 1$

$\therefore \log\left(\frac{1}{2} + \left(\frac{1}{2}\right)^2 + \cdots\right) = \log 1 = 0.$

$\therefore$ The required value $= 1 + 0 = 1$.

53. Given, $|x + 2|^{\log_{10} x^2 + 6x + 9} = 1$

As the RHS = 1

The exponent of $x + 2$ should be 0 ($a^0 = 1$)

or $|x + 2| = 1$

$\Rightarrow \log_{10} x^2 + 6x + 9 = 0$ or $x + 2 = \pm 1$

$x^2 + 6x + 9 = 1$ or $x = -1$ or -3

$x = -2$ or -4

$x = -1$ or -3

when $x = -3$, $\log_{10}(x^2 + 6x + 9)$ is not defined.

When $x = -2$, $|x + 2| = 0$ which is not possible.

$x = -4$, or -1.

54. Given, $\log_p pq = x$

$\log_p p + \log_p q = x$

$1 + \log_p q = x$

$\log_p q = x - 1$

$$\log_q pq = \log_q p + \log_q q$$

$$= \frac{1}{x-1} + 1 = \frac{1+x-1}{x-1} = \frac{x}{x-1}.$$

55. Given, $\log_{1/8}(\log_4(x^2-5)) > 0$

Here $\log_4 x^2 - 5 > 0$

$x^2 - 5 > 4^0 \Rightarrow x^2 - 5 > 1$

$\Rightarrow x^2 - 6 > 0 \Rightarrow x^2 - (\sqrt{6})^2 > 0$

$(x-\sqrt{6})(x+\sqrt{6}) > 0$

$\therefore x \in (-\infty, -\sqrt{6}) \cup (\sqrt{6}, \infty)$ (1)

And $\log_{1/8}(\log_4 x^2 - 5) > 0$

$\Rightarrow \log_4(x^2 - 5) < \left(\frac{1}{8}\right)^0$

$x^2 - 5 < 4^1$

$\Rightarrow x^2 - 9 < 0$

$(x-3)(x+3) < 0$

$\therefore x \in (-3, 3)$ (2)

From Eqs. (1) and (2), we have,

$x \in (-3, -\sqrt{6}) \cup (\sqrt{6}, 3)$.

56. $pqr = (\log_a b + \log_a c)(\log_b c + \log_b a)(\log_c a + \log_c b)$

$= (\log_a c + 1 + \log_a c \cdot \log_b c + \log_b c)(\log_c a + \log_c b)$

$= 1 + \log_a b + \log_c a + \log_c b + \log_b c + \log_a c + \log_b a + 1$

$= 2 + (\log_a b + \log_a c) + (\log_c a + \log_c b) + (\log_b c + \log_b a)$

$= 2 + \log_a bc + \log_b ac + \log_c ab$

$= 2 + p + q + r.$

57. Given, $\log_2 p + \log_8 p + \log_{32} p = \frac{46}{5}$

$$\log_2 p + \left(\frac{1}{3}\right)\log_2 p + \left(\frac{1}{5}\right)\log_2 p = \frac{46}{5}$$

$$\log_2 p\left(1 + \frac{1}{3} + \frac{1}{5}\right) = \frac{46}{5}$$

$$\left(\frac{15+5+3}{15}\right)\log_2 p = \frac{46}{5}$$

$$\left(\frac{23}{15}\right)\log_2 p = \frac{46}{5}$$

$$\log_2 p = \frac{46}{5} \times \frac{15}{23}$$

$\log_2 p = 6$

$p = 2^6 = 64.$

58. We know that AM $(a, b) \geq$ GM (a, b)

AM $(\log_q p, \log_p q) \geq$ GM $(\log_q p, \log_p q)$

$$\frac{|\log_q p + \log_p q|}{2} \geq \sqrt{\log_p q \cdot \log_q p}$$

$\Rightarrow |\log_q p + \log_p q| \geq 2.$

$\therefore$ The least value is 2.

59. Given, $\log_{48} 81 = x$

$\log_{48} 3^4 = x$

$4 \log_{48} 3 = x$

$$\log_3 48 = \frac{4}{x}$$

$$\log_3 3(16) = \frac{4}{x}$$

$$\log_3 3 + \log_3 16 = \frac{4}{x}$$

$$1 + \log_3 4^2 = \frac{4}{x}$$

$$2\log_3 4 = \left(\frac{4}{x}\right) - 1$$

$$\log_3 4 = \frac{4-x}{2x}.$$

Consider $\log_3 12 = \log_3 3(4)$

$= \log_3 3 + \log_3 4$

$$\Rightarrow 1 + \frac{4-x}{2x}$$

$$\Rightarrow \log_3 12 = \frac{x+4}{2x}$$

$$\log_{12} 3 = \frac{2x}{x+4}.$$

60. Given, $\log_l p$, $\log_m p$, $\log_n p$ are in AP.

$\Rightarrow \log_p l$, $\log_p m$ and $\log_p n$ are in HP.

$$\log_p m = \frac{2\log_p l \cdot \log_p n}{\log_p l + \log_p n}$$

$$\frac{\log_p m}{\log_p l} = \frac{2\log_p n}{\log_p ln}$$

$\Rightarrow \log_l m = \log_{ln} n^2$

$\Rightarrow (ln)^{\log_l m} = n^2.$